Dear

This 2
of the Michelin Guide
to Great Britain and Ireland
offers the latest selection
of hotels and restaurants.

Independently compiled by our inspectors,
the Guide provides travellers
with a wide choice of establishments
at all levels of comfort and price.

We are committed to providing readers
with the most up to date information
and this edition has been produced
with the greatest care.

That is why only this year's guide
merits your complete confidence

Thank you for your comments,
which are always appreciated.

Bon voyage

Contents

3 Dear Reader

5 to 12 How to use this guide

43 County abbreviations

44 Starred establishments

45 Further establishments which merit your attention

Particularly pleasant hotels and restaurants

Hotels, restaurants, town plans, sights... and maps

49 England

London *Pages bordered in red*

533 Wales

567 Scotland

649 Northern Ireland

659 Channel Islands

671 Isle of Man

673 Republic of Ireland

719 Major hotel groups

720 Distances

722 Atlas: main roads and principal shipping routes

728 European dialling codes

732 Michelin maps and guides

Choosing
a hotel or restaurant

This guide offers a selection of hotels and restaurants to help the motorist on his travels. In each category establishments are listed in order of preference according to the degree of comfort they offer.

CATEGORIES

	Luxury in the traditional style	
	Top class comfort	
	Very comfortable	
	Comfortable	
	Quite comfortable	
	Simple comfort	
	Other recommended accommodation, at moderate prices	
without rest.	The hotel has no restaurant	
	The restaurant also offers accommodation	with rm

PEACEFUL ATMOSPHERE AND SETTING

Certain establishments are distinguished in the guide by the red symbols shown below.
Your stay in such hotels will be particularly pleasant or restful, owing to the character of the building, its decor, the setting, the welcome and services offered, or simply the peace and quiet to be enjoyed there.

to	Pleasant hotels
to	Pleasant restaurants
« Park »	Particularly attractive feature
	Very quiet or quiet, secluded hotel
	Quiet hotel
sea	Exceptional view
	Interesting or extensive view

The maps located at the beginning of each regional section in the guide indicate places with such peaceful, pleasant hotels and restaurants.

By consulting them before setting out and sending us your comments on your return you can help us with our enquiries.

Hotel facilities

In general the hotels we recommend have full bathroom and toilet facilities in each room. However, this may not be the case for certain rooms in categories , , and .

30 rm	Number of rooms
	Lift (elevator)
	Air conditioning
TV	Television in room
	Establishment either partly or wholly reserved for non-smokers
	Telephone in room: outside calls connected by the operator
	Telephone in room: direct dialling for outside calls
	Rooms accessible to disabled people
	Outdoor or indoor swimming pool
	Exercise room - Sauna
	Garden
9	Hotel tennis court - Golf course and number of holes
	Fishing available to hotel guests. A charge may be made
150	Equipped conference hall: maximum capacity
	Hotel garage (additional charge in most cases)
P	Car park for customers only
	Dogs are not allowed in all or part of the hotel
Fax	Telephone document transmission
May-October	Dates when open, as indicated by the hotelier
season	Probably open for the season - precise dates not available Where no date or season is shown, establishments are open all year round
LL35 OSB	Postal code
(Forte)	Hotel Group (See list at end of the Guide)

Animals

It is forbidden to bring domestic animals (dogs, cats...) into Great Britain and Ireland.

Cuisine

STARS

Certain establishments deserve to be brought to your attention for the particularly fine quality of their cooking. **Michelin stars** are awarded for the standard of meals served. For each of these restaurants we indicate three culinary specialities typical of their style of cooking to assist you in your choice.

- ✿✿✿ **Exceptional cuisine, worth a special journey**
  Superb food, fine wines, faultless service, elegant surroundings. One will pay accordingly!
- ✿✿ **Excellent cooking, worth a detour**
  Specialities and wines of first class quality. This will be reflected in the price.
- ✿ **A very good restaurant in its category**
  The star indicates a good place to stop on your journey.
  But beware of comparing the star given to an expensive « de luxe » establishment to that of a simple restaurant where you can appreciate fine cooking at a reasonable price.

THE RED « Meals »

Whilst appreciating the quality of the cooking in restaurants with a star, you may, however, wish to find some serving a perhaps less elaborate but nonetheless always carefully prepared meal.
Certain restaurants seem to us to answer this requirement. We bring them to your attention by marking them with a red « Meals » in the text of the Guide.

Please refer to the map of ✿ and Meals rated restaurants located at the beginning of each regional section in the guide.

Alcoholic beverages-conditions of sale

The sale of alcoholic drinks is governed in Great Britain and Ireland by licensing laws which vary greatly from country to country.
Allowing for local variations, restaurants may stay open and serve alcohol with a bona fide meal during the afternoon. Hotel bars and public houses are generally open between 11am and 11pm at the discretion of the licensee. Hotel residents, however, may buy drinks outside the permitted hours at the discretion of the hotelier.
Children under the age of 14 are not allowed in bars.

Prices

Prices quoted are valid for autumn 1994. Changes may arise if goods and service costs are revised.
Your recommendation is self-evident if you always walk into a hotel guide in hand.
Hotels and restaurants in bold type have supplied details of all their rates and have assumed responsibility for maintaining them for all travellers in possession of this guide.
Prices are given in £ sterling, except for the Republic of Ireland where Irish pounds (punt) are quoted. Where no mention **s., t.,** or **st.** is shown, prices may be subject to the addition of service charge, V.A.T., or both (V.A.T. does not apply in the Channel Islands).

MEALS

Meals 13.00/24.00	**Set meals** - Lunch 13.00, dinner 24.00 - including cover charge, where applicable
Meals 15.00/25.00	See page 7
s.	Service only included
t.	V.A.T. only included
st.	Service and V.A.T. included
🍷 6.00	Price of 1/2 bottle or carafe of house wine
Meals a la carte 20.00/25.00	**A la carte meals** - The prices represent the range of charges from a simple to an elaborate 3 course meal and include a cover charge where applicable
☕ 8.50	Charge for full cooked breakfast (i.e. not included in the room rate) Continental breakfast may be available at a lower rate

⌂ : Dinner in this category of establishment will generally be offered from a fixed price menu of limited choice, served at a set time to residents only. Lunch is rarely offered. Many will not be licensed to sell alcohol.

ROOMS

rm 50.00/80.00	Lowest price 50.00 per room for a comfortable single and highest price 80.00 per room for the best double
rm ☕ 55.00/75.00	Full cooked breakfast (whether taken or not) is included in the price of the room

SHORT BREAKS

Many hotels offer a special rate for a stay of two nights which comprises dinner, room and breakfast usually for a minimum of two people. Please enquire at hotel for rates.

DEPOSITS - CREDIT CARDS

Some hotels will require a deposit, which confirms the commitment of customer and hotelier alike. Make sure the terms of the agreement are clear.

Access AE Diners VISA JCB	Credit cards accepted by the establishment: Access (MasterCard, Eurocard) - American Express - Diners Club - Visa - Japan Card Bank

Towns

✉ York	Postal address
01225 Bath	STD dialling code (name of exchange indicated only when different from name of the town). Omit 0 when dialling from abroad
401 M 27, ⑩	Michelin map and co-ordinates or fold
West Country G.	See the Michelin Green Guide England : The West Country
pop. 1057	Population
ECD : Wednesday	Early closing day (shops close at midday)
BX **A**	Letters giving the location of a place on the town map
18	Golf course and number of holes (handicap usually required, telephone reservation strongly advised)
✱, ⩽	Panoramic view, viewpoint
✈	Airport
🚗 ✆ 261 1234	Place with a motorail connection; further information from telephone number listed
⛴	Shipping line
⛴	Passenger transport only *see list of companies at the end of the Guide*
ℹ	Tourist Information Centre

Standard Time

In winter standard time throughout the British Isles is Greenwich Mean Time (G.M.T.). In summer British clocks are advanced by one hour to give British Summer Time (B.S.T.). The actual dates are announced annually but always occur over weekends in March and October.

Sights

STAR-RATING

★★★	Worth a journey
★★	Worth a detour
★	Interesting
AC	Admission charge

LOCATION

See	Sights in town
Envir.	On the outskirts
Exc.	In the surrounding area
N, S, E, W	The sight lies north, south, east or west of the town
A 22	Take road A 22, indicated by the same symbol on the Guide map
2 m.	Mileage

Town plans

Hotels – Restaurants

Sights

Place of interest and its main entrance
Interesting place of worship

Roads

Motorway
Interchanges : complete, limited
Dual carriageway with motorway characteristics
Main traffic artery
Primary route
(network currently being reclassified)
One-way street – Unsuitable for traffic, street subject to restrictions
Pedestrian street
Piccadilly P Shopping street – Car park
Gateway – Street passing under arch – Tunnel
15'5 Low headroom (16'6" max.) on major through routes
Station and railway
Funicular – Cable-car
B Lever bridge – Car ferry

Various signs

Tourist Information Centre
Mosque – Synagogue
Communications tower or mast – Ruins
Garden, park, wood – Cemetery
Stadium – Racecourse – Golf course
Golf course (with restrictions for visitors)
View – Panorama
Monument – Fountain – Hospital
Pleasure boat harbour – Lighthouse
Airport – Underground station
Ferry services :
passengers and cars
Main post office with poste restante, telephone
Public buildings located by letter :
C H County Council Offices – Town Hall
M T U Museum – Theatre – University, College
POL Police (in large towns police headquarters)

London

BRENT SOHO Borough – Area
Borough boundary – Area boundary

North is at the top on all town plans.

Car, tyres

The wearing of seat belts in Great Britain is obligatory for drivers, front seat passengers and rear seat passengers where seat belts are fitted. It is illegal for front seat passengers to carry children on their lap.

In the Republic of Ireland seat belts are compulsory, if fitted, for drivers and front seat passengers. Children under 12 are not allowed in front seats unless in a suitable safety restraint.

MICHELIN TYRE SUPPLIERS

ATS Tyre dealers

The location of the nearest ATS tyre dealer can be obtained by contacting the address below between 9am and 5pm.

ATS HOUSE
180-188 Northolt Rd.
Harrow,
Middlesex HA2 OED
(0181) 423 2000

MOTORING ORGANISATIONS

The major motoring organisations in Great Britain and Ireland are the Automobile Association and the Royal Automobile Club. Each provides services in varying degrees for non-resident members of affiliated clubs.

AUTOMOBILE ASSOCIATION
Fanum House
BASINGSTOKE, Hants., RG21 2EA
✆ (01256) 20123

AUTOMOBILE ASSOCIATION
108-110 Great-Victoria St.
BELFAST, BT2 7AT
✆ 01 232-328924

AUTOMOBILE ASSOCIATION
23 Rock Hill
BLACKROCK
Co-Dublin
✆ 01 283-3555

ROYAL AUTOMOBILE CLUB
RAC House, Lansdowne Rd.
CROYDON, Surrey CR9 2JA
✆ (0181) 686 2525

ROYAL AUTOMOBILE CLUB
RAC House, 79 Chichester St.
BELFAST, BT1 4JR
✆ 01 232-240261

ROYAL AUTOMOBILE CLUB
RAC IRELAND
New Mount House
22-24 Lower Mount St.
DUBLIN 2
✆ 01 760113

Ami lecteur

Cette 22e édition du Guide Michelin
Great Britain and Ireland
propose une sélection actualisée
d'hôtels et de restaurants.

Réalisée en toute indépendance,
par nos inspecteurs,
elle offre au voyageur de passage
un large choix d'adresses
à tous les niveaux de confort et de prix.

Toujours soucieux d'apporter
à nos lecteurs l'information la plus récente,
nous avons mis à jour cette édition
avec le plus grand soin.

C'est pourquoi, seul,
le Guide de l'année en cours
mérite votre confiance.

Merci de vos commentaires
toujours appréciés.

MICHELIN vous souhaite « Bon voyage ! »

Sommaire

13 Ami lecteur

15 à 22 Comment se servir du guide

43 Abréviations des comtés

44 Les établissements à étoiles

45 Autres tables qui méritent votre attention

Hôtels et restaurants particulièrement agréables

Hôtels, restaurants, plans de ville, curiosités... et cartes

49 England

Londres *Pages bordées de rouge*

533 Wales

567 Scotland

649 Northern Ireland

659 Channel Islands

671 Isle of Man

673 Republic of Ireland

719 Principales chaînes hôtelières

720 Distances

722 Atlas : principales routes et liaisons maritimes

728 Indicatifs téléphoniques européens

732 Cartes et Guides Michelin

Le choix
d'un hôtel, d'un restaurant

Ce guide vous propose une sélection d'hôtels et restaurants établie à l'usage de l'automobiliste de passage. Les établissements, classés selon leur confort, sont cités par ordre de préférence dans chaque catégorie.

CATÉGORIES

🏨🏨🏨🏨🏨	Grand luxe et tradition	XXXXX
🏨🏨🏨🏨	Grand confort	XXXX
🏨🏨🏨	Très confortable	XXX
🏨🏨	De bon confort	XX
🏨	Assez confortable	X
	Simple mais convenable	
	Autre ressource hôtelière conseillée, à prix modérés	
Without rest.	L'hôtel n'a pas de restaurant	
	Le restaurant possède des chambres	with rm

AGRÉMENT ET TRANQUILLITÉ

Certains établissements se distinguent dans le guide par les symboles rouges indiqués ci-après. Le séjour dans ces hôtels se révèle particulièrement agréable ou reposant.
Cela peut tenir d'une part au caractère de l'édifice, au décor original, au site, à l'accueil et aux services qui sont proposés, d'autre part à la tranquillité des lieux.

🏨🏨🏨🏨🏨 à	Hôtels agréables
XXXXX à X	Restaurants agréables
« Park »	Élément particulièrement agréable
	Hôtel très tranquille ou isolé et tranquille
	Hôtel tranquille
≤ sea	Vue exceptionnelle
≤	Vue intéressante ou étendue.

Les localités possédant des établissements agréables ou tranquilles sont repérées sur les cartes placées au début de chacune des régions traitées dans ce guide.
Consultez-les pour la préparation de vos voyages et donnez-nous vos appréciations à votre retour, vous faciliterez ainsi nos enquêtes.

L'installation

Les chambres des hôtels que nous recommandons possèdent, en général, des installations sanitaires complètes. Il est toutefois possible que dans les catégories 🏘, 🏠, ⛱ et ⌂, certaines chambres en soient dépourvues.

30 ch	Nombre de chambres
	Ascenseur
	Air conditionné
TV	Télévision dans la chambre
	Établissement entièrement ou en partie réservé aux non-fumeurs
	Téléphone dans la chambre relié par standard
	Téléphone dans la chambre, direct avec l'extérieur
	Chambres accessibles aux handicapés physiques
	Piscine : de plein air ou couverte
	Salle de remise en forme – Sauna
	Jardin de repos
9	Tennis à l'hôtel – Golf et nombre de trous
	Pêche ouverte aux clients de l'hôtel (éventuellement payant)
150	Salles de conférences : capacité maximum
	Garage dans l'hôtel (généralement payant)
P	Parking réservé à la clientèle
	Accès interdit aux chiens (dans tout ou partie de l'établissement)
Fax	Transmission de documents par télécopie
May-October	Période d'ouverture, communiquée par l'hôtelier
season	Ouverture probable en saison mais dates non précisées. En l'absence de mention, l'établissement est ouvert toute l'année.
LL35 OSB	Code postal de l'établissement
(Forte)	Chaîne hôtelière (voir liste en fin de guide)

Animaux

L'introduction d'animaux domestiques (chiens, chats...) est interdite en Grande-Bretagne et en Irlande.

La table

LES ÉTOILES

Certains établissements méritent d'être signalés à votre attention pour la qualité de leur cuisine. Nous les distinguons par **les étoiles de bonne table**.
Nous indiquons, pour ces établissements, trois spécialités culinaires qui pourront orienter votre choix.

✿✿✿ **Une des meilleures tables, vaut le voyage**
Table merveilleuse, grands vins, service impeccable, cadre élégant... Prix en conséquence.

✿✿ **Table excellente, mérite un détour**
Spécialités et vins de choix... Attendez-vous à une dépense en rapport.

✿ **Une très bonne table dans sa catégorie**
L'étoile marque une bonne étape sur votre itinéraire.
Mais ne comparez pas l'étoile d'un établissement de luxe à prix élevés avec celle d'une petite maison où à prix raisonnables, on sert également une cuisine de qualité.

« Meals »

Tout en appréciant les tables à « étoiles », on peut souhaiter trouver sur sa route un repas plus simple mais toujours de préparation soignée. Certaines maisons nous ont paru répondre à cette préoccupation.
Le mot « **Meals** » rouge les signale à votre attention dans le texte de ce guide.
Consultez les cartes des localités (étoiles de bonne table et **Meals**) *placées au début de chacune des régions traitées dans ce guide.*

La vente de boissons alcoolisées

En Grande-Bretagne et en Irlande, la vente de boissons alcoolisées est soumise à des lois pouvant varier d'une région à l'autre.
D'une façon générale, les hôtels, les restaurants et les pubs peuvent demeurer ouverts l'après-midi et servir des boissons alcoolisées dans la mesure où elles accompagnent un repas suffisamment consistant. Les bars ferment après 23 heures.
Néanmoins, l'hôtelier a toujours la possibilité de servir, à sa clientèle, des boissons alcoolisées en dehors des heures légales.
Les enfants au-dessous de 14 ans n'ont pas accès aux bars.

Les prix

Les prix que nous indiquons dans ce guide ont été établis en automne 1994. Ils sont susceptibles de modifications, notamment en cas de variations des prix des biens et services.

Entrez à l'hôtel le guide à la main, vous montrerez ainsi qu'il vous conduit là en confiance.

Les prix sont indiqués en livres sterling (1 £ = 100 pence), sauf en République d'Irlande où ils sont donnés en « Punts ».
Lorsque les mentions **s.**, **t.**, ou **st.** ne figurent pas, les prix indiqués peuvent être majorés d'un pourcentage pour le service, la T.V.A., ou les deux. (La T.V.A. n'est pas appliquée dans les Channel Islands.)
Les hôtels et restaurants figurent en gros caractères lorsque les hôteliers nous ont donné tous leurs prix et se sont engagés, sous leur propre responsabilité, à les appliquer aux touristes de passage porteurs de notre guide.

REPAS

Meals 13.00/24.00	**Repas à prix fixe** - Déjeuner 13.00, diner 24.00. Ces prix s'entendent couvert compris
Meals 15.00/25.00	Voir page 17
s.	Service compris
t.	T.V.A. comprise
st.	Service et T.V.A. compris (prix nets)
6.00	Prix de la 1/2 bouteille ou carafe de vin ordinaire
Meals à la carte 20.00/25.00	**Repas à la carte** - Le 1er prix correspond à un repas simple mais soigné, comprenant : petite entrée, plat du jour garni, dessert. Le 2e prix concerne un repas plus complet, comprenant : hors-d'œuvre, plat principal, fromage ou dessert. Ces prix s'entendent couvert compris
8.50	Prix du petit déjeuner à l'anglaise, s'il n'est pas compris dans celui de la chambre. Un petit déjeuner continental peut être obtenu à moindre prix

: Dans les établissements de cette catégorie, le dîner est servi à heure fixe exclusivement aux personnes ayant une chambre. Le menu, à prix unique, offre un choix limité de plats. Le déjeuner est rarement proposé. Beaucoup de ces établissements ne sont pas autorisés à vendre des boissons alcoolisées.

CHAMBRES

rm 50.00/80.00	Prix minimum 50.00 d'une chambre pour une personne et prix maximum 80.00 de la plus belle chambre occupée par deux personnes
rm 55.00/75.00	Le prix du petit déjeuner à l'anglaise est inclus dans le prix de la chambre, même s'il n'est pas consommé

« SHORT BREAKS »

Certains hôtels proposent des conditions avantageuses ou « Short Break » pour un séjour minimum de 2 nuits. Ce forfait calculé par personne, pour 2 personnes au minimum, comprend la chambre, le diner et le petit déjeuner. Se renseigner auprès de l'hôtelier.

LES ARRHES - CARTES DE CRÉDIT

Certains hôteliers demandent le versement d'arrhes. Il s'agit d'un dépôt-garantie qui engage l'hôtelier comme le client. Bien faire préciser les dispositions de cette garantie.

AE VISA JCB	Cartes de crédit acceptées par l'établissement : Access (Eurocard) - American Express - Diners Club - Visa - Japan Card Bank

Les villes

✉ York	Bureau de poste desservant la localité
01225 Bath	Indicatif téléphonique interurbain suivi, si nécessaire, de la localité de rattachement (De l'étranger, ne pas composer le 0)
401 M 27, ⑩	Numéro des cartes Michelin et carroyage ou numéro du pli
West Country G.	Voir le guide vert Michelin England : The West Country
pop. 1057	Population
ECD : Wednesday	Jour de fermeture des magasins (après-midi seulement)
BX **A**	Lettres repérant un emplacement sur le plan
18	Golf et nombre de trous (Handicap généralement demandé, réservation par téléphone vivement recommandée)
✳, ←	Panorama, point de vue
✈	Aéroport
☎ 261 1234	Localité desservie par train-auto. Renseignements au numéro de téléphone indiqué
	Transports maritimes
	Transports maritimes (pour passagers seulement) *Voir liste des compagnies en fin de guide*
ℹ	Information touristique

Heure légale

Les visiteurs devront tenir compte de l'heure officielle en Grande Bretagne : une heure de retard sur l'heure française.

Les curiosités

INTÉRÊT

★★★	Vaut le voyage
★★	Mérite un détour
★	Intéressant
AC	Entrée payante

SITUATION

See	Dans la ville
Envir.	Aux environs de la ville
Exc.	Excursions dans la région
N, S, E, W	La curiosité est située : au Nord, au Sud, à l'Est, à l'Ouest
A 22	On s'y rend par la route A 22, repérée par le même signe sur le plan du Guide
2 m.	Distance en miles

Les plans

@ ●a **Hôtels - Restaurants**

Curiosités

Bâtiment intéressant et entrée principale

Édifice religieux intéressant

Voirie

M 1 Autoroute
échangeurs : complet, partiel

Route à chaussées séparées de type autoroutier

Grand axe de circulation

A 2 Itinéraire principal (Primary route)
réseau en cours de révision

Sens unique - Rue impraticable, réglementée

Rue piétonne

Piccadilly P Rue commerçante - Parc de stationnement

Porte - Passage sous voûte - Tunnel

15'5 Passage bas (inférieur à 16'6") sur les grandes voies de circulation

Gare et voie ferrée

Funiculaire - Téléphérique, télécabine

B Pont mobile - Bac pour autos

Signes divers

Information touristique

Mosquée - Synagogue

Tour ou pylône de télécommunication - Ruines

Jardin, parc, bois - Cimetière

Stade - Hippodrome - Golf

Golf (réservé)

Vue - Panorama

Monument - Fontaine - Hôpital

Port de plaisance - Phare

Aéroport - Station de métro

Transport par bateau :
passagers et voitures

Bureau principal de poste restante, téléphone

Bâtiment public repéré par une lettre :

C H Bureau de l'Administration du Comté - Hôtel de ville

M T U Musée - Théâtre - Université, grande école

POL. Police (commissariat central)

Londres

BRENT SOHO Nom d'arrondissement (borough) - de quartier (area)

Limite de « borough » - d'« area »

Les plans de villes sont disposés le Nord en haut.

La voiture, les pneus

En Grande-Bretagne, le port de la ceinture de sécurité est obligatoire pour le conducteur et le passager avant ainsi qu'à l'arrière, si le véhicule en est équipé. La loi interdit au passager avant de prendre un enfant sur ses genoux.

En République d'Irlande, le port de la ceinture de sécurité est obligatoire pour le conducteur et le passager avant, si le véhicule en est équipé. Les enfants de moins de 12 ans ne sont pas autorisés à s'asseoir à l'avant, sauf si le véhicule est muni d'un système d'attache approprié.

FOURNISSEURS DE PNEUS MICHELIN

ATS Spécialistes du pneu

Des renseignements sur le plus proche point de vente de pneus ATS pourront être obtenus en s'informant entre 9 h et 17 h à l'adresse indiquée ci-dessous.

ATS HOUSE
180-188 Northolt Rd.
Harrow,
Middlesex HA2 OED
(0181) 423 2000

AUTOMOBILE CLUBS

Les principales organisations de secours automobile dans le pays sont l'Automobile Association et le Royal Automobile Club, toutes deux offrant certains de leurs services aux membres de clubs affilés.

AUTOMOBILE ASSOCIATION
Fanum House
BASINGSTOKE, Hants., RG21 2EA
✆ (01256) 20123

AUTOMOBILE ASSOCIATION
108-110 Great-Victoria St.
BELFAST, BT2 7AT
✆ 01232-328924

AUTOMOBILE ASSOCIATION
23 Rock Hill
BLACKROCK
Co-Dublin
✆ 01 283-3555

ROYAL AUTOMOBILE CLUB
RAC House, Lansdowne Rd,
CROYDON, Surrey CR9 2JA
✆ (0181) 686 2525

ROYAL AUTOMOBILE CLUB
RAC House, 79 Chichester St.
BELFAST, BT1 4JR
✆ 01232-240261

ROYAL AUTOMOBILE CLUB
RAC IRELAND New Mount House
22-24 Lower Mount St.
DUBLIN 2
✆ 01 760113

Amico Lettore

Questa 22esima edizione
della Guida Michelin
Great Britain and Ireland
propone una selezione aggiornata
di alberghi e ristoranti.

Realizzata dai nostri ispettori
in piena autonomia
offre al viaggiatore di passaggio
un'ampia scelta a tutti i livelli
di comfort e prezzo.

Con l'intento di fornire
ai nostri lettori
l'informazione più recente,
abbiamo aggiornato questa edizione
con la massima cura.
Per questo solo la Guida dell'anno
in corso merita pienamente
la vostra fiducia.

Grazie delle vostre segnalazioni
sempre gradite.

Michelin vi augura « Buon Viaggio ! »

Sommario

23 Amico Lettore

25 a 32 Come servirsi della guida

43 Abbreviazioni delle contee

44 Gli esercizi con stelle

45 Altre tavole particolarmente interessanti
Alberghi e ristoranti ameni

Alberghi, ristoranti, piante di città, curiosità... e Carte

49 England

Londra *Pagine bordate di rosso*

533 Wales

567 Scotland

649 Northern Ireland

659 Channel Islands

671 Isle of Man

673 Republic of Ireland

719 Principali catene alberghiere

720 Distanze

722 Carta : principali strade e collegamenti marittimi

728 Indicativi telefonici dei paesi europei

732 Carte e guide Michelin

La scelta
di un albergo, di un ristorante

Questa guida Vi propone una selezione di alberghi e ristoranti stabilita ad uso dell'automobilista di passaggio. Gli esercizi, classificati in base al confort che offrono, vengono citati in ordine di preferenza per ogni categoria.

CATEGORIE

🏨🏨🏨🏨🏨	Gran lusso e tradizione	XXXXX
🏨🏨🏨🏨	Gran confort	XXXX
🏨🏨🏨	Molto confortevole	XXX
🏨🏨	Di buon confort	XX
🏨	Abbastanza confortevole	X
	Semplice, ma conveniente	
	Altra risorsa, consigliata per prezzi contenuti	
without rest.	L'albergo non ha ristorante	
	Il ristorante dispone di camere	with rm

AMENITÀ E TRANQUILLITÀ

Alcuni esercizi sono evidenziati nella guida dai simboli rossi indicati qui di seguito. Il soggiorno in questi alberghi dovrebbe rivelarsi particolarmente ameno o riposante.
Ciò può dipendere sia dalle caratteristiche dell'edifico, dalle decorazioni non comuni, dalla sua posizione e dal servizio offerto, sia dalla tranquillità dei luoghi.

🏨🏨🏨🏨🏨 a	Alberghi ameni
XXXXX a X	Ristoranti ameni
« Park »	Un particolare piacevole
	Albergo molto tranquillo o isolato e tranquillo
	Albergo tranquillo
< sea	Vista eccezionale
<	Vista interessante o estesa

Le località che possiedono degli esercizi ameni o tranquilli sono riportate sulle carte che precedono ciascuna delle regioni trattate nella guida.

Consultatele per la preparazione dei Vostri viaggi e, al ritorno, inviateci i Vostri pareri ; in tal modo agevolerete le nostre inchieste.

Installazioni

Le camere degli alberghi che raccomandiamo possiedono, generalmente, delle installazioni sanitarie complete. È possibile tuttavia che nelle categorie , , e alcune camere ne siano sprovviste.

30 rm	Numero di camere
	Ascensore
	Aria condizionata
	Televisione in camera
	Esercizio riservato completamente o in parte ai non fumatori
	Telefono in camera collegato con il centralino
	Telefono in camera comunicante direttamente con l'esterno
	Camere di agevole accesso per i minorati fisici
	Piscina : all'aperto, coperta
	Palestra - Sauna
	Giardino da riposo
	Tennis appartenente all'albergo - Golf e numero di buche
	Pesca aperta ai clienti dell' albergo (eventualmente a pagamento)
150	Sale per conferenze : capienza massima
	Garage nell'albergo (generalmente a pagamento)
	Parcheggio riservato alla clientela
	Accesso vietato ai cani (in tutto o in parte dell'esercizio)
Fax	Trasmissione telefonica di documenti
May-October	Periodo di apertura, comunicato dall'albergatore
season	Probabile apertura in stagione, ma periodo non precisato. Gli esercizi senza tali menzioni sono aperti tutto l'anno.
LL35 OSB	Codice postale dell' esercizio
(Forte)	Catena alberghiera (Vedere la lista alla fine della Guida)

Animali

L'introduzione di animali domestici (cani, gatti...), in Gran Bretagna e in Irlanda, è vietata.

La tavola

LE STELLE

Alcuni esercizi meritano di essere segnalati alla Vostra attenzione per la qualità tutta particolare della loro cucina. Noi li evidenziamo con le « **stelle di ottima tavola** ».
Per questi ristoranti indichiamo tre specialità culinarie e alcuni vini locali che potranno aiutarVi nella scelta.

✿✿✿ **Una delle migliori tavole, vale il viaggio**
Tavola meravigliosa, grandi vini, servizio impeccabile, ambientazione accurata... Prezzi conformi.

✿✿ **Tavola eccellente, merita una deviazione**
Specialità e vini scelti... AspettateVi una spesa in proporzione.

✿ **Un'ottima tavola nella sua categoria**
La stella indica una tappa gastronomica sul Vostro itinerario. Non mettete però a confronto la stella di un esercizio di lusso, dai prezzi elevati, con quella di un piccolo esercizio dove, a prezzi ragionevoli, viene offerta una cucina di qualità.

« Meals »

Pur apprezzando le tavole a « stella », si desidera alle volte consumare un pasto più semplice ma sempre accuratamente preparato.
Alcuni esercizi ci son parsi rispondenti a tale esigenza e sono contraddistinti nella guida con « **Meals** » in rosso.

Consultate le carte delle località con stelle e con **Meals** che precedono ciascuna delle regioni trattate nella guida.

La vendita di bevande alcoliche

In Gran Bretagna e Irlanda la vendita di bevande alcoliche è soggetta a leggi che possono variare da una regione all'altra.
In generale gli alberghi, i ristoranti e i pubs possono restare aperti il pomeriggio e servire bevande alcoliche nella misura in cui queste accompagnano un pasto abbastanza consistente.
I bars chiudono dopo le ore 23.00.
L'albergatore ha tuttavia la possobilità di servire alla clientela bevande alcoliche anche oltre le ore legali.
Ai ragazzi inferiori ai 14 anni è vietato l'accesso ai bar.

I prezzi

I prezzi che indichiamo in questa guida sono stati stabiliti nel l'autunno 1994. Potranno pertanto subire delle variazioni in relazione ai cambiamenti dei prezzi di beni e servizi.

Entrate nell'albergo o nel ristorante con la guida alla mano, dimostrando in tal modo la fiducia in chi vi ha indirizzato.

Gli alberghi e i ristoranti vengono menzionati in carattere grassetto quando gli albergatori ci hanno comunicato tutti i loro prezzi e si sono impegnati, sotto la propria responsabilità, ad applicarli ai turisti di passaggio, in possesso della nostra guida.
I prezzi sono indicati in lire sterline (1 £ = 100 pence) ad eccezione per la Repubblica d'Irlanda dove sono indicati in « punts ».
Quando non figurano le lettere **s.**, **t.**, o **st.** i prezzi indicati possono essere maggiorati per il servizio o per l'I.V.A. o per entrambi. (L'I.V.A. non viene applicata nelle Channel Islands).

PASTI

Meals 13.00/24.00	**Prezzo fisso** – Pranzo 13.00, cena 24.00. Questi prezzi comprendono il coperto
Meals 15.00/25.00	Vedere p. 27
s.	Servizio compreso
t.	I.V.A. compresa
st.	Servizio ed I.V.A. compresi (prezzi netti)
🍷 6.00	Prezzo della mezza bottiglia o di una caraffa di vino
Meals a la carte 20.00/25.00	**Alla carta** – Il 1° prezzo corrisponde ad un pasto semplice comprendente : primo piatto, piatto del giorno con contorno, dessert. Il 2° prezzo corrisponde ad un pasto più completo comprendente : antipasto, piatto principale, formaggio e dessert Questi prezzi comprendono il coperto
☕ 8.50	Prezzo della prima colazione inglese se non è compreso nel prezzo della camera. Una prima colazione continentale può essere ottenuta a minor prezzo

⌂ : Negli alberghi di questa categoria, la cena viene servita, ad un'ora stabilita, esclusivamente a chi vi allogia. Il menu, a prezzo fisso, offre una scelta limitata di piatti. Raramente viene servito anche il pranzo. Molti di questi esercizi non hanno l'autorizzazione a vendere alcolici.

CAMERE

rm 50.00/80.00	Prezzo minimo 50.00 per una camera singola e prezzo massimo 80.00 per la camera più bella per due persone
rm ☕ 55.00/75.00	Il prezzo della prima colazione inglese è compreso nel prezzo della camera anche se non viene consumata

« SHORT BREAKS »

Alcuni alberghi propongono delle condizioni particolarmente vantaggiose o short break per un soggiorno minimo di due notti.
Questo prezzo, calcolato per persona e per un minimo di due persone, comprende : camera, cena e prima colazione. Informarsi presso l'albergatore.

LA CAPARRA - CARTE DI CREDITO

Alcuni albergatori chiedono il versamento di una caparra. Si tratta di un deposito-garanzia che impegna tanto l'albergatore che il cliente. Vi raccomandiamo di farVi precisare le norme riguardanti la reciproca garanzia di tale caparra.

AE VISA JCB	Carte di credito accettate dall'esercizio Access (Eurocard) - American Express - Diners Club - Visa - Japan Card Bank

Le città

✉ York	Sede dell'ufficio postale
01225 Bath	Prefisso telefonico interurbano (nome del centralino indicato solo quando differisce dal nome della località). Dall'estero non formare lo 0
401 M 27, ⑩	Numero della carta Michelin e del riquadro o numero della piega
West Country G.	Vedere la Guida Verde Michelin England : The West Country
pop. 1057	Popolazione
ECD : Wednesday	Giorno di chiusura settimanale dei negozi (solo pomeriggio)
BX **A**	Lettere indicanti l'ubicazione sulla pianta
18	Golf e numero di buche (handicap generalmente richiesto, prenotazione telefonica vivamente consigliata)
✻, ⋞	Panorama, punto di vista
✈	Aeroporto
☎ 261 1234	Località con servizio auto su treno. Informarsi al numero di telefono indicato
⛴	Trasporti marittimi
	Trasporti marittimi (solo passeggeri) *Vedere la lista delle compagnie alla fine della Guida*
ℹ	Ufficio informazioni turistiche

Ora legale

I visitatori dovranno tenere in considerazione l'ora ufficiale in Gran Bretagna : un'ora di ritardo sull'ora italiana.

Le curiosità

GRADO DI INTERESSE

★★★	Vale il viaggio
★★	Merita una deviazione
★	Interessante
AC	Entrata a pagamento

UBICAZIONE

See	Nella città
Envir.	Nei dintorni della città
Exc.	Nella regione
N, S, E, W	La curiosità è situata : a Nord, a Sud, a Est, a Ovest
A 22	Ci si va per la strada A 22 indicata con lo stesso segno sulla pianta
2 m.	Distanza in miglia

Le piante

a ● a — **Alberghi – Ristoranti**

Curiosità

Edificio interessante ed entrata principale
Costruzione religiosa interessante

Viabilità

M 1 — Autostrada
4 4 — svincoli : completo, parziale,
Strada a carregiate separate di tipo autostradale
Asse principale di circolazione
A 2 — Itinerario principale
(« Primary route », rete stradale in corso di revisione)
Senso unico – Via impraticabile, a circolazione regolamentata
Via pedonale
Piccadilly P — Via commerciale – Parcheggio
Porta – Sottopassaggio – Galleria
15'5 — Sottopassaggio (altezza inferiore a 16'6") sulle grandi vie di circolazione
Stazione e ferrovia
Funicolare – Funivia, Cabinovia
B — Ponte mobile – Battello per auto

Simboli vari

Ufficio informazioni turistiche
Moschea – Sinagoga
Torre o pilone per telecomunicazione – Ruderi
Giardino, parco, bosco – Cimitero
9 — Stadio – Ippodromo – Golf
Golf riservato
Vista – Panorama
Monumento – Fontana – Ospedale
Porto per imbarcazioni da diporto – Faro
Aeroporto – Stazione della Metropolitana
Trasporto con traghetto :
passeggeri ed autovetture
Ufficio centrale di fermo posta, telefono
Edificio pubblico indicato con lettera :
C H — Sede dell'Amministrazione di Contea – Municipio
M T U — Museo – Teatro – Università, grande scuola
POL — Polizia (Questura, nelle grandi città)

Londra

BRENT SOHO — Nome del distretto amministrativo (borough) – del quartiere (area)
Limite del « borough » – di « area »

Le piante topografiche sono orientale col Nord in alto.

L'automobile, I pneumatici

In Gran Bretagna, l'uso delle cinture di sicurezza è obbligatorio per il conducente e il passeggero del sedile anteriore, nonchè per i sedili posteriori, se ne sono equipaggiati. La legge non consente al passaggero d'avanti di tenere un bambino sulle ginocchia.

Nella Repubblica d'Irlanda, l'uso delle cinture di sicurezza è obbligatorio per il conducente e il passeggero d'avanti, se il veicolo ne è equipaggiato. I bambini di meno di 12 anni non sono autorizzati a viaggiare sul sedile anteriore, a meno che questo non sia fornito di un sistema di ritenuta espressamente concepito per loro.

RIVENDITORI DI PNEUMATICI MICHELIN

ATS Specialista in pneumatici

Potrete avere delle informazioni sul più vicino punto vendita di pneumatici ATS, rivolgendovi, tra le 9 e le 17, all'indirizzo indicato qui di seguito :

ATS HOUSE
180-188 Northolt Rd.
Harrow,
Middlesex HA2 OED
(0181) 423 2000

AUTOMOBILE CLUBS

Le principali organizzazioni di soccorso automobilistico sono l'Automobile Association ed il Royal Automobile Club : entrambe offrono alcuni loro servizi ai membri dei club affiliati.

AUTOMOBILE ASSOCIATION
Fanum House
BASINGSTOKE, Hants., RG21 2EA
✆ (01256) 20123

AUTOMOBILE ASSOCIATION
108-110 Great-Victoria St.
BELFAST, BT2 7AT
✆ 01232-328924

AUTOMOBILE ASSOCIATION
23 Rock Hill
BLACKROCK
Co-Dublin
✆ 01 283-3555

ROYAL AUTOMOBILE CLUB
RAC House, Lansdowne Rd,
CROYDON, Surrey CR9 2JA
✆ (0181) 686 2525

ROYAL AUTOMOBILE CLUB
RAC House, 79 Chichester St.
BELFAST, BT1 4JR
✆ 01232-240261

ROYAL AUTOMOBILE CLUB
RAC IRELAND New Mount House
22-24 Lower Mount St.
DUBLIN 2
✆ 01 760113

Lieber Leser

Die 22. Ausgabe
des MICHELIN-Hotelführers
Great Britain and Ireland
bietet Ihnen
eine aktualisierte Auswahl
an Hotels und Restaurants.

Von unseren unabhängigen
Hotelinspektoren ausgearbeitet,
beitet der Hotel führer dem
Reisenden eine Große Auswahl
an Hotels und Restaurants
in jeder Kategorie sowohl was den Preis
als auch den Komfort anbelangt.

Stets bemüht,
unseren Lesern die neueste
Information anzubieten,
wurde diese Ausgabe
mit größter Sorgfalt erstellt.

Deshalb sollten Sie immer
nur dem aktuellen Hotelführer
Ihr Vertrauen schenken.

Ihre Kommentare sind uns
immer willkommen.

MICHELIN wünscht Ihnen "Gute Reise !"

Inhaltsverzeichnis

S. 33 Lieber Leser

S. 35 bis 42 Zum Gebrauch dieses Führers

43 Abkürzungen der Grafschaften

S. 44 Die Stern-Restaurants

S. 45 Weitere empfehlenswerte häuser

Angenehmen Hotels und Restaurants

Hotels, Restaurants, Stadtpläne, Sehenswürdigkeiten...
Karten

S. 49 England

London *Rot umrandete Seiten*

S. 533 Wales

S. 567 Scotland

S. 649 Northern Ireland

S. 659 Channel Islands

S. 671 Isle of Man

S. 673 Republic of Ireland

S. 719 Die wichtigsten Hotelketten

S. 720 Entfernungen

S. 722 Atlas : Hauptverkehrsstraßen und -schiffsverbindungen

S. 728 Telefon-Vorwahlnummern europäischer Länder

S. 732 Michelin-Karten und -Führer

Wahl

eines Hotels, eines Restaurants

Die Auswahl der in diesem Führer aufgeführten Hotels und Restaurants ist für Durchreisende gedacht. In jeder Kategorie drückt die Reihenfolge der Betriebe (sie sind nach ihrem Komfort klassifiziert) eine weitere Rangordnung aus.

KATEGORIEN

꜒	Großer Luxus und Tradition	XXXXX
	Großer Komfort	XXXX
	Sehr komfortabel	XXX
	Mit gutem Komfort	XX
	Mit ausreichendem Komfort	X
	Bürgerlich	
	Preiswerte, empfehlenswerte Gasthäuser und Pensionen	
without rest.	Hotel ohne Restaurant	
	Restaurant vermietet auch Zimmer	with rm

ANNEHMLICHKEITEN

Manche Häuser sind im Führer durch rote Symbole gekennzeichnet (s. unten). Der Aufenthalt in diesen Hotels ist wegen der schönen, ruhigen Lage, der nicht alltäglichen Einrichtung und Atmosphäre und dem gebotenen Service besonders angenehm und erholsam.

bis	Angenehme Hotels
XXXXX bis X	Angenehme Restaurants
« Park »	Besondere Annehmlichkeit
	Sehr ruhiges, oder abgelegenes und ruhiges Hotel
	Ruhiges Hotel
sea	Reizvolle Aussicht
	Interessante oder weite Sicht

Die den einzelnen Regionen vorangestellten Übersichtskarten, auf denen die Orte mit besonders angenehmen oder ruhigen Häusern eingezeichnet sind, helfen Ihnen bei der Reisevorbereitung. Teilen Sie uns bitte nach der Reise Ihre Erfahrungen und Meinungen mit. Sie helfen uns damit, den Führer weiter zu verbessern.

Einrichtung

Die meisten der empfohlenen Hotels verfügen über Zimmer, die alle oder doch zum größten Teil mit einer Naßzelle ausgestattet sind. In den Häusern der Kategorien , , und kann diese jedoch in einigen Zimmern fehlen.

30 rm	Anzahl der Zimmer
	Fahrstuhl
	Klimaanlage
TV	Fernsehen im Zimmer
	Hotel ganz oder teilweise reserviert für Nichtraucher
	Zimmertelefon mit Außenverbindung über Telefonzentrale
	Zimmertelefon mit direkter Außenverbindung
	Für Körperbehinderte leicht zugängliche Zimmer
	Freibad, Hallenbad
	Fitneßcenter – Sauna
	Liegewiese, Garten
9	Hoteleigener Tennisplatz – Golfplatz und Lochzahl
	Angelmöglichkeit für Hotelgäste, evtl. gegen Gebühr
150	Konferenzräume : Höchstkapazität
	Hotelgarage (wird gewöhnlich berechnet)
P	Parkplatz reserviert für Gäste
	Hunde sind unerwünscht (im ganzen Haus bzw. in den Zimmern oder im Restaurant)
Fax	Telefonische Dokumentenübermittlung
May-October	Öffnungszeit, vom Hotelier mitgeteilt
season	Unbestimmte Öffnungszeit eines Saisonhotels. Die Häuser, für die wir keine Schließungszeiten angeben, sind im allgemeinen ganzjährig geöffnet
LL35 OSB	Angabe des Postbezirks (hinter der Hoteladresse)
(Forte)	Hotelkette (Liste am Ende des Führers)

Tiere

Das Mitführen von Haustieren (Hunde, Katzen u. dgl.) bei der Einreise in Großbritannien und Irland ist untersagt.

Küche

DIE STERNE

Einige Häuser verdienen wegen ihrer überdurchschnittlich guten Küche Ihre besondere Beachtung. Auf diese Häuser weisen die Sterne hin.

Bei den mit « **Stern** » ausgezeichneten Betrieben nennen wir drei kulinarische Spezialitäten, die Sie probieren sollten.

✿✿✿ **Eine der besten Küchen : eine Reise wert**
Ein denkwürdiges Essen, edle Weine, tadelloser Service, gepflegte Atmosphäre ... entsprechende Preise.

✿✿ **Eine hervorragende Küche : verdient einen Umweg**
Ausgesuchte Menus und Weine ... angemessene Preise.

✿ **Eine sehr gute Küche : verdient Ihre besondere Beachtung**
Der Stern bedeutet eine angenehme Unterbrechung Ihrer Reise.
Vergleichen Sie aber bitte nicht den Stern eines sehr teuren Luxusrestaurants mit dem Stern eines kleineren oder mittleren Hauses, wo man Ihnen zu einem annehmbaren Preis eine ebenfalls vorzügliche Mahlzeit reicht.

« Meals »

Wir glauben, daß Sie neben den Häusen mit « Stern » auch solche Adressen interessieren werden, die einfache, aber sorgfältig zubereitete Mahlzeiten anbieten.

« Meals » im Text weist auf solche Haüser hin.

Siehe Karten der Orte mit « Stern » und « Meals », die den einzelnen im Führer behandelten Regionen vorangestellt sind.

Ausschank alkoholischer Getränke

In Großbritannien und Irland unterliegt der Ausschank alkoholischer Getränke gesetzlichen Bestimmungen, die in den einzelnen Gegenden verschieden sind.

Generell können Hotels, Restaurants und Pubs nachmittags geöffnet sein und alkoholische Getränke ausschenken, wenn diese zu einer entsprechend gehaltvollen Mahlzeit genossen werden. Die Bars schließen nach 23 Uhr.

Hotelgästen können alkoholische Getränke jedoch auch außerhalb der Ausschankzeiten serviert werden.

Kindern unter 14 Jahren ist der Zutritt zu den Bars untersagt.

Preise

Die in diesem Führer genannten Preise wurden uns im Herbst 1994 angegeben. Sie können sich mit den Preisen von Waren und Dienstleistungen ändern.

Halten Sie beim Betreten des Hotels den Führer in der Hand. Sie zeigen damit, daß Sie aufgrund dieser Empfehlung gekommen sind.

Die Preise sind in Pfund Sterling angegeben (1 £ = 100 pence) mit Ausnahme der Republik Irland who sie in Punts angegeben sind.

Wenn die Buchstaben **s.**, **t.**, oder **st.** nicht hinter den angegebenen Preisen aufgeführt sind, können sich diese um den Zuschlag für Bedienung und/oder MWSt erhöhen (keine MWSt auf den Channel Islands).

Die Namen der Hotels und Restaurants, die ihre Preise genannt haben, sind fett gedruckt. Gleichzeitig haben sich diese Häuser verpflichtet, die von den Hoteliers selbst angegebenen Preise den Benutzern des Michelin-Führers zu berechnen.

MAHLZEITEN

Meals 13.00/24.00	**Feste Menupreise** – Mittagessen 13.00, Abendessen 24.00 (inkl. Couvert)
Meals 15.00/25.00	Siehe Seite 37
s.	Bedienung inkl.
t.	MWSt inkl.
st.	Bedienung und MWSt inkl.
🍷 6.00	Preis für 1/2 Flasche oder eine Karaffe Tafelwein
Meals a la carte 20.00/25.00	**Mahlzeiten « à la carte »** – Der erste Preis entspricht einer einfachen aber sorgfältig zubereiteten Mahlzeit, bestehend aus kleiner Vorspeise, Tagesgericht mit Beilage und Nachtisch. Der zweite Preis entspricht einer reichlicheren Mahlzeit mit Vorspeise, Hauptgericht, Käse oder Nachtisch (inkl. Couvert)
☕ 8.50	Preis des englischen Frühstücks, wenn dieser nicht im Übernachtungspreis enthalten ist. Einfaches, billigeres Frühstück (Continental breakfast) erhältlich

⌂ : In dieser Hotelkategorie wird ein Abendessen normalerweise nur zu bestimmten Zeiten für Hotelgäste angeboten. Es besteht aus einem Menu mit begrenzter Auswahl zu festgesetztem Preis. Mittagessen wird selten angeboten. Viele dieser Hotels sind nicht berechtigt, alkoholische Getränke auszuschenken.

ZIMMER

rm 50.00/80.00	Mindestpreis 50.00 für ein Einzelzimmer und Höchstpreis 80.00 für das schönste Doppelzimmer
rm ☕ 55.00/75.00	Übernachtung mit englischem Frühstück, selbst wenn dieses nicht eingenommen wird

« SHORT BREAKS »

Einige Hotels bieten Vorzugskonditionen für einen Mindestaufenthalt von zwei Nächten (Short Break). Der Preis ist pro Person kalkuliert, bei einer Mindestbeteiligung von zwei Personen und schließt das Zimmer, das Abendessen und das Frühstück ein.

ANZAHLUNG - KREDITKARTEN

Einige Hoteliers verlangen eine Anzahlung. Diese ist als Garantie sowohl für den Hotelier als auch für den Gast anzusehen.

AE VISA JCB	Vom Haus akzeptierte Kreditkarten : Access (Eurocard) - American Express - Diners Club - Visa (Carte Bleue) - Japan Card Bank

Städte

✉ York	Zuständiges Postamt
01225 Bath	Vorwahlnummer und evtl. zuständiges Fernsprechamt (bei Gesprächen vom Ausland aus wird die erste Null weggelassen)
401 M 27, ⑩	Nummer der Michelin-Karte und Koordinaten des Planfeldes oder Faltseite
West Country G.	Siehe auch den grünen Michelinführer « England : The West Country »
pop. 1057	Einwohnerzahl
ECD : Wednesday	Tag, an dem die Läden nachmittags geschlossen sind
BX **A**	Markierung auf dem Stadtplan
18	Öffentlicher Golfplatz und Lochzahl (Handicap erforderlich, telefonische Reservierung empfehlenswert)
	Rundblick, Aussichtspunkt
	Flughafen
☎ 261 1234	Ladestelle für Autoreisezüge - Nähere Auskünfte unter der angegebenen Telefonnummer
	Autofähre
	Personenfähre *Liste der Schiffahrtsgesellschaften am Ende des Führers*
i	Informationsstelle

Uhrzeit

In Großbritannien ist eine Zeitverschiebung zu beachten und die Uhr gegenüber der deutschen Zeit um 1 Stunde zurückzustellen.

Sehenswürdigkeiten

BEWERTUNG

★★★	Eine Reise wert
★★	Verdient einen Umweg
★	Sehenswert
AC	Eintritt (gegen Gebühr)

LAGE

See	In der Stadt
Envir.	In der Umgebung der Stadt
Exc.	Ausflugsziele
N, S, E, W	Im Norden (N), Süden (S), Osten (E), Westen (W) der Stadt
A 22	Zu erreichen über die Straße A 22
2 m.	Entfernung in Meilen

Stadtpläne

a ● a	**Hotels – Restaurants**
	Sehenswürdigkeiten
	Sehenswertes Gebäude mit Haupteingang
	Sehenswerter Sakralbau
	Straßen
M 1	Autobahn
4 4	Anschlußstellen : Autobahneinfahrt und/oder-ausfahrt,
	Schnellstraße mit getrennten Fahrbahnen
	Hauptverkehrsstraße
A 2	Fernverkehrsstraße (Primary route) Netz wird z.z. neu eingestuft
	Einbahnstraße – Gesperrte Straße, mit Verkehrsbeschränkungen
	Fußgängerzone
Piccadilly P	Einkaufsstraße – Parkplatz
	Tor – Passage – Tunnel
15'5	Unterführung (Höhe angegeben bis 16′6″) auf Hauptverkehrsstraßen
	Bahnhof und Bahnlinie
	Standseilbahn – Seilschwebebahn
B	Bewegliche Brücke – Autofähre
	Sonstige Zeichen
	Informationsstelle
	Moschee – Synagoge
	Funk-, Fernsehturm – Ruine
	Garten, Park, Wäldchen – Friedhof
	Stadion – Pferderennbahn – Golfplatz
	Golfplatz (Zutritt bedingt erlaubt)
	Aussicht – Rundblick
	Denkmal – Brunnen – Krankenhaus
	Jachthafen – Leuchtturm
	Flughafen – U-Bahnstation
	Schiffsverbindungen : Autofähre
	Hauptpostamt (postlagernde Sendungen), Telefon
	Öffentliches Gebäude, durch einen Buchstaben gekennzeichnet :
C H	Sitz der Grafschaftsverwaltung – Rathaus
M T U	Museum – Theater – Universität, Hochschule
POL.	Polizei (in größeren Städten Polizeipräsidium)
	London
BRENT SOHO	Name des Verwaltungsbezirks (borough) – des Stadtteils (area)
	Grenze des « borough » – des « area »

Die Stadtpläne sind eingenordet (Norden = oben).

Das Auto, die Reifen

In Großbritannien herrscht Anschnallpflicht für Fahrer, Beifahrer und auf dem Rücksitz, wenn Gurte vorhanden sind. Es ist verboten, Kinder auf den Vordersitzen auf dem Schoß zu befördern. In Irland besteht für den Fahrer und den Beifahrer Anschnallpflicht, wenn Gurte vorhanden sind. Kinder unter 12 Jahren dürfen allerdings nicht auf den Vordersitzen befördert werden, es sei denn es existiert ein entsprechender Kindersitz.

LIEFERANTEN VON MICHELIN-REIFEN

ATS Reifenhändler

Die Anschrift der nächstgelegenen ATS-Verkaufsstelle erhalten Sie auf Anfrage (9-17 Uhr) bei

ATS HOUSE
180-188 Northolt Rd.
Harrow,
Middlesex HA2 OED
(0181) 423 2000

AUTOMOBILCLUBS

Die wichtigsten Automobilclubs des Landes sind die Automobile Association und der Royal Automobile Club, die den Mitgliedern der der FIA angeschlossenen Automobilclubs Pannenhilfe leisten und einige ihrer Dienstleistungen anbieten.

AUTOMOBILE ASSOCIATION
Fanum House
BASINGSTOKE, Hants., RG21 2EA
✆ (01256) 20123

AUTOMOBILE ASSOCIATION
108-110 Great-Victoria St.
BELFAST, BT2 7AT
✆ 01232-328924

AUTOMOBILE ASSOCIATION
23 Rock Hill
BLACKROCK
Co-Dublin
✆ 01 283-3555

ROYAL AUTOMOBILE CLUB
RAC House, Lansdowne Rd.
CROYDON, Surrey CR9 2JA
✆ (0181) 686 2525

ROYAL AUTOMOBILE CLUB
RAC House, 79 Chichester St.
BELFAST, BT1 4JR
✆ 01232-240261

ROYAL AUTOMOBILE CLUB
RAC IRELAND
New Mount House
22-24 Lower Mount St.
DUBLIN 2
✆ 01 760113

County abbreviations
Abréviations des comtés
Abbreviazioni delle contee
Abkürzungen der Grafschaften

England

Avon	Avon
Bedfordshire	Beds.
Berkshire	Berks.
Buckinghamshire	Bucks.
Cambridgeshire	Cambs.
Cheshire	Ches.
Cleveland	Cleveland
Cornwall	Cornwall
Cumbria	Cumbria
Derbyshire	Derbs.
Devon	Devon
Dorset	Dorset
Durham	Durham
East Sussex	E. Sussex
Essex	Essex
Gloucestershire	Glos.
Greater Manchester	Gtr. Manchester
Hampshire	Hants.
Hereford and Worcester	Heref. & Worcs.
Hertfordshire	Herts.
Humberside	Humbs.
Isle of Wight	I.O.W.
Kent	Kent
Lancashire	Lancs.
Leicestershire	Leics.
Lincolnshire	Lincs.
Merseyside	Mersey.
Norfolk	Norfolk
Northamptonshire	Northants.
Northumberland	Northd
North Yorkshire	N. Yorks.
Nottinghamshire	Notts.
Oxfordshire	Oxon.
Shropshire	Shrops.
Somerset	Somerset
South Yorkshire	S. Yorks.
Staffordshire	Staffs.
Suffolk	Suffolk
Surrey	Surrey
Tyne and Wear	Tyne and Wear
Warwickshire	Warks.
West Midlands	W. Mids.
West Sussex	W. Sussex
West Yorkshire	W. Yorks.
Wiltshire	Wilts.

Wales

Clwyd	Clwyd
Dyfed	Dyfed
Gwent	Gwent
Gwynedd	Gwynedd
Mid Glamorgan	M. Glam.
Powys	Powys
South Glamorgan	S. Glam.
West Glamorgan	W. Glam.

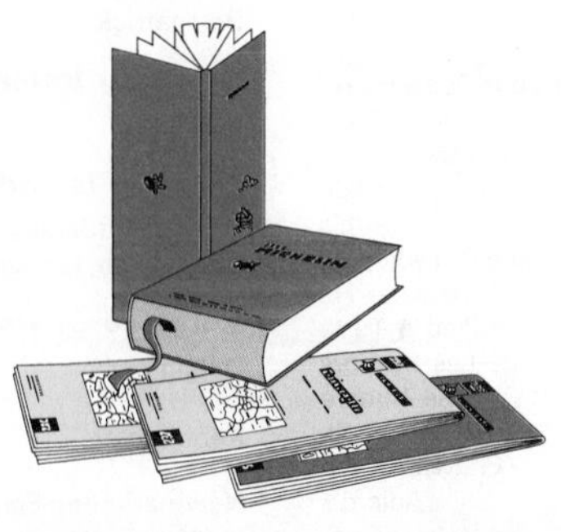

Starred establishments

Les établissements à étoiles

Gli esercizi con stelle

Die Stern-Restaurants

✿✿✿

England

Bray-on-Thames Waterside Inn
London La Tante Claire
London Chez Nico at Ninety Park Lane (at Grosvenor House H.)
– The Restaurant, Marco Pierre White (at Hyde Park H.)

✿✿

England

Bristol Lettonie
London Le Gavroche
Longridge Paul Heathcote's
Oxford Le Manoir aux Quat' Saisons
Reading L'Ortolan

Scotland

Ullapool Altnaharrie Inn

✿

England

Baslow Fischer's at Baslow Hall
Bath Lucknam Park
Bourton-on-the-Water Lords of the Manor
Bradford Restaurant Nineteen
Bristol Harvey's
Broadway Buckland Manor
Brockenhurst Le Poussin
Bury Normandie
Chagford Gidleigh Park
Cheltenham Epicurean
– Le Champignon Sauvage
Chester Arkle (at Chester Grosvenor H.)
Earl Stonham Mr. Underhill's
Faversham Read's
Grantham Harry's Place
Great Malvern Croque-en-Bouche
London Aubergine
– MPW's, The Canteen
– Capital
– Connaught
– Four Seasons (at Four Seasons H.)
– Fulham Road
– Grill Room at the Café Royal
– Halkin
– Leith's
– Oak Room (at Le Meridien Piccadilly H.)
– Oriental (at Dorchester H.)
– Pied à Terre
– Les Saveurs
– The Square
Newcastle upon Tyne 21 Queen St.
New Milton Chewton Glen
Norwich Adlard's
Oakham Hambleton Hall
Plymouth Chez Nous
Storrington Manley's
Stroud Oakes
Taplow Waldo's (at Cliveden)
Taunton Castle
Truro Pennypots
Waterhouses Old Beams
Winteringham Winteringham Fields

Wales

Pwllheli Plas Bodegroes

Scotland

Aberfoyle Braeval Old Mill
Balloch Georgian Room (at Cameron House H.)
Fort William Inverlochy Castle
Gullane La Potinière
Port Appin Airds
Portpatrick Knockinaam Lodge

Northern Ireland

Belfast Roscoff

Channel Islands

St. Helier (Jersey) Shai
St. Saviour (Jersey) Longueville Manor

Republic of Ireland

Dublin The Commons
– Patrick Guilbaud
Kenmare Park
– Sheen Falls Lodge
Newmarket-on-Fergus Dromoland Castle

Further establishments which merit your attention

Autres tables qui méritent votre attention
Altre tavole particolarmente interessanti
Weitere empfehlenswerte Häuser

Meals

England

Barnsley	Peano
Bath	Hole in the Wall
Blackpool	River House
Blakeney	Morston Hall
Bridgnorth	Old Vicarage
Brimfield	Poppies
Calstock	Danescombe Valley
Cheltenham	Epicurean Bistro
Dorking	Partners West Street
Drewsteignton	Hunts Tor House
Eastbourne	Hungry Monk
Fowey	Food for Thought
Frampton-on-Severn	Savery's
Goring	Leatherne Bottel
Harrogate	Millers, the Bistro
Hastings	Röser's
Keyston	Pheasant Inn
King's Lynn	Congham Hall
–	Rococo
Ledbury	Five Bridges
Leeds	Leodis Brasserie
London	Alastair Little
–	Al Bustan
–	Al San Vincenzo
–	Bibendum
–	Bistrot Bruno
–	Le Caprice
–	Chutney Mary
–	Clarke's
–	Fifth Floor (at Harvey Nichols)
–	Greenhouse
–	Hilaire
–	Ivy
–	Kensington Place
–	Malabar
–	Nico Central
–	Percy's
–	Le Pont de la Tour
–	Simply Nico
Maiden Newton	Le Petit Canard
Midhurst	Cowdray Room (at Angel H.)
Milford-on-Sea	Rocher's
Moulsford	Beetle & Wedge
Newcastle upon Tyne	Forsters
–	Horton Grange
Old Burghclere	Dew Pond
Padstow	Seafood
Pateley Bridge	Dusty Miller
Portsmouth	Bistro Montparnasse
Royal Tunbridge Wells	Cheevers
Rushlake Green	Stone House
Shepton Mallet	Bowlish House
Storrington	Old Forge
Tadworth	Gemini
Torquay	Table
Totnes	Floyd's Inn (sometimes)
Towcester	Vine House
Ullswater	Sharrow Bay Country House
Wiveliscombe	Langley House

Wales

Llanrwst	Chandlers Brasserie
Llansanffraid Glan Conwy	Old Rectory

Scotland

Achiltibuie	Summer Isles
Glasgow	Ubiquitous Chip
Gullane	Greywalls
Kingussie	The Cross
Linlithgow	Champany Inn
Muir of Ord	Dower House
Mull (Isle of)	Tiroran House
Newtonmore	Ard-na-Coille

Northern Ireland

Portrush	Ramore

Channel Islands

Gorey (Jersey)	Jersey Pottery (Garden Rest.)
–	Village Bistro

Republic of Ireland

Adare	Mustard Seed
Ahakista	Shiro
Bunratty	MacCloskey's
Castlebaldwin	Cromleach Lodge
Cork	Cliffords
Dingle	Doyle's Seafood Bar
Dublin	Clarets
–	Ernie's
Gorey	Marlfield House
Kenmare	d'Arcy's Old Bank House
Moycullen	Drimcong House
Navan	Dunderry Lodge

Particularly pleasant Hotels

Hôtels agréables

Alberghi ameni

Angenehme Hotels

England

London Claridge's
– Dorchester
– Savoy
New Milton Chewton Glen
Taplow Cliveden

Republic of Ireland

Straffan Kildare H & Country Club

England

Aylesbury Hartwell House
Bath Lucknam Park
Ipswich Hintlesham Hall
London Connaught
– 47 Park Street
Melton Mowbray Stapleford Park
Oxford Le Manoir aux Quat'Saisons
Ston Easton Ston Easton Park
Uckfield Horsted Place

Wales

Llyswen Llangoed Hall

Scotland

Dunkeld Kinnaird
Fort William Inverlochy Castle

Republic of Ireland

Kenmare Park
– Sheen Falls Lodge

England

Bath Homewood Park
Bourton-on-the-Water Lower Slaughter Manor
Broadway Buckland Manor
Castle Combe Manor House
Chagford Gidleigh Park
Cheltenham On the Park
Chipping Campden Charingworth Manor
East Grinstead Gravetye Manor
Evershot Summer Lodge
Gillingham Stock Hill Country House
Grasmere Michael's Nook Country House
Kidderminster Brockencote Hall
Leeds 42 The Calls
London Blakes
– Durley House
– Goring
– Halkin
– The Milestone
– 22 Jermyn Street
– Pelham
Newbury Hollington House
Oakham Hambleton Hall
Royal Leamington Spa Mallory Court
Sandiway Nunsmere Hall
Sutton Coldfield New Hall
York Middlethorpe Hall

Scotland

Arisaig Arisaig House
Eriska (Isle of) Isle of Eriska
Glasgow One Devonshire Gardens
Port Appin Airds

Wales

Llandudno Bodysgallen Hall

Channel Islands

St Saviour (Jersey) Longueville Manor

Republic of Ireland

Gorey Marlfield House
Mallow Longueville House
Rathnew Tinakilly House

England

Bibury Swan
Bradford-on-Avon Woolley Grange
Brampton Farlam Hall
Cuckfield Ockenden Manor
King's Lynn Congham Hall
Lewdown Lewtrenchard Manor
Liskeard Well House
London Sydney House
Oxford Old Parsonage
Prestbury White House Manor
Purton Pear Tree at Purton
South Molton Whitechapel Manor
Tetbury Calcot Manor
Ullswater Sharrow Bay Country House
– Old Church
Wareham Priory
Windermere Holbeck Ghyll
Woodstock Feathers

Wales

Llandrillo Tyddyn Llan Country House
Machynlleth Ynyshir Hall
Talsarnau Maes-y-Neuadd

Scotland

Aberfeldy Farleyer House
Achiltibuie Summer Isles
Alloa Gean House
Ballater Tullich Lodge
Gullane Greywalls
Kentallen Ardsheal House
Lewis & Harris (Isle of) Ardvourlie Castle
Mull (Isle of) Tiroran House
Portpatrick Knockinaam Lodge
Skye (Isle of) Kinloch Lodge
Ullapool Altnaharrie Inn
Whitebridge Knockie Lodge

Northern Ireland

Annalong Glassdrumman Lodge

Republic of Ireland

Cashel Bay Cashel House
Castlebaldwin Cromleach Lodge
Donegal St Ernan's House
Letterfrack Rosleague Manor

England

Blakeney Morston Hall
Branscombe The Look Out
Buttermere Pickett Howe
Calne Chilvester Hill House
Calstock Danescombe Valley
Canterbury Thruxted Oast (without rest)
Chipping Campden Malt House
Cranbrook Old Cloth Hall
Dulverton Ashwick House
Grasmere White Moss House
Horley Langshott Manor
Leominster The Marsh
Marlborough Old Vicarage (without rest)
Melksham Sandridge Park
Otley Otley House
Porlock Oaks
Rushlake Green Stone House
Sedgeford Sedgeford Hall
Swaffham Strattons
Teignmouth Thomas Luny House
Tintagel Trebrea Lodge
Tonbridge Goldhill Mill (without rest)
Wiveliscombe Langley House
York 4 South Parade (without rest)

Wales

Betws-y-Coed Tan-y-Foel
Llansanffraid Glan Conwy Old Rectory

Scotland

Arran (Isle of) Kilmichael Country House
Auchencairn Collin House
Banff Eden House
Lewis & Harris (Isle of) Scarista House
Maybole Ladyburn
Muir of Ord Dower House
Nairn Lochloy House
Oban Glenfeochan House

Republic of Ireland

Bunclody Clohamon House
Kanturk Assolas Country House
Kilkenny Blanchville House
Leenane Delphi Lodge
Wicklow Old Rectory

England

Benenden Crit Hall
Bethersden Little Hodgeham
Billingshurst Old Wharf (without rest)
Bovey Tracey Willmead Farm (without rest)
Chipping Campden Holly Mount (without rest)
Cirencester Shawswell Country House
Cockermouth Low Hall
Coniston Appletree Holme
Crackington Haven Manor Farm
East Retford Old Plough
Faversham Frith Farm House
Grindon Porch Farmhouse
Hayling Island Cockle Warren Cottage
Honiton Cokesputt House
Hutton-Le-Hole Burnley House
Iron Bridge Severn Lodge
Lewes Millers (without rest)
Norwich Old Rectory
St Blazey Nanscawen House
Seaford Old Parsonage
Stow-on-the-Wold College House
Tetbury Tavern House (without rest)
Thame Upper Green Farm (without rest)
Thoralby Littleburn
Wiveliscombe Jews Farm House
Worcester Upton House
Wroxham Garden Cottage (without rest)

Wales

Bala Fron Feuno Hall
Cowbridge Stembridge Farmhouse (without rest)

Scotland

Edinburgh Drummond House (without rest)
– Sibbet House (without rest)
– 28 Northumberland Street (without rest)
Fort William Grange (without rest)
Mull (Isle of) Ardfenaig

Northern Ireland

Belfast Cottage (without rest)
Coleraine Greenhill House

Republic of Ireland

Dublin Anglesea Town House (without rest)

Particularly pleasant Restaurants

Restaurants agréables

Ristoranti ameni

Angenehme Restaurants

XXXXX

England

London — **Oak Room** (at Le Meridien Piccadilly H.)

XXXX

England

Bray-on-Thames — Waterside Inn (with rm)
London — Oriental (at Dorchester H.)
London — Grill Room at the Café Royal
Taplow — Waldo's (at Cliveden)
Winteringham — Winteringham Fields (with rm)

XXX

England

Baslow — Fischer's at Baslow Hall (with rm)
Bradford — Restaurant Nineteen (with rm)
Cheltenham — Epicurean
Emsworth — 36 on the Quay
Henley-on-Thames — Stonor Arms (with rm)
London — Le Pont de la Tour
– — Quaglino's
Lymington — Gordleton Mill (with rm)
Moreton-in-Marsh — Marsh Goose
Moulsford — Beetle & Wedge (with rm)
Reading — L'Ortolan
Romsey — Old Manor House
Sheffield — Old Vicarage
Winchcombe — Wesley House (with rm)

Wales

Pwllheli — Plas Bodegroes (with rm)

Scotland

Kingussie — The Cross (with rm)
Peat Inn — Peat Inn

Republic of Ireland

Navan — Dunderry Lodge

XX

England

Cheltenham — Epicurean Bistro
Earl Stonham — Mr Underhill's
Eastbourne — Hungry Monk
Fowey — Food for Thought
Goring — Leatherne Bottel
Halford — Sykes House
Newcastle upon Tyne — Horton Grange (with rm)
Padstow — Seafood (with rm)
Salisbury — Howard's House (with rm)
Waterhouses — Old Beams (with rm)

Wales

Brechfa — Ty Mawr Country House (with rm)
Llanrwst — Cae'r Berllan (with rm)

Republic of Ireland

Adare — Mustard Seed
Ahakista — Shiro
Shanagarry — Ballymaloe House (with rm)

X

England

Thirsk — Crab & Lobster

Channel Islands

Jersey (Gorey) Jersey Pottery (Garden Rest)

Republic of Ireland

Kenmare — Lime Tree

England

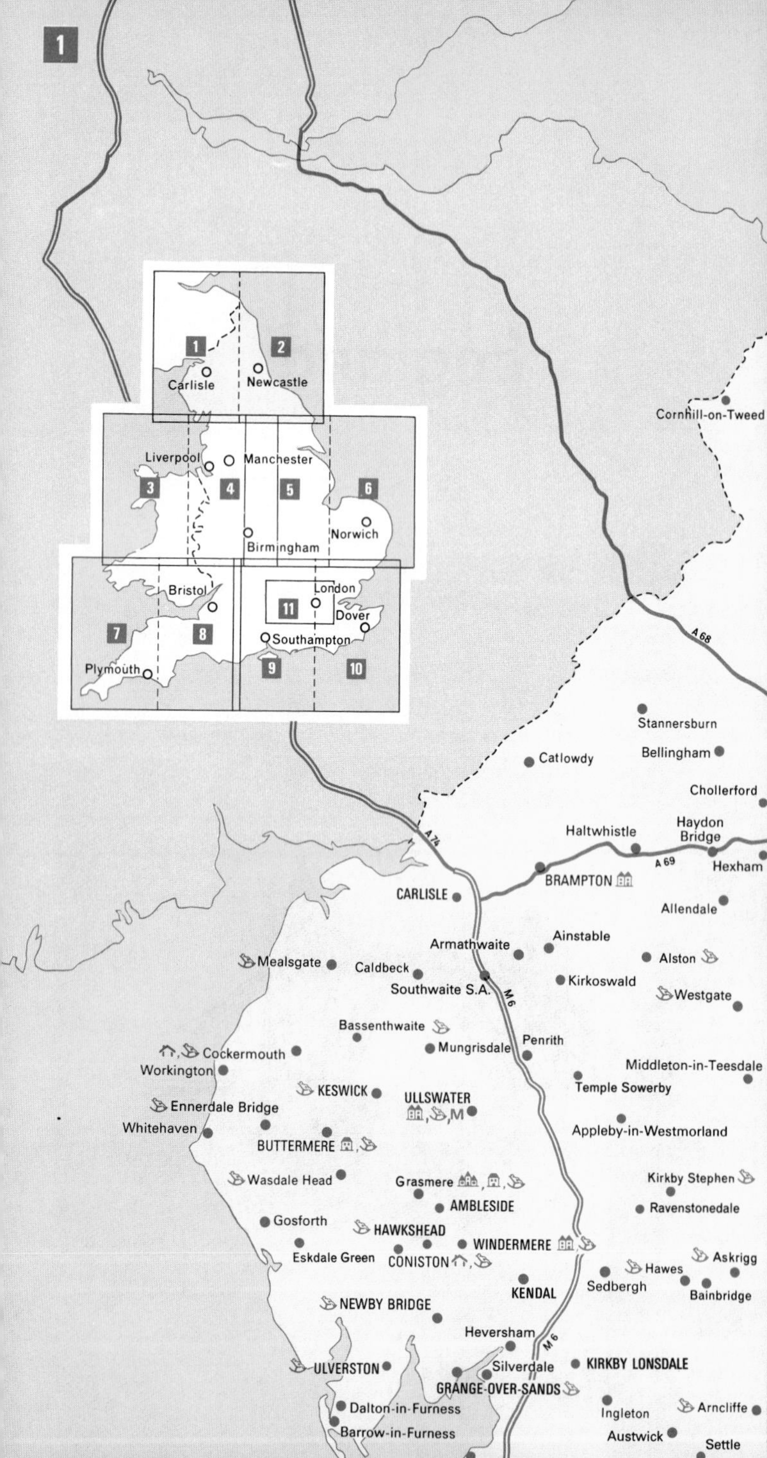
1
1
2
Carlisle
Newcastle
Liverpool
Manchester
3
4
5
6
Norwich
Birmingham
Bristol
London
11
Dover
7
8
Southampton
Plymouth
9
10
Cornhill-on-Tweed
A 68
Stannersburn
Catlowdy
Bellingham
Chollerford
A 74
Haltwhistle
Haydon Bridge
A 69
Hexham
BRAMPTON
CARLISLE
Allendale
Armathwaite
Ainstable
Mealsgate
Caldbeck
Alston
Southwaite S.A.
Kirkoswald
M6
Westgate
Bassenthwaite
Mungrisdale
Penrith
Cockermouth
Workington
Middleton-in-Teesdale
Temple Sowerby
KESWICK
ULLSWATER
M
Ennerdale Bridge
Whitehaven
Appleby-in-Westmorland
BUTTERMERE
Wasdale Head
Grasmere
Kirkby Stephen
AMBLESIDE
Ravenstonedale
Gosforth
HAWKSHEAD
WINDERMERE
Eskdale Green
CONISTON
Askrigg
Hawes
Sedbergh
KENDAL
Bainbridge
NEWBY BRIDGE
Heversham
M6
ULVERSTON
Silverdale
KIRKBY LONSDALE
GRANGE-OVER-SANDS
Dalton-in-Furness
Ingleton
Arncliffe
Barrow-in-Furness
Austwick
Settle

Place with at least :

a hotel or restaurant .... ● Ripon
a pleasant hotel or restaurant .... 🏨, ⌂, ✕
a quiet, secluded hotel .... 🪑
a restaurant with .... ✿, ✿✿, ✿✿✿, **Meals** (M)
See this town for establishments
located in its vicinity .... **LEICESTER**

Localité offrant au moins :

une ressource hôtelière .... ● Ripon
un hôtel ou restaurant agréable .... 🏨, ⌂, ✕
un hôtel très tranquille, isolé .... 🪑
une bonne table à .... ✿, ✿✿, ✿✿✿, **Meals** (M)
Localité groupant dans le texte
les ressources de ses environs .... **LEICESTER**

La località possiede come minimo :

una risorsa alberghiera .... ● Ripon
Albergo o ristorante ameno .... 🏨, ⌂, ✕
un albergo molto tranquillo, isolato .... 🪑
un'ottima tavola con .... ✿, ✿✿, ✿✿✿, **Meals** (M)
La località raggruppa nel suo testo
le risorse dei dintorni .... **LEICESTER**

Ort mit mindestens :

einem Hotel oder Restaurant .... ● Ripon
ein angenehmes Hotel oder Restaurant .... 🏨, ⌂, ✕
einem sehr ruhigen und abgelegenen Hotel .... 🪑
einem Restaurant mit .... ✿, ✿✿, ✿✿✿, **Meals** (M)
Ort mit Angaben über Hotels und Restaurants
in seiner Umgebung .... **LEICESTER**

Berwick-upon-Tweed
BAMBURGH
Belford
Seahouses
Wooler
Powburn 🪑
ALNWICK
Alnmouth
Rothbury
Kirkwhelpington
Ashington
Morpeth
A 696
Whitley Bay
Tynemouth
Corbridge
Wylam
✿NEWCASTLE UPON TYNE
M, ✕✕ with rm.
GATESHEAD
South Shields
Ebchester
Burnopfield
Sunderland
Washington
Carterway Heads
Washington S.A.
Blanchland
Chester-le-Street
DURHAM
Crook
Bowburn
A1
Hamsterley 🪑
HARTLEPOOL
Bishop Auckland
Redcar
STOCKTON-ON-TEES
BARNARD CASTLE
Staithes
Thornaby-on-Tees
Middlesbrough
Loftus 🪑
Greta Bridge
DARLINGTON 🪑
Yarm
Great Ayton 🪑
WHITBY
Stokesley
Scotch Corner
Reeth
Robin Hood's Bay
Moulton
🪑 GREAT BROUGHTON
🪑 RICHMOND
Goathland
Rosedale Abbey
🪑, ⌂
Patrick Brompton
NORTHALLERTON 🪑
Hutton-le-Hole ⌂
Thoralby
Lastingham 🪑
W. Witton
Bedale
Leeming Bar
Kirkbymoorside
SCARBOROUGH 🪑
🪑 MIDDLEHAM
E. Witton
Pickhill
Appleton le Moors
PICKERING
MASHAM
THIRSK ✕, 🪑
HELMSLEY
Hunmanby
KETTLEWELL
Hovingham
Ripon
EASINGWOLD
MALTON
M PATELEY BRIDGE
Sheriff Hutton 🪑
Bridlington

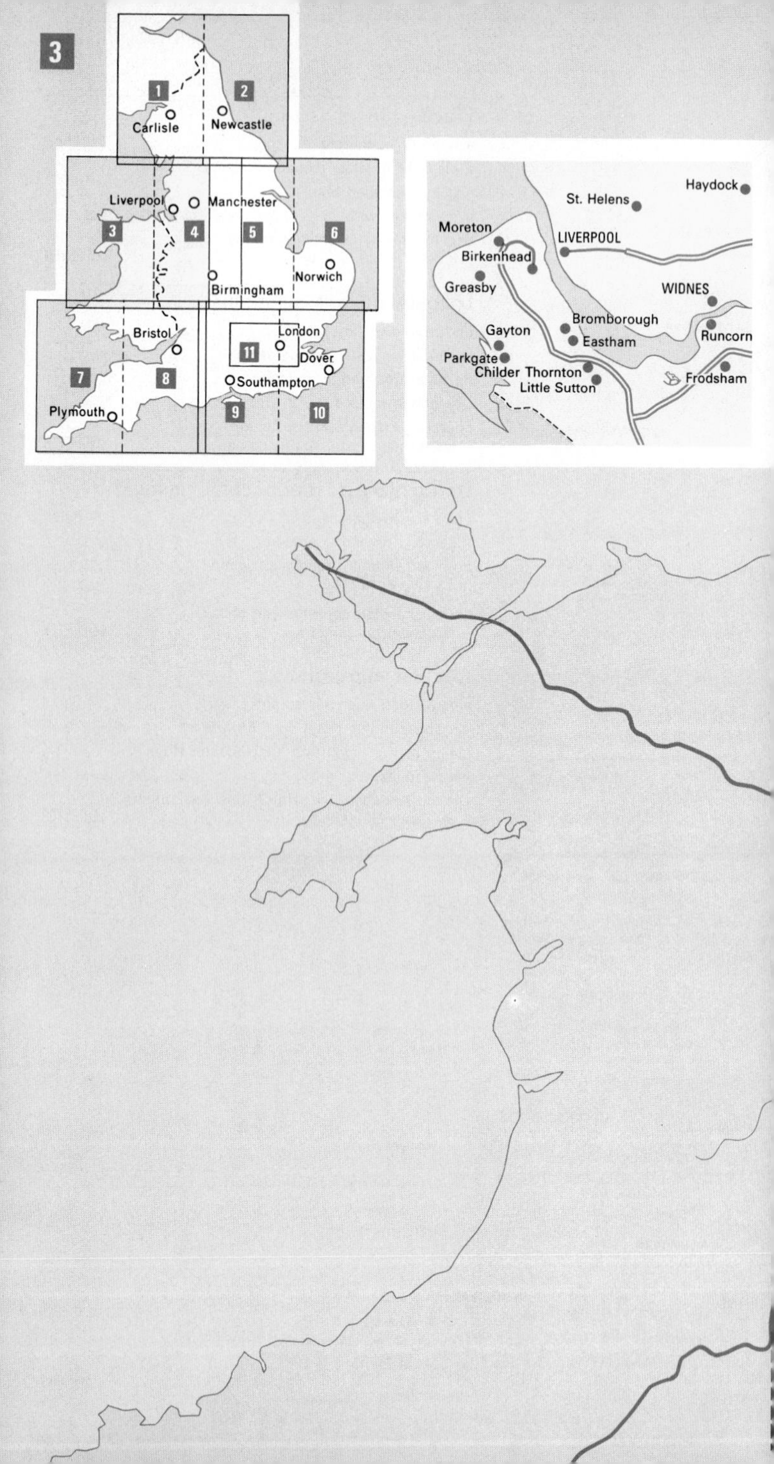
3
1
2
Carlisle
Newcastle
Liverpool
Manchester
3
4
5
6
Norwich
Birmingham
Bristol
London
11
Dover
7
8
Plymouth
Southampton
9
10
Haydock
St. Helens
Moreton
LIVERPOOL
Birkenhead
Greasby
WIDNES
Bromborough
Gayton
Eastham
Runcorn
Parkgate
Childer Thornton
Little Sutton
Frodsham

4
Dalton-in-Furness
Barrow-in-Furness
Ingleton
Arncliffe
Ripon
M PATELEY BRIDGE
Austwick
Settle
Grassington
Morecambe
LANCASTER
Long Preston
Hetton
Burnsall
RIPLEY
Bolton Abbey
Forton S.A.
Pilling
Whitewell
Slaidburn
SKIPTON
M, HARROGATE
M6
Fleetwood
GARSTANG
Grindleton
Barnoldswick
Ilkley
Chipping
Sawley
Keighley
Otley
Thornton Cleveleys
St-Michaels-on-Wyre
CLITHEROE
Haworth
Bingley
Harewood
Hurst Green
Colne
Shipley
M, BLACKPOOL
Kirkham
Goosnargh
Longridge
Whalley
Burnley
with rm. BRADFORD
M LEEDS
LYTHAM ST. ANNE'S
PRESTON
BLACKBURN
Clayton-le-Moors
Hebden Bridge
Brighouse
Batley
M 62
Rawtenstall
HALIFAX
Dewsbury
Clayton le Woods
Hartshead Moor S.A.
Mere Brow
CHORLEY
Ramsbottom
Southport
HUDDERSFIELD
Charnock Richard S.A.
Rochdale
Mawdesley
Kirkburton
Horwich
BURY
Marsden
Woolley E
Parbold
Adlington
Formby
Standish
BOLTON
Birch S.A.
Meltham
Shelley
Clayton
Blackrod
Holmfirth
Prestwich
Oldham
Ormskirk
WIGAN
MANCHESTER
Ashton-under-Lyne
Ashton-in-Makerfield
Burtonwood S.A.
Sale
Denton
Hyde
Glossop
ROTHERH
M 62
Stockport
Marple
Hayfield
ALTRINCHAM
Hope
SHEFFIELD
WARRINGTON
Cheadle
Castleton
Daresbury
BRAMHALL
Disley
Hathersage
Poynton
Chinley
KNUTSFORD
WILMSLOW
Grindleford
M 56
Alderley Edge
Prestbury
Dronfie
Hartford
Eyam
Buxton
Baslow
Weaverham
MACCLESFIELD
BAKEWELL
Sandiway
CHESTER
Holmes Chapel
Rowsley
Tarporley
Longnor
Tattenhall
M6
Congleton
Hartington
Winster
MATLOCK
Beeston
Sandbach
BROXTON
Crewe
Alsager
LEEK
Grindon
Alfreton
Cheddleton
NANTWICH
STOKE-ON-TRENT
Thorpe
MALPAS
Waterhouses
with rm.
Newcastle-under-Lyme
Belpe
Ashbourne
Stone
DERBY
Uttoxeter
Wem
Eccleshall
Doveridge
Oswestry
Hodnet
Tutbury
Woodseaves
Stafford
BURTON-UPON-TRENT
Shawbury
Newport
Ashby de la Zouch
Rugeley
SHREWSBURY
Penkridge
TELFORD
Cannock
Armitage
Coalvill
A 5
Lichfield
M 54
Iron Bridge
Shifnal
Hilton Park S.A.
TAMWORTH
Market Bosworth
Tamworth S.A.
R. Severn
Aldridge
Earl Sh
Much Wenlock
Wolverhampton
Walsall
SUTTON COLDFIELD
Hinckle
Church Stretton
Atherstone
M BRIDGNORTH
Coleshill
Dudley
NUNEATON
Ditton Priors
BIRMINGHAM
STOURBRIDGE
M 6
Frankley S.A.
Knowle
Craven Arms
Diddlebury
Hopton Wafers
SOLIHULL
KIDDERMINSTER
COV
LEINTWARDINE
Ludlow
Bucknell
Hopwood
Hockley Heath
Bewdley
Kenilwor
Knighton
Stourport-on-Severn
Hartlebury
Bromsgrove
M Brimfield
Royal Leamington Sp
Tenbury Wells
ABBERLEY
Redditch
Shrawley
Studley
Henley-in-Arden
WARWICK
LEOMINSTER
Ombersley
DROITWICH
KINGTON
Alcester
WORCESTER
STRATFORD-UPON-AVON
Bromyard
Weobley
Knightwick
Ullingswick
Whitney-on-Wye
Halford
4
Oxhill
GREAT MALVERN
M5
Bredwardine
HEREFORD
Upton upon Severn
HAY-ON-WYE
EVESHAM
BROADWAY
CHIPPING CAMPDEN
M, LEDBURY
Blockley
Fownhope
Moreton-in-Mars

5
Ripon
EASINGWOLD
MALTON
PATELEY BRIDGE
BOROUGHBRIDGE
Sheriff Hutton
Bridlington
RIPLEY
Knaresborough
GREAT DRIFFIELD
M, HARROGATE
YORK
Wetherby
Pocklington
Otley
Brandesburton
Harewood
Market Weighton
Bingley
Shipley
A1
BEVERLEY
South Cave
Little Weighton
Selby
M LEEDS
Wressle
M 62
Monk Fryston
A 63
KINGSTON-UPON-HULL
Batley
M 62
Ferrybridge S.A.
Dewsbury
WAKEFIELD
Winteringham with rm
HUDDERSFIELD
Wentbridge
Barnsdale Bar
Woolley Edge S.A.
SCUNTHORPE
Great Grimsby
Shelley
Clayton West
Cleethorpes
Barnsley M
DONCASTER
Epworth
Binbrook
North Somercotes
ROTHERHAM
M 18
Bawtry
Hope
SHEFFIELD
Gringley
Market Rasen
Louth
Blyth
Hathersage
East Retford
Todwick
Grindleford
Dronfield
Markham Moor
East Barkwith
Clowne
Worksop
A1
Eyam
Baslow, with rm.
R. Trent
LINCOLN
BAKEWELL
Chesterfield
Horncastle
Rowsley
Longnor
Woodhall Spa
Winster
MATLOCK
South Normanton
Grindon
Alfreton
M 1
Beckingham
Thorpe
Southwell
NEWARK-ON-TRENT
with rm.
A 17
Boston
Gunthorpe
Sleaford
Ashbourne
Belper
NOTTINGHAM
DERBY
Bingham
GRANTHAM
Doveridge
CASTLE DONINGTON
Colsterworth
Tutbury
UPON-TRENT
Spalding
Whaplode
LOUGHBOROUGH
Bourne
Ashby de la Zouch
MELTON MOWBRAY
Armitage
Coalville
Markfield
Market Deeping
Market Bosworth
OAKHAM
STAMFORD
Tamworth S.A.
LEICESTER
Earl Shilton
PETERBOROUGH
UPPINGHAM
Blaby
Hinckley
Atherstone
Coleshill
NUNEATON
Stilton
M 69
Corby
MARKET HARBOROUGH
OUNDLE
Chatteris
M 6
Lutterworth
Desborough
Knowle
Husbands Bosworth
Aldwincle
COVENTRY
Kettering
Keyston M
Hockley Heath
RUGBY
Old
Thrapston S.A.
Huntingdon
ST. IVES
Kenilworth
Dunchurch
M 1
Wellingborough
Royal Leamington Spa
DAVENTRY
Holdenby
Buckden
Rushden
WARWICK
NORTHAMPTON
ST. NEOTS
Weedon Bec
Castle Ashby
A 45
STRATFORD-UPON-AVON
A1
M 40
Horton
A 428
Sandy
Roade
Halford
Oxhill
M TOWCESTER
Stoke Bruerne
BEDFORD
Culworth
Newport Pagnell
Melbourn
STONY STRATFORD
MILTON KEYNES
CHIPPING CAMPDEN
BANBURY
Flitwick
Aspley Guise
Blockley
Brackley
Woburn
Letchworth
Moreton-in-Marsh

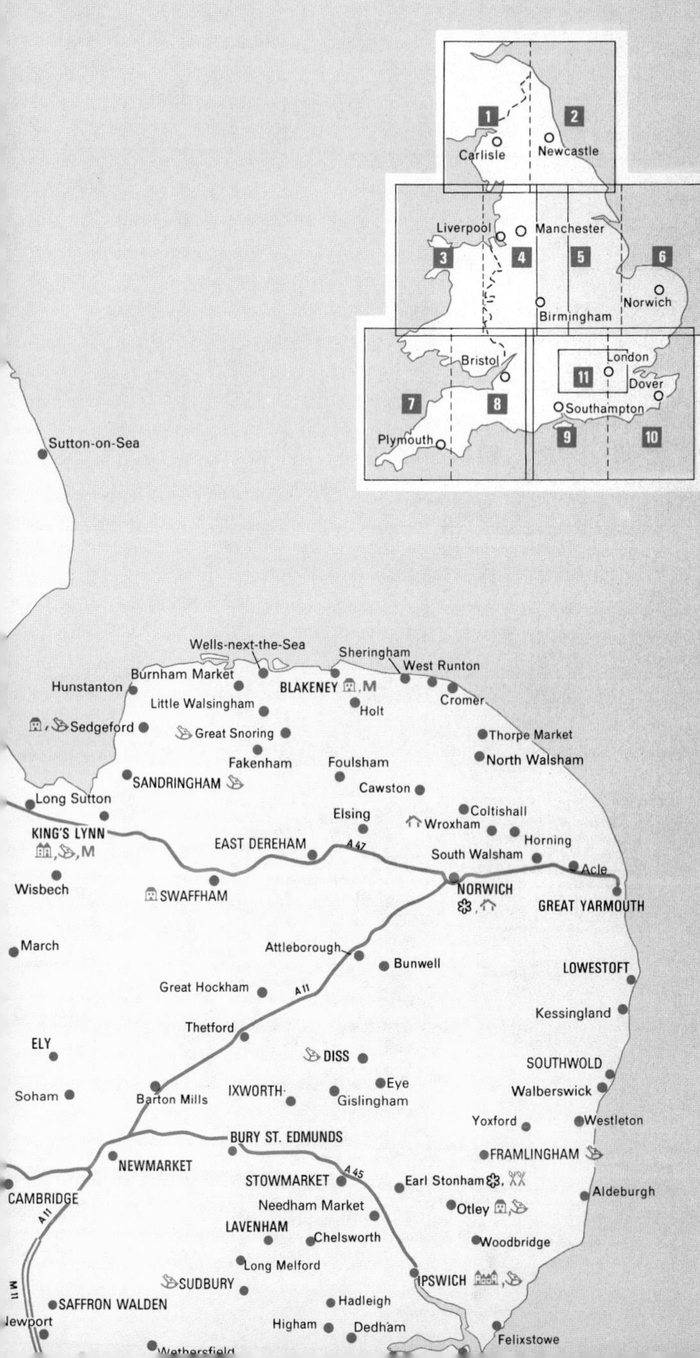
1
2
Carlisle
Newcastle
Liverpool
Manchester
3
4
5
6
Norwich
Birmingham
Bristol
London
11
Dover
7
8
Southampton
Plymouth
9
10
Sutton-on-Sea
Wells-next-the-Sea
Sheringham
West Runton
Burnham Market
Hunstanton
BLAKENEY
M
Cromer
Little Walsingham
Holt
Sedgeford
Great Snoring
Thorpe Market
Fakenham
Foulsham
North Walsham
SANDRINGHAM
Cawston
Long Sutton
Elsing
Coltishall
KING'S LYNN
M
Wroxham
Horning
EAST DEREHAM
A 47
South Walsham
Acle
Wisbech
SWAFFHAM
NORWICH
GREAT YARMOUTH
March
Attleborough
Bunwell
LOWESTOFT
Great Hockham
A 11
Kessingland
Thetford
ELY
DISS
SOUTHWOLD
Eye
Soham
Barton Mills
IXWORTH
Gislingham
Walberswick
Yoxford
Westleton
BURY ST. EDMUNDS
FRAMLINGHAM
NEWMARKET
STOWMARKET
A 45
Earl Stonham
Aldeburgh
CAMBRIDGE
Needham Market
Otley
A 11
LAVENHAM
Chelsworth
Woodbridge
Long Melford
M 11
SUDBURY
IPSWICH
SAFFRON WALDEN
Hadleigh
Higham
Dedham
Felixstowe

7

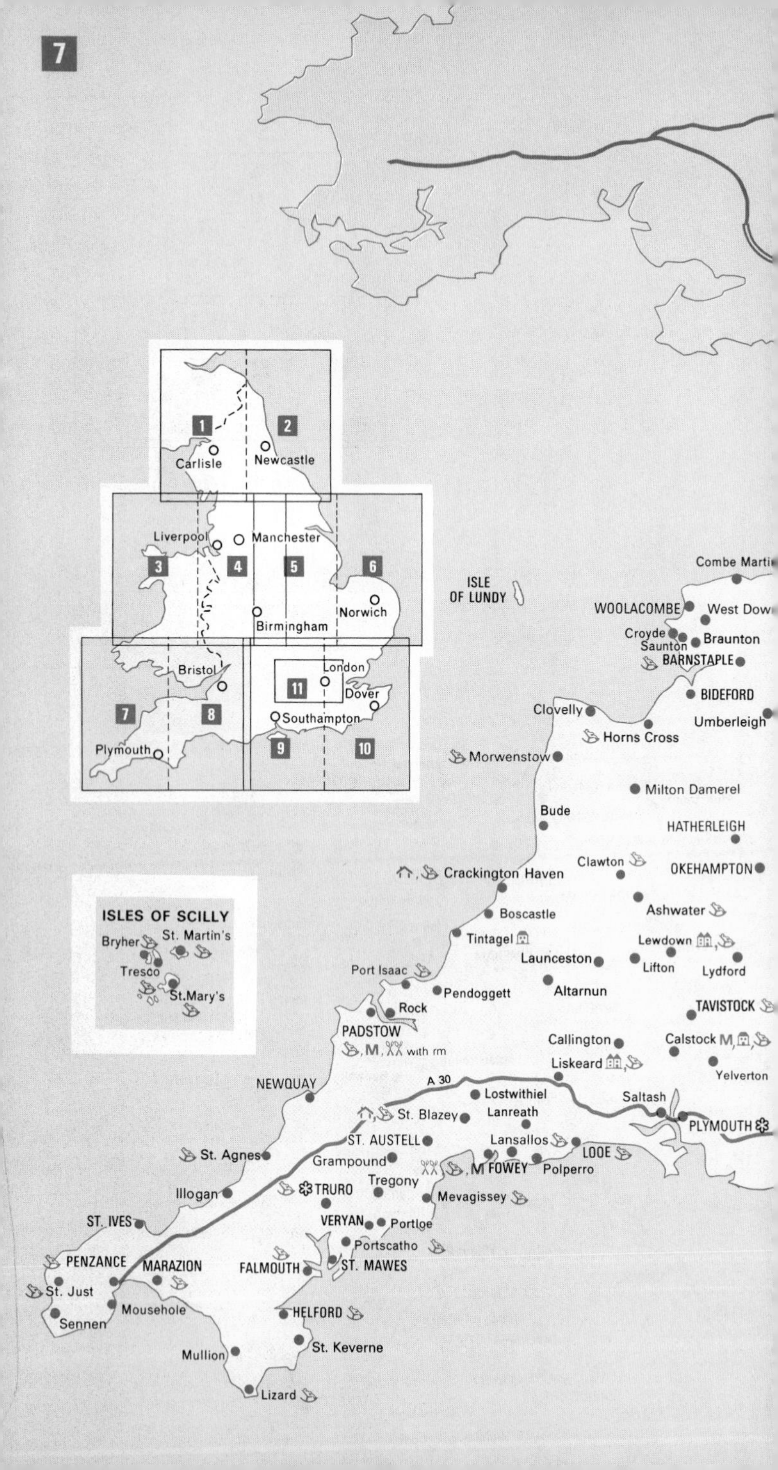

1
Carlisle
2
Newcastle
Liverpool
Manchester
3
4
5
6
Norwich
Birmingham
Bristol
London
11
Dover
7
8
Southampton
Plymouth
9
10

ISLES OF SCILLY
Bryher
St. Martin's
Tresco
St.Mary's

ISLE OF LUNDY

Combe Martin
WOOLACOMBE
West Down
Croyde
Saunton
Braunton
BARNSTAPLE
BIDEFORD
Clovelly
Umberleigh
Horns Cross
Morwenstow
Milton Damerel
Bude
HATHERLEIGH
Clawton
OKEHAMPTON
Crackington Haven
Ashwater
Boscastle
Tintagel
Lewdown
Launceston
Lifton
Lydford
Port Isaac
Pendoggett
Altarnun
Rock
TAVISTOCK
PADSTOW
M, with rm
Callington
Calstock M,
Liskeard
Yelverton
NEWQUAY
A 30
Lostwithiel
Saltash
St. Blazey
Lanreath
PLYMOUTH
ST. AUSTELL
Lansallos
LOOE
St. Agnes
Grampound
M FOWEY
Polperro
Tregony
TRURO
Mevagissey
Illogan
ST. IVES
VERYAN
Portloe
Portscatho
PENZANCE
MARAZION
FALMOUTH
ST. MAWES
St. Just
Mousehole
HELFORD
Sennen
St. Keverne
Mullion
Lizard

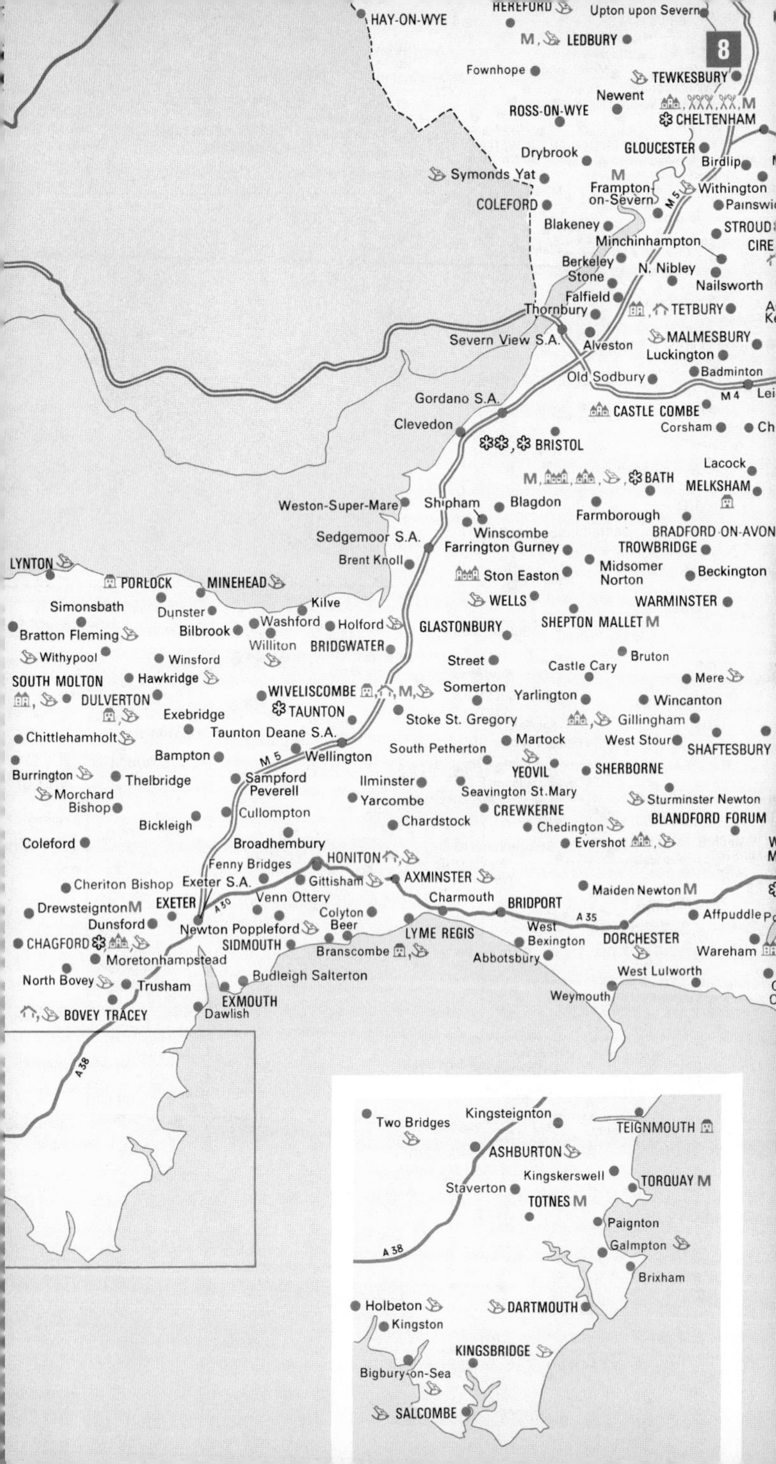

8
HAY-ON-WYE
HEREFORD
Upton upon Severn
LEDBURY
Fownhope
TEWKESBURY
Newent
ROSS-ON-WYE
CHELTENHAM
Drybrook
GLOUCESTER
Birdlip
Symonds Yat
Frampton-on-Severn
Withington
COLEFORD
Painswi
M 5
Blakeney
STROUD
Minchinhampton
CIRE
Berkeley
Stone
N. Nibley
Nailsworth
Falfield
Thornbury
TETBURY
Severn View S.A.
Alveston
MALMESBURY
Luckington
Old Sodbury
Badminton
M 4
Gordano S.A.
CASTLE COMBE
Clevedon
Corsham
BRISTOL
Lacock
BATH
MELKSHAM
Weston-Super-Mare
Shipham
Blagdon
Farmborough
Winscombe
BRADFORD-ON-AVON
Sedgemoor S.A.
Farrington Gurney
TROWBRIDGE
Brent Knoll
Midsomer Norton
LYNTON
Ston Easton
Beckington
PORLOCK
MINEHEAD
WELLS
WARMINSTER
Simonsbath
Dunster
Kilve
Washford
Holford
GLASTONBURY
SHEPTON MALLET
Bratton Fleming
Bilbrook
Williton
BRIDGWATER
Withypool
Winsford
Street
Bruton
Castle Cary
SOUTH MOLTON
Hawkridge
Mere
WIVELISCOMBE
Somerton
Yarlington
Wincanton
DULVERTON
TAUNTON
Exebridge
Stoke St. Gregory
Gillingham
Taunton Deane S.A.
Chittlehamholt
Martock
West Stour
SHAFTESBURY
Bampton
M 5
Wellington
South Petherton
YEOVIL
SHERBORNE
Burrington
Thelbridge
Sampford Peverell
Ilminster
Seavington St. Mary
Morchard Bishop
Yarcombe
Sturminster Newton
Cullompton
CREWKERNE
Bickleigh
Chardstock
Chedington
BLANDFORD FORUM
Coleford
Broadhembury
Evershot
HONITON
Fenny Bridges
Exeter S.A.
Gittisham
AXMINSTER
Cheriton Bishop
Maiden Newton
Venn Ottery
Charmouth
BRIDPORT
Drewsteignton
EXETER
A 30
Colyton
A 35
Affpuddle
Dunsford
Beer
West Bexington
Newton Poppleford
LYME REGIS
DORCHESTER
CHAGFORD
SIDMOUTH
Branscombe
Wareham
Moretonhampstead
Abbotsbury
West Lulworth
North Bovey
Budleigh Salterton
Trusham
Weymouth
EXMOUTH
BOVEY TRACEY
Dawlish
A 38
Kingsteignton
Two Bridges
TEIGNMOUTH
ASHBURTON
Kingskerswell
Staverton
TORQUAY
TOTNES
Paignton
A 38
Galmpton
Brixham
Holbeton
DARTMOUTH
Kingston
KINGSBRIDGE
Bigbury-on-Sea
SALCOMBE

9
EVESHAM
BROADWAY
CHIPPING CAMPDEN
Blockley
with rm.
Moreton-in-Marsh
Winchcombe
Great Tew
STOW-ON-THE-WOLD
Guiting Power
Kingham
Churchill
Chadlington
BOURTON-ON-THE WATER
Milton-under-Wychwood
Charlbury
Shipton-under-Wychwood
Woodstock
Northleach
Minster Lovell
BURFORD
WITNEY
Bibury
Lew
Coln St. Aldwyns
Clanfield
Stanton Harcourt
Meysey Hampton
Ashton Keynes
Cricklade
Lyford
Purton
SWINDON
M 4
Leigh Delamere S.A.
Hilmarton
Chippenham
Aldbourne
Calne
Hungerford
Kintbury
MARLBOROUGH
DEVIZES
HURSTBOURNE TARRANT
ANDOVER
Amesbury
Middle Wallop
Sutton Scotney S.A.
Hindon
STOCKBRIDGE
with rm.
SALISBURY
WINCHESTER
New Alresford
Alvediston
Ampfield
Cranborne
ROMSEY
Eastleigh
M 27
Rownhams S.A.
Brook
Cadnam
FORDINGBRIDGE
Southampton
RINGWOOD
A 31
Lyndhurst
WIMBORNE MINSTER
Burley
Brockenhurst
Ferndown
BEAULIEU
New Milton
CHRISTCHURCH
Lymington
with rm.
Poole
Milford-on-Sea
M
Bournemouth
Freshwater
Totland
Corfe Castle
Swanage
BANBURY
Brackley
Deddington
Chipping Norton
Cherwell Valley S.A.
Enstone
Steeple Aston
Middleton Stoney
Chesterton
Weston-on-the-Green
MILTON KEYNES
Aspley Guise
Woburn
Buckingham
Leighton Buzzard
Flitwick
Toddington S.A.
Letchworth
HITCHIN
STEVENAGE
Great Offley
Luton
DUNSTABLE
Mentmore
Ivinghoe
Flamstead
Harpenden
M 1
M 40
11
M 4
M 3
M 25
GODALMING
Cranleigh
Gatwick Airport
Alton
Four Marks
Grayshott
Haslemere
HORSHAM
Rogate
Billingshurst
Petersfield
MIDHURST
PETWORTH
PULBOROUGH
Ashington
HENFIELD
Steyning
Findon
A 27
M 27
Worthing
Botley
Shedfield
Wickham
Denmead
Amberley
Storrington
M,
Fontwell
ARUNDEL
M 27
Fareham
Emsworth
Havant
A 27
CHICHESTER
Sarisbury
PORTSMOUTH AND SOUTHSEA
M
Littlehampton
Lee-on-the-Solent
Hayling Island
East Wittering
Cowes
Seaview
Alverstone
ISLE OF WIGHT
Shanklin
Chale
VENTNOR
Niton

10
SAFFRON WALDEN
Hadleigh
Newport
Higham
Dedham
Felixstowe
Baldock
Wethersfield
Clavering
Thaxted
Manningtree
Harwich and Dovercourt
STANSTED AIRPORT
Earls Colne
Standon
Braintree
Coggeshall
COLCHESTER
BISHOP'S STORFORD
Great Dunmow
Felsted
Frinton-on-Sea
WARE
Hertford
Witham
West Mersea
CHELMSFORD
Maldon
South Woodham Ferrers
Burnham-on-Crouch
M 11
M 25
Basildon
LONDON
Southend-on-Sea
North Stifford
Gravesend
Rochester
Medway S.A.
Birchington
Whitstable
Herne Bay
Broadstairs
Cobham
Newington
RAMSGATE
M 20
West Malling
FAVERSHAM
Selling
Sandwich
Warren Street
CANTERBURY
Wingham
MAIDSTONE
Lenham
DEAL
M 23
Pluckley
Wye
Edenbridge
Brenchley
Horley
Penshurst
Frittenden
ROYAL TUNBRIDGE WELLS
ASHFORD
Turners Hill
Bethersden
DOVER
Goudhurst
Biddenden
EAST GRINSTEAD
CRANBROOK
Folkestone
CRAWLEY
Hartfield
Wadhurst
Hythe
FOREST ROW
Tenterden
Hawkhurst
Ardingly
Crowborough
Benenden
A 259
Ticehurst
Cuckfield
MAYFIELD
Wittersham
Sedlescombe
Heathfield
Haywards Heath
Uckfield
RYE
Rushlake Green
Battle
Hickstead
Halland
Winchelsea
Lewes
Herstmonceux
A 27
Bexhill
A 23
BRIGHTON AND HOVE
HAILSHAM
Hastings and St. Leonards
Alfriston
Pevensey
Rottingdean
EASTBOURNE
SEAFORD
1
2
Carlisle
Newcastle
Liverpool
Manchester
3
4
5
6
Norwich
Birmingham
Bristol
London
11
Dover
7
8
Southampton
Plymouth
9
10

11
LONDON
Thames
M 1
M 4
M 11
M 20
M 23
M 25
M 3
M 40
A 4
A 11
A 20
A 23
A 40
A 41
A 316
OXFORD
Horton-cum-Studley
Waddesdon
Aylesbury
Aston Clinton
Tring
Long Crendon
THAME
ABINGDON
Chislehampton
Dorchester
Sutton Courtenay
Harwell
WALLINGFORD
Chinnor
Ibstone
Great Missenden
Speen
High Wycombe
Little Chalfont
Amersham
Chenies
Chipperfield
HEMEL HEMPSTEAD
Kings Langley
Watford
St.Albans
Welwyn
Welwyn Garden City
Hatfield
Brookmans Park
Hertingfordbury
Stanstead Abbots
Sawbridgeworth
Harlow
Cheshunt
Waltham Abbey
South Mimms S.A.
Radlett
Borehamwood
Elstree
Buckhurst Hill
Ingatestone
Brentwood
East Horndon
Thurrock S.A.
Dartford
Farningham
BRANDS HATCH
Wrotham Heath
SEVENOAKS
Westerham
TONBRIDGE
Godstone
REDHILL
Reigate
Dorking
Tadworth
Epsom
ESHER
COBHAM
Walton-on-Thames
Weybridge
Chobham
Ripley
Ockham
GUILDFORD
BEACONSFIELD
Chalfont St. Peter
Gerrards Cross
Nettlebed
Moulsford with rm.
with rm.
HENLEY-ON-THAMES
Goring
Streatley
Marlow
Hurley-on-Thames
MAIDENHEAD
Cookham
Taplow
Burnham
Slough
Knowl Hill
with rm.
Bray-on-Thames
Sonning-on-Thames
Windsor
Staines
Egham
Shepperton
Chertsey
Yattendon
Bradfield
READING
Wokingham
Bracknell
ASCOT
Thatcham
NEWBURY
Padworth
Silchester
Old Burghclere
Stratfield Turgis
Crowthorne
Bagshot
Yateley
Camberley
Frimley
Fleet S.A.
Fleet
Farnborough
HOOK
BASINGSTOKE
North Waltham
Crondall
Odiham
FARNHAM

ABBERLEY Heref. and Worcs. 403 404 M 27 – pop. 654 – ECD : Wednesday – ✉ Worcester – ☎ 01299.
♦London 137 – ♦Birmingham 27 – Worcester 13.

The Elms (Q.M.H.) ⛱, WR6 6AT, W : 2 m. on A 443 ℘ 896666, Telex 337105, Fax 896804, ≤, « Queen Anne mansion », ⛱, park, 🎾 – TV ☎ P – 🏛 40. AE VISA
Meals (bar lunch Monday to Saturday)/dinner 24.00 **t.** and a la carte 22.50/31.50 **t.** 6.25 – 8.75 – **24 rm** 92.00/128.00 **t.**, 1 suite – SB.

Manor Arms ⛱, Abberley Village, WR6 6BN, ℘ 896507, ⛱ – TV ☎ P
10 rm.

at Little Witley SW : 4 m. by A 443 – ✉ Worcester – ☎ 01886 :

Ribston House ⛱, Bank Rd, WR6 6LS, ℘ 888750, Fax 888750, ⛱ – P. ✗
Booking essential – **Meals** (communal dining) – **3 rm** (dinner included) 35.00/70.00 **s.** – SB.

ABBOTSBURY Dorset 403 404 M 32 **The West Country G.** – pop. 422 – ☎ 01305.
See : Town★★ - Chesil Beach★★ - Swannery★ *AC* – Sub-Tropical Gardens★ *AC*.
Envir. : St. Catherine's Chapel★, ½ m. uphill (30 mn rtn on foot).
Exc. : Maiden Castle★★ (≤★) NE : 7½ m.
♦London 146 – Exeter 50 – Bournemouth 44 – Weymouth 10.

Ilchester Arms, 9 Market St., DT3 4JR, ℘ 871243, Fax 871225 – ⇔ rest TV ☎ P. VISA. ✗
Meals a la carte 9.50/16.25 **t.** 3.10 – **10 rm** 35.00/80.00 **st.** – SB.

The Guide is updated annually so renew your Guide every year.

ABBOT'S SALFORD Warks. 403 404 O 27 – see Evesham (Heref. and Worcs.).

ABINGDON Oxon. 403 404 Q 28 **Great Britain G.** – pop. 30 771 – ECD : Thursday – ☎ 01235.
See : Town★ – County Hall★.
18 Drayton Park, Steventon Rd, Drayton, ℘ 550607.
Abbey House, Abbey Close, OX14 3JD ℘ 522711.
♦London 64 – ♦Oxford 6 – Reading 25.

Upper Reaches (Forte), Thames St., OX14 3JA, ℘ 522311, Fax 555182 – ⇔ TV ☎ P – 🏛 70. AE VISA JCB
Meals 11.95/18.95 **st.** and a la carte 6.95 – 8.50 – **25 rm** 85.00/95.00 **st.** – SB.

Abingdon Lodge, Marcham Rd, OX14 1TZ, W : 1 m. on A 415 ℘ 553456, Fax 554117 – ⇔ rm TV ☎ P – 🏛 140. AE VISA
Meals 8.25/10.95 **st.** and dinner a la carte – 5.95 – **63 rm** 65.00/80.00 **st.** – SB.

Crown and Thistle, Bridge St., OX14 3HS, ℘ 522556, Fax 553281 – TV ☎ P. ✗
21 rm.

Thame Lane House, 1 Thame Lane, Culham, OX14 3DS, SE : 1 ¾ m. on A 415 ℘ 524177, ⛱ – ⇔ rm TV P. VISA. ✗
Meals - French *(closed Monday lunch and Sunday dinner)* (booking essential) 18.50/26.50 **st.** 5.50 – **5 rm** 27.00/54.00 **st.**

at Clifton Hampden SE : 3¾ m. on A 415 – ✉ Abingdon – ☎ 01867 :

Barley Mow, OX14 3EH, on Long Wittenham Rd ℘ 307847, Fax 407836, ⛱ – TV ☎ P. AE VISA. ✗
Meals (in bar lunchtime and Sunday to Tuesday)/dinner a la carte 13.15/19.35 **t.** 3.75 – **4 rm** 30.95/34.95 **t.** – SB.

at Frilford W : 3¾ m. on A 415 – ✉ Abingdon – ☎ 01865 :

Dog House, Frilford Heath, OX13 6QJ, NE : 1 ¼ m. by A 338 on Cothill rd ℘ 390830, Fax 390860, ⛱ – ⇔ rm TV ☎ ♿ P. AE VISA
Meals a la carte 10.15/19.40 **t.** – **19 rm** 60.00/69.00 **t.** – SB.

ACLE Norfolk 404 Y 26 **Great Britain G.** – pop. 2 208 – ☎ 01493.
Envir. : The Broads★.
♦London 118 – Great Yarmouth 8 – ♦Norwich 11.

Forte Travelodge without rest., Acle by Pass, NR1 3BE, on A 47 at junction with B 1140 ℘ 751970, Reservations (Freephone) 0800 850950 – TV ♿ P. AE VISA. ✗
40 rm 33.50 **t.**

ADDERBURY Oxon. 403 404 Q 27 – see Banbury.

ADLINGTON Ches. – see Macclesfield.

ADLINGTON Lancs. 402 404 M 23 – pop. 5 653 – ECD : Wednesday – ☎ 01257.
♦London 217 – ♦Liverpool 35 – ♦Manchester 21 – Preston 16.

Gladmar, Railway Rd, PR6 9RG, ℘ 480398, Fax 482681, ⛱ – TV ☎ P. AE VISA. ✗
Meals 8.50/13.50 **st.** 3.50 – **20 rm** 37.00/58.00 **st.**

AFFPUDDLE Dorset 403 404 N 31 The West Country G. – pop. 447 – ✉ Dorchester – ☎ 01305.
Envir. : Moreton Church★★, S : 2½ m. by B 3390.
Exc. : Bere Regis (St. John the Baptist Church★★) NE : 3½ m. by B 3390 and A 35.
♦London 121 – Bournemouth 19 – Exeter 60 – ♦Southampton 47 – Weymouth 14.

Old Vicarage without rest., DT2 7HH, ℘ 848315, « Tastefully furnished Georgian house », – TV P.
closed 5 days Christmas – **3 rm** 22.50/40.00.

AINSTABLE Cumbria 401 402 L 19 – ✉ Carlisle – ☎ 01768.
♦London 304 – ♦Carlisle 19 – Kendal 45 – Lancaster 62.

New Crown Inn, CA4 9QQ, ℘ 896273 – TV P
Meals *(closed Monday lunch except Bank Holidays)* (in bar) 7.50 **t.** (lunch) and a la carte 8.10/15.95 **t.** 3.00 – **3 rm** 27.50/50.00 **t.** – SB.

ALBERBURY Shrops. 402 403 L 25 – see Shrewsbury.

ALBRIGHTON Shrops. 402 403 L 25 – see Shrewsbury.

ALBURY Surrey – see Guildford.

ALCESTER Warks. 403 404 O 27 – ☎ 01789.
♦London 104 – ♦Birmingham 20 – Cheltenham 27 – Stratford-upon-Avon 8.

Kings Court, Kings Coughton, B49 5QQ, N: 1½ m. on A 435 ℘ 763111, Fax 400242, – TV ☎ & P – 100. AE VISA
accommodation closed 24 to 30 December – **Meals** *(closed 25 December)* a la carte 11.30/17.55 **t.** 5.20 – **42 rm** 49.00/64.00 **t.** – SB.

Throckmorton Arms, Coughton, B49 5HX, N : 2¼ m. on A 435 ℘ 762879, Fax 762654 – TV ☎ P
10 rm.

ALDBOURNE Wilts. 403 404 P 29 – pop. 2 194 – ☎ 01672.
♦London 77 – ♦Oxford 36 – ♦Southampton 53 – Swindon 9.

Raffles, 1 The Green, SN8 2BW, ℘ 40700, Fax 40038 – AE VISA
closed lunch Monday and Saturday, Sunday dinner, 2-3 weeks August, 25 to 31 December and Bank Holidays – **Meals** (restricted menu Friday dinner) a la carte 12.65/21.55 **t.** 4.80.

ALDEBURGH Suffolk 404 Y 27 – pop. 2 654 – ECD : Wednesday – ☎ 01728.
18 Thorpeness Golf Hotel, Thorpeness ℘ 452176.
The Cinema, High St., IP15 5AU ℘ 453637 (summer only).
♦London 97 – ♦Ipswich 24 – ♦Norwich 41.

Wentworth, Wentworth Rd, IP15 5BD, ℘ 452312, Fax 454343, ← – TV ☎ P. AE VISA
closed 27 December-9 January – **Meals** 14.75/17.50 and a la carte – **31 rm** 52.50/105.00 **t.** – SB.

White Lion, Market Cross Pl., IP15 5BJ, ℘ 452720, Fax 452986, ← – TV ☎ P – 100. AE VISA
Meals (bar lunch)/dinner 16.95 **st.** and a la carte 5.45 – **38 rm** 57.50/100.00 **st.** – SB.

Brudenell (Forte), The Parade, IP15 5BU, ℘ 452071, Fax 454082, ← – TV ☎ P – 45. AE VISA JCB
Meals 10.95/16.95 **t.** and a la carte 6.50 – 8.50 – **47 rm** 55.00/65.00 **t.** – SB.

Uplands, Victoria Rd, IP15 5DX, ℘ 452420, Fax 454872, – rest TV ☎ P. AE VISA
Meals (dinner only) 15.00 **t.** and a la carte – **20 rm** 32.00/65.00 **t.** – SB.

Austins with rm, 243-247 High St., IP15 5DN, ℘ 453932, Fax 453668 – TV ☎. VISA
Meals *(closed Sunday dinner to non-residents and Monday)* (dinner only and Sunday lunch)/dinner 19.75 **t.** 3.75 – 7.50 – **7 rm** 47.75/70.00 **t.**

New Regatta, 171-173 High St., IP15 5AN, ℘ 452011, Fax 452011 – AE VISA
closed Sunday, Monday and Bank Holidays – **Meals** a la carte 14.15/18.15 **t.**

ALDERHOLT Hants. – see Fordingbridge.

ALDERLEY EDGE Ches. 402 403 404 N 24 – pop. 4 482 – ECD : Wednesday – ☎ 01625.
18 Wilmslow, Great Warford, Mobberley ℘ (01565) 872148 – 9 Brook Lane ℘ 585583.
♦London 187 – Chester 34 – ♦Manchester 14 – ♦Stoke-on-Trent 25.

Alderley Edge, Macclesfield Rd, SK9 7BJ, ℘ 583033, Fax 586343, – TV ☎ P – 120. AE VISA
Meals (see ***Alderley Edge*** below) – 8.50 – **32 rm** 87.00/125.00 **st.**

De Trafford Arms (Premier), London Rd, SK9 7AA, ℘ 583881, Fax 586625 – TV ☎ P. – **37 rm.**

Alderley Edge, (at Alderley Edge H.) Macclesfield Rd, SK9 7BJ, ℘ 583033, Fax 586343, – P. AE VISA.
Meals 16.50/20.50 **t.** and a la carte 8.50.

ALDRIDGE W. Mids. 402 403 404 O 26 – pop. 17 549 – ECD : Thursday – ✉ Walsall – ☎ 01922.

♦London 130 – ♦Birmingham 12 – Derby 32 – ♦Leicester 40 – ♦Stoke-on-Trent 38.

Plan : see Birmingham p.3

Fairlawns, 178 Little Aston Rd, WS9 0NU, E : 1 m. on A 454 ✆ 55122, Fax 743210 – rm rest – 80. VISA CT **n**
Meals *(closed Saturday lunch, Sunday dinner and Bank Holidays)* 12.95/22.50 **st.** and a la carte 5.00 – **31 rm** 45.00/80.00 **st.**, 4 suites – SB.

ATS 106 Leighswood Rd, Walsall ✆ 51968/53970

ALDWINCLE Northants. 402 404 S 26 – pop. 310 – ✉ Kettering – ☎ 01832.

♦London 84 – ♦Cambridge 40 – ♦Leicester 40 – Northampton 26 – Peterborough 18.

The Maltings without rest., NN14 3EP, ✆ 720233, Fax 720326, – . VISA.
3 rm 32.00/43.00 **st.**

ALFRETON Derbs 402 403 404 P 24 – pop. 21 117 – ECD : Wednesday – ☎ 01773.

18 Shirland, Lower Delves ✆ 834935 – 18 Ormonde Fields, Nottingham Rd, Codnor, Ripley ✆ 742987.

♦London 134 – Derby 13 – ♦Nottingham 19 – ♦Sheffield 27.

Granada, Old Swanwick Colliery Rd, DE55 1HJ, S : ¾ m. by A 61 at junction with A 38 ✆ 520040, Fax 521087 – rm rest – 50.
Meals (grill rest.) – **61 rm.**

Le Guide change, changez de guide Michelin tous les ans.

ALFRISTON E. Sussex 404 U 31 – pop. 1 721 – ECD : Wednesday – ✉ Polegate – ☎ 01323.

♦London 66 – Eastbourne 9 – Lewes 10 – Newhaven 8.

Deans Place, BN26 5TW, ✆ 870248, Fax 870918, heated, – rest – 150
36 rm.

Star Inn (Forte), High St., BN26 5TA, ✆ 870495, Fax 870922 – – 30. VISA JCB
Meals 13.95/15.95 **t.** and dinner a la carte 6.95 – 8.95 – **34 rm** 72.50/102.50 **t.** – SB.

Moonrakers, High St., BN26 5TD, ✆ 870472. VISA
closed 21 January to 12 February – **Meals** (dinner only and Sunday lunch)/dinner 17.95 **t.** and a la carte 4.50.

ALLENDALE Northd. 401 402 N 19 – pop. 2 123 – ✉ Hexham – ☎ 01434.

9 High Studdon, Allenheads Rd ✆ (0191) 267 5875.

♦London 314 – ♦Carlisle 39 – ♦Newcastle upon Tyne 33.

Bishop Field without rest., NE47 9EJ, W : 1 m. on Whitfield rd ✆ 683248, , –
closed January and February – **3 rm** 20.00/40.00.

Thornley House, NE47 9NH, W : ¾ m. on Whitfield rd ✆ 683255, –
Meals (communal dining) 9.50 **st.** – **3 rm** 21.00/35.00 **st.**

ALLESLEY W. Mids. 403 404 P 26 – see Coventry.

ALNE N. Yorks. – see Easingwold.

ALNMOUTH Northd. 401 402 P 17 **Great Britain G.** – pop. 586 – ECD : Wednesday – ☎ 01665.

Envir. : Warkworth Castle★ *AC*, S : 4 m. by B 1338 and A 1068.

9 Alnmouth Village, Marine Rd. ✆ 830370.

♦London 314 – ♦Edinburgh 90 – ♦Newcastle upon Tyne 37.

Marine House, 1 Marine Rd, NE66 2RW, ✆ 830349, ←, – . VISA
Meals 13.95 5.50 – **10 rm** (dinner included) 78.00 **t.** – SB.

High Buston Hall , High Buston, NE66 3QH, SW: 2 ¼ m. by B 1338 and A 1068 ✆ 830341, « Georgian house », – .
closed January – **Meals** (by arrangement) (communal dining) 20.00 4.25 – **3 rm** 35.00/59.00 **s.** – SB.

The Grange without rest., NE66 2RJ, ✆ 830401, ←, – .
5 rm 21.00/48.00 **st.**

ALNWICK Northd. 401 402 O 17 **Great Britain G.** – pop. 7 419 – ECD : Wednesday – ☎ 01665.

See : Town ★ – Castle★★ *AC*.

Exc. : Dunstanburgh Castle★ *AC*, NE : 8 m. by B 1340 and Dunstan rd (last 2½ m. on foot).

9 Swansfield Park ✆ 602632.

The Shambles, NE66 1TN ✆ 510665.

♦London 320 – ♦Edinburgh 86 – ♦Newcastle upon Tyne 34.

White Swan, Bondgate Within, NE66 1TD, 602109, Fax 510400 – rest – 150. AE VISA
Meals (bar lunch Monday to Saturday)/dinner 15.95 **st.** 4.65 – **55 rm** 54.50/70.00 **st.** – SB.

Oaks, South Rd, NE66 2PN, SE : ½ m. 510014, Fax 603219 – . AE VISA JCB
Meals 12.75/18.50 **st.** and a la carte 3.95 – **13 rm** 45.00/65.00 **st.** – SB.

Bondgate House, 20 Bondgate Without, NE66 1PN, 602025, Fax 602554 – . VISA.
Meals (by arrangement) 11.00 **st.** 4.00 – **8 rm** 22.00/36.00 **st.** – SB.

John Blackmore's, 1 Dorothy Forster Court, Narrowgate, NE66 1NL, 604465 – . AE VISA
closed Sunday, Monday and January – **Meals** (dinner only) 16.50 **t.** and a la carte.

at Eglingham NW : 7 m. on B 6346 – Alnwick – 01665 :

Ogle House, NE66 2TZ, 578264, –
Meals 15.00 **st.** 3.75 – **3 rm** 23.50/39.00 **st.** – SB.

ALPORT Derbs. – see Bakewell.

ALSAGER Ches. 402 403 404 N 24 **Great Britain G.** – pop. 11 912 – Stoke-on-Trent (Staffs.) – 01270.

Envir. : Little Moreton Hall★★ *AC*, NE : 4 m. by A 50 and A 34.

London 180 – Chester 36 – Liverpool 49 – Manchester 32 – Stoke-on-Trent 11.

Manor House, Audley Rd, ST7 2QQ, SE : ¾ m. 884000, Fax 882483, – rm – 200. AE VISA.
Meals *(closed Saturday lunch)* 10.95/17.50 **t.** and a la carte 4.50 – **57 rm** 54.00/94.00 **t.** – SB.

La guida cambia, cambiate la guida ogni anno.

ALSTON Cumbria 401 402 M 19 – pop. 2 065 – ECD : Tuesday – 01434.

Alston Moor, The Hermitage 381675.

The Railway Station, CA9 3JB 381696.

London 309 – Carlisle 28 – Newcastle upon Tyne 45.

Lovelady Shield Country House , Nenthead Rd, CA9 3LF, E : 2 ½ m. on A 689 381203, Fax 381515, , , – rest . AE VISA
closed 5 January-3 February – **Meals** (bar lunch)/dinner 26.50 **t.** 4.30 – **12 rm** (dinner included) 72.50/169.00 **t.** – SB.

Nent Hall Country House, CA9 3LQ, E : 2 ½ m. on A 689 381584, Fax 382668, – . AE VISA
Meals 22.50 **st.** (dinner) and a la carte 10.85/15.85 **st.** – **18 rm** 47.00/85.00 **st.** – SB.

ALTARNUN Cornwall 403 G 32 – Launceston – 01566.

London 279 – Exeter 56 – Plymouth 36 – Truro 39.

Penhallow Manor , PL15 7SJ, 86206, Fax 86179, – .
7 rm.

ALTON Hants. 404 R 30 – pop. 16 356 – ECD : Wednesday – 01420.

Old Odiham Rd 82042.

7 Cross and Pillory Lane, GU34 1HL 88448.

London 53 – Reading 24 – Southampton 29 – Winchester 18.

Swan (Forte), High St., GU34 1AT, 83777, Fax 87975 – – 50
36 rm.

Grange, London Rd, GU34 4EG, NE : 1 m. on A 339 86565, Fax 541346, – – 80. AE VISA
closed 25 to 31 December – **Meals** (bar lunch Saturday) a la carte 10.40/19.20 **t.** 4.50 – **28 rm** 49.50/125.00 **t.** – SB.

Alton House, Normandy St., GU34 1DW, 80033, Fax 89222, heated, , – – 130. AE VISA
closed 25 and 26 December – **Meals** 7.95/11.95 **t.** and a la carte 4.00 – 5.95 – **39 rm** 48.00/55.00 **t.** – SB.

ALTRINCHAM Gtr. Manchester 402 403 404 N 23 – pop. 39 528 – ECD : Wednesday – 0161.

Altrincham Municipal, Stockport Rd, Timperley 928 0761 – Ringway, Hale Mount, Hale Barns 904 9609.

Stamford New Road, WA14 1EJ 941 7337.

London 191 – Chester 30 – Liverpool 30 – Manchester 8.

Cresta Court, Church St., WA14 4DP, on A 56 ✆ 927 7272, Fax 926 9194 – rm rest – 250.
Meals 8.95 **st.** and a la carte 4.50 – **138 rm** 55.50/70.00 **st.** – SB.

Woodland Park, Wellington Rd, WA15 7RG, off A 560 ✆ 928 8631, Fax 941 2821 – rest – 200.
Meals *(closed lunch Saturday and Sunday)* 11.00 **t.** (dinner) and a la carte 17.40/23.70 **t.** – **45 rm** 69.50/95.00 **t.** – SB.

Pelican Country Inn (Premier), Manchester Rd, West Timperley, WA14 5NH, N : 2 m. on A 56 ✆ 962 7414, Fax 962 3456 – rm.
48 rm.

George and Dragon (Premier), Manchester Rd, WA14 4PH, on A 56 ✆ 928 9933, Fax 929 8060 – rm
47 rm.

at Hale SE : 1 m. on B 5163 – ✉ Altrincham – ☎ 0161 :

Ashley (De Vere), Ashley Rd, WA15 9SF, ✆ 928 3794, Fax 926 9046 – rm – 200.
Meals (light lunch Monday to Saturday)/dinner 14.25 **st.** and a la carte – **47 rm** 55.00/65.00 **st.** – SB.

Est, Est, Est!, 183 Ashley Rd, WA15 9SD, ✆ 928 1811.
closed 25 December – **Meals** - Italian 9.95 **t.** and a la carte.

at Halebarns SE : 3 m. on A 538 – ✉ Altrincham – ☎ 0161 :

Four Seasons, Manchester Airport, Hale Rd, WA15 8XW, ✆ 904 0301, Fax 980 1787, – rm rest – 120.
Meals (bar lunch Saturday and Bank Holidays) 15.95/16.95 **st.** and a la carte 6.25 – 9.50 – **90 rm** 92.50/113.50 **st.**, 4 suites.

at Bowdon SW : 1 m. – ✉ Altrincham – ☎ 0161 :

Bowdon Croft, Green Walk, WA14 2SN, ✆ 928 1718, Fax 928 1718, «19C house», – rest.
Meals (booking essential) (residents only) 15.00/19.50 **st.** 4.50 – **9 rm** 60.00/89.00 **st.**

Bowdon, Langham Rd, WA14 2HT, ✆ 928 7121, Fax 927 7560 – – 130.
Meals (bar lunch Monday to Saturday)/dinner 15.95 **st.** and a la carte – **82 rm** 58.00/79.00 **st.** – SB.

ATS 74 Oakfield Rd ✆ 928 7024

ALVEDISTON Wilts. 404 N 30 – ✉ Salisbury – ☎ 01722 :

Crown Inn with rm, SP5 5JY, ✆ 780335, « Part 17C inn », –.
Meals a la carte 11.70/21.90 **t.** 4.80 – **3 rm** 25.00/40.00 **t.**

ALVELEY Shrops. – see Bridgnorth.

ALVERSTONE I.O.W. 403 404 Q 32 – see Wight (Isle of).

ALVESTON Avon 403 404 M 29 – pop. 3 620 – ECD : Wednesday – ✉ Bristol – ☎ 01454.
♦London 127 – ♦Bristol 11 – Gloucester 23 – Swindon 42.

Alveston House, BS12 2LJ, on A 38 ✆ 415050, Fax 415425, – – 85.
Meals 10.75/17.00 **st.** and a la carte 5.50 – **30 rm** 65.50/79.50 **st.** – SB.

Forte Posthouse, Thornbury Rd, BS12 2LL, on A 38 ✆ 412521, Fax 413920, heated, – rm – 100.
Meals a la carte approx. 15.00 **t.** 5.50 – **74 rm** 56.00/69.50 **st.**

ALWALTON Cambs. 402 404 T 26 – see Peterborough.

AMBERLEY Glos. 403 404 N 28 – see Stroud.

AMBERLEY W. Sussex 404 S 31 **Great Britain G.** – pop. 525 – ✉ Arundel – ☎ 01798.
Envir. : Bignor Roman Villa (mosaics★) *AC*, NW : 3½ m. by B 2139 via Bury.
♦London 56 – ♦Brighton 24 – ♦Portsmouth 31.

Amberley Castle, BN18 9ND, SW : ½ m. on B 2139 ✆ 831992, Fax 831998, « 14C castle, 12C origins », , park – rest – 40.
Meals 16.50/25.50 **st.** and a la carte 7.50 – **14 rm** 80.00/225.00 **st.** – SB.

AMBLESIDE Cumbria 402 L 20 **Great Britain G.** – pop. 3 353 – ECD : Thursday – ☎ 0153 94.
Envir. : Lake Windermere★★ – Dove Cottage, Grasmere★ *AC* AY **A** – Brockhole National Park Centre★ *AC*, SE : 3 m. by A 591 AZ.
Exc. : Wrynose Pass★★, W : 7½ m. by A 593 AY – Hard Knott Pass★★, W : 10 m. by A 593 AY.
Old Courthouse, Church St., LA22 0BT ✆ 32582 (summer only) AZ – Main Car Park, Waterhead, LA22 0EN ✆ 32729 (summer only) BY.
♦London 278 – ♦Carlisle 47 – Kendal 14.

AMBLESIDE GRASMERE

Lake Rd . . . . AZ

Borrans Rd. . . . . BY 2
Broadgate . . . . BZ 3
Cheapside . . . . AZ 4
Church St. . . . . AZ 6
Compston St . . . . AZ 8
Easedale Rd. . . . . BZ 10
Kelswick Rd . . . . AZ 12
King St . . . . AZ 13
Market Pl . . . . AZ 14
North Rd . . . . AZ 17
Old Lake Rd. . . . . AZ 20
St. Mary's Lane. . . . . AZ 22
Smithy Brow . . . . AZ 23
Swan Hill . . . . AY 24

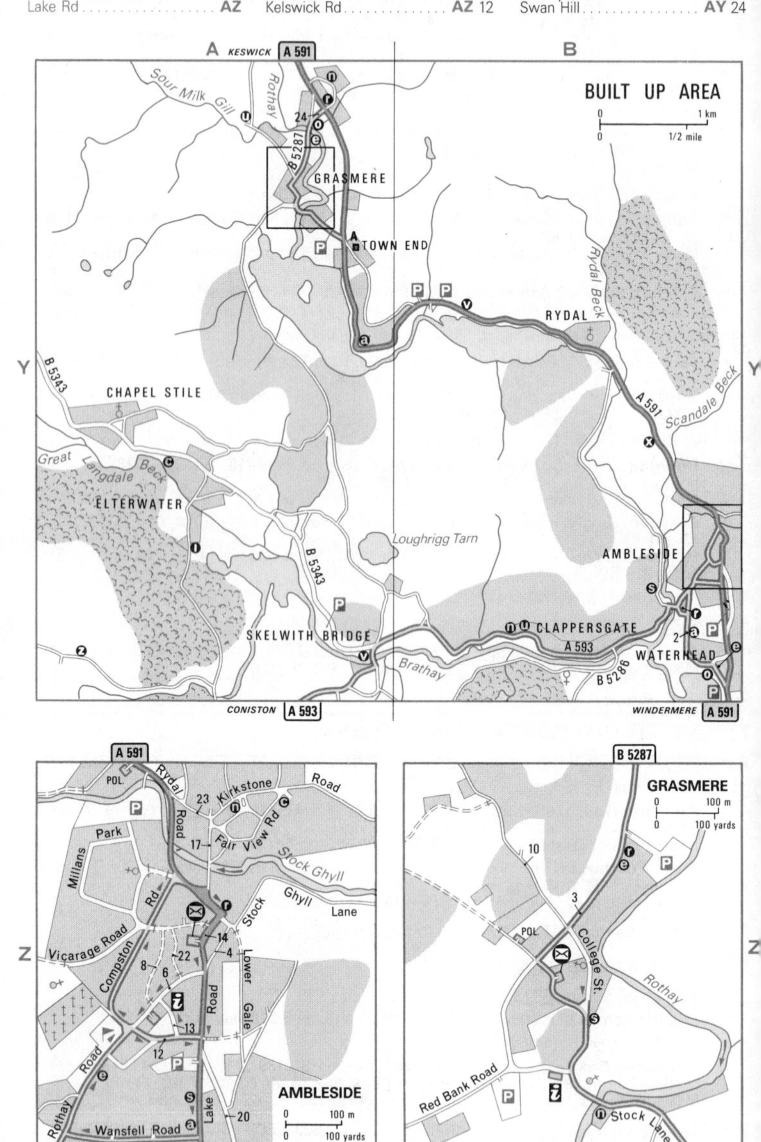

Town plans : *roads most used by traffic and those on which guide listed hotels and restaurants stand are fully drawn; the beginning only of lesser roads is indicated.*

Rothay Manor, Rothay Bridge, LA22 0EH, S : ½ m. on A 593 ℘ 33605, Fax 33607, <, « Regency style country house », – rest TV ☎ & P. AE VISA. BY r
closed 2 January-10 February – **Meals** (buffet lunch Monday to Saturday)/dinner 25.00 **t.** 4.50 – **15 rm** 72.00/125.00 **t.**, 3 suites – SB.

Kirkstone Foot Country House, Kirkstone Pass Rd, LA22 9EH, NE : ¼ m. ℘ 32232, Fax 32232, – rest TV ☎ P. AE VISA AZ c
closed first 2 weeks January – **Meals** (dinner only) 19.75 **t.** 4.25 – **15 rm** (dinner included) 52.00/116.00 **t.** – SB.

Salutation, Lake Rd, LA22 9BX, ℘ 32244, Fax 34157 – rest TV ☎ P. VISA JCB AZ r
Meals (bar lunch)/dinner 18.00 **st.** and a la carte 4.85 – **29 rm** 59.50/109.00 **st.**

Borrans Park, Borrans Rd, LA22 0EN, ℘ 33454, – TV ☎ & P. VISA. BY a
Meals (dinner only) 16.00 **st.** 3.75 – **12 rm** 27.50/75.00 **st.** – SB.

Laurel Villa, Lake Rd, LA22 0DB, ℘ 33240 – TV P. VISA. AZ s
closed 24 to 26 December – **Meals** (dinner only) 25.00 **t.** 5.00 – **8 rm** 50.00/60.00 **t.**

Elder Grove, Lake Rd, LA22 0DB, ℘ 32504 – rest TV ☎ P. AE VISA AZ a
mid February-mid November – **Meals** (bar lunch)/dinner 16.50 **t.** and a la carte 4.00 – **12 rm** 26.50/53.00 **t.** – SB.

Riverside, Under Loughrigg, LA22 9LJ, ℘ 32395, Fax 32395, – rest TV ☎ P. VISA. BY s
March-mid November – **Meals** (bar lunch)/dinner 18.00 **st.** and a la carte 5.50 – **10 rm** (dinner included) 60.00/100.00 **t.** – SB.

Rothay Garth, Rothay Rd, LA22 0EE, ℘ 32217, Fax 34400, – TV ☎ P. AE VISA JCB. AZ e
Meals 9.50/19.50 **st.** and a la carte 5.20 – **15 rm** 45.00/90.00 **st.**, 1 suite – SB.

Drunken Duck Inn, Barngates, LA22 0NG, SW : 3 m. by A 593 off B 5286 ℘ 36347, Fax 36781 – TV ☎ P. AE VISA BY
closed Christmas Day – **Meals** (in bar) approx. 11.50 **t.** – **9 rm** 50.00/69.00 **t.** – SB.

Crow How, Rydal Rd, LA22 9PN, NW : ½ m. on A 591 ℘ 32193, <, – TV P. VISA BY x
closed December and January – **Meals** 12.00 **st.** 4.25 – **9 rm** 25.00/59.00 **st.** – SB.

Chapel House, Kirkstone Rd, LA22 9DZ, ℘ 33143 – . AZ n
closed January-February (restricted service November and December) – **Meals** 15.00 **st.** – **10 rm** (dinner included) 37.00/79.50 **st.** – SB.

at Waterhead S : 1 m. on A 591 – BY – ⊠ Ambleside – 0153 94 :

Low Wood, LA23 1LP, SE : ½ m. on A 591 ℘ 33338, Fax 34072, <, squash – rest TV ☎ P – 340. AE VISA JCB
Meals (bar lunch)/dinner 19.50 **st.** 4.95 – **99 rm** 47.00/129.00 **st.** – SB.

Wateredge, Borrans Rd, LA22 0EP, ℘ 32332, Fax 32332, <, « Part 17C fishermen's cottages, lakeside setting », – rest TV ☎ P. AE VISA. BY o
closed December and January – **Meals** (light lunch)/dinner 26.90 **t.** – **23 rm** (dinner included) 71.00/162.00 **t.** – SB.

Regent, Borrans Rd, LA22 0ES, ℘ 32254, Fax 31474, – rest TV ☎ P. VISA BY e
Meals (bar lunch)/dinner 25.00 **t.** and a la carte 5.50 – **21 rm** 50.00/90.00 **t.** – SB.

at Clappersgate W : 1 m. on A 593 – BY – ⊠ Ambleside – 0153 94 :

Nanny Brow Country House, LA22 9NF, ℘ 32036, Fax 32450, <, « Landscaped gardens », – TV ☎ P. AE VISA BY u
Meals (dinner only) 29.75 **t.** and a la carte 6.00 – **15 rm** (dinner included) 75.00/130.00 **t.**, 3 suites – SB.

Grey Friar Lodge, LA22 9NE, ℘ 33158, <, – TV P. BY n
March-October – **Meals** (residents only) (dinner only) 15.00 **st.** 3.70 – **8 rm** 29.50/60.00 **st.**

at Skelwith Bridge W : 2½ m. on A 593 – AY – ⊠ Ambleside – 0153 94 :

Skelwith Bridge, LA22 9NJ, ℘ 32115, Fax 34254 – rest TV ☎ P. VISA AY v
Meals (bar lunch Monday to Saturday)/dinner 17.75 **st.** 4.85 – **29 rm** 25.50/110.00 **st.** – SB.

at Little Langdale W : 4½ m. by A 593 – ⊠ Langdale – 0153 94 :

Three Shires Inn, LA22 9NZ, ℘ 37215, <, – rest P. AY z
closed January – **Meals** (bar lunch)/dinner 17.00 **st.** and a la carte 4.00 – **10 rm** 43.00/66.00 **st.** – SB.

at Elterwater W : 4 ½ m. by A 593 off B 5343 – AY – ✉ Ambleside – ☎ 0153 94 :

Langdale H. & Country Club, Great Langdale, LA22 9JD, NW : 1 ¼ m. on B 5343 ☎ 37302, Fax 37694, Fö, ≘s, ▢, park, squash – ⇔ rest ▣ ☎ ⓟ – ⚑ 90. ▣ AE ⓞ VISA AY c
Meals 25.00 **t.** (dinner) and a la carte 14.00/28.50 **t.** ¼ 5.00 – **65 rm** ☐ 77.00/130.00 **t.** – SB.

Eltermere Country House ⑤, LA22 9HY, ☎ 37207, ≤, ⚘ – ▣ ⓟ. ※ AY i
Meals *(closed Monday to Thursday December and January)* (dinner only) 17.50 **st.** ¼ 4.85 – **18 rm** ☐ (dinner included) 33.00/75.00 **st.** – SB.

at Great Langdale W : 6 m. by A 593 on B 5343 - AY – ✉ Ambleside – ☎ 0153 94 :

Long House ⑤, LA22 9JS, ☎ 37222, ≤ Langdale valley, ⚘ – ⇔ ⓟ. ▣ VISA. ※
closed December and January – **Meals** (by arrangement) 13.00 – **3 rm** ☐ -/50.00 **st.** – SB.

AMERSHAM (Old Town)

Bucks. 404 S 28 – pop. 17 629 – ECD : Thursday – ☎ 01494.

♦London 29 – Aylesbury 16 – ♦Oxford 33.

Crown (Forte), 16 High St., HP7 0DH, ☎ 721541, Fax 431283, « Former coaching inn », ⚘ – ⇔ rest ▣ ☎ ⓟ – ⚑ 30
22 rm, 1 suite.

King's Arms, High St., HP7 0DJ, ☎ 726333, Fax 433480 – ⓟ. ▣ AE ⓞ VISA JCB
closed Sunday dinner, Monday and 26 to 30 December – **Meals** 11.50/24.00 **t.** and a la carte ¼ 3.90.

Romna, 20-22 The Broadway, HP7 0HP, ☎ 433732 – ▤. ▣ AE ⓞ VISA
Meals - Indian (buffet lunch Sunday) 8.00/20.00 **t.** and a la carte.

AMESBURY

Wilts. 403 404 O 30 **The West Country G.** – pop. 6 656 – ECD : Monday – ☎ 01980.

Envir. : Stonehenge★★★ *AC*, W : 2 m. by A 303.

Exc. : Wilton (Wilton House★★★ *AC*, Royal Wilton Carpet Factory★ *AC*) SW : 13 m. by A 303, B 3083 and A 36.

Ⓘ Redworth House, Flower Lane, SP4 7HE ☎ 622833/623255.

♦London 87 – ♦Bristol 52 – Taunton 66.

Forte Travelodge without rest., SP4 7AS, N : ¼ m. at junction of A 303 with A 345 ☎ 624966, Reservations (Freephone) 0800 850950 ▣ ♿ ⓟ. ▣ AE VISA. ※
32 rm 33.50 **t.**

Mandalay, 15 Stonehenge Rd, SP4 7BA, ☎ 623733, ⚘ – ⇔ ▣ ⓟ
Meals (by arrangement) – **3 rm.**

AMPFIELD

Hants. 403 404 P 30 – pop. 1 523 – ECD : Wednesday – ✉ Romsey – ☎ 01794.

⛳18 Ampfield (Par Three), Winchester Rd ☎ 368480.

♦London 79 – Bournemouth 31 – Salisbury 19 – ♦Southampton 11 – Winchester 7.

Potters Heron (Country Club), Winchester Rd, SO51 9ZF, on A 31 ☎ (01703) 266611, Fax 251359, ≘s – ⧉ ⇔ ▣ ☎ ♿ ⓟ – ⚑ 140. ▣ AE ⓞ VISA. ※
Meals *(closed Saturday lunch)* 13.50/15.95 **t.** and a la carte – ☐ 7.50 – **54 rm** 65.00 **t.** – SB.

Keats, Winchester Rd, SO51 9BQ, on A 31 ☎ 368252 – ⓟ. ▣ AE ⓞ VISA JCB
closed Sunday and Monday – **Meals** - Italian 9.20 **t.** (lunch) and a la carte 16.10/22.20 **t.** ¼ 5.00.

AMPNEY CRUCIS

Glos. 403 404 O 28 – see Cirencester.

ANDOVER

Hants. 403 404 P 30 – pop. 30 632 – ECD : Wednesday – ☎ 01264.

⛳9 51 Winchester Rd ☎ 323980.

Ⓘ Town Mill House, Bridge St., SP10 1BL ☎ 324320.

♦London 74 – Bath 53 – Salisbury 17 – Winchester 11.

Ashley Court, Micheldever Rd, SP11 6LA, by London Street and Wolversdene Rd ☎ 357344, Fax 356755, Fö, ⚘ – ⇔ rm ▣ ☎ ⓟ – ⚑ 120. ▣ AE VISA JCB
Meals 10.50/12.50 **t.** and a la carte ¼ 4.75 – **35 rm** ☐ 54.50/85.00 **t.** – SB.

Danebury, High St., SP10 1NX, ☎ 323332, Fax 334021 – ⇔ rm ▣ ☎ ⓟ
21 rm.

White Hart, Bridge St., SP10 1BH, ☎ 352266, Fax 323767 – ⇔ rm ▣ ☎ ⓟ – ⚑ 65. ▣ AE ⓞ VISA
Meals (bar lunch)/dinner 14.95 **t.** and a la carte – ☐ 7.95 – **20 rm** 55.00/65.00 **t.** – SB.

at Barton Stacey SE : 5 ½ m. by A 303 – ✉ Andover – ☎ 01264 :

Forte Travelodge without rest., SO21 3NP, on A 303 ☎ 720260, Reservations (Freephone) 0800 850950 – ▣ ♿ ⓟ. ▣ AE VISA. ※
20 rm 33.50 **t.**

ATS 51a New St. ☎ 323606/7

ANSTY

Warks. – see Coventry (West Midlands).

APPLEBY-IN-WESTMORLAND Cumbria 402 M 20 – pop. 2 570 – ECD : Thursday – 0176 83.

Appleby, Brackenber Moor 51432.

Moot Hall, Boroughgate, CA16 6XD 51177.

London 285 – Carlisle 33 – Kendal 24 – Middlesbrough 58.

Appleby Manor, Roman Rd, CA16 6JB, E : 1 m. by B 6542 and Station Rd 51571, Fax 52888, – – 40. AE VISA JCB
Oak Room : **Meals** 17.95/19.95 **st.** and a la carte 5.95 – **30 rm** 69.00/108.00 **st.** – SB.

Tufton Arms, Market Sq., CA16 6XA, 51593, Fax 52761, – – 120. AE VISA
Meals 16.50 **t.** (dinner) and a la carte 12.00/26.75 **t.** 3.75 – **17 rm** 40.00/120.00 **t.**, 2 suites – SB.

Royal Oak Inn, Bongate, CA16 6UN, SE : ½ m. on B 6542 51463, Fax 52300 – rest . AE VISA
closed 25 December – **Meals** a la carte 7.95/16.00 **t.** – **9 rm** 30.00/70.00 **t.** – SB.

APPLETON LE MOORS N. Yorks 402 R 21 – 01751.

Appleton Hall Country House, YO6 6TF, 417227, Fax 417540, – rest . AE VISA
Meals (dinner only and Sunday lunch)/dinner 18.95 **t.** 5.00 – **8 rm** (dinner included) 51.00/102.00 **t.**, 2 suites.

ARDINGLY W. Sussex 404 T 30 – 01444.

London 37 – Brighton 20 – Crawley 11.

Ardingly Inn, Street Lane, RH17 6UA, 892214, Fax 892635, – . AE VISA
Meals a la carte 9.80/15.40 **t.** 4.50 – **6 rm** 30.00/40.00 **t.**

ARMATHWAITE Cumbria 401 402 L 19 – Carlisle – 0169 74.

London 302 – Carlisle 17 – Kendal 46 – Lancaster 60.

Dukes Head, Front St., CA4 9PB, 72226, –
Meals a la carte 11.60/14.80 **t.** 3.95 – **6 rm** 22.50/45.00 **st.** – SB.

ARMITAGE Staffs. 402 403 404 O 25 – pop. 4 426 – Rugeley – 01543.

London 135 – Birmingham 25 – Derby 26 – Stoke-on-Trent 25.

Old Farmhouse, Rugeley Rd, WS15 4AT, on A 513 490353, Fax 491932 – . AE VISA
closed Saturday lunch, Sunday dinner, Monday, last 2 weeks August and first 2 weeks January – **Meals** 7.95/12.95 **t.** and a la carte 4.90.

ARNCLIFFE N. Yorks. 402 N 21 – pop. 467 – Skipton – 01756.

London 232 – Kendal 41 – Leeds 41 – Preston 50 – York 52.

Amerdale House, BD23 5QE, 770250, Fax 770250, – rest . VISA.
mid March-mid November – **Meals** (dinner only) 23.00 **t.** 4.80 – **11 rm** (dinner included) 63.50/113.00 **t.**

ARUNDEL W. Sussex 404 S 31 **Great Britain G.** – pop. 3 817 – ECD : Wednesday – 01903.

See : Castle* *AC.*

61 High St., BN18 9AJ 882268.

London 58 – Brighton 21 – Southampton 41 – Worthing 9.

Norfolk Arms, 22 High St., BN18 9AD, 882101, Fax 884275 – – 100. AE VISA JCB
Meals 9.95/19.95 **t.** 5.35 – **34 rm** 41.95/63.90 **t.** – SB.

Arundel, 16-18 Chichester Rd, BN18 0AD, W : 1 m. on A 27 882677, Fax 884154 – rm – 140
27 rm.

Howards, Crossbush, BN18 9PQ, E : 1 m. on A 27 882655, Fax 883384 – . AE VISA.
closed 24 to 26 December – **Meals** (carving rest.) 13.95/16.50 **t.** and a la carte 4.00 – **9 rm** 47.50/65.00 **st.** – SB.

Arundel Park Inn, Station Rd, BN18 9JL, E : ½ m. on A 27 882588, Fax 883808 – . VISA.
Meals a la carte 10.70/17.70 **t.** 5.00 – **12 rm** 32.00/48.00 **t.**

Portreeves Acre without rest., The Causeway, BN18 9JL, 883277, –
3 rm 18.00/40.00 **t.**

at Burpham NE : 3 m. by A 27 – Arundel – 01903 :

Burpham Country, Old Down, BN18 9RJ, 882160, – rest . VISA.
Meals (dinner only) 16.00 **t.** 4.00 – **10 rm** 36.00/66.00 **t.** – SB.

George and Dragon, BN18 9RR, 883131. AE VISA
closed Sunday dinner – **Meals** (dinner only and Sunday lunch)/dinner 15.50/18.50 **t.** 4.75.

at Walberton W : 3 m. by A 27 off B 2132 – ✉ Arundel – ☎ 01243 :

Stakis Arundel, Avisford Park, Yapton Lane, BN18 0LS, on B 2132 ☎ 551215, Fax 552485, ←, ≘s, heated, ⊠, ⛳9, ⚘, park, ⚔, squash – ⊁ rest TV ☎ & P – 300. VISA.
Meals *(closed Saturday lunch)* (buffet lunch) 16.50/25.00 **st.** and dinner a la carte – **121 rm** ☐ 70.00/120.00 **st.**, 5 suites – SB.

ASCOT Berks. 404 R 29 – pop. 150244 (inc Sunningdale) – ECD : Wednesday – ☎ 01344.

⛳18 Mill Ride, North Ascot ☎ 886777.

♦London 36 – Reading 15.

Royal Berkshire (Hilton) ⛰, London Rd, Sunninghill, SL5 OPP, E : 2 m. on A 329 ☎ 23322, Fax 27100, « Queen Anne mansion », ⚚, ≘s, ⊠, ⚘, park, ⚔, squash – TV ☎ P – 75. VISA JCB
Meals (see **Stateroom** below) – ☐ 14.00 – **60 rm** 120.00/205.00 **t.**, 3 suites – SB.

Berystede (Forte), Bagshot Rd, Sunninghill, SL5 9JH, S : 1 ½ m. on A 330 ☎ 23311, Fax 872301, heated, ⚘, park – |♦| ⊁ rm TV ☎ P – 120. VISA JCB
Meals 15.50/21.00 **st.** and a la carte 8.50 – ☐ 9.50 – **90 rm** 95.00/130.00 **st.**, 1 suite – SB.

Royal Foresters, London Rd, SL5 8DR, W : 1 ½ m. on A 329 ☎ 884747, Fax 884115 – TV ☎ P. VISA.
closed 25 and 26 December – **Meals** (Beefeater grill) a la carte 8.30/17.40 **st.** – ☐ 4.95 – **33 rm** 39.50 **st.**

XXX **Stateroom** (at Royal Berkshire H.), London Rd, Sunninghill, SL5 0PP, E : 2 m. on A 329 ☎ 23322, Fax 27100, ⚘ – P. VISA JCB
Meals (booking essential) 16.00/36.00 **t.** and a la carte.

XX **Ciao Ninety,** 6 Hermitage Par., High St., SL5 7TE, ☎ 22285 – ▤. VISA
closed Saturday lunch – **Meals** - Italian 12.00 **t.** (lunch) and a la carte 15.80/23.90 **t.** 3.50.

at Sunninghill S : 1 ½ m. by A 329 on B 3020 – ✉ Ascot – ☎ 01344 :

Highclere, Kings Rd, SL5 9AD, ☎ 25220, Fax 872528 – TV ☎ P. VISA.
Meals (in bar Sunday dinner) a la carte 15.50/20.50 **t.** 5.80 – **11 rm** ☐ 55.00/90.00 **st.**

XX **Jade Fountain,** 38 High St., SL5 9NE, ☎ 27070 – ▤. VISA
closed 24 to 27 December – **Meals** - Chinese (Canton, Peking) 16.50/21.00 **st.** and a la carte 4.00.

ASENBY N. Yorks. – see Thirsk.

ASHBOURNE Derbs. 402 403 404 O 24 **Great Britain G.** – pop. 6 300 – ☎ 01335.

Envir. : Dovedale★★ (Ilam Rock★) NW : 6 m. by A 515.

⛳9 Clifton ☎ 342078.

ℹ 13 Market Pl., DE6 1EU ☎ 343666.

♦London 146 – Derby 14 – ♦Manchester 48 – ♦Nottingham 33 – ♦Sheffield 44.

Callow Hall ⛰, Mappleton Rd, DE6 2AA, W : ¾ m. by Union St. ☎ 343403, Fax 343624, ⚲, ⚘, park – ⊁ rest TV ☎ & P. VISA.
closed 25 and 26 December – **Meals** *(closed Sunday dinner to non-residents)* (lunch by arrangement)/dinner 27.50 **t.** and a la carte 8.95 – **16 rm** ☐ 65.00/140.00 **t.** – SB.

Ashbourne Lodge, Derby Rd, DE6 1XH, SE : 1 m. on A 52 ☎ 346666, Fax 346549 – |♦| ⊁ rm ▤ rest TV ☎ & P – 200. VISA.
Meals (light lunch Monday to Saturday)/dinner 14.95 **st.** and a la carte – **48 rm** ☐ 59.00/75.00 **st.**, 2 suites – SB.

ATS Airfield Ind. Est., Blenheim Rd ☎ 344644

ASHBURTON Devon 403 I 32 **The West Country G.** – pop. 3 660 – ECD : Wednesday – ☎ 01364.

Envir. : Dartmoor National Park★★ (Brent Tor ←★★, Haytor Rocks ←★).

♦London 220 – Exeter 20 – ♦Plymouth 23.

Holne Chase ⛰, TQ13 7NS, W : 3 m. on Two Bridges rd ☎ 631471, Fax 631453, ←, ⚲, ⚘, park – ⊁ rest TV ☎ P – 30. VISA
Meals 13.00/21.50 **st.** and a la carte 5.50 – **14 rm** ☐ 47.50/110.00 **st.** – SB.

Ashburton, 79 East St., TQ13 7AL, ☎ 652784, Fax 652784, ⚘ – ⊁ TV ☎
Meals -Vegetarian (booking essential) 5.00/10.00 **st.** 3.00 – **6 rm** 18.00/36.00 **st.**

Gages Mill, Buckfastleigh Rd, TQ13 7JW, SW : 1 m. on old A 38 ☎ 652391, ⚘ – ⊁ rest P.
closed February and December – **Meals** (by arrangement) 9.50 **t.** 3.50 – **8 rm** ☐ 22.50/45.00 **t.**

at Holne W : 4 ½ m. by Two Bridges rd – ✉ Ashburton – ☎ 01364 :

Wellpritton Farm ⛰, TQ13 7RX, E : 1 m. ☎ 631273 – ⊁ rm P.
closed 25 and 26 December – **Meals** (by arrangement) – **4 rm** ☐ 16.00/36.00.

Prices For full details of the prices quoted in the guide, consult the introduction.

ASHBY DE LA ZOUCH Leics. 402 403 404 P 25 – pop. 12 083 – ECD : Wednesday – 01530.

Willesley Park, Measham Rd 411532.

North St., LE65 1HU 411767.

London 119 – Birmingham 29 – Leicester 18 – Nottingham 22.

Fallen Knight, Kilwardby St., LE65 2FQ, 412230, Fax 417596 – 50.
Meals 12.95/14.95 **t.** and a la carte 4.00 – **24 rm** 62.00/112.00 **t.**

Rajni, 48 Tamworth Rd, LE65 2PR, S : ½ m. on B 5006 560349 –
closed Friday lunch and 25 December – **Meals** - Indian a la carte 6.65/15.85 **t.**

ATS Kilwardby St. 412791

ASHFORD Kent 404 W 30 – pop. 41 790 – ECD : Wednesday – 01233.

Ashford Manor, Fordbridge Rd 252049, off A 308.

Lydd Airport : (01797) 320401.

18 The Churchyard, TN23 1QG 629165.

London 56 – Canterbury 14 – Dover 24 – Hastings 30 – Maidstone 19.

Eastwell Manor (Q.M.H.), Eastwell Park, Boughton Lees, TN25 4HR, N : 3 m. by A 28 on A 251 635751, Fax 635530, « Reconstructed period mansion in formal gardens », park, – rest – 80.
Meals 16.50/28.00 **t.** and a la carte 7.75 – **20 rm** 100.00/175.00 **t.**, 3 suites – SB.

Ashford International (Q.M.H.), Simone Weil Av., TN24 8UX, 611444, Group Telex 96498, Fax 627708, – rm – 400.
Meals (in bar Saturday lunch and Sunday) (carving lunch) 12.90/16.90 **st.** 6.25 – 9.50 – **198 rm** 82.50 **st.**, 2 suites – SB.

Forte Posthouse, Canterbury Rd, TN24 8QQ, 625790, Fax 643176, – rm – 120.
Meals a la carte approx. 15.00 **t.** 5.50 – **60 rm** 56.00 **st.**

Master Spearpoint, Canterbury Rd, Kennington, TN24 9QR, NE : 2 m. on A 28 636863, Fax 610119, – – 60.
Meals (carving lunch) a la carte 9.60/18.50 **t.** – **35 rm** 51.00/59.50 **t.** – SB.

at Hothfield NW : 3½ m. by A 20 – Ashford – 01233 :

Holiday Inn Garden Court, Maidstone Rd, TN26 1AR, N : 1 m. on A 20 713333, Fax 712082, – rm rest – 25.
Meals (bar lunch)/dinner 12.95 **st.** – 7.50 – **104 rm** 57.50 **st.** – SB.

Travel Inn, Maidstone Rd, Hothfield Common, TN26 1AP, on A 20 712571, Fax 713945 – rm
Meals (Beefeater grill) a la carte approx. 16.00 **t.** – 4.95 – **40 rm** 33.50 **t.**

ATS Henwood Ind. Est., Hythe Rd, Henwood 622450/624891

ASHFORD-IN-THE-WATER Derbs. 402 403 404 O 24 – see Bakewell.

ASHINGTON Northd. 401 402 P 18 – pop. 60 724 (Warsbeck) – 01670.

London 303 – Edinburgh 102 – Newcastle upon Tyne 17.

Lakeside, Queen Elizabeth II Country Park, Woodhorn, NE63 9AT, N : 2½ m. by A 197 on A 189 862001, Fax 860986, – – 130.
Meals (bar lunch Monday, Tuesday and Saturday) 8.50/16.95 **t.** 4.95 – **20 rm** 55.00/65.00 **t.** – SB.

ASHINGTON W. Sussex 404 S 31 – pop. 1 748 – ECD : Wednesday – Pulborough – 01903.

London 50 – Brighton 20 – Worthing 9.

Mill House, Mill Lane, RH20 3BZ, 892426, Fax 892855, – – 40
12 rm.

Willows, London Rd, RH20 3JR, on A 24 892575 –
closed Saturday lunch, Sunday dinner and Monday – **Meals** 15.50/18.25 **t.** 3.95.

ATS Lintonville Terr. 817013/817038

ASHPRINGTON Devon 403 I 32 – see Totnes.

ASHTON-IN-MAKERFIELD Gtr. Manchester 402 M 23 – Wigan – 01942.

London 199 – Liverpool 21 – Manchester 20.

Bay Horse (Premier), 53 Warrington Rd, WN4 9PJ, S : ½ m. on A 49 725032, Fax 719302 – rm
Meals (grill rest.) – **28 rm.**

Si vous cherchez un hôtel tranquille,
consultez d'abord les cartes de l'introduction
ou repérez dans le texte les établissements indiqués avec le signe ou .

ASHTON KEYNES Wilts. 403 404 O 29 – pop. 1 682 – ☎ 01285.

♦London 98 – ♦Bristol 40 – Gloucester 27 – ♦Oxford 42 – Swindon 14.

2 Cove House, SN6 6NS, (behind White Hart Inn) ☎ 861221, – rest. *closed Christmas* – **Meals** (by arrangement) (communal dining) 16.50 – **3 rm** 33.00/50.00 **st.**

ASHTON-UNDER-LYNE Gtr. Manchester 402 403 404 N 23 – pop. 44 384 – ECD : Tuesday – ☎ 0161.

♦London 209 – ♦Leeds 40 – ♦Manchester 7 – ♦Sheffield 34.

York House, York Pl., off Richmond St., OL6 7TT, ☎ 330 5899, Fax 343 1613, – 40. AE VISA JCB
Meals *(closed Saturday lunch and Sunday)* 9.50/15.00 **st.** and a la carte 4.75 – **34 rm** 46.00/66.00 **st.** – SB.

Woodlands with rm, 33 Shepley Rd, Audenshaw, M34 5DL, S : 2 m. by A 635, Audenshaw Rd and Guide Lane (A 6017) on B 6169 ☎ 336 4241 – . VISA
closed Saturday lunch, Sunday, Monday, 1 week Easter, 2 weeks August and 1 week Christmas – **Meals** 15.95 **t.** and a la carte – **3 rm** 40.00/60.00 **t.**

ASHWATER Devon 403 H 31 – ✉ Beaworthy – ☎ 01409.

Blagdon Manor Country, EX21 5DF, NW : 2 m. by Holsworthy rd on Blagdon rd ☎ 211224, Fax 211633, ≤, « Part 17C Manor », – . VISA.
Meals (residents only) (communal dining) (dinner only) 25.00 **st.** – **7 rm** 45.00/90.00 **st.**

ASKRIGG N. Yorks. 402 N 21 – pop. 1 002 – ✉ Leyburn – ☎ 01969.

♦London 251 – Kendal 32 – ♦Leeds 70 – York 63.

King's Arms, Market Sq., DL8 3HQ, ☎ 650258, Fax 650635, « Part 18C, part 19C coaching inn » – rest . AE VISA JCB
***Clubroom :* Meals** 25.00 **st.** 5.00 – ***Silks Grill :* Meals** 3.50/12.50 **st.** 5.00 – **10 rm** 55.00/95.00 **t.** – SB.

Winville, Main St., DL8 3HG, ☎ 650515, Fax 650594, – . VISA
Meals 17.95 **st.** and a la carte 4.00 – **10 rm** 40.00/64.00 **st.** – SB.

Helm Country House, Helm, DL8 3JF, W: 1 ¼m, turning right at No Through Rd sign ☎ 650443, ≤, « Part 17C stone cottage » – .
closed November-2 January – **Meals** 14.50 5.00 – **3 rm** 45.00/58.00.

ASPLEY GUISE Beds. 404 S 27 – pop. 2 236 – ☎ 01908.

18 Woburn Sands, West Hill ☎ 582264 – 18 Millbrook, Ampthill ☎ (01525) 840252.

♦London 52 – Bedford 13 – Luton 16 – ♦Northampton 22.

Moore Place, The Square, MK17 8DW, ☎ 282000, Fax 281888, – – 50. AE VISA
closed 25 to 30 December – **Meals** *(closed Saturday lunch)* 17.50/18.50 **st.** and a la carte 10.95 – **53 rm** 65.00/95.00 **st.**, 1 suite – SB.

ASTON CLINTON Bucks. 404 R 28 – pop. 3 980 – ECD : Wednesday – ✉ Aylesbury – ☎ 01296.

♦London 42 – Aylesbury 4 – ♦Oxford 26.

Bell Inn, London Rd, HP22 5HP, ☎ 630252, Fax 631250, « Courtyard and gardens » – – 150. AE VISA JCB
Meals 17.50/22.50 **t.** and a la carte – **15 rm** 79.00/89.00 **st.**, 6 suites – SB.

ATHERSTONE Warks. 403 404 P 26 – pop. 8 047 – ☎ 01827.

♦London 120 – ♦Birmingham 22 – ♦Coventry 15 – ♦Leicester 30.

Chapel House with rm, Friars Gate, CV9 1EY, ☎ 718949, Fax 717702, « Part Georgian former dower house », – . AE VISA.
closed 25 and 26 December – **Meals** *(closed Sunday)* (dinner only) 29.00 6.25 – **11 rm** 42.00/60.00 **t.** – SB.

ATTLEBOROUGH Norfolk 404 X 26 – pop. 7 604 – ECD : Wednesday – ☎ 01953.

♦London 94 – ♦Cambridge 47 – ♦Norwich 15.

Sherbourne House, Norwich Rd, NR17 2JX, NE : ½ m. ☎ 454363, Fax 453509, – . VISA.
closed 25 and 26 December – **Meals** *(closed Tuesday lunch, Sunday dinner and Monday to non-residents)* 12.95/15.00 **t.** and dinner a la carte – **7 rm** 27.00/65.00 **st.** – SB.

ATS London Rd ☎ 453883

AUSTWICK N. Yorks. 402 M 21 – ✉ Lancaster – ☎ 0152 42.

♦London 259 – Kendal 28 – Lancaster 20 – ♦Leeds 46.

The Traddock, LA2 8BY, ☎ 51224, Fax 51224, – rest . VISA.
Meals 9.00/20.00 **st.** and lunch a la carte 4.00 – **11 rm** 35.00/65.00 **st.** – SB.

AVON Hants. – see Ringwood.

AXMINSTER Devon 403 L 31 **The West Country G.** – pop. 5 181 – ECD : Wednesday – ☎ 01297.
Envir. : Lyme Regis★ - The Cobb★, SE : 5½ m. by A 35 and A 3070.
ℹ The Old Courthouse, Church St., EX13 5AQ ✆ 34386 (summer only).
♦London 156 – Exeter 27 – Lyme Regis 5.5 – Taunton 22 – Yeovil 24.

Fairwater Head ⛰, Hawkchurch, EX13 5TX, NE : 3¾ m. by A 35 off B 3165 ✆ 678349, ⋖ Axe Vale, 🌳 – ⊬ rest TV ☎ P. AE VISA.
closed January and February – **Meals** (bar lunch Monday to Saturday)/dinner 20.50 **t.** and a la carte 5.00 – **21 rm** (dinner included) 69.00/148.00 **t.** – SB.

at Membury N : 4½ m. by A 35 and Stockland rd – ✉ Axminster – ☎ 01404 :

Lea Hill ⛰, EX13 7AQ, ✆ 881881, ⋖, « Part 14C Devon longhouse », 🌳 – ⊬ TV ☎ P. AE VISA.
closed 15 January to 10 February – **Meals** (bar lunch)/dinner 15.95 **t.** 4.95 – **9 rm** 38.00/84.00 **t.** – SB.

AYLESBURY Bucks. 404 R 28 **Great Britain G.** – pop. 145 931 (Vale of Aylesbury) – ECD : Thursday – ☎ 01296.
Envir. : Waddesdon Manor (Collection★★) NW : 5½ m. by A 41.
18 Weston Turville, New Rd ✆ 24084 – 9 Hulcott Lane, Bierton ✆ 399644.
ℹ County Hall, Walton St., HP20 1UA ✆ 382308/383095.
♦London 46 – ♦Birmingham 72 – Northampton 37 – ♦Oxford 22.

Hartwell House ⛰, Oxford Rd, HP17 8NL, SW : 2 m. on A 418 ✆ 747444, Fax 747450, ⋖, « Part Jacobean, part Georgian house, former residence of Louis XVIII », 🏋, ♨, 🏊, 🎣, 🌳, park, 🎾 – 🛗 ⊬ rest TV ☎ P – 🪑 80. AE VISA.
Meals 16.50/38.00 **st.** and a la carte 5.95 – 12.50 – **34 rm** 95.00/215.00 **st.**, 13 suites – SB.

Forte Posthouse, Aston Clinton Rd, HP22 5AA, SE : 2 m. on A 41 ✆ 393388, Fax 392211, 🏋, ♨, 🏊, 🌳 – ⊬ rm ▤ rest TV ☎ ♿ P – 🪑 100. AE VISA
Meals (bar lunch Saturday) a la carte approx. 15.00 **t.** 5.50 – **92 rm** 59.50/69.50 **st.**, 2 suites.

Holiday Inn Garden Court without rest., Buckingham Rd, HP19 3FY, N : 1 m. on A 413 ✆ 398839, Fax 394108 – ⊬ TV ☎ ♿ P – 🪑 30. AE VISA JCB.
40 rm 49.00 **st.**

Horse and Jockey, Buckingham Rd, HP19 3QL, ✆ 23803, Fax 395142 – TV ☎ P. AE VISA.
closed Christmas and New Year – **Meals** (in bar) approx. 12.00 – **24 rm** 46.00/56.00 **t.**

ATS Gatehouse Way ✆ 433177

BABBACOMBE Devon 403 J 32 – see Torquay.

BADBY Northants. – see Daventry.

BADMINTON Avon 403 404 N 29 – pop. 2 167 – ☎ 01454.
♦London 114 – ♦Bristol 19 – Gloucester 26 – Swindon 33.

Petty France, Dunkirk, GL9 1AF, NW : 3 m. on A 46 ✆ 238361, Fax 238768, 🌳 – ⊬ rest TV ☎ P – 🪑 25. AE VISA
Meals 19.50 **t.** (dinner) and a la carte 5.75 – **20 rm** 65.00/110.00 **t.** – SB.

Bodkin House, Dunkirk, GL9 1AF, NW : 3 m. on A 46 ✆ 238310, Fax 238422 – TV ☎ P. AE VISA JCB.
Meals *(closed Sunday dinner)* 8.95/13.95 **t.** and a la carte 4.00 – **8 rm** 49.00/65.00 **t.** – SB.

BAGINTON Warks. 403 404 P 26 – see Coventry.

BAGSHOT Surrey 404 R 29 – pop. 5 190 – ECD : Wednesday – ☎ 01276.
♦London 37 – Reading 17 – ♦Southampton 49.

Pennyhill Park ⛰, London Rd, GU19 5ET, SW : 1 m. on A 30 ✆ 471774, Fax 473217, ⋖, ♨, 🏊 heated, 9, 🎣, 🌳, park, 🎾 – ⊬ rm TV ☎ P – 🪑 50. AE VISA JCB.
Meals 17.95/28.00 **t.** and dinner a la carte 7.50 – 13.00 – **70 rm** 120.00/184.00 **st.**, 6 suites – SB.

Cricketers, London Rd, GU19 5HR, N : ½ m. on A 30 ✆ 473196, Fax 451357, 🌳 – TV ☎ P. AE VISA.
Meals (Beefeater grill) a la carte 6.00/19.50 **t.** 4.25 – 4.95 – **27 rm** 39.50 **st.**

BAINBRIDGE N. Yorks. 402 N 21 – pop. 474 – ECD : Wednesday – ✉ Wensleydale – ☎ 01969.
♦London 249 – Kendal 31 – ♦Leeds 68 – York 61.

Rose and Crown, DL8 3EE, ✆ 650225, Fax 650735 – TV P. VISA
Meals a la carte 13.50/20.05 **st.** 4.95 – **12 rm** 44.00/72.00 **st.** – SB.

BAKEWELL Derbs. 402 403 404 O 24 **Great Britain G.** – pop. 3 818 – ECD : Thursday – ☏ 01629.
Envir. : Chatsworth*** (Park and Garden***) *AC*, NE : 2½ m. by A 619 – Haddon Hall** *AC*, SE : 2 m. by A 6.
Old Market Hall, Bridge St., DE4 5DS ☏ 813227.
♦London 160 – Derby 26 – ♦Manchester 37 – ♦Nottingham 33 – ♦Sheffield 17.

Rutland Arms, The Square, DE45 1BT, ☏ 812812, Fax 812309 – 80. AE VISA
Meals 9.50/17.50 **st.** and lunch a la carte 5.50 – **36 rm** 49.50/88.00 **st.** – SB.

Milford House, Mill St., DE45 1DA, ☏ 812130,
April-October – **Meals** (by arrangement) 15.30 **t.** 3.50 – **12 rm** 35.00/70.00 **t.** – SB.

at Hassop N : 3½ m. by A 619 on B 6001 – ✉ Bakewell – ☏ 01629 :

Hassop Hall ⛰, DE45 1NS, ☏ 640488, Fax 640577, ≤, « Part 16C hall », park, – AE VISA JCB.
accommodation closed 3 days at Christmas – **Meals** *(closed Monday lunch and Sunday dinner)* 14.00/28.00 **t.** 5.75 – 8.95 – **13 rm** 70.00/125.00 **t.**

at Great Longstone N : 4 m. by A 619 off B 6001 – ✉ Bakewell – ☏ 01629 :

Croft ⛰, DE45 1TF, ☏ 640278, – rest VISA.
closed 4 January-2 February – **Meals** (dinner only) 21.00 **t.** 4.25 – **9 rm** 55.00/90.00 **t.** – SB.

at Alport S : 4 m. by A 6 off B 5056 – ✉ Bakewell – ☏ 01629 :

Rock House without rest., DE45 1LG, ☏ 636736,
4 rm 20.00/40.00.

at Ashford-in-the-Water NW : 1 ¾ m. by A 6 and A 6020 on B 6465 – ✉ Bakewell – ☏ 01629 :

Riverside Country House, Fennel St., DE45 1QF, ☏ 814275, Fax 812873, AE VISA.
Meals 19.50 **t.** (dinner) and lunch a la carte 5.50 – 5.00 – **15 rm** 75.00/99.00 **t.** – SB.

BALDERSTONE Lancs. – see Blackburn.

BALDOCK Herts. 404 T 28 – pop. 6 237 – ECD : Thursday – ☏ 01462.
♦London 42 – Bedford 20 – ♦Cambridge 21 – Luton 15.

Forte Travelodge without rest., A 1 Great North Road, Hinxworth (southbound carriageway), SG7 5EX, NW : 3 m. by A 507 on A 1 ☏ 835329, Reservations (Freephone) 0800 850950 – AE VISA.
40 rm 33.50 **t.**

BALSALL COMMON W. Mids. – see Coventry.

BAMBER BRIDGE Lancs. 402 M 22 – see Preston.

BAMBURGH Northd. 401 402 O 17 **Great Britain G.** – pop. 582 – ECD : Wednesday – ☏ 01668.
See : Castle* *AC*.
♦London 337 – ♦Edinburgh 77 – ♦Newcastle upon Tyne 51.

Lord Crewe Arms, Front St., NE69 7BL, ☏ 214243, Fax 214273 – VISA
closed 4 January - 1 March – **Meals** (bar lunch)/dinner 17.95 **t.** – **23 rm** 34.00/62.00 **t.** – SB.

at Waren Mill W : 2¾ m. on B 1342 – ✉ Belford – ☏ 01668 :

Waren House ⛰, NE70 7EE, ☏ 214581, Fax 214484, ≤, AE VISA.
Meals (dinner only) 22.50 **st.** 6.50 – **5 rm** 74.00/124.00 **st.**, 2 suites – SB.

BAMPTON Devon 403 J 31 – ✉ Tiverton – ☏ 01398.
♦Lancaster 192 – Exeter 23 – Minehead 21 – Taunton 21.

Bark House, Oakfordbridge, EX16 9HZ, W : 3 m. by B 3227 on A 396 ☏ 5236, VISA
March-November – **Meals** (residents only) (dinner only) 15.50 5.00 – **6 rm** 19.00/56.00 **st.**

BANBURY Oxon. 403 404 P 27 **Great Britain G.** – pop. 37 463 – ECD : Tuesday – ☏ 01295.
Exc. : Upton House* *AC*, NW : 7 m. by A 422.
18 Cherwell Edge, Chacombe ☏ 711591.
Banbury Museum, 8 Horsefair, OX16 0AA ☏ 259855.
♦London 76 – ♦Birmingham 40 – ♦Coventry 25 – ♦Oxford 23.

Whately Hall (Forte), Horsefair, by Banbury Cross, OX16 0AN, ☏ 263451, Fax 271736, « Part 17C hall », – 80. AE VISA JCB.
Meals *(closed Saturday lunch)* 10.95/17.95 **st.** 6.70 – 8.50 – **72 rm** 60.00/70.00 **st.**, 2 suites – SB.

Banbury Moat House (Q.M.H) 27-29 Oxford Rd, OX16 9AH, ✆ 259361, Telex 838967, Fax 270954 – ⇆ rm TV ☎ P – 80
48 rm.

Easington House, 50 Oxford Rd, OX16 9AN, ✆ 270181, Fax 269527, – TV ☎ P. AE VISA
Meals *(closed Sunday and Bank Holidays)* (dinner only) a la carte 11.25/21.50 **st.** 4.75 – **12 rm** 45.00/70.00 **st.** – SB.

Prospect without rest., 70 Oxford Rd, OX16 9AN, ✆ 268749, – TV P. AE VISA.
9 rm 32.00/48.00 **st.**

at Adderbury S : 3 m. on A 423 – ✉ Banbury – 01295 :

Red Lion, The Green, OX17 3LU, ✆ 810269, Fax 811906, « Part 16C inn » – ⇆ rest TV ☎ P
Meals a la carte 12.90/19.45 **st.** 3.50 – **14 rm** 39.95/49.95 **st.** – SB.

at North Newington W : 2 ¼ m. by B 4035 – ✉ Banbury – 01295 :

La Madonette Country without rest., OX15 6AA, ✆ 730212, Fax 730363, , – TV ☎ P. VISA.
5 rm 32.00/55.00 **st.**

at Wroxton NW : 3 m. by A 41 on A 422 – ✉ Banbury – 01295 :

Wroxton House, Silver St., OX15 6QB, ✆ 730777, Fax 730800 – ⇆ rest TV ☎ P – 50. AE VISA JCB
Meals 15.50/23.50 **st.** and a la carte 4.95 – **32 rm** 79.00/125.00 **st.** – SB.

at Shenington NW : 6 m. by A 41 off A 422 – ✉ Banbury – 01295 :

Sugarswell Farm , OX15 6HW, NW : 2 ¼ m. on Edge Hill rd ✆ 680512, Fax 680512, , – ⇆ P.
Meals (by arrangement) 18.00 – **3 rm** 35.00/60.00.

ATS Beaumont Ind. Est., Beaumont Close ✆ 253525

Great Britain and Ireland are covered entirely
at a scale of 16 miles to 1 inch by our map « Main roads » 986.

BANTHAM Devon – see Kingsbridge.

BARFORD Warks. 403 404 P 27 – see Warwick.

BAR HILL Cambs. 404 U 27 – see Cambridge.

BARKWITH Lincs. 402 404 T 24 – see East Barkwith.

BARNARD CASTLE Durham 402 O 20 **Great Britain G.** – pop. 4 783 – ECD : Thursday – 01833.

See : Bowes Museum★ *AC.*

Exc. : Raby Castle★ *AC,* NE : 6 ½ m. by A 688.

18 Harmire Rd ✆ 37237.

43 Galgate, DL12 8EL ✆ 690909.

♦London 258 – ♦Carlisle 63 – ♦Leeds 68 – ♦Middlesbrough 31 – ♦Newcastle upon Tyne 39.

Jersey Farm , Darlington Rd, DL12 8TA, E : 1 ½ m. on A 67 ✆ 638223, Fax 631988, park – TV ☎ P – 150. VISA
Meals (carving rest.) (bar lunch Monday to Saturday)/dinner 14.00 **t.** 4.00 – **16 rm** 45.00/65.00 **t.**, 4 suites – SB.

at Romaldkirk NW : 6 m. by A 67 on B 6277 – ✉ Barnard Castle – 01833 :

Rose and Crown, DL12 9EB, ✆ 650213, Fax 650828, « Part 18C coaching inn » – ⇆ rest TV ☎ P. VISA
closed 25 and 26 December – **Meals** *(closed Sunday dinner)* (bar lunch Monday to Saturday)/dinner 24.95 **st.** 5.60 – **10 rm** 54.00/75.00 **st.**, 2 suites – SB.

BARNARD GATE Oxon. 403 404 P 28 – see Witney.

BARNOLDSWICK Lancs. – 01282.

Monks House, 5 Manchester Rd, BB8 5NZ, ✆ 814423.
Meals 6.00 **s.** – **4 rm** 16.00/32.00 **s.**

BARNSDALE BAR W. Yorks. 402 404 Q 23 – ✉ Pontefract – 01977.

♦London 181 – ♦Leeds 22 – ♦Nottingham 53 – ♦Sheffield 26.

Forte Travelodge without rest., WF8 3JB, on A 1 ✆ 620711, Reservations (Freephone) 0800 850950 – TV ♿ P. AE VISA.
56 rm 33.50 **t.**

BARNSLEY Glos. 403 404 O28 – see Cirencester.

BARNSLEY S. Yorks. 402 404 P 23 – pop. 76 783 – ECD : Thursday – ☎ 01226.

18 Wakefield Rd, Staincross ☎ 382856 – 18 Silkstone, Field Head, Elmhirst Lane ☎ 790328 – 9 Wombwell Hillies, Wentworth View, Wombwell ☎ 754433.

56 Eldon St., S70 2JL ☎ 206757.

London 177 – Leeds 21 – Manchester 36 – Sheffield 15.

Ardsley Moat House (Q.M.H.), Doncaster Rd, Ardsley, S71 5EH, E: 2 ¾ m. on A 635 ☎ 289401, Fax 205374, – rest – 250. AE VISA
closed 26 and 27 December – **Meals** *(closed lunch Saturday and Bank Holidays)* 10.75/17.35 **st.** and a la carte 5.50 – 8.75 – **73 rm** 55.00/70.00 **st.** – SB.

Forte Travelodge without rest., Doncaster Rd, S70 3PE, E: 2 ½ m. on A 635 ☎ 298799, Reservations (Freephone) 0800 850950 – . AE VISA.
32 rm 33.50 **t.**

Periquito, Regent St., S70 2HQ, ☎ 731010, Fax 248719, – rm – 150. AE VISA JCB
Meals (bar lunch)/dinner 11.75 **t.** and a la carte – 6.50 – **51 rm** 38.00 **st.**

XX **Restaurant Peano,** 102 Dodworth Rd, S70 6HL, on A 628 ☎ 244990 – . AE VISA
closed Saturday lunch, Sunday, Monday, 1 week January and 1 week September – **Meals** 11.95 **st.** and a la carte 19.40/24.35 **st.**

ATS Huddersfield Rd ☎ 281888/287406

ATS Wombwell Lane, Aldham Bridge, Wombwell ☎ 753511

Benutzen Sie für weite Fahrten in Europa die ***Michelin-Länderkarten*** *:*
970 Europa, 980 Griechenland, 984 Deutschland, 985 Skandinavien-Finnland,
986 Großbritannien-Irland, 987 Deutschland-Österreich-Benelux, 988 Italien,
989 Frankreich, 990 Spanien-Portugal, 991 Jugoslawien.

BARNSTAPLE Devon 403 H 30 **The West Country G.** – pop. 20 740 – ECD : Wednesday – ☎ 01271.

See : Town★ - Long Bridge★.

Envir. : Arlington Court★★ (Carriage Collection★) *AC*, NE : 6 m. by A 39.

18, 9 Chulmleigh, Leigh Rd ☎ (01769) 80519.

to the Isle of Lundy (Lundy Co.) (2 h 15 mn).

North Devon Library, Tuly St., EX31 1TY ☎ 388583/388584.

London 222 – Exeter 40 – Taunton 51.

Park, Taw Vale, EX32 9AE, ☎ 72166, Fax 78558 – – 100. AE VISA.
Meals 7.50/13.50 **st.** and a la carte 4.25 – **41 rm** 47.00/59.00 **st.**

XX **Lynwood House** with rm, Bishops Tawton Rd, EX32 9DZ, S : 1 ½ m. by A 361 and Newport rd ☎ 43695, Fax 79340 – . AE VISA
Meals *(closed Sunday)* 13.95 **t.** (lunch) and a la carte 18.30/42.50 **t.** 8.50 – **5 rm** 40.50/60.50 **st.**

at Bishop's Tawton S : 2 ¾ m. by A 39 on A 377 – ✉ Barnstaple – ☎ 01271 :

Downrew House , EX32 0DY, SE : 1 ½ m. on Chittlehampton rd ☎ 42497, Fax 23947, heated, , park, – – 40. VISA
Meals (bar lunch)/dinner 17.50 **st.** and a la carte 4.40 – **11 rm** (dinner included) 68.00/130.00 **st.** – SB.

Halmpstone Manor , EX32 0EA, SE : 3 m. by Chittlehampton rd ☎ 830321, Fax 830826, , , park – rest . AE VISA
closed December and January – **Meals** (lunch by arrangement)/dinner 17.50/27.50 **t.** 5.70 – **5 rm** 65.00/130.00 **t.** – SB.

ATS Pottington Ind. Est., Braunton Rd ☎ 42294/5

BARROW-IN-FURNESS Cumbria 402 K 21 – pop. 73 125 – ☎ 01229.

18 Rakesmoore Lane, Hawcoat ☎ 825444 – 18 Furness, Walney Island ☎ 471232.

Forum 28, Duke St., LA14 1HU ☎ 870156.

London 295 – Kendal 34 – Lancaster 47.

Abbey House, Abbey Rd, LA13 0PA, NE : 2 m. on A 590 ☎ 838282, Fax 820403, « Lutyens house », , park – – 100. AE VISA
Meals a la carte 17.00/26.75 **t.** 4.95 – 7.25 – **30 rm** 69.95/104.95 **t.** – SB.

Arlington House, 200/202 Abbey Rd, LA14 5LD, ☎ 831976 – . VISA.
Meals *(closed Sunday)* (dinner only) 18.50 **st.** 4.50 – **8 rm** 51.00/70.00 **t.**

ATS 149-151 Ainslie St. ☎ 828513/828663

BARTON MILLS Suffolk. 404 V 26 – pop. 866 – ☎ 01638.

London 72 – Cambridge 21 – Ipswich 37 – Norwich 40.

Forte Travelodge without rest., Fiveways Roundabout, IP28 6AE, on A 11 ☎ 717675, Reservations (Freephone) 0800 850950 – . AE VISA.
32 rm 33.50 **t.**

BARTON STACEY Hants. 403 404 P 30 – see Andover.

BARTON UNDER NEEDWOOD Staffs. – see Burton-upon-Trent.

BARWICK Somerset 403 404 M 31 – see Yeovil.

BASFORD Staffs. – see Stoke-on-Trent.

BASILDON Essex 404 V 29 – pop. 94 800 – ECD : Wednesday – 01268.

Clayhill Lane, Sparrow's Hearne, Kingswood 533297 – , Langdon Hills, Lower Dunton Rd, Bulphan 548444 – Pipps Hill, Cranes Farm Rd 523456.

London 30 – Chelmsford 17 – Southend-on-Sea 13.

Forte Posthouse, Cranes Farm Rd, SS14 3DG, NW : 2 1/4 m. by A 176 off A 1235 533955, Fax 530119, – rm – 250. VISA JCB
Meals a la carte approx. 15.00 **t.** 5.50 – **110 rm** 56.00/69.50 **st.**

Travel Inn, Felmores, East Mayne, SS13 1BW, N : 1 1/2 m. on A 132 522227, Fax 530092 – rm . VISA.
closed Christmas – **Meals** (Beefeater grill) a la carte approx. 16.00 **t.** – 4.95 – **32 rm** 33.50 **t.**

Campanile, A 127 Southend Arterial Rd, Pipp's Hill, SS14 3AE, NW : 1 m. on A 176 530810, Fax 286710 – – 30
97 rm.

MICHELIN Distribution Centre, Bramston Link, Southfields Industrial Area, Laindon, SS15 6TX, 491150, Fax 491163

ATS Archers Field 525177

BASINGSTOKE Hants. 403 404 Q 30 – pop. 73 027 – 01256.

Test Valley, Micheldever Rd, Overton 771737 – Weybrooks Park, Sherborne, St Johns 20347.

Willis Museum, Old Town Hall, Market Pl., RG21 1QD 817618.

London 55 – Reading 17 – Southampton 31 – Winchester 18.

Plan on next page

Audleys Wood (Mt. Charlotte Thistle), Alton Rd, RG25 2JT, S : 1 1/2 m. on A 339 817555, Fax 817500, « Gothic Renaissance mansion », park – rm – 50. VISA JCB Z v
Meals *(closed Saturday lunch)* 17.95/27.00 **st.** and a la carte 7.20 – 8.75 – **69 rm** 89.00/109.00 **st.**, 2 suites – SB.

Hilton National, Old Common Rd, Black Dam, RG21 3PR, 460460, Fax 840441, – rm rest – 150. VISA. Z i
Meals (carving rest.) 9.50/16.50 **st.** and dinner a la carte – 9.50 – **141 rm** 69.50 **st.** – SB.

Forte Posthouse, Grove Rd, RG21 3EE, S : 1 m. at junction of A 339 with A 30 468181, Fax 840081 – rm – 150. VISA JCB Z e
Meals a la carte approx. 15.00 **t.** 5.50 – **84 rm** 56.00/69.50 **st.**

Travel Inn, Worting Rd, RG22 6PG, 811477, Fax 819329 – rm . VISA. Z c
Meals (Beefeater grill) a la carte approx. 16.00 **t.** – 4.95 – **49 rm** 33.50 **t.**

Forte Travelodge, Stag & Hounds, Winchester Road, RG22 6HN, 843566, Reservations (Freephone) 0800 850950 – . VISA. Z u
Meals (Harvester grill) a la carte approx. 16.00 **t.** – 5.50 – **32 rm** 33.50 **t.**

Fernbank without rest., 4 Fairfields Rd, RG21 3DR, 21191, Fax 21191 – . VISA. Y a
closed Christmas – **16 rm** 27.00/44.00.

at Oakley W : 4 3/4 m. on B 3400 – Z – Oakley – 01256 :

Beach Arms, RG23 7EP, on B 3400 780210, Fax 780557, – – 25. VISA.
closed 25 and 26 December – **Meals** (bar lunch Monday to Saturday)/dinner 9.95 **st.** and a la carte – **32 rm** 55.00/75.00 **t.**

ATS Moniton Trading Est., West Ham Lane 51431/2

ATS Armstrong Rd, Daneshill East 462448

BASINGSTOKE

London Street . . . . Y 19
Upper Church Street . . . . Y 24
Winchester Street . . . . Y 27

Aldermaston Road . . . . Z 2
Beaconsfield Road . . . . Y 3
Buckland Avenue . . . . Z 5
Chequers Road . . . . Y 6
Church Street . . . . Y 7
Churchill Way . . . . Z 9
Churchill Way East . . . . Z 10
Council Road . . . . Y 12
Cross Street . . . . Y 13
Fairfields Road . . . . Y 14
Houndmills Road . . . . Z 17
New Road . . . . Y 20
Reading Road . . . . Z 22
Southern Ringway . . . . Z 23
Victoria Street . . . . Y 25
Wote Street . . . . Y 28

North is at the top on all town plans.

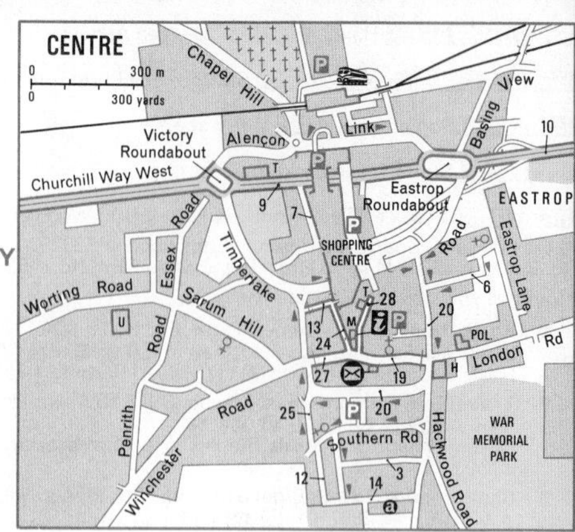

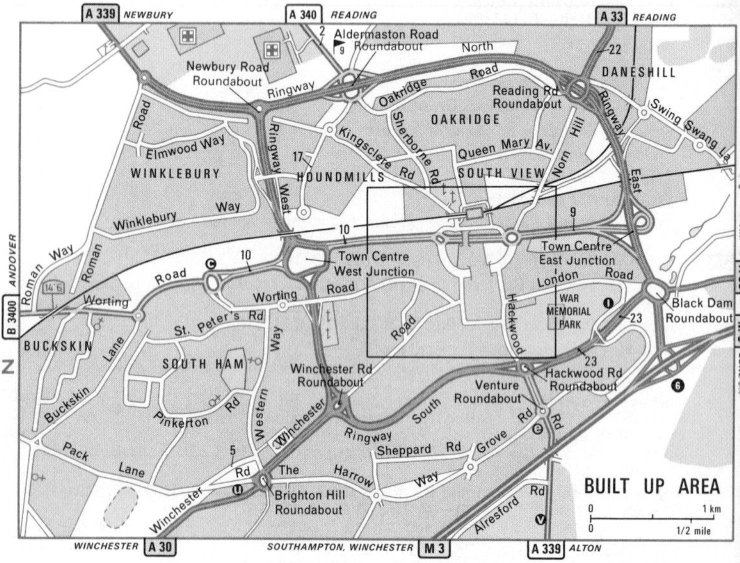

BUILT UP AREA

BASLOW Derbs. 402 403 404 P 24 **Great Britain G.** – pop. 1 757 – ECD : Wednesday – ✉ Bakewell – ☎ 01246.

See : Chatsworth★★★ (Park and Garden★★★) *AC*.

♦London 161 – Derby 27 – ♦Manchester 35 – ♦Sheffield 13.

Cavendish, DE45 1SP, on A 619 ☎ 582311, Fax 582312, ≤ Chatsworth Park, – rest TV ☎ P – 25. AE VISA
Meals 24.75 **t.** and a la carte – ☐ 8.65 – **23 rm** 83.00/125.00 **t.** – SB.

XXX ✿ **Fischer's at Baslow Hall** (Fischer) with rm, Calver Rd, DE45 1RR, on A 623 ☎ 583259, Fax 583818, « Edwardian manor house », – rest TV ☎ P. AE VISA
closed 25 and 26 December – **Meals** *(closed Sunday dinner to non-residents)* 17.50/36.00 **t.** – **5 rm** ☐ 70.00/120.00 **t.** 1 suite – SB
Spec. Roast saddle of Derbyshire lamb with a garden herb crust, Jugged hare with pasta and seasonal garnishes, Gratin of Yorkshire rhubarb with stuffed prunes and vanilla ice cream.

XX **Cafe Max**
Meals *(closed Sunday)* a la carte 14.20/23.40 **t.**

BASSENTHWAITE Cumbria 401 402 K 19 – pop. 433 – ☎ 017687.

◆London 300 – ◆Carlisle 24 – Keswick 7.

- **Armathwaite Hall** 🔇, CA12 4RE, W : 1 ½ m. on B 5291, ✉ Keswick ☎ 76551, Fax 76220, ≤ Bassenthwaite Lake, « Part 18C mansion in extensive grounds », Ⅰ₆, ≘s, ⊠, ⛟, ⛰, park, 🎾 – 🛗 ⇆ rest 📺 ☎ 🅟 – 🏛 100. 🅢 AE ⓞ VISA
  Meals 13.95/28.95 **t.** and dinner a la carte – **43 rm** ☕ 50.00/184.00 **t.** – SB.

- **Overwater Hall** 🔇, CA5 1HH, NE : 2¼ m. on Uldale rd, ✉ Ireby ☎ 76566, Fax 76566, ≤, ⛰, park – 📺 ☎ 🅟. 🅢 VISA
  Meals (dinner only and Sunday lunch)/dinner 18.95 **t.** – **13 rm** ☕ (dinner included) 51.00/102.00 **t.** – SB.

- **Pheasant Inn,** CA13 9YE, SW : 3 ¼ m. by B 5291 off A 66, ✉ Cockermouth ☎ 76234, Fax 76002, « 16C inn », ⛰ – ⇆ rest 🅟. 🅢 VISA. ✂
  closed 25 December – **Meals** 21.00 **st.** (dinner) and lunch a la carte 10.00/15.45 **st.** 🍷 4.20 – **20 rm** ☕ 52.00/96.00 **st.** – SB.

To visit a town or region: use the Michelin Green Guides.

BATH Avon 403 404 M 29 **The West Country G.** – pop. 78 689 – ECD : Monday and Thursday – ☎ 01225.

See : City★★★ – Royal Crescent★★★ AV (No 1 Royal Crescent★★ *AC* AV **D**) – The Circus★★★ AV – Museum of Costume★★★ *AC* AV **M2** – Royal Photographic Society National Centre of Photography★★ *AC* BV **M4** – Roman Baths★★ *AC* BX **B** – Holburne Museum and Crafts Study Centre★★ *AC* Y **M1** – Pump Room★ BX **A** – Assembly Rooms★ AV – Bath Abbey★ BX – Pulteney Bridge★ BV – Bath Industrial Heritage Centre★ *AC* AV **M3**.

Envir. : Lansdown Crescent★★ (Somerset Place★) Y – Claverton (American Museum★★ *AC*, Claverton Pumping Station★ *AC*) E : 3 m. by A 36 Y – Camden Crescent★ Y – Beckford Tower and Museum *AC* (prospect★) Y **M6**.

Exc. : Corsham Court★★ *AC*, NE : 8½ m. by A 4 – Dyrham Park★ *AC*, N : 6½ m. by A 4 and A 46 – Norton St. Philip (George Inn★) S : 7¼ m. by A 367 – Z – and B 3110.

18, 9 Tracy Park, Bath Rd, Wick ☎ (0117) 937 2251 – 18 Lansdown ☎ 425007 – 18 Sham Castle, North Rd ☎ 425182 – 9 Entry Hill ☎ 834248.

ℹ The Colonnades, 11-13 Bath St., BA1 1SW ☎ 462831.

◆London 119 – ◆Bristol 13 – ◆Southampton 63 – Taunton 49.

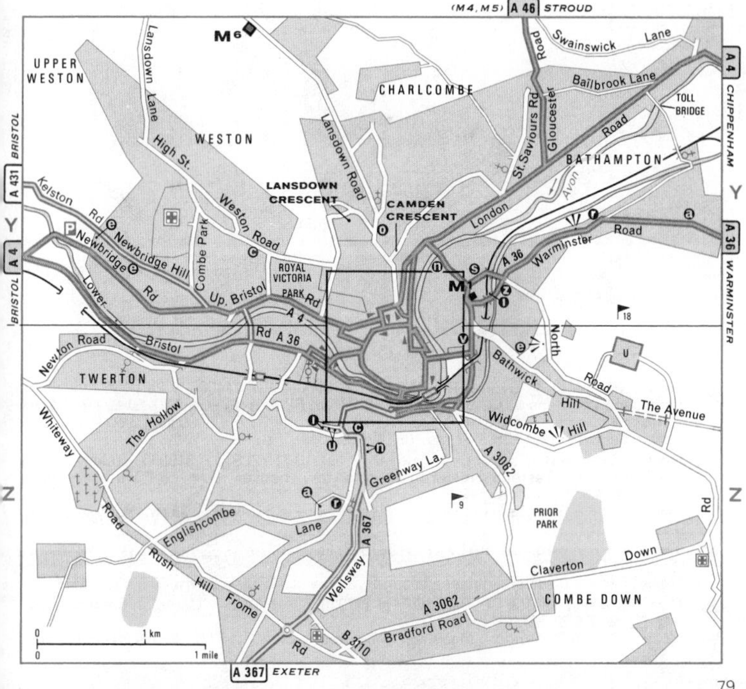

BATH

Gay Street	AV	
Green Street	BV	21
Milsom Street	BV	
New Bond Street	BV	31
Ambury	BX	2
Argyle Street	BV	3
Bennett Street	AV	4
Bridge Street	BVX	6
Broad Quay	BX	7
Chapel Row	AVX	9
Charles Street	AX	10
Charlotte Street	AV	12
Cheap Street	BX	13
Churchill Bridge	BX	14
Circus Place	AV	16
Grand Parade	BX	17
Great Stanhope Street	AV	18
Guinea Lane	BV	23
Henry Street	BX	24
Lower Borough Walls	BX	26
Monmouth Place	AVX	28
Monmouth Street	AX	30
New Orchard Street	BX	32
Nile Street	AV	34
Northgate Street	BVX	35
Old Bond Street	BX	36
Orange Grove	BX	38
Pierrepont Street	BX	39
Quiet Street	BV	41
Russell Street	AV	42
Southgate Street	BX	43
Stanley Road	BX	45
Terrace Walk	BX	46
Upper Borough Walls	BX	48
Westgate Buildings	AX	49
Westgate Street	ABX	50
Wood Street	AV	52
York Street	BX	53

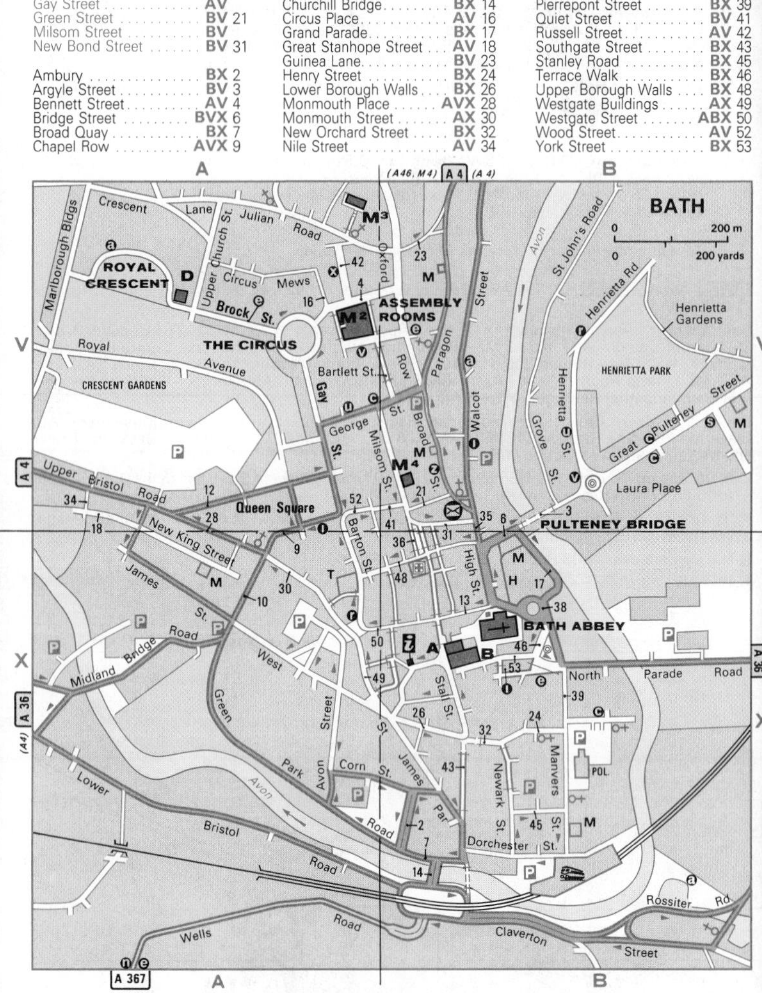

Bath Spa (Forte) Sydney Rd, BA2 6JF, ☎ 444424, Fax 444006, « Part 19C mansion in landscaped gardens », Fɑ, ≘s, ⊠, ✂ – |♦| ⋡ rm ▣ ☎ & ℗ – 🏠 120. AE ⓓ VISA JCB
Alfresco Colonnade : **Meals** 18.00/25.00 and a la carte 17.50/22.00 **st.** 8.50 – (see also *Vellore* below) – ⊐ 12.75 – **91 rm** 109.00/169.00 **st.**, 7 suites – SB. Y **z**

Royal Crescent (Q.M.H.), 16 Royal Cres., BA1 2LS, ☎ 319090, Telex 444251, Fax 339401, ⩽, « Tastefully restored Georgian town houses », – |♦| ▣ ☎ – 🏠 60. AE ⓓ VISA AV **a**
Meals 19.75/32.50 **st.** and dinner a la carte 8.00 – ⊐ 11.50 – **38 rm** 98.00/205.00 **st.**, 4 suites – SB.

The Priory, Weston Rd, BA1 2XT, ☎ 331922, Fax 448276, ⩽, heated, – ⋡ rest ▣ ☎ ℗. AE ⓓ VISA Y **c**
Meals 20.50/27.00 **st.** and dinner a la carte 8.00 – ⊐ 12.00 – **21 rm** 89.00/200.00 **st.**

Queensberry, Russell St., BA1 2QF, ☎ 447928, Fax 446065, « Georgian town houses » – |♦| ▣ ☎. AE VISA. AV **x**
closed 24 to 29 December – **Meals** (see *Olive Tree* below) – ⊐ 7.50 – **22 rm** 89.00/164.00 **st.** – SB.

Hilton National, Walcot St., BA1 5BJ, ℘ 463411, Fax 464393, ⛶, ☐, ☐ – |‡| ⇔ ☐ ☎ ⇔ Ⓟ – ⛫ 240. ☐ AE ⓞ VISA JCB BV **i**
Meals (bar lunch Saturday) 9.95/17.50 **st.** and a la carte – ☐ 10.25 – **148 rm** 84.00/104.00 **st.**, 2 suites – SB.

Fountain House without rest., 9-11 Fountain Buildings, Lansdown Rd, BA1 5DV, ℘ 338622, Fax 445855 – |‡| ☐ ☎. ☐ AE ⓞ VISA BV **e**
14 suites 92.00/168.00 **st.**.

Francis (Forte), Queen Sq., BA1 2HH, ℘ 424257, Telex 449162, Fax 319715 – |‡| ⇔ ☐ ☎ Ⓟ – ⛫ 80. ☐ AE ⓞ VISA JCB AV **i**
Meals (bar lunch Saturday) 10.95/17.95 **st.** and a la carte ⚱ 6.50 – ☐ 8.50 – **92 rm** 75.00/95.00 **st.**, 1 suite – SB.

Lansdown Grove, Lansdown Rd, BA1 5EH, ℘ 315891, Fax 448092, ⛶ – |‡| ☐ ☎ Ⓟ – ⛫ 90. ☐ AE ⓞ VISA Y **o**
Meals (bar lunch Monday to Saturday)/dinner 10.50/25.00 **t.** ⚱ 5.95 – **44 rm** ☐ 55.00/115.00 **t.** – SB.

Pratt's, South Par., BA2 4AB, ℘ 460441, Fax 448807 – |‡| ☐ ☎ – ⛫ 50 BX **c**
46 rm.

Stakis Bath, Widcombe Basin, BA2 4JP, ℘ 338855, Fax 428941 – |‡| ☐ ☎ Ⓟ – ⛫ 80. ☐ AE ⓞ VISA BX **a**
Meals 13.50/17.50 **st.** and a la carte ⚱ 5.25 – ☐ 8.50 – **96 rm** 65.00/70.00 **t.**

Compass Abbey, North Par., BA1 1LG, ℘ 461603, Fax 447758 – |‡| ☐ ☎ – ⛫ 40. ☐ AE ⓞ VISA BX **e**
Meals *(closed lunch Monday to Friday)*/dinner 15.50 **t.** and dinner a la carte ⚱ 4.20 – **54 rm** ☐ 55.00/89.00 **t.** – SB.

Brompton House without rest., St. John's Rd, Bathwick, BA2 6PT, ℘ 420972, Fax 420505, ⛶ – ⇔ ☐ ☎ Ⓟ. ☐ AE VISA. ✻ Y **n**
closed Christmas and New Year – **18 rm** ☐ 35.00/65.00 **st.**

Dukes, Great Pulteney St., BA2 4DN, ℘ 463512, Telex 449227, Fax 483733 – ⇔ rest ☐ ☎. ☐ AE ⓞ VISA BV **s**
Meals (bar lunch)/dinner 13.50 **t.** ⚱ 5.50 – **22 rm** 45.00/75.00 **t.** – SB.

Sydney Gardens without rest., Sydney Rd, BA2 6NT, ℘ 464818, ≤, ⛶ – ⇔ ☐ ☎ Ⓟ. ☐ AE VISA Y **i**
closed Christmas and 3 weeks January – **6 rm** ☐ 55.00/69.00 **st.**

Siena, 25 Pulteney Rd, BA2 4EZ, ℘ 425495, Fax 469029, ⛶ – ⇔ rest ☐ ☎ Ⓟ – ⛫ 25. ☐ VISA JCB. ✻ Z **v**
Meals (bar lunch)/dinner 17.50 **t.** and a la carte – **14 rm** ☐ 42.50/75.00 **t.** – SB.

Bloomfield House without rest., 146 Bloomfield Rd, BA2 2AS, ℘ 420105, Fax 481958, ≤, ⛶ – ⇔ ☐ ☎ Ⓟ. ☐ VISA. ✻ Z **r**
6 rm ☐ 35.00/85.00 **st.**

Paradise House without rest., 86-88 Holloway, BA2 4PX, ℘ 317723, Fax 482005, ≤, ⛶ – ☐ ☎. ☐ AE VISA. ✻ Z **c**
closed 22 to 28 December – **9 rm** ☐ 40.00/65.00 **st.**

Holly Lodge without rest., 8 Upper Oldfield Park, BA2 3JZ, ℘ 424042, Fax 481138, ≤, ⛶ – ⇔ ☐ ☎ Ⓟ. ☐ AE ⓞ VISA. ✻ Z **i**
6 rm ☐ 48.00/85.00 **st.**

Arden without rest., 73 Great Pulteney St., BA2 4DL, ℘ 466601, Fax 465548 – ☐ ☎. ☐ VISA JCB. ✻ BV **c**
closed November - 1st week February – **Meals** (booking essential) – **10 rm** ☐ 35.00/74.00 **st.**

Cranleigh without rest., 159 Newbridge Hill, BA1 3PX, ℘ 310197, Fax 423143 – ⇔ ☐ Ⓟ. ☐ VISA Y **e**
5 rm ☐ 35.00/58.00 **st.**

Haydon House without rest., 9 Bloomfield Park, off Bloomfield Rd, BA2 2BY, ℘ 427351, Fax 444919, ⛶ – ⇔ ☐ ☎. ☐ AE VISA. ✻ Z **a**
5 rm ☐ 40.00/70.00 **st.**

Leighton House without rest., 139 Wells Rd, BA2 3AL, ℘ 314769, ⛶ – ☐ ☎ Ⓟ. ☐ VISA. ✻ AX **e**
8 rm ☐ 42.00/65.00 **st.**

Somerset House, 35 Bathwick Hill, BA2 6LD, ℘ 466451, Fax 317188, ≤, ⛶ – ⇔ ☎ Ⓟ. ☐ AE VISA Z **e**
Meals (dinner only Monday to Saturday and Sunday lunch November-May)/dinner 18.00 **st.** ⚱ 3.75 – **10 rm** ☐ (dinner included) 41.50/98.00 **st.** – SB.

Villa Magdala without rest., Henrietta Rd, BA2 6LX, ℘ 466329, Fax 483207, ⛶ – ☐ ☎ Ⓟ. ☐ VISA. ✻ BV **r**
17 rm ☐ 45.00/66.00 **t.**

Bath Tasburgh without rest., Warminster Rd, Bathampton, BA2 6SH, ☎ 425096, Fax 463842, ←, – TV ☎ P. AE VISA. Y r
13 rm 36.00/72.00 **st.**

Laura Place without rest., 3 Laura Pl., Great Pulteney St., BA2 4BH, ☎ 463815, Fax 310222 – TV ☎ P. AE VISA. BV v
closed Christmas-February – **8 rm** 50.00/85.00 **st.**

Dorian House without rest., 1 Upper Oldfield Park, BA2 3JX, ☎ 426336, Fax 444699, – TV ☎ P. AE VISA. Z u
8 rm 42.00/70.00 **st.**

Orchard Lodge without rest., Warminster Rd, Bathampton, BA2 6XG, ☎ 466115, Fax 446050, – rest TV ☎ P. VISA Y a
14 rm 45.00/59.00 **st.**

Cheriton House without rest., 9 Upper Oldfield Park, BA2 3JX, ☎ 429862, Fax 428403, – TV P. VISA. Z u
closed Christmas and New Year – **9 rm** 35.00/58.00 **st.**

Blairgowrie House without rest., 55 Wellsway, BA2 4RT, ☎ 332266 – TV. Z n
3 rm 34.00/48.00 **st.**

Rosemary House, 63 Wellsway, BA2 4RT, ☎ 425667 – TV. Z n
closed Christmas and New Year – **Meals** (by arrangement) – **3 rm** (dinner included) 34.50/69.00 **st.** – SB.

Greenways without rest., 1 Forester Rd, Bathwick, BA2 6QF, ☎ 310132, Fax 310132 – TV Y s
3 rm 35.00/56.00 **t.**

Kennard without rest., 11 Henrietta St., BA2 6LL, ☎ 310472, Fax 460054 – TV ☎. AE VISA BV u
13 rm 35.00/60.00 **st.**

Oakleigh without rest., 19 Upper Oldfield Park, BA2 3JX, ☎ 315698, Fax 448223 – TV P. VISA. Z i
4 rm 35.00/60.00 **st.**

Brocks without rest., 32 Brock St., BA1 2LN, ☎ 338374, Fax 338374 – TV. VISA. AV e
closed 7 to 21 January – **8 rm** 22.00/54.00 **t.**

Oldfields without rest., 102 Wells Rd, BA2 3AL, ☎ 317984, Fax 444471, – TV P. VISA. AX n
closed 25 and 26 December – **14 rm** 30.00/65.00 **st.**

XXXX **Vellore** (at Bath Spa H.), Sydney Rd, BA2 6JF, ☎ 444424, Fax 444006, – P. AE VISA JCB Y z
Meals (dinner only) 34.00/40.00 **st.** and a la carte 9.00.

XX **Clos du Roy,** 1 Seven Dials, Saw Close, BA1 1EN, ☎ 444450, Fax 460218 – AE VISA JCB AX r
Meals 11.95/18.50 **t.** and a la carte 4.50.

XX **Hole in the Wall,** 16 George St., BA1 2EH, ☎ 425242, Fax 425242 – VISA AV u
closed Sunday and Christmas – **Meals** 13.50 **t.** (lunch) and a la carte approx. 19.00 **t.** 5.00.

XX **Garlands,** 7 Edgar Buildings, George St., BA1 2EE, ☎ 442283 – AE VISA AV c
closed Monday and first 2 weeks January – **Meals** (booking essential) 11.95/20.00 **t.**

XX **Olive Tree** (at Queensberry H.), Russell St., BA1 2QF, ☎ 447928, Fax 446065 –
closed Sunday – **Meals** 10.50/19.00 **t.** and a la carte 6.00. AV x

XX **Sukhothai,** 90a Walcot St., BA1 5BG, ☎ 462463, Fax 462463 – . AE VISA BV a
closed Sunday – **Meals** - Thai 10.00/22.00 **t.** and a la carte.

X **New Moon,** Seven Dials, Saw Close, BA1 1EN, ☎ 444407 – AE VISA JCB AX r
closed 1 January – **Meals** 7.95 **t.** (lunch) and a la carte 13.90/20.40 **t.** 6.10.

X **Tilleys Bistro,** 3 North Parade Passage, BA1 1NX, ☎ 484200 – . VISA BX i
closed Sunday lunch and 24 to 29 December – **Meals** 6.60 **t.** (lunch) and dinner a la carte 12.50/15.90 **t.**

X **Woods,** 9-13 Alfred St., BA1 2QX, ☎ 314812, Fax 443146 – AE VISA AV v
closed Sunday dinner, 24 to 26 December and 1 January – **Meals** 10.00/19.00 **t.** and a la carte.

X **Moon and Sixpence,** 6a Broad St., BA1 5LJ, ☎ 460962 – AE JCB BV z
Meals 13.50/18.50 **t.** and a la carte 5.35.

at Box NE : 5 ½ m. on A 4 - Y – ✉ Corsham (Wilts.) – ☎ 01225 :

Hermitage without rest., Bath Rd, SN14 9DT, ☎ 744187, Fax 744187, heated, – P by A 4 Y
5 rm 35.00/48.00.

Manor Farm without rest., Wadswick, SN14 9JB, SE : 2 m. by A 365 off B 3109 ☎ 810700, Fax 810307, « Working Farm », , park – TV P. VISA by A 4 Y
3 rm 25.00/45.00 **s.**

at Colerne (Wilts.) NE : 6 ½ m. by A 4 – Y – and Bannerdown rd – ✉ Bath – ☎ 01225 :

Lucknam Park ⑤, SN14 8AZ, N : ½ m. on Marshfield rd ☎ 742777, Fax 743536, ≤, « Early 18C country house in park », ⛉, ≘, ⬚, ⛲, ⚔ – ⛔ rest ⬚ ☎ ⓟ – 🔏 25. AE ⓘ VISA JCB. ⚓
Meals 22.50/39.50 **t.** 9.00 – **38 rm** ⊐ 115.00/215.00 **t.**, 4 suites – SB
Spec. Wild and farmed salmon prepared three ways, Supreme of Trelough duck with sautéed foie gras and a sherry sauce, Hot chocolate pudding with a vanilla sauce and caramelised fruits.

at Bathford E : 3 ½ m. by A 4 – Y – off A 363 – ✉ Bath – ☎ 01225 :

Orchard ⑤ without rest., 80 High St., BA1 7TG, ☎ 858765, « Georgian house », ⛲ – ⛔ ⬚ ⓟ. ⚓
closed December and January – **4 rm** ⊐ 55.00 **st.**

Old School House, Church St., BA1 7RR, ☎ 859593, Fax 859590, ⛲ – ⛔ ⬚ ☎ ⓟ. VISA. ⚓
Meals (by arrangement) 25.00 **st.** 5.50 – **4 rm** ⊐ 45.00/65.00 **st.** – SB.

at Monkton Combe SE : 4 ½ m. by A 36 – ✉ Bath – ☎ 01225 :

Monks Hill ⑤ without rest., ☎ 833028, ≤Limpley Stoke Valley, ⛲ – ⛔ ⬚ ⓟ. AE ⓘ VISA. ⚓
3 rm ⊐ 45.00/65.00 **st.**

at Limpley Stoke (Lower) SE : 5 ½ m. by A 36 - Y - off B 3108 – ✉ Bath – ☎ 01225 :

Cliffe, Cliffe Drive, Crowe Hill, BA3 6HY, ☎ 723226, Fax 723871, ≤, ⛱ heated, ⛲ – ⛔ rest ⬚ ☎ ⓟ. AE VISA JCB
Meals 15.00 **t.** (lunch) and a la carte 15.75/21.25 **t.** – **11 rm** ⊐ 66.50/97.00 **t.** – SB.

at Winsley (Wilts) SE : 6 ½ m. by A 36 – Y – on B 3108 – ✉ Bradford-on-Avon – ☎ 01225 :

Burghope Manor ⑤ without rest., BA15 2LA, off B 3108 ☎ 723557, Fax 723113, « 13C manor house », ⛲ – ⛔ ⬚ ⓟ. AE VISA JCB. ⚓
closed Christmas – **5 rm** ⊐ 45.00/65.00 **t.**

at Hinton Charterhouse S : 5 ¾ m. by A 367 – Z – on B 3110 – ✉ Bath – ☎ 01225 :

Homewood Park ⑤, BA3 6BB, E : 1 ¼ m. on A 36 (North) ☎ 723731, Fax 723820, ≤, « Part Georgian country house », ⛲, park, ⚔ – ⛔ rest ⬚ ☎ ⓟ. AE ⓘ VISA. ⚓
Meals 19.50/29.50 **st.** and dinner a la carte 30.50/35.00 **st.** 6.50 – **15 rm** ⊐ 90.00/140.00 **st.** – SB.

Green Lane House without rest., Green Lane, BA3 6BL, ☎ 723631 – AE VISA. ⚓
4 rm ⊐ 32.00/49.00.

at Norton St. Philip (Somerset) S : 7 ¼ m. by A 367 – Z – on B 3110 – ✉ Bath (Avon) – ☎ 01373 :

Monmouth Lodge without rest., BA3 6LH, ☎ 834367, ⛲ – ⛔ ⬚ ⓟ. ⚓
closed 15 to 31 December – **3 rm** ⊐ 38.00/50.00. by A 367

The Plaine without rest., BA3 6LE, ☎ 834723, Fax 834101, « 16C cottages » – ⛔ ⬚ ⓟ. AE VISA. ⚓
closed Christmas – **3 rm** ⊐ 30.00/50.00 **s.**

at Corston W : 4 m. by A 4 on A 39 – ✉ Bath – ☎ 01225 :

Old Court House without rest., BA2 9AP, ☎ 874228, « Part 16C », ⛲ – ⛔ ⬚ ⓟ. ⚓
3 rm ⊐ 40.00/50.00 **t.**

at Bitton NW : 5 ¾ m. by A 4 - Y - on A 431 – ✉ Bristol – ☎ 0117 :

Gaites House ⑤, Swineford, BS15 6LR, SE : ¾ m. on A 431 ☎ 932 9800, Fax 932 8882, ≤, ⛲ – ⛔ rm ⬚ ☎ ⓟ by A 431 Y
Meals (by arrangement) (dinner only) (residents only) (communal dining) 17.50 and a la carte – **3 rm** ⊐ 45.00/80.00.

ATS London Rd ☎ 338899/338924

BATHFORD Avon 403 404 M 29 – see Bath.

BATLEY W. Yorks. 402 O 22 – ☎ 01924.

♦London 205 – ♦Leeds 9 – ♦Manchester 40 – ♦Middlesbrough 76 – ♦Sheffield 31.

Alder House, Towngate Rd, Healey Lane, WF17 7HR, ☎ 444777, Fax 442644, ⛲ – ⬚ ☎ ⓟ – 🔏 80. AE VISA
Meals (in bar Sunday dinner and Bank Holidays) 10.75/16.50 **st.** and dinner a la carte 4.75 – ⊐ 6.00 – **21 rm** 39.50/65.00 **t.** – SB.

BATTLE E. Sussex 404 V 31 **Great Britain G.** – pop. 5 732 – ☎ 01424.

See : Town★ – Abbey and Site of the Battle of Hastings★ *AC*.

ℹ 88 High St., TN33 0AQ ☎ 773721.

◆London 55 – ◆Brighton 34 – Folkestone 43 – Maidstone 30.

Netherfield Place 🔇, TN33 9PP, NW : 2 m. by A 2100 on Netherfield rd ☎ 774455, Fax 774024, ≤, « Georgian style country house », 🌳, park, 🎾 – TV ☎ P – 🏛 50. 💳 AE ⓓ VISA. 🚫
closed last week December and first 2 weeks January – **Meals** 15.95/22.50 **t.** and a la carte 🍷 5.50 – **14 rm** ☐ 58.00/125.00 **t.** – SB.

Powdermills 🔇, Powdermill Lane, TN33 0SP, S : 1½ m. by A 2100 on B 2095 ☎ 775511, Fax 774540, ≤, « Part Georgian gunpowdermill, antiques », 🏊, 🎣, 🌳, park – TV ☎ P – 🏛 250. 💳 AE ⓓ VISA
Meals (see ***Orangery*** below) – **23 rm** ☐ 45.00/85.00 **st.** – SB.

Burnt Wood, Powdermill Rd, TN33 0SU, S : 2 m. on B 2095 ☎ 775151, Fax 775151, ≤, 🏊 heated, 🌳, park, 🎾 – TV ☎ P
Meals 10.66/17.50 **t.** – **10 rm** ☐ 40.00/65.00 **t.** – SB.

George, 23 High St., TN33 0EA, ☎ 774466, Fax 774853 – TV ☎ P – 🏛 50. 💳 AE ⓓ VISA JCB
Meals 12.00 and a la carte – **22 rm** ☐ 50.00/70.00 **st.** – SB.

Little Hemingfold 🔇, Telham, TN33 0TT, SE : 1 ¾ m. on A 2100 ☎ 774338, ≤, « Lakeside setting », 🎣, 🌳, park, 🎾 – 🚭 rest TV ☎ P. 💳 AE VISA
Meals 19.50 **st.** 🍷 5.00 – **12 rm** ☐ 35.00/65.00 **st.** – SB.

XX **Orangery** (at Powdermills H.), Powdermill Lane, TN33 0SP, S : 1½ m. by A 2100 on B 2095 ☎ 775511, Fax 774540, 🌳 – P. 💳 AE ⓓ VISA
Meals 13.50/17.50 **t.** and dinner a la carte 🍷 5.50.

Town plans : *roads most used by traffic and those on which guide- listed hotels and restaurants stand are fully drawn; the beginning only of lesser roads is indicated.*

BAWTRY S. Yorks 402 403 404 Q 23 – ✉ Doncaster – ☎ 01302.

⛳18 Austerfield Park, Cross Lane ☎ 710841.

◆London 157 – ◆Leeds 37 – Lincoln 30 – ◆Nottingham 36 – ◆Sheffield 20.

Crown (Forte), High St., DN10 6JW, ☎ 710341, Fax 711798 – 🚭 TV ☎ P – 🏛 150. 💳 AE ⓓ VISA
Meals (bar lunch Monday to Saturday)/dinner 16.95 **st.** and a la carte 🍷 5.50 – ☐ 8.50 – **57 rm** 40.00/50.00 **st.** – SB.

BEACONSFIELD Bucks. 404 S 29 – pop. 10 543 – ECD : Wednesday and Saturday – ☎ 01494.

◆London 26 – Aylesbury 19 – ◆Oxford 32.

De Vere Bellhouse, Oxford Rd, HP9 2XE, E : 1 ¾ m. on A 40 ☎ (01753) 887211, Fax 888231, Ⅎ₆, ≘s, 🏊, 🌳, squash – 🛗 🚭 rm TV ☎ P – 🏛 450. 💳 AE ⓓ VISA
Meals *(closed Saturday lunch)* 18.50 **st.** and a la carte – **133 rm** ☐ 110.00/155.00 **st.**, 3 suites – SB.

XX **Leigh House,** 53 Wycombe End, HP9 1LX, ☎ 676348, Fax 676348 – ▤. 💳 AE ⓓ VISA
closed 25-26 December – **Meals** - Chinese (Peking) 9.50/24.00 **t.** and a la carte.

XX **La Lanterna,** 57 Wycombe End, HP9 1LX, ☎ 675210 – ▤. 💳 AE ⓓ VISA
closed Sunday – **Meals** - Italian 13.50/18.50 **t.** and a la carte 🍷 4.95.

XX **China Diner,** 7 The Highway, Station Rd, Beaconsfield New Town, HP9 1QD, ☎ 678346 – 💳 AE ⓓ VISA
closed 25 and 26 December – **Meals** - Chinese 10.00/20.00 **t.** and a la carte 🍷 4.00.

at Wooburn Common SW : 3½ m. by A 40 – ✉ Beaconsfield – ☎ 01628 :

Chequers Inn 🔇, Kiln Lane, HP10 0JQ, SW : 1 m. on Bourne End rd ☎ 529575, Fax 850124 – TV ☎ P – 🏛 45. 💳 AE VISA. 🚫
Meals 14.95/17.95 **t.** and a la carte – **17 rm** ☐ 72.50/90.00 **t.** – SB.

BEARSTED Kent 404 V 30 – see Maidstone.

BEAULIEU Hants. 403 404 P 31 **Great Britain G.** – pop. 726 – ECD : Tuesday and Saturday – ✉ Brockenhurst – ☎ 01590.

See : Town★★ - National Motor Museum★★ *AC*.

Envir. : Buckler's Hard★ (Maritime Museum★ *AC*) SE : 2 m.

◆London 102 – Bournemouth 24 – ◆Southampton 13 – Winchester 23.

Montagu Arms, Palace Lane, SO42 7ZL, ☎ 612324, Fax 612188, « Part 18C inn, gardens » – 🚭 rest TV ☎ P – 🏛 30. 💳 AE ⓓ VISA
Meals 14.95/23.90 **t.** – **22 rm** ☐ 67.90/95.90 **t.**, 2 suites – SB.

at Bucklers Hard S : 2 ½ m. – ✉ Brockenhurst – ☎ 01590 :

Master Builder's House, SO42 7XB, ☎ 616253, Fax 616297, ≤, – rm ☎ – 40.
Meals 12.50/15.45 **t.** and a la carte – **23 rm** 55.00/100.00 **st.** –.

BECKINGHAM Lincs. 402 404 R 24 – pop. 263 – ✉ Fenton Claypole – ☎ 01636.
♦London 124 – Leicester 43 – Lincoln 20 – ♦Nottingham 28 – ♦Sheffield 46.

Black Swan, Hillside, LN5 0RF, ☎ 626474, – . VISA
closed Monday, 1 week August and Christmas-New Year – **Meals** (booking essential) (lunch by arrangement)/dinner 22.00 **t.**

BECKINGTON Somerset 403 404 N 30 – ✉ Bath (Avon) – ☎ 01373 :

Forte Travelodge without rest., BA3 6SF, on A 36 ☎ 830251, Reservations (Freephone) 0800 850950 – . AE VISA.
40 rm 33.50 **t.**

Woolpack Inn with rm, BA3 6SP, ☎ 831244, Fax 831233, « Part 16C inn », – ☎ . VISA
Meals 12.00/23.00 **t.** and a la carte **t.** 5.50 – **10 rm** 49.50/84.50 **t.** – SB.

BECKWITHSHAW N. Yorks. 402 P 22 – see Harrogate.

BEDALE N. Yorks. 402 P 21 – pop. 3 319 – ECD : Thursday – ✉ Darlington – ☎ 01677.
Leyburn Rd ☎ 422568.
Bedale Hall, DL8 1AA ☎ 424604 (summer only).
♦London 225 – ♦Leeds 45 – ♦Newcastle upon Tyne 30 – York 38.

Hyperion House without rest., 88 South End, DL8 2DS, ☎ 422334, –
closed Christmas and New Year – **4 rm** 17.00/34.00.

Plummer's, 7-10 North End, DL8 1AF, ☎ 423432 – AE VISA
Meals 8.95 **st.** (lunch) and a la carte 10.70/16.95 **st.**

BEDFORD Beds. 404 S 27 – pop. 75 632 – ECD : Thursday – ☎ 01234.
Bedfordshire, Bromham Rd, Biddenham ☎ 353241 – Mowsbury, Kimbolton Rd ☎ 216374/771041.
10 St. Paul's Sq., MK40 1SL ☎ 215226.
♦London 59 – ♦Cambridge 31 – Colchester 70 – ♦Leicester 51 – Lincoln 95 – Luton 20 – ♦Oxford 52 – Southend-on-Sea 85.

Barns (Country Club), Cardington Rd, MK44 3SA, E : 2 m. on A 603 ☎ 270044, Fax 273102, , – rm ☎ – 120. AE VISA.
Meals (bar lunch Saturday) 10.50/18.00 **t.** and a la carte 5.75 – 7.50 – **49 rm** 65.00/90.00 **t.** – SB.

Bedford Swan, The Embankment, MK40 1RW, ☎ 346565, Fax 212009, – ☎ – 300. AE VISA
Meals 12.50 **st.** and a la carte 4.95 – **114 rm** 66.00/76.00 **st.**, 1 suite – SB.

Wayfarer, 403 Goldington Rd, Goldington, MK40 0DS, E : 2 m. on A 428 ☎ 272707, Fax 272707, – ☎ – 30. AE VISA JCB.
Meals (grill rest.) a la carte 6.85/16.60 **t.** – **29 rm** 55.00/65.00 **st.** – SB.

Edwardian House, 15 Shakespeare Rd, MK41 2DZ, ☎ 211156, Fax 262492 – ☎ . AE VISA.
closed 24 December-2 January – **Meals** (lunch by arrangement)/dinner 18.50 **st.** 3.95 – **19 rm** 38.50/48.00 **st.**

Hertford House without rest., 57 de Parys Av., MK40 2TP, ☎ 350007, Fax 353468, – . VISA.
16 rm 25.00/45.00 **t.**

at Houghton Conquest S : 6 ½ m. by A 6 – ✉ Bedford – ☎ 01234 :

Knife and Cleaver with rm, MK45 3LA, ☎ 740387, Fax 740900, – ☎ . AE VISA
closed Sunday night and 27 to 30 December – **Meals** *(closed dinner Bank Holidays)* (bar lunch Saturday) 11.50/16.50 **st.** and a la carte 5.50 – **9 rm** 41.00/66.00 **st.**

at Marston Moretaine SW : 6 ¼ m. by A 6 off A 421 – ✉ Bedford – ☎ 01234 :

Forte Travelodge without rest., Beancroft Rd junction, MK43 0PZ, on A 421 ☎ 766755, Reservations (Freephone) 0800 850950 – TV & P. AE VISA.
32 rm 33.50 **t.**

at Clapham NW : 2 m. on A 6 – ✉ Bedford – ☎ 01234 :

Woodlands Manor, Green Lane, MK41 6EP, ☎ 363281, Fax 272390, – TV ☎ P – 30
24 rm, 1 suite.

MICHELIN Distribution Centre, H.T. Centre, Hammond Rd, Elms Farm Industrial Estate, MK41 0LG, ☎ 271100, Fax 269453

ATS 3 London Rd ☎ 358838

BEER Devon 403 K 31 **The West Country G.** – pop. 1 415 – ✉ Seaton – ☎ 01297.

Envir. : Seaton (≤★★) N : ¾ m.

18 Axe Cliff, Squires Lane, Axmouth, Seaton ☎ 24371.

London 170 – Exeter 22 – Taunton 28.

Anchor Inn, Fore St., EX12 3ET, ☎ 20386, ≤ – TV. VISA.
closed 3 days at Christmas – **Meals** *(closed 25 December)* 10.00 **t.** (lunch) and a la carte 10.75/18.00 **t.** 5.00 – **8 rm** 30.00/60.00 **t.**

To visit a town or region: use the Michelin Green Guides.

BEESTON Ches. 402 403 404 L 24 – pop. 196 – ✉ Tarporley – ☎ 01829.

London 186 – Chester 15 – Liverpool 40 – Shrewsbury 32.

Wild Boar, Whitchurch Rd, Bunbury, CW6 9NW, on A 49 ☎ 260309, Fax 261081, « Part 17C timbered house » – rest TV ☎ & P – 50. AE VISA
Meals 12.75/18.75 **t.** and a la carte 5.25 – **37 rm** 62.50/97.00 **t.** – SB.

BELCHAMP WALTER Essex 404 W 27 – see Sudbury.

BELFORD Northd. 401 402 O 17 – pop. 1 177 – ECD : Thursday – ☎ 01668.

London 335 – Edinburgh 71 – Newcastle upon Tyne 49.

Blue Bell, Market Pl., NE70 7NE, ☎ 213543, Fax 213787, – rest TV ☎ & P. AE VISA
Meals (bar lunch)/dinner 20.00 **st.** and a la carte 5.25 – **17 rm** 40.00/92.00 **t.** – SB.

Purdy Lodge, Adderstone Services, NE70 7JU, on A 1 at junction with B 1341 ☎ 213000, Fax 213111 – TV & P. AE VISA
Meals (bar lunch)/dinner a la carte 8.75/15.20 **st.** – **20 rm** 35.00 **st.** – SB.

BELLINGHAM Northd. 401 402 N 18 – ✉ Hexham – ☎ 01434.

9 Bellingham ☎ 220530.

Main St., NE48 2BQ ☎ 220616.

London 315 – Carlisle 48 – Newcastle upon Tyne 33.

Riverdale Hall, NE48 2JT, E : ½ m. ☎ 220254, Fax 220457, ≤, – TV ☎ P. AE VISA
Meals 7.75/17.50 **t.** and a la carte 4.95 – **21 rm** 40.00/78.00 **t.** – SB.

Westfield House, NE48 2DP, ☎ 220340, – P. VISA.
Meals (communal dining) (by arrangement) 13.50 **s.** – **5 rm** 36.00/52.00 **s.**

BELPER Derbs. 402 403 404 P 24 – pop. 16 960 – ☎ 01332.

London 141 – Derby 8 – Manchester 55 – Nottingham 17.

Makeney Hall Country House, Makeney, Milford, DE56 0RU, S : 2 m. by A 6 ☎ 842999, Fax 842777, – rm TV ☎ & P – 180. AE VISA
Meals *(closed Saturday lunch)* 12.00/19.50 **st.** and dinner a la carte 8.00 – 6.00 – **44 rm** 65.00/135.00 **st.**, 1 suite – SB.

BENENDEN Kent 404 V 30 – ✉ Cranbrook – ☎ 01580.

London 50 – Hastings 20 – Maidstone 20.

Crit Hall, Cranbrook Rd, TN17 4EU, W : 1 m. on B 2086 ☎ 240609, Fax 241743, – TV P.
closed mid December-mid January – **Meals** (communal dining) 16.50 **st.** 4.00 – **3 rm** 28.00/50.00 **st.**

BEPTON W. Sussex – see Midhurst.

BERKELEY Glos. 403 404 M 28 **Great Britain G.** – pop. 1 550 – ECD : Wednesday – 01453.

See : Berkeley Castle★★ *AC*.

Exc. : Wildfowl and Wetlands Trust, Slimbridge★ *AC*, NE : 6½ m. by B 4066 and A 38.

London 129 – Bristol 20 – Cardiff 50 – Gloucester 18.

- **Prince of Wales,** Berkeley Rd, GL13 9HD, NE : 2½ m. by B 4066 on A 38 ☎ 810474, Fax 511370, – – 200
  Meals 6.95/12.95 **st.** and a la carte – 5.95 – **41 rm** 35.00/55.00 **st.**
- **Old School House,** 34 Canonbury St., GL13 9BG, ☎ 811711 – . VISA.
  Meals 10.50/16.00 **t.** and a la carte 4.95 – **7 rm** 40.00/55.00 **t.** – SB.

BERKSWELL W. Mids. 403 404 P 26 – see Coventry.

BERWICK-UPON-TWEED Northd. 401 402 O 16 **Great Britain and Scotland G.** – pop. 12 772 – ECD : Thursday – 01289.

See : Town★ - Walls★.

Envir. : Foulden★, NW : 5 m. – Paxton House (Chippendale furniture★) *AC*, W : 5 m. by A 6105, A 1 and B 6461.

Exc. : SW : Tweed Valley★★ – Eyemouth Museum★ *AC*, N : 7½ m. by A 1 and A 1107 – Holy Island★ (Priory ruins★ *AC*, Lindisfarne Castle★ *AC*) SE : 9 m. by A 1167 and A 1.

Goswick Beal ☎ 387256 – Magdalene Fields ☎ 306384.

Castlegate Car Park, TD15 1JS ☎ 330733.

London 349 – Edinburgh 57 – Newcastle upon Tyne 63.

- **Marshall Meadows**, TD15 1UT, N : 2¾ m. by A 1167 and A 1 ☎ 331133, Fax 331438, , park, – . VISA.
  Meals 12.50 **st.** (dinner) and a la carte 11.00/15.50 **st.** 4.25 – **17 rm** 55.00/68.00 **st.**, 1 suite – SB.
- **Harberton,** 181 Main St., Spittal, TD15 1RP, SE : 2¼ m. by A 1167 ☎ 308813, ←, –
  closed Christmas and New Year – **Meals** 10.00 – **5 rm** 17.50/44.00.

ATS 78-80 Church St. ☎ 305720/308222

BETHERSDEN Kent 404 W 30 – pop. 1 341 – ✉ Ashford – 01233.

London 63 – Folkestone 20 – Maidstone 27.

- **Little Hodgeham**, Smarden Rd, TN26 3HE, W : 2 m. ☎ 850323, « 15C cottage, antique furniture », , – .
  mid March-August – **Meals** (by arrangement) (communal dining) – **3 rm** (dinner included) 58.00/101.00 **s.** – SB.

BEVERLEY Humbs. 402 S 22 **Great Britain G.** – pop. 12 914 – ECD : Thursday – ✉ Kingston-upon-Hull – 01482.

See : Town★ - Minster★★ – St. Mary's Church★.

The Westwood ☎ 867190.

Guildhall, Register Sq., HU17 9AU ☎ 867430/883898.

London 188 – Kingston-upon-Hull 8 – Leeds 52 – York 29.

- **Beverley Arms** (Forte), North Bar Within, HU17 8DD, ☎ 869241, Fax 870907 – – 60. AE VISA JCB
  Meals 11.25/17.95 **st.** and a la carte 6.50 – 8.50 – **57 rm** 56.00/80.00 **st.** – SB.
- **Kings Head,** 38 Market Pl., HU17 9AH, ☎ 868103, Fax 871201 – . AE VISA
  accommodation closed 25 December – **Meals** 10.50 **t.** and a la carte 4.50 – **12 rm** 39.50/49.50 **t.** – SB.
- **Lairgate,** 30 Lairgate, HU17 8EP, ☎ 882141, Fax 861067 – . VISA.
  Meals 9.50/20.00 **t.** and a la carte 4.95 – **22 rm** 40.00/65.00 **t.**
- **Cerutti 2,** Beverley Station, Station Sq., HU17 0AS, ☎ 866700 – . VISA
  closed Sunday and Bank Holidays – **Meals** a la carte 12.90/18.70 **t.** 5.00.

at Tickton NE : 3½ m. by A 1035 – ✉ Kingston-upon-Hull – 01964 :

- **Tickton Grange,** HU17 9SH, on A 1035 ☎ 543666, Fax 542556, – – 60. AE VISA
  Meals 12.95/22.95 **t.** 5.95 – 6.95 – **18 rm** 53.50 **t.**

at Walkington SW : 3½ m. by A 164 – ✉ Beverley – 01482 :

- **Manor House** with rm, Northlands, Newbald Rd, HU17 8RT, NE : 1 m. by Northgate ☎ 881645, Fax 866501, « Late 19C house, conservatory », – . VISA.
  closed Bank Holidays – **Meals** *(closed Sunday)* (dinner only) 15.00 **t.** and a la carte **t.** 4.50 – 8.50 – **7 rm** 70.00/100.00 **t.** – SB.

ATS 379 Grovehill Rd ☎ 868655/882644

BEWDLEY Heref. and Worcs. 402 403 404 N 26 – ☎ 01299.

♦London 145 – ♦Birmingham 23 – Shrewsbury 34 – Worcester 21.

XX **Somewhere Nice,** 78-80 Load St., ✆ 404584
closed 2 to 18 January – **Meals** *(closed Sunday dinner, Monday and Bank Holidays)* (dinner only and Sunday lunch)/dinner 16.00 **st.** and a la carte 5.50.

BEXHILL E. Sussex 404 V 31 – pop. 34 625 – ECD : Wednesday – ☎ 01424.

Cooden Beach ✆ 842040 – Highwoods, Ellerslie Lane ✆ 212625.

De La Warr Pavilion, Marina, TN40 1DP ✆ 212023.

♦London 66 – ♦ Brighton 32 – Folkestone 42.

Jarvis Cooden Beach, Cooden Sea Rd, Cooden Beach, TN39 4TT, W : 2 m. on B 2182 ✆ 842281, Fax 846142, ≤, heated, – TV ☎ P – 160. AE VISA
Meals 12.15/15.00 **st.** and a la carte 4.25 – **41 rm** 60.00/90.00 – SB.

X **Lychgates,** 5a Church St., Old Town, TN40 2HE, ✆ 212193 – VISA
closed Sunday, Monday, 2 weeks in summer and 25 December – **Meals** (booking essential) 10.00/21.95 5.50.

BIBURY Glos. 403 404 O 28 **Great Britain G.** – pop. 570 – ECD : Wednesday – ✉ Cirencester – ☎ 01285.

See : Village★.

♦London 86 – Gloucester 26 – ♦Oxford 30.

Swan, GL7 5NW, ✆ 740695, Fax 740473, « Attractively furnished inn with gardens and trout stream », – rest TV ☎. AE VISA JCB.
Meals 15.95/35.00 **st.** and a la carte – **18 rm** 97.00/210.00 **st.** – SB.

Cotteswold House without rest., Arlington, GL7 5ND, on B 4425 ✆ 740609 – TV P.
3 rm 22.00/38.00.

BICKLEIGH Devon 403 J 31 **The West Country G.** – pop. 227 – ECD : Tuesday – ✉ Tiverton – ☎ 01884.

See : Village★★ - Bickleigh Mill Craft Centre and Farms★★ *AC* – Bickleigh Castle★ *AC.*

Envir. : Tiverton : Museum★ *AC,* N : 2½ m. by A 396 – Knightshayes Court★ *AC,* N : 4 m. by A 396.

Exc. : Uffculme (Coldharbour Mill★★ *AC*) NE : 7½ m.

Post Hill Tiverton ✆ 252114.

♦London 195 – Exeter 9 – Taunton 31.

Bickleigh Cottage Country, Bickleigh Bridge, EX16 8RJ, on A 396 ✆ 855230, « Part 17C thatched cottage, riverside setting », – P. VISA.
April-October – **Meals** (residents only) (dinner only) 11.50 **t.** – **9 rm** 22.50/50.00 **t.**

Fisherman's Cot, EX16 8RW, on A 396 ✆ 855237, Fax 855241, , – rm TV ☎ P. VISA.
Meals (carving lunch)/dinner a la carte 9.95/12.70 **t.** 6.25 – **23 rm** 46.00/66.00 **t.** – SB.

BIDDENDEN Kent 404 V 30 **Great Britain G.** – pop. 2 205 – ✉ Ashford – ☎ 01580.

Envir. : Sissinghurst Castle★ *AC,* W : 3 m. by A 262.

♦London 51 – Folkestone 29 – Hastings 23 – Maidstone 14.

XX **West House,** 28 High St., TN27 8AH, ✆ 291341 – P. VISA
closed Sunday dinner, Monday, 1 week January, 1 week April and 1 week October – **Meals** - Italian 12.50 **st.** and a la carte 4.95.

BIDEFORD Devon 403 H 30 **The West Country G.** – pop. 13 066 – ECD : Wednesday – ☎ 01237.

See : Bridge★★ – Burton Art Gallery★ *AC.*

Envir. : Appledore★, N : 2 m.

Exc. : Clovelly★★, W : 11 m. by A 39 and B 3237 – Lundy Island★★, NW : by ferry – Great Torrington (Dartington Crystal★ *AC*) SE : 7½ m. by A 386.

Royal North Devon, Golf Links Rd, Westward Ho ✆ 473824 – Torrington, Weare Trees ✆ (01805) 622229.

to the Isle of Lundy (Lundy Co.) (2 h 15 mn).

Victoria Park, The Quay, EX39 2QQ ✆ 477676/421853.

♦London 231 – Exeter 43 – ♦Plymouth 58 – Taunton 60.

Durrant House, Heywood Rd, Northam, EX39 3QB, N : 1 m. on A 386 ✆ 472361, Fax 421709, , – TV ☎ P – 300. AE VISA
Meals 7.50/15.00 **t.** and a la carte 5.40 – **123 rm** 56.00/81.00 **t.**, 2 suites – SB.

New Bridge, Northam, EX39 3QA, N : 1 m. on A 386 ✆ 474989, Fax 474989 – rest TV ☎ P. VISA.
Meals (dinner only and Sunday lunch)/dinner 12.00 **t.** – **10 rm** 30.00/70.00 **t.**

Orchard Hill, Orchard Hill, Northam, EX39 2QY, N : ¾ m. by A 386 ✆ 472872, Fax 423803, – TV P. VISA.
Meals (dinner only) a la carte 9.50/16.45 **st.** 2.80 – **9 rm** 33.00/50.00 **st.** – SB.

at Instow N : 3 m. on A 39 – ✉ Bideford – ☎ 01271 :

Commodore, Marine Par., EX39 4JN, ℘ 860347, Fax 861233, ≤ Taw and Torridge estuaries, – TV ☎ P. AE VISA.
Meals 8.75/18.00 **t.** and a la carte 4.25 – **20 rm** (dinner included) 50.00/115.00 **t.** – SB.

at Eastleigh NE : 2 ½ m. by A 386 (via Old Barnstaple Rd) – ✉ Bideford – ☎ 01271 :

Pines, EX39 4PA, ℘ 860561, Fax 860561, ≤, – TV ☎ P
Meals (by arrangement) 9.95 3.50 – **5 rm** 25.00/40.00 **st.** – SB.

ATS New Rd ℘ 472451

BIGBURY-ON-SEA Devon 403 I 33 – pop. 600 – ECD : Thursday – ✉ Kingsbridge – ☎ 01548.

London 196 – Exeter 42 – Plymouth 17.

Burgh Island, TQ7 4AU, S : ½ m. by sea tractor ℘ 810514, Fax 810243, ≤ Bigbury Bay, « Island setting, Art Deco », park, – TV ☎. AE VISA.
closed Monday to Thursday January-February – **Meals** (booking essential) 18.50/28.00 **t.** and a la carte 5.50 –, **14 suites** (dinner included) 174.00/210.00 **t.** – SB.

Henley, Folly Hill, TQ7 4AR, ℘ 810240, Fax 810020, ≤ Bigbury Bay and Bolt Tail, – TV ☎ P. VISA
Meals (dinner only) 12.50 – **8 rm** (dinner included) 40.00/90.00 **st.** – SB.

BILBROOK Somerset 403 J 30 – ✉ Minehead – ☎ 01984.

London 179 – Bristol 56 – Minehead 7 – Taunton 17.

Dragon House, TA24 6HQ, on A 39 ℘ 40215, Fax 41340, – TV ☎ P
9 rm.

BILBROUGH N. Yorks. 402 Q 22 – see York.

BILLESLEY Warks. – see Stratford-upon-Avon.

BILLINGSHURST W. Sussex 404 S 30 – pop. 5 770 – ECD : Wednesday – ☎ 01403.

London 44 – Brighton 24 – Guildford 25 – Portsmouth 40.

Forte Travelodge without rest., Five Oaks, Stane St., RH14 9AE, N : 1 m. on A 29 ℘ 782711, Reservations (Freephone) 0800 850950 – TV P. AE VISA.
26 rm 33.50 **t.**

Old Wharf without rest., Wharf Farm, Newbridge, RH14 0JG, W : 1 ¾ m. on A 272 ℘ 784096, Fax 784096, ≤, « Restored canalside warehouse », park – TV ☎ P. AE VISA.
closed 2 weeks Christmas-New Year – **4 rm** 35.00/55.00 **t.**

Gables, Pulborough Rd, Parbrook, RH14 9EU, S : ½ m. on A 29 ℘ 782571 – P. AE VISA
closed Saturday lunch, Sunday dinner, Monday, 1 week January, 2 weeks August and Bank Holidays 13.50/18.95 **t.**

BILSBURROW Lancs. – see Garstang.

BINBROOK Lincs. 402 404 T 23 – ☎ 01472.

London 162 – Great Grimsby 10 – Lincoln 26 – Scunthorpe 32.

Hoe Hill, Swinhope, LN3 6HX, NE : 1 m. on B 1203 ℘ 398206, – P.
Meals (by arrangement) (communal dining) 12.00 – **3 rm** 15.00/30.00 **s.**

BINGHAM Notts. 402 404 R 25 – ☎ 01949.

London 125 – Lincoln 28 – Nottingham 11 – Sheffield 35.

Bingham Court, Ming House, Market St., NG13 8AB, ℘ 831831, Fax 838833 – TV ☎ P. VISA.
Meals (see *Yeung Sing* below) – **15 rm** 39.00/49.50 **t.**

Yeung Sing (at Bingham Court H.), Ming House, Market St., NG13 8AB, ℘ 831222, Fax 838833 – P. VISA
Meals - Chinese (Canton) (dinner only and Sunday lunch)/dinner 18.00 **t.** and a la carte.

ATS 1 Moorbridge Rd ℘ 837717

BINGLEY W. Yorks. 402 O 22 – pop. 28 196 – ECD : Tuesday – ✉ Bradford – ☎ 01274.

18 St. Ives Est. ☎ 562436.

♦London 204 – Bradford 6 – Skipton 13.

Jarvis Bankfield, Bradford Rd, BD16 1TU, SE : 1 ½ m. on A 650 ☎ 567123, Fax 551331, – rm rest – 200.
Meals (carving rest.) (bar lunch Saturday and Bank Holidays) 9.95/15.00 **st.** and a la carte – 8.00 – **103 rm** 79.00/89.00 **st.** – SB.

Hallbank, Beck Lane, BD16 4DD, ☎ 565296, Fax 565296 – rest .
closed Christmas – **Meals** 12.00 **st.** 3.50 – **9 rm** 40.00/50.00 **st.**

Holroyd House, Beck Rd, Micklethwaite, BD16 3JN, N : 1 ¾ m. by A 650 and Micklethwaite Lane ☎ 562464, –
Meals (by arrangement) 11.00 **s.** – **3 rm** 18.00/36.00 – SB.

BIRCHINGTON Kent 404 X 29 – ☎ 01843.

♦London 71 – ♦Dover 20 – Maidstone 40 – Margate 5.

Crown Inn (Cherry Brandy House), Ramsgate Rd, Sarre, CT7 0LF, SW : 4 m. on A 28 ☎ 847808, Fax 847914 – rm
Meals (bar lunch)/dinner a la carte 8.70/20.00 **t.** 2.95 – **12 rm** 43.50/66.75 **t.** – SB.

BIRCH SERVICE AREA Gtr. Manchester 402 ㉒ 403 ③ 404 ⑩ – ✉ Heywood (Lancs.) – ☎ 0161.

Granada Lodge without rest., OL10 2QH, on M 62, between junctions 18 and 19 ☎ 655 3403, Fax 655 3358, Reservations (Freephone) 0800 555300 – .
4.00 – **39 rm** 39.95 **st.**

BIRDLIP Glos. 403 404 N 28 **Great Britain G.** – ECD : Saturday – ✉ Gloucester – ☎ 01452.

Envir. : Crickley Hill Country Park (≤★) N : 1 ½ m. by B 4070 and A 417.

♦London 107 – ♦Bristol 51 – Gloucester 9 – ♦Oxford 44 – Swindon 24.

Royal George, GL4 8JH, ☎ 862506, Fax 862277, – rm – 100.
Meals 12.50/14.95 **t.** and a la carte – **34 rm** 49.50/59.50 **t.** – SB.

Kingshead House, GL4 8JH, ☎ 862299 – .
closed Saturday lunch, Sunday dinner, Monday, 26-27 December and 1 January – **Meals** 23.50 **t.** and lunch a la carte 15.45/21.50 **t.**

BIRKENHEAD Mersey. 402 403 K 23 – pop. 99 075 – ECD : Thursday – ☎ 0151.

18 Arrowe Park, Woodchurch ☎ 677 1527 – 18 Prenton, Golf Links Rd, Prenton ☎ 608 1461.

to Liverpool and Wallasey (Mersey Ferries).

Woodside Visitors Centre, Woodside Ferry Terminal, L41 6DU ☎ 647 6780.

♦London 222 – ♦Liverpool 2.

Plan : see Liverpool p. 3

Bowler Hat, 2 Talbot Rd, Oxton, L43 2HH, ☎ 652 4931, Fax 653 8127, – – 200. AX
Meals (bar lunch Saturday) 9.95/19.05 **t.** and a la carte 4.95 – **32 rm** 59.50/102.50 **t.**

Beadles, 15 Rosemount, Oxton, L43 5SG, ☎ 653 9010 – AX
closed Sunday, Monday and 2 weeks August-September – **Meals** (dinner only) a la carte approx. 19.00 **t.** 3.50.

ATS 40 Mill Lane, Wallasey, Wirral ☎ 638 1949/8606

BIRMINGHAM W. Mids. 403 404 O 26 **Great Britain G.** – pop. 961 041 – ECD : Wednesday – 0121.

See : City★ – Museum and Art Gallery★★ JZ **M2** – Barber Institute of Fine Arts★★ (at Birmingham University) EX – Museum of Science and Industry★ JY **M3** – Cathedral of St. Philip (stained glass portrayals★) KYZ.

Envir. : Aston Hall★★ FV **M.**

Exc. : Black Country Museum★, Dudley, NW : 10 m. by A 456 and A 4123 AU.

18 Edgbaston, Church Rd 454 1736, FX – 18 Hilltop, Park Lane, Handsworth 554 4463, CU – 18 Hatchford Brook, Coventry Rd, Sheldon 743 9821, HX – 18 Brand Hall, Heron Rd, Oldbury, Warley 552 7475, BU – 9 Harborne Church Farm, Vicarage Rd, Harborne 427 1204, EX.

Birmingham Airport : 767 5511, E : 6½ m. by A 45 DU.

Convention & Visitor Bureau, 2 City Arcade, B2 4TX 643 2514 – Convention & Visitor Bureau, National Exhibition Centre, B40 1NT 780 4321 – Birmingham Airport, Information Desk, B26 3QJ 767 7145/7146.

♦London 122 – ♦Bristol 91 – ♦Liverpool 103 – ♦Manchester 86 – ♦Nottingham 50.

Town plans : Birmingham pp. 2-7
Except where otherwise stated see pp. 6 and 7

Hyatt Regency, 2 Bridge St., B1 2JZ, 643 1234, Telex 335097, Fax 616 2323, ≤, ₺, ≘s, ☒ – ⛓ ⇔ rm ▤ ☑ ☎ ⇔ – 🏃 250. AE ① VISA. ✻ JZ **a**
Meals (see ***Number 282*** below) – ☐ 12.00 – **315 rm** 99.00 **st.**, 4 suites – SB.

Swallow, 12 Hagley Rd, B16 8SJ, 452 1144, Fax 456 3442, ₺, ☒ – ⛓ ⇔ rm ▤ ☑ ☎ ♿ Ⓟ – 🏃 25. AE ① VISA p. 4 FX **c**
Langtrys : **Meals** (closed Sunday and Bank Holidays) a la carte 22.65/32.90 **st.** 8.00 – (see also ***Sir Edward Elgar's*** below) – **94 rm** ☐ 125.00/145.00 **st.**, 4 suites – SB.

Midland, 128 New St., B2 4JT, 643 2601, Telex 338419, Fax 628 5005 – ⛓ ☑ ☎ – 🏃 200 KZ **r**
109 rm, 2 suites.

Holiday Inn, Central Sq., Holliday St., B1 1HH, 631 2000, Fax 643 9018, ₺, ≘s, ☒ – ⛓ ⇔ rm ▤ ☑ ☎ ♿ Ⓟ – 🏃 150. AE ① VISA JZ **z**
Meals 9.50/17.00 **st.** and a la carte – ☐ 9.95 – **284 rm** 99.00/108.00 **st.**, 3 suites.

Copthorne, Paradise Circus, B3 3HJ, 200 2727, Telex 339026, Fax 200 1197, ₺, ≘s, ☒ – ⛓ ⇔ rm ▤ rest ☑ ☎ ♿ Ⓟ – 🏃 180 JZ **e**
209 rm, 3 suites.

Jonathan's, 16-24 Wolverhampton Rd, Oldbury, B68 0LH, W : 4 m. by A 456 429 3757, Fax 434 3107, « Authentic Victorian furnishings and memorabilia » – ⇔ rest ☑ ☎ Ⓟ. AE ① VISA. ✻ p. 2 BU **e**
Meals - English (closed Sunday dinner) 12.50/30.00 **t.** and a la carte 5.75 – **19 rm** ☐ 69.00/80.00 **st.** 11 suites – SB.

Grand (Q.M.H.), Colmore Row, B3 2DA, 236 7951, Fax 233 1465 – ⛓ ⇔ rm ▤ rest ☑ ☎ – 🏃 500. AE ① VISA JKY **c**
closed 27 to 31 December – **Meals** (bar lunch Saturday) 12.00/18.00 **st.** and a la carte. 4.75 – ☐ 9.50 – **171 rm** 85.00/100.00 **st.**, 2 suites – SB.

Plough and Harrow (Forte), 135 Hagley Rd, Edgbaston, B16 8LS, 454 4111, Fax 454 1868, ⚘ – ⛓ ⇔ ☑ ☎ Ⓟ – 🏃 70. AE ① VISA JCB p. 4 EX **a**
Meals *(closed Saturday lunch)* 11.25/16.95 **t.** and a la carte 5.50 – ☐ 8.50 – **42 rm** 70.00/78.00 **st.**, 2 suites – SB.

Forte Crest, Smallbrook Queensway, B5 4EW, 643 8171, Fax 631 2528, ₺, ≘s, ☒, squash – ⛓ ⇔ rm ▤ ☑ ☎ Ⓟ – 🏃 630 KZ **o**
252 rm, 1 suite.

Strathallan Thistle (Mt. Charlotte Thistle), 225 Hagley Rd, Edgbaston, B16 9RY, 455 9777, Telex 336680, Fax 454 9432 – ⛓ ⇔ rm ▤ rest ☑ ☎ Ⓟ – 🏃 200. AE ① VISA JCB p. 4 EX **i**
Meals *(closed Saturday lunch)* 9.25/17.25 **t.** and a la carte 5.25 – ☐ 8.95 – **163 rm** 75.00/85.00 **t.**, 4 suites – SB.

Novotel, 70 Broad St., B1 2HT, 643 2000, Telex 335556, Fax 643 9796, ₺, ≘s – ⛓ ⇔ rm ▤ rest ☑ ☎ ♿ Ⓟ – 🏃 300. AE ① VISA p. 4 FV **a**
Meals 12.00/14.00 **st.** and a la carte 4.95 – ☐ 7.50 – **148 rm** 69.00/79.00 **st.**

Chamberlain, Alcester St., B12 0PJ, 606 9000, Fax 606 9001 – ⛓ ⇔ rest ▤ rest ☑ ☎ ⇔ – 🏃 400. AE ① VISA. ✻ FX **r**
Meals *(closed Saturday lunch)* (carving rest.) 5.00/7.50 **st.** – **250 rm** 35.00 **st.**

Royal Angus Thistle (Mt. Charlotte Thistle), St. Chad's, Queensway, B4 6HY, 236 4211, Telex 336889, Fax 233 2195 – ⛓ ⇔ rm ☑ ☎ Ⓟ – 🏃 140 KY **s**
131rm, 2 suites.

Apollo (Mt. Charlotte Thistle), 243 Hagley Rd, Edgbaston, B16 9RA, 455 0271, Telex 336759, Fax 456 2394 – ⛓ ⇔ rm ▤ rest ☑ ☎ Ⓟ – 🏃 150. AE ① VISA JCB
Meals *(closed Saturday lunch)* (carving lunch) 9.95/12.80 **st.** and a la carte 5.20 – ☐ 8.75 – **124 rm** 53.00/85.00 **st.**, 2 suites – SB. p. 4 EX **o**

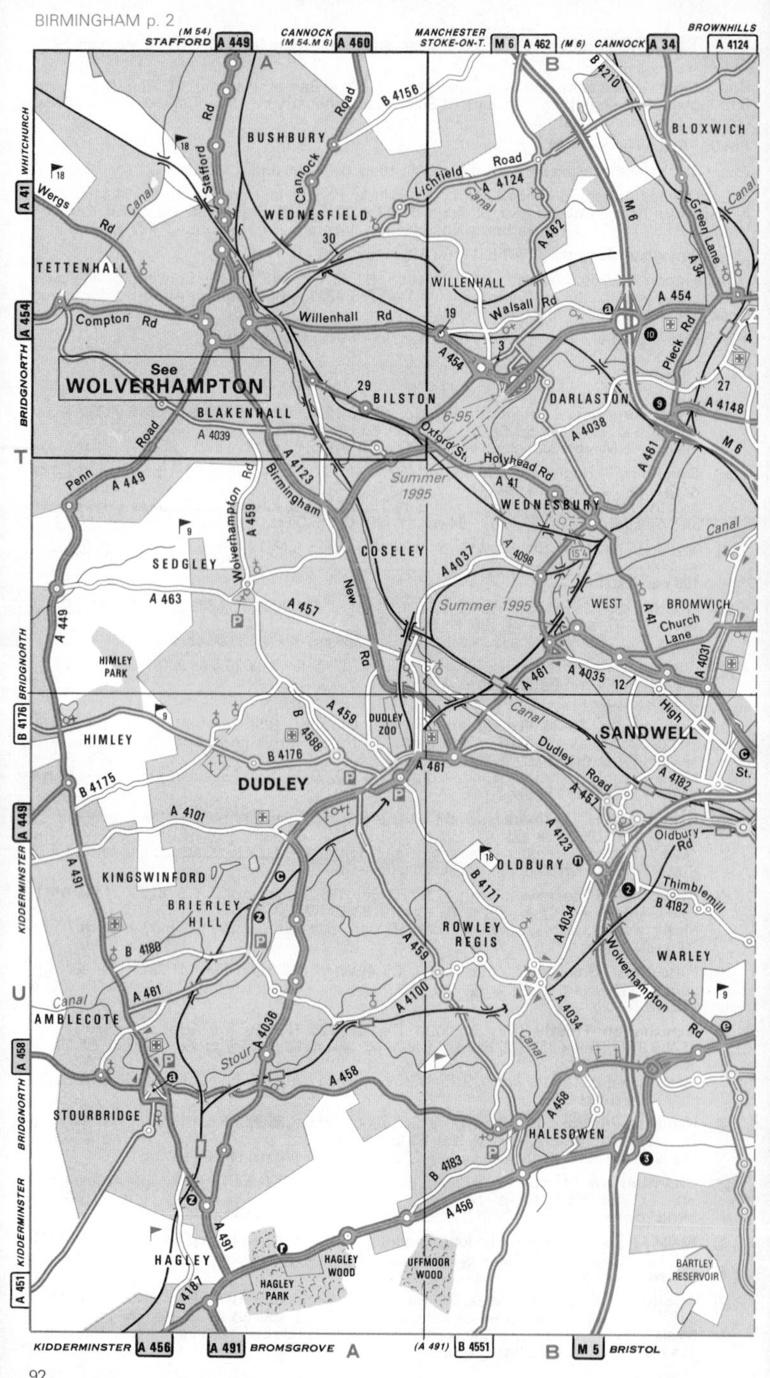
(M 54) STAFFORD A 449
CANNOCK (M 54.M 6) A 460
MANCHESTER STOKE-ON-T. M 6 A 462 (M 6)
CANNOCK A 34
BROWNHILLS A 4124
WHITCHURCH A 41
BRIDGNORTH A 454
BRIDGNORTH B 4176
KIDDERMINSTER A 449
BRIDGNORTH A 458
KIDDERMINSTER A 451
KIDDERMINSTER A 456
A 491 BROMSGROVE
(A 491) B 4551
M 5 BRISTOL
BUSHBURY
WEDNESFIELD
BLOXWICH
TETTENHALL
WILLENHALL
See WOLVERHAMPTON
BLAKENHALL
BILSTON
DARLASTON
WEDNESBURY
SEDGLEY
COSELEY
WEST BROMWICH
HIMLEY PARK
HIMLEY
DUDLEY
DUDLEY ZOO
SANDWELL
KINGSWINFORD
BRIERLEY HILL
OLDBURY
ROWLEY REGIS
WARLEY
AMBLECOTE
STOURBRIDGE
HALESOWEN
HAGLEY
HAGLEY PARK
HAGLEY WOOD
UFFMOOR WOOD
BARTLEY RESERVOIR
Summer 1995
6-95
Wergs Rd
Compton Rd
Stafford Rd
Cannock Road
Lichfield Road
Willenhall Rd
Walsall Rd
Green Lane
Pleck Rd
Penn Road
Wolverhampton Rd
Birmingham New Rd
Oxford St.
Holyhead Rd
Church Lane
High St.
Dudley Road
Oldbury Rd
Thimblemill
Wolverhampton Rd
Canal
Stour

BIRMINGHAM AND WOLVERHAMPTON

ENLARGED AREA

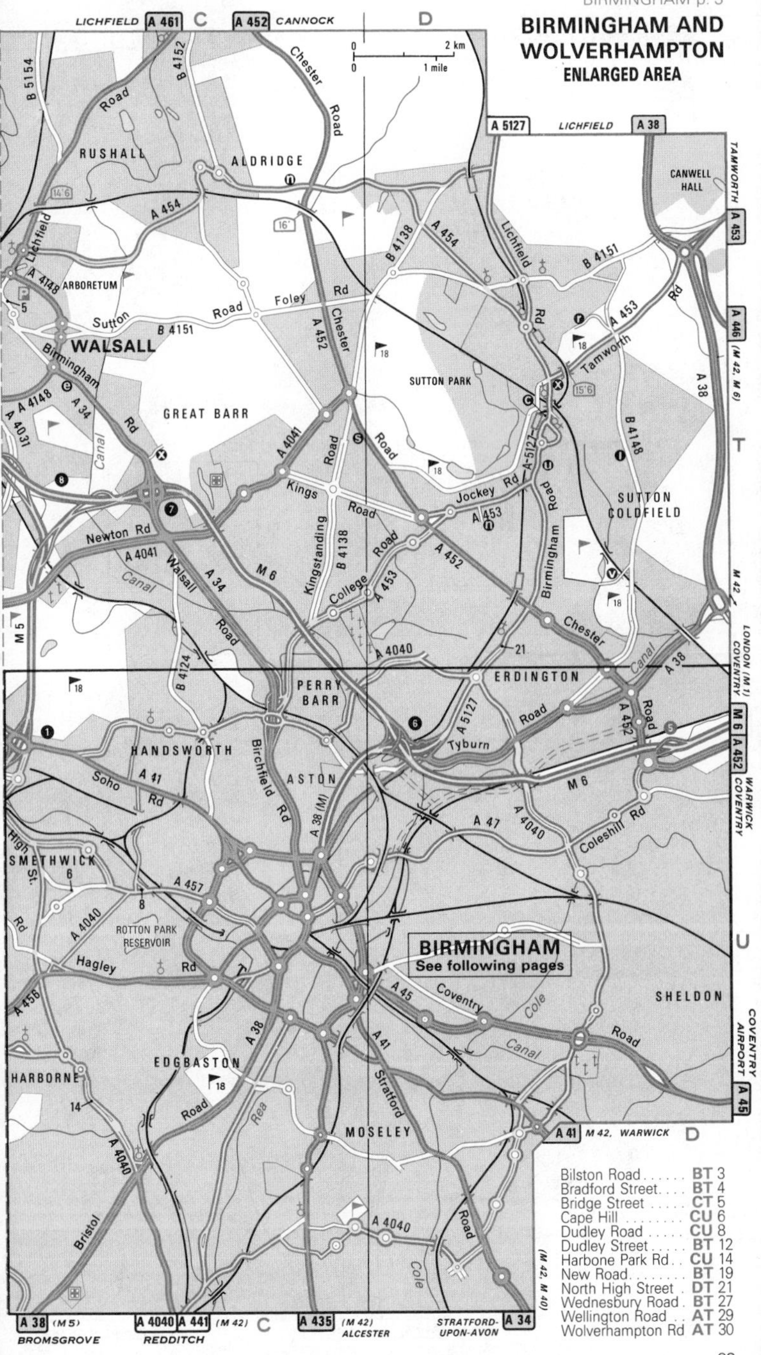

Street	Grid	No.
Bilston Road	BT	3
Bradford Street	BT	4
Bridge Street	CT	5
Cape Hill	CU	6
Dudley Road	CU	8
Dudley Street	BT	12
Harbone Park Rd	CU	14
New Road	BT	19
North High Street	DT	21
Wednesbury Road	BT	27
Wellington Road	AT	29
Wolverhampton Rd	AT	30

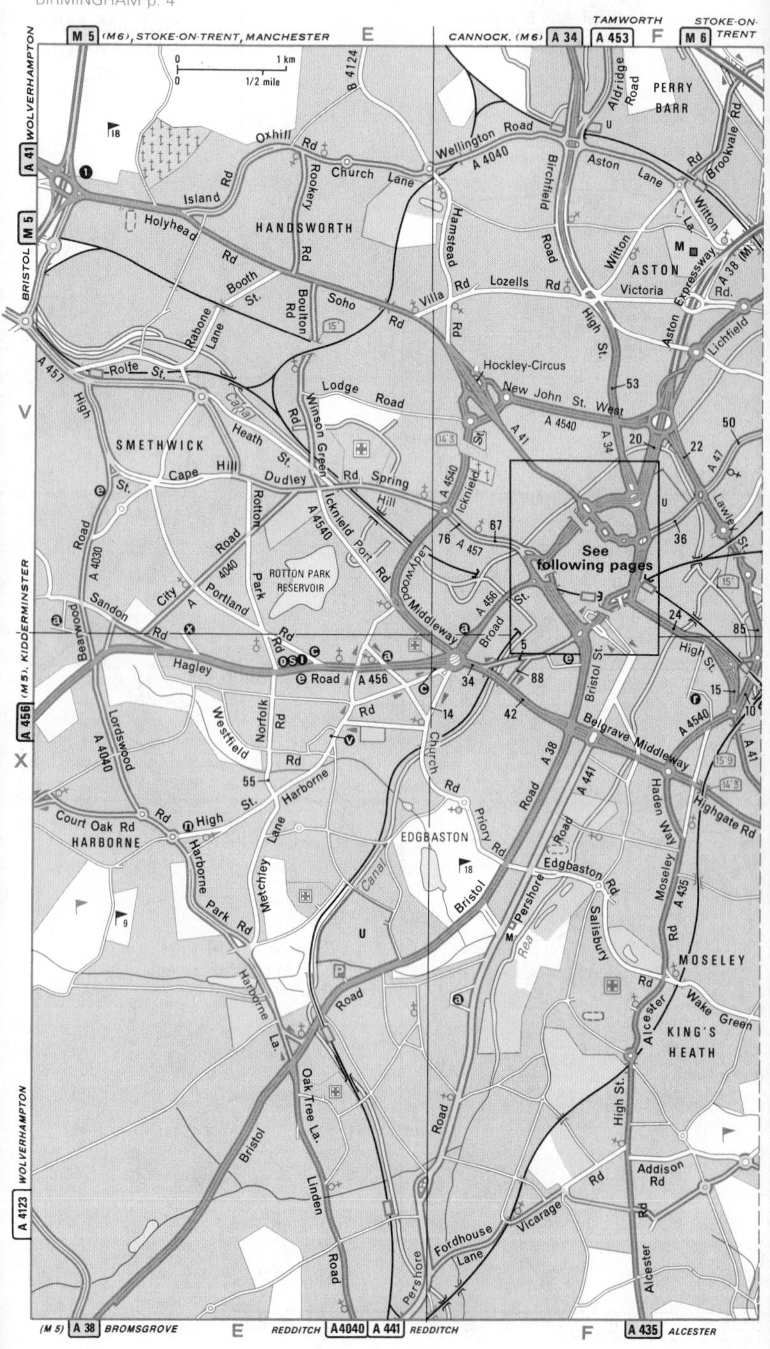
M 5 (M6), STOKE-ON-TRENT, MANCHESTER
CANNOCK (M6) A 34
TAMWORTH A 453
M 6 STOKE-ON-TRENT
PERRY BARR
HANDSWORTH
ASTON
SMETHWICK
ROTTON PARK RESERVOIR
See following pages
EDGBASTON
HARBORNE
MOSELEY
KING'S HEATH
A 41 WOLVERHAMPTON
M 5 BRISTOL
A 456 (M 5), KIDDERMINSTER
A 4123 WOLVERHAMPTON
(M 5) A 38 BROMSGROVE
REDDITCH A4040 A 441 REDDITCH
A 435 ALCESTER

BUILT UP AREA

Bath Row .... FX 5
Bordesley Middleway .... FX 10
Calthorpe Rd .... FX 14
Camp Hill .... FX 15
Corporation St. .... FV 20
Darmouth Middleway .... FV 22
Digbeth .... FV 24
Dudley Park Rd .... GX 25
High St. .... GV 31
Islington Row Middleway .... FX 34
Jennen's Rd .... FV 36
Lee Bank Middleway .... FX 42
Nechell's Parkway .... FV 50
New Town Row .... FV 53
Nursery Rd .... EX 55
Saltley Rd .... GV 66
Sand Pits Parade .... FV 67
Solihull Lane .... GX 74
Summer Hill Rd .... FV 76
Watery Lane .... FV 85
Westley Rd .... GX 87
Wheeley's Lane .... FX 88

For Street Index see Birmingham p. 7

CENTRE

Albert St. . . . . **KZ** 2
Bull St. . . . . **KY** 13
Dale End . . . . **KZ** 21
Hall St. . . . . **JY** 29
Holloway Circus . . . . **JZ** 32
James Watt Queensway . . **KY** 35
Jennen's Rd . . . . **KY** 36
Lancaster Circus . . . . **KY** 39
Lancaster St. . . . . **KY** 41
Masshouse Circus . . . . **KY** 43
Moor St. Queensway . . . . . **KZ** 46
Navigation St. . . . . **JZ** 49
Newton St. . . . . **KY** 52
Paradise Circus . . . . **JZ** 56
Priory Queensway. . . . . **KY** 57
St Chads Circus . . . . **JKY** 62
St Chads Ringway . . . . **KY** 63
St Martin's Circus . . . . **KZ** 64
Shadwell St. . . . . **KY** 70
Smallbrook Queensway . . . **KZ** 71
Snow Hill Queensway . . . . **KY** 73
Summer Row. . . . . **JY** 77
Temple Row . . . . **KZ** 80
Waterloo St. . . . . **JZ** 84

For Street Index
see Birmingham p. 7

« Short Breaks » (SB)

Many hotels now offer a special rate for a stay of 2 nights which includes dinner, bed and breakfast.

STREET INDEX TO BIRMINGHAM TOWN PLANS

Bull Ring Centre p. 6 **KZ**
Corporation St. p. 6 **KYZ**
New St. p. 6 **JKZ**
Paradise Forum
Shopping Centre p. 6 **JZ**

Addison Rd p. 4 **FX**
Albert St. p. 6 **KZ** 2
Alcester Rd p. 4 **FX**
Aldridge Rd p. 4 **FV**
Alum Rock Rd p. 5 **GV**
Aston Expressway p. 4 **FV**
Aston Lane p. 4 **FV**
Aston St. p. 6 **KY**
Bath Row p. 4 **FX** 5
Bearwood Rd p. 4 **EV**
Belgrave Middleway p. 4 **FX**
Birchfield Rd p. 4 **FV**
Booth St. p. 4 **EV**
Bordesley Green p. 5 **GV**
Bordesley Green Rd p. 5 **GV**
Bordesley Middleway p. 4 **FX** 10
Boulton Rd p. 4 **EV**
Bowyer Rd p. 5 **GV**
Bradford Rd p. 5 **HV**
Bristol Rd p. 4 **EX**
Bristol St. p. 4 **FX**
Broad St. p. 4 **FV**
Bromford Lane p. 5 **GV**
Bromford Rd p. 5 **HV**
Brook Lane p. 5 **GX**
Brookvale Rd p. 4 **FV**
Bull Ring p. 6 **KZ**
Bull Ring Centre p. 6 **KZ**
Bull St. p. 6 **KY** 13
Calthorpe Rd p. 4 **FX** 14
Camp Hill p. 4 **FX** 15
Cape Hill p. 4 **EV**
Caroline St. p. 6 **JY**
Cattell Rd p. 5 **GV**
Centenary Square p. 6 **JZ**
Charlotte St p. 6 **JY**
Chester Rd p. 5 **HV**
Church Lane p. 4 **EV**
Church Rd
EDGBASTON p. 4 **FX**
Church Rd SHELDON p. 5 **HX**
Church Rd YARDLEY p. 5 **HX**
Church St. p. 6 **JY**
City Rd p. 4 **EV**
Coleshill Rd p. 5 **HV**
College Rd p. 5 **GX**
Colmore Circus p. 6 **KY**
Colmore Row p. 6 **JZ**
Commercial St. p. 6 **JZ**
Constitution Hill p. 6 **JY**
Corporation St. p. 4 **FV** 20
Court Oak Rd p. 4 **EX**
Coventry Rd p. 5 **GX**
Dale End p. 6 **KZ** 21
Darmouth
Middleway p. 4 **FV** 22
Digbeth p. 4 **FV** 24
Dudley Park Rd p. 5 **GX** 25
Dudley Rd p. 4 **EV**
Edgbaston Rd p. 4 **FX**
Edmund St. p. 6 **JYZ**
Fordhouse Lane p. 4 **FX**
Fox Hollies Rd p. 5 **GX**
Golden Hillock Rd p. 5 **GX**
Gravelly Hill p. 5 **GV**
Gravelly Hill Junction p. 5 **GV**
Great Charles St. p. 6 **JY**
Hadden Way p. 4 **FX**
Hagley Rd p. 4 **EX**
Hall St. p. 6 **JY** 29
Hampstead Rd p. 4 **FV**
Harborne Lane p. 4 **EX**
Harborne Park Rd p. 4 **EX**
Harborne Rd p. 4 **EX**
Heath St. p. 4 **EV**
Highfield Rd p. 5 **GX**
Highfield Rd SALTLEY p. 5 **GV**
Highgate Rd p. 4 **FX**
High St. p. 6 **KZ**
High St. ASTON p. 4 **FV**
High St.
BORDESLEY p. 4 **FX**
High St. HARBORNE p. 4 **EX**
High St.
KING'S HEATH p. 4 **FX**
High St. SALTLEY p. 5 **GV** 31
High St. SMETHWICK p. 4 **EV**
Hill St. p. 6 **JZ**
Hob's Moat Rd p. 5 **HX**
Hockley Circus p. 4 **FV**
Hockley Hill p. 6 **JY**
Holliday St. p. 6 **JZ**
Holloway Circus p. 6 **JZ** 32
Holloway Head p. 6 **JZ**
Holyhead Rd p. 4 **EV**
Hurst St. p. 6 **KZ**
Icknield Port Rd p. 4 **EV**
Icknield St. p. 4 **FV**
Island Rd p. 4 **EV**
Islington Row
Middleway p. 4 **FX** 34
James Watt
Queensway p. 6 **KY** 35
Jennen's Rd p. 4 **FV** 36
Kingsbury Rd p. 5 **HV**
Ladywood Middleway p. 4 **EV**
Lancaster Circus p. 6 **KY** 39
Lancaster St. p. 6 **KY** 41
Lawley St. p. 4 **FV**
Lee Bank Middleway p. 4 **FX** 42
Lichfield Rd p. 4 **FV**
Linden Rd p. 4 **EX**
Livery St. p. 6 **JY**
Lodge Rd p. 4 **EV**
Lordswood Rd p. 4 **EX**
Lozells Rd p. 4 **FV**
Ludgate Hill p. 6 **JY**
Masshouse Circus p. 6 **KY** 43
Metchley Lane p. 4 **EX**
Moor St. Queensway p. 6 **KZ** 46
Moseley Rd p. 4 **FX**
Navigation St. p. 6 **JZ** 49
Nechell's Parkway p. 4 **FV** 50
Newhall St. p. 6 **JY**
New John St. West p. 4 **FV**
Newport Rd p. 5 **HV**
New St. p. 6 **JZ**
Newton St. p. 6 **KY** 52
New Town Row p. 4 **FV** 53
Norfolk Rd p. 4 **EX**
Nursery Rd p. 4 **EX** 55
Oak Tree Lane p. 4 **EX**
Olton Bd East p. 5 **GX**
Oxhill Rd p. 4 **EV**
Paradise Circus p. 6 **JZ** 56
Park St. p. 6 **KZ**
Pershore Rd p. 4 **FX**
Pershore St. p. 6 **KZ**
Portland Rd p. 4 **EV**
Princip St. p. 6 **KY**
Priory Queensway p. 6 **KY** 57
Priory Rd p. 4 **FX**
Rabone Lane p. 4 **EV**
Richmond Rd p. 5 **HX**
Robin Hood Lane p. 5 **GX**
Rolfe St. p. 4 **EV**
Rookery Rd p. 4 **EV**
Rotton Park Rd p. 4 **EV**
St Chads Circus p. 6 **JY** 62
St Chads Ringway p. 6 **KY** 63
St Martin's Circus p. 6 **KZ** 64
St Paul's Square p. 6 **JY**
Salisbury Rd p. 4 **FX**
Saltley Rd p. 5 **GV** 66
Sandon Rd p. 4 **EV**
Sand Pits Parade p. 4 **FV** 67
Severn St. p. 6 **JZ**
Shadwell St. p. 6 **KY** 70
Shaftmoor Lane p. 5 **GX**
Sheaf Lane p. 5 **HX**
Sheldon Heath Rd p. 5 **HX**
Shirley Rd p. 5 **GX**
Smallbrook
Queensway p. 6 **KZ** 71
Small Heath Highway p. 5 **GX**
Snow Hill Queensway p. 6 **KY** 73
Soho Rd p. 4 **EV**
Solihull Lane p. 5 **GX** 74
Spring Hill p. 4 **EV**
Station Rd p. 5 **HV**
Stechford Lane p. 5 **HV**
Steelhouse Lane p. 6 **KY**
Stockfield Rd p. 5 **GX**
Stoney La. MOSELEY p. 5 **GX**
Stoney La. SHELDON p. 5 **HX**
Stratford Rd p. 5 **GX**
Suffolk St. p. 6 **JZ**
Summer Hill Rd p. 4 **FV** 76
Summer Row p. 6 **JY** 77
Temple Row p. 6 **KZ** 80
Tyburn Rd p. 5 **GV**
Vicarage Rd p. 4 **FX**
Victoria Rd p. 4 **FV**
Villa Rd p. 4 **FV**
Wagon Lane p. 5 **HX**
Wake Green Rd p. 4 **FX**
Warwick Rd p. 5 **GX**
Washwood Heath Rd p. 5 **GV**
Waterloo St. p. 6 **JZ** 84
Watery Lane p. 4 **FV** 85
Wellington Rd p. 4 **FV**
Westfield Rd p. 4 **EX**
Westley Rd p. 5 **GX** 87
Wheeley's Lane p. 4 **FX** 88
Whittal St p. 6 **KY**
Winson Green Rd p. 4 **EV**
Witton Lane p. 4 **FV**
Witton Rd p. 4 **FV**
Wood End Rd p. 5 **GV**
Yardley Rd p. 5 **HX**
Yardley Wood Rd p. 5 **GX**

«Short Breaks» (SB)

De nombreux hôtels proposent des conditions avantageuses pour un séjour de deux nuits comprenant la chambre, le dîner et le petit déjeuner.

Asquith House, 19 Portland Rd, off Hagley Rd, Edgbaston, B16 9HN, ☎ 454 5282, Fax 456 4668, « Attractive furnishings », – TV ☎. VISA. p. 4 EX **c**
closed Christmas – **Meals** (by arrangement Sunday dinner and Bank Holidays) 16.15/29.95 **t.** and a la carte 4.00 – **10 rm** 50.60/61.80 **t.**

Westbourne Lodge, 27-29 Fountain Rd, Edgbaston, B17 8NJ, ☎ 429 1003, Fax 429 1003, – TV ☎ P. VISA p. 4 EV **x**
Meals 9.95/15.95 **st.** 4.80 – **18 rm** 39.50/56.00 **st.** – SB.

Copperfield House, 60 Upland Rd, Selly Park, B29 7JS, ☎ 472 8344, Fax 472 8344, – rest TV ☎ P. VISA p. 4 FX **a**
Meals (bar lunch)/dinner 15.95 **st.** – **17 rm** 47.50/69.50 **st.** – SB.

Bearwood Court, 360-366 Bearwood Rd, Bearwood, B66 4ET, ☎ 429 9731, Fax 429 6175 – TV ☎ P. VISA. EV **e**
Meals (bar lunch)/dinner 10.50 **st.** and a la carte 3.50 – **24 rm** 28.00/46.00 **st.**

Travel Inn, 20-22 Bridge St., B1 2JH, ☎ 633 4820, Fax 633 4779 – rm TV P – 40. VISA. JZ **c**
Meals (Beefeater grill) a la carte approx. 16.00 **t.** – 4.95 – **54 rm** 33.50 **t.**

New Cobden (Friendly), 166-174 Hagley Rd, Edgbaston, B16 9NZ, ☎ 454 6621, Fax 456 2935, – rm TV ☎ P – 100. VISA. p. 4 EX **e**
Meals 13.50 **st.** and dinner a la carte 5.50 – 6.75 – **230 rm** 54.75/70.00 **st.** – SB.

Hagley Court, 229 Hagley Rd, Edgbaston, B16 9RP, ☎ 454 6514, Fax 456 2722 – TV ☎ P. VISA. p. 4 EX **s**
closed 24 December-2 January – **Meals** *(closed Friday to Sunday)* (dinner only) 13.50 **st.** and a la carte 4.50 – **27 rm** 43.00/64.00 **st.** – SB.

Campanile, 55 Irving St., B1 1DH, ☎ 622 4925, Fax 622 4195 – TV ☎ P – 25. VISA. p. 4 FX **e**
Meals (grill rest.) 9.85 **t.** 4.65 – 4.25 – **47 rm** 35.75 **t.**

XXXX **Sir Edward Elgar's** (at Swallow H.), 12 Hagley Rd, B16 8SJ, ☎ 452 1144, Fax 456 3442 – P. VISA p. 4 FX **c**
closed Saturday lunch – **Meals** 16.50/30.00 **st.** and a la carte 8.00.

XXX Sloans, 27-29 Chad Sq., Hawthorne Rd, Edgbaston, B15 3TQ, ☎ 455 6697, Fax 454 4335 p. 4 EX **v**

XX **Number 282** (at Hyatt Regency H.), 2 Bridge St., B1 2JZ, ☎ 643 1234, Fax 616 2323 – . VISA JZ **a**
Meals 12.75/50.00 **st.** and a la carte.

XX **Henry's,** 27 St. Paul's Sq., B3 1RB, ☎ 200 1136 – . VISA JY **a**
closed Sunday and Bank Holidays – **Meals** - Chinese (Canton) 13.00 **t.** and a la carte 5.80.

XX **Dynasty,** 93-103 Hurst St., B5 4TE, ☎ 622 1410 – VISA KZ **e**
closed 25 and 26 December – **Meals** - Chinese 10.00 **t.** (dinner) and a la carte approx. 14.60 **t.**

XX **Henry Wong,** 283 High St., Harborne, B17 9QH, ☎ 427 9799 – . VISA p. 4 EX **n**
closed Sunday and Bank Holidays – **Meals** - Chinese (Canton) 13.00 **t.** and a la carte 5.80.

XX **Maharaja,** 23-25 Hurst St., B5 4AS, ☎ 622 2641 – . VISA KZ **i**
closed last week July – **Meals** - North Indian 7.50/10.75 and a la carte.

XX **Franzl's,** 151 Milcote Rd, Bearwood, Smethwick, B67 5BN, ☎ 429 7920, Fax 429 1615 – VISA p. 4 EV **a**
closed Sunday, Monday and first 3 weeks August – **Meals** - Austrian (dinner only) 12.95/19.65 **t.** 4.50.

at Hall Green SE : 5 ¾ m. by A 41 on A 34 – ✉ Birmingham – 0121 :

Robin Hood (Toby), Stratford Rd, B28 9ES, ☎ 745 9900, Fax 733 1075 – rm TV ☎ P GX **a**
Meals (grill rest.) – **30 rm.**

at Birmingham Airport SE : 9 m. by A 45 – DU – ✉ Birmingham – 0121 :

Novotel, Passenger Terminal, B26 3QL, ☎ 782 7000, Telex 338158, Fax 782 0445 – rm rest TV ☎ – 35. VISA
closed 25 December – **Meals** a la carte 12.40/23.40 **st.** 4.95 – 7.50 – **195 rm** 69.00/121.00 **st.**

Forte Posthouse, Coventry Rd, B26 3QW, on A 45 ☎ 782 8141, Fax 782 2476 – rm TV ☎ P – 150. VISA JCB
Meals a la carte approx. 15.00 **t.** 5.50 – **136 rm** 56.00/69.50 **st.**

at National Exhibition Centre SE : 9 ½ m. on A 45 – DU – ✉ Birmingham – 0121 :

Birmingham Metropole, Bickenhill, B40 1PP, ☎ 780 4242, Telex 336129, Fax 780 3923 – rm TV ☎ P – 2 000. VISA
Terrace : **Meals** French – ***Primavera :*** **Meals** Italian – **787 rm** 135.00/205.00 **t.**, 15 suites – SB.

Arden, Coventry Rd, B92 0EH, ☎ (01675) 443221, Fax 443221, – TV ☎ P – 200. VISA
Meals (bar lunch Saturday) 13.00/15.00 **t.** and a la carte 4.85 – 7.00 – **146 rm** 65.00/89.50 **t.**

at Northfield SW : 6 m. by A 38 – CU – ✉ Birmingham – ☎ 0121 :

Norwood, 87-89 Bunbury Rd, B31 2ET, via Church rd ☎ 411 2202, Fax 411 2202, – TV ☎ P. AE VISA
closed 24 to 26 December – **Meals** *(closed Sunday and Bank Holidays)* (dinner only) 15.00 5.00 – **15 rm** 54.75/59.75 **st.**

at Oldbury W : 7 ¾ m. by A 456 on A 4123 – ✉ Birmingham – ☎ 0121 :

Forte Travelodge without rest., Wolverhampton Rd, B69 2BH, on A 4123 ☎ 552 2967, Reservations (Freephone) 0800 850950 – TV P. AE VISA. p. 2 BU **n**
33 rm 33.50 **t.**

at Great Barr NW : 6 m. on A 34 – ✉ Birmingham – ☎ 0121 :

Forte Posthouse, Chapel Lane, B43 7BG, ☎ 357 7444, Fax 357 7503, – rm TV ☎ P – 120. AE VISA JCB. CT **x**
Meals a la carte approx. 15.00 **t.** 5.50 – **192 rm** 56.00/69.50 **st.**

at West Bromwich NW : 6 m. on A 41 – ✉ Birmingham – ☎ 0121 :

Moat House Birmingham (Q.M.H.) Birmingham Rd, B70 6RS, ☎ 553 6111, Fax 525 7403 – rm rest TV ☎ P – 180. AE VISA JCB BU **c**
Meals 9.95/14.50 **st.** and a la carte 5.75 – 8.50 – **172 rm** 64.50/72.00 **st.** – SB.

MICHELIN Distribution Centre, Valepits Rd, Garrett's Green, B33 0YD, ☎ 789 7100, Fax 789 7323 p. 5 HX

ATS 1558 Pershore Rd., Stirchley ☎ 458 2951
ATS 158 Slade Rd, Erdington ☎ 327 2783
ATS 1189 Chester Rd, Erdington ☎ 373 6104/382 7533
ATS 94 Aldrige Rd, Perry Barr ☎ 356 5925/6632
ATS 314 Bearwood Rd, Bearwood ☎ 420 2000
ATS 427 Bordesley Green, Bordesley Green ☎ 772 6514
ATS 43 Whitmore Rd, Small Heath ☎ 772 2571
ATS 341 Dudley Rd, Winson Green ☎ 454 2588/2536
ATS Dudley Rd, Halesowen ☎ 550 2464
ATS 947 Bristol Rd South, Northfield ☎ 475 1244
ATS Bromford Rd, Oldbury, West Bromwich ☎ 552 6131
ATS 87 Old Meeting St., West Bromwich ☎ 553 3495

BIRTLE Gtr. Manchester – see Bury.

BISHOP AUCKLAND Durham 401 402 P 20 – pop. 23 560 – ECD : Wednesday – ☎ 01388.

High Plains, Durham Rd ☎ 602198 – Aycliffe, School Aycliffe Lane, Newton Aycliffe ☎ (01325) 310820 – Woodham G. & C.C., Burnhill Way, Newton Aycliffe ☎ (01325) 318346.

London 253 – Carlisle 73 – Middlesbrough 24 – Newcastle upon Tyne 28 – Sunderland 25.

Park Head, Park View Terrace, New Coundon, DL14 8QB, NE : 1 ¾ m. by A 689 on A 688 ☎ 661727, Fax 661727 – TV ☎ P. AE VISA
Meals (carving lunch Sunday) 5.95/11.95 **t.** and a la carte 3.75 – **31 rm** 42.00/85.00 **st.** – SB.

ATS Cockton Hill ☎ 603681

BISHOPS FROME Heref. and Worcs. – see Ledbury.

BISHOP'S HULL Somerset – see Taunton.

BISHOP'S STORTFORD Herts. 404 U 28 – pop. 22 535 – ECD : Wednesday – ☎ 01279.

Stansted Airport : ☎ 680500, NE : 3 ½ m..

The Old Monastery, Windhill, CM23 2ND ☎ 652274 ext : 251.

London 34 – Cambridge 27 – Chelmsford 19 – Colchester 33.

The Cottage, 71 Birchanger Lane, CM23 5QA, NE : 2 ¼ m. by B 1383 on Birchanger rd ☎ 812349, « Part 17C and 18C cottages », – TV P. VISA.
Meals (by arrangement) 11.00 **st.** 4.00 – **15 rm** 28.00/44.00 **st.**

at Hatfield Heath SE : 6 m. on A 1060 – ✉ Bishop's Stortford – ☎ 01279 :

Down Hall Country House, CM22 7AS, S : 1 ½ m. ☎ 731441, Fax 730416, ←, « 19C Italianate mansion », park, – TV ☎ P – 200. AE VISA JCB.
Meals 15.50/17.50 **t.** and a la carte – 9.25 – **103 rm** 80.00/135.00 **st.** – SB.

ATS 14 Burnt Mill, Harlow ☎ 421965

BISHOP'S TAWTON Devon 403 H30 – see Barnstaple.

BITTON Avon 403 404 M 29 – see Bath.

BLABY Leics. 402 403 404 Q 26 – pop. 6 538 pop. 7 030 – ☎ 0116.

London 100 – Coventry 10 – Leicester 4 – Northampton 38.

Time Out, 15 Enderby Rd, LE8 3GD, ☎ 278 7898, Fax 278 7898, – TV ☎ P – 40. AE VISA.
closed 26 to 30 December – **Meals** *(closed Saturday lunch and Sunday dinner)* 11.95/15.95 **t.** and a la carte – **25 rm** 59.50/79.50 **st.** – SB.

BLACKBURN Lancs. 402 M 22 – pop. 136 612 – ECD : Thursday – ☎ 01254.

18 Pleasington ☎ 202177 – 18 Wilpshire, 72 Whalley Rd ☎ 248260/249691 – 9 Great Harwood, Harwood Bar ☎ 884391.

King George's Hall, Northgate, BB2 1AA ☎ 53277.

London 228 – Leeds 47 – Liverpool 39 – Manchester 24 – Preston 11.

Blackburn Moat House (Q.M.H.), Yew Tree Drive, Preston New Rd, BB2 7BE, NW : 2 m. at junction of A 677 with A 6119 ☎ 264441, Telex 63271, Fax 682435 – rm – 350
96 rm, 2 suites.

at Mellor NW : 4 m. by A 677 – ✉ Blackburn – ☎ 01254 :

Millstone, Church Lane, BB2 7JR, ☎ 813333, Fax 812628 – rm. AE VISA
Meals *(closed Saturday lunch)* 11.95/18.00 **st.** and a la carte 6.95 – **20 rm** 59.00/88.00 **st.**, 1 suite – SB.

at Langho N : 4½ m. on A 666 – ✉ Whalley – ☎ 01254 :

XXX **Northcote Manor** with rm, Northcote Rd, BB6 8BE, N : ½ m. on A 59 at junction with A 666 ☎ 240555, Fax 246568, – . AE VISA.
closed 1 January – **Meals** 16.00/27.00 **t.** and a la carte – **14 rm** 64.00/95.00 **t.** – SB.

at Balderstone NW : 6½ m. by A 677 off A 59 – ✉ Blackburn – ☎ 01254 :

Boddington Arms, Myerscough Rd, BB2 7LE, on A 59 ☎ 813900, Fax 814079 – . AE VISA.
Meals (grill rest.) 6.00/11.00 **t.** and a la carte – 4.95 – **20 rm** 45.00 **st.**

ATS Pendle St., Copy Nook ☎ 55963/59272/665115

Prices For full details of the prices quoted in the guide, consult the introduction.

BLACKPOOL Lancs. 402 K 22 **Great Britain G.** – pop. 146 069 – ECD : Wednesday – ☎ 01253.
See : Tower★ *AC* AY **A**.

18 Blackpool Park, North Park Drive ☎ 393960, BY – 9 Poulton-le-Fylde, Myrtle Farm, Breck Rd ☎ 892444.

Blackpool Airport : ☎ 343434, S : 3 m. by A 584.

1 Clifton St., FY1 1LY ☎ 321623/325212 – 87a Coronation St., FY1 4PD ☎ 321891 – Pleasure Beach, 525 Ocean Boulevard, South Promenade, FY4 1PL ☎ 403223 (summer only).

London 246 – Leeds 88 – Liverpool 56 – Manchester 51 – Middlesbrough 123.

Plan opposite

Imperial (Forte), North Promenade, FY1 2HB, ☎ 23971, Fax 751784, ≤, – rm – 400. AE VISA JCB AY **c**
Meals 15.75 **st.** (dinner) and a la carte 11.80/27.35 **st.** 6.50 – 9.75 – **175 rm** 84.00/120.00 **st.**, 8 suites – SB.

Pembroke, North Promenade, FY1 2JQ, ☎ 23434, Telex 677469, Fax 27864, ≤, – rm rest – 500. AE VISA JCB AY **x**
***The Promenade* : Meals** (buffet rest.) 13.95/15.95 **st.** 7.50 – ***The Crystal Room* : Meals** (dinner only) a la carte 17.40/27.20 **st.** 7.50 – **268 rm** 106.00/132.00 **st.**, 6 suites – SB.

Village H. & Leisure Club, East Park Drive, FY3 8LL, ☎ 838866, Fax 798800, 18, squash – rm – 600. AE VISA. BZ **a**
Meals (grill rest.) 6.95/15.50 **t.** and a la carte 8.75 – **166 rm** 85.00/95.00 **t.** – SB.

Libertys on the Square without rest., Cocker Square, North Promenade, FY1 1RX, ☎ 291155, ≤ – . VISA. AY **n**
2.95 – **24 rm** 39.50 **t.**

Savoy, Queens Promenade, FY2 9SJ, ☎ 352561, Fax 500735 – – 300. AE VISA AY **a**
Meals (bar lunch Monday to Saturday)/dinner 12.50 **t.** and a la carte 5.75 – **125 rm** 35.00/109.50 **st.**, 6 suites – SB.

Clifton, Talbot Sq., FY1 1ND, ☎ 21481, Fax 27345 – – 80. AE VISA AY **v**
Meals 6.50/9.95 **st.** 4.00 – **77 rm** 65.00/95.00 **t.**, 2 suites – SB.

Warwick, 603-609 New South Promenade, FY4 1NG, ☎ 342192, Fax 405776, – – 50. AE VISA JCB BZ **u**
Meals (bar lunch)/dinner 12.95 **st.** 4.50 – **50 rm** 40.00/78.00 **st.** – SB.

Shellard, 18-20 Dean St., South Shore, FY4 1AU, ☎ 342679 – . VISA. AZ **a**
closed January – **Meals** (dinner only) 12.50 **t.** 4.25 – **20 rm** 27.00/54.00 **t.**

Brabyn's, 1-5 Shaftesbury Av., North Shore, FY2 9QQ, ☎ 354263, Fax 352915 – . AE VISA BY **i**
Meals 6.00/12.00 **st.** 4.50 – **25 rm** 25.00/55.00 **st.** – SB.

Berwyn, 1-2 Finchley Rd, Gynn Sq., FY1 2LP, ☎ 352896, Fax 594391 – . VISA. AY **e**
4.00 – **20 rm** (dinner included) 34.00/70.00 **t.** – SB.

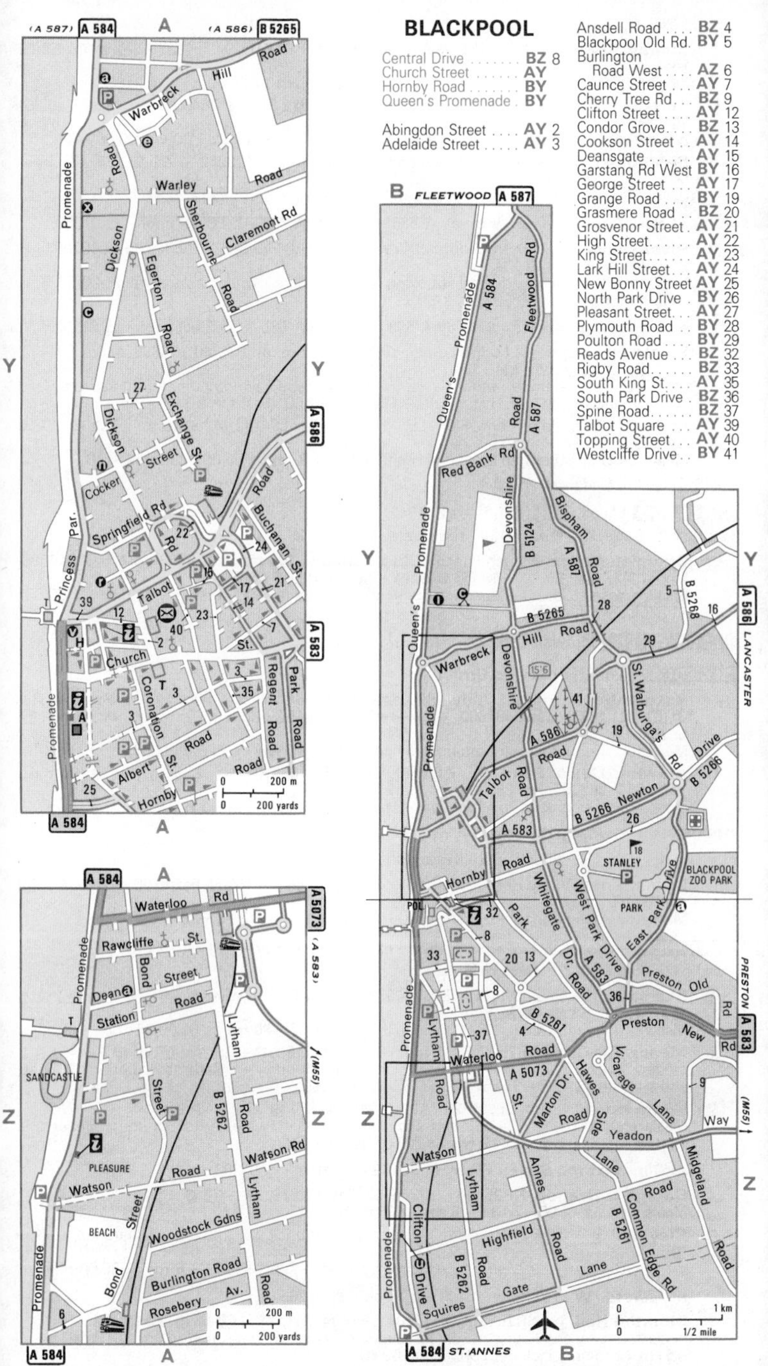

BLACKPOOL
Central Drive BZ 8
Church Street AY
Hornby Road BY
Queen's Promenade BY
Abingdon Street AY 2
Adelaide Street AY 3
Ansdell Road BZ 4
Blackpool Old Rd. BY 5
Burlington Road West AZ 6
Caunce Street AY 7
Cherry Tree Rd. BZ 9
Clifton Street AY 12
Condor Grove BZ 13
Cookson Street AY 14
Deansgate AY 15
Garstang Rd West BY 16
George Street AY 17
Grange Road BY 19
Grasmere Road BZ 20
Grosvenor Street AY 21
High Street AY 22
King Street AY 23
Lark Hill Street AY 24
New Bonny Street AY 25
North Park Drive BY 26
Pleasant Street AY 27
Plymouth Road BY 28
Poulton Road BY 29
Reads Avenue BZ 32
Rigby Road BZ 33
South King St. AY 35
South Park Drive BZ 36
Spine Road BZ 37
Talbot Square AY 39
Topping Street AY 40
Westcliffe Drive BY 41
(A 587) A 584
(A 586) B 5265
A 586
A 583
A 5073
(A 583)
(M55)
A 584
FLEETWOOD A 587
LANCASTER
PRESTON
ST. ANNES
Warbreck Hill Road
Warley Road
Claremont Rd
Sherbourne Road
Egerton Road
Dickson Road
Exchange St.
Cocker Street
Springfield Rd
Buchanan St.
Princess Par.
Promenade
Talbot Rd
Church St.
Coronation St.
Regent Road
Park Road
Albert Road
Hornby Road
Waterloo Rd
Rawcliffe St.
Bond Street
Dean Road
Station Road
Lytham Road
Watson Road
Watson Rd
Woodstock Gdns
Burlington Road
Rosebery Av.
SANDCASTLE
PLEASURE BEACH
Queen's Promenade
Fleetwood Rd
Red Bank Rd
Devonshire Road
Bispham Road
St. Walburga's Rd
Newton Drive
STANLEY PARK
BLACKPOOL ZOO PARK
East Park Drive
West Park Drive
Whitegate Dr.
Preston Old Rd
Preston New Rd
Vicarage Lane
Marton Dr.
Hawes Side Lane
Yeadon Way
Midgeland Road
Common Edge Rd
Highfield Road
Squires Gate Lane
Clifton Drive
POL.
0 200 m
0 200 yards
0 1 km
0 1/2 mile

Sunray, 42 Knowle Av., off Queens Promenade, FY2 9TQ, ✆ 351937 – TV ☎ P. AE VISA — BY c
closed 15 December-5 January – **Meals** 10.00 **s.** – **9 rm** 25.00/50.00 **s.** – SB.

Burlees, 40 Knowle Av., off Queen's Promenade, FY2 9TQ, ✆ 354535 – rest TV P. VISA. — BY c
closed mid November-January – **Meals** 8.50 **st.** 4.00 – **9 rm** 21.00/46.00 **st.** – SB.

September Brasserie, 15-17 Queen St., FY1 1PU, ✆ 23282 – AE VISA JCB. — AY r
closed Sunday and Monday – **Meals** 15.95 **t.** (dinner) and a la carte 10.80/22.90 **t.**

at Little Thornton NE : 5 m. by A 586 – BY – off A 588 – ✉ Blackpool – 01253 :

River House with rm, Skippool Creek, Wyre Rd, FY5 5LF, ✆ 883497, Fax 892083, ←, – TV ☎ P. AE VISA
Meals *(closed Sunday dinner)* (booking essential) 18.50 **t.** and a la carte 25.00/36.50 **t.** 7.50 – **5 rm** 55.00/80.00 **t.** – SB.

at Little Singleton NE : 6 m. by A 586 – BY – on A 585 – ✉ Blackpool – 01253 :

Singleton Lodge, Lodge Lane, FY6 8LT, S : ½ m. on B 5260 ✆ 883854, Fax 894432, – TV ☎ P. AE VISA
closed 25-26 December and 1 January – **Meals** *(closed Sunday dinner)* (dinner only and Sunday lunch)/dinner 15.50 **t.** 4.50 – **12 rm** 52.00/70.00 **t.** – SB.

Mains Hall, 86 Mains Lane, FY6 7LE, ✆ 885130, Fax 894132, – rm TV ☎ P. AE VISA
Meals 12.95/25.00 **st.** and dinner a la carte 4.75 – **9 rm** 55.00/125.00 **st.** – SB.

ATS Clifton Rd, Marton ✆ 695033/4

BLACKROD Lancs. 402 404 M 23 – 01942.

◆London 220 – Burnley 25 – ◆Liverpool 31 – ◆Manchester 16 – Preston 18.

Georgian House, Manchester Rd, BL6 5RU, SE : 1 ½ m. by B 5408 on A 6 ✆ 814598, Fax 813427, – TV ☎ P – 200. AE VISA
Meals *(closed Saturday lunch)* 9.60/18.50 **st.** and a la carte 5.60 – **100 rm** 80.00/114.25 **st.** – SB.

BLACKWATER Cornwall 403 E 33 – see Truro.

BLAGDON Avon 403 L 30 – ✉ Bristol.

Butcombe Farm, Aldwick Lane, BS18 6UW, N : 1 ½ m. by Station Rd ✆ (01761) 462380, Fax 462300, ←, « Farmhouse of 15C origin », heated, , park – TV ☎ P
Meals (by arrangement) (communal dining) 18.50 **t.** – **6 rm** 35.00/49.00 **t.**

Aldwick Court Farm, Aldwick Lane, BS18 TRF, N : 2 ¼ m. by Station Rd ✆ (01934) 862305, Fax 863308, , park, – TV P
closed mid December - mid January – **Meals** (by arrangement) – **3 rm** 28.00/42.00 **s.**

BLAKENEY Glos. 403 404 M 28 – 01594.

◆London 134 – ◆Bristol 31 – Gloucester 16 – Newport 31.

Lower Viney, Viney Hill, GL15 4LT, S : ¾ m. by A 48 ✆ 516000, Fax 516018, – TV P. VISA
Meals (by arrangement) 18.00 **st.** 4.20 – **6 rm** 30.00/40.00 **t.** – SB.

BLAKENEY Norfolk 404 X 25 – pop. 1 628 – ECD : Wednesday – ✉ Holt – 01263.

◆London 127 – King's Lynn 37 – ◆Norwich 28.

Blakeney, The Quay, NR25 7NE, ✆ 740797, Fax 740795, ←, , , – rest TV ☎ P – 150. AE VISA
Meals (light lunch)/dinner 15.00 **t.** and a la carte 4.50 – **60 rm** 61.00/158.00 **t.** – SB.

Manor, The Quay, NR25 7ND, ✆ 740376, Fax 741116, – rest TV ☎ P
closed 2 to 23 January – **Meals** (bar lunch Monday to Saturday)/dinner 14.50 **st.** and a la carte 4.25 – **37 rm** 25.00/78.00 **st.** – SB.

White Horse, 4 High St., NR25 7AL, ✆ 740574 – TV P. AE VISA.
Meals *(closed dinner Sunday and Monday)* (bar lunch Monday to Saturday)/dinner a la carte 9.70/16.50 **t.** 3.25 – **9 rm** 30.00/70.00 **t.** – SB.

at Cley next the Sea E : 1 ½ m. on A 149 – ✉ Holt – 01263 :

George & Dragon, NR25 7RN, ✆ 740652, Fax 741275, – TV P
Meals a la carte 7.65/17.10 **t.** – **8 rm** 30.00/65.00 **t.**

Cley Mill, NR25 7NN, ✆ 740209, ←, « 18C redbrick windmill on saltmarshes », – P
closed 10 January - 28 February – **Meals** (by arrangement) 15.50 **t.** – **6 rm** 29.00/59.00 **t.**

at Morston W : 1 ½ m. on A 149 – ✉ Holt – 01263 :

Morston Hall, NR25 7AA, ✆ 741041, Fax 741041, – TV ☎ P. AE VISA
closed January and February – **Meals** (dinner only and Sunday lunch)/dinner 22.00 **st.** 4.50 – **5 rm** (dinner included) 90.00/140.00 **st.**

BLANCHLAND Northd. 401 402 N 19 – pop. 135 – ECD : Monday and Tuesday – ✉ Consett (Durham) – ☎ 01434.

♦London 298 – ♦Carlisle 47 – ♦Newcastle upon Tyne 24.

Lord Crewe Arms ♨, DH8 9SP, ✆ 675251, Fax 675337, « Part 13C abbey », 🌳 – TV ☎ – 🏛 25. MC AE ⦿ VISA
Meals (bar lunch Monday to Saturday)/dinner 26.00 **t.** 🍷 6.50 – **18 rm** ☕ 75.00/98.00 **t.** – SB.

BLANDFORD FORUM Dorset 403 404 N 31 **The West Country G.** – pop. 7 957 – ECD : Wednesday – ☎ 01258.

See : Town★.

Envir. : Kingston Lacy★★ *AC*, SE : 5½ m. by B 3082 – Royal Signals Museum★, NE : 2 m. by B 3082.

Exc. : Milton Abbas★, SW : 8 m. by A 354.

⛳9 Ashley Wood, Tarrant Rawston ✆ 452253 – ⛳18 The Mid Dorset, Belchalwell ✆ 861386.

ℹ Marsh and Ham Car Park, West St., DT11 7AW ✆ 454770.

♦London 124 – Bournemouth 17 – Dorchester 17 – Salisbury 24.

Crown, West St., DT11 7AJ, ✆ 456626, Fax 451084, 🎣, 🌳 – 🚭 rm TV ☎ P – 🏛 100. MC AE ⦿ VISA
closed 24 December - 1 January – **Meals** *(closed Saturday lunch)* 10.50 **t.** and a la carte 🍷 4.95 – **31 rm** ☕ 64.00/74.00 **t.**, 1 suite – SB.

XX **La Belle Alliance** with rm, Portman Lodge, White Cliff Mill St., DT11 7BP, ✆ 452842 – 🚭 rest TV ☎ P. MC AE VISA
closed first 2 weeks January – **Meals** *(closed Sunday and Monday)* (dinner only) 20.00 **st.** and a la carte 🍷 4.95 – **6 rm** ☕ 48.00/66.00 **st.** – SB.

at Pimperne NE : 2½ m. on A 354 – ✉ Blandford Forum – ☎ 01258 :

Anvil, Salisbury Rd, DT11 8UQ, ✆ 453431 – TV ☎ P. MC AE ⦿ VISA
Meals a la carte 12.55/20.45 **st.** 🍷 5.00 – **9 rm** ☕ 42.50/65.00 **t.**

Fairfield House, Church Rd, DT11 8UB, ✆ 456756, Fax 480053, 🌳 – 🚭 TV ♿ P. MC AE ⦿ VISA. 🐕
Meals *(closed Sunday)* (dinner only) a la carte 14.90/22.15 **st.** – **5 rm** ☕ 36.00/64.00 **t.** – SB.

at Tarrant Monkton NE : 5½ m. by A 354 – ✉ Blandford Forum – ☎ 01258 :

Langton Arms, DT11 8RX, ✆ 830225, 🌳 – TV ☎ P. MC VISA
Meals (bar lunch Monday to Saturday)/dinner 15.00 🍷 3.50 – **6 rm** ☕ 35.00/49.00 **st.**

at Farnham NE : 7½ m. by A 354 – ✉ Blandford Forum – ☎ 01725 :

Museum, DT11 8DE, ✆ 516261, 🌳 – TV ☎ P. MC VISA. 🐕
closed 25-26 December – **Meals** (booking essential) a la carte 13.40/20.40 **t.** – **4 rm** ☕ 35.00/50.00 **st.**

BLAWITH Cumbria 402 K 21 – see Coniston.

BLEDINGTON Glos. 403 404 P 28 – see Stow-on-the-Wold.

BLOCKLEY Glos. 403 404 O 27 – pop. 1 668 – ECD : Thursday – ✉ Moreton-in-Marsh – ☎ 01386.

♦London 89 – ♦Birmingham 40 – Gloucester 29 – ♦Oxford 33.

Crown Inn, High St., GL56 9EX, ✆ 700245, Fax 700247, « Converted 17C coach house and cottages » – TV ☎ P. MC AE ⦿ VISA
Meals 7.95/19.95 **t.** and a la carte 🍷 4.95 – **21 rm** ☕ 53.00/114.00 **t.** – SB.

Lower Brook House without rest., Lower St., GL56 9DS, ✆ 700286, « Part 17C cottages », 🌳 – P
4 rm ☕ -/45.00.

BLUNSDON Wilts. 403 404 O 29 – see Swindon.

BLYTH Notts. 402 403 404 Q 23 – pop. 1 867 – ✉ Worksop – ☎ 01909.

♦London 166 – Doncaster 13 – Lincoln 30 – ♦Nottingham 32 – ♦Sheffield 20.

Granada Lodge without rest., Hilltop roundabout, S81 8HG, N : ¾ m. by B 6045 at junction of A 1 (M) with A 614 ✆ 591841, Fax 591831, Reservations (Freephone) 0800 555300 – 🚭 TV ☎ ♿ P. MC AE VISA. 🐕
☕ 4.00 – **39 rm** 39.95 **st.**

Forte Travelodge without rest., A 1 southbound, S81 8EL, SE : 1 m. by A 634 on A 1 ✆ 591775, Reservations (Freephone) 0800 850950 – TV ♿ P. MC AE VISA. 🐕
32 rm 33.50 **t.**

BODENHAM Heref. and Worcs. 403 L 29 – see Leominster.

BODINNICK-BY-FOWEY Cornwall – see Fowey.

BODYMOOR HEATH Staffs. 402 403 404 O 26 – see Tamworth.

BOLDON Tyne and Wear 401 402 O 19 – see Newcastle upon Tyne.

BOLLINGTON Ches. 402 403 404 N 24 – see Macclesfield.

BOLTON Gtr. Manchester 402 404 M 23 – pop. 143 960 – ECD : Wednesday – 01204.

Regent Park, Links Rd, Chorley New Road ✆ 495421 – Lostock Park ✆ 843278 – Bolton, Old Links, Chorley Old Rd, Monserrat ✆ 840050.

Town Hall, Victoria Sq, BL1 1RU ✆ 364333.

London 214 – Burnley 19 – Liverpool 32 – Manchester 11 – Preston 23.

Bolton Moat House (Q.M.H.), 1 Higher Bridge St., BL1 2EW, ✆ 383338, Fax 380777, « Cloisters restaurant in 19C church », – rm rest – 300. VISA
Meals *(closed Saturday lunch)* (carving lunch) (bar lunch Saturday) 10.75/15.50 **st.** and a la carte – 7.50 – **126 rm** 83.00/99.00 **st.**, 2 suites – SB.

Beaumont (Forte), Beaumont Rd, BL3 4TA, SW : 2½ m. on A 58 ✆ 651511, Fax 61064 – rm – 120. VISA JCB.
Meals 6.95/14.80 **st.** and a la carte 4.65 – 7.95 – **95 rm** 53.50 **st.** – SB.

Pack Horse (De Vere), Nelson Sq., Bradshawgate, BL1 1DP, ✆ 27261, Fax 364352 – – 275. VISA
Meals (buffet lunch Monday to Saturday) (dancing Friday evening)/dinner 13.00 **st.** and a la carte 6.00 – **72 rm** 55.00/100.00 **st.** – SB.

Broomfield, 33-35 Wigan Rd, Deane, BL3 5PX, SW : 1 ½ m. on A 676 ✆ 61570, Fax 650932 – rest . VISA
Meals *(closed Sunday)* (residents only)(dinner only) 10.95 **st.** and a la carte 4.00 – **15 rm** 26.50/40.00 **st.** – SB.

at Egerton N : 3½ m. on A 666 – ✉ Bolton – 01204 :

Egerton House, Blackburn Rd, BL7 9PL, ✆ 307171, Fax 593030, – rm – 150.
Meals *(closed Saturday lunch)* 10.95/22.00 **t.** and a la carte 5.25 – 6.95 – **32 rm** 72.50/87.50 **t.** – SB.

at Bromley Cross N : 4 m. by A 666 on B 6472 – ✉ Bolton – 01204 :

Last Drop Village, Hospital Rd, BL7 9PZ, ✆ 591131, Fax 304122, « Village created from restored farm buildings », , , squash – rm – 200. VISA
Meals (bar lunch Saturday) 10.75/16.95 **t.** and a la carte – **80 rm** 72.50/87.50 **t.**, 3 suites – SB.

ATS Foundry St. ✆ 22144/27841/388681
ATS Moss Bank Way, Astley Bridge, Bolton (ASDA car park) ✆ 300057
ATS Chorley Rd, Fourgates, Westhoughton ✆ 813024

BOLTON ABBEY N. Yorks. 402 O 22 **Great Britain G.** – pop. 122 – ✉ Skipton – 01756.

See : Bolton Priory★ *AC*.

London 216 – Harrogate 18 – Leeds 23 – Skipton 6.

Devonshire Arms Country House, BD23 6AJ, ✆ 710441, Telex 51218, Fax 710564, , « Part 17C restored coaching inn », , , , park, – – 150. VISA
Burlington – **Meals** 17.95/30.00 **st.** and a la carte 7.95 – **40 rm** 95.00/150.00 **st.**, 1 suite – SB.

BONCHURCH I.O.W. 403 404 Q 32 – see Wight (Isle of).

BOREHAMWOOD Herts. 404 T 29 – pop. 28 298 – 0181.

Civic Offices, Elstree Way, WD6 1WA ✆ 207 2277/7496.

London 10 – Luton 20.

Plan : see Greater London (North West)

Elstree Moat House (Q.M.H.), Barnet By-Pass, WD6 5PU, at junction of A 5135 with A 1 ✆ 953 1622, Fax 207 3194, , – rm rest – 100. VISA CT s
Meals (bar lunch Saturday and Bank Holidays) 12.95/21.00 **t.** and a la carte – 9.95 – **130 rm** 94.00/110.00 **st.** – SB.

Oaklands (Toby), Studio Way, WD6 5JY, off Elstree Way (A 5135) ✆ 905 1455, Fax 905 1370 – rm – 35. VISA CT i
Meals (grill rest.) 8.80 **t.** and a la carte – **38 rm** 65.00/75.00 **t.**

BOROUGHBRIDGE N.Yorks 402 P 21 – 01423 :

Rose Manor, Horsefair, YO5 9LL, ✆ 322245, Fax 324920, – rm – 200. VISA.
Meals (bar lunch Monday to Saturday)/dinner 16.50 **st.** and a la carte – 7.90 – **17 rm** 59.00/78.00 – SB.

at Brafferton Helperby NE : 5 m. by B 6265 and Easingwold rd on Helperby rd – ✉ York – ☎ 01423 :

Brafferton Hall, YO6 2NZ, ☎ 360352, Fax 360352, – TV P. VISA.
Meals (by arrangement) (communal dining) 17.00 – **3 rm** 30.00/55.00.

Laurel Farmhouse, YO6 2NZ, ☎ 360436, , park, – TV P
Meals (by arrangement) (communal dining) 12.00 **s.** 2.00 – **3 rm** 19.00/38.00 **st.**

BORROWDALE Cumbria 402 K 20 – see Keswick.

BOSCASTLE Cornwall 403 F 31 **The West Country G.** – ☎ 01840.

See : Village★.

◆London 260 – Bude 14 – Exeter 59 – ◆Plymouth 43.

St. Christopher's, High St., PL35 0BD, S : ½ m. by B 3266 ☎ 250412 – rest TV P. VISA
closed November-January – **Meals** 9.00 **st.** – **9 rm** 17.50/35.00 **t.** – SB.

Old Coach House without rest., Tintagel Rd, PL35 0AS, S : ¾ m. on B 3263 ☎ 250398 – TV P. AE VISA.
March-October – **6 rm** 15.00/44.00 **t.**

BOSHAM W. Sussex 404 R 31 – see Chichester.

BOSTON Lincs. 402 404 T 25 **Great Britain G.** – pop. 53 226 – ECD : Thursday – ☎ 01205.

See : St. Botolph's Church★.

Cowbridge, Horncastle Rd ☎ 362306.

Blackfriars Arts Centre, Spain Lane, PE21 6HP ☎ 356656.

◆London 122 – Lincoln 35 – ◆Nottingham 55.

Friendly Stop Inn, Bicker Bar Roundabout, PE20 3AN, SW : 8 m. at junction of A 17 with A 52 ☎ 820118, Fax 820228, – rm rest TV P – 60. AE VISA.
Meals 9.75 **st.** and dinner a la carte 4.75 – 5.75 – **55 rm** 36.50 **st.** – SB.

ATS London Rd ☎ 362854

BOTLEY Hants. 403 404 Q 31 – pop. 2 156 – ECD : Thursday – ✉ Southampton – ☎ 01489.

Botley Park H. & C.C., Winchester Rd, Boorley Green ☎ 780888 ext : 444.

◆London 83 – ◆Portsmouth 17 – ◆Southampton 6 – Winchester 11.

Botley Park, Winchester Rd, Boorley Green, SO32 2UA, NW : 1 ½ m. on B 3354 ☎ 780888, Fax 789242, , park, , squash – rest TV P – 200. AE VISA
Meals 13.25/19.95 **t.** and a la carte 4.95 – 8.95 – **100 rm** 84.00/177.00 **t.** – SB.

Cobbett's, 15 The Square, SO3 2EA, ☎ 782068, Fax 799641 – P. VISA
closed Monday and Saturday lunch, Sunday, 2 weeks summer, 2 weeks winter and Bank Holidays.
Meals - French 23.00 **t.** 6.00.

BOUGHTON Kent – see Faversham.

BOUGHTON MONCHELSEA Kent – see Maidstone.

BOURNE Lincs. 402 404 S 25 – pop. 9 988 – ECD : Wednesday – ☎ 01778.

◆London 101 – ◆Leicester 42 – Lincoln 35 – ◆Nottingham 42.

Bourne Eau House, 30 South St., PE10 9LY, on A 15 ☎ 423621, « Part Elizabethan and Georgian house », – TV P.
Meals *(closed Sunday)* (residents only) (communal dining) (dinner only) 18.00 **st.** – **3 rm** 35.00/60.00 **st.**

Toft House, Main Rd, Toft, PE10 0JT, SW : 3 m. by A 151 on A 6121 ☎ 590614, Fax 590264, – TV P – 80. VISA.
Meals *(closed Sunday dinner)* (bar lunch)/dinner 14.50 **t.** 3.80 – **22 rm** 40.00/60.00 **t.**

ATS 18 Abbey Rd ☎ 422811

BOURNE END Herts. 404 S 28 – see Hemel Hempstead.

BOURNEMOUTH Dorset 403 404 O 31 **The West Country G.** – pop. 151 302 – ECD : Wednesday – ☎ 01202.

See : Compton Acres★★ (English Garden ≤★★★) *AC* AX – Bournemouth Museums★ (Russell-Cotes Art Gallery and Museum *AC* DZ - Shelley Rooms *AC* EX).

Queens Park, Queens Park West Drive ☎ 396198/302611, DV – Meyrick Park ☎ 2090307 CY.

Bournemouth (Hurn) Airport : ☎ 593939, N : 5 m. by Hurn - DV.

Westover Rd, BH1 2BU ☎ 789789.

◆London 114 – ◆Bristol 76 – ◆Southampton 34.

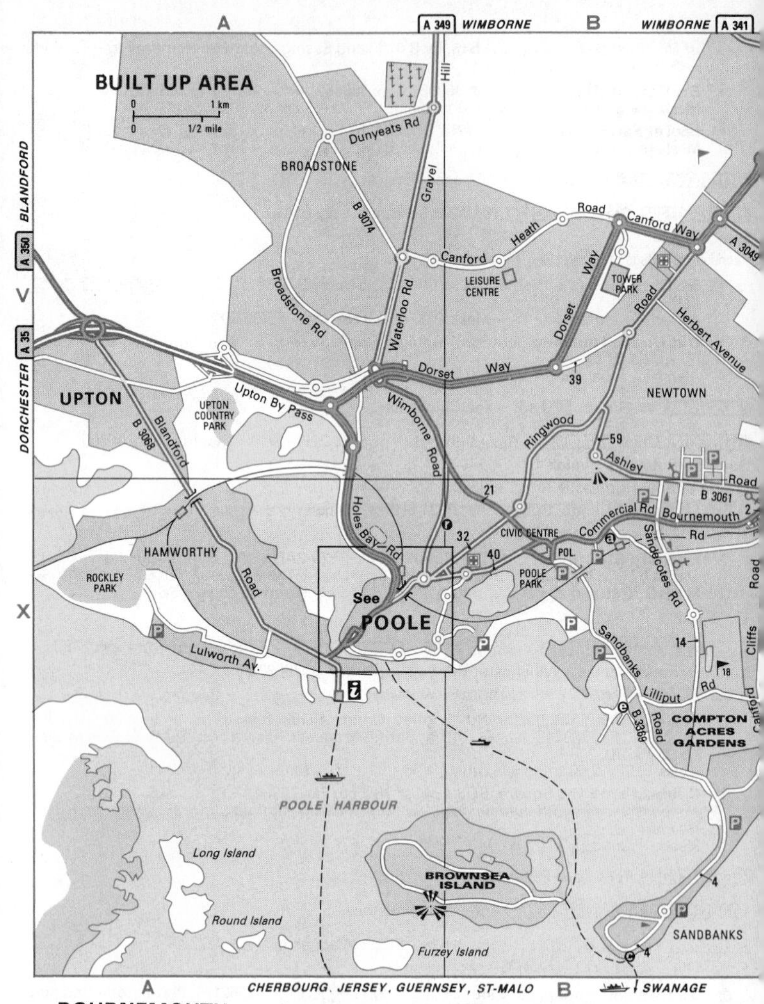

BOURNEMOUTH AND POOLE

Old Christchurch Road .... **DY**
Square (The) .... **CY** 63
Westover Road .... **DZ** 75

Archway Road .... **BX** 2
Banks Road .... **BX** 4
Boscombe Overcliff Road .... **EX** 6
Boscombe Spa Road ..... **DX** 7
Branksome Wood Road .... **CY** 9
Chessel Avenue .... **EX** 10
Clarendon Road .... **CX** 12
Commercial Road .... **CY** 13
Compton Avenue .... **BX** 14
Cranleigh Road .... **EV** 16
Durley Road .... **CZ** 17
Ensbury Park Road .... **CV** 19
Exeter Road .... **CDZ** 20
Fernside Road .... **ABX** 21
Fir Vale Road .... **DY** 23
Gervis Place .... **DY** 24
Gloucester Road .... **EV** 26
Hinton Road .... **DZ** 27
Lansdowne (The) .... **DY** 28
Lansdowne Road .... **DY** 30
Leven Avenue .... **CX** 31
Longfleet Road .... **BX** 32
Madeira Road .... **DY** 34
Manor Road .... **EY** 35
Meyrick Road .... **EYZ** 36
Old Wareham Road ...... **BV** 39
Parkstone Road .... **BX** 40
Pinecliff Road .... **CX** 42
Post Office Road .... **CY** 43
Priory Road .... **CZ** 45
Queen's Road .... **CX** 46
Richmond Hill .... **CY** 47
Richmond Park Road ..... **DV** 48
Russell Cotes Road .... **DZ** 49
St. Michael's Road .... **CZ** 51
St. Paul's Road .... **EY** 52
St. Peter's Road .... **DY** 53
St. Stephen's Road .... **CY** 55
St. Swithuns Road South .... **EY** 56
Seabourne Road .... **EV** 57
Seamoor Road .... **CX** 58
Sea View Road .... **BV** 59
Southbourne Grove .... **EX** 61
Southbourne Overcliff Drive .... **EX** 62
Suffolk Road .... **CY** 64
Surrey Road .... **CX** 66
Triangle (The) .... **CY** 67
Upper Hinton Road .... **DZ** 68
Wessex Way .... **CX** 70
West Cliff Promenade .... **CZ** 71
Western Road .... **CX** 73

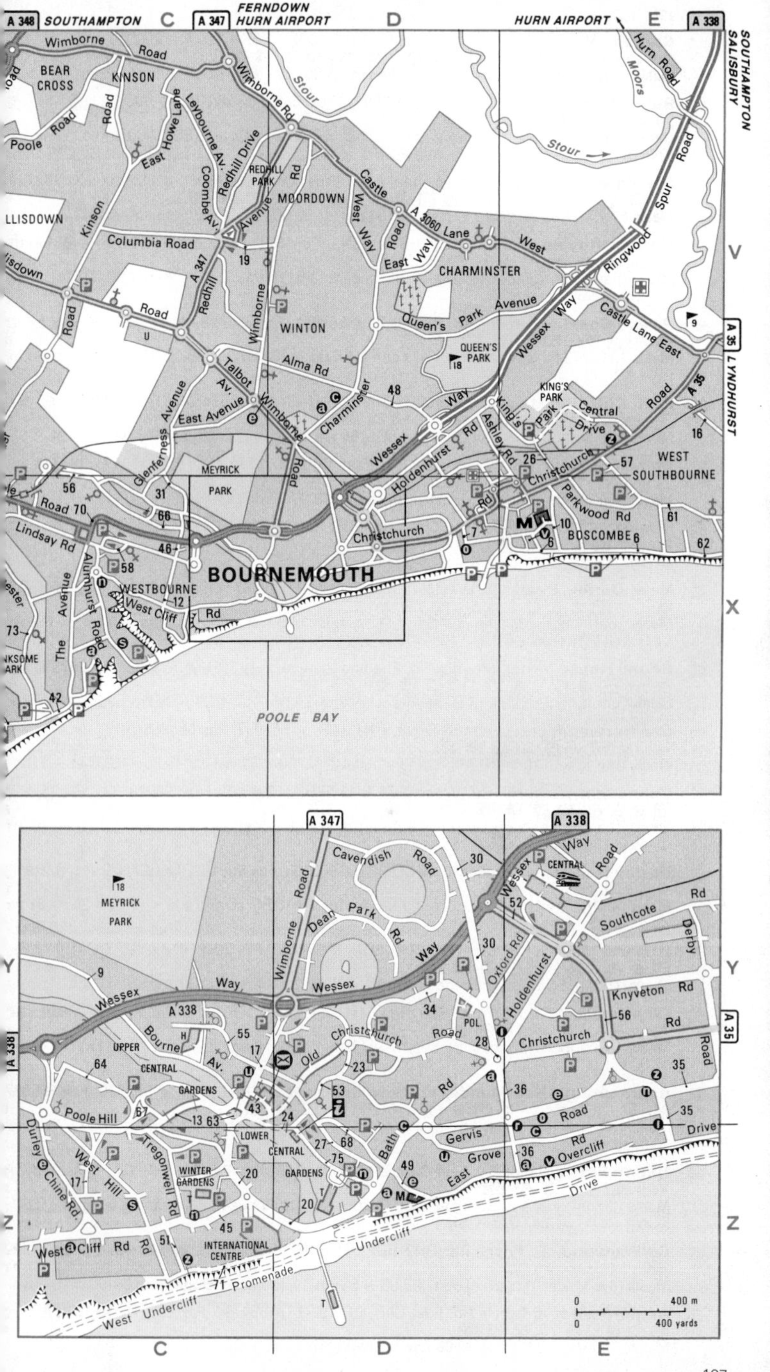
A 348 SOUTHAMPTON
A 347 FERNDOWN HURN AIRPORT
HURN AIRPORT
A 338
SOUTHAMPTON SALISBURY
BEAR CROSS
KINSON
ELLISDOWN
REDHILL PARK
MOORDOWN
WINTON
CHARMINSTER
QUEEN'S PARK
KING'S PARK
MEYRICK PARK
BOURNEMOUTH
WESTBOURNE
BOSCOMBE
WEST SOUTHBOURNE
POOLE BAY
A 35 LYNDHURST
Wimborne Road
Castle Lane West
Castle Lane East
Wessex Way
Christchurch Road
Holdenhurst Rd
Stour
CENTRAL
UPPER CENTRAL GARDENS
LOWER CENTRAL GARDENS
WINTER GARDENS
INTERNATIONAL CENTRE
West Undercliff Promenade
Undercliff Drive
Overcliff Drive
400 m
400 yards

Carlton, Meyrick Rd, East Overcliff, BH1 3DN, ℘ 552011, Fax 299573, ≤, heated, – rest – 160. VISA EZ a
Meals 12.50/23.50 **st.** and a la carte – **65 rm** 95.00/120.00 **st.**, 5 suites – SB.

Royal Bath (De Vere), Bath Rd, BH1 2EW, ℘ 555555, Fax 554158, ≤, – 500. VISA. DZ a
Oscars : **Meals** *(closed Sunday and Christmas-New Year)* 15.50/27.60 and a la carte – **124 rm** 95.00/152.00 **t.**, 7 suites – SB.

Swallow Highcliff, 105 St. Michael's Rd, West Cliff, BH2 5DU, ℘ 557702, Fax 292734, ≤, heated, – 500. VISA CZ z
Meals 11.75/17.95 **st.** and a la carte – **154 rm** 90.00/135.00 **st.**, 3 suites – SB.

Norfolk Royale, Richmond Hill, BH2 6EN, ℘ 551521, Fax 299729, – rm rest – 90. VISA. CY u
Meals (bar lunch)/dinner 18.00 **t.** and a la carte 5.00 – 8.75 – **90 rm** 90.00/120.00 **st.**, 5 suites – SB.

Palace Court, Westover Rd, BH1 2BZ, ℘ 557681, Fax 554918, ≤, – 250. VISA. DZ n
Meals 10.50/18.50 **st.** and dinner a la carte 6.00 – **104 rm** 95.00/138.00 **st.**, 6 suites – SB.

East Cliff Court, East Overcliff Drive, BH1 3AN, ℘ 554545, Fax 557456, ≤, heated – 100. VISA EZ v
Meals (bar lunch)/dinner 14.25 **st.** 4.50 – **68 rm** (dinner included) 49.00/98.00 **st.** – SB.

Marsham Court, Russell-Cotes Rd, East Cliff, BH1 3AB, ℘ 552111, Fax 294744, ≤, heated – 200. VISA. DZ e
Meals (bar lunch)/dinner 16.00 **st.** – **85 rm** 49.00/98.00 **st.**, 1 suite – SB.

Miramar, 19 Grove Rd, East Overcliff, BH1 3AU, ℘ 556581, Fax 299573, ≤, – rest – 80 DZ u
39 rm.

New Durley Dean, 28 Westcliff Rd, BH2 5HE, ℘ 557711, Fax 292815, – rest – 80. VISA. CZ a
Meals (bar lunch Monday to Saturday)/dinner 14.90 **st.** and a la carte 5.95 – **112 rm** 58.00/131.00 **st.** – SB.

Round House (Forte), Meyrick Rd, The Lansdowne, BH1 2PR, ℘ 553262, Fax 557698 – rm – 100. VISA JCB. DY a
Meals (bar lunch)/dinner 13.80 **st.** and a la carte 4.95 – 6.95 – **98 rm** 53.50 **st.** – SB.

Chesterwood, East Overcliff Drive, BH1 3AR, ℘ 558057, Fax 556285, ≤, heated – rest. VISA EZ
Meals (bar lunch)/dinner 12.00 **t.** and a la carte 4.50 – **51 rm** 45.00/110.00 **st.** – SB.

Connaught, West Hill Rd, West Cliff, BH2 5PH, ℘ 298020, Fax 298028, – . VISA CZ s
Meals (bar lunch Monday to Saturday)/dinner 18.50 **st.** and a la carte 4.95 – **59 rm** 48.00/96.00 **st.**, 1 suite – SB.

Durley Hall, Durley Chine Rd, BH2 5JS, ℘ 500100, Fax 500103, – – 120. CZ e
Meals (buffet lunch Monday to Saturday)/dinner 16.50 **st.** and a la carte 4.25 – **81 rm** 43.00/86.00 **st.** – SB.

Queens, Meyrick Rd, East Cliff, BH1 3DL, ℘ 554415, Fax 294810, – rest – 200. VISA EYZ
Meals 8.50/18.50 **t.** and dinner a la carte – **110 rm** 44.50/109.00 **t.** – SB.

Courtlands, 16 Boscombe Spa Rd, East Cliff, BH5 1BB, ℘ 302442, Fax 309880, heated – rest – 45. VISA DX
Meals (bar lunch Monday to Saturday)/dinner 21.00 **t.** and a la carte – **58 rm** 44.90/82.00 **t.**

Bournemouth Heathlands, 12 Grove Rd, East Cliff, BH1 3AY, ℘ 553336, Fax 555937, heated – 250. VISA EZ
Meals (bar lunch Monday to Saturday)/dinner 16.50 **st.** 4.50 – **113 rm** 49.00/78.00 **st.**, 2 suites – SB.

Hinton Firs, 9 Manor Rd, East Cliff, BH1 3HB, ℘ 555409, Fax 299607, heated – rest. VISA. EY
Meals (dinner only and Sunday lunch October-May)/dinner 12.50 **st.** and a la carte 3.80 – **52 rm** 46.00/94.00 **st.** – SB.

Collingwood, 11 Priory Rd, BH2 5DF, ℘ 557575, – rest. VISA CZ
Meals (bar lunch)/dinner 15.95 **t.** 3.95 – **54 rm** (dinner included) 35.00/90.00 **t.** – SB.

Anglo-Swiss, 16 Gervis Rd, East Cliff, BH1 3EQ, ℘ 554794, Fax 299615, – – 70. VISA EY
Meals 10.00/15.00 **t.** 4.95 – **68 rm** 35.00/100.00 **st.** – SB.

Belvedere, 14 Bath Rd, BH1 2EU, ☎ 297556, Fax 294699 – TV ☎ P. VISA JCB. DYZ **c**
Meals (bar lunch Monday to Saturday)/dinner 12.75 **t.** and a la carte – **62 rm** 45.50/83.00 **t.** – SB.

Tudor Grange, 31 Gervis Rd, East Cliff, BH1 3EE, ☎ 291472, – TV ☎ P. VISA EY **o**
Meals (dinner only) 8.00 **st.** 4.50 – **12 rm** 20.00/60.00 **st.** – SB.

Cliff House, 113 Alumhurst Rd, Alum Chine, BH4 8HS, ☎ 763003, – TV P. CX **s**
mid March-October and Christmas – **Meals** (dinner only) 12.00 **st.** 2.50 – **11 rm** (dinner included) 37.00/74.00 **st.** – SB.

Sinclair's, 31 Alumhurst Rd, BH4 8EN, ☎ 752777, Fax 752778 – TV ☎ P. VISA. CX **n**
Meals 8.50/12.00 **st.** and dinner a la carte 7.00 – **21 rm** 33.00/45.00 **st.**

Wood Lodge, 10 Manor Rd, East Cliff, BH1 3EY, ☎ 290891, – rest TV P. VISA EY **z**
closed January and February – **Meals** (dinner only) 11.50 4.40 – **15 rm** 28.00/56.00 **t.**

Silver Trees without rest., 57 Wimborne Rd, BH3 7AL, ☎ 556040, Fax 556040, – TV P. AE VISA CV **e**
5 rm 23.00/40.00.

Valberg, 1A Wollstonecraft Rd, Boscombe, BH5 1JQ, ☎ 394644, – rest TV P EX **v**
Meals (by arrangement) – **10 rm** 15.00/38.00 **st.** – SB.

Salathai, 1066 Christchurch Rd, Boscombe East, BH7 6DS, ☎ 420772 – AE VISA EV **z**
closed Sunday and 25-26 December – **Meals** - Thai 7.95/14.25 **t.** and a la carte.

Noble House, 3-5 Lansdowne Rd, BH1 1RZ, ☎ 291277 – AE VISA JCB DEY **i**
closed 25-26 December – **Meals** - Chinese a la carte 13.60/20.40 **t.**

Sophisticats, 43 Charminster Rd, BH8 8UE, ☎ 291019 CV **a**
closed Sunday, 2 weeks January, and 2 weeks July – **Meals** (dinner only) a la carte 18.25/22.65 **t.** 4.00.

Helvetia, 61 Charminster Rd, BH8 8UE, ☎ 555447 – AE VISA DV **c**
closed Sunday lunch – **Meals** - Swiss 22.35 **t.** (dinner) and a la carte **t.** 5.45.

ATS 892 Christchurch Rd, Boscombe ☎ 424457 ATS 1 Fernside Rd, Poole ☎ 733301/733326

BOURTON-ON-THE-WATER Glos. 403 404 O 28 **Great Britain G.** – pop. 2 999 – ECD : Saturday – ☎ 01451.

See : Town★.

◆London 91 – ◆Birmingham 47 – Gloucester 24 – ◆Oxford 36.

Dial House, The Chestnuts, High St., GL54 2AN, ☎ 822244, Fax 810126, – TV ☎ P. AE VISA
Meals 9.95/17.00 **t.** and dinner a la carte 6.25 – **10 rm** 39.50/96.00 **t.** – SB.

Lansdowne Villa, Lansdowne, GL54 2AT, ☎ 820673 – rest TV P.
Meals 10.50 **st.** 5.25 – **12 rm** 24.00/39.50 **st.**

Coombe House without rest., Rissington Rd, GL54 2DT, ☎ 821966, Fax 810477, – TV P. AE VISA.
closed 24, 25 and 31 December – **7 rm** 36.00/65.00 **st.**

Broadlands, Clapton Row, GL54 2DN, ☎ 822002 – rest TV P
closed January – **Meals** 10.50 **st.** – **11 rm** 30.00/39.50 **st.**

Triangle without rest., Station Rd, GL54 2ER, ☎ 821037, – P.
May-October – **3 rm** 32.00/42.00 **s.**

at Little Rissington E : 1 ¾ m. on Little Rissington rd – ✉ Bourton-on-the-Water – ☎ 01451 :

Touchstone without rest., GL54 2ND, ☎ 822481, – TV P
closed 15 December-15 February – **3 rm** 25.00/38.00 **st.**

at Great Rissington SE : 3¼ m. – ✉ Cheltenham – ☎ 01451 :

Lamb Inn, GL54 2LP, ☎ 820388, Fax 820724, « Part 17C Cotswold stone inn », – P. AE VISA
closed 25 and 26 December – **Meals** (bar lunch)/dinner a la carte 12.25/17.70 **t.** 4.80 – **13 rm.**

at Lower Slaughter NW : 1 ¾ m. by A 429 – ✉ Cheltenham – ☎ 01451 :

Lower Slaughter Manor, GL54 2HP, ☎ 820456, Fax 822150, « 17C manor house, gardens », – rest TV ☎ P – 25. AE VISA.
closed 3 weeks January – **Meals** 17.95/33.00 **t.** 8.50 – **14 rm** (dinner included) 145.00/290.00 **t.**, 2 suites – SB.

Washbourne Court, GL54 2HS, ☎ 822143, Fax 821045, « Part 17C house in picturesque village », – rest TV ☎ P. AE VISA
Meals (light lunch)/dinner 23.95 **t.** and a la carte – **12 rm** 75.00/125.00 **t.**, 6 suites – SB.

at Upper Slaughter NW : 2 ¾ m. by A 429 – ✉ Cheltenham – ☎ 01451 :

Lords of the Manor ⑤, GL54 2JD, ☏ 820243, Fax 820696, ≤, « Part 17C manor house », ⚲, ⛱, park – ⚹ rest ▣ ☎ Ⓟ – 🏔 30. ⬚ AE ⓓ VISA JCB. ⚹
closed 1 to 15 January – **Meals** 10.95/29.50 **st.** and dinner a la carte approx. 33.50 **t.** 5.65 – **29 rm** ⊡ 80.00/195.00 **st.** – SB
Spec. Terrine of salmon and brill with spinach, soft herbs and Niçoise salad, Rib eye of Aberdeen Angus on celeriac puree with tomato and thyme sauce, Fine apple tart on caramel sauce with sultana and Calvados ice cream.

BOVEY TRACEY Devon 403 I 32 **The West Country G.** – pop. 4 884 – ECD : Wednesday – ✉ Newton Abbot – ☎ 01626.

See : St. Peter, St. Paul and St. Thomas of Canterbury Church★.

Envir. : Dartmoor National Park★★ (Brent Tor ≤★★, Haytor Rocks ≤★).

18 Newton Abbot ☏ 52460.

♦London 214 – Exeter 14 – ♦Plymouth 32.

Edgemoor, Haytor Rd, TQ13 9LE, W : 1 m. on B 3387 ☏ 832466, Fax 834760, ⛱ – ⚹ rest ▣ ☎ Ⓟ – 🏔 50. ⬚ AE ⓓ VISA
closed 1st week January – **Meals** (booking essential) 11.75/22.70 **t.** and lunch a la carte 4.15 – **12 rm** ⊡ 44.75/89.50 **t.**

Coombe Cross, Coombe Cross, TQ13 9EY, E : ½ m. on B 3344 ☏ 832476, Fax 835298, Lδ, ≘s, ⬚, ⛱ – ⚹ rest ▣ ☎ Ⓟ. ⬚ AE ⓓ VISA
closed December – **Meals** (bar lunch)/dinner 17.95 **st.** 6.00 – **24 rm** ⊡ 37.00/74.00 – SB.

Willmead Farm ⑤ without rest., TQ13 9NP, NW : 2 ¾ m. by A 382 ☏ (01647) 277214, ≤, « Part 14C thatched farmhouse », ⛱, park – ⚹ Ⓟ. ⚹
closed Christmas and New Year (booking essential) – **3 rm** ⊡ 30.00/47.00 **st.**

Front House Lodge, East St., TQ13 9EL, ☏ 832202, Fax 834931, ⛱ – ⚹ ▣ Ⓟ. ⬚ AE VISA. ⚹
Meals (by arrangement) 15.00 **st.** – **6 rm** ⊡ 25.00/40.00 – SB.

at Haytor W : 2½ m. on B 3387 – ✉ Bovey Tracey – ☎ 01364 :

Bel Alp House ⑤, TQ13 9XX, on B 3387 ☏ 661217, Fax 661292, ≤ countryside, « Country house atmosphere », ⛱ – |‡| ⚹ rest ▣ ☎ ♿ Ⓟ. ⬚ VISA
Booking essential November-March – **Meals** (booking essential) (dinner only) 33.00 **t.** 6.00 – **9 rm** ⊡ 72.00/144.00 **t.** – SB.

at Haytor Vale W : 3½ m. by B 3387 – ✉ Newton Abbot – ☎ 01364.

Rock Inn, TQ13 9XP, ☏ 661305, Fax 661242, « 18C inn », ⛱ – ⚹ ▣ ☎ Ⓟ. ⬚ AE VISA. ⚹
Meals 7.95/25.00 **t.** and a la carte 5.95 – **10 rm** ⊡ 25.95/65.00 **t.** – SB.

BOWBURN Durham 401 402 P 19 – pop. 3 748 – ☎ 0191.

♦London 265 – Durham 3 – ♦Middlesbrough 20.

Road Chef Lodge without rest., Tursdale, DH6 5NP, at junction of A 1(M) with A 177 ☏ 377 3666, Fax 377 1448, Reservations (Freephone) 0800 834719 – ⚹ ▣ ☎ ♿ Ⓟ. ⚹
closed Christmas – ⊡ 4.75 – **38 rm** 35.50 **t.**

BOWDON Gtr. Manchester 402 403 404 M 23 – see Altrincham.

BOWLAND BRIDGE Cumbria – see Newby Bridge.

BOWNESS-ON-WINDERMERE Cumbria 402 L 20 - see Windermere.

BOX Avon 403 404 M 29 – see Bath.

BRACKENTHWAITE FELL Cumbria – see Buttermere.

BRACKLEY Northants. 403 404 Q 27 – pop. 9 113 – ECD : Wednesday – ☎ 01280.

ℹ 2 Bridge St., NN13 5EP ☏ 700111.

♦London 67 – ♦Birmingham 53 – Northampton 21 – ♦Oxford 21.

Crown, 20 Market Pl., NN13 5DP, ☏ 702210, Fax 701840 – ▣ ☎ – 🏔 60. ⬚ AE ⓓ VISA
Meals a la carte approx. 11.00 **t.** – **19 rm** ⊡ 55.00/70.00 **t.** – SB.

ATS Station Building, Northampton Rd ☏ 702000/703188

We suggest :

For a successful tour, that you prepare it in advance.
***Michelin maps** and **guides** will give you much useful information on route planning, places of interest, accommodation, prices etc.*

BRACKNELL Berks. 404 R 29 – pop. 50 325 – ECD : Wednesday – 01344.

Downshire Easthampstead Park, Wokingham 302030.

The Look Out, Countryside Heritage Centre, Nine Mile Ride, RG12 4QW 868196.

London 35 – Reading 11.

Coppid Beech, John Nike Way, RG12 8TF, NW : 3 m. by A 329 on B 3408 303333, Fax 301200, – rm rest – 350.
Rowans : **Meals** *(closed Saturday lunch)* 15.95/25.00 **t.** and a la carte 8.25 – **205 rm** 105.00/295.00 **st.** – SB.

Hilton National, Bagshot Rd, RG12 3QJ, S : 2 m. on A 322 424801, Fax 487454, – rm rest – 200.
Meals (light lunch Saturday) 14.95/18.95 **st.** and a la carte 7.95 – 10.95 – **167 rm** 96.00/130.00 **st.** – SB.

BRADFIELD Berks. 403 404 Q 29 – pop. 1 570 – Reading – 01734.

London 56 – Oxford 28 – Reading 7.

Boot Farm without rest., Southend Rd., Southend, RG7 6ES, SW : 2 m. 744298, –
4 rm 16.00/38.00 **t.**

BRADFIELD COMBUST Suffolk – see Bury St. Edmunds.

BRADFORD W. Yorks. 402 O 22 **Great Britain G.** – pop. 293 336 – ECD : Wednesday – 01274.

See : City★.

West Bowling, Newall Hall, Rooley Lane 724449, BY – Chellow Grange, Haworth Rd 542767, AX - Woodhall Hills, Pudsey 564771/554594, BX – Bradford Moor, Scarr Hall, Pollard Lane 638313, BX – East Bierley, South View Rd 681023, BX – Brighouses Road, Queensbury 882155, AY.

Leeds and Bradford Airport : (0113) 250 9696, NE : 6 m. by A 658 BX.

National Museum of Photography, Film & TV, Pictureville, BD1 1NQ 753678.

London 212 – Leeds 9 – Manchester 39 – Middlesbrough 75 – Sheffield 45.

Plan of Enlarged Area : see Leeds

Stakis Bradford, Hall Ings, BD1 5SH, 734734, Fax 306146 – rm rest – 700. BZ **e**
Meals *(closed Saturday lunch)* (carving lunch) 8.00/16.95 **st.** and a la carte 6.50 – 8.95 – **116 rm** 79.00 **st.**, 4 suites – SB.

Tong Village (Country Club), The Pastures, Tong Lane, BD4 0RP, SE : 4 3/4 m. by A 650 - BY - and B 6135 on Tong Lane 854646, Fax 853661, – rm – 250.
Meals a la carte 13.65/21.95 **t.** 4.95 – 7.50 – **58 rm** 65.00 **t.**, 1 suite – SB.

Guide Post, Common Rd, Low Moor, BD12 0ST, S : 3 m. by A 641 off A 638 607866, Fax 671085 – – 100. on plan of Leeds AX **c**
Meals *(closed Saturday lunch)* 8.95/14.95 **t.** and a la carte 3.65 – **43 rm** 50.00/85.00 **st.**

Novotel Bradford, Euroway Trading Estate, Merrydale Rd, BD4 6SA, S : 3 1/2 m. by A 641 and A 6117 off M 606 683683, Telex 517312, Fax 651342, heated – rm – 300. on plan of Leeds AX **a**
Meals a la carte 11.75/22.85 **st.** 4.95 – 7.50 – **125 rm** 39.50 **st.** – SB.

Park Drive, 12 Park Drive, Heaton, BD9 4DR, 480194, Fax 484869, – . AX **e**
Meals (light lunch)/dinner 12.50 **st.** and a la carte – **11 rm** 46.00/56.00 **st.** – SB.

Brow Top Farm without rest., Baldwin Lane, Clayton, BD14 6PS, SW : 4 1/2 m. by A 647 - AY - off Baldwin Lane 882178, « Working farm », – .
3 rm 20.00/30.00.

Restaurant Nineteen (Smith) with rm, 19 North Park Rd, Heaton, BD9 4NT, 492559, Fax 483827 – . AX **n**
closed Sunday, 2 weeks August-September and 1 week Christmas – **Meals** (dinner only) 26.00 **t.** – **4 rm** 65.00/80.00 **t.** – SB
Spec. Sautéed scallops with leeks and soya ginger, Roast Gressingham duck with cashew nut and corn pancake, plum sauce, Elderflower ice cream with warm grapes in Muscat.

Bombay Brasserie, Simes St., Westgate, BD1 3RB, 737564, « Former Baptist church » – . AZ **a**
Meals - Indian a la carte 12.00/16.10 **t.** 4.00.

at Gomersal SE : 7 m. by A 650 on A 651 – BY – Bradford – 01274 :

Gomersal Park, Moor Lane, BD19 4LJ, NW : 1 1/2 m. by A 651 off A 652 869386, Fax 861042, – – 250.
Meals 9.95/25.00 **st.** and a la carte 5.25 – 7.25 – **49 rm** 70.00/80.00 **st.**, 1 suite – SB.

ATS 8 Cranmer Rd 632233/632106
ATS 177 Thornton Rd 731141/723015
ATS Tong Street (ASDA) 680155

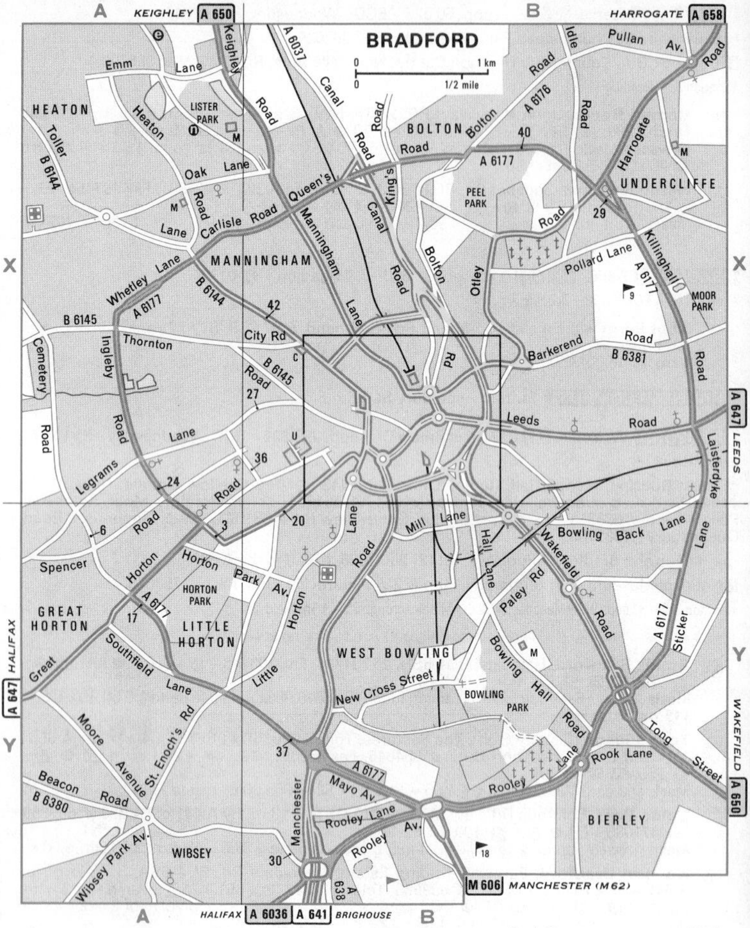

BRADFORD

0 1 km
0 1/2 mile

KEIGHLEY A 650
HARROGATE A 658
LEEDS A 647
WAKEFIELD A 650
MANCHESTER (M62) M 606
HALIFAX A 6036
A 641 BRIGHOUSE
HALIFAX A 647

HEATON
LISTER PARK
MANNINGHAM
BOLTON
PEEL PARK
UNDERCLIFFE
MOOR PARK
HORTON PARK
GREAT HORTON
LITTLE HORTON
WEST BOWLING
BOWLING PARK
BIERLEY
WIBSEY

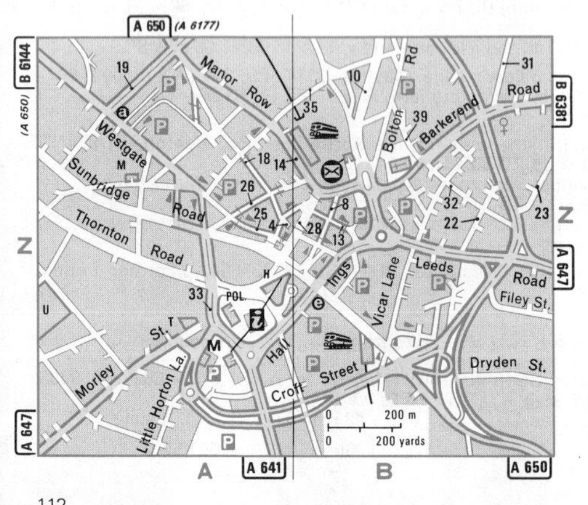

Bank Street AZ 4
Broadway BZ 8
Charles Street BZ 13
Market Street BZ 28

All Saints Road AY 3
Beckside Road AY 6
Canal Road BZ 10
Cheapside BZ 14
Cross Lane AY 17
Darley Street AZ 18
Drewton Road AZ 19
Easby Road BY 20
East Parade BZ 22
Harris Street BZ 23
Horton Grange Road AX 24
Ivegate AZ 25
Kirkgate AZ 26
Listerhills Road BX 27
Northcote Road BX 29
Odsal Road BY 30
Otley Road BZ 31
Peckover Street BZ 32
Prince's Way AZ 33
School Street BZ 35
Shearbridge Road BX 36
Smiddles Lane BY 37
Stott Hill BZ 39
Valley View Grove BX 40
White Abbey Road BX 42

BRADFORD-ON-AVON Wilts. 403 404 N 29 The West Country G. – pop. 8 815 – ECD : Wednesday – ☎ 01225.

See : Town★★ - Saxon Church of St. Lawrence★★ – Bridge★.

Envir. : Great Chalfield Manor★ (All Saints★) *AC*, NE : 3 m. by B 3109 – Westwood Manor★ *AC*, S : 1½ m. by B 3109 – Top Rank Tory (≤★).

Exc. : Bath★★★, NW : 7½ m. by A 363 and A 4 – Corsham Court★★ *AC*, NE : 6½ m. by B 3109 and A 4.

ℹ The Library, Bridge St., BA15 1BY ✆ 865797.

London 118 – Bristol 24 – Salisbury 35 – Swindon 33.

Woolley Grange, Woolley Green, BA15 1TX, NE : ¾ m. by B 3107 on Woolley St. ✆ 864705, Fax 864059, ≤, « 17C manor house », heated, – rest TV ☎ P – 40. AE VISA
Meals 28.00/25.00 **st.** and lunch a la carte 4.90 – **18 rm** 90.00/165.00 **st.**, 2 suites – SB.

Widbrook Grange, Trowbridge Rd, Widbrook, BA15 1UH, SE : 1 m. on A 363 ✆ 864750, Fax 862890, , park – rest TV ☎ P – 25. AE VISA.
Meals (by arrangement)(residents only)(dinner only) 18.50 **t.** 6.00 – **18 rm** 30.00/85.00 **t.**, 1 suite.

Georgian Lodge, 25 Bridge St., BA15 1BY, ✆ 862268, Fax 722417 – TV. AE VISA.
Meals *(closed Monday lunch)* a la carte 13.50/20.00 **st.** 4.25 – **10 rm** 30.00/100.00 **st.** – SB.

Bradford Old Windmill, 4 Masons Lane, BA15 1QN, on A 363 ✆ 866842, Fax 866842, ≤, – TV P. AE VISA.
Meals - Ethnic Vegetarian (by arrangement) (communal dining) 18.00 **st.** – **4 rm** 39.00/75.00 **s.**

Priory Steps, Newtown, off Market St., BA15 1NQ, ✆ 862230, Fax 866248, ≤, « 17C weavers cottages », – TV P. VISA.
Meals (by arrangement) 15.00 **st.** 3.75 – **5 rm** 40.00/56.00 **st.**

at Monkton Farleigh NW : 4 m. by A 363 – ✉ Bradford-on-Avon – ☎ 01225 :

Fern Cottage without rest., 74 Monkton Farleigh, BA15 2QJ, ✆ 859412, Fax 859018, – TV P
3 rm 25.00/45.00 **st.**

The Guide is updated annually so renew your Guide every year.

BRADWELL Derbs. 402 403 404 O 24 – ✉ Sheffield – ☎ 01433.

London 181 – Derby 51 – Manchester 32 – Sheffield 16 – Stoke-on-Trent 41.

Stoney Ridge without rest., Granby Rd, S30 2HU, W : ¾ m. by Gore Lane ✆ 620538, , – TV P
3 rm 22.00/46.00 **st.**

BRAFFERTON HELPERBY N. Yorks 402 P 21 – see Boroughbridge.

BRAINTREE Essex 404 V 28 – pop. 30 975 – ECD : Thursday – ☎ 01376.

18 Kings Lane, Stisted ✆ 346079 – 9 Towerlands, Panfield Rd ✆ 552487/326802.

ℹ Town Hall Centre, Market Sq., CM7 6YG ✆ 550066.

London 45 – Cambridge 38 – Chelmsford 12 – Colchester 15.

White Hart, Bocking End, CM7 6AB, ✆ 321401, Fax 552628, – rm TV ☎ P – 40. AE VISA.
Meals *(closed dinner 25 December)* (grill rest.) a la carte 11.65/18.50 **t.** 5.25 – **31 rm** 59.50/71.00 **t.** – SB.

ATS 271-275 Rayne Rd ✆ 323306

BRAITHWAITE Cumbria 401 402 K 20 – see Keswick.

BRAMHALL Ches. 402 403 404 N 23 – ✉ Stockport – ☎ 0161.

London 190 – Chesterfield 35 – Manchester 11.

Bramhall Moat House (Q.M.H.), Bramhall Lane South, SK7 2EB, on A 5102 ✆ 439 8116, Telex 668464, Fax 440 8071, – rm TV ☎ P – 110. AE VISA.
closed 25 to 30 December – **Meals** (bar lunch)/dinner 13.50 **st.** and a la carte 5.90 – 7.50 – **65 rm** 65.00/75.00 **st.** – SB.

at Woodford S : 2 m. on A 5102 – ✉ Bramhall – ☎ 0161 :

Olivers, 547 Chester Rd, SK7 1PR, on A 5102 ✆ 440 8715 – P. AE VISA
closed Saturday lunch, Sunday dinner and Monday – **Meals** 6.50/9.95 **t.** and a la carte 4.90.

BRAMHOPE W. Yorks. 402 P 22 – see Leeds.

BRAMLEY Surrey 404 S 30 – see Guildford.

BRAMLEY S. Yorks. 402 403 404 Q 23 – see Rotherham.

BRAMPTON Cumbria 401 402 L 19 **Great Britain G.** – pop. 3 957 – ECD : Thursday – ☎ 0169 77.
Envir. : Hadrian's Wall★★, NW : by A 6077.
Talkin Tarn ☎ 2255.
Moot Hall, Market Square, CA8 1RWA ☎ 3433 (summer only).
♦London 317 – ♦Carlisle 9 – ♦Newcastle upon Tyne 49.

- **Farlam Hall** ⊗, CA8 2NG, SE : 2 ¾ m. on A 689 ☎ 46234, Fax 46683, ≤, « Gardens » – TV ☎ P. AE VISA
  closed 25 to 31 December – **Meals** (dinner only) 29.00 **t.** 5.25 – **12 rm** (dinner included) 92.00/205.00 **t.** – SB.
- **Kirby Moor,** Longtown Rd, CA8 2AB, N : ½ m. on A 6071 ☎ 3893, Fax 41847, – TV ☎ P. AE VISA
  closed 25-26 December – **Meals** (light lunch)/dinner 11.95 **t.** and a la carte 5.55 – **6 rm** 36.50/46.00 **t.** – SB.

at Kirkcambeck N : 7 ¾ m. by A 6071 and Walton rd – ✉ Brampton – ☎ 0169 77 :

- **Cracrop Farm** ⊗, CA8 2BW, W : 1 m. by B 6318 on Stapleton rd ☎ 48245, Fax 48333, « Working farm », – TV P. AE.
  closed Christmas – **Meals** (by arrangement) (communal dining) 14.00 **st.** – **4 rm** 20.00/40.00 **st.**

at Lanercost NE : 2 m. by A 689 – ✉ Brampton – ☎ 0169 77 :

- **Abbey Bridge Inn,** CA8 2HG, ☎ 2224, Fax 2224 – rm P. VISA
  Meals a la carte 12.50/21.00 **st.** – **7 rm** 20.00/50.00 **st.** – SB.

at Talkin S : 2 ¾ m. by B 6413 – ✉ Brampton – ☎ 0169 77 :

- **Hullerbank** ⊗, CA8 1LB, NW : ½ m. by Hallbankgate rd ☎ 46668, « Working farm », – P
  Meals (by arrangement) (communal dining) 12.00 **st.** – **3 rm** 25.00/38.00 **st.**

BRANDESBURTON Humbs. 402 T 22 – ✉ Great Driffield – ☎ 01964.
♦London 197 – ♦Kingston-upon-Hull 16 – York 37.

- **Burton Lodge,** YO25 8RU, S : ½ m. on A 165 ☎ 542847, Fax 542847, 18, – rest TV ☎ P. AE VISA
  Meals (residents only)(dinner only) 14.00 **st.** 4.00 – **9 rm** 35.00/45.00 **st.** – SB.

BRANDON Warks. 403 404 P 26 – see Coventry (W. Mids.).

BRANDS HATCH Kent – ✉ Dartford – ☎ 01474.
9 Corinthian, Gay Dawn Farm, Fawkham, Dartford ☎ 707559.
♦London 22 – Maidstone 18.

- Brands Hatch Thistle (Mt. Charlotte Thistle), DA3 8PE, on A 20 ☎ 854900, Fax 853220 – rm rest TV ☎ P – 270
  135 rm, 2 suites.

at Fawkham E : 1 ½ m. by A 20 – ✉ Ash Green – ☎ 01474 :

- **Brands Hatch Place,** DA3 8NQ, ☎ 872239, Fax 879652, park, squash – rest TV ☎ P – 120. AE VISA.
  Meals *(closed Saturday lunch)* 17.50/18.50 **t.** and a la carte – **29 rm** 75.00/120.00 **t.**

BRANSCOMBE Devon 403 K 32 **The West Country G.** – pop. 501 – ECD : Thursday – ✉ Seaton – ☎ 01297.
See : Village★.
Envir. : Seaton (≤★★) NW : 3 m.
♦London 167 – Exeter 20 – Lyme Regis 11.

- **The Look Out** ⊗, EX12 3DP, S : ¾ m. by Beach rd ☎ 680262, Fax 680272, ≤ cliffs and Beer Head, « Tastefully converted coastguards cottages », – rest TV P
  closed 1 week Christmas – **Meals** *(closed Monday)* (dinner only) 22.00 **t.** 5.55 – **5 rm** 54.00/86.00 **t.** – SB.
- **Masons Arms,** EX12 3DJ, ☎ 680300, Fax 680500, « 14C inn » – TV ☎ P – 80. VISA
  Meals (bar lunch Monday to Saturday)/dinner 24.00 **st.** 5.50 – **21 rm** 22.00/80.00 – SB.

BRANSTON Lincs. 402 404 S 24 – see Lincoln.

BRANSTON Staffs. – see Burton-upon-Trent.

BRATTON FLEMING Devon 403 I 30 – ✉ Barnstaple – ☎ 01598.
♦London 228 – Barnstaple 6 – Exeter 46 – Taunton 36.

- **Bracken House** ⊗, EX31 4TG, ☎ 710320, ≤, – rest TV P. VISA
  mid March-mid November – **Meals** (dinner only) 14.00 **t.** 3.50 – **8 rm** (dinner included) 51.00/92.00 **t.** – SB.

BRAUNSTONE Leics. 402 403 404 Q 26 – see Leicester.

BRAUNTON Devon 403 H 30 **The West Country G.** – pop. 7 563 – ECD : Wednesday – ☎ 01271.
See : Town★ - St. Brannock's Church★.
Envir. : Braunton Burrows★, W : 3 m. by B 3231.
18, 18 Saunton ✆ 812436.
♦London 226 – Exeter 47 – Taunton 58.

XX **Grays Country,** Knowle, EX33 2NA, N : 1 ¼ m. on A 361 ✆ 812809, – . VISA
closed Sunday and Monday – **Meals** (dinner only) a la carte 16.40/22.40 **t.** 5.50.

BRAY-ON-THAMES Berks. 404 R 29 – pop. 8 121 – ✉ Maidenhead – ☎ 01628.
♦London 34 – Reading 13.

Plan : see Maidenhead

Monkey Island, SL6 2EE, SE : ¾ m. by Old Mill Lane ✆ 23400, Fax 784732, ←, « Island on River Thames », , – rm – 120. VISA. X
closed 26 December-mid January – **Meals** (bar lunch Saturday) 18.50/23.50 **t.** and a la carte – 8.50 – **23 rm** 80.00/95.00 **t.**, 2 suites.

XXXX ✪✪✪ **Waterside Inn** (Roux) with rm, Ferry Rd, SL6 2AT, ✆ 20691, Fax 784710, « ← Thames-side setting », – rest . VISA JCB. X **s**
closed 26 December-27 January – **Meals** - French (closed Tuesday lunch, Sunday dinner from 3rd weekend October-2nd weekend April, Monday and Bank Holidays) 29.00/ 62.50 **st.** and a la carte 55.50/76.00 **st.** 11.50 – **7 rm** 120.00/210.00 **st.**, 1 suite
Spec. Tronçonnettes de homard poêlées minute au Porto blanc, Filets de lapereau grillés aux marrons glacés, Soufflé chaud aux framboises.

BREADSALL Derbs. – see Derby.

BREDONS NORTON 403 404 N 28 – see Tewkesbury.

BREDWARDINE Heref. and Worcs. 403 L 27 – ✉ Hereford – ☎ 01981.
♦London 150 – Hereford 12 – Newport 51.

Bredwardine Hall , HR3 6DB, ✆ 500596, –
March-October – **Meals** 12.00 **st.** 4.00 – **5 rm** 35.00/50.00 **st.** – SB.

BRENCHLEY Kent 404 V 30 – pop. 2 756 – ✉ Tonbridge – ☎ 01892.
18 Moatlands, Watermans Lane ✆ 724400.
♦London 44 – ♦Brighton 41 – Hastings 28 – Maidstone 15.

Bull Inn, High St., TN12 7NQ, ✆ 722701 – rm .
Meals *(closed 25 December)* a la carte 8.15/17.65 **st.** 3.75 – **4 rm** 24.00/45.00 **t.** – SB.

BRENT ELEIGH Suffolk – see Lavenham.

BRENT KNOLL Somerset 403 L 30 – pop. 1 142 – ECD : Wednesday and Saturday – ✉ Highbridge – ☎ 01278.
18 Brean, Coast Rd, Burnham-on-Sea ✆ 751595.
♦London 151 – ♦Bristol 33 – Taunton 21.

Battleborough Grange, Bristol Rd, TA9 4HJ, E : 2 m. on A 38 ✆ 760208, Fax 760208, – – 90. VISA.
Meals *(closed Sunday dinner in winter)* 15.00 **t.** and a la carte 4.20 – **16 rm** 42.50/ 65.00 **st.** – SB.

BRENTWOOD Essex 404 V 29 – pop. 70 597 – ECD : Thursday – ☎ 01277.
18 King George's Playing Fields ✆ 218714 – 18 Bentley, Ongar Road ✆ 373179 – 9, 18, Warley Park, Magpie Lane, Little Warley ✆ 224891.
Old House, 5 Shenfield Rd, CM15 8AG ✆ 200300.
♦London 22 – Chelmsford 11 – Southend-on-Sea 21.

Marygreen Manor, London Rd, CM14 4NR, SW : 1 ¼ m. on A 1023 ✆ 225252, Telex 995182, Fax 262809, – – 55. VISA.
Meals 19.50/25.00 **t.** and a la carte 4.90 – 8.50 – **32 rm** 88.00/99.50 **st.**, 1 suite – SB.

Forte Posthouse, Brook St., CM14 5NF, SW : 1 ¾ m. on A 1023 ✆ 260260, Fax 264264, , , – rm – 100. VISA.
Meals a la carte approx. 15.00 4.65 – **111 rm** 59.50/69.50 **st.**

ATS Fairfield Rd ✆ 211079 — ATS Unit 30, Wash Rd, Hutton Ind. Est., Hutton ✆ 262877

BRIDGNORTH Shrops. 402 403 404 M 26 **Great Britain G.** – pop. 50 511 – ECD : Thursday – ☎ 01746.
Exc. : Ironbridge Gorge Museum★★ *AC* (The Iron Bridge★★ - Coalport China Museum★★ - Blists Hill Open Air Museum★★ - Museum of the River and Visitor Centre★) NW : 8 m. by B 4373.
18 Stanley Lane ✆ 763315.
The Library, Listley St., WV16 4AW ✆ 763358.
♦London 146 – ♦Birmingham 26 – Shrewsbury 20 – Worcester 29.

Cross Lane House, Astley Abbotts, WV16 4SJ, N : 1 ¾ m. on B 4373 ℘ 764887, Fax 762962, ≤, – rest. **Meals** (residents only)(dinner only) 23.50 **st.** 4.75 – **9 rm** 47.50/52.50 **st.**

Croft, 11 St. Mary's St., WV16 4DW, ℘ 762416 – rest. **Meals** (by arrangement) 12.95 **t.** 5.25 – **12 rm** 23.50/50.00 **st.** – SB.

at Worfield NE : 4 m. by A 454 – ✉ Bridgnorth – 01746 :

Old Vicarage, WV15 5JZ, ℘ 716497, Fax 716552, –. **Meals** *(closed Saturday lunch)* (lunch by arrangement Monday to Friday)/dinner 17.50/26.50 **t.** 7.50 – **12 rm** 65.00/88.00 **t.**, 2 suites – SB.

at Hampton Loade SE : 6 ¼ m. by A 442 – ✉ Bridgnorth – 01746 :

Haywain, WV15 6HD, ℘ 780404, Fax 780533, –. **Meals** *(closed Sunday dinner and Monday)* (dinner only and Sunday lunch)/dinner 15.50/25.00 **st.** 4.20.

at Alveley SE : 7 m. by A 442 – ✉ Bridgnorth – 01746 :

Mill, Birdsgreen, WV15 6HL, NE : ¾ m. ℘ 780437, Fax 780850, park – – 200. **Meals** 7.70/18.75 **t.** and a la carte 5.25 – **21 rm** 42.50/103.00 **t.** – SB.

Per spostarvi più rapidamente utilizzate le carte Michelin "Grandi Strade" :
n° 970 Europa, *n°* 980 Grecia, *n°* 984 Germania, *n°* 985 Scandinavia-Finlanda,
n° 986 Gran Bretagna-Irlanda, *n°* 987 Germania-Austria-Benelux, *n°* 988 Italia,
n° 989 Francia, *n°* 990 Spagna-Portogallo, *n°* 991 Jugoslavia.

BRIDGWATER

BRIDGWATER Somerset 403 L 30 **The West Country G.** – pop. 30 782 – ECD : Thursday – 01278.

See : Town★ – Castle Street★ – St. Mary's★ – Admiral Blake Museum★ *AC.*

Envir. : Westonzoyland (St. Mary's Church★★) SE : 4 m. by A 372 – North Petherton (Church Tower★★) S : 3 ½ m. by A 38.

Exc. : Stogursey Priory Church★★, NW : 14 m. by A 39.

18 Enmore Park, Enmore ℘ 671244.

50 High St., TA6 3BL ℘ 427652 (summer only).

♦London 160 – ♦Bristol 39 – Taunton 11.

Watergate, 10-11 West Quay, TA6 3DB, ℘ 423847, Fax 423847 –. *closed 25 and 26 December* – **Meals** *(closed Sunday)* 17.50 **t.** and a la carte 3.75 – **8 rm** 37.00/47.00 **t.** – SB.

Friarn Court, 37 St. Mary St., TA6 3LX, ℘ 452859, Fax 452988 –. **Meals** *(closed Sunday)* (dinner only) 13.50 **st.** and a la carte 4.50 – 3.00 – **11 rm** 39.90/59.90 **st.** – SB.

at North Petherton S : 3 m. on A 38 – ✉ Bridgwater – 01278 :

Walnut Tree Inn, TA6 6QA, ℘ 662255, Fax 663946 – rest – 90. **Meals** 7.50/13.00 **t.** and a la carte 5.20 – **27 rm** 52.00/88.00 **t.**, 1 suite – SB.

ATS Friarn St. ℘ 455891/455795

BRIDLINGTON

BRIDLINGTON Humbs. 402 T 21 **Great Britain G.** – pop. 32 163 – ECD : Thursday – 01262.

Envir. : Flamborough Head★, NE : 5 ½ m. by B 1255 and B 1259 – Burton Agnes Hall★ *AC*, SW : 6 m. by A 166.

18 Belvedere Rd ℘ 672092/606367 – 18 Flamborough Head, Lighthouse Rd, Flamborough ℘ 850333.

25 Prince St., YO15 2NP ℘ 673474/606383.

♦ London 236 – ♦Kingston-upon-Hull 29 – York 41.

Expanse, North Marine Drive, YO15 2LS, ℘ 675347, Fax 675347, ≤ –. **Meals** 7.75/13.95 **st.** and dinner a la carte – **48 rm** 29.50/65.00 **st.** – SB.

ATS Springfield Av. ℘ 675571

BRIDPORT

BRIDPORT Dorset 403 L 31 **The West Country G.** – pop. 7 2785 – ECD : Thursday – 01308.

Exc. : Parnham House★★ *AC*, N : 6 m. by A 3066 – Lyme Regis★ - The Cobb★, W : 11 m. by A 35 and A 3052.

18 Bridport and West Dorset, East Cliff, West Bay ℘ 422597.

32 South St., DT6 3NQ ℘ 424901.

♦London 150 – Exeter 38 – Taunton 33 – Weymouth 19.

Roundham House, Roundham Gdns, West Bay Rd, DT6 4BD, S : 1 m. by B 3157 ℘ 422753, Fax 421145, ≤, 🌳 – ⇆ rest TV ☎ P. AE ① VISA. ✂
closed November-January – **Meals** (bar lunch)/dinner 15.95 **t.** 3.95 – **8 rm** 30.50/59.00 **t.**

Britmead House, 154 West Bay Rd, DT6 4EG, S : 1 m. on B 3157 ℘ 422941, 🌳 – ⇆ rest TV P. AE ① VISA JCB. ✂
Meals 12.00 **st.** 3.95 – **7 rm** 30.00/52.00 **st.** – SB.

Riverside, West Bay, DT6 4EZ, ℘ 422011. VISA
Meals - Seafood (closed late November-early March) (booking essential) a la carte 12.50/24.00 **t.** 5.50.

at Powerstock NE : 4 m. by A 3066 – ✉ Bridport – ☎ 01308 :

Three Horseshoes Inn, DT6 3TF, ℘ 485328 – TV P
4 rm.

at Shipton Gorge SE : 3 m. by A 35 – ✉ Bridport – ☎ 01308 :

Innsacre with rm, Shipton Lane, DT6 4LJ, N : 1 m. ℘ 456137, Fax 427277, 🌳 – ⇆ rest TV P. VISA
closed 2 weeks November and Christmas – **Meals** *(closed Sunday and Monday to non-residents except Bank Holidays)* (dinner only) 17.70/26.30 **t.** and a la carte 6.00 – **6 rm** 45.00/66.00 **t.** – SB.

ATS Victoria Grove ℘ 423661/2

BRIGHOUSE W. Yorks. 402 O 22 – pop. 32 597 – ☎ 01484.
♦London 213 – Bradford 12 – Burnley 28 – ♦Manchester 35 – ♦Sheffield 39.

Forte Crest, Clifton Village, HD6 4HW, SE : 1 m. on A 644 ℘ 400400, Fax 400068, Fø, ≘s, ⊠ – ⇆ rm TV ☎ & P – 🏛 200
92 rm, 2 suites.

Brook's, 6 Bradford Rd, HD6 1RW, ℘ 715284 – ⇆. VISA
closed Sunday, 2 weeks January and 1 week August – **Meals** (dinner only) 11.75 **t.** and a la carte.

BRIGHTON AND HOVE E. Sussex 404 T 31 **Great Britain G.** – pop. 228 946 (inc. Hove) – ☎ 01273.

See : Town★★ - Royal Pavilion★★★ *AC* CZ – Seafront★★ – The Lanes★ BCZ – St. Bartholomew's★ *AC* CX **B** – Art Gallery and Museum (20C decorative arts★) CY **M.**

Envir. : Devil's Dyke (≤★) NW : 5 m. by Dyke Rd (B 2121) BY.

18 East Brighton, Roedean Rd ℘ 604838 CV – 18 The Dyke, Dyke Rd ℘ 857296, BV – 18 Hollingbury Park, Ditchling Rd ℘ 552010, CV – 18 Waterhall, Devils Dyke Rd ℘ 508658, AV – 18 Pyecombe ℘ 845372, BV.

✈ Shoreham Airport : ℘ 452304, W : 8 m. by A 27 AV.

i 10 Bartholomew Sq., BN1 1JS ℘ 323755 Church Road, BN3 3BQ ℘ 778087.

King Alfred Leisure Centre, Kingsway, BN3 2WW ℘ 746100.

♦London 53 – ♦Portsmouth 48 – ♦Southampton 61.

Plans on following pages

Grand (De Vere), Kings Rd, BN1 2FW, ℘ 321188, Fax 202694, ≤, Fø, ≘s, ⊠ – 🛗 TV ☎ 🚗 – 🏛 800. AE ① VISA BZ **v**
Meals 16.00/32.00 **t.** and a la carte 5.75 – **195 rm** 130.00/160.00 **t.**, 5 suites – SB.

Brighton Thistle (Mt. Charlotte Thistle), Kings Rd, BN1 2GS, ℘ 206700, Fax 820692, ≤, Fø, ≘s, ⊠ – 🛗 ⇆ rm ▤ TV ☎ & 🚗 – 🏛 300. AE ① VISA JCB CZ **n**
Meals (carving rest.) 14.50 **st.** and a la carte 6.00 – (see also ***La Noblesse*** below) – 9.75 – **200 rm** 115.00/159.00 **st.**, 4 suites – SB.

Brighton Metropole, Kings Rd, BN1 2FU, ℘ 775432, Fax 207764, ≤, Fø, ≘s, ⊠ – 🛗 ⇆ rm ▤ rest TV ☎ – 🏛 1200. AE ① VISA JCB BZ **s**
Meals 17.50/17.95 and a la carte 6.45 – **312 rm** 125.00/165.00 **t.**, 16 suites – SB.

Bedford, Kings Rd, BN1 2JF, ℘ 329744, Fax 775877, ≤ – 🛗 ▤ rest TV ☎ 🚗 – 🏛 450. AE ① VISA BZ **c**
Meals (carving rest.) 10.95/16.95 **st.** and a la carte 7.50 – **125 rm** 97.00/155.00 **st.**, 4 suites – SB.

Old Ship, Kings Rd, BN1 1NR, ℘ 329001, Fax 820718 – 🛗 ⇆ TV ☎ 🚗 – 🏛 300. AE ① VISA CZ **c**
Meals (dancing Saturday evening) 14.50/20.00 **st.** and a la carte – **149 rm** 65.00/125.00 **st.**, 3 suites – SB.

Topps, 17 Regency Sq., BN1 2FG, ℘ 729334, Fax 203679 – 🛗 TV ☎. AE ① VISA. ✂ BZ **a**
Meals *(closed Sunday, Wednesday and January)* (dinner only) 18.95 **st.** 3.95 – **15 rm** 45.00/79.00 **st.** – SB.

Brighton Oak, West St., BN1 2RQ, ℘ 220033, Fax 778000 – 🛗 ⇆ rm ▤ rest TV ☎ & – 🏛 200. AE ① VISA. ✂ BZ **i**
Meals (bar lunch Monday to Saturday)/dinner 12.25 **st.** and a la carte – 6.75 – **136 rm** 44.00/54.00 **st.**, 2 suites – SB.

BRIGHTON AND HOVE

Churchill Square Shopping Centre . . . BYZ
George Street . . . AV 10
London Road . . . CX
North Street . . . CZ
Western Road . . . ABY
Adelaide Crescent . . . AY 2
Brunswick Place . . . AY 3
Brunswick Square . . . AYZ 4
Carlton Terrace . . . AV 5
Chatham Place . . . BX 6
Denmark Road . . . BY 7
East Street . . . CZ 8
Eastern Road . . . CV 9
Gladstone Terrace . . . CX 12
Gloucester Place . . . CY 13
Gloucester Road . . . CY 14
Goldsmid Road . . . BX 15
Grand Junction Road . . . CZ 16
Hollingbury Park Av . . . BV 17
Hollingdean Road . . . CV 18
Hove Street . . . AV 19
Market Place . . . CX 20
Marlborough Place . . . CY 21
Montpelier Place . . . BY 22
Old Steine . . . CZ 23
Pavillon Parade . . . CZ 26
Richmond Place . . . CY 27
Richmond Terrace . . . CX 28
St. George's Place . . . CY 30
St. Peter's Place . . . CX 31
Terminus Road . . . BCX 32
Upper Lewes Road . . . CX 33
Warren Road . . . CV 37
Waterloo Place . . . CX 39
Wellington Road . . . AV 40
York Place . . . CY 42

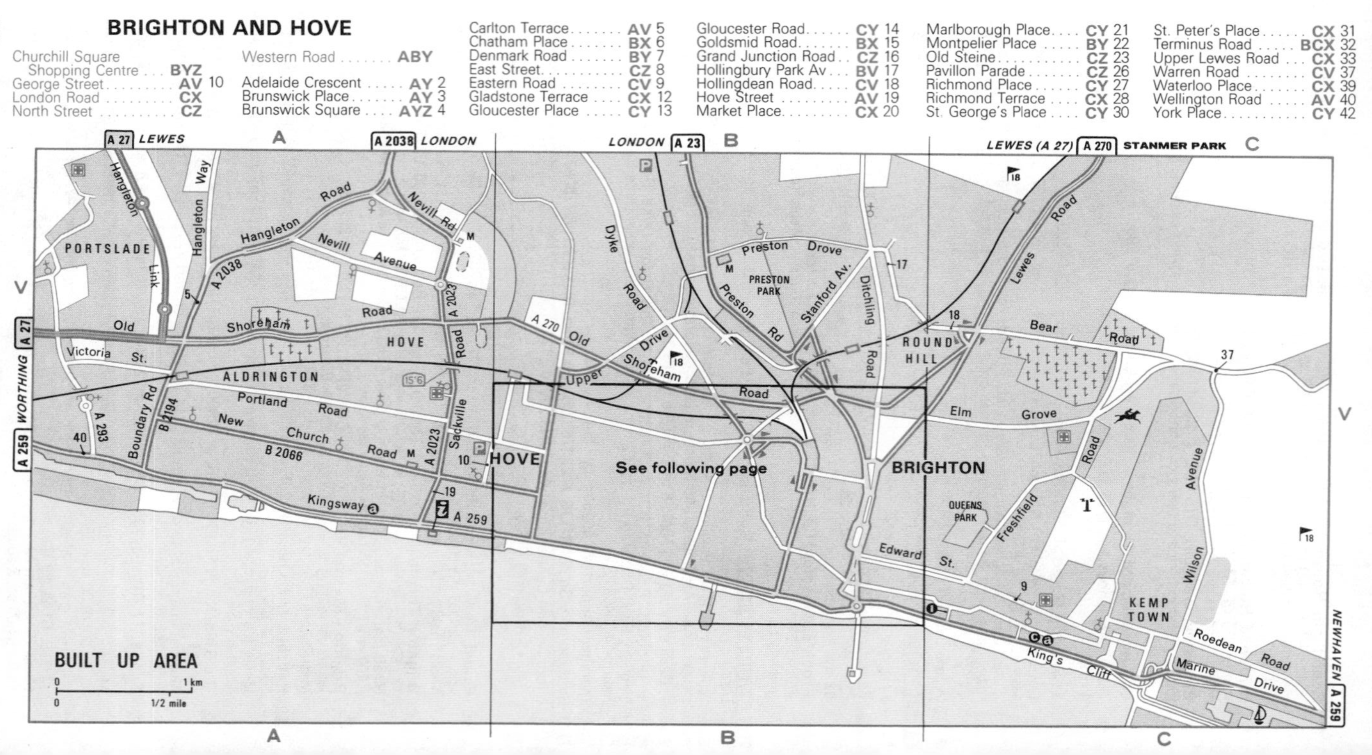

BRIGHTON
HOVE
CENTRE
ROYAL PAVILION
THE LANES
CHURCHILL SQ. SHOPPING CENTRE
THE BRIGHTON CENTRE
ST. ANN'S WELL GARDENS
A 2073
A 259
A 23
A 270
B 2185
B 2066
(A 27)
B 2119
B 2118
B 2120
B 2121
B 2122
A 2010
Ditchling
Viaduct Road
London Rd
New England St.
England Rd
Southover St.
Albion Hill
Sussex St.
Carlton Hill
John St.
Grand Parade
Edward Street
James's St.
Marine Parade
Madeira Drive
Trafalgar Street
North Road
Church St.
North St.
Queen's Road
West St.
King's Road
Buckingham Road
Buckingham Pl.
Dyke Road
Dyke Rd
New Road
Old Shoreham Road
Vernon Ter.
Clifton Hill
Upper North St.
Western Road
Montpelier Road
Preston St.
Davigdor Road
Lansdowne Road
Holland Road
Palmeira Avenue
Selborne Rd
Wilbury Road
First Avenue
Second Av.
The Drive
Eaton Road
Cromwell Road
Tisbury Road
Grand Avenue
Norton Rd
Third Av.
Church Road
Fourth Av.
Kingsway
POL.
X
Y
Z
A
B
C
0
300 m
300 yards
For names of numbered streets, see previous page.

Adelaide, 51 Regency Sq., BN1 2FF, ℘ 205286, Fax 220904 – rest. AE VISA. BZ z
Meals *(closed Sunday and Wednesday)* (residents only)(dinner only) 14.50 **st.** 4.00 – **12 rm** 38.00/75.00 **st.**

Dove, 18 Regency Sq., BN1 2FG, ℘ 779222, Fax 746912 – rest. AE VISA JCB. BZ e
Meals (by arrangement) (residents only) (dinner only) 13.50 **st.** 3.00 – **10 rm** 32.00/78.00 **st.** – SB.

Twenty One, 21 Charlotte St., BN2 1AG, ℘ 686450, Fax 607711 – AE VISA JCB. CV i
Meals *(closed Sunday and Monday)* (by arrangement) (dinner only) 15.95 **st.** 4.10 – **6 rm** 35.00/68.00 **st.** CZ n

Allendale, 3 New Steine, BN2 1PB, ℘ 675436, Fax 602603 – rest. AE VISA. CZ u
closed 20 December-9 January – **Meals** (by arrangement) 14.00 **st.** – **13 rm** 30.00/66.00 **st.** – SB.

Prince Regent without rest., 29 Regency Sq., BN1 2FH, ℘ 329962, Fax 748162 – AE VISA JCB. BZ u
20 rm 30.00/80.00 **t.**

Kempton House, 33-34 Marine Par., BN2 1TR, ℘ 570248, Fax 570248, – AE VISA CZ a
Meals (by arrangement) – **12 rm** 35.00/50.00 **st.**

New Steine without rest., 12a New Steine, BN2 1PB, ℘ 681546 – CZ v
closed January and February – **11 rm** 16.00/43.00 **st.**

La Noblesse (at Brighton Thistle H.), Kings Rd, BN1 2GS, ℘ 206700, Fax 820692 – CZ n
Meals *(closed Saturday lunch and Sunday)* 17.50/23.00 **st.** 6.00.

Langan's Bistro, 1 Paston Pl., Kemp Town, BN2 1HA, ℘ 606933, Fax 675685 – CV a
closed Saturday lunch, Sunday dinner, Monday, last 2 weeks August and first 2 weeks January – **Meals** 14.50 **t.** (lunch) and a la carte 23.00/25.90 **t.**

New Dynasty, 33 Preston St., BN1 2HP, ℘ 202708, Fax 822716 – AE VISA BZ x
Meals - Chinese 15.00/25.00 **t.** and a la carte.

La Marinade, 77 St. Georges Rd, Kemp Town, BN2 1EF, ℘ 600992 – AE VISA CV c
closed Saturday lunch, Sunday dinner and Monday – **Meals** 10.75/23.00 **t.** and a la carte 5.35.

Whytes, 33 Western St., BN1 2PG, ℘ 776618 – AE VISA BZ o
closed Sunday – **Meals** (dinner only) 17.95 **t.**

Black Chapati, 12 Circus Par., off New England Rd, BN1 4GW, ℘ 699011 – AE VISA
closed Sunday dinner, Monday, 1 week June and 1 week Christmas – **Meals** - Indian Specialities (booking essential) (lunch by arrangement Tuesday to Saturday) (buffet lunch Sunday) a la carte 16.25/20.50 **t.** CX a

Le Grandgousier, 15 Western St., BN1 2PG, ℘ 772005 – AE VISA BY x
closed Saturday lunch and 22 December-3 January – **Meals** - French 5.00/20.00 **t.**

Foggs, 5 Little Western St., BN1 2PU, ℘ 735907 – AE VISA JCB BY e
closed 25 to 30 December – **Meals** (dinner only) a la carte 15.55/21.30 **t.** 3.50.

at Hove – Hove – 01273 :

Imperial, First Av., BN3 2GU, ℘ 777320, Fax 777310 – 100. AE VISA AZ e
Meals 11.55 **st.** and a la carte – **75 rm** 60.00/80.00 – SB.

Whitehaven, 34 Wilbury Rd, BN3 3JP, ℘ 778355, Fax 731177, – AE VISA. AX c
Meals *(closed Saturday lunch and Sunday)* 14.50/19.95 **st.** 4.95 – **17 rm** 52.50/75.00 **st.** – SB.

Claremont House, Second Av., BN3 2LL, ℘ 735161, Fax 324764, – AE VISA JCB AY c
Meals 6.50/11.50 **st.** and a la carte 3.50 – **12 rm** 45.00/58.00 **st.** – SB.

Le Classique, 37 Waterloo St., BN3 1AY, ℘ 734140 – AE VISA BY i
closed Sunday – **Meals** - French (dinner only) 15.00 **t.** and a la carte 4.25.

Quentin's, 42 Western Rd, BN3 1JD, ℘ 822734. AE VISA AZ a
closed Saturday lunch, Sunday, Monday and 2 weeks August-September – **Meals** a la carte 13.20/16.75 **t.** 5.50.

ATS 40 Bristol Gdns ℘ 680150/686344 ATS Franklin Rd, Portslade ℘ 415327/414488

BRIMFIELD Heref. and Worcs. 403 404 L 27 **Great Britain G.** – pop. 626 – Ludlow (Shrops.) – 01584 – **Envir.** : Berrington Hall★ *AC*, S : 3 m. by A 49.
London 149 – Birmingham 41 – Hereford 21 – Shrewsbury 32 – Worcester 33.

Forte Travelodge without rest., Woofferton, SY8 4AL, N : ½ m. on A 49 ℘ 711695, Reservations (Freephone) 0800 850950 – AE VISA.
32 rm 33.50 **t.**

XX **Poppies** (at The Roebuck) with rm, SY8 4NE, ✆ 711230, Fax 711654 – TV ☎ P. AE VISA. ✻
closed 2 weeks February and 1 week October – **Meals** *(closed Sunday and Monday)* 20.00 **t.** (lunch) and dinner a la carte 26.90/32.00 **t.** 8.00 – **3 rm** 45.00/60.00 **t.**

BRIMSCOMBE Glos. 403 404 N 28 – see Stroud.

BRISTOL Avon 403 404 M 29 **The West Country G.** – pop. 376 146 – 0117.

See : City★★ – St. Mary Redcliffe★★ DZ – The Georgian House★★ AX **A** – Industrial Museum★★ CZ **M2** – SS Great Britain★★ *AC* AX **B** – The Old City★ CYZ : Theatre Royal★★ CZ **T** – Merchant Seamen's Almshouses★ **K** – St. Stephen's City★ CY **D** – St. John the Baptist★ CY – Cathedral District★ CYZ (Bristol Cathedral★, Lord Mayor's Chapel★) – Bristol "Exploratory"★ DZ – John Wesley's New Room★ DY **E** – City Museum and Art Gallery★ AX **M.**

Envir. : Clifton★★ AX (Suspension Bridge★★★, R.C. Cathedral of SS. Peter and Paul★★ **F**, Bristol Zoological Gardens★★ *AC*, Village★) – Blaise Hamlet★★ - Blaise Castle House Museum★, NW : 5 m. by A 4018 and B 4057 AV.

Exc. : Bath★★★, SE : 13 m. by A 4 BX – Chew Magna★ (Stanton Drew Stone Circles★ *AC*) S : 8 m. by A 37 – BX – and B 3130 – Clevedon★ (Clevedon Court★ *AC*, ≤★) W : 11½ m. by A 370, B 3128 – AX – and B 3130.

18 Mangotsfield, Carsons Rd ✆ 9565501, BV – 18 Beggar Bush Lane, Failand ✆ (01275) 393117/393474, AX – 18 West Town lane, Knowle, Fairway, Brislington ✆ 9776341, BX – 18 Long Ashton ✆ (01275) 392229, AX – 18 Stockwood Vale, Stockwood Lane, Keynsham ✆ 9866505, BX.

Bristol Airport : ✆ (01275) 474444, SW : 7 m. by A 38 AX.

✆ 0345 090700.

St. Nicholas Church, St. Nicholas St., BS1 1UE ✆ 260767 – Bristol Airport, BS19 3DY ✆ (01275) 474444.

♦London 121 – ♦Birmingham 91.

Plans on following pages

Swallow Royal, College Green, BS1 5TA, ✆ 925 5100, Fax 925 1515, Ꮀ, ≘s, – rm TV ☎ & P – 250. AE VISA JCB. ✻ CZ **a**
Terrace : **Meals** 15.75/19.75 **st.** and a la carte 4.50 – *Palm Court* : **Meals** (dinner only) 26.00 **st.** and a la carte 4.50 – **227 rm** 99.50/119.00 **st.**, 15 suites – SB.

Bristol Marriott, 2 Lower Castle St., Old Market, BS1 3AD, ✆ 929 4281, Fax 922 5838, ≤, Ꮀ, ≘s, – rm TV ☎ & P – 600. AE VISA DY **s**
Le Chateau : **Meals** *(closed Sunday)* (dinner only) 19.95 **st.** 8.00 – *The Brasserie* : **Meals** 14.95 **st.** 5.25 – 10.25 – **280 rm** 105.00/115.00 **t.**, 9 suites.

Holiday Inn Crowne Plaza Bristol, Victoria St., BS1 6HY, ✆ 925 5010, Fax 925 5040, Ꮀ – rm rest TV ☎ & P – 200. AE VISA JCB. ✻ DZ **a**
Spires : **Meals** (bar lunch Saturday) a la carte 12.20/24.50 **st.** 6.75 – 10.00 – **132 rm** 100.00/195.00 **st.** – SB.

Grand (Mt. Charlotte Thistle), Broad St., BS1 2EL, ✆ 929 1645, Telex 449889, Fax 922 7619 – rm rest TV ☎ P – 600. AE VISA JCB CY **a**
Meals *(closed Saturday lunch)* 14.50/17.50 **st.** and a la carte – 10.00 – **178 rm** 85.00/95.00 **st.**, 4 suites – SB.

Avon Gorge (Mt. Charlotte Thistle), Sion Hill, Clifton, BS8 4LD, ✆ 973 8955, Fax 923 8125, ≤ – rm TV ☎ – 100. AE VISA JCB AX **x**
Meals 10.75/14.25 **st.** and a la carte 5.10 – **74 rm** 75.00/85.00 **st.**, 2 suites – SB.

Hilton National Bristol, Redcliffe Way, BS1 6NJ, ✆ 926 0041, Telex 449240, Fax 923 0089, Ꮀ, ≘s, – rm rest TV ☎ P – 300. AE VISA JCB DZ **n**
Meals (bar lunch Saturday) 12.95/18.75 **t.** and a la carte 5.95 – 10.50 – **201 rm** 89.00/175.00 **st.** – SB.

Berkeley Square, 15 Berkeley Sq., BS8 1HB, ✆ 925 4000, Fax 925 2970 – TV ☎. AE VISA AX **i**
Meals *(closed Sunday dinner)* (bar lunch Monday to Saturday)/dinner 15.50 **t.** and a la carte 5.25 – 9.50 – **42 rm** 76.00/99.00 **st.**, 1 suite – SB.

St. Vincent Rocks (Forte), Sion Hill, Clifton, BS8 4BB, ✆ 973 9251, Fax 923 8139, ≤ – TV ☎ P – 50. AE VISA AX **c**
Meals (dinner only and Sunday lunch)/dinner 19.95 **s.** and a la carte 5.85 – 8.95 – **46 rm** 75.00/103.00 **st.** – SB.

Westbury Park without rest., 37 Westbury Rd, BS9 3AU, ✆ 962 0465, Fax 962 8607 – TV ☎. AE VISA AV **u**
8 rm 25.00/48.50 **st.**

Forte Travelodge, Cribbs Causeway, BS10 8TL, junction 17, M5 ✆ 501530 – TV & P. AE VISA. ✻ AV **e**
Meals (Harvester grill) a la carte approx. 16.00 **t.** – **40 rm** 33.50 **t.**

Downlands without rest., 33 Henleaze Gdns, BS9 4HH, ✆ 962 1639, Fax 962 1639 – TV. VISA AV **s**
9 rm 23.00/46.00 **s.**

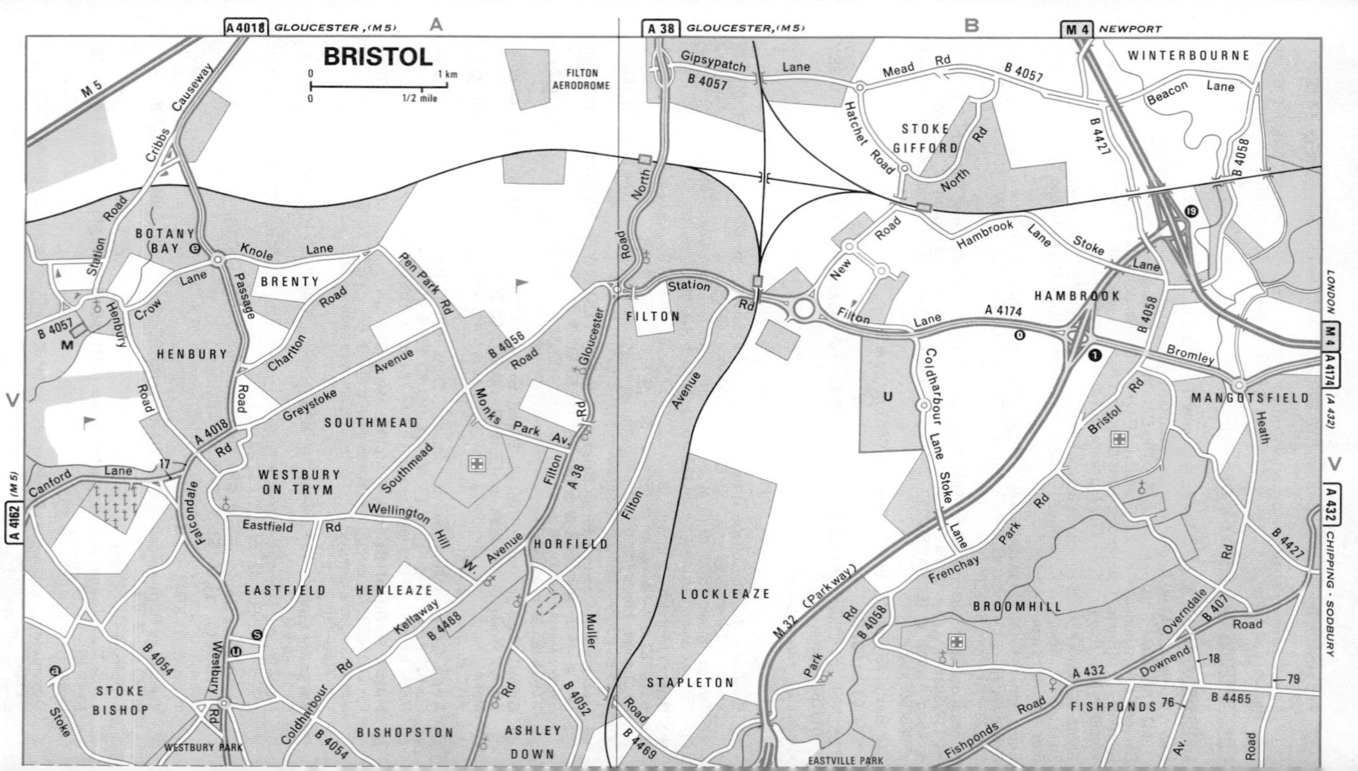

A 4018 GLOUCESTER, (M5)
A
A 38 GLOUCESTER, (M5)
B
M 4 NEWPORT
LONDON M 4 A 4174 (A 432)
A 432 CHIPPING - SODBURY
A 4162 (M 5)
BRISTOL
0 1 km
0 1/2 mile
FILTON AERODROME
WINTERBOURNE
STOKE GIFFORD
HAMBROOK
MANGOTSFIELD
BROOMHILL
FISHPONDS
EASTVILLE PARK
LOCKLEAZE
STAPLETON
FILTON
HORFIELD
ASHLEY DOWN
BISHOPSTON
HENLEAZE
EASTFIELD
SOUTHMEAD
WESTBURY ON TRYM
BRENTY
HENBURY
BOTANY BAY
STOKE BISHOP
WESTBURY PARK
M 5
Cribbs Causeway
Station Road
Knole Lane
Crow Lane
Henbury Road
Passage Road
Charlton Road
Pen Park Rd
B 4056 Road
Gloucester Rd
Greystoke Avenue
A 4018 Rd
Monks Park Av.
Canford Lane
Falcondale Rd
Southmead Road
Wellington Hill W.
Eastfield Rd
Filton Avenue
A 38
Kellaway Av.
B 4468
Muller Road
Westbury Rd
Coldharbour Rd
B 4054
B 4052
B 4469
Gipsypatch Lane
B 4057
Mead Rd
Hatchet Road
North Rd
North Road
Station Rd
New Road
Hambrook Lane
Stoke Lane
Filton Lane
A 4174
Coldharbour Lane
Stoke Lane
B 4427
B 4058
Bromley Heath
Bristol Rd
Frenchay Park Rd
M 32 (Parkway)
Park Rd
Overndale Road
B 407
Downend Road
A 432
Fishponds Road
B 4465
Av.
Road
17
18
76
79

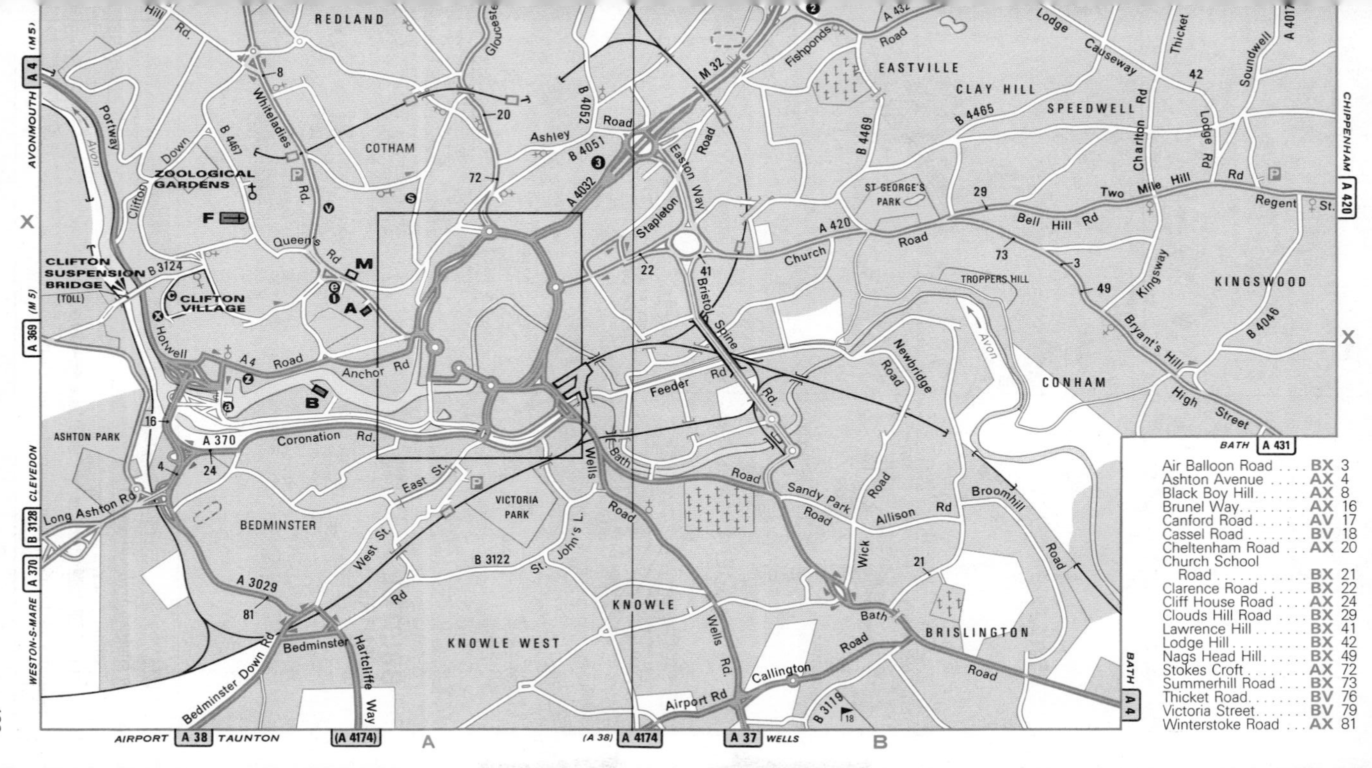

CHIPPENHAM A 420
BATH A 431
BATH A 4
AVONMOUTH A 4 (M 5)
A 369 (M 5)
CLEVEDON B 3128
WESTON-S-MARE A 370
AIRPORT A 38 TAUNTON
(A 4174)
(A 38) A 4174
A 37 WELLS
A
B
X
REDLAND
COTHAM
EASTVILLE
CLAY HILL
SPEEDWELL
KINGSWOOD
CONHAM
TROPPERS HILL
ST GEORGE'S PARK
ZOOLOGICAL GARDENS
CLIFTON SUSPENSION BRIDGE (TOLL)
CLIFTON VILLAGE
ASHTON PARK
BEDMINSTER
VICTORIA PARK
KNOWLE
KNOWLE WEST
BRISLINGTON
Avon
Portway
Whiteladies Rd.
Queen's Rd
Hotwell Road
Anchor Rd
Coronation Rd.
Long Ashton Rd
Bedminster Down Rd
Hartcliffe Way
Wells Rd.
Airport Rd
Callington Road
Bath Road
Sandy Park Road
Wick Road
Allison Rd
Broomhill Road
Newbridge Road
Feeder Rd
Bristol Spine Rd.
Easton Way
Stapleton Road
Church Road
Bell Hill Rd
Two Mile Hill Rd
Regent St.
Bryant's Hill
High Street
Kingsway
Charlton Rd
Lodge Rd
Lodge Causeway
Fishponds Road
Thicket
Soundwell
Ashley Road
Gloucester
Clifton Down
East St.
West St.
St. John's L.
A 4
A 370
A 3029
A 4032
A 420
A 432
A 4017
M 32
B 4052
B 4051
B 4467
B 3124
B 4465
B 4469
B 4046
B 3122
B 3119
Air Balloon Road . . . . BX 3
Ashton Avenue . . . . . AX 4
Black Boy Hill. . . . . . . AX 8
Brunel Way. . . . . AX 16
Canford Road . . . . . . AV 17
Cassel Road . . . . BV 18
Cheltenham Road . . . AX 20
Church School Road . . . . BX 21
Clarence Road . . . . . . BX 22
Cliff House Road . . . . AX 24
Clouds Hill Road . . . . BX 29
Lawrence Hill . . . . BX 41
Lodge Hill. . . . . BX 42
Nags Head Hill. . . . . . BX 49
Stokes Croft . . . . AX 72
Summerhill Road . . . . BX 73
Thicket Road. . . . . BV 76
Victoria Street. . . . . . . BV 79
Winterstoke Road . . . AX 81

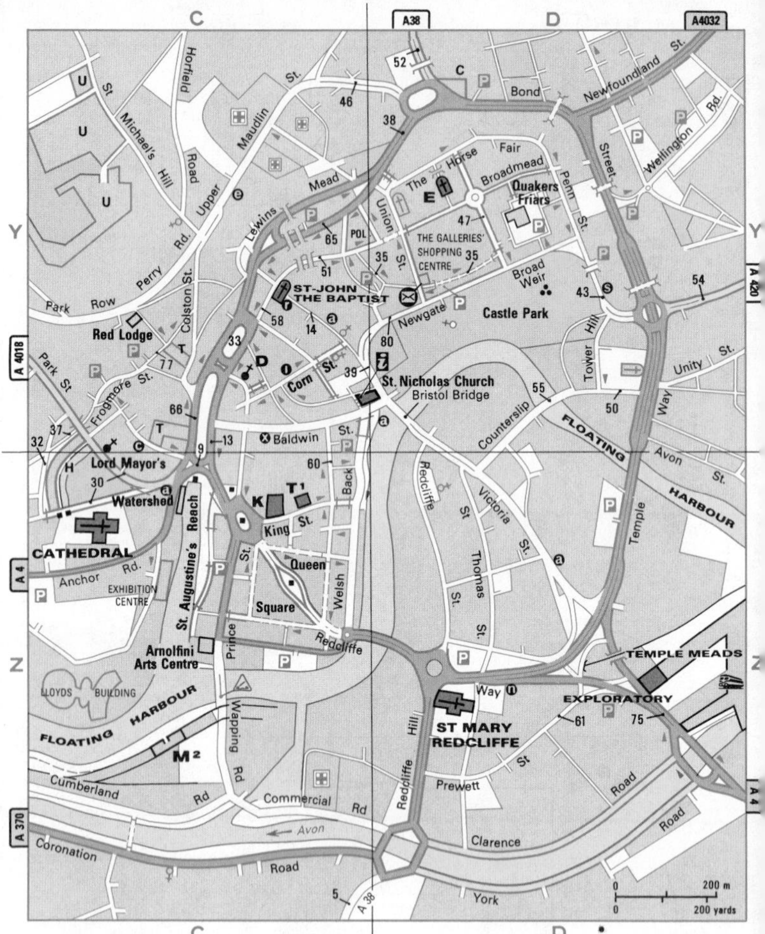

BRISTOL
CENTRE

- Broadmead . . . . DY
- Fairfax Street . . . . CDY 35
- Galleries' (The) Shopping Centre . . . . . . DY
- Horse Fair (The) . . . . DY
- Merchant Street . . . . DY 47
- Nelson Street . . . . CY 51
- Park Street . . . . CY
- Bedminster Parade . . . . CZ 5
- Bridgehead . . . . CZ 9
- Broad Quay . . . . CYZ 13
- Broad Street . . . . CY 14
- College Green . . . . CZ 30
- College Street. . . . . CYZ 32
- Colston Avenue . . . . CY 33
- Frog Lane . . . . CY 37
- Haymarket. . . . . DY 38
- High Street. . . . . CDY 39
- Lower Castle St. . . . . DY 43
- Marlborough St. . . . . CDY 46
- Narrow Plain . . . . DY 50
- North Street . . . . DY 52
- Old Market St. . . . . DY 54
- Passage Street . . . . DY 55
- Quay Street. . . . . CY 58
- Queen Charlotte St. . . . . . . CZ 60
- Redcliffe Mead Lane . . . . . DZ 61
- Rupert Street. . . . . CY 65
- St. Augustine's Parade. . . . CY 66
- Temple Gate . . . . DZ 75
- Trenchard Street. . . . . CY 77
- Wine Street. . . . . DY 80

When travelling for business or pleasure in England, Wales, Scotland and Ireland:

– use the series of five maps (nos 401, 402, 403, 404 and 405) at a scale of 1:400 000

– they are the perfect complement to this Guide

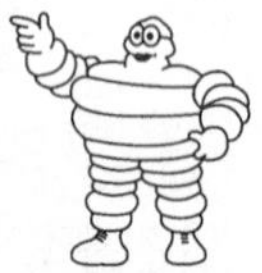

XXX ✿ **Harveys,** 12 Denmark St., BS1 5DQ, ☎ 927 5034, Fax 927 5003, « Medieval cellars and wine museum » – ▤. AE VISA CY **c**
closed Saturday lunch, Sunday and Bank Holidays – **Meals** 16.00/30.00 **st.** and a la carte 23.00/36.00 **st.**
Spec. Sautéed fresh langoustines in creamed hazelnut oil, Breast of pigeon with roasted goose liver, shallots and a grenadine sauce, Harvey's speciality apple dessert.

XX ✿✿ **Lettonie** (Blunos), 9 Druid Hill, Stoke Bishop, BS9 1EW, ☎ 968 6456, Fax 968 6943 – AE VISA AV **a**
closed Sunday, Monday, 2 weeks summer, 10 days Christmas and Bank Holidays – **Meals** - French (booking essential) 17.95/34.50 **t.** 6.85
Spec. Squat lobster and pike tortellini with a lobster butter sauce, Stuffed leg of rabbit braised in cider with a sage cream sauce, Gooseberry and elderflower ice cream.

XX **Markwicks,** 43 Corn St., BS1 1HT, ☎ 926 2658, Fax 926 2658 – AE VISA CY **i**
closed Saturday lunch, Sunday, 1 week Easter, last 2 weeks August and 10 days Christmas-New Year – **Meals** 15.00/19.50 **t.** and a la carte.

XX **Hunt's,** 26 Broad St., BS1 2HG, ☎ 926 5580, Fax 926 5580 – AE VISA CY **r**
closed Saturday lunch, Sunday, Monday, 1 week Easter, 1 week August and 10 days Christmas – **Meals** 13.50 **st.** (lunch) and a la carte 21.70/27.40 **st.** 5.95.

XX **China Palace,** 18a Baldwin St., BS1 1SE, ☎ 926 2719, Fax 925 6168 – ▤. AE VISA JCB CY **x**
Meals - Chinese a la carte 24.95/28.70 **t.** 4.50.

XX **Glass Boat,** Welsh Back, nr Bristol Bridge, BS1 4SB, ☎ 929 0704. AE VISA DY **a**
closed Sunday and 1 to 20 January – **Meals** 9.95/15.95 **t.** and a la carte 5.25.

XX **Michaels,** 129 Hotwell Rd, BS8 4RU, ☎ 927 6190, Fax 925 3629 – ⅔. AE VISA AX **z**
closed 29 August-2 September, 26 December and 1 January – **Meals** (dinner only and Sunday lunch)/dinner 23.95 **t.** 4.50.

XX **Du Gourmet,** 43 Whiteladies Rd, BS8 2LS, ☎ 973 6230, Fax 923 7394 – ▤. AE VISA AX **v**
closed Saturday lunch and Sunday – **Meals** a la carte 15.35/22.65 **t.** 4.45.

X **Jameson's,** 30-32 Upper Maudlin St., BS2 8DJ, ☎ 927 6565, Fax 927 6835. AE VISA CY **e**
closed Bank Holidays – **Meals** (dinner only and Sunday lunch)/dinner 18.95 **t.** and a la carte 4.50.

X **Bistro Twenty One,** 21 Cotham Road South, Kingsdown, BS6 5TZ, ☎ 942 1744 – AE VISA JCB AX **s**
closed Saturday lunch and Sunday – **Meals** 12.95 **t.** and a la carte.

X **Howards,** 1a/2a Avon Crescent, Hotwells, BS1 6XQ, ☎ 926 2921 – AE VISA AX **a**
closed Saturday lunch and Sunday – **Meals** 13.00/15.00 **st.** and a la carte.

X **Danton,** 2 Upper Byron Pl., The Triangle, BS8 1JY, ☎ 926 8314 – AE VISA AX **e**
closed Saturday lunch, Sunday, 1 week Christmas and Bank Holidays – **Meals** 15.00 **t.** (lunch) and a la carte 16.60/21.40 **t.** 7.95.

at Patchway N : 6 ½ m. on A 38 – BV – ✉ Bristol – ☎ 01454 :

Aztec, Aztec West Business Park, BS12 4TS, N : 1 m. by A 38 ☎ 201090, Fax 201593, squash – rm ▤ rest – 200. AE VISA
Meals (bar lunch Saturday) 11.95/18.00 **st.** and a la carte 6.95 – **86 rm** 83.00/112.00 **st.**, 2 suites – SB.

Stakis Bristol, Woodlands Lane, Bradley Stoke, BS12 4JF, N : 1 m. by A 38 ☎ 201144, Fax 612022, – rm ▤ rest – 85. AE VISA
Meals (bar lunch Saturday and Bank Holidays) (carving lunch) 12.50/20.50 **t.** and dinner a la carte – 9.25 – **108 rm** 92.00/102.00 **t.**, 2 suites – SB.

at Hambrook NE : 5 ½ m. by M 32 on A 4174 – ✉ Bristol – ☎ 0117 :

Forte Crest, Filton Rd, BS16 1QX, ☎ 956 4242, Fax 956 9735, park – rm ▤ rest – 500 BV **o**
193 rm, 4 suites.

at Winterbourne NE : 7 ½ m. by M 32 and A 4174 on B 4058 – BV – ✉ Bristol – ☎ 01454 :

Jarvis Grange H. & Country Club, Northwoods, BS17 1RP, NW : 2 m. by B 4057 on B 4427 ☎ 777333, Fax 777447, – rm – 150. AE VISA
Meals *(closed Saturday lunch)* 13.95/16.95 **st.** and a la carte – 8.25 – **52 rm** 85.00/95.00 **st.** – SB.

at Saltford SE : 7 ½ m. on A 4 – BX – ✉ Bristol – ☎ 01225 :

Brunel's Tunnel House, High St., BS18 3BQ, off Beech Rd ☎ 873873, Fax 874875, – rest . AE VISA
closed 24 to 26 December – **Meals** (by arrangement) 13.50 **st.** 4.00 – **7 rm** 47.00/55.25 **st.** – SB.

at Chelwood SE : 8 ½ m. by A 37 – BX – on A 368 – ✉ Bristol – ☎ 01761 :

Chelwood House, BS18 4NH, SW : ¾ m. on A 37 ☎ 490730, Fax 490730 (ext. 504), – rest . AE VISA JCB
closed first 2 weeks January – **Meals** *(closed Sunday dinner to non-residents)* (bar lunch Monday to Saturday)/dinner a la carte 17.10/26.10 **t.** 5.50 – **11 rm** 49.00/94.00 **st.** – SB.

at Hunstrete SE : 10 m. by A 4 and A 37 – BX – off A 368 – ✉ Bristol – ☎ 01761.

Hunstrete House 🐎, BS18 4NS, ☎ 490490, Fax 490732, ←, « 18C country house, gardens and deer park », ⛱ heated, 🎾 – 🚭 rest TV ☎ P. 🅰 AE ⓓ VISA. ✂
Meals 15.00/25.00 **st.** and dinner a la carte – **22 rm** ☐ 95.00/135.00 **t.**, 1 suite – SB.

at Stanton Wick S : 9 m. by A 37 and A 368 on Stanton Wick rd - BX – ✉ Bristol – ☎ 01761.

Carpenters Arms, BS18 4BX, ☎ 490202, Fax 490763 – 🚭 rm TV ☎ P. 🅰 AE ⓓ VISA. ✂
closed 25 December – **Meals** a la carte 11.15/23.00 **t.** 🍷 5.75 – **12 rm** ☐ 45.50/59.50 **st.** – SB.

ATS 68-72 Avon St. ☎ 971 1269
ATS 551 Gloucester Rd, Horfield ☎ 951 4525
ATS 58-60 Broad St., Staple Hill ☎ 956 4741/ 956 5396/956 4594/ 957 1483
ATS 34-38 St. Johns Lane, Bedminster ☎ 977 6418/977 0674

BRIXHAM Devon 403 J 32 **The West Country G.** – pop. 15 171 – ECD : Wednesday – ☎ 01803.

Envir. : Berry Head★ (←★★★) NE : 1½ m.

ℹ The Old Market House, The Quay, TQ5 8TB ☎ 852861.

◆London 230 – Exeter 30 – ◆Plymouth 32 – Torquay 8.

Lobster Pot, 13a The Quay, TQ5 8AW, ☎ 853131 – 🅰 AE ⓓ VISA
closed 7 to 28 February and 24 to 26 December – **Meals** - Seafood (closed lunch Saturday, Sunday and January-March) (live music most evenings) a la carte 15.15/32.25 **t.** 🍷 4.95.

BROAD CAMPDEN Glos. – see Chipping Campden.

BROAD CHALKE Wilts. 403 404 O 30 – see Salisbury.

BROADHEMBURY Devon 403 K 31 – ✉ Honiton – ☎ 01404.

◆London 191 – Exeter 17 – Honiton 5 – Taunton 23.

Drewe Arms, EX14 0NF, ☎ 841267, « Part 13C thatched inn », 🌳 – P
Meals - Seafood 17.95 **t.** and a la carte 🍷 3.95.

BROADSTAIRS Kent 404 Y 29 – pop. 23 691 (inc. St. Peter's) – ECD : Wednesday – ☎ 01843.

⛳18, ⛳9 North Foreland, Kingsgate, Broadstairs ☎ 862140.

ℹ 6b High St., CT10 1IH ☎ 862242.

◆London 78 – ◆Dover 21 – Maidstone 47.

Castlemere, 15 Western Esplanade, CT10 1TD, ☎ 861566, Fax 866379, ←, 🌳 – TV ☎ P. 🅰 VISA
Meals (light lunch)/dinner 15.95 **st.** 🍷 4.20 – **36 rm** ☐ 37.50/76.00 **st.** – SB.

Marchesi, 18 Albion St., CT10 1LU, ☎ 862481, Fax 861509, ← – P. 🅰 AE ⓓ VISA
closed Sunday dinner and 26 to 30 December – **Meals** 10.50/17.00 **st.** and a la carte 🍷 4.95.

BROADWATER Herts. – see Stevenage.

BROADWAY Heref. and Worcs. 403 404 O 27 **Great Britain G.** – pop. 2 775 – ECD : Thursday – ☎ 01386.

See : Town★.

Envir. : Country Park (Broadway Tower ✳★★), SE : 2 m. by A 44 – Snowshill Manor★ (Terrace Garden★) *AC*, S : 2½m..

⛳18 Willersey Hill ☎ 858997.

ℹ 1 Cotswold Court, WR12 7AA ☎ 852937 (summer only).

◆London 93 – ◆Birmingham 36 – Cheltenham 15 – Worcester 22.

Lygon Arms, High St., WR12 7DU, ☎ 852255, Fax 858611, « Part 16C inn », Lб, ≘s, 🎾, 🌳, 🎾 – TV ☎ P – 🏛 80. 🅰 AE ⓓ VISA JCB
Meals 20.50/32.00 **t.** and a la carte 29.20/41.75 **t.** – ☐ 8.75 – **60 rm** 90.00/145.00, 5 suites – SB.

Broadway, The Green, WR12 7AA, ☎ 852401, Fax 853879, 🌳 – 🚭 rm TV ☎ P. 🅰 AE VISA. ✂
Meals (bar lunch Monday to Saturday)/dinner 8.50 **t.** and a la carte – **20 rm** ☐ 45.00/ 80.00 **t.** – SB.

Collin House 🐎, Collin Lane, WR12 7PB, NW : 1¼ m. by A 44 ☎ 858354, ⛱, 🌳 – P. 🅰 VISA. ✂
closed 24 to 29 December – **Meals** 15.00/22.00 **st.** 🍷 5.00 – **7 rm** ☐ 45.00/86.00 **st.** – SB.

Small Talk Lodge, Keil Close, 32 High St., WR12 7DP, ☎ 858953 – 🚭 rest TV P. 🅰 VISA. ✂
closed February – **Meals** (by arrangement) 16.00 **st.** 🍷 4.50 – **8 rm** ☐ 30.00/50.00 **st.** – SB.

Windrush House without rest., Station Rd, WR12 7DE, ☎ 853577, 🌳 – 🚭 TV P
5 rm ☐ 30.00/40.00.

Whiteacres without rest., Station Rd, WR12 7DE, ☎ 852320, 🌳 – TV P. ✂
March-October – **6 rm** ☐ 30.00/42.00 **st.**

Olive Branch, 78 High St., WR12 7AJ, ☎ 853440, Fax 853440, 🌳 – 🚭 rest TV P. AE. ✂
closed 23 to 31 December – **Meals** (by arrangement) 9.50 **st.** – **7 rm** ☐ 19.50/48.00 **st.**

XX **Hunters Lodge,** High St., WR12 7DT, ✆ 853247, – VISA
closed Sunday dinner, Monday to Wednesday, first 3 weeks February and first 3 weeks August – **Meals** (dinner only and lunch Saturday and Sunday)/dinner 18.50 **t.** and a la carte 4.40.

at Willersey (Glos.) N : 2 m. on B 4632 – ✉ Broadway – ✆ 01386 :

Old Rectory without rest., Church St., WR12 7PN, ✆ 853729, – VISA.
closed Christmas – **8 rm** 50.00/115.00 **st.**

at Willersey Hill (Glos.) E : 2 m. by A 44 – ✉ Broadway – ✆ 01386 :

Dormy House, WR12 7LF, ✆ 852711, Telex 338275, Fax 858636, – rest – 200. VISA
closed 25 and 26 December – **Meals** (bar lunch Saturday) 14.00/25.50 **t.** and a la carte 5.00 – **46 rm** 58.00/116.00 **t.**, 3 suites – SB.

at Buckland (Glos.) SW : 2 ¼ m. by B 4632 – ✉ Broadway – ✆ 01386 :

Buckland Manor, WR12 7LY, ✆ 852626, Fax 853557, ≤, « Part 13C manor in extensive gardens », heated, – rest . VISA.
Meals a la carte 29.30/38.30 **t.** 5.50 – **13 rm** 155.00/290.00 **t.** – SB
Spec. Pithivier of Cornish scallops with caviar and chives, Garlic and herb coated rack of lamb, roasted with a rosemary jus, Glazed summer berries with a basket of homemade cinnamon ice cream.

at Wormington (Glos.) SW : 4 ¼ m. by B 4632 on Wormington rd – ✉ Broadway – ✆ 01386 :

Leasow House without rest., Laverton Meadows, WR12 7NA, E : 1 ¼ m. ✆ 584526, Fax 584596, ≤, – . VISA
7 rm 40.00/60.00 **s.**

BROADWELL Glos. 403 404 O 28 – see Stow-on-the-Wold.

BROCKENHURST Hants. 403 404 P 31 **Great Britain G.** – pop. 7 680 – ECD : Wednesday – ✆ 01590.
Envir. : New Forest★★ (Rhinefield Ornamental Drive★★, Bolderwood Ornamental Drive★★).
18 Brockenhurst Manor, Sway Rd ✆ 623332.
London 99 – Bournemouth 17 – Southampton 14 – Winchester 27.

Rhinefield House, Rhinefield Rd, SO42 7QB, NW : 3 m. ✆ 622922, Fax 622800, « Victorian country mansion, formal gardens », heated, park, – rm – 80. VISA.
Meals 14.00/19.95 **st.** and a la carte 5.00 – **34 rm** 70.00/105.00 **st.** – SB.

Careys Manor, Lyndhurst Rd, SO42 7RH, on A 337 ✆ 623551, Fax 622799, – – 100. VISA
Meals (dancing Saturday evening) 13.95/19.95 **t.** and a la carte – (see also ***Le Blaireau*** below) – **79 rm** 69.00/159.00 **t.** – SB.

Balmer Lawn, Lyndhurst Rd, SO42 7ZB, on A 337 ✆ 23116, Telex 477649, Fax 23864, ≤, heated, squash – – 100. VISA
Meals *(closed Saturday lunch)* (bar lunch)/dinner 15.00 **st.** and a la carte 4.75 – **55 rm** 55.00/90.00 **st.** – SB.

Whitley Ridge, Beaulieu Rd, SO42 7QL, E : 1 m. on B 3055 ✆ 22354, Fax 22856, – . VISA JCB
Meals (dinner only and Sunday lunch)/dinner 19.00 **t.** and a la carte 4.75 – **13 rm** 56.00/106.00 **st.** – SB.

Cottage without rest., Sway Rd, S042 7SH, ✆ 22296, – . VISA.
7 rm 32.00/60.00 **st.** – SB.

XXX **Le Poussin** (Aitken), The Courtyard, rear of 49-55 Brookley Rd, SO42 7RB, ✆ 623063, Fax 622912 – . VISA
closed Sunday dinner, Monday and Tuesday – **Meals** (booking essential) 10.00/30.00 **t.**
Spec. Tagliatelle with wild mushrooms, Trio of meats with a red wine and rosemary sauce, Rich chocolate truffle cake with white chocolate ice cream.

X **Le Blaireau** (at Carey's Manor H.), SO42 7RH, ✆ 623032 – . VISA
Meals - French 7.95/15.95 **t.** and a la carte.

BROMBOROUGH Mersey. 402 403 L 24 – pop. 14 518 – ✉ Wirral – ✆ 0151.
18 Raby Hall Rd ✆ 334 2155 – 18 Ellesmere Port, Chester Rd, Hooton, South Wirral, Ches. ✆ 339 7689.
London 210 – Chester 14 – Liverpool 6.5 – Manchester 46.

The Village H. & Leisure Club, Pool Lane, L62 4UE, on A 41 ✆ 643 1616, Fax 643 1420, squash – rm rest – 200. VISA
Meals *(closed Saturday lunch)* 8.00/12.00 **t.** and a la carte 4.50 – **89 rm** 73.50/83.50 **t.**

Travel Inn, High St., L62 7HZ, ✆ 334 2917, Telex 628225, Fax 334 0443 – rm – 80. VISA.
Meals (Beefeater grill) a la carte approx. 16.00 **t.** – 4.95 – **32 rm** 33.50 **t.**

BROME Suffolk 404 X 26 – see Diss (Norfolk).

BROMLEY CROSS Gtr. Manchester 402 404 M 23 – see Bolton.

BROMSGROVE Heref. and Worcs. 403 404 N 26 – pop. 24 576 – ECD : Thursday – 01527.

Bromsgrove Golf Centre, Stratford Rd ℘ 570505.

Bromsgrove Museum, 26 Birmingham Rd, B61 0DD ℘ 831809.

London 117 – Birmingham 14 – Bristol 71 – Worcester 13.

Stakis Bromsgrove, Birmingham Rd, B61 0JB, N : 2½ m. on A 38 ℘ (0121) 447 7888, Fax 447 7273, – rm rest – 80. AE VISA JCB
Meals *(closed Saturday lunch)* 12.50/17.95 **st.** and dinner a la carte 5.50 – 8.95 – **130 rm** 90.00/100.00 **st.**, 10 suites – SB.

Pine Lodge, 85 Kidderminster Rd, B61 9AB, W : 1 m. on A 448 ℘ 576600, Fax 878981, – rm rest – 200. AE VISA
Meals (light lunch Saturday) 13.95/16.50 **st.** and a la carte – **112 rm** 85.00/95.00 **st.**, 2 suites – SB.

Perry Hall (Jarvis), 13 Kidderminster Rd, B61 7JN, ℘ 579976, Fax 575998, – rm – 70. AE VISA
Meals 10.95/15.95 **t.** and a la carte 6.00 – 8.00 – **58 rm** 72.00/92.00 **st.** – SB.

Bromsgrove Country, 249 Worcester Rd, Stoke Heath, B61 7JA, SW : 2 m. ℘ 835522, Fax 871257, – rm . VISA.
closed Christmas-New Year – **Meals** *(closed Friday to Sunday)* (residents only) (dinner only) 12.00 **st.** 4.50 – **10 rm** 45.00/49.00 **st.**

XXX **Grafton Manor** with rm, Grafton Lane, B61 7HA, SW : 1 ¾ m. by Worcester Rd ℘ 579007, Fax 575221, « 16C and 18C manor », , park – . AE VISA.
Meals *(closed Saturday lunch)* 18.00/32.50 **st.** 6.25 – **7 rm** 85.00/125.00 **st.**, 2 suites – SB.

BROMYARD Heref. and Worcs. 403 404 M 27 – pop. 3 401 – 01885.

T.I.C. & Heritage Centre, 1 Rowberry St., HR7 4DX ℘ 482038.

London 138 – Hereford 15 – Leominster 13 – Worcester 14.

Falcon, Broad St., HR7 4BT, ℘ 483034, Fax 488818 – . VISA
Meals (carving rest.) 5.95/8.00 **st.** 4.50 – **8 rm** 39.50/49.50 **st.**

Granary , Church House Farm, HR7 4NA, N : 4 ¼ m. by B 4214, Edvin Loach rd and Ripplewood rd ℘ 410345, « Working Farm » –
Meals a la carte approx. 12.50 **t.** 3.75 – **5 rm** 20.00/40.00 **t.**

BROOK Hants. 403 404 P 31 – ECD : Tuesday – Lyndhurst – 01703.

London 92 – Bournemouth 24 – Southampton 14.

Bell, SO43 7HE, ℘ 812214, Fax 813958, – . AE VISA
Meals (bar lunch)/dinner 23.50 **t.** and a la carte – **25 rm** 45.00/90.00 **t.** – SB.

BROOKMANS PARK Herts. 404 T 28 – pop. 5 238 – 01707.

London 21 – Luton 21.

XX **Villa Rosa,** 3 Great North Rd, AL9 6LB, SE : 1 ¾ m. on A 1000 ℘ 651444 – . AE VISA
closed Saturday lunch, Sunday and Bank Holidays – **Meals** - Italian a la carte 14.05/22.90 **t.** 4.50.

BROUGHTON Lancs. 402 L 22 – see Preston.

BROUGHTON S. Humbs. 402 S 23 – see Scunthorpe.

BROXTED Essex 404 U 28 – see Stansted Airport.

BROXTON Ches. 402 403 L 24 – pop. 417 – 01829.

London 197 – Birmingham 68 – Chester 12 – Manchester 44 – Stoke-on-Trent 29.

Broxton Hall Country House Whitchurch Rd, CH3 9JS, on A 41 at junction with A 534 ℘ 782321, Fax 782330, – . AE VISA
closed 25 and 26 December – **Meals** 10.00/22.90 **t.** and lunch a la carte **t.** 5.00 – **11 rm** 55.00/75.00 **t.** – SB.

Egerton Arms, Whitchurch Rd, CH3 9JW, on A 41 at junction with A 534 ℘ 782241 –
Meals (grill rest.) – **8 rm.**

at Carden Park W : 1½ m. on A 41 – Chester – 01829 :

Birches, CH3 9DQ, ℘ 731000, Fax 250539, , , , , park, – rest – 160
80 rm, 3 suites.

BRUSHFORD Somerset 403 J 30 – see Dulverton.

When looking for a quiet hotel
use the maps found in the introductory pages
or look for establishments with the sign or .

BRUTON Somerset 403 404 M 30 **The West Country G.** – pop. 2 111 – ☎ 01749.

Exc. : Stourhead★★★ *AC*, W : 8 m. by B 3081.

♦London 118 – ♦Bristol 27 – Bournemouth 44 – Salisbury 35 – Taunton 36.

XX **Truffles,** 95 High St., BA10 0AR, ℘ 812255 – VISA
closed Sunday dinner and Monday – **Meals** 13.50/20.95 **st.** 4.50.

BRYHER Cornwall 403 ㉚ – see Scilly (Isles of).

BUCKDEN Cambs. 404 T 27 – pop. 2 534 – ✉ Huntingdon – ☎ 01480.

♦London 65 – Bedford 15 – ♦Cambridge 20 – Northampton 31.

Lion, High St., PE18 9XA, ℘ 810313, Fax 811070, « Part 15C inn » – TV ☎ P. AE VISA
Meals 8.00/17.00 **t.** and a la carte 3.50 – **15 rm** 55.00/72.00 **t.** – SB.

BUCKHURST HILL Essex 404 ㊸ – pop. 11 243 – ECD : Wednesday – ☎ 0181.

♦London 13 – Chelmsford 25.

Plan : see Greater London (North-East)

Roebuck (Forte), North End, IG9 5QY, ℘ 505 4636, Fax 504 7826 – TV ☎ P – 200. AE VISA JCB HT **u**
Meals 10.25/16.95 **st.** and a la carte 3.80 – 8.50 – **29 rm** 60.00/70.00 **st.** – SB.

BUCKINGHAM Bucks. 403 404 Q 27 **Great Britain G.** – pop. 10 774 – ECD : Thursday – ☎ 01280.

Exc. : Claydon House★ *AC*, S : 8 m. by A 413.

18 Silverstone, Silverstone Rd, Stowe ℘ 850005.

♦London 64 – ♦Birmingham 61 – Northampton 20 – ♦Oxford 25.

Villiers, 3 Castle St., MK18 1BS, ℘ 822444, Fax 822113 – rest TV ☎ P – 250. AE VISA
Meals (bar lunch)/dinner 15.75 **st.** – **34 rm** 58.00/70.00 **st.**, 1 suite.

Buckingham Lodge, Buckingham Ring Rd, MK18 1RY, W : 1 ¼ m. by A 413 on A 421 ℘ 822622, Fax 823074, – rm rest TV ☎ P – 160. AE VISA
Meals 7.75/10.50 **st.** and a la carte 4.50 – 5.95 – **70 rm** 63.00/82.00 – SB.

We suggest :

For a successful tour, that you prepare it in advance.
***Michelin maps** and **guides** will give you much useful information on route planning, places of interest, accommodation, prices etc.*

BUCKLAND Glos. 403 404 O 27 – see Broadway (Heref. and Worc.).

BUCKLERS HARD Hants. 403 404 P 31 – see Beaulieu.

BUCKLOW HILL Ches. 402 403 404 M 24 – see Knutsford.

BUCKNELL Shrops. 403 L 26 – pop. 898 – ☎ 01547.

♦London 158 – ♦Birmingham 55 – Hereford 29 – Shrewsbury 31.

Bucknell House without rest., SY7 0AD, on B 4367 ℘ 530248, , park, – TV P
closed December and January – **3 rm** 21.00/36.00 **s.**

BUDE Cornwall 403 G 31 **The West Country G.** – pop. 6 512 – ECD : Thursday – ☎ 01288.

See : The Breakwater★★ – Compass Point (≤★).

Envir. : Poughill★★ (Church★★) N : 2½ m. - E : Tamar River★★ – Kilkhampton (Church★) NE : 5½ m. by A 39 – Stratton (Church★) E : 1½ m. – Launcells (Church★) E : 3 m. by A 3072 – Marhamchurch (St. Morwenne's Church★) SE : 2½m. by A 39 – Poundstock★ (≤★★, church★, guildhouse★) S : 4½ m. by A 39.

Exc. : Jacobstow (Church★) S : 7 m. by A 39.

18 Burn View ℘ 352006.

The Crescent Car Park, EX23 8LE ℘ 354240.

♦London 252 – Exeter 51 – ♦Plymouth 44 – Truro 53.

Hartland, EX23 8JY, ℘ 355661, Fax 355664, ≤, heated – TV ☎ P
Easter-October and Christmas – **Meals** 13.00/20.00 **t.** 4.20 – **29 rm** 39.95/70.00 **t.** – SB.

Camelot, Downs View, EX23 8RE, ℘ 352361, Fax 355470, – rest TV ☎ P. VISA
Meals (dinner only) 14.00 **st.** and a la carte 4.50 – **21 rm** (dinner included) 38.00/76.00 **st.** – SB.

Bude Haven, Flexbury Av., EX23 8NS, ℘ 352305, – rest TV P. AE VISA
Meals (bar lunch)/dinner 9.00 **st.** 3.50 – **11 rm** 18.00/38.00 **st.**

Meva Gwin, Upton, EX23 0LY, S : 1 ¼ m. on coast rd ℘ 352347, ≤ – rest TV P.
closed January - mid April – **Meals** 8.50 **st.** 3.25 – **13 rm** 18.00/44.00 **st.**

BUDLEIGH SALTERTON Devon 403 K 32 **The West Country G.** – pop. 4 710 – ✆ 01395.

Envir. : East Budleigh (Church*) N : 2½m. by A 376 – Bicton* (garden*) *AC*, N : 3 m. by A 376.

18 East Devon, North View Rd ☎ 442018.

Fore St., EX9 6NG ☎ 445275.

♦London 215 – Exeter 16 – ♦Plymouth 55.

- **Long Range,** Vales Rd, EX9 6HS, by Raleigh Rd ☎ 443321, – rest. *closed January and February* – **Meals** 12.50 **st.** 3.50 – **6 rm** 21.50/43.00 **st.** – SB.

BUDOCK WATER Cornwall – see Falmouth.

BULKINGTON Warks. 403 404 P 26 – see Nuneaton.

BUNWELL Norfolk 404 X 26 – pop. 795 – ECD : Monday and Wednesday – ✆ 01953.

♦London 102 – ♦Cambridge 51 – ♦Norwich 16.

- **Bunwell Manor**, Bunwell St., NR16 1QU, NW : 1 m. ☎ 788304, – AE VISA
  Meals 12.95 **t.** and a la carte 3.90 – **10 rm** 40.00/65.00 **t.** – SB.

BURBAGE Wilts. 403 404 O 29 – see Marlborough.

Les prix	Pour toutes précisions sur les prix indiqués dans ce guide, reportez-vous à l'introduction.

BURFORD Oxon. 403 404 P 28 – pop. 1 807 – ECD : Wednesday – ✆ 01993.

18 ☎ 822149.

The Brewery, Sheep St., 0X18 4LP ☎ 823558.

♦London 76 – ♦Birmingham 55 – Gloucester 32 – ♦Oxford 20.

- **Bay Tree,** 12-14 Sheep St., OX18 4LW, ☎ 822791, Fax 823008, « 16C house, antique furnishings », – AE VISA
  Meals (see *Bay Tree* below) – **20 rm** 55.00/115.00 **t.**, 2 suites – SB.
- **Golden Pheasant,** 91 High St., OX18 4QA, ☎ 823223, Fax 822621 – rest AE VISA.
  Meals a la carte 9.45/17.60 **t.** – **12 rm** 50.00/98.00 **t.** – SB.
- **Lamb Inn,** Sheep St., OX18 4LR, ☎ 823155, Fax 822228, « Part 14C inn, antique furnishings », – rest VISA
  closed 25 and 26 December – **Meals** (bar lunch Monday to Saturday)/dinner 20.00 4.50 – **13 rm** 50.00/80.00 **t.** – SB.
- **Andrews** without rest., 99 High St., OX18 4QA, ☎ 823151, Fax 823240, – VISA.
  closed 25 and 26 December – **8 rm** 50.00/85.00 **t.**
- **Inn For All Seasons,** The Barringtons, OX18 4TN, W : 3¼ m. on A 40 ☎ (01451) 844324, Fax 844375, – AE VISA.
  Meals *(closed Sunday dinner)* 8.00/15.75 **t.** and a la carte 4.75 – **10 rm** 39.50/70.00 **t.** – SB.
- XX **Bay Tree** (at Bay Tree H.), 12-14 Sheep St., OX18 4LW, ☎ 822791, Fax 823008, – AE VISA
  Meals 12.95/21.90 **t.** and dinner a la carte 4.95.

at Fulbrook NE : ¾ m. on A 361 – ✉ Burford – ✆ 01993 :

- **Elm House**, Meadow Lane, OX18 4BW, ☎ 823611, Fax 873937, – VISA.
  Meals 17.50 **s.** – **7 rm** 33.00/65.00 **s.**

BURLAND Ches. – see Nantwich.

BURLEY Hants. 403 404 O 31 **Great Britain G.** – pop. 1 438 – ECD : Wednesday – ✉ Ringwood – ✆ 01425.

Envir. : New Forest** (Rhinefield Ornamental Drive**, Bolderwood Ornamental Drive**).

9 Burley, Ringwood ☎ 402431.

♦London 102 – Bournemouth 17 – ♦Southampton 17 – Winchester 30.

- Burley Manor, Ringwood Rd, BH24 4BS, ☎ 403522, Fax 403227, heated, – – 80
  30 rm.
- **Toad Hall,** The Cross, BH24 4AB, ☎ 403448, Fax 402505 – AE VISA
  Meals (dinner only and Sunday lunch)/dinner 15.45 **t.** 4.00 – **8 rm** 40.00/60.00 **t.** – SB.

BURN BRIDGE N. Yorks. 402 P 22 – see Harrogate.

BURNHAM Bucks. 404 S 29 – pop. 11 169 – ECD : Thursday – ✆ 01628.

♦London 33 – ♦Oxford 37 – Reading 17.

- Burnham Beeches Moat House (Q.M.H.), Grove Rd, SL1 8DP, NW : 1 m. by Britwell Rd ☎ 603333, Fax 603994, , park, – rm – 180
  73 rm, 2 suites.

BURNHAM MARKET Norfolk 404 W 25 **Great Britain G.** – pop. 898 – ☎ 01328.

Envir. : Holkham Hall★★ *AC*, E : 3 m. by B 1155.

♦London 128 – ♦Cambridge 71 – ♦Norwich 36.

Hoste Arms, The Green, PE31 8HD, ☎ 738257, Fax 730103, « 17C inn », – rest TV ☎ P. VISA
Meals (bar lunch)/dinner 16.50 **t.** and a la carte **t.** 5.50 – **15 rm** 47.00/72.00 **st.** – SB.

BURNHAM-ON-CROUCH Essex 404 W 29 – pop. 7 067 – ECD : Wednesday – ☎ 01621.

♦London 52 – Chelmsford 19 – Colchester 32 – Southend-on-Sea 25.

Contented Sole, 80 High St., CM0 8AA, ☎ 782139. VISA
closed Sunday dinner, Monday, last 2 weeks September and 24 December-24 January – **Meals** 11.00/17.50 **t.** and a la carte.

BURNLEY Lancs. 402 N 22 – pop. 91 130 – ☎ 01282.

9, 18 Towneley, Towneley Park, Todmorden Rd ☎ 451636 – 18 Glen View ☎ 421045.

Burnley Mechanics, Manchester Rd, BB11 1JA ☎ 455485.

♦London 236 – Bradford 32 – ♦Leeds 37 – ♦Liverpool 55 – ♦Manchester 25 – ♦Middlesbrough 104 – Preston 22 – ♦Sheffield 68.

Oaks, Colne Rd, Reedley, BB10 2LF, NE : 2½ m. on A 56 ☎ 414141, Fax 33401, , , – rm TV ☎ P – 150. AE VISA
Quills : **Meals** *(closed Saturday lunch)* (dinner only) 18.00 **st.** 6.95 – **56 rm** 79.00/108.00 **st.** – SB.

Rosehill House, Rosehill Av., Manchester Rd, BB11 2PW, ☎ 453931, Fax 455628, – TV ☎ P. AE VISA
Meals (lunch by arrangement)/dinner 12.50 **t.** and a la carte 4.50 – **20 rm** 42.50/58.50 **t.** – SB.

Forte Travelodge without rest., Cavalry Barracks, Barracks Rd, BB11 4AS, W : ½ m. at junction of A 671 with A 679 ☎ 416039, Reservations (Freephone) 0800 850950 – TV P. AE VISA.
32 rm 33.50 **t.**

ATS Healey Wood Rd ☎ 22409/38423/51624

BURNOPFIELD Durham 401 402 O 19 – ☎ 01207.

18 Beamish Park, Beamish, Stanley ☎ (0191) 370 1133 – 18 Hobson Municipal, Hobson, Newcastle-upon-Tyne ☎ 271605.

♦London 287 – ♦Middlesbrough 48 – ♦Newcastle upon Tyne 13.

Burnbrae without rest., Leazes Villas, NE16 6HN, ☎ 270432, – TV P. VISA.
6 rm 22.00/60.00 **s.**

BURNSALL N. Yorks. 402 O 21 – pop. 108 – ECD : Monday and Thursday – ✉ Skipton – ☎ 01756.

♦London 223 – Bradford 26 – ♦Leeds 29.

Red Lion, BD23 6BU, ☎ 720204, Fax 720292 – rest TV ☎ P. VISA.
Meals (bar lunch Monday to Saturday)/dinner 16.95 **t.** 5.70 – **11 rm** (dinner included) 54.50/95.00 **t.** – SB.

BURNT YATES N. Yorks. – see Ripley.

BURPHAM W. Sussex 404 S 30 – see Arundel.

BURRINGTON Devon 403 I 31 – pop. 533 – ECD : Saturday – ☎ 01769.

♦London 260 – Barnstaple 14 – Exeter 28 – Taunton 50.

Northcote Manor , EX37 9LZ, NW : 1½ m. by Barnstaple rd ☎ 560501, Fax 60770, , , park, – rest TV ☎ P. AE VISA JCB
March-October – **Meals** (booking essential) (dinner only) 20.50 **t.** 4.90 – **11 rm** 51.00/104.00 **t.** – SB.

BURSTALL Suffolk – see Ipswich.

BURTON-UPON-TRENT Staffs. 402 403 404 O 25 – pop. 59 040 – ECD : Wednesday – 01283.

Branston, Burton Rd 543207 – , Craythorne Road, Stretton 564329.

Unit 40, Octagon Centre, New St., DE14 3TN 516609.

London 128 – Birmingham 29 – Leicester 27 – Nottingham 27 – Stafford 27.

Stanhope Arms, Ashby Rd East, DE15 0PU, SE : 2½ m. on A 50 217954, Fax 226199, – – 100. VISA.
Meals a la carte 7.60/15.85 **t.** 3.65 – 5.95 – **23 rm** 45.00/50.00 **t.**

Queens, 2-5 Bridge St., DE14 1SY, 564993, Fax 517556 – – 100. AE VISA.
Meals *(closed Saturday lunch)* 7.95/12.50 **t.** and a la carte 7.95 – **24 rm** 59.50/79.50 **t.**, 3 suites.

at Stretton N : 3½ m. by A 50 off A 5121 – Burton-upon-Trent – 01283 :

Dovecliff Hall with rm, Dovecliff Rd, DE13 0DJ, 531818, Fax 516546, <, « Carefully restored Georgian house », , park – . AE VISA.
closed 1 week December and 2 weeks summer – **Meals** *(closed Saturday lunch, Sunday dinner, Monday and Bank Holidays)* 11.50/19.50 **st.** and dinner a la carte 10.00 – **7 rm** 55.00/105.00 **t.** – SB.

at Rolleston-on-Dove N : 3 ¾ m. by A 50 on Rolleston Rd – Burton-upon-Trent – 01283 :

Brookhouse Inn, Brookside, DE13 9AA, 814188, Fax 813644, « Part 17C house, antiques », – . AE VISA.
Meals *(closed Saturday lunch and Sunday dinner)* 13.25 **t.** (lunch) and a la carte 16.65/30.25 **t.** 4.25 – **19 rm** 65.00/85.00 **t.** – SB.

at Newton Solney NE : 3 m. by A 50 on B 5008 – Burton-upon-Trent – 01283 :

Newton Park (Jarvis), DE15 0SS, 703568, Fax 703214, – rm – 100
51 rm.

at Branston SW : 1½ m. on A 5121 – Burton-upon-Trent – 01283 :

Riverside , Riverside Drive, off Warren Lane, DE14 3EP, 511234, Fax 511441, , – – 150. AE VISA
Meals *(closed Saturday lunch)* 10.50/15.95 **t.** and a la carte 4.95 – **22 rm** 55.00/65.00 **t.**

Old Vicarage, 2 Main St., DE14 3EX, 533222, Fax 540258 – . AE VISA
closed Sunday dinner, Monday, and first 2 weeks August – **Meals** 10.95/21.50 **st.** 5.00.

at Barton-under-Needwood SW : 5 m. by A 5121 on A 38 – Burton-upon-Trent – 01283 :

Forte Travelodge without rest., Lichfield Rd, DE13 8EG, on A 38 (northbound carriageway) 716343, Reservations (Freephone) 0800 850950 – . AE VISA.
20 rm 33.50 **t.**

Forte Travelodge without rest., DE13 8EG, on A 38 (southbound carriageway) 716784, Reservations (Freephone) 0800 850950 – . AE VISA.
40 rm 33.50 **t.**

ATS All Saints Rd 565994/563170

BURTONWOOD SERVICE AREA Ches. 402 M 23 – Warrington – 01925.

Forte Travelodge without rest., WA5 3AY, M 62 (westbound carriageway) 710376, Reservations (Freephone) 0800 850950 – . AE VISA.
40 rm 33.50 **t.**

BURY Gtr. Manchester 402 N 23 403 ② 404 N 23 – pop. 61 785 – ECD : Tuesday – 0161.

Unsworth Hall, Blackford Bridge 766 4897 – Lowes Park, Hill Top, Walmersley 764 1231.

Derby Hall, Market St., BL9 0BW 705 5111.

London 211 – Leeds 45 – Liverpool 35 – Manchester 9.

Est, Est, Est!, 703 Manchester Rd, BL9 9SS, on A 56 766 4869 – . AE VISA
closed Saturday lunch, and 25-26 December – **Meals** - Italian 9.95 **t.** and a la carte.

at Walmersley N : 1 ¾ m. on A 56 – Bury – 01706 :

Red Hall, Manchester Rd, BL9 5NA, N : 1 ¼ m. on A 56 822476, Fax 828086 – rest – 35. AE VISA.
closed 26 December-3 January – **Meals** *(closed lunch Monday and Saturday)* 15.00 **st.** and a la carte 4.90 – **20 rm** 50.00/60.00 **st.**

at Birtle NE : 3 m. by B 6222 – ✉ Bury – ☎ 0161 :

⌂ ❀ **Normandie,** Elbut Lane, BL9 6UT, ☎ 764 1170, Fax 764 4866, ≤ – |$| TV ☎ P. VISA AE ⊙ VISA
closed 12 to 18 April, 26 December-7 January and Bank Holidays – **Meals** - French (closed Monday and Saturday lunch and Sunday) (booking essential) 15.00/18.95 **t.** and a la carte 6.35 – **23 rm** ☐ 49.00/79.00 **t.**
Spec. Terrine of wild duck and wood pigeon with lentils, Noisettes of lamb with a red wine sauce and young vegetables, Manadarin flavoured crème brûlée.

ATS John St. ☎ 764 2830/6860

BURY ST. EDMUNDS Suffolk 404 W 27 **Great Britain G.** – pop. 30 563 – ECD : Thursday – ☎ 01284.

See : Town★ - Abbey and Cathedral★★.

Envir. : Ickworth House★ *AC*, SW : 3 m. by A 143.

18 Fornham Park, St. John's Hill Plantation, The Street ☎ 706777.

ℹ 6 Angel Hill, IP33 1UZ ☎ 764667.

♦London 79 – ♦Cambridge 27 – ♦Ipswich 26 – ♦Norwich 41.

⌂ **Angel,** 3 Angel Hill, IP33 1LT, ☎ 753926, Fax 750092 – ⇔ rest TV ☎ P – 🏛 140. VISA AE ⊙ VISA
Meals 13.95/19.75 **st.** and a la carte – **41 rm** ☐ 65.00/95.00 **st.**, 1 suite – SB.

⌂ **Priory,** Tollgate, IP32 6EH, N : 1 ¾ m. by A 1101 on B 1106 ☎ 766181, Fax 767604, ⛲ – ⇔ rm TV ☎ P – 🏛 60. VISA AE ⊙ VISA. ✂
Meals *(closed Saturday lunch)* 17.50 **st.** and a la carte – **27 rm** ☐ 59.00/89.00 **st.** – SB.

⌂ **Butterfly,** Symonds Rd, IP32 7BW, SE : 1 ½ m. by A 1302 and A 134 at junction with A 45 ☎ 760884, Fax 755476 – TV ☎ P – 🏛 40. VISA AE ⊙ VISA
Meals 10.85/11.95 **t.** and a la carte 4.50 – ☐ 6.50 – **66 rm** 49.00 **t.** – SB.

⌂ Suffolk (Forte), 38 The Buttermarket, IP33 1DL, ☎ 753995, Fax 750973 – ⇔ TV ☎ 🚗 P – 🏛 25
33 rm.

⌂ **Ounce House,** 13 Northgate St., IP33 1HP, ☎ 761779, Fax 768315, ⛲ – ⇔ TV ☎ P. VISA ⊙ VISA. ✂
Meals (by arrangement) (communal dining) 18.50 **st.** 3.50 – **4 rm** ☐ 35.00/72.00 **st.**

⌂ **Olde White Hart** without rest., 35 Southgate St., IP33 2AZ, ☎ 755547, Fax 724770 – ⇔ TV ☎ P. VISA AE ⊙ VISA. ✂
10 rm ☐ 39.50/69.50 **st.**

✗ **Mortimer's,** 31 Churchgate St., IP33 1RG, ☎ 760623, Fax 752561. VISA AE ⊙ VISA JCB
closed 2 weeks August-September, 24 December-6 January and Bank Holidays – **Meals** - Seafood (closed Saturday lunch and Sunday) a la carte 11.85/23.30 **t.** 2.90.

at Rougham Green SE : 4 m. by A 1302 and A 134 off A 45 – ✉ Bury St. Edmunds – ☎ 01359.

⌂ **Ravenwood Hall,** IP30 9JA, ☎ 270345, Fax 270788, 🏊 heated, ⛲, park, 🎾 – TV ☎ P – 🏛 120. VISA AE ⊙ VISA
Meals 16.95 **t.** and a la carte 6.95 – **14 rm** ☐ 59.00/97.00 **t.** – SB.

at Bradfield Combust SE : 4 ½ m. on A 134 – ✉ Bury St. Edmunds – ☎ 01284.

✗✗ **Bradfield House** with rm, Sudbury Rd, IP30 0LR, ☎ 386301, Fax 386301, ⛲ – TV ☎ P. VISA VISA. ✂
closed 26 to 30 December – **Meals** *(closed Sunday)* (dinner only) 18.50 **st.** and a la carte 4.50 – **4 rm** ☐ 45.00/65.00 **st.** – SB.

ATS Units 1 and 3, Ailwin Rd, Moreton Hall Ind. Est. ☎ 705610

BUTTERMERE Cumbria 402 K 20 – pop. 139 – ✉ Cockermouth – ☎ 0176 87.

♦London 306 – ♦Carlisle 35 – Kendal 43.

⌂ **Bridge,** CA13 9UZ, ☎ 70252, Fax 70252, ≤ – ⇔ rest ☎ P. VISA VISA
Meals (bar lunch)/dinner 17.50 **st.** 5.50 – **22 rm** ☐ (dinner included) 45.00/90.00 **t.** – SB.

at Brackenthwaite Fell NW : 4 m. on B 5289 – ✉ Cockermouth – ☎ 01900.

⌂ **Pickett Howe** 🔇, CA13 9UY, ☎ 85444, ≤, « Part 17C longhouse », ⛲ – ⇔ TV ☎ P. VISA VISA. ✂
April-mid November – **Meals** (residents only) (communal dining) (dinner only) 3.70 – **4 rm** ☐ (dinner included) -/110.00 **st.**

BUTTERTON Staffs. – see Leek.

BUXTON Derbs. 402 403 404 O 24 – pop. 19 502 – ECD : Wednesday – 01298.

Buxton and High Peak, Townend 23453.

The Cresent, SK17 6BQ 25106.

London 172 – Derby 38 – Manchester 25 – Stoke-on-Trent 24.

Lee Wood, 13 Manchester Rd, SK17 6TQ, on A 5004 23002, Fax 23228, – rm – 100. AE VISA
closed 24 to 29 December – **Meals** 9.95/21.00 **st.** and a la carte 5.00 – **38 rm** 64.00/86.00 **t.** – SB.

Brookfield Hall, Long Hill, SK17 6SU, NW : 1 3/4 m. on A 5004 24151, Fax 24151, ≤, « Victorian country house », – . AE VISA
Meals (dinner only and Sunday lunch)/dinner 17.50 **t.** and a la carte 4.00 – **7 rm** 47.50/75.00 **t.**

Coningsby, 6 Macclesfield Rd, SK17 9AH, 26735, – .
closed December and January – **Meals** (by arrangement) (communal dining) 13.50 **s.** 3.00 – **3 rm** 35.00/45.00 **s.**

Lakenham, 11 Burlington Rd, SK17 9AL, 79209 –
Meals (by arrangement) 12.00 **st.** – **6 rm** 28.00/44.00 **st.**

ATS Staden Lane, off Ashbourne Rd 25608/25655

BYFORD Heref. and Worcs. 403 L 27 – see Hereford.

CADNAM Hants. 403 404 P 31 – pop. 1 882 – ECD : Wednesday – 01703.

London 91 – Salisbury 16 – Southampton 8 – Winchester 19.

Walnut Cottage without rest., Old Romsey Rd, SO40 2NP, off A 31 812275, – .
closed 24 to 26 December – **3 rm** 28.00/42.00 **s.**

CALCOT Glos. – see Tetbury.

CALDBECK Cumbria 401 402 K 19 – pop. 688 – Wigton – 0169 74.

London 308 – Carlisle 13 – Keswick 16 – Workington 23.

Parkend, Park End, CA7 8HH, SW : 1 1/2 m. on B 5299 78494, « Converted 17C farmhouse », – rest . AE VISA
closed 8 to 31 January – **Meals** a la carte approx. 14.00 **t.** 4.25 – **3 rm** 32.00/48.00 **t.**

CALLINGTON Cornwall 403 H 32 **The West Country G.** – pop. 4 265 – ECD : Wednesday – 01579.

Exc. : Launceston★ - Castle★ (≤★) St. Mary Magdalene★, South Gate★, N : 11 1/2 m. by A 388.

London 252 – Exeter 51 – Penzance 67 – Plymouth 14.

Coachmakers Arms, Newport Sq., PL17 7AS, 82567 – . AE VISA.
closed 24 to 26 December – **Meals** a la carte 6.00/13.90 **st.** 3.50 – **4 rm** 24.00/37.00 **st.**

CALNE Wilts. 403 404 O 29 **The West Country G.** – pop. 13 894 – ECD : Wednesday – 01249.

Envir. : Bowood House★ *AC*, (Library ≤★) SW : 2 m. by A 4 – Avebury★★ (The Stones★, Church★) E : 6 m. by A 4.

Bowood G. & C.C., Derry Hill 822228.

London 91 – Bristol 33 – Swindon 17.

Chilvester Hill House, SN11 OLP, W : 3/4 m. by A 4 on Bremhill rd 813981, Fax 814217, heated, – rest . AE VISA.
Meals (booking essential) (residents only) (communal dining) (dinner only) 22.00 **st.** 4.35 – **3 rm** 50.00/75.00 **st.**

ATS Unit 4, Maundrell Rd., Portemarsh Ind. Est. 821622

CALSTOCK Cornwall 403 H 32 **The West Country G.** – pop. 5 964 – Tavistock – 01822.

Envir. : Tamar River★★ – Cotehele★ *AC*, SW : 1 m. - Morwellham★ *AC*, NE : 1 1/2 m.

London 246 – Exeter 48 – Plymouth 22.

Danescombe Valley, Lower Kelly, PL18 9RY, W : 1/2 m. 832414, Fax 832414, ≤ Viaduct and Tamar Valley, « Country house atmosphere » – rest . AE VISA.
closed Wednesday, Thursday and November to Easter except Christmas – **Meals** (dinner only) 30.00 **st.** 3.75 – **5 rm** 75.00/130.00 **st.**

CAMBERLEY Surrey 404 R 29 – pop. 45 108 – ECD : Wednesday – 01276.

London 40 – Reading 13 – Southampton 48.

Frimley Hall (Forte), Lime Av. via Conifer Drive, GU15 2BG, E : 3/4 m. off Portsmouth Rd (A 325) 28321, Fax 691253, – – 60. AE VISA
Meals 14.95/18.95 **t.** and a la carte 7.20 – 8.50 – **66 rm** 98.00 **t.** – SB.

CAMBRIDGE Cambs. 404 U 27 **Great Britain G.** – pop. 91 933 – ECD : Thursday – ☎ 01223.

See : Town*** – St. John's College*** *AC* Y – King's College** (King's College Chapel***) Z The Backs** YZ – Fitzwilliam Museum** Z **M1** – Trinity College** Y – Clare College* Z **B** – Kettle's Yard* Y **M2** – Queen's College* *AC* Z.

18 Cambridgeshire Moat House Hotel, Bar Hill ☎ (01954) 780555 X.

Cambridge Airport : ☎ 61133, E : 2 m. on A 1303 X.

Wheeler St., CB2 3QB ☎ 322640.

♦London 55 – ♦Coventry 88 – ♦Kingston-upon-Hull 137 – ♦Ipswich 54 – ♦Leicester 74 – ♦Norwich 61 – ♦Nottingham 88 – ♦Oxford 100.

Plan on next page

Garden House (Q.M.H.), Granta Pl., off Mill Lane, CB2 1RT, ☎ 63421, Fax 316605, ←, – rm TV ☎ P – 250. AE VISA. Z **n**
Meals 18.95/23.00 **t.** and a la carte – 9.95 – **118 rm** 80.00/160.00 **t.** – SB.

University Arms (De Vere), Regent St., CB2 1AD, ☎ 351241, Fax 315256 – TV ☎ P – 300. AE VISA Z **e**
Meals 11.50/17.00 **st.** and a la carte 6.00 – **114 rm** 96.00/115.00, 1 suite – SB.

Holiday Inn, Downing St., CB2 3DT, ☎ 464466, Fax 464440, – rm TV ☎ P – 150. AE VISA JCB Z **a**
Meals *(bar lunch Monday to Friday)* /dinner 9.95/18.50 **st.** and a la carte 6.95 – 9.95 – **197 rm** 89.00/139.00 **st.**, 2 suites.

Arundel House, 53 Chesterton Rd, CB4 3AN, ☎ 67701, Fax 67721 – rest TV ☎ P – 50. AE VISA. Y **u**
closed 25 and 26 December – **Meals** 9.95/14.95 **t.** and a la carte 4.15 – 2.25 – **105 rm** 28.00/75.00 **t.** – SB.

Gonville, Gonville Pl., CB1 1LY, ☎ 66611, Fax 315470 – rest TV ☎ P – 200. AE VISA Z **r**
Meals 12.50/14.50 **t.** and a la carte 5.00 – **64 rm** 68.00/85.00 **t.**

Centennial, 63-71 Hills Rd, CB2 1PG, ☎ 314652, Fax 315443 – rm TV ☎ P. AE VISA. X **x**
closed 23 December-2 January – **Meals** (lunch by arrangement)/dinner 17.00 **t.** and a la carte 4.00 – **39 rm** 55.00/75.00 **t.** – SB.

Cambridge Lodge, 139 Huntingdon Rd, CB3 0DQ, ☎ 352833, Fax 355166, – TV ☎ P. AE VISA X **i**
Meals 14.95/19.95 **t.** and a la carte 4.00 – **11 rm** 50.00/65.00 **st.**

XX **22 Chesterton Road,** 22 Chesterton Rd, CB4 3AX, ☎ 351880 – AE VISA Y **c**
closed Sunday, Monday and 1 week Christmas – **Meals** (dinner only) 19.95 **t.**

X **Michel's Brasserie,** 21-24 Northampton St., CB3 0AD, ☎ 353110 – AE VISA Y **e**
closed 25 to 27 December and 1 to 3 January – **Meals** 7.45/14.95 **t.** and a la carte.

at Impington N : 2 m. on B 1049 at junction with A 14 – X – ✉ Cambridge – ☎ 01223 :

Forte Posthouse, Lakeview, Bridge Rd, CB4 4PH, ☎ 237000, Fax 233426, , , , – rm TV ☎ P – 60. AE VISA
Meals a la carte approx. 15.00 5.50 – **118 rm** 59.50/69.50 **st.**

at Fowlmere S : 8 ¾ m. by A 1309 – X – and A 10 on B 1368 – ✉ Royston (Herts.) – ☎ 01763 :

XX **Chequers,** High St., SG8 7SR, ☎ 208369 – P. AE VISA
closed Christmas Day – **Meals** 14.25 **t.** (lunch) and dinner a la carte 16.00/25.10 **t.** 4.35.

X **Maguire's,** High St., SG8 7SR, ☎ 208444 – P. AE
closed 25-26 December – **Meals** 16.50/20.50 **t.** and a la carte 4.65.

at Duxford S : 9 ½ m. by A 1309 – X – A 1301 and A 505 on B 1379 – ✉ Cambridge – ☎ 01223 :

Duxford Lodge, Ickleton Rd, CB2 4RU, ☎ 836444, Fax 832271, – TV ☎ P – 30. AE VISA
closed 27 to 30 December – **Meals** *(closed Saturday lunch)* 14.00/15.50 **st.** and a la carte 4.25 – **15 rm** 67.00/87.50 **st.** – SB.

at Bar Hill NW : 5 ½ m. by A 1307 – X – off A 14 – ✉ Bar Hill – ☎ 01954 :

Cambridgeshire Moat House (Q.M.H.), CB3 8EU, ☎ 780555, Fax 780010, , , 18, , , squash – TV ☎ P – 180. AE VISA
Meals *(closed Saturday lunch)* 15.95/16.75 **st.** and a la carte 6.50 – 6.95 – **99 rm** 65.00/78.00 **st.** – SB.

at Lolworth Service Area NW : 6 m. by A 1307 – X – on A 14 – ✉ Cambridge – ☎ 01954 :

Forte Travelodge without rest., CB3 8DR, (northbound carriageway) ☎ 781335, Reservations (Freephone) 0800 850950 – TV P. AE VISA.
20 rm 33.50 **t.**

CAMBRIDGE

Grafton Centre . . . Y
Lion Yard Centre . . Z
Market Hill. . . . . . . Z 18
Market Street . . . . Y 19
Petty Cury . . . . Z 27
Rose Crescent . . . Y 28
St. Andrew's St. . . Z 30
Sidney Street . . . . Y 34
Trinity Street . . . . . Y 36

Bridge Street. . . . . Y 2
Corn Exchange St. Z 6
Downing Street. . . Z 7
Free School Lane . Z 12

Hobson Street . . . Y 14
King's Parade . . . . Z 15
Madingley Rd . X, Y 16
Magdalene St. . . . Y 17
Milton Road . . . . . Y 20
Newmarket Road . Y 21
Northampton St. . Y 22
Parker Street . . . . . Z 23
Peas Hill. . . . . Z 25
Pembroke Street . . Z 26
St. John's Street . . Y 31
Short Street . . . . . Y 32
Trumpington Road Z 37
Wheeler Street . . . Z 39

COLLEGES

CHRIST'S	Y	A	NEW HALL	X	D
CHURCHILL	X	B	NEWNHAM	X	E
CLARE	Z	B	PEMBROKE	Z	N
CORPUS CHRISTI	Z	G	PETERHOUSE	Z	O
DARWIN	Z	D	QUEENS'	Z	
DOWNING	Z	E	RIDSLEY HALL	Z	Q
EMMANUEL	Z	F	ST CATHARINE'S	Z	R
FITZWILLIAM COLLEGE	X	G	ST EDMUNDS HOUSE	Y	U
GONVILLE AND CAIUS	Y	G	ST JOHN'S	Y	
HARVEY COURT	Z	K	SELWYN	X	F
HUGUES HALL	Z	J	SIDNEY SUSSEX	Y	P
JESUS	Y	K	TRINITY	Y	
KING'S	Z		TRINITY HALL	Y	V
LUCY CAVENDISH	Y	O	WESTMINSTER	Y	W
MAGDALENE	Y	N	WOLFSON	X	U

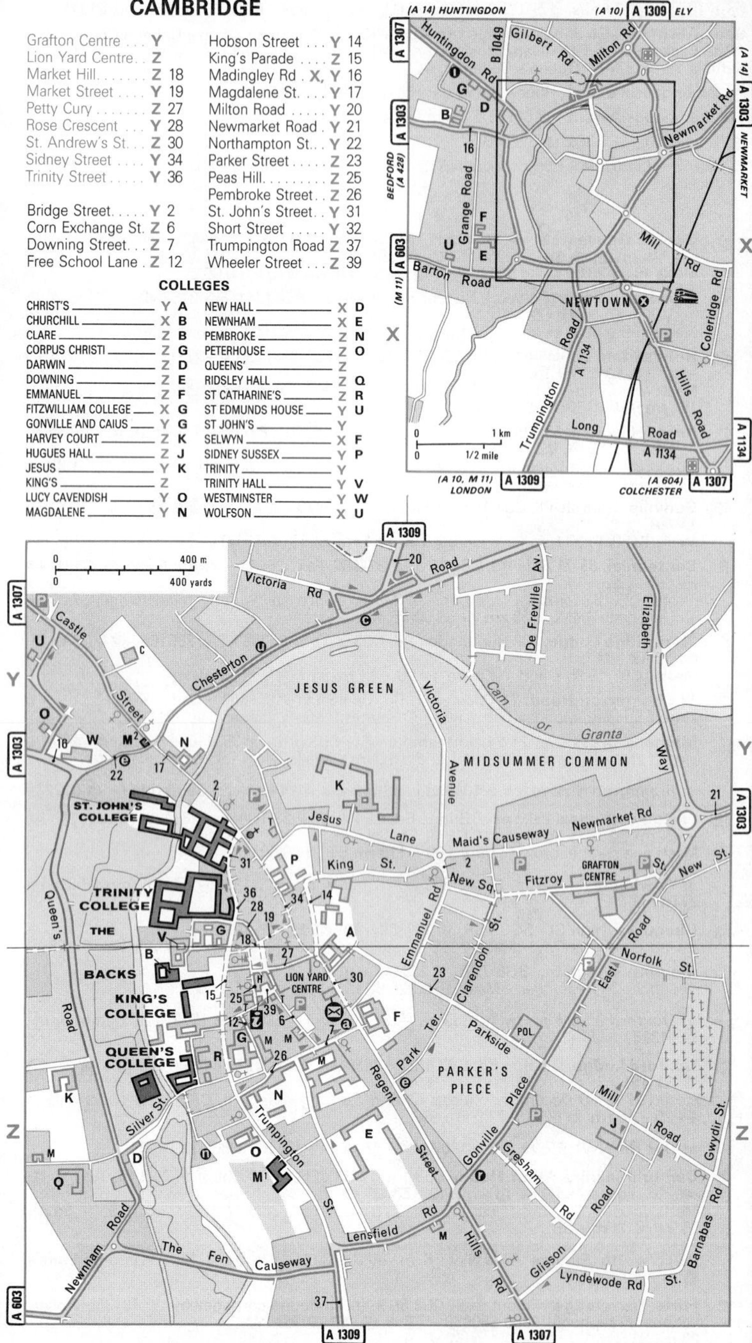

at Swavesey Service Area NW : 8 m. by A 1307 on A 14 – X – ✉ Cambridge – ☎ 01954 :

Forte Travelodge without rest., CB4 5QR, (southbound carriageway) ✆ 789113, Reservations (Freephone) 0800 850950 – TV. AE VISA.
36 rm 33.50 **t.**

ATS 143 Histon Rd ✆ 61695

CANNOCK Staffs. 402 403 404 N 25 **Great Britain G.** – pop. 88 833 – ECD : Thursday – ☎ 01543.

Exc. : Weston Park★★ *AC*, W : 11 m. by A 5.

Cannock Park Municipal, Stafford Rd ✆ 578850.

♦London 135 – ♦Birmingham 20 – Derby 36 – ♦Leicester 51 – Shrewsbury 32 – ♦Stoke-on-Trent 28.

Roman Way, Watling St., Hatherton, WS11 1SH, SW : 1 ¼ m. by A 4601 on A 5 ✆ 572121, Fax 502749 – rm TV – 120. AE VISA
Meals (bar lunch Saturday)/dinner a la carte 12.75/24.00 **t.** 6.00 – **56 rm** 61.00/64.00 **t.** – SB.

Travel Inn, Watling St., WS11 1SJ, SW : 1 m. at junction of A 4601 with A 5 ✆ 572721, Fax 466130 – rm TV – 100. AE VISA.
Meals (Beefeater grill) a la carte approx. 16.00 **t.** – 4.95 – **38 rm** 33.50 **st.**

ATS Cannock Rd, Chadsmoor ✆ 574580/504985 ATS Cannock Rd, Heath Hayes ✆ 274200

CANON PYON Heref. and Worcs. 403 L 27 – see Hereford.

CANTERBURY Kent 404 X 30 **Great Britain G.** – pop. 34 546 – ECD : Thursday – ☎ 01227.

See : City★★★ - Cathedral★★★ Y – St. Augustine's Abbey★★ *AC* YZ **K** – King's School★ Y **B** – Mercery Lane★ Y **12** – Christ Church Gate★ Y **A** – Weavers★ Y **D** – Hospital of St. Thomas the Martyr, Eastbridge★ Y **E** – Poor Priests Hospital★ *AC* Y **M1** – St. Martin's Church★ Y **N** – West Gate★ *AC* Y **R.**

34 St. Margaret's St., CT1 2TG ✆ 766567.

♦London 59 – ♦Brighton 76 – ♦Dover 15 – Maidstone 28 – Margate 17.

Plan on next page

County, High St., CT1 2RX, ✆ 766266, Fax 451512 – TV – 180. AE VISA JCB. Y **n**
Meals (see ***Sullys*** below) – 8.50 – **72 rm** 69.00/93.00 **t.**, 1 suite.

Chaucer (Forte), 63 Ivy Lane, CT1 1TU, ✆ 464427, Fax 450397 – TV – 100. AE VISA JCB Z **c**
Meals (bar lunch Saturday) 9.95/17.95 **t.** and a la carte 6.95 – 8.50 – **42 rm** 60.00/80.00 **t.** – SB.

Falstaff (Country Club), 8-12 St. Dunstan's St., CT2 8AF, ✆ 462138, Fax 463525 – rm TV – 60. AE VISA Y **a**
Meals 11.95/16.95 **st.** 5.00 – 7.50 – **24 rm** 65.00/85.00 **st.** – SB.

Thanington without rest., 140 Wincheap, CT1 3RY, ✆ 453227, Fax 453225, – TV. AE VISA JCB Z **s**
10 rm 45.00/62.00 **t.**

Victoria, 59 London Rd, CT2 8JY, ✆ 459333, Fax 781552 – TV. AE VISA. Y **i**
Meals (grill rest.) 7.45/18.15 **t.** 4.65 – **33 rm** 39.95/43.95 **t.** – SB.

Pilgrims, 15 The Friars, CT1 2AS, ✆ 464531, Fax 762514 – TV. VISA. Y **c**
Meals dinner a la carte 12.95/16.00 **t.** – **15 rm** 45.00/75.00 **t.**

Ebury, 65-67 New Dover Rd, CT1 3DX, ✆ 768433, Fax 459187, – rest TV. AE VISA. Z **r**
closed mid December-mid January – **Meals** (dinner only) (light dinner Sunday) a la carte 16.00 **t.** and a la carte 4.00 – **15 rm** 41.00/62.00 **t.** – SB.

Pointers, 1 London Rd, CT2 8LR, ✆ 456846, Fax 831131 – TV. AE VISA JCB Y **e**
closed Christmas-16 January – **Meals** (dinner only) 12.95 **t.** 4.50 – **14 rm** 38.00/55.00 **t.** – SB.

Ann's House without rest., 63 London Rd, CT2 8JZ, ✆ 768767, Fax 768172, – TV. AE VISA. Y **r**
18 rm 18.00/46.00 **st.**

Magnolia House, 36 St. Dunstan's Terr., CT2 8AX, ✆ 765121, Fax 765121, – TV. AE VISA. Y **s**
Meals (November to February)(by arrangement) 15.00 **t.** – **6 rm** 36.00/80.00 **t.** – SB.

Alexandra House without rest., 1 Roper Rd, CT2 7EH, ✆ 767011, Fax 786671, – TV. Y **u**
7 rm 21.00/46.00.

CANTERBURY

Burgate . . . . Y
Butchery Lane . . . . Y 5
Guildhall Street . . . . Y 6
High Street . . . . Y 8
Mercery Lane . . . . Y 12
Palace Street . . . . Y
St. George's Street . . . . Z 17
St. Margaret's Street . . . . . . YZ 18
St. Peter's Street . . . . Y 20

Beercart Lane . . . . YZ 2
Borough (The) . . . . Y 4
Lower Bridge Street . . . . Z 9
Lower Chantry Lane . . . . Z 10
Rhodaus Town . . . . Z 13
Rosemary Lane . . . . Z 14
St. George's Place . . . . Z 16
St. Mary's Street . . . . Z 19
St. Radigund's Street . . . . . . Y 21
Upper Bridge Street . . . . Z 23
Watling Street . . . . Z 25

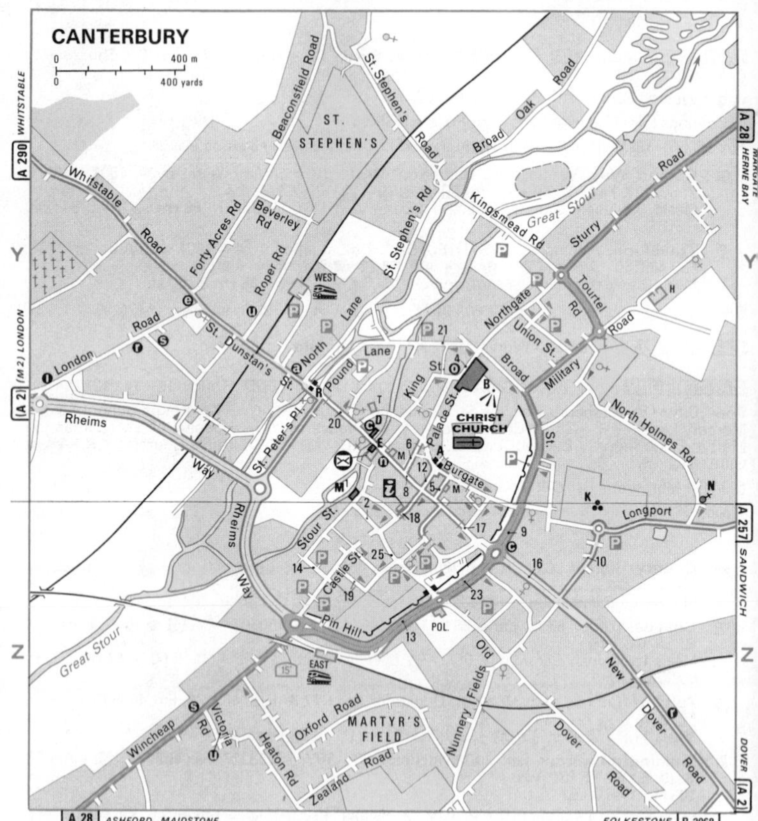

⌂ **Highfield** without rest., Summer Hill, Harbledown, CT2 8NH, ✆ 462772, ⌂ – Ⓟ. VISA. ✶ by Rheims way Y
closed Christmas-New Year – **8 rm** ☐ 29.00/52.00 **st.**

Clare Ellen without rest., 9 Victoria Rd, CT1 3SG, ✆ 760205, Fax 784482, ⌂ – TV Ⓟ. VISA Z **u**
6 rm ☐ 23.00/46.00 **s.**

⌂ **Zan Stel Lodge** without rest., 140 Old Dover Rd, CT1 3NX, ✆ 453654, ⌂ – TV Ⓟ. ✶
4 rm ☐ 20.00/46.00 **st.** by Old Dover Rd Z

XXX **Sullys** (at County H.), High St., CT1 2RX, ✆ 766266, Fax 451512 – Ⓟ. AE VISA JCB Y **n**
Meals 12.50/18.00 **t.** and a la carte.

XX **Tuo e Mio,** 16 The Borough, CT1 2DR, ✆ 761471 – AE VISA Y **o**
closed Tuesday lunch, Monday, last 2 weeks February and last 2 weeks August – **Meals** - Italian a la carte 14.25/22.00 **t.** 3.75.

at Chartham SW : 3 ¼ m. by A 28 – Z – ✉ Canterbury – ☎ 01227 :

⌂ **Thruxted Oast** without rest., Mystole, CT4 7BX, SW : 1 ¼ m. by Rattington St. and Cockering Rd on Mystole Lane ✆ 730080, ←, ⌂ – TV Ⓟ. AE VISA. ✶
closed Christmas – **3 rm** ☐ 65.00/75.00.

at Chartham Hatch W : 3¼ m. by A 28 – Z – ✉ Canterbury – ☎ 01227 :

Howfield Manor, Howfield Lane, CT4 7HQ, SE : 1 m. ☎ 738294, Fax 731535, – TV ☎ P – 80. AE VISA.
Meals (see *Old Well* below) – **13 rm** 62.50/95.00 **st.** – SB.

Old Well (at Howfield Manor H.), Howfield Lane, CT4 7HQ, SE : 1 m. ☎ 738294, Fax 731535, – P. AE VISA
Meals 13.95/18.95 **st.** and a la carte 4.95.

ATS 29 Sturry Rd ☎ 464867/765021

CARBIS BAY Cornwall 403 D 33 – see St. Ives.

CARCROFT S. Yorks. 402 403 404 Q 23 – see Doncaster.

CARDEN PARK Ches. – see Broxton.

CARLISLE Cumbria 401 402 L 19 **Great Britain G.** – pop. 100 562 – ECD : Thursday – ☎ 01228.

See : Town★ - Cathedral★ (Painted Ceiling★) AY **E** – Tithe Barn★ BY **A**.

Envir. : Hadrian's Wall★★, N : by A 7 AY.

18 Aglionby ☎ 513303 BY – 18 Stoneyholme ☎ 34856, BY – 9 Dalston Hall, Dalston ☎ 710165, AZ.

Carlisle Airport ☎ 573641, NW : 5½m. by A 7 BY and B 6264 – **Terminal** : Bus Station, Lowther Street.

☎ 0345 090700.

Carlisle Visitor Centre, Old Town Hall, Green Market, CA3 8JH ☎ 512444.

♦London 317 – ♦Blackpool 95 – ♦Edinburgh 101 – ♦Glasgow 100 – ♦Leeds 124 – ♦Liverpool 127 – ♦Manchester 122 – ♦Newcastle upon Tyne 59.

CARLISLE

Botchergate . . . . **BZ**
Castle Street . . . . **BY** 6
English Street . . . . **BY** 13
Scotch Street. . . . . **BY** 19
The Lanes Shopping Centre . . . . **BY**

Annetwell Street . . . . **AY** 2
Bridge Street. . . . . **AY** 3
Brunswick Street . . . . **BZ** 4
Cecil Street . . . . **BZ** 5
Charlotte Street . . . . **AZ** 7
Chiswick Street . . . . **BY** 8
Church Street . . . . **AY** 10
Eden Bridge. . . . . **BY** 12
Lonsdale Street . . . . **BY** 14

Lowther Street. . . . . **BY** 15
Port Road. . . . . **AY** 16
St. Marys Gate . . . . **BY** 17
Spencer Street . . . . **BY** 20
Tait Street. . . . . **BZ** 21
Victoria Viaduct . . . . **ABZ** 24
West Tower Street . . . . **BY** 26
West Walls . . . . **ABY** 27
Wigton Road . . . . **AZ** 29

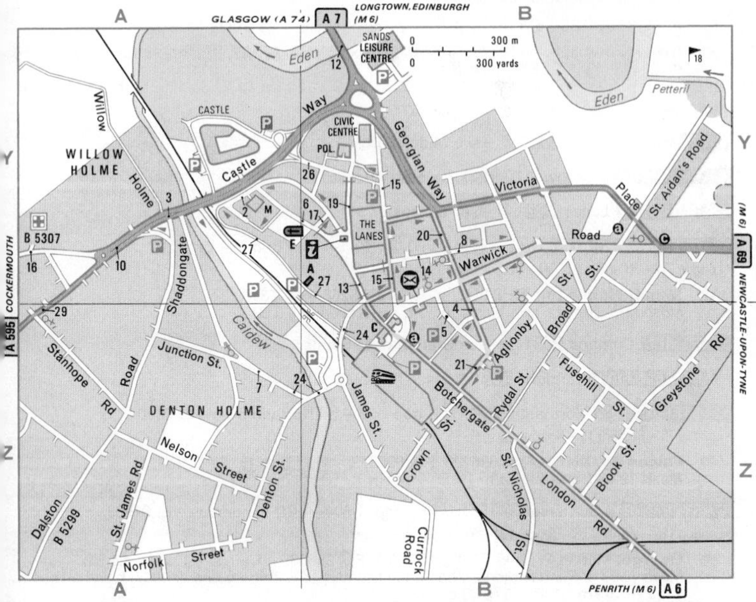

Cumbrian, Court Sq., CA1 1QY, ℘ 31951, Telex 64287, Fax 47799 – rm – 300. BZ a
Meals *(closed lunch Saturday and Sunday)* 9.50/14.95 **st.** and a la carte 4.95 – **70 rm** 79.50/95.00 **st.**

Cumbria Park, 32 Scotland Rd, CA3 9DG, N : 1 m. on A 7 ℘ 22887, Fax 22887 – – 100. BY
closed 25 and 26 December – **Meals** (bar lunch Sunday) 16.50 **t.** (dinner) and a la carte 15.85/23.30 **t.** – **49 rm** 70.00/82.00 **t.** – SB.

Swallow Hilltop, London Rd, CA1 2PQ, SE : 1 m. on A 6 ℘ 29255, Fax 25238, – rm – 500. BZ
Meals (bar lunch Monday to Saturday)/dinner 16.50 **st.** and a la carte 7.00 – **92 rm** 75.00/90.00 **st.** – SB.

Gosling Bridge (Premier), Kingstown Rd, CA3 0AT, N : 1 ¾ m. on A 7 ℘ 515294, Fax 515220 – . BY
Meals (bar lunch)/dinner a la carte 7.90/18.40 **st.** 2.95 – 3.45 – **30 rm** -/39.50 **st.** – SB.

Beeches without rest., Wood St., CA1 2SF, E : 1 ½ m. by A 69 off Victoria Rd ℘ 511962 – . BY
3 rm 25.00/35.00 **st.**

Avondale, 3 St. Aidan's Rd, CA1 1LT, ℘ 23012 – BY a
Meals (by arrangement) (communal dining) 6.50 – **3 rm** 22.00/38.00.

Courtfield House, 169 Warwick Rd, CA1 1LP, ℘ 22767 – BY c
Meals (by arrangement) 7.00 – **4 rm** 25.00/35.00 **s.**

at Kingstown N : 3 m. by A 7 – BY – at junction 44 of M 6 – ✉ Carlisle – 01228 :

Forte Posthouse, Park House Rd, Kingstown, CA3 0HR, on A 7 ℘ 31201, Fax 43178, – rm – 60.
Meals a la carte approx. 15.00 **t.** 5.50 – **93 rm** 56.00 **st.**

at Crosby-on-Eden NE : 4 ½ m. by A 7 and A 689 – BY – on B 6264 – ✉ Carlisle – 01228 :

Crosby Lodge with rm, High Crosby, CA6 4QZ, ℘ 573618, Fax 573428, ←, « 18C country mansion », – rest .
closed 24 December-mid January – **Meals** 15.00/29.00 **t.** and a la carte 6.75 – **11 rm** 65.00/90.00 **t.** – SB.

at Faugh E : 8 ¼ m. by A 69 – BY – ✉ Carlisle – 01228 :

String of Horses Inn, Heads Nook, CA4 9EG, ℘ 70297, Fax 70675, « Elaborately furnished 17C inn », heated – rest .
accommodation closed 24 and 25 December – **Meals** 12.95/16.95 **t.** and a la carte 4.00 – **14 rm** 58.00/98.00 **t.** – SB.

at Wetheral SE : 6 ¼ m. by A 6 – BZ – ✉ Carlisle – 01228 :

Crown, CA4 8ES, on B 6263 ℘ 561888, Fax 561637, squash – rm – 175.
Meals (bar lunch Saturday) 11.95/18.00 **st.** 6.95 – **50 rm** 72.00/128.00 **st.**, 1 suite – SB.

ATS Rosehill Ind. Est., Montgomery Way ℘ 25277

CARLTON N. Yorks. 402 O 21 – see Middleham.

CARLYON BAY Cornwall 403 F 33 – see St. Austell.

CARNFORTH Lancs. 402 L 21 – see Lancaster.

CARTERWAY HEADS Northd 401 402 O 19 – ✉ Shotley Bridge – 01207.

♦London 272 – ♦Carlisle 59 – ♦Newcastle upon Tyne 21.

Manor House Inn, DH8 9LX, on A 68 ℘ 55268 – .
closed Christmas Day – **Meals** 16.50 **t.** and a la carte 3.50.

CARTMEL Cumbria 402 L 21 – see Grange-over-Sands.

CARTMELL FELL Cumbria 402 L 21 – see Newby Bridge.

CASTLE ASHBY Northants. 404 R 27 – pop. 138 – ✉ Northampton – 01604.

♦London 76 – Bedford 15 – Northampton 11.

Falcon, NN7 1LF, ℘ 696200, Fax 696673, – .
Meals 19.00 **t.** and a la carte 4.50 – **14 rm** 59.50/75.00 **t.** – SB.

CASTLE CARY Somerset 403 404 M 30 – pop. 1 904 – ECD : Thursday – 01963.

♦London 125 – ♦Bristol 28 – Taunton 31 – Yeovil 13.

George, Market Pl., BA7 7AH, ℘ 350761, Fax 350035 – rest .
Meals *(closed Sunday dinner)* (bar lunch Monday to Saturday)/dinner 16.00 **t.** and a la carte 3.75 – **15 rm** 45.00/70.00 **t.** – SB.

XX **Bond's** with rm, Ansford Hill, Ansford, BA7 7JP, N : 3/4 m. by Ansford Rd on A 371 ✆ 350464, Fax 350464, – TV ☎ P. VISA.
closed 1 week Christmas – **Meals** (dinner only) 12.50 **st.** and a la carte 4.25 – **7 rm** 38.00/80.00 – SB.

CASTLE COMBE Wilts. 403 404 N 29 **The West Country G.** – pop. 347 – ✉ Chippenham – 01249.
See : Village★★.
◆London 110 – ◆Bristol 23 – Chippenham 6.

Manor House, SN14 7HR, ✆ 782206, Fax 782159, « Part 14C manor house in park », heated, 18, , , – rest TV ☎ P. AE VISA
Meals 16.95/32.00 **t.** and a la carte – 10.00 – **34 rm** 95.00/295.00 **t.**, 2 suites – SB.

at Ford S : 1 3/4 m. on A 420 – ✉ Chippenham – 01249 :

White Hart Inn, SN14 8RP, ✆ 782213, Fax 783075 – TV ☎ P. AE VISA
Meals 12.75/14.00 **t.** and a la carte 5.50 – **11 rm** 43.00/59.00 **t.** – SB.

at Nettleton Shrub W : 2 m. by B 4039 on Nettleton rd (Fosse Way) – ✉ Chippenham – 01249 :

Fosse Farmhouse, SN14 7NJ, ✆ 782286, Fax 783066, – rest TV P. AE VISA
Meals 15.00/25.00 **t.** and dinner a la carte 8.50 – **6 rm** 40.00/110.00 **t.** – SB.

CASTLE DONINGTON Leics. 402 403 404 P 25 – pop. 6 313 – ✉ Derby – 01332.
East Midlands Airport : ✆ 810621, S : by B 6540 and A 453.
◆London 123 – ◆Birmingham 38 – ◆Leicester 23 – ◆Nottingham 13.

Hilton National, East Midlands Airport, Derby Rd, Lockington, DE7 2RH, E : 3 1/4 m. by B 6540 on A 453 at junction with A 6 and M 1 ✆ (01509) 674000, Telex 341031, Fax 672412, , , – rm TV ☎ P – 250. AE VISA JCB
Meals (bar lunch Saturday) 12.95/16.95 **st.** and dinner a la carte 5.65 – ***Zen*** **: Meals** Japanese (Teppan Yaki) (closed Sunday) 12.00/30.00 **st.** 5.65 – 10.50 – **151 rm** 95.00/140.00 **st.**, 1 suite.

Donington Thistle (Mt. Charlotte Thistle), East Midlands Airport, DE74 2SH, SE : 3 1/4 m. by B 6540 on A 453 ✆ 850700, Telex 377632, Fax 850823, , , – rm rest TV ☎ P – 220. AE VISA JCB
Meals (bar lunch Saturday and Bank Holidays) 14.00/19.95 **st.** and a la carte 6.25 – 8.95 – **108 rm** 85.00/140.00 **st.**, 2 suites – SB.

Priest House, Kings Mills, DE74 2RR, W : 1 3/4 m. by Park Lane ✆ 810649, Fax 811141, ≤, « Riverside setting », , park – TV ☎ P – 130. AE VISA.
Meals 10.95/16.50 **t.** and a la carte 5.50 – **43 rm** 74.00/84.00 **t.**, 2 suites – SB.

Donington Manor, High St., DE74 2PP, ✆ 810253, Fax 850330 – TV ☎ P – 80. AE VISA.
closed 26 to 31 December – **Meals** 7.90/8.75 **st.** and a la carte 4.40 – **36 rm** 54.00/72.50 **st.**

at Isley Walton SW : 1 3/4 m. by B 6540 on A 453 – ✉ Derby – 01332 :

Park Farmhouse, Melbourne Rd, DE74 2RN, W : 3/4 m. ✆ 862409, Fax 862364, ≤ – TV ☎ P. AE VISA JCB
closed Christmas – **Meals** (residents only) (dinner only) approx. 16.00 **st.** 3.50 – **9 rm** 38.00/56.00 **st.** – SB.

CASTLETON Derbs. 402 403 404 O 23 **Great Britain G.** – pop. 689 – ECD : Wednesday – ✉ Sheffield (South Yorks.) – 01433.
Envir. : Blue John Caverns★ *AC*, W : 1 m.
◆London 181 – Derby 49 – ◆Manchester 30 – ◆Sheffield 16 – ◆Stoke-on-Trent 39.

Ye Olde Nags Head, S30 2WH, ✆ 620248, Fax 621604 – TV ☎ P. AE VISA.
Meals 14.00/16.85 **t.** and a la carte – **8 rm** 42.50/86.00 **st.** – SB.

CATLOWDY Cumbria 401 402 L 18 – ✉ Carlisle – 01228.
◆London 333 – ◆Carlisle 16 – ◆Dumfries 36 – Hawick 31 – ◆Newcastle upon Tyne 65.

Bessiestown Farm, CA6 5QP, ✆ 577219, , , park – TV P. AE VISA.
Meals (by arrangement) 10.00 **st.** 3.50 – **4 rm** 24.00/43.00 **st.** – SB.

CAWSTON Norfolk 404 X 25 **Great Britain G.** – pop. 2 265 – ✉ Norwich – 01603.
Envir. : Blicking Hall★★ *AC*, NE : 5 m. by B 1145 and B 1354.
◆London 122 – Cromer 15 – King's Lynn 42 – ◆Norwich 13.

Grey Gables, Norwich Rd, NR10 4EY, S : 1 m. ✆ 871259, , – rest TV ☎ P. VISA
closed 24 to 26 December – **Meals** (lunch by arrangement)/dinner 21.50 **st.** 5.50 – **8 rm** 20.00/60.00 **st.** – SB.

CERNE ABBAS Dorset 403 404 M 31 – see Dorchester.

CHADDESLEY CORBETT Heref. and Worcs. 403 404 N 26 – see Kidderminster.

CHADLINGTON Oxon. 403 404 P 28 – pop. 1 310 – ☎ 01608.
♦London 74 – Cheltenham 32 – ♦Oxford 18 – Stratford-upon-Avon 25.

- **Manor** ⑤, OX7 3LX, ☎ 676711, Fax 676674, ≤, 🏡, park – ⇔ rest TV ☎ P. VISA.
  Meals (dinner only) 25.50 **st.** 4.50 – **7 rm** 60.00/120.00 **st.** – SB.
- **Chadlington House,** OX7 3LZ, ☎ 676437, Fax 676503, 🏡 – ⇔ rest TV ☎ P. AE VISA JCB.
  closed December and January – **Meals** (residents only) (dinner only) 15.00 **st.** 4.50 – **10 rm** 35.00/70.00 **st.** – SB.

CHAGFORD Devon 403 I 31 **The West Country G.** – pop. 1 417 – ECD : Wednesday – ☎ 01647.
Envir. : Dartmoor National Park★★ (Brent Tor ≤★★, Haytor Rocks ≤★).
♦London 218 – Exeter 17 – ♦Plymouth 28.

- ✿ **Gidleigh Park** ⑤, TQ13 8HH, NW : 2 m. by Gidleigh Rd ☎ 432367, Fax 432574, ≤ Teign Valley, woodland and Meldon Hill, « Timbered country house, water garden », park, 🎾 – ⇔ rest TV ☎ P. AE VISA
  Meals (booking essential) 50.00/60.00 **st.** 8.75 – **13 rm** (dinner included) 200.00/365.00 **st.**, 2 suites
  Spec. Salad of scallops and potatoes with truffle vinaigrette, Stuffed rabbit with fricassee of wild mushrooms, Chocolate and orange confit mousse.
- **Thornworthy House** ⑤, Thornworthy, TQ13 8EY, SW : 3 m. by Fernworthy rd on Thornworthy rd ☎ 433297, Fax 433297, ≤, « Country house atmosphere », 🏡, park, 🎾 – ⇔ rest TV P.
  Meals (by arrangement) (dinner only) 20.00 **st.** 3.50 – 5.00 – **4 rm** 17.00/55.00 **st.**
- **Bly House** ⑤ without rest., Nattadon Hill, TQ13 8BW, E : ¼ m. ☎ 432404, 🏡, 🎾 – TV P
  6 rm 30.00/54.00 **st.**

at Sandy Park NE : 2¼ m. on A 382 – ✉ Chagford – ☎ 01647 :

- **Mill End,** TQ13 8JN, on A 382 ☎ 432282, Fax 433106, « Country house with water mill », 🎣, 🏡 – TV ☎ P. AE VISA
  closed 5 to 16 December and 9 to 19 January – **Meals** (lunch by arrangement)/dinner 24.50 **t.** 5.55 – **17 rm** 35.00/80.00 **t.** – SB.
- **Great Tree** ⑤, TQ13 8JS, on A 382 ☎ 432491, Fax 432562, ≤, « Country house atmosphere », 🎣, 🏡, park – ⇔ rest TV ☎ P. AE VISA.
  Meals (bar lunch)/dinner 19.95 **t.** 2.80 – **12 rm** 50.00/98.00 **t.** – SB.

at Easton Cross NE : 1½ m. on A 382 – ✉ Chagford – ☎ 01647 :

- **Easton Court,** TQ13 8JL, ☎ 433469, Fax 433469, « Part 15C thatched house », 🏡 – ⇔ rest TV ☎. AE VISA
  closed January – **Meals** (dinner only) 24.00 **t.** 4.00 – **7 rm** (dinner included) 64.00/116.00 **st.** – SB.

CHALE I.O.W. – see Wight (Isle of).

CHALFONT ST.PETER Bucks. 404 S 29 – pop. 14 135 – ✉ Chalfont St. Giles – ☎ 01494.
⛳18 Harewood Downs, Cokes Lane, Chalfont St. Giles ☎ 762308.
♦London 24 – ♦Oxford 43.

- XXX **Water Hall,** Amersham Rd, SL9 OPA, N : ½ m. on A 413 ☎ 873430 – P. AE VISA
  closed Sunday dinner and 1 to 5 January – **Meals** - French 14.50/19.50 **st.** and a la carte 5.00.

CHAPELTOWN N. Yorks. 402 403 404 P 23 – see Sheffield.

CHARDSTOCK Devon 403 L 31 **The West Country G.** – pop. 4 456 – ✉ Axminster – ☎ 01460.
Envir. : Chard (Museum★) *AC*, N : 3 m. by A 358.
♦London 160 – Exeter 31 – Lyme Regis 9.5 – Taunton 20 – Yeovil 21.

- **Tytherleigh Cot,** EX13 7BN, ☎ 221170, Fax 221291, ≘s, heated, 🏡 – ⇔ rest TV ☎ P. VISA.
  Meals (dinner only) 25.75 **t.** 6.95 – **19 rm** 49.00/123.00 **t.** – SB.

CHARINGWORTH Glos. – see Chipping Campden.

CHARLBURY Oxon. 403 404 P 28 – pop. 2 694 – ☎ 01608.
♦London 72 – ♦Birmingham 50 – ♦Oxford 15.

- **Bell,** Church St., OX7 3PP, ☎ 810278, Fax 811447 – TV ☎ P – 50. AE VISA JCB
  Meals 13.50 **t.** and a la carte 4.95 – **14 rm** 50.00/75.00 **t.** – SB.
- **Bull at Charlbury,** Sheep St., OX7 3RR, ☎ 810689 – TV P. VISA.
  Meals *(closed Sunday dinner and Monday to non-residents)* (bar lunch)/dinner a la carte approx. 15.85 **t.** – **5 rm** 45.00/55.00 **st.**

CHARLECOTE Warks. 403 404 P 27 – see Stratford-upon-Avon.

CHARLESTOWN Cornwall 403 F 32 – see St. Austell.

CHARLTON W. Sussex 404 R 31 – see Chichester.

CHARMOUTH Dorset 403 L 31 – pop. 1 497 – ECD : Thursday – ✉ Bridport – ☎ 01297.
♦London 157 – Dorchester 22 – Exeter 31 – Taunton 27.

White House, 2 Hillside, The Street, DT6 6PJ, ☎ 560411, Fax 560702 – TV ☎ P. AE VISA.
closed December and January – **Meals** (dinner only) 18.50 **st.** 5.50 – **10 rm** 36.00/112.00 **st.** – SB.

Hensleigh, Lower Sea Lane, DT6 6LW, ☎ 560830 – rest TV P. VISA
March-October – **Meals** 11.00 **st.** 4.45 – **11 rm** 25.00/50.00 **t.** – SB.

Newlands House, Stonebarrow Lane, DT6 6RA, ☎ 560212, – TV P
March-October – **Meals** (by arrangement) 13.50 **st.** – **12 rm** 22.50/50.00 **st.** – SB.

CHARNOCK RICHARD SERVICE AREA Lancs. 402 L 23 – ✉ Chorley – ☎ 01257.
♦London 212 – ♦Liverpool 27 – ♦Manchester 31 – Preston 10.

Forte Travelodge, Mill Lane, PR7 5LR, M6 between junctions 27 and 28 (northbound carriageway) ☎ 791746, Reservations (Freephone) 0800 850950 – TV P – 50. AE VISA
Meals (grill rest.) (dinner only) approx. 16.00 **t.** – **100 rm** 33.50 **t.**

CHARTHAM Kent 404 X 30 – see Canterbury.

CHARTHAM HATCH Kent 404 X 30 – see Canterbury.

CHATTERIS Cambs. 402 404 U 26 – pop. 7 261 – ☎ 01345.
♦London 85 – ♦Cambridge 26 – ♦Norwich 71.

Cross Keys, 16 Market Hill, PE16 6BA, ☎ 693036, Fax 693036 – ☎ P. AE VISA
Meals a la carte 8.95 **t.** (lunch) and a la carte 12.95/17.20 **t.** 6.00 – **7 rm** 32.50/45.00 **st.** – SB.

CHEADLE Ches. 402 403 N 23 – ☎ 0161.
♦London 200 – ♦Manchester 7 – ♦Stoke-on-Trent 33.

Village H. & Leisure Club, Cheadle Rd, SK8 1HW, S : ¾ m. by A 5149 ☎ 428 0404, Fax 428 1191, squash – rm TV ☎ P – 200. AE VISA.
Meals *(closed Saturday lunch)* (grill rest.) 12.00 **st.** and dinner a la carte – **73 rm** 74.00/89.00 **st.** – SB.

CHEDDLETON Staffs. 402 403 404 N 24 – pop. 4 088 – ✉ Leek – ☎ 01538.
♦London 125 – ♦Birmingham 48 – Derby 33 – ♦Manchester 42 – ♦Stoke-on-Trent 11.

Choir Cottage, Ostlers Lane, via Hollows Lane, ST13 7HS, ☎ 360561 – TV ☎ P.
closed Christmas and New Year – **Meals** (by arrangement) – **3 rm** 39.00/54.00 **st.**

CHEDINGTON Dorset 403 L 31 – pop. 100 – ✉ Beaminster – ☎ 01935.
18 Halstock, Common Lane ☎ 891689 – 9, 18, Chedington Court, South Perrott ☎ 891413.
♦ London 148 – Dorchester 17 – Taunton 25.

Chedington Court, DT8 3HY, ☎ 891265, Fax 891442, countryside, « Country house in landscaped gardens », 9, park – TV ☎ P. AE VISA
closed 2 January-2 February – **Meals** (dinner only) 27.50 **st.** 4.50 – **10 rm** 57.50/121.00 **st.** – SB.

Hazel Barton without rest., DT8 3HY, ☎ 891613, Fax 891370, – TV ☎ P
4 rm.

CHELMSFORD Essex 404 V 28 – pop. 91 109 – ECD : Wednesday – ☎ 01245.
E Block, County Hall, Market Rd, CM1 1GG ☎ 283400.
♦London 33 – ♦Cambridge 46 – ♦Ipswich 40 – Southend-on-Sea 19.

South Lodge, 196 New London Rd, CM2 0AR, ☎ 264564, Fax 492827 – rm TV ☎ P – 35. AE VISA.
Meals 14.00 **st.** and a la carte 5.00 – 3.50 – **41 rm** 45.00/75.00 **st.**

County, 29 Rainsford Rd, CM1 2QA, ☎ 491911, Fax 492762 – TV ☎ P – 150. AE VISA
closed 27 to 30 December – **Meals** 12.95/16.95 **st.** and a la carte 7.00 – **35 rm** 63.00/79.00 **st.** – SB.

Travel Inn Chelmsford Service Area, Colchester Rd, Springfield, NE : at junction of A 12 with A 138 and A 130 ☎ 464008, Fax 464010 – rm TV P – 60. AE VISA.
Meals (grill rest.) a la carte approx. 16.00 **t.** – 4.95 – **60 rm** 33.50 **t.**

at Great Baddow SE : 3 m. by A 130 – ✉ Chelmsford – ☎ 01245 :

Pontlands Park, West Hanningfield Rd, CM2 8HR, ☎ 476444, Fax 478393, heated, park – TV ☎ P – 40. AE VISA.
closed first week January – **Meals** *(closed Monday and Saturday lunch and Sunday dinner to non-residents)* 12.00/17.00 **t.** and a la carte 8.00 – 9.00 – **16 rm** 75.00/110.00 **t.**, 1 suite.

ATS 375 Springfield Rd ☎ 257795
ATS Chelmer Village Centre, Springfield (ASDA car park) ☎ 465676
ATS Town Centre, Inchbonnie Rd, South Woodham Ferrers (ASDA car park) ☎ 324999

CHELSWORTH Suffolk 404 W 27 – pop. 141 – Ipswich – 01449.

London 68 – Colchester 21 – Ipswich 16.

Peacock Inn, The Street, IP7 7HU, 740758, – rm . VISA.
Meals *(closed dinner Sunday and Monday)* a la carte 9.00/18.00 **t.** – **3 rm** 35.00/45.00 **t.** – SB.

CHELTENHAM Glos. 403 404 N 28 **Great Britain G.** – pop. 103 115 – 01242.

See : Town★ – Pittville Pump Room★ *AC* A **A.**

Exc. : Sudeley Castle★ (Paintings★) *AC*, NE : 7 m. by B 4632 A.

Cleeve Hill (0124 267) 2025 A – Cotswold Hills, Ullenwood 522421, A.

77 Promenade, GL50 1PP 522878.

London 99 – Birmingham 48 – Bristol 40 – Gloucester 9 – Oxford 43.

Plan opposite

Queen's (Forte), Promenade, GL50 1NN, 514724, Fax 224145, – rm – 200. AE VISA JCB B **n**
Meals 16.00/23.00 **st.** and a la carte 6.50 – 9.75 – **74 rm** 65.00/130.00 **st.** – SB.

Cheltenham Park, Cirencester Rd, Charlton Kings, GL53 8EA, 222021, Fax 226935, park – rm rest – 350. AE VISA JCB. A **e**
Meals 14.95/18.50 **st.** and a la carte 6.50 – 8.50 – **153 rm** 78.00/98.00 **st.**, 1 suite – SB.

On the Park, 38 Evesham Rd, GL52 2AH, 518898, Fax 511526 – . AE VISA. C **r**
Meals 14.50/19.50 **st.** and a la carte 5.50 – 7.75 – **12 rm** 70.00/85.00 **t.** – SB.

Golden Valley Thistle (Mt. Charlotte Thistle), Gloucester Rd, GL51 0TS, W : 2 m. on A 40 232691, Fax 221846, – rm rest – 220. AE VISA JCB. A
Meals 14.50/21.50 **st.** and a la carte 5.75 – 8.75 – **120 rm** 85.00/95.00 **st.**, 4 suites – SB.

Prestbury House, The Burgage, GL52 3DN, NE : 1 ½ m. by Prestbury Rd (B 4632) off New Barn Lane 529533, Fax 227076, – – 30. AE VISA. A **r**
Meals 15.50/21.50 **st.** and a la carte 6.50 – **17 rm** 65.00/80.00 **st.** – SB.

Charlton Kings, London Rd, Charlton Kings, GL52 6UU, 231061, Fax 241900, – . AE VISA A **c**
Meals (bar lunch)/dinner 25.00 **t.** and a la carte – **14 rm** 49.00/84.00 **t.** – SB.

Lypiatt House, Lypiatt Rd, GL50 2QW, 224994, Fax 224996 – . VISA. B **c**
Meals (dinner only)(by arrangement) 16.50 **st.** 4.55 – **10 rm** 48.00/70.00 **st.**

Milton House, 12 Royal Parade, Bayshill Rd, GL50 3AY, 582601, Fax 222326 – . AE VISA. B **e**
Meals (by arrangement) (dinner only) 16.00/25.00 **t.** – **8 rm** 37.50/66.00 **t.**

Regency House, 50 Clarence Sq., GL50 4JR, 582718, Fax 262697, – . AE VISA C **c**
closed 24 December to 2 January – **Meals** (by arrangement) (dinner only) 15.95 **st.** 4.00 – **8 rm** 32.50/48.00 **st.** – SB.

Stretton Lodge, Western Rd, GL50 3RN, 528724, Fax 570771, – . AE VISA. B **v**
Meals (by arrangement) (dinner only) 15.00 **st.** – **5 rm** 37.50/65.00 **st.** – SB.

Travel Inn, Tewkesbury Rd, Uckington, GL51 9SL, NW : 1 ¾ m. on A 4019 at junction with B 4634 233847, Fax 244887 – rm . AE VISA. A **a**
Meals (Beefeater grill) a la carte approx. 16.00 **t.** – 4.95 – **40 rm** 33.50 **t.**

Hannaford's, 20 Evesham Rd, GL52 2AB, 515181, Fax 515181 – . AE VISA. C **u**
closed 24 to 31 December – **Meals** (by arrangement) 15.00 4.00 – **8 rm** 29.00/52.00 – SB.

Hunting Butts Farm, Swindon Lane, GL50 4NZ, N : 1 ½ m. by A 435 524982, « Working farm », – rest A **n**
Meals (by arrangement) 9.00 – **7 rm** 21.00/37.00 **st.**

Abbey, 16 Bath Par., GL53 7HN, 516053, Fax 513034, – . AE VISA C **e**
Meals (by arrangement) 14.50 **st.** 3.50 – **11 rm** 35.00/58.00 **st.**

Hollington House, 115 Hales Rd, GL52 6ST, 256652, Fax 570280, – rest . AE VISA. A **s**
Meals (by arrangement) approx. 13.50 **t.** – **9 rm** 28.00/59.00 **t.** – SB.

Beaumont House, 56 Shurdington Rd, GL53 0JE, 245986, Fax 520044, – rest . VISA A **u**
Meals (by arrangement) 13.95 **st.** 3.95 – **18 rm** 32.00/55.00 **st.** – SB.

Battledown, 125 Hales Rd, GL52 6ST, 233881, – rest . A **x**
Meals 11.00 **st.** – **7 rm** 26.00/44.00 **st.**

CHELTENHAM

High Street . . . . BC
Pittville Street . . . . C 26
Portland Street . . . . C 27
Promenade (The) . . . . . BC 28
Regent Arcade
Shopping Centre C
Winchcombe
Street . . . . C 38

Berkeley Street . . . . C 4
Clarence Street . . . . C 6
Crescent Terrace . . . . B 7
Deep Street . . . . A 9
Dunalley Street . . . . C 10
Henrietta Street . . . . C 13
High Street
(PRESTBURY) . . . . A 14
Keynsham Road . . . . C 15
Knapp Road . . . . B 16
Montpellier Avenue . . . . . B 17

Montpellier Walk . . . . B 18
North Street . . . . C 20
Norwood Road . . . . B 21
Oriel Road . . . . C 22
Regent Street . . . . C 29
Rodney Road . . . . C 30
Royal Well Road . . . . . . BC 32
St. James Street . . . . C 33
St. Margaret's Road . . . . . C 35
Sandford Mill Road . . . . . C 36
Sandford Terrace . . . . . . C 37

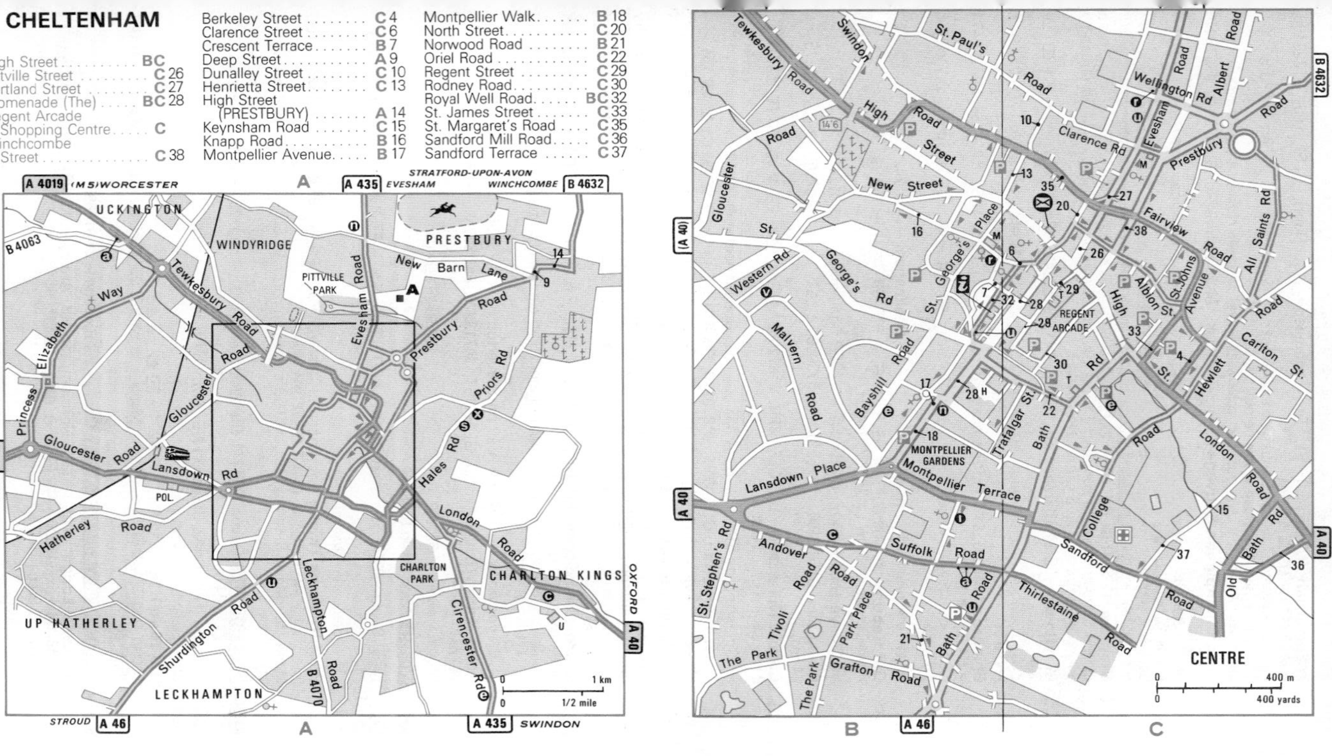

XXX ✿ **Epicurean** (McDonald), 81, The Promenade (1st Floor), GL51 1PJ, ✆ 222466, Fax 222474 – AE VISA B **u**
closed Sunday, 2 weeks January and 2 weeks August – **Meals** a la carte 17.50/50.00 **t.** 7.50 (see also ***Epicurean Bistro*** below)
Spec. Salmon tartar with a caviar crust, Duck confit with foie gras and a stew of haricot beans, Glazed lemon tart.

XX ✿ **Le Champignon Sauvage** (Everitt-Matthias), **24-26 Suffolk Rd, GL50 2AQ,** ✆ **573449** – AE VISA B **a**
closed Saturday lunch, Sunday, 2 weeks June, 2 weeks Christmas and Bank Holidays – **Meals** 17.50/27.00 **t.** 3.95
Spec. Fillet of cod with cinnamon, garnished with shredded leek and lemon butter, Fillet of Cotswold beef with an onion tart Tatin and celeriac purée, Iced gingerbread soufflé with an orange and liquorice sorbet.

XX **Staithes,** 12 Suffolk Rd, GL50 2AQ, ✆ 260666 – AE VISA B **a**
closed Sunday, 2 weeks summer, 1 week Christmas and Bank Holidays – **Meals** (lunch by arrangement)/dinner a la carte 13.85/24.40 **t.**

XX **Mayflower,** 32-34 Clarence St., GL50 3NX, ✆ 522426, Fax 251667 – AE VISA B **r**
closed Sunday lunch and 25 to 27 December – **Meals** - Chinese 11.00/27.00 **t.** and a la carte.

XX **Epicurean Bistro,** 81 The Promenade (Ground floor), GL51 1PS, ✆ 222466, Fax 222474 – AE VISA B **u**
closed Sunday, 2 weeks January and 2 weeks August – **Meals** a la carte 14.00/16.50 **t.** 7.50.

at Woolstone N : 6 ¼ m. by A 435 – A – ✉ Cheltenham – ☎ 01242 :

Old Rectory without rest., GL52 4RG, ✆ 673766,
April-October – **3 rm** 25.00/39.00 **st.**

at Cleeve Hill NE : 4 m. on B 4632 – A – ✉ Cheltenham – ☎ 01242 :

Rising Sun, GL52 3PX, ✆ 676281, Fax 673069, rm – 75
24 rm.

Cleeve Hill without rest., GL52 3PR, ✆ 672052, AE VISA.
9 rm 45.00/75.00 **st.**

at Colesbourne SE : 7 m. on A 435 – A – ✉ Cheltenham – ☎ 01242 :

Colesbourne Inn, GL53 9NP, ✆ 870376, Fax 870397, AE VISA
Meals (bar lunch)/dinner 11.95 **t.** and a la carte 4.25 – **9 rm** 34.00/50.00 **t.** – SB.

at Shurdington SW : 3 ¾ m. on A 46 – A – ✉ Cheltenham – ☎ 01242 :

Greenway, GL51 5UG, ✆ 862352, Fax 862780, « Part 17C Cotswold country house, gardens » – 30. AE VISA.
Meals *(closed lunch Saturday and Bank Holidays)* 17.00/25.00 **st.** 5.50 – **19 rm** 77.50/160.00 **st.** – SB.

Allards, Shurdington Rd, GL51 5XA, ✆ 862498, Fax 863017, AE VISA JCB.
Meals (bar lunch Monday to Friday)/dinner 13.95 **t.** and a la carte 3.95 – **12 rm** 38.00/60.00 **t.** – SB.

at Staverton W : 4 ¼ m. by A 40 on Staverton rd – A – ✉ Cheltenham – ☎ 01452 :

White House, Gloucester Rd, GL51 0ST, ✆ 713226, Fax 857590 – 180
48 rm, 1 suite.

ATS Chosen View Rd ✆ 521288 ATS 99-101 London Rd ✆ 519814

CHELWOOD Avon – see Bristol.

CHENIES Bucks. 404 S 28 – pop. 2 240 – ECD : Thursday – ✉ Rickmansworth (Herts.) – ☎ 01923.

♦London 30 – Aylesbury 18 – Watford 7.

Bedford Arms Thistle (Mt. Charlotte Thistle), WD3 6EQ, ✆ 283301, Fax 284825, « 16C inn », rm AE VISA JCB
Meals (bar lunch Saturday) 15.00/18.50 **t.** and a la carte 6.50 – 8.75 – **10 rm** 95.00/150.00 **t.** – SB.

CHERITON BISHOP Devon 403 I 31 **The West Country G.** – pop. 754 – ECD : Wednesday – ✉ Exeter – ☎ 01647.

Exc. : Crediton (Holy Cross Church★) NE : 6½m. by A 30.

♦London 211 – Exeter 10 – ♦Plymouth 51.

Old Thatch Inn, EX6 6HJ, ✆ 24204 – VISA.
closed first 2 weeks November – **Meals** a la carte 6.95/12.55 **st.** 3.90 – **3 rm** 33.00/45.00 **st.**

CHERWELL VALLEY SERVICE AREA Oxon. – ✉ Bicester – ☎ 01869.

Granada Lodge without rest., Northampton Rd, Ardley, OX6 9RD, M40, junction 10 ✆ 346060, Fax 345030 – AE VISA.
64 rms 39.95 **t.**

Le Guide change, changez de ***guide Michelin*** *tous les ans.*

CHERTSEY Surrey 404 S 29 ㊷ – ☎ 01932.

⛳, ⛳ Foxhills, Stonehill Rd, Ottershaw ✆ 872050.

♦London 28.

Crown, 7 London St., KT16 8AP, ✆ 564657, Fax 570839 – ⇔ rm TV ☎ ♿ P – 🎤 100. AE ◑ VISA
Meals a la carte 12.70/22.40 **st.** – **30 rm** ☕ 80.00/115.00 **st.**

CHESHUNT Herts. 404 T 28 – pop. 49 525 – ✉ Broxbourne – ☎ 01992.

⛳ Cheshunt Park, Park Lane ✆ 629777.

♦London 22 – ♦Cambridge 40 – ♦Ipswich 70 – Luton 34 – Southend-on-Sea 39.

Cheshunt Marriott, Halfhide Lane, Turnford, EN10 6NG, NW : 1 ¼ m. on B 176 ✆ 451245, Fax 440120, Fō, 🏊 – 🛗 ⇔ rm ▤ TV ☎ ♿ P – 🎤 120. AE ◑ VISA JCB
Meals *(closed Saturday lunch)* 11.00/15.95 **t.** and a la carte 🍷 5.95 – **127 rm** ☕ 79.50/89.50 **st.**, 12 suites – SB.

CHESTER Ches. 402 403 L 24 **Great Britain G.** – pop. 80 154 – ECD : Wednesday – ☎ 01244.

See : City★★ - The Rows★★ – Cathedral★ – City Walls★.

Envir. : Chester Zoo★ *AC*, N : 3 m. by A 5116.

⛳ Upton-by-Chester, Upton Lane ✆ 381183 – ⛳ Curzon Park ✆ 675130.

ℹ Town Hall, Northgate St., CH1 2HJ ✆ 317962 – Chester Visitor Centre, Vicars Lane, CH1 1QX ✆ 351609/318916.

♦London 207 – Birkenhead 7 – ♦Birmingham 91 – ♦Liverpool 19 – ♦Manchester 40 – Preston 52 – ♦Sheffield 76 – ♦Stoke-on-Trent 38.

CHESTER

Street	No.
Bridge Street	3
Eastgate Street	5
Northgate Street	18
Watergate Street	
Boughton	2
Frodsham Street	6
Grosvenor Park Road	7
Grosvenor Street	8
Handbridge	10
Little St. John Street	12
Liverpool Road	13
Lower Bridge Street	15
Nicholas Street	17
Parkgate Road	20
Pepper Street	21
St. John Street	23
St. Martins Way	24
Vicar's Lane	25

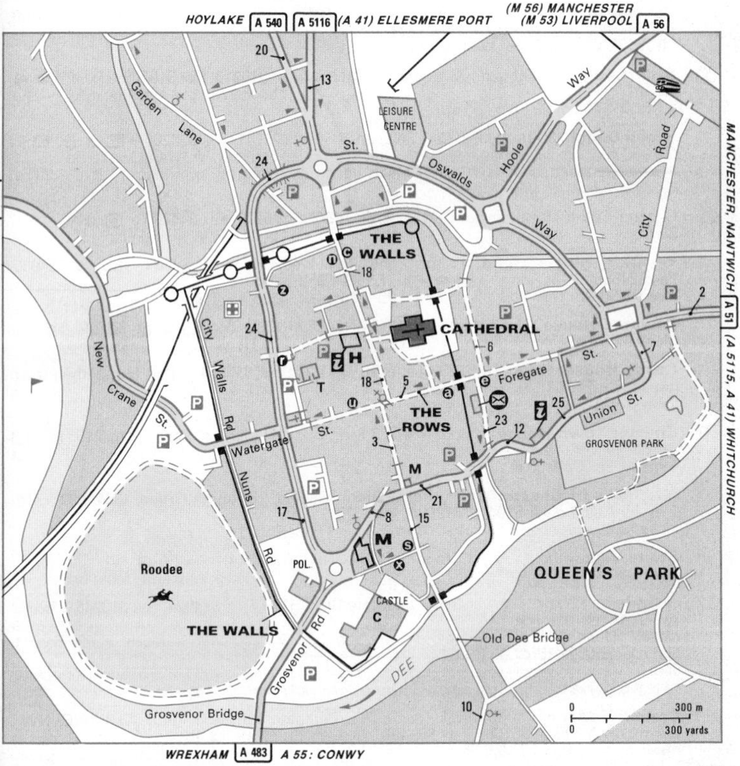

Chester Grosvenor, Eastgate St., CH1 1LT, 324024, Fax 313246, – 250. a
closed 25 and 26 December – ***Brasserie :*** **Meals** a la carte 14.50/26.95 **t.** 5.25 – (see also ***Arkle*** below) – 9.95 – **83 rm** 115.00/170.00, 3 suites.

Crabwall Manor, Parkgate Rd, Mollington, CH1 6NE, NW : 2 ¼ m. on A 540 851666, Telex 61220, Fax 851400, « Part 16C manor », – rest – 80.
Meals (see ***Crabwall Manor*** below) – 7.70 – **42 rm** 98.50/125.00 **t.**, 6 suites.

Moat House International (Q.M.H.), Trinity St., CH1 2BD, 322330, Fax 316118, – rm rest – 500. r
closed 25 to 27 December – **Meals** *(closed Saturday lunch and lunches Monday to Friday in July and August)* 12.00/18.45 **st.** and a la carte 5.50 – 9.00 – **146 rm** 90.00/125.00 **st.**, 6 suites – SB.

Mollington Banastre, Parkgate Rd, Mollington, CH1 6NN, NW : 2 ¼ m. on A 540 851471, Fax 851165, squash – rm – 250.
Meals 10.95/20.50 **st.** and a la carte 8.50 – **64 rm** 77.00/130.00 **st.** – SB.

Hoole Hall, Warrington Rd, Hoole, CH2 3PD, NE : 2 m. on A 56 350011 – rm – 100.
Meals 7.95/15.25 **t.** and a la carte – **99 rm** 55.00/65.00 **t.** – SB.

Redland without rest., 64 Hough Green, CH4 8JY, SW : 1 m. by A 483 on A 5104 671024, Fax 681309, « Victorian town house », –
13 rm 40.00/70.00 **st.**

Blossoms (Forte), St. John St., CH1 1HL, 323186, Fax 346433 – – 100
63 rm 80.00/90.00, 1 suite. e

Forte Posthouse, Wrexham Rd, CH4 9DL, S : 2 m. on A 483 680111, Fax 674100, – rm rest – 100.
Meals a la carte approx. 15.00 **t.** 5.50 – **105 rm** 56.00/69.50 **st.**

Cavendish, 42-44 Hough Green, CH4 8JQ, SW : 1 m. by A 483 on A 5104 675100, Fax 682946, –
Meals 15.00 **st.** – **18 rm** 39.50/65.00 **t.** – SB.

Alton Lodge without rest., 78 Hoole Rd, CH2 3NT, 310213, Fax 319206 –
by Hoole Way and Hoole Rd
5.50 – **16 rm** 29.50/32.50 **st.**

Green Bough, 60 Hoole Rd, CH2 3NL, on A 56 326241, Fax 326265 –
by Hoole Way and Hoole Rd
closed Christmas and New Year – **Meals** (lunch by arrangement)/dinner 12.25 **t.** – **20 rm** 38.00/55.00 **t.** – SB.

Chester Court, 48 Hoole Rd, CH2 3NL, on A 56 320779, Fax 344795 –
20 rm. by Hoole Way and Hoole Rd

Ye Olde King's Head (Premier), 48/50 Lower Bridge St., CH1 1RS, 324855, Fax 324855, « 16C inn » – s
Meals 5.95/20.00 **st.** and a la carte 4.95 – **8 rm** 42.95/46.40 **st.**

Edwards House, 61-63 Hoole Rd, CH2 3NJ, 318055 –
Meals 12.50 **st.** 4.00 – **8 rm** 29.00/39.00 **st.** by Hoole Way and Hoole Rd

Castle House without rest., 23 Castle St., CH1 2DS, 350354, « Part Elizabethan town house » – x
5 rm 22.00/44.00.

Chester Town House without rest., 23 King St., CH1 2AH, 350021, Fax 315345 – z
4 rm 35.00/48.00 **st.**

Mitchell's of Chester without rest., Green Gables, 28 Hough Green, CH4 8JQ, SW : 1 m. by A 483 on A 5104 679004, –
closed 22 December-8 January – **4 rm** 23.00/38.00 **st.**

Stone Villa without rest., 3 Stone Pl., CH2 3NR, 345014 –
6 rm 22.00/40.00 **st.** by Hoole Way and Hoole Rd

Arkle (at Chester Grosvenor H.), Eastgate St., CH1 1LT, 324024, Fax 313246 – a
closed Monday lunch, Sunday dinner, and 25-26 December – **Meals** 37.00/46.00 **t.** and a la carte 28.15/47.00 **t.** 8.50
Spec. 'Landes' duck liver with jellied pork cheeks and crackling salad, A pot roast of wild rabbit with juniper scented cabbage and morels, Lightly spiced bread and butter pudding soufflé with orange preserve.

Crabwall Manor (at Crabwall Manor H.), Parkgate Rd, Mollington, CH1 6NE, NW : 2 ¼ m. on A 540 851666, Fax 851400, – n
Meals (a la carte) 24.70/35.75 **t.**

XX **Chester Rows,** 24 Watergate Row, CH1 2LD, ☎ 316003, « Part 15C and 17C town house » – AE VISA JCB u
Meals a la carte 11.75/19.75 **t.** 5.40.

XX **Garden House,** 1 Rufus Court, off Northgate St., CH1 2JH, ☎ 320004, Fax 327604 – VISA c
Meals *(closed Sunday)* a la carte 16.65/21.50 **t.**

X **Blue Bell,** 65 Northgate St., CH1 2HQ, ☎ 317758, « Converted 15C inn ». VISA
closed 25 and 26 December – **Meals** 10.00/15.00 **t.** and a la carte 6.50.

at Mickle Trafford NE : 2 ½ m. by A 56 – ✉ Chester – ☎ 01244 :

Royal Oak (Toby), Warrington Rd, CH2 4EX, on A 56 ☎ 301391, Fax 301948 – TV ☎ P. AE VISA
Meals (grill rest.) 7.95/10.95 **t.** and a la carte **36 rm** 59.00/66.00 **t.**

at Rowton SE : 3 m. by A 41 – ✉ Chester – ☎ 01244 :

Rowton Hall, Rowton Lane, CH3 6AD, ☎ 335262, Fax 335464, – TV ☎ & P – 200. AE VISA
closed 25 to 27 December – **Meals** 10.50/16.50 **t.** and a la carte 6.00 – **42 rm** 72.00/125.00 **t.** – SB.

at Two Mills NW : 5 ¾ m. on A 540 at junction with A 550 – ✉ Ledsham – ☎ 0151 :

Tudor Rose Lodge, Parkgate Rd, L66 9PD, ☎ 339 2399, Fax 347 1725 – TV ☎ & P
31 rm.

at Puddington NW : 7 ¼ m. by A 540 – ✉ South Wirral – ☎ 0151 :

XXX **Craxton Wood** with rm, Parkgate Rd, L66 9PB, on A 540 ☎ 339 4717, Fax 339 1740, ≤, « Gardens », park – TV ☎ P. AE VISA.
closed first week January and last 2 weeks August – **Meals** *(closed Sunday and Bank Holidays)* 19.85 **st.** and a la carte 6.50 – **13 rm** 49.50/98.50 **st.**, 1 suite – SB.

MICHELIN Distribution Centre, Sandycroft Industrial Estate, Glendale Av., Sandycroft, Deeside, CH5 2QP, ☎ 537373, Fax 537453 by A 548

ATS 7 Bumpers Lane, Sealand Trading Est. ☎ 375154

CHESTERFIELD Derbs. 402 403 404 P 24 – pop. 99 403 – ECD : Wednesday – ☎ 01246.

18 Chesterfield Municipal, Murray House, Crow Lane ☎ 273887 – 18 Grassmoor, North Wingfield Rd ☎ 856044.

Peacock Information Centre, Low Pavement, S40 1PB ☎ 207777.

London 152 – Derby 24 – Nottingham 25 – Sheffield 12.

Forte Travelodge without rest., Brimington Rd North, Wittington Moor, S41 9BE, N : 2 m. on A 61 ☎ 455411, Reservations (Freephone) 0800 850950 – TV & P. AE VISA
20 rm 33.50 **t.**

ATS 512 Sheffield Rd ☎ 452281

CHESTER-LE-STREET Durham 401 402 P 19 – pop. 52 641 – ECD : Wednesday – ☎ 0191.

18 Lumley Park ☎ 388 3218 – 18 Roseberry Grange, Grange Villa ☎ 370 0670.

London 275 – Durham 7 – Newcastle upon Tyne 8.

Lumley Castle, DH3 4NX, E : 1 m. on B 1284 ☎ 389 1111, Fax 387 1437, « 13C castle », – TV ☎ P – 150. AE VISA.
closed 25-26 December and 1 January – **Meals** (bar lunch Saturday) 13.50/21.50 **st.** and a la carte – **60 rm** 79.50/125.00 **st.**, 1 suite – SB.

MICHELIN Distribution Centre, Drum Rd Industrial Estate, Drum Rd, DH3 2AF, ☎ 410 7762, Fax 492 0717

CHESTERTON Oxon. 404 Q 28 – ✉ Bicester – ☎ 01869.

18 Chesterton , Bicester ☎ 241204.

London 69 – Birmingham 65 – Northampton 36 – Oxford 15.

XX **Bignell Park** with rm, OX6 8UE, on A 4095 ☎ 241444, Fax 241444, – TV ☎ P. AE VISA.
Meals *(closed Saturday lunch)* 15.00/27.50 **t.** and a la carte 5.50 – **5 rm** 57.50/75.00 **t.** – SB.

Pleasant hotels and restaurants are shown in the Guide by a red sign.

Please send us the names of any where you have enjoyed your stay.

Your Michelin Guide will be even better.

... XXXXX ... X

CHICHESTER W. Sussex 404 R 31 **Great Britain G.** – pop. 26 050 – ECD : Thursday – 01243.

See : City★ – Cathedral★ BZ **A** – St. Mary's Hospital★ BY **D** – Pallant House★ *AC* BZ **M.**

Envir. : Fishbourne Roman Palace (mosaics★) *AC* AZ **R.**

Exc. : Weald and Downland Open Air Museum★ *AC*, N : 6 m. by A 286 AY.

18 Goodwood 785012, AY – 18, 9 Chichester Golf Centre, Hoe Farm, Hunston 533833, AZ.

29a South Street, PO19 1AH 775888.

♦London 69 – ♦Brighton 31 – ♦Portsmouth 18 – ♦Southampton 30.

CHICHESTER

East Street .... BZ
North Street .... BYZ
South Street .... BZ

Birdham Road .... AZ 2
Bognor Road .... AZ 3
Cathedral Way .... AZ 4
Chapel Street .... BY 6
Chichester Arundel Road .... AY 7
East Pallant .... BZ 9
Florence Road .... AZ 10
Hornet (The) .... BZ 12
Kingsham Road .... BZ 13
Lavant Road .... AY 14
Little London .... BY 15
Market Road .... BZ 16
Northgate .... BY 17
North Pallant .... BZ 19
St. James's .... AZ 21
St. John's Street .... BZ 23
St. Martin's Square .... BY 24
St. Pancras .... BY 25
St. Paul's Road .... BY 27
Sherborne Road .... AZ 28
Southgate .... BZ 29
South Pallant .... BZ 31
Spitalfield Lane .... BY 32
Stockbridge Road .... AZ 33
Tower Street .... BY 35
Westhampnett Road .... AYZ 36

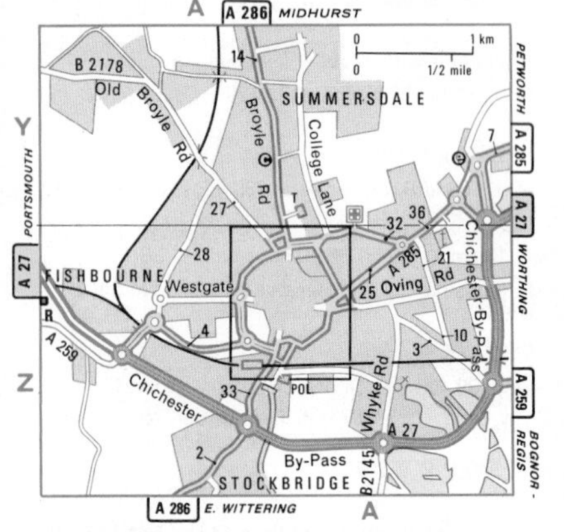

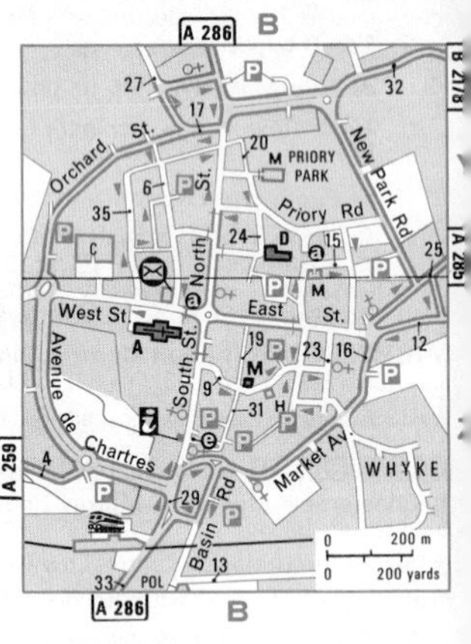

Dolphin and Anchor (Forte), West St., PO19 1QE, 785121, Fax 533408 – 180. AE VISA BZ **a**
Meals 11.25/16.95 **t.** and a la carte – 8.50 – **49 rm** 55.00/120.00 **t.** – SB.

Jarvis Chichester, Westhampnett, PO19 4UL, 786351, Fax 782371, – rm – 300. AE VISA AY **e**
Meals (bar lunch Saturday) 10.50/15.00 **t.** and a la carte – 8.25 – **76 rm** 70.00/95.00 **t.**, 1 suite – SB.

Suffolk House, 3 East Row, PO19 1PD, 778899, Fax 787282, – . AE VISA BY **a**
Meals *(closed Sunday lunch)* 7.50/14.50 **st.** and a la carte 3.75 – **11 rm** 43.50/65.00 **st.** – SB.

Crouchers Bottom, Birdham Rd, Apuldram, PO20 7EH, SW : 2 ½ m. on A 286 784995, Fax 539797, – . AE VISA. AZ
closed 1 week Christmas – **Meals** (dinner only) 19.50 **st.** 4.25 – **6 rm** 49.00/79.00 **st.** – SB.

Droveway, 30a Southgate, PO19 1DR, 528832. AE VISA BZ **e**
closed Sunday, Monday and first 2 weeks January – **Meals** 14.00/19.50 **t.** and a la carte.

Comme ça, 67 Broyle Rd, PO19 4BD, on A 286 788724, Fax 530052, – . AE VISA AY **c**
closed Sunday dinner and Monday – **Meals** - French 16.75 **t.** and a la carte 4.80.

Cafe de Chine, 117 St. Pancras, PO19 4LH, E : ¼ m. on A 285 784232 – . AE VISA BY
Meals - Chinese (lunch by arrangement Saturday and Sunday) 6.00/15.00 **t.** and a la carte.

at Charlton N : 6¼ m. by A 286 – AY – Chichester – 01243 :

Woodstock House, PO18 0HU, 811666, Fax 811666, – . VISA
closed Sunday and 25-26 December – **Meals** (dinner only) a la carte approx. 17.00 **t.** 4.00 – **10 rm** 38.50/76.00 **t.** – SB.

at Halnaker NE : 3¼ m. on A 285 – BY – Chichester – 01243 :

Old Store without rest., Stane St., PO18 0QL, on A 285 531977, – . VISA.
7 rm 25.00/50.00 **st.**

at Chilgrove N : 6 ½ m. by A 286 – AY – on B 2141 – ✉ East Marden – ☎ 01243 :

✗✗ **White Horse Inn,** 1 High St., PO18 9HX, ✆ 535219, Fax 535301 – ⓟ. VISA
closed Sunday dinner, Monday, February and last week October – **Meals** 17.50/23.00 **t.** and a la carte ⅟ 4.50.

at Goodwood NE : 3 ½ m. by A 27 – AY – on East Dean Rd – ✉ Chichester – ☎ 01243 :

Goodwood Park (Country Club), PO18 0QB, ✆ 775537, Fax 533802, park, squash – TV ☎ ⓟ – 120. AE VISA
Meals *(closed Saturday lunch to non-residents)* 8.50/30.00 **t.** and a la carte ⅟ 5.75 – 9.00 – **87 rm** 75.00 **st.**, 1 suite – SB.

at Bosham W : 4 m. by A 259 – AZ – ✉ Chichester – ☎ 01243 :

Millstream, Bosham Lane, PO18 8HL, ✆ 573234, Fax 573459, – TV ☎ ⓟ – 45. AE VISA
Meals 12.75/18.25 **t.** ⅟ 4.60 – **29 rm** 59.00/109.00 **t.** – SB.

Hatpins without rest., Bosham Lane, PO18 8HG, ✆ 572644, – TV ⓟ.
3 rm 32.50/50.00.

at Chidham W : 6 m. by A 259 – AZ – ✉ Chichester – ☎ 01243 :

Old Rectory without rest., Cot Lane, West Chidham, PO18 8TA, ✆ 572088, – TV ⓟ
4 rm 20.00/48.00 **st.**

ATS Terminus Rd Ind Est. ✆ 773100

CHIDHAM W. Sussex – see Chichester.

CHILDER THORNTON Ches. – ✉ Wirral – ☎ 0151.

Travel Inn, New Chester Rd, L66 1QW, on A 41 ✆ 339 8101 – rm TV ⓟ. AE VISA
Meals (grill rest.) a la carte approx. 16.00 **t.** – 4.95 – **31 rm** 33.50 **t.**

CHILGROVE W. Sussex 404 R 31 – see Chichester.

CHILLINGTON Devon 403 I 33 – see Kingsbridge.

CHINLEY Derbs. 402 403 404 O 23 – ✉ Stockport (Ches.) – ☎ 01663.
London 187 – Manchester 24 – Sheffield 25.

Ashen Clough, SK12 6AF, N : 1 ½ m. by Maynestone Rd ✆ 750311, ←, park – rm ⓟ
Meals (by arrangement) (communal dining) 18.50 ⅟ 3.75 – **3 rm** 41.50/63.00.

CHINNOR Oxon. 404 R 28 **The West Country G.** – pop. 5 949 – ☎ 01494.
Exc. : Ridgeway Path★★.
London 45 – Oxford 19.

✗ **Sir Charles Napier Inn,** Sprigg's Alley, by Bledlow Ridge rd, OX9 4BX, SE : 2 ½ m. ✆ 483011, Fax 484929, – ⓟ. VISA
closed Sunday dinner and Monday – **Meals** a la carte 21.00/25.50 **t.** ⅟ 5.00.

CHIPPENHAM Wilts. 403 404 N 29 **The West Country G.** – pop. 25 794 – ECD : Wednesday – ☎ 01249.
See : Yelde Hall★.
Envir. : Corsham Court★★ *AC*, SW : 3 ½ m. by A 4 – Sheldon Manor★ *AC*, W : 1 ½ m. by A 420 – Biddestone★, W : 4 ½ m. – Bowood House★ *AC* (Library ←★) SE : 5 m. by A 4 and A 342.
Exc. : Castle Combe★★, NW : 6 m. by A 420 and B 4039.
Monkton Park (Par Three) ✆ 653928.
The Neeld Hall, High St., SN15 3ER ✆ 657733.
London 106 – Bristol 27 – Southampton 64 – Swindon 21.

Stanton Manor, Stanton St. Quinton, SN14 6DQ, N : 5 m. by A 429 ✆ (01666) 837552, Fax 837022, – TV ☎ ⓟ. AE VISA
closed 26 December-8 January – **Meals** *(closed Sunday lunch)* 18.00 **st.** and a la carte – **10 rm** 68.00/82.00 **st.** – SB.

ATS Cocklebury Rd ✆ 653541

CHIPPERFIELD Herts. 404 ㊷ – pop. 1 680 – ECD : Wednesday – ✉ Kings Langley – ☎ 01923.
London 27 – Hemel Hempstead 5 – Watford 6.

Two Brewers Inn (Forte), The Common, WD4 9BS, ✆ 265266, Fax 261884 – TV ☎ ⓟ – 25. AE VISA JCB
Meals (bar lunch Monday to Saturday)/dinner 15.95 **st.** and a la carte ⅟ 6.70 – 8.50 – **20 rm** 70.00/85.00 **st.** – SB.

CHIPPING Lancs. 402 M 22 – pop. 1 392 – ✉ Preston – ☎ 01995.

♦London 233 – Lancaster 30 – ♦Leeds 54 – ♦Manchester 40 – Preston 12.

Gibbon Bridge Country House ⛰, PR3 2TQ, E : 1 m. on Clitheroe rd ☎ 61456, Fax 61277, ←, ⛹, ≘s, 🌳, ✂ – 🛗 📺 ☎ ♿ 🅟. 🅂 AE ⓓ VISA. ✂
Meals 10.00/18.00 **t.** and a la carte 🍷 4.85 – **13 rm** ☕ 59.00/70.00 **t.**, **17 suites** 80.00/150.00 **t.** – SB.

CHIPPING CAMPDEN Glos. 403 404 O 27 **Great Britain G.** – pop. 1 997 – ECD : Thursday – ☎ 01386.

See : Town★.

Envir. : Hidcote Manor Garden★★ *AC*, NE : 2½ m.

🅘 Woolstaplers Hall Museum, High St., GL55 6HB ☎ 840101 (summer only).

♦London 93 – Cheltenham 21 – ♦Oxford 37 – Stratford-upon-Avon 12.

Cotswold House, The Square, GL55 6AN, ☎ 840330, Fax 840310, « Attractively converted Regency town house », 🌳 – ⇔ rest 📺 ☎ 🅟. 🅂 AE ⓓ VISA. ✂
closed 24 to 28 December – **Meals** (light lunch Monday to Saturday)/dinner 26.50 **t.** – **15 rm** ☕ 69.50/135.00 **st.** – SB.

Seymour House, High St., GL55 6AH, ☎ 840429, Fax 840369, « Mature grapevine in restaurant », 🌳 – 📺 ☎ 🅟. 🅂 AE VISA. ✂
Meals 14.50/26.00 **st.** and a la carte 🍷 5.00 – **13 rm** ☕ 53.00/132.00 **t.**, 3 suites – SB.

Noel Arms, High St., GL55 6AT, ☎ 840317, Fax 841136 – 📺 ☎ 🅟 – 🏛 35. 🅂 AE ⓓ VISA. ✂
Meals (bar lunch Monday to Saturday)/dinner 17.95 **st.** 🍷 8.50 – **26 rm** ☕ 60.00/80.00 **st.** – SB.

Caminetto, Old Kings Arms Pantry, High St., GL55 6HB, ☎ 840934 – 🅂 VISA
closed Monday lunch, Sunday and 3 weeks Easter – **Meals** - Italian a la carte 10.00/22.25 **t.** 🍷 4.85.

at Mickleton N : 3 ¼ m. by B 4035 and B 4081 on B 4632 – ✉ Chipping Campden – ☎ 01386 :

Three Ways, GL55 6SB, ☎ 438429, Fax 438118, 🌳 – 📺 ☎ 🅟 – 🏛 75. 🅂 AE ⓓ VISA
Meals (bar lunch Monday to Saturday)/dinner 16.50 **st.** – **40 rm** ☕ 44.00/88.00 **st.** – SB.

Holly Mount without rest., High St., GL55 6SL, ☎ 438243, Fax 438858, 🌳 – 📺 🅟
3 rm ☕ 33.00/42.00 **s.**

at Charingworth E : 3 m. by B 4035 – ✉ Chipping Campden – ☎ 01386 :

Charingworth Manor ⛰, GL55 6NS, on B 4035 ☎ 593555, Fax 593353, ←, « Part early 14C manor house with Jacobean additions », ≘s, 🏊, 🌳, park, ✂ – ⇔ rest 📺 ☎ 🅟 – 🏛 30. 🅂 AE ⓓ VISA
Meals 17.50/29.50 **st.** 🍷 6.50 – **24 rm** ☕ 90.00/220.00 **st.** – SB.

at Broad Campden S : 1 ¼ m. by B 4081 – ✉ Chipping Campden – ☎ 01386 :

Malt House ⛰, GL55 6UU, ☎ 840295, Fax 841334, « 17C house », 🌳 – ⇔ rest 📺 🅟. 🅂 VISA
Meals *(closed Monday)* (residents only) (communal dining) (dinner only) 23.50 **st.** 🍷 6.25 – **5 rm** ☕ 42.50/87.50 **st.** – SB.

CHIPPING NORTON Oxon 403 404 P 28 **Great Britain G.** – pop. 5 386 – ECD : Thursday – ☎ 01608.

Envir. : Chastleton House★★, NW : 4 m. by A 44.

⛳18 Lyneham ☎ (01993) 831841.

♦London 77 – ♦Birmingham 44 – Gloucester 36 – ♦Oxford 21.

White Hart, High St., OX7 5AD, ☎ 642572, Fax 644143 – 📺 ☎ 🅟 – 🏛 50. 🅂 AE ⓓ VISA. ✂
Meals a la carte 6.95/13.85 **t.** – **21 rm** ☕ 50.00/80.00 **st.** – SB.

CHISELDON Wilts. 403 404 O 29 – see Swindon.

CHISLEHAMPTON Oxon. 404 Q 28 – ✉ Oxford – ☎ 01865.

♦London 55 – ♦Oxford 7.

Coach and Horses, OX44 7UX, ☎ 890255, Fax 891995 – 📺 ☎ 🅟. 🅂 AE ⓓ VISA. ✂
closed 26 to 30 December – **Meals** *(closed Sunday dinner)* 11.95 **st.** and a la carte – **9 rm** ☕ 45.00/50.00 **st.** – SB.

CHITTLEHAMHOLT Devon 403 I 31 – pop. 194 – ✉ Umberleigh – ☎ 01769.

♦London 216 – Barnstaple 14 – Exeter 28 – Taunton 45.

Highbullen ⛰, EX37 9HD, ☎ 540561, Fax 540492, ←, ≘s, 🏊 heated, 🏊, ⛳9, 🎣, 🌳, park, ✂, squash – ⇔ rest 📺 ☎ 🅟 – 🏛 25. ✂
Meals (bar lunch)/dinner 18.50 **st.** 🍷 4.75 – ☕ 2.50 – **37 rm** (dinner included) 60.00/140.00 **st.** – SB.

La guida cambia, cambiate la guida ogni anno.

CHOBHAM Surrey 404 S 29 – ✉ Woking – ☎ 01276.
◆London 35 – Reading 21 – ◆Southampton 53.

Knaphill Manor without rest., Carthouse Lane, GU21 4XT, SW : 1 m. by Castle Grove Rd and Guildford Rd ✆ 857962, ≤, ⛱, 🎾 – TV P. VISA.
closed Easter and Christmas – **3 rm** 40.00/65.00 **s.**

Quails, 1 Bagshot Rd, GU24 8BP, ✆ 858491 – ▤. AE VISA
closed Saturday lunch, Sunday dinner, and Monday – **Meals** 14.50/16.95 **t.** and a la carte 4.75.

CHOLLERFORD Northd. 401 402 N 18 **Great Britain G.** – pop. 813 – ✉ Hexham – ☎ 01434.
Envir. : Hadrian's Wall★★ – Chesters★ (Bath House★) *AC*, W : ½ m. by B 6318.
◆London 303 – ◆Carlisle 36 – ◆Newcastle upon Tyne 21.

George (Swallow), NE46 4EW, ✆ 681611, Fax 681727, ≤, « Riverside gardens », ℒ₆, ⌂s, ⛆, 🎣 – ⇔ rm TV ☎ ♿ P – 🔺 65. AE VISA
Meals 13.50/22.50 **st.** and a la carte 5.50 – **48 rm** 85.00/115.00 **st.** – SB.

CHORLEY Lancs. 402 404 M 23 – pop. 34 618 – ECD : Wednesday – ☎ 01257.
⛳18 Duxbury Park, Duxbury Hall Rd ✆ 265380 – ⛳18 Shaw Hill Hotel Preston Rd, Whittle-le-Woods ✆ 269221.
◆London 222 – ◆Blackpool 30 – ◆Liverpool 32 – ◆Manchester 26.

Yarrow Bridge (Premier), Bolton Rd, PR7 4AB, S : 1 m. on A 6 ✆ 265989, Fax 23082 – ⇔ rm TV ☎ ♿ P
Meals (grill rest.) – **29 rm.**

at Whittle-le-Woods N : 2 m. on A 6 – ✉ Chorley – ☎ 01257 :

Shaw Hill H. Golf & Country Club , Preston Rd, PR6 7PP, ✆ 269221, Fax 261223, ⛳18 – TV ☎ P – 🔺 200. AE VISA
***Vardon* : Meals** *(closed lunch Saturday and Bank Holidays)* 10.95/18.95 **st.** and a la carte – **22 rm** 49.50/95.00 **st.** – SB.

Parkville Country House, 174 Preston Rd, PR6 7HE, ✆ 261881, Fax 273171, ⛱ – TV ☎ P. AE VISA JCB.
Meals *(closed Sunday)* (dinner only) a la carte approx. 20.00 **t.** 4.50 – **13 rm** 48.00/60.00 **st.** – SB.

ATS 18 Westminster Rd ✆ 262000/265472

CHORLTON CUM HARDY Gtr. Manchester 402 403 404 N 23 – see Manchester.

CHRISTCHURCH Dorset 403 404 O 31 **The West Country G.** – pop. 40 865 – ECD : Wednesday – ☎ 01202.
See : Town★ – Priory★.
Envir. : Hengistbury Head★ (≤★★) SW : 4½ m. by A 35 and B 3059.
⛳18 Highcliffe Castle, 107 Lymington Rd, Highcliffe-on-Sea ✆ (01425) 272953 – ⛳9 Iford Bridge, Barrack Rd, Iford ✆ 473817.
ℹ 23 High St., BH23 1AB ✆ 471780.
◆London 111 – Bournemouth 6 – Salisbury 26 – ◆Southampton 24 – Winchester 39.

Travel Inn, Somerford Rd, BH23 3QG, E : 2 m. by A 35 on B 3059 ✆ 485376, Fax 474939 – ⇔ rm TV ♿ P. AE VISA.
Meals (Beefeater grill) a la carte approx. 16.00 **t.** 5.60 – 4.95 – **38 rm** 33.50 **t.**

Splinters Brasserie, 12 Church St., BH23 1BW, ✆ 483454, Fax 483454 – AE VISA
closed 15 January to 2 February – **Meals** 14.50/22.50 **t.** 5.00.

at Mudeford SE : 2 m. – ✉ Christchurch – ☎ 01202 :

Avonmouth (Forte), 95 Mudeford, BH23 3NT, ✆ 483434, Fax 479004, ≤, ⛆ heated, ⛱ – ⇔ TV ☎ P – 🔺 60. AE VISA
Meals (bar lunch Monday to Saturday)/dinner 15.95 **st.** 6.75 – 8.50 – **41 rm** 65.00/90.00 **st.** – SB.

Waterford Lodge, 87 Bure Lane, Friars Cliff, BH23 4DN, ✆ (01425) 278801, Fax 279130, ⛱ – TV ☎ P – 🔺 80. AE VISA JCB
Meals 13.50 **t.** (lunch) and a la carte 22.25/28.75 **t.** 4.80 – **17 rm** 76.00/99.00 **t.** – SB.

at Winkton N : 2 m. on B 3347 – ✉ Christchurch – ☎ 01202 :

Fisherman's Haunt, Salisbury Rd, BH23 7AS, ✆ 477283, Fax 484071, ⛱ – TV ☎ P
20 rm.

CHURCHILL Oxon. 403 404 P 28 – pop. 502 – ✉ Chipping Norton – ☎ 01608.
◆London 79 – ◆Birmingham 46 – Cheltenham 29 – ◆Oxford 23 – Swindon 31.

Forge House without rest., OX7 6NJ, ✆ 658173 – TV P.
4 rm 32.00/54.00 **st.**

CHURCH STRETTON Shrops. 402 403 L 26 **Great Britain G.** – pop. 4 161 – ECD : Wednesday – ☎ 01694.

Envir. : Wenlock Edge★, E : by B 4371.

Trevor Hill ☎ 722281.

London 166 – Birmingham 46 – Hereford 39 – Shrewsbury 14.

Mynd House, Ludlow Rd, Little Stretton, SY6 6RB, SW : 1 m. on B 4370 ☎ 722212, Fax 724180, – TV ☎ P. AE
closed January and 2 weeks summer – **Meals** (booking essential) (bar lunch)/dinner 14.95 **st.** 4.40 – **7 rm** 40.00/75.00 **st.**, 1 suite – SB.

Rectory Farm without rest., Woolstaston, SY6 6NN, NW : 5½ m. by A 49 ☎ 751306, ≤, « 17C timbered house », – TV P
closed January – **3 rm** 25.00/38.00 **st.**

Belvedere, Burway Rd, SY6 6DP, ☎ 722232, Fax 722232, – P. VISA
Meals (by arrangement) 9.00 **st.** – **12 rm** 21.00/46.00 **st.**

ATS Crossways ☎ 722526/722112

CHURT Surrey 404 R 30 – see Farnham.

CIRENCESTER Glos. 403 404 O 28 **Great Britain G.** – pop. 17 085 – ECD : Thursday – ☎ 01285 :

See : Town★ – Church of St. John the Baptist★ – Corinium Museum★ (Mosaic pavements★) *AC*.

Envir. : Fairford : Church of St. Mary★ (stained glass windows★★) E : 7 m. by A 417.

Cheltenham Rd ☎ 653939.

Corn Hall, Market Pl., GL7 2NW ☎ 654180.

London 97 – Bristol 37 – Gloucester 19 – Oxford 37.

Jarvis Fleece, Market Pl., GL7 2NZ, ☎ 658507, Fax 651017 – TV ☎ P – 35. AE VISA
Meals (bar lunch Monday to Saturday) 10.95/15.95 **st.** and dinner a la carte – 8.25 – **30 rm** 65.00/90.00 **st.** – SB.

Wimborne House, 91 Victoria Rd, GL7 1ES, ☎ 653890, – TV P.
closed Christmas-New Year – **Meals** (by arrangement) 8.00 **st.** – **5 rm** 25.00/35.00 **t.**

Harry Hare's, 3 Gosditch St., GL7 2AG, ☎ 652375, Fax 641691, – AE VISA
Meals a la carte 13.40/23.95 **t.** 3.95.

at Rendcomb N : 6¼ m. by A 417 off A 435 – ✉ Cirencester – ☎ 01285 :

Shawswell Country House, GL7 7HD, N : 1½ m. on No Through Rd ☎ 831779, ≤, « Part 17C and 18C house », , park – TV P.
closed December and January – **Meals** (by arrangement) 16.50 **st.** – **5 rm** 35.00/50.00 **st.**

at Barnsley NE : 4 m. by A 429 on B 4425 – ✉ Cirencester – ☎ 01285 :

Village Pub, GL7 5EF, ☎ 740421 – TV ☎ P. AE VISA
closed 25 December – **Meals** a la carte 9.50/14.40 **st.** 4.50 – **5 rm** 29.00/45.00 **st.**

at Ampney Crucis E : 2¾ m. by A 417 – ✉ Cirencester – ☎ 01285 :

Crown of Crucis, GL7 5RS, ☎ 851806, Fax 851735, – rest TV ☎ P – 80. AE VISA
closed 25 December – **Meals** (bar lunch)/dinner 15.00 **t.** and a la carte 4.85 – **25 rm** 49.00/64.00 **t.** – SB.

Waterton Garden Cottage, GL7 5RY, S : ½ m. by Driffield rd turning right into unmarked driveway ☎ 851303, « Converted Victorian stables, walled garden », heated – rm P.
Booking essential – **Meals** (by arrangement) 20.00 – **3 rm** 25.00/45.00 **s.**

at Ewen SW : 3¼ m. by A 429 – ✉ Cirencester – ☎ 01285 :

Wild Duck Inn, Drake's Island, GL7 6BY, ☎ 770310, Fax 770310, « Part 16C former farm buildings », – TV ☎ P. AE VISA
Meals a la carte 11.45/20.90 **t.** – 5.00 – **9 rm** 48.00/75.00 **t.**

at Kemble SW : 4 m. by A 433 on A 429 – ✉ Cirencester – ☎ 01285 :

Smerrill Barns without rest., GL7 6BW, on A 429 ☎ 770907, Fax 770907 – TV P. VISA.
7 rm 25.00/50.00 **s.**

at Stratton NW : 1¼ m. on A 417 – ✉ Cirencester – ☎ 01285 :

Stratton House, Gloucester Rd, GL7 2LE, ☎ 651761, Fax 640024, – TV ☎ P – 150. AE VISA
Meals (bar lunch Monday to Saturday)/dinner 15.75 **t.** and a la carte 5.45 – **41 rm** 46.95/65.90 **t.**

ATS 1 Mercian Close, Watermoor End ☎ 657761

CLANFIELD Oxon. 403 404 P 28 – pop. 1 709 – ECD : Wednesday and Saturday – ☎ 0136 781.
♦London 76 – ♦Oxford 20 – Swindon 17.

XXX **Plough at Clanfield** with rm, Bourton Rd, OX18 2RB, on A 4095 ℘ 222, Fax 596, « Small Elizabethan manor house », – rest TV ☎ P. VISA JCB.
Meals 14.50/33.95 **t.** 6.40 – **6 rm** 65.00/100.00 **t.** – SB.

CLAPHAM Beds. 404 S 27 – see Bedford.

CLAPPERSGATE Cumbria – see Ambleside.

CLAUGHTON Lancs. 402 M 21 – see Lancaster.

CLAVERING Essex 404 U 28 – pop. 1 663 – ✉ Saffron Walden – ☎ 01799.
♦London 44 – ♦Cambridge 25 – Colchester 44 – Luton 29.

X **Cricketers,** CB11 4QT, ℘ 550442, Fax 550882 – P. VISA
Meals (bar lunch Monday to Saturday)/dinner 19.00 **st.**

CLAWTON Devon 403 H 31 **The West Country G.** – pop. 292 – ✉ Holsworthy – ☎ 01409.
Envir. : W : Tamar River★★.
♦London 240 – Exeter 39 – ♦Plymouth 36.

Court Barn, EX22 6PS, W : ½ m. ℘ 27219, Fax 27309, – rm TV ☎ P. AE VISA
Meals (booking essential) 10.50/20.00 **t.** and lunch a la carte 4.25 – **8 rm** 30.00/75.00 **t.** – SB.

CLAYGATE Surrey 404 ㊷ – see Esher.

CLAYTON-LE-MOORS Lancs 402 M 22 – pop. 6 146 – ECD : Wednesday – ✉ Accrington – ☎ 01254.
♦London 232 – Blackburn 3.5 – Lancaster 37 – ♦Leeds 44 – Preston 14.

Dunkenhalgh, Blackburn Rd, BB5 5JP, SW : 1 ½ m. on A 678 ℘ 398021, Fax 872230, , – rm TV ☎ P – 400. AE VISA
Meals (bar lunch Saturday) 9.00/17.50 **t.** and a la carte 4.95 – 6.95 – **78 rm** 77.50/92.00 **t.**, 1 suite – SB.

Sparth House, Whalley Rd, BB5 5RP, ℘ 872263, Fax 872263, – rest TV ☎ P – 100. VISA.
Meals *(closed Sunday dinner)* 14.95 **st.** and a la carte 4.50 – **16 rm** 48.25/80.75 **t.**

CLAYTON-LE-WOODS Lancs. – pop. 14 272 – ✉ Chorley – ☎ 01772.
♦London 220 – ♦Liverpool 31 – ♦Manchester 26 – Preston 5.5.

Pines, Preston Rd, PR6 7ED, on A 6 at junction with B 5256 ℘ 38551, Fax 629002, – rm TV ☎ P – 200. AE VISA.
closed 25 and 26 December – **Meals** 9.50/18.50 **t.** and a la carte – **37 rm** 50.00/85.00 **t.**, 2 suites – SB.

CLAYTON WEST W. Yorks 402 404 P 23 – ✉ Huddersfield – ☎ 01484.
♦London 190 – ♦Leeds 19 – ♦Manchester 35 – ♦Sheffield 24.

Bagden Hall, Wakefield Rd, Scissett, HD8 9LE, SW : 1 m. on A 636 ℘ 865330, Fax 861001, 9, , park – TV ☎ P – 90
Meals *(closed Sunday dinner)* 8.95/15.95 **t.** and a la carte – **17 rm** 60.00/80.00 **st.** – SB.

CLEARWELL Glos. – see Coleford.

CLEETHORPES Humbs. 402 404 U 23 – pop. 33 238 – ECD : Thursday – ☎ 01472.
42-43 Alexandra Rd, DN35 8LE ℘ 200220.
♦London 171 – Boston 49 – Lincoln 38 – ♦Sheffield 77.

Plan : see Great Grimsby

Kingsway, Kingsway, DN35 0AE, ℘ 601122, Fax 601381, ← – TV ☎ P. AE VISA. BZ **a**
closed 25 and 26 December – **Meals** 11.50/15.25 **t.** and a la carte 4.60 – **50 rm** 55.00/80.00 **t.** – SB.

CLEEVE HILL Glos. 403 404 N 28 – see Cheltenham.

CLEVEDON Avon 403 L 29 – ☎ 01275.
♦London 137 – ♦Bristol 13 – Taunton 36.

X Il Giardino, 12 The Beach, BS21 7QU, ℘ 878832
Meals - Italian (booking essential).

CLEY NEXT THE SEA Norfolk 404 X 25 – see Blakeney.

CLIFTON HAMPDEN Oxon. 403 404 Q 29 – see Abingdon.

CLITHEROE Lancs 402 M 22 – pop. 13 548 – ☎ 01200.
Whalley Rd ℘ 22618.
12-14 Market Pl., BB7 2DA ℘ 25566.
♦London 64 – ♦Blackpool 35 – ♦Manchester 31.

Brooklyn, 32 Pimlico Rd, BB7 2AH, ℘ 28268 TV. AE VISA.
Meals 10.50 **s.** – **4 rm** 25.00/38.00 **s.** – SB.

Auctioneer, New Market St., BB7 2JW, ℘ 27153 – AE VISA
closed Monday – **Meals** 6.25/15.75 **t.** and lunch a la carte 4.90.

at Waddington N : 1 ¾ m. on B 6478 – ✉ Clitheroe – ☎ 01200.

Peter Barn without rest., Rabbit Lane, via Cross Lane, BB7 3JH, NW : 1 ½ m. by B 6478 ℘ 28585, – P.
closed 24 December to 1 January – **3 rm** 26.00/39.00.

ATS Salthill Rd ℘ 23011

CLOVELLY Devon 403 G 31 **The West Country G.** – ✉ Bideford – ☎ 01237.
See : Village★★.
Exc. : Hartland : Hartland Church★ – Hartland Quay★ (viewpoint★★) – Hartland Point ≤★★★, W : 6 ½ m. by B 3237 and B 3248.
♦London 241 – Barnstaple 18 – Exeter 52 – Penzance 92.

Red Lion, The Quay, EX39 5TF, ℘ 431237, Fax 431044, ≤ – TV P. VISA.
Meals (bar lunch)/dinner 20.75 **t.** 4.40 – **12 rm** 39.00/63.00 **st.** – SB.

CLOWNE Derbs. 402 403 404 Q 24 **Great Britain G.** – pop. 7 234 – ECD : Wednesday – ☎ 01246.
Exc. : Bolsover Castle★ *AC*, S : 6 m. by B 6417 and A 632.
♦London 156 – Derby 40 – Lincoln 35 – ♦Nottingham 30 – ♦Sheffield 12.

Van Dyk, Worksop Rd, S43 4TD, N : ¾ m. by A 618 on A 619 ℘ 810219, Fax 819566 – TV P – 120. AE VISA
Meals *(closed Sunday dinner)* 17.50 **t.** and a la carte 5.20 – **16 rm** 40.00/50.00 **st.**

CLYST ST. GEORGE Devon – see Exeter.

COALVILLE Leics. 402 403 404 P 25 – pop. 28 772 – ☎ 01530.
Snibston Discovery Park, Ashby Rd, LE6 3LN ℘ 813608.
♦London 115 – ♦Birmingham 32 – ♦Leicester 15 – ♦Nottingham 25.

Hermitage Park, Whitwick Rd, LE67 3FA, off High St. ℘ 814814, Fax 814202, – rest TV P – 30. AE VISA.
Meals 9.95/11.95 **t.** and a la carte 5.95 – **24 rm** 59.50/64.50 **t.**, 1 suite.

COATHAM MUNDEVILLE Durham 402 P 20 – see Darlington.

COBHAM Kent 404 V 29 – pop. 13 795 (inc. Oxshott) – ✉ Gravesend – ☎ 01474.
Silvermere, Redhill Rd ℘ 867275.
♦London 27 – Maidstone 13 – Rochester 6.

Ye Olde Leather Bottle, The Street, DA12 3BZ, ℘ 814327, Fax 812086, « 17C inn », – TV P. AE VISA.
Meals *(closed Saturday lunch and Sunday dinner)* 11.45 **t.** and a la carte – 4.00 – **7 rm** 35.95 **t.**

COBHAM Surrey 404 S 30 – pop. 10 252 – ECD : Wednesday – ☎ 01932.
♦London 24 – Guildford 10.

Plan : see Greater London (South-West)

Hilton National, Seven Hills Rd South, KT11 1EW, W : 1 ½ m. by A 245 ℘ 864471, Fax 868017, , , park, , squash – rm TV P – 300. AE VISA JCB by A 3 AZ
Meals (bar lunch Saturday) (dancing Friday and Saturday evenings) 15.50/23.50 **t.** and a la carte 7.00 – 10.75 – **149 rm** 85.00/130.00 **st.**, 3 suites – SB.

Cedar House, Mill Rd, KT11 3AN, ℘ 863424, Fax 862023, – TV P. AE VISA. by A 307 AZ
closed 25 December to 1 January – **Meals** *(closed Sunday dinner and Monday)* (dinner only and Sunday lunch)/dinner 19.95 **t.** and a la carte 4.65 – **6 rm** 40.00/80.00 **t.**

at Stoke D'Abernon SE : 1 ½ m. on A 245 – AZ – ✉ Cobham – ☎ 01372.

Woodlands Park, Woodlands Lane, KT11 3QB, on A 245 ℘ 843933, Fax 842704, , park, – TV P – 300. AE VISA.
Meals *(closed Saturday lunch)* 10.75/14.25 **t.** and a la carte 6.50 – 8.95 – **57 rm** 100.00/130.00 **t.**, 1 suite – SB.

COCKERMOUTH Cumbria 401 402 J 20 – pop. 7 702 – ECD : Thursday – 01900.

Embleton ℘ (017687) 76223.

Town Hall, Market Place, CA13 9NP ℘ 822634.

London 306 – Carlisle 25 – Keswick 13.

Trout, Crown St., CA13 0EJ, ℘ 823591, Fax 827514, – – 50.
Meals 7.95/16.95 **t.** and a la carte 5.15 – **23 rm** 54.95/79.95 **t.** – SB.

Low Hall, Brandlingill, CA13 0RE, S : 3¼ m. by A 5086 on Lorton rd ℘ 826654, ≤, – .
March-October – **Meals** 18.00 **st.** 4.50 – **5 rm** 20.00/70.00 **st.**

COGGESHALL Essex 404 W 28 – pop. 5 220 – ECD : Wednesday – ✉ Colchester – 01376.

London 49 – Braintree 6 – Chelmsford 16 – Colchester 9.

White Hart, Market End, CO6 1NH, ℘ 561654, Fax 561789, « Part 15C guildhall », – .
Meals - Italian (closed Sunday dinner) 13.95/14.95 **t.** and a la carte 5.50 – **18 rm** 61.50/97.00 **t.**

Baumann's Brasserie, 4-6 Stoneham St., CO6 1TT, ℘ 561453 –
closed Saturday lunch, Sunday dinner, Monday and first 2 weeks January – **Meals** 9.95 **t.** (lunch) and a la carte 19.00/23.95 **t.**

COLCHESTER Essex 404 W 28 **Great Britain G.** – pop. 87 476 – ECD : Thursday – 01206.

See : Castle and Museum★ *AC.*

Birch Grove, Layer Rd ℘ 734276 – , Earls Colne ℘ (01787) 224466.

1 Queen St., CO1 2PJ ℘ 712920.

London 52 – Cambridge 48 – Ipswich 18 – Luton 76 – Southend-on-Sea 41.

Red Lion, 43 High St., CO1 1DJ, ℘ 577986, Fax 578207, « Part 15C inn » – – 40.
Meals 9.95 **st.** and a la carte 5.00 – **24 rm** 50.00/70.00 **st.** – SB.

George, 116 High St., CO1 1TD, ℘ 578494, Fax 761732, – – 80.
Meals 8.95/21.00 **t.** and dinner a la carte 4.95 – 8.75 – **47 rm** 53.00/69.00 **st.** – SB.

Butterfly, Old Ipswich Rd, CO7 7QY, NE : 4 ¼ m. by A 1232 at junction of A 12 with A 120 ℘ 230900, Fax 231095 – rm – 80. .
Meals 10.85/11.95 **t.** and a la carte 4.50 – 6.50 – **50 rm** 49.00/80.00 **t.** – SB.

Rose and Crown, East St., Eastgates, CO1 2TZ, ℘ 866677, Fax 866616 – – 100. .
Meals 13.95/21.50 **t.** and a la carte 3.85 – **30 rm** 55.00/99.00 **t.** – SB.

Warehouse Brasserie, 12a Chapel St. North, CO2 7AT, ℘ 765656 – .
closed Good Friday lunch and 25-26 December – **Meals** *(closed Sunday dinner)* a la carte 12.20/18.15 **t.** 3.75.

at Nayland N : 6½ m. by A 134 – ✉ Colchester – 01206 :

Martha's Vineyard, 18 High St., CO6 4JF, ℘ 262888 –
closed Sunday, Monday, 2 weeks summer and 2 weeks winter – **Meals** (dinner only) 20.00 **t.** 5.00.

at Stoke by Nayland N : 8½ m. by A 134 on B 1087 – ✉ Colchester – 01206 :

Angel Inn with rm, Polstead St., CO6 4SA, ℘ 263245, Fax 337324, « Part timbered 17C inn » – .
closed 25-26 December – **Meals** a la carte 11.70/19.45 **t.** 3.70 – **6 rm** 44.00/57.50 **t.**

at Eight Ash Green W : 4 m. by A 604 – ✉ Colchester – 01206 :

Forte Posthouse, Abbotts Lane, CO6 3QL, at junction of A 604 with A 12 ℘ 767740, Fax 766577, – rm – 50.
Meals a la carte approx. 15.00 **t.** 5.50 – **110 rm** 56.00/69.50 **st.**

at Marks Tey W : 5 m. by A 12 at junction with A 120 – ✉ Colchester – 01206 :

Marks Tey, London Rd, CO6 1DU, on B 1408 ℘ 210001, Fax 212167, – rm – 200.
Meals 9.95/13.95 **t.** and a la carte 4.95 – 6.00 – **109 rm** 53.50/56.50 **t.**, 1 suite – SB.

ATS East Hill ℘ 866484/867471
ATS Telford Way, Severalls Park Ind. Est. ℘ 845641
ATS 451 Ipswich Rd ℘ 841404

COLEBROOK Devon 403 H 32 – see Plymouth.

COLEFORD Devon 403 I 31 – ✉ Crediton – 01363.

London 214 – Barnstaple 29 – Exeter 14 – Taunton 42.

New Inn, EX17 5BZ, ℘ 84242, Fax 85044, « Part 13C thatched inn » – rm .
Meals (in bar) a la carte 8.90/14.85 **t.** 4.50 – **3 rm** 32.00/49.50 **st.** – SB.

COLEFORD Glos. 403 404 M 28 **Great Britain G.** – pop. 8 246 – ECD : Thursday – ☎ 01594.
Envir. : W : Wye Valley★.
Forest of Dean, Lords Hills ☏ 832583 – Forest Hills, Mile End Rd ☏ 810620.
27 Market Place, GL16 8AE ☏ 836307.
London 143 – Bristol 28 – Gloucester 19 – Newport 29.

- **Speech House** (Forte), Forest of Dean, GL16 7EL, NE : 3 m. by B 4028 on B 4226 ☏ 822607, Fax 823658, – rm – 40. AE VISA
  Meals (bar lunch Monday to Saturday)/dinner 17.95 **t.** and a la carte 6.70 – 8.50 – **14 rm** 50.00/115.00 **t.** – SB.

at Clearwell S : 2 m. by B 4228 – ✉ Coleford – ☎ 01594.

- **Wyndham Arms,** GL16 8JT, ☏ 833666, Fax 836450 – – 40. AE VISA
  Meals 10.75/15.25 **t.** and a la carte 5.25 – **17 rm** 35.00/60.00 **t.** – SB.
- **Tudor Farmhouse,** GL16 8JS, ☏ 833046, Fax 837093, – rm . AE VISA JCB.
  Meals *(closed Sunday)* (dinner only) 15.95 **t.** – **8 rm** 42.50/59.00 **t.**, 1 suite – SB.

COLERNE Wilts. 403 404 M 29 – see Bath (Avon).

COLESBOURNE Glos. 403 404 N 28 – see Cheltenham.

COLESHILL Warks. 403 404 O 26 – pop. 6 511 – ECD : Monday and Thursday – ✉ Birmingham (W. Mids.) – ☎ 01675.
London 113 – Birmingham 8 – Coventry 11.

- Swan, High St., B46 3BL, ☏ 464107, Fax 467493 – – 60
  32 rm.
- Coleshill, 152 High St., B46 3BG, ☏ 465527, Fax 464013 – – 150
  23 rm.

During the season, particularly in resorts, it is wise to book in advance.

COLNE Lancs. 402 N 22 – pop. 19 094 – ☎ 01282.
Law Farm, Skipton Old Rd ☏ 863391 – Ghyll Brow, Barnoldswick ☏ 842466.
London 234 – Manchester 29 – Preston 26.

- **West Lynn Country House,** Barrowford Rd, BB8 9QW, W : ½ m. on B 6247 ☏ 869199, Fax 869199, – . VISA.
  Meals *(closed Sunday dinner)* (dinner only and Sunday lunch)/dinner 12.95 **st.** and a la carte 4.95 – **12 rm** 39.50/49.50 **st.** – SB.
- **Higher Slipper Hill Farm** , Foulridge, BB8 7LY, NW : 3¾ m. by A 56 and B 6251 on Barrowford rd ☏ 863602, ←, – . AE VISA.
  Meals (residents only) (dinner only) a la carte 11.15/18.00 **st.** 7.95 – **9 rm** 38.80/50.55 **t.**

ATS Corporation St. (ASDA) ☏ 864616

COLN ST. ALDWYNS Glos. – ✉ Cirencester – ☎ 01285.
London 101 – Bristol 53 – Gloucester 20 – Swindon 15.

- **New Inn,** GL7 5AN, ☏ 750651, Fax 750657, « 16C inn » – . AE VISA.
  Meals (bar lunch)/dinner 16.50 **t.** and a la carte 4.00 – 3.00 – **14 rm** 45.00/80.00 **t.** – SB.

COLSTERWORTH Lincs. 402 404 S 25 – pop. 1 107 – ☎ 01476.
London 105 – Grantham 8 – Leicester 29 – Nottingham 32 – Peterborough 14.

- **Granada Lodge** without rest., Granada Service Area, NG33 5JR, at A 151/A 1 (southbound carriageway) ☏ 860686, Fax 861078, Reservations (Freephone) 0800 555300 – – 30. AE VISA.
  4.00 – **36 rm** 39.95 **st.**
- **Forte Travelodge** without rest., NG33 5JJ, E : ½ m. by B 6403 on A 1 (southbound carriageway) ☏ 861181, Reservations (Freephone) 0800 850950 – . AE VISA
  32 rm 33.50 **t.**
- **Forte Travelodge** without rest., New Fox, South Witham, LE15 8AU, S : 3 m. by B 6403 on A 1 (northbound carriageway) ☏ (01572) 767586, Reservations (Freephone) 0800 850950 – . AE VISA
  32 rm 33.50 **t.**

COLTISHALL Norfolk 404 Y 25 **Great Britain G.** – pop. 1 414 – ✉ Norwich – ☎ 01603.
Envir. : The Broads★.
London 133 – Norwich 8.

- **Norfolk Mead** , Church St., NR12 7DN, ☏ 737531, Fax 737521, heated, , , park – rest . AE VISA.
  closed 25 to 30 December – **Meals** *(closed Sunday dinner and Bank Holidays)* (dinner only and Sunday lunch)/dinner 24.75 **t.** and a la carte – **10 rm** 55.00/85.00 **t.** – SB.
- XX **Norfolk Place,** Point House, High St., NR12 7AA, ☏ 738991. AE VISA
  closed Sunday, Monday, Tuesday and January – **Meals** (dinner only) 16.50/26.50 **st.** 4.00.

COLYTON Devon 403 K 31 **The West Country G.** – pop. 2 435 – ☎ 01297.

See : Town★ - Church★.

Envir. : Axmouth (<★) SE : 3 m. by B 3161, A 3052 and B 3172.

♦London 160 – Exeter 23 – Lyme Regis 7.

- **Old Bakehouse,** Lower Church St., EX13 6ND, ℘ 552518, Fax 552182 – rm TV P. AE VISA JCB
  Meals a la carte 9.95/12.95 **t.** and a la carte 4.00 – **6 rm** 18.00/36.00 **t.** – SB.
- **Swallows Eaves,** Colyford, EX13 6QJ, SE : 1 1/4 m. on A 3052 ℘ 553184, – TV P.
  closed January – **Meals** (dinner only) 18.50 **st.** – **8 rm** 35.00/59.00 **st.** – SB.

COMBE MARTIN Devon 403 H 30 – pop. 3 165 – ECD : Wednesday – ✉ Ilfracombe – ☎ 01271.

See : Ilfracombe : Hillsborough (<★★) *AC*, Capstone Hill★ (<★), St. Nicholas' Chapel (<★) *AC*.

Cross St., EX34 0DH ℘ 883319 (summer only).

♦London 218 – Exeter 56 – Taunton 58.

- **Coulsworthy Country House** , EX34 0PD, SE : 2 1/2 m. by A 399 and Hunters Inn rd ℘ 882463, <, « Country house atmosphere », heated, , – rest TV P. AE VISA
  closed 8 December-8 February – **Meals** *(closed Sunday dinner to non residents)* (dinner only and Sunday lunch)/dinner 25.00 **st.** – **9 rm** 51.00/114.00 **st.** – SB.
- **Rone House,** King St., EX34 0AD, ℘ 883428, Fax 883428, heated, – TV P. VISA
  March-October – **Meals** (dinner only) 10.00 **t.** and a la carte 3.00 – **10 rm** 18.00/36.00 **t.** – SB.
- **Just Johnsons,** King St., EX34 0BS, ℘ 883568 – VISA
  closed Monday and Tuesday in winter and Sunday – **Meals** (dinner only) a la carte 14.80/19.50 3.70.

COMPTON ABBAS Dorset – see Shaftesbury.

CONGLETON Ches. 402 403 404 N 24 **Great Britain G.** – pop. 21 539 – ECD : Wednesday – ☎ 01260.

Envir. : Little Moreton Hall★★ *AC*, SW : 3 m. by A 34.

Biddulph Rd ℘ 273540.

Town Hall, High St., CW12 1BN ℘ 271095.

♦London 183 – ♦Liverpool 50 – ♦Manchester 25 – ♦Sheffield 46 – ♦Stoke-on-Trent 13.

- **Sandhole Farm** without rest., Hulme Walfield, CW12 2JH, N : 2 1/4 m. on A 34 ℘ 224419, Fax 224766, , park – TV ☎ P. VISA
  13 rm 25.00/42.00 **st.**

ATS Brookside ℘ 273720

CONISTON Cumbria 402 K 20 **Great Britain G.** – pop. 1 304 – ☎ 0153 94.

Envir. : Coniston Water★ – Brantwood★ *AC*, SE : 2 m. on east side of Coniston Water.

16 Yewdale Rd, LA21 8DU ℘ 41533 (summer only).

♦London 285 – ♦Carlisle 55 – Kendal 22 – Lancaster 42.

- **Coniston Lodge,** Sunny Brow, LA21 8HH, ℘ 41201 – TV ☎ P. AE VISA.
  Meals *(closed Sunday and Monday)* (dinner only) 18.50 **st.** 5.90 – **6 rm** 39.00/68.00 **t.** – SB.
- **Sun,** LA21 8HQ, ℘ 41248, <, – rest TV ☎ P
  closed 24 to 26 December – **Meals** (bar lunch)/dinner a la carte 15.00 **t.** 5.30 – **11 rm** 33.00/66.00 **t.** – SB.

at Torver SW : 2 1/4 m. on A 593 – ✉ Coniston – ☎ 0153 94 :

- **Wheelgate Country House,** Little Arrow, LA21 8AU, NE : 3/4 m. on A 593 ℘ 41418, « Part 17C farmhouse », – TV P. AE VISA.
  closed November and December – **Meals** (dinner only) 17.00 **st.** 5.25 – **8 rm** 32.50/65.00 **st.** – SB.
- **Old Rectory,** LA21 8AX, ℘ 41353, Fax 41156, <, – TV P
  Meals *(closed Sunday)* (residents only) (dinner only) 15.50 **st.** 4.95 – **7 rm** 40.00/72.00 **t.**
- **Arrowfield,** Little Arrow, LA21 8AU, NE : 3/4 m. on A 593 ℘ 41741, <, – TV P.
  March-November – **Meals** (by arrangement) 13.00 **st.** 3.00 – **5 rm** 20.00/44.00 **st.**

at Water Yeat S : 6 1/2 m. by A 593 on A 5084 – ✉ Ulverston – ☎ 01229 :

- **Water Yeat,** LA12 8DJ, ℘ 885306, – rm P.
  closed January – **Meals** (by arrangement) 14.00 **st.** – **7 rm** 21.00/55.00 **st.** – SB.

at Blawith S : 7 1/4 m. by A 593 on A 5084 – ✉ Ulverston – ☎ 01229 :

- **Appletree Holme** , LA12 8EL, W : 1 m. taking unmarked road opposite church and then right hand fork ℘ 885618, <, – TV ☎ P. VISA.
  Meals 23.50 3.75 – **4 rm** (dinner included) 65.00/118.00 **st.**

CONSTANTINE BAY Cornwall 403 E 32 – see Padstow.

COOKHAM Berks. 404 R 29 **Great Britain G.** – pop. 5 752 – ECD : Wednesday and Thursday – ✉ Maidenhead – ☎ 01628.

See : Stanley Spencer Gallery★ *AC.*

♦London 32 – High Wycombe 7 – Reading 16.

XX **Alfonso's,** 19 Station Hill Par., SL6 9BR, ✆ 525775 – VISA JCB
closed Saturday lunch, Sunday, 2 weeks August and Bank Holidays – **Meals** 12.50/16.50 **t.** and a la carte.

XX **Peking Inn,** 49 High St., SL6 9SL, ✆ 520900 – ▤. VISA
Meals - Chinese (Peking) 12.00/20.00 **t.** and a la carte.

COPDOCK Suffolk 404 X 27 – see Ipswich.

COPTHORNE W. Sussex 404 T 30 – see Crawley.

CORBRIDGE Northd. 401 402 N 19 **Great Britain G.** – pop. 3 533 – ECD : Thursday – ☎ 01434.

Envir. : Hadrian's Wall★★, N : 3 m. by A 68 – Corstopitum★ *AC,* NW :½m..

Hill St., NE45 5AA ✆ 632815 (summer only).

♦London 300 – Hexham 3 – ♦Newcastle upon Tyne 18.

Lion of Corbridge, Bridge End, NE45 5AX, ✆ 632504, Fax 632571 – TV ☎ ♿ P. VISA.
Meals 7.75/18.00 **t.** and dinner a la carte 4.80 – **14 rm** 46.00/53.50 **t.** – SB.

Riverside without rest., Main St., NE45 5LE, ✆ 632942, Fax 633883 – TV P. VISA
closed mid December-mid January – **10 rm** 25.00/48.00 **st.**

Wheatsheaf, St. Helens St., NE45 5HE, ✆ 632020, Fax 632801 – TV ☎ P. VISA.
Meals (bar lunch)/dinner 11.95 **t.** and a la carte 3.50 – **6 rm** 39.50/49.50 **t.**

Low Barns, Thornbrough, NE45 5LX, E : 1¼ m. on B 6530 ✆ 632408, – rest TV P. VISA
Meals (by arrangement) 14.00 **st.** – **3 rm** 28.00/42.00 **st.**

XXX **Ramblers Country House,** Farnley, NE45 5RN, S : 1 m. on Riding Mill Rd ✆ 632424 – P. VISA
closed Sunday dinner, Monday, 1 week February and 2 weeks July – **Meals** - German (lunch by arrangement)/dinner 16.95 **t.** and a la carte 3.85.

XX **Valley,** The Old Station House, Station Rd, NE45 5AY, S : ½ m. by Riding Mill rd ✆ 633434, Fax 633923 – VISA
closed Sunday and 25 December – **Meals** - Indian (dinner only) a la carte 10.30/18.60 **st.**

CORBY Northants. 404 R 26 **Great Britain G.** – pop. 53 044 – ☎ 01536.

Envir. : Boughton House★★ *AC,* S : 5½ m. by A 6116 and A 43.

18 Priors Hall, Stamford Rd, Weldon ✆ 260756.

Civic Centre, George St., NN17 1QB ✆ 407507.

♦London 100 – ♦Leicester 26 – Northampton 22 – Peterborough 24.

Carlton Manor, Geddington Rd, NN18 8ET, SE : 1 ¾ m. on A 6116 ✆ 401020, Fax 400767, – TV ☎ P – 190. VISA
Meals 12.75/14.75 **st.** and a la carte – 6.50 – **72 rm** 65.00/75.00 **t.**, 2 suites – SB.

Rockingham Forest, Rockingham Rd, NN17 1AE, ✆ 401348, Fax 66383 – rm TV ☎ P – 400
68 rm.

ATS St. Jame's Rd ✆ 269519

CORFE CASTLE Dorset 403 404 N 32 **The West Country G.** – pop. 1 335 – ✉ Wareham – ☎ 01929.

See : Castle★★ (≤★★) *AC.*

♦London 129 – Bournemouth 18 – Weymouth 23.

Mortons House, 45 East St., BH20 5EE, ✆ 480988, Fax 480820, ≤, « Elizabethan manor », – TV ☎ P. VISA
Meals 15.00/22.50 **t.** – **16 rm** 55.00/96.00 **t.**, 1 suite – SB.

CORNHILL-ON-TWEED Northd. 401 402 N 17 – pop. 317 – ECD : Thursday – ☎ 01890.

♦London 345 – ♦Edinburgh 49 – ♦Newcastle upon Tyne 59.

Coach House, Crookham, TD12 4TD, E : 4 m. on A 697 ✆ 820293, – rest ♿ P. VISA
Easter-October – **Meals** 14.50 **st.** 4.50 – **9 rm** 19.00/62.00 **t.**

CORSE LAWN Heref. and Worcs. – see Tewkesbury (Glos.).

CORSHAM Wilts. 403 404 N 29 **The West Country G.** – pop. 11 259 – ECD : Wednesday – 01249.

See : Corsham Court** *AC* – **Envir.** : Castle Combe**, N : 5½ m. - Biddestone*, N : 2 m.

Exc. : Bath***, SW : 9 m. by A 4.

London 110 – Bristol 22 – Swindon 25.

- Rudloe Park, Leafy Lane, SN13 0PA, W : 2 m. by B 3353 on A 4 (01225) 810555, Fax 811412, ←, – rest – 80. VISA
  Meals 15.95/20.95 **st.** 5.50 – **11 rm.**
- **Methuen Arms,** 2 High St., SN13 0HB, 714867, Fax 712004, – . VISA.
  Meals *(closed Sunday dinner)* 12.00/18.00 **t.** and a la carte 4.25 – **25 rm** 47.00/65.00 **st.** – SB.

CORSTON Avon 403 404 M 29 – see Bath.

COSGROVE Northants. 404 R 27 – see Stony Stratford.

COSHAM Hants. 403 404 Q 31 – see Portsmouth and Southsea.

COVENTRY W. Mids. 403 404 P 26 **Great Britain G.** – pop. 294 387 – ECD : Thursday – 01203.

See : City* - Cathedral*** *AC* AV – Old Cathedral* AV **A** – Museum of British Road Transport* *AC* AV **M1**.

18 Finham Park 411123 BZ – 18 Windmill Village, Birmingham Rd, Allesley 407241, – 9 Sphinx, Siddeley Av., Stoke 451361.

Coventry Airport : 301717, S : 3½ m. by Coventry Rd BZ.

Bayley Lane, CV1 5RN 832303/832304,.

London 100 – Birmingham 18 – Bristol 96 – Nottingham 52.

Plans on following pages

- **De Vere,** Cathedral Sq., CV1 5RP, 633733, Fax 225299 – rest – 400. VISA — AV **n**
  Meals (bar lunch Saturday) 12.00/22.50 **t.** and a la carte – **180 rm** 85.00/95.00 **st.**, 10 suites – SB.
- **Brooklands Grange,** Holyhead Rd, CV5 8HX, 601601, Fax 601277 – . VISA. — AY **e**
  Meals *(closed lunch Saturday and Bank Holidays)* 15.95 **st.** and a la carte – **30 rm** 50.00/90.00 **st.** – SB.
- **Leofric,** Broadgate, CV1 1LZ, 221371, Fax 551352 – rest – 600. VISA. — AV **r**
  Meals 15.00 **t.** (dinner) and a la carte 12.40/23.35 4.50 – 7.50 – **89 rm** 79.50/94.50 **st.**, 5 suites – SB.
- **Travel Inn,** Rugby Rd, Binley Woods, CV3 2TA, at junction of A 46 with A 428 636585, Fax 431178 – rm – 32. VISA. — BZ **n**
  Meals (grill rest.) a la carte approx. 16.00 **t.** – 4.95 – **50 rm** 33.50 **t.**
- **Campanile,** Abbey Rd, Whitley, CV3 4BJ, SE : 2½ m. by A 4114 off A 444 639922, Fax 306898 – rm . VISA — BZ **a**
  Meals 9.85 **t.** and a la carte 2.65 – **51 rm** 40.00/44.25 **t.**
- **Crest** without rest., 39 Friars Rd, CV1 2LJ, 227822, Fax 227244 – . — AV **e**
  closed 25 December-1 January – **4 rm** 22.00/40.00 **s.**
- **Baccara** without rest., 20 Park Rd, CV1 2LD, 226530 – . — AV **i**
  7 rm 16.00/32.00 **st.**
- **Ashbourne** without rest., 33 St. Patricks Rd, CV1 2LP, 229518 – . — AV **a**
  closed 24 December-2 January – **5 rm** 18.00/38.00 **st.**
- **Abigail** without rest., 39 St. Patricks Rd, CV1 2LP, 221378 – — AV **x**
  closed 2 weeks Christmas-New Year – **5 rm** 16.00/32.00 **s.**

at Longford N : 4 m. on A 444 – ✉ Coventry – 01203 :

- **Novotel,** Wilsons Lane, CV6 6HL, 365000, Fax 362422, heated – rm rest – 250. VISA — BV **v**
  Meals 8.50/10.50 **st.** and a la carte – 7.50 – **98 rm** 53.00/63.00 **st.**

at Walsgrave NE : 3 m. on A 4600 – ✉ Coventry – 01203 :

- **Hilton National,** Paradise Way, The Triangle, CV2 2ST, NE : 1 m. by A 4600 603000, Telex 311333, Fax 603011, , , – rm – 600. VISA JCB — BX **c**
  Meals (bar lunch Saturday) 12.50/16.95 **t.** and a la carte 7.50 – 10.25 – **169 rm** 90.00/110.00 **st.**, 3 suites – SB.
- Forte Crest, Hinckley Rd, CV2 2HP, NE : ½ m. on A 4600 613261, Fax 621736, , , – rm rest – 425 — BX **e**
  145 rm, 2 suites.
- Campanile, Wigston Rd off Hinckley Rd, CV2 2SD, NE : ½ m. by A 4600 622311, Telex 317454, Fax 602362 – rm — BX **a**
  47 rm.

COVENTRY

Street	Grid	Street	Grid	Street	Grid
Broadgate	AV 6	Far Gosford Street	AV 13	Queen Victoria Road	AV 35
Corporation Street	AV	Gosford Street	AV 15	St. Johns (Ringway)	AV 38
Shopping Precincts	AV	Greyfriars Lane	AV 16	St. Nicholas (Ringway)	AV 39
Bayley Lane	AV 3	Hales Street	AV 17	Swanswell (Ringway)	AV 40
Bishop Street	AV 5	Hearsall Lane	AY 21	Trinity Street	AV 41
Burges	AV 7	High Street	AV 22	Upper Well Street	AV 43
Earl Street	AV 10	Ironmonger Row	AV 23	Vecqueray Street	AV 45
Fairfax Street	AV 12	Jordan Well	AV 26	Victoria Street	AV 46
		Leicester Row	AV 29	Warwick Row	AV 49
		Light Lane	AV 30	White Street	AV 51
		Little Park Street	AV 31	Windsor Street	AV 52
		Primrose Hill Street	AV 34	White Friars (Ringway)	AV 54

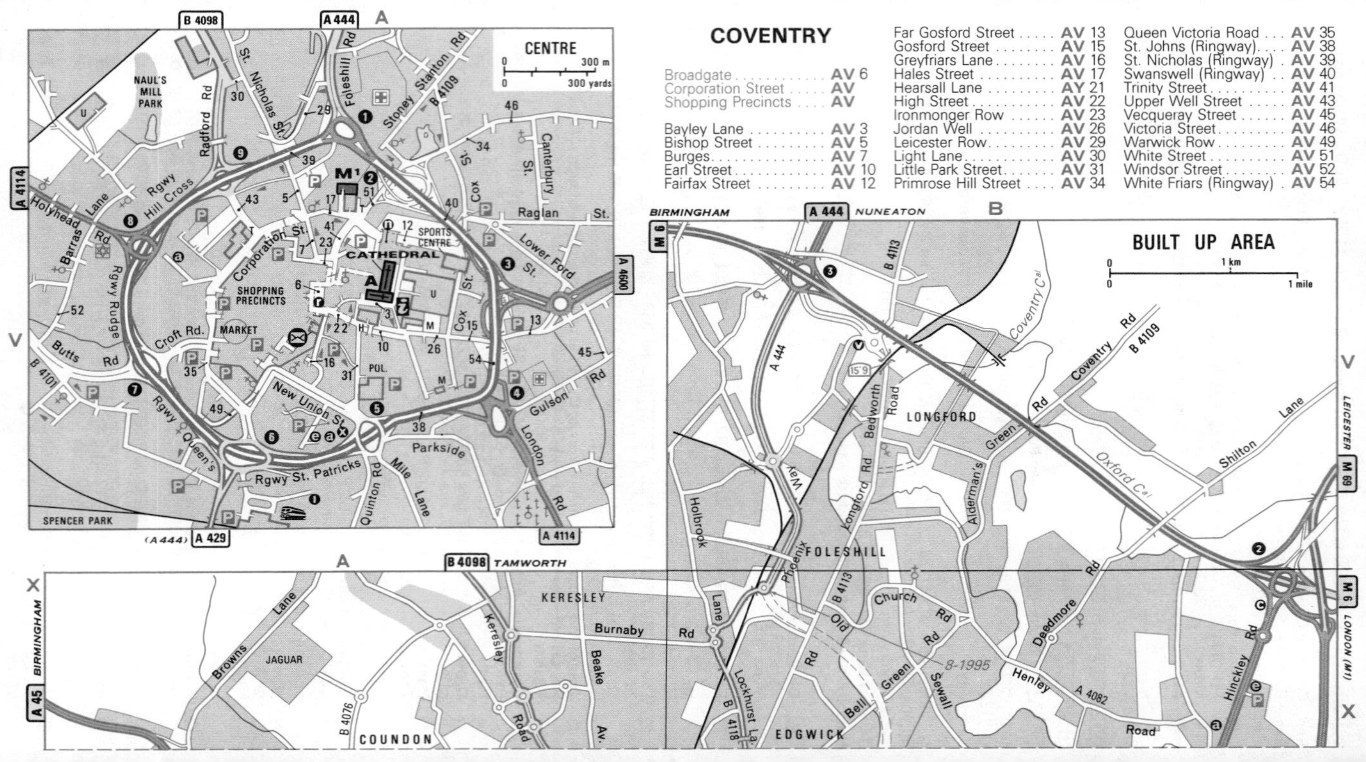

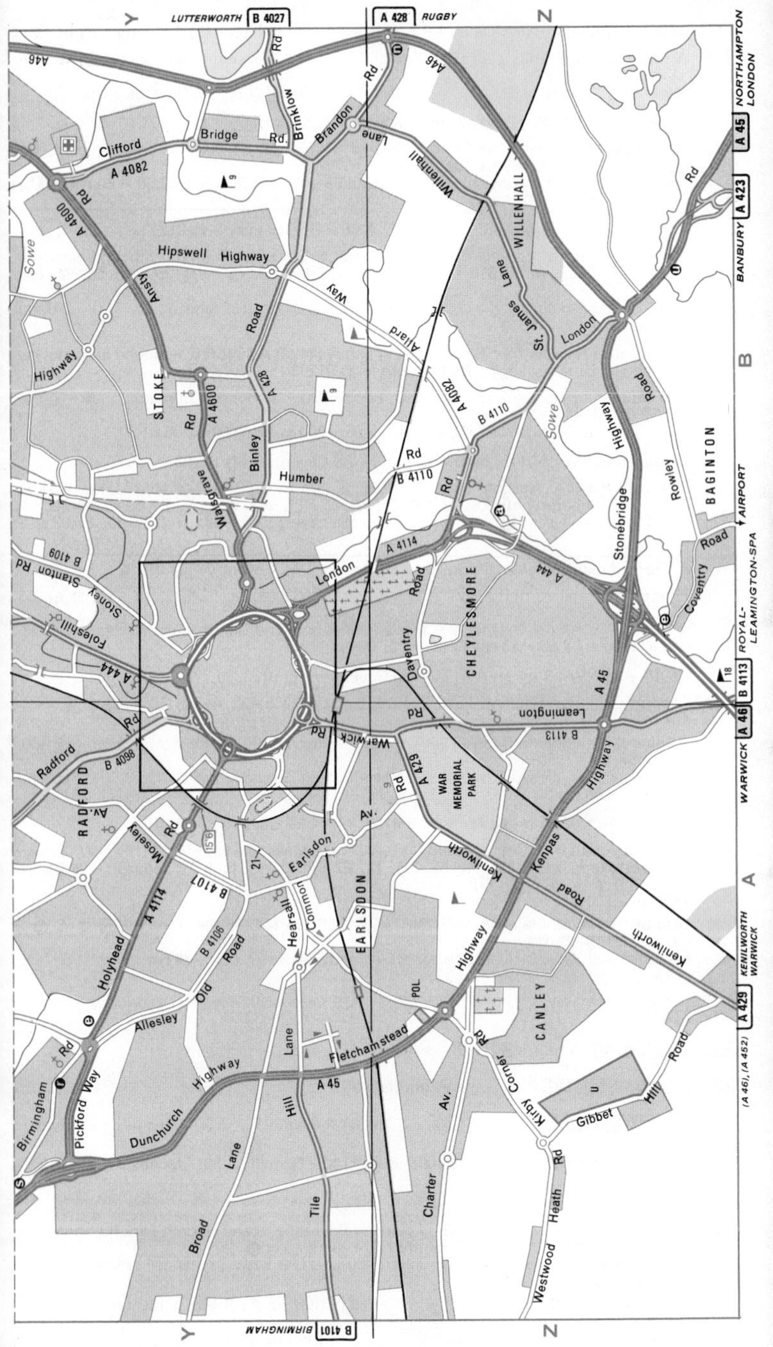

LUTTERWORTH B 4027
A 428 RUGBY
NORTHAMPTON LONDON A 45
BANBURY A 423
B
AIRPORT
ROYAL-LEAMINGTON-SPA B 4113
WARWICK A 46
A
KENILWORTH WARWICK A 429
(A 46), (A 452)
B 4101 BIRMINGHAM
Y
Z
A 46
Clifford Bridge Rd.
A 4082
Brinklow Rd
Brandon Rd
Willenhall Lane
WILLENHALL
A 4600 Rd
Sowe
Hipswell Highway
Ansty
Road
Allard Way
St. James Lane
London
Highway
STOKE
Rd A 4600
A 428
A 4082
B 4110
Binley
Humber Rd
B 4110
Rd
Walsgrave
Sowe
Highway
Road
Rowley
BAGINTON
Stonebridge
Coventry Road
B 4109
Stanton Rd
Stoney
Foleshill
A 444
A 4114
London
Road
Daventry
CHEYLESMORE
A 444
A 45
Leamington Rd
B 4113
Warwick Rd
A 429
Rd
WAR MEMORIAL PARK
Radford Rd
B 4098
RADFORD
Av.
Moseley
Rd
A 4114
B 4107
Earlsdon
Av.
EARLSDON
Kenilworth
Kenpas
Highway
Road
Kenilworth
Hearsall
Common
B 4106
Road
Old
Holyhead
Allesley
Highway
Highway
POL.
CANLEY
Rd
Corner
Kirby
Fletchamstead
Lane
Hill
A 45
Gibbet
Hill
Road
Birmingham
Rd
Pickford Way
Dunchurch
Broad
Lane
Tile
Charter
Av.
Rd
Heath
Westwood

at Ansty (Warks.) NE : 5 ¾ m. by A 4600 – BY – on B 4065 – ✉ Coventry – ☎ 01203 :

Ansty Hall, CV7 9HZ, ☎ 612222, Fax 602155, « 17C mansion », park – TV ☎ P – 80. VISA
Meals 9.95/22.50 **st.** and dinner a la carte 4.95 – **30 rm** 80.00/100.00 **st.** – SB.

at Brandon (Warks.) E : 6 m. on A 428 – BZ – ✉ Coventry – ☎ 01203 :

Brandon Hall (Forte), Main St., CV8 3FW, ☎ 542571, Fax 544909, park, squash – TV ☎ P – 90. VISA JCB
Meals (bar lunch Saturday) 10.95/25.45 **st.** and a la carte 6.70 – 8.50 – **60 rm** 60.00/94.00 **st.** – SB.

at Ryton on Dunsmore SE : 4 ¾ m. by A 45 – ✉ Coventry – ☎ 01203 :

Coventry Knight (Country Club), London Rd, CV8 3DY, on A 45 (northbound carriageway) ☎ 301585, Fax 301610 – rm rest TV ☎ P – 250. VISA. BZ **u**
Meals *(closed Saturday lunch)* 8.95/14.95 **st.** and dinner a la carte – 7.50 – **47 rm** 59.00 **st.**, 2 suites – SB.

at Baginton (Warks.) S : 3 m. by A 4114 and A 444 off A 45 (off westbound carriageway and Howes Lane turning) – ✉ Coventry – ☎ 01203 :

Old Mill, Mill Hill, CV8 2BS, ☎ 303588, Fax 307070, « Converted corn mill », – TV ☎ P. VISA. BZ **e**
Meals (grill rest.) a la carte 7.50/16.40 **t.** 3.95 – **20 rm** 60.00/65.00 **t.**

at Berkswell W : 6 ½ m. by B 4101 – AY – ✉ Coventry – ☎ 01203 :

Nailcote Hall, Nailcote Lane, CV7 7DE, S : 1 ½ m. on B 4101 ☎ 466174, Fax 470720, « Part 17C timbered house », – TV ☎ P – 100. VISA.
Meals (booking essential) 17.75/24.50 **t.** and a la carte 5.00 – **38 rm** 95.00/165.00 **st.** – SB.

at Balsall Common W : 6 ¾ m. by B 4101 – AY – ✉ Coventry – ☎ 01676 :

Haigs, 273 Kenilworth Rd, CV7 7EL, on A 452 ☎ 533004, Fax 534572, – TV ☎ P. VISA
closed 24 December-5 January – **Meals** (dinner only and Sunday lunch)/dinner 17.40 **st.** and a la carte 4.80 – **13 rm** 49.95/65.00 **st.**

at Allesley NW : 3 m. on A 4114 – ✉ Coventry – ☎ 01203 :

Coventry Hill, Rye Hill, CV5 9PH, ☎ 402151, Fax 402235 – rm TV ☎ P – 110
184 rm. AXY **s**

Allesley, Birmingham Rd, CV5 9GP, ☎ 403272, Fax 405190 – rest TV ☎ P – 400. VISA AY **r**
accommodation closed Christmas – **Meals** *(closed Saturday lunch)* 12.50/13.50 **st.** and a la carte – **90 rm** 90.00/110.00 **st.** – SB.

at Meriden NW : 6 m. by A 45 on B 4102 – AX – ✉ Coventry – ☎ 01676 :

Forest of Arden H. & Country Club (Country Club), Maxstoke Lane, CV7 7HR, NW : 2 ¾ m. by Maxstoke rd ☎ 522335, Fax 523711, park, squash – rm rest TV ☎ P – 150
150 rm, 2 suites.

Manor (De Vere), Main Rd, CV7 7NH, ☎ 522735, Fax 522186, – rm TV ☎ P – 275. VISA
Meals *(closed Saturday lunch)* 15.95/16.50 **t.** and a la carte 4.50 – **74 rm** 85.00/95.00 **t.** – SB.

ATS Ashmore Lake Way, Willenhall ☎ (01902) 602555/605098
ATS Kingswood Close, off Holbrook Lane, Holbrooks ☎ 638554

COWAN BRIDGE Cumbria 402 M 21 – see Kirkby Lonsdale.

COWES I.O.W. 403 404 PQ 31 – see Wight (Isle of).

CRACKINGTON HAVEN Cornwall 403 G 31 **The West Country G.** – ECD : Tuesday – ✉ Bude – ☎ 01840.

Envir. : Poundstock★ (≤★★, church★, guildhouse★) NE : 5½m. by A 39 – Jacobstow (Church★) E : 3 ½ m.

London 262 – Bude 11 – Truro 42.

Manor Farm, EX23 0JW, SE : 1 ¼ m. by Boscastle rd and Church Park Rd, then take first right ☎ 230304, « Part 11C manor », park – P.
Meals (communal dining) (dinner only) 15.00 3.00 – **5 rm** (dinner included) 42.00/84.00 **s.** – SB.

Trevigue, EX23 0LQ, SE : 1 ¼ m. on High Cliff rd ☎ 230418, « 16C farmhouse » – rest P.
closed November-January – **Meals** 15.00 3.50 – **6 rm** 35.00/55.00.

CRANBORNE Dorset 403 404 O 31 – pop. 667 – ☎ 01725.

Crane Valley, Verwood ℘ (01202) 814088.

London 107 – Bournemouth 21 – Salisbury 18 – Southampton 30.

Fleur De Lys, Wimborne St., BH21 5PP, on B 3078 ℘ 517282, Fax 517765 – TV P. AE VISA.
Meals (bar lunch)/dinner 11.95 **st.** and a la carte 4.95 – **8 rm** 27.00/50.00 **st.** – SB.

La Fosse with rm, London House, The Square, BH21 5PR, ℘ 517604, Fax 517778 – rest TV. AE VISA.
accommodation closed Christmas and New Year – **Meals** *(closed Saturday lunch and Sunday dinner)* 10.50/12.95 **t.** and a la carte 4.50 – **3 rm** 27.50/48.00 **t.** – SB.

CRANBROOK Kent 404 V 30 **Great Britain G.** – pop. 4 670 – ECD : Wednesday – ☎ 01580.

Envir. : Sissinghurst Castle★ *AC*, NE : 2½m. by A 229 and A 262.

Vestry Hall, Stone St., TN17 3HA ℘ 712538 (summer only).

London 53 – Hastings 19 – Maidstone 15.

Kennel Holt, Goudhurst Rd, TN17 2PT, NW : 2 ¼ m. by A 229 on A 262 ℘ 712032, Fax 715495, « Gardens » – rest TV ☎ P. AE VISA.
Meals *(closed Sunday dinner to non-residents and Monday)* (lunch by arrangement)/dinner 18.50 **t.** 4.75 – **9 rm** 90.00/110.00 **st.**

Old Cloth Hall, TN17 3NR, E : 1 m. by Tenterden Rd ℘ 712220, Fax 712220, ≤, « Tudor manor house, gardens », park – TV P.
closed Christmas – **Meals** *(unlicensed)* (residents only) (dinner only) 25.00 **st.** – **3 rm** 35.00/95.00 **st.**

Hartley Mount, TN17 3QX, S : ½ m. on A 229 ℘ 712230, Fax 715733 – TV ☎ P. AE VISA.
Meals 12.95/15.50 **st.** and a la carte 4.75 – **5 rm** 55.00/90.00 **st.** – SB.

at Sissinghurst NE : 1 ¾ m. by B 2189 on A 262 – ✉ Cranbrook – ☎ 01580 :

Rankins, The Street, TN17 2JH, ℘ 713964 – VISA
closed Sunday dinner, Monday, Tuesday and Bank Holidays – **Meals** 18.50/23.50 **st.** 3.90.

CRANLEIGH Surrey 404 S 30 – pop. 11 479 – ECD : Wednesday – ☎ 01483.

Fernfell G. & C.C., Barhatch Lane ℘ 268855.

London 42 – Brighton 36 – Reading 36 – Southampton 58.

La Barbe Encore, High St., GU6 8AE, ℘ 273889 – AE VISA
closed Saturday lunch, Sunday dinner, Monday, 25-26 December and 1 January – **Meals** - French 14.95/17.95 **t.** 6.75.

CRANTOCK Cornwall 403 E 32 – see Newquay.

CRAVEN ARMS Shrops. 402 403 L 26 **Great Britain G.** – ☎ 01588.

Envir. : Wenlock Edge★, NE : by B 4368.

London 170 – Birmingham 47 – Hereford 32 – Shrewsbury 21.

Old Rectory, Hopesay, SY7 8HD, W : 3 ¾ m. by B 4368 ℘ 660245, ≤, « Part 17C », – TV P.
closed Christmas – **Meals** (by arrangement) (communal dining) 17.00 5.00 – **3 rm** 30.00/60.00.

CRAWLEY W. Sussex 404 T 30 – pop. 87 644 – ECD : Wednesday – ☎ 01293.

(2x) Cottesmore, Buchan Hill ℘ 528256 – Tilgate Forest, Titmus Drive, Tilgate ℘ 530103 – Gatwick Manor, London Rd ℘ 538587 – Horsham Rd, Pease Pottage ℘ 521706.

London 33 – Brighton 21 – Lewes 23 – Royal Tunbridge Wells 23.

Plan of enlarged Area : see Gatwick

Holiday Inn London Gatwick, Langley Drive, Tushmore Roundabout, RH11 7SX, ℘ 529991, Telex 877311, Fax 515913 – rm rest TV ☎ P – 250. AE VISA JCB — BY **n**
Meals 9.95/16.95 **st.** and dinner a la carte 6.25 – 9.95 – **215 rm** 88.00 **st.**, 2 suites.

George (Forte), High St., RH10 1BS, ℘ 524215, Fax 548565 – TV ☎ P – 50. AE VISA JCB. — BY **o**
Meals (dinner only and Sunday lunch)/dinner 16.95 **t.** and a la carte 6.95 – 8.50 – **81 rm** 55.00/65.00 **st.** – SB.

Goffs Park, 45 Goffs Park Rd, Southgate, RH11 8AX, ℘ 535447, Fax 542050 – TV ☎ P – 80. AE VISA. — AZ **s**
Meals *(closed Saturday lunch)* (dancing Friday and Saturday evenings) 13.00 **t.** and a la carte 4.75 – 7.75 – **64 rm** 49.00 **st.**

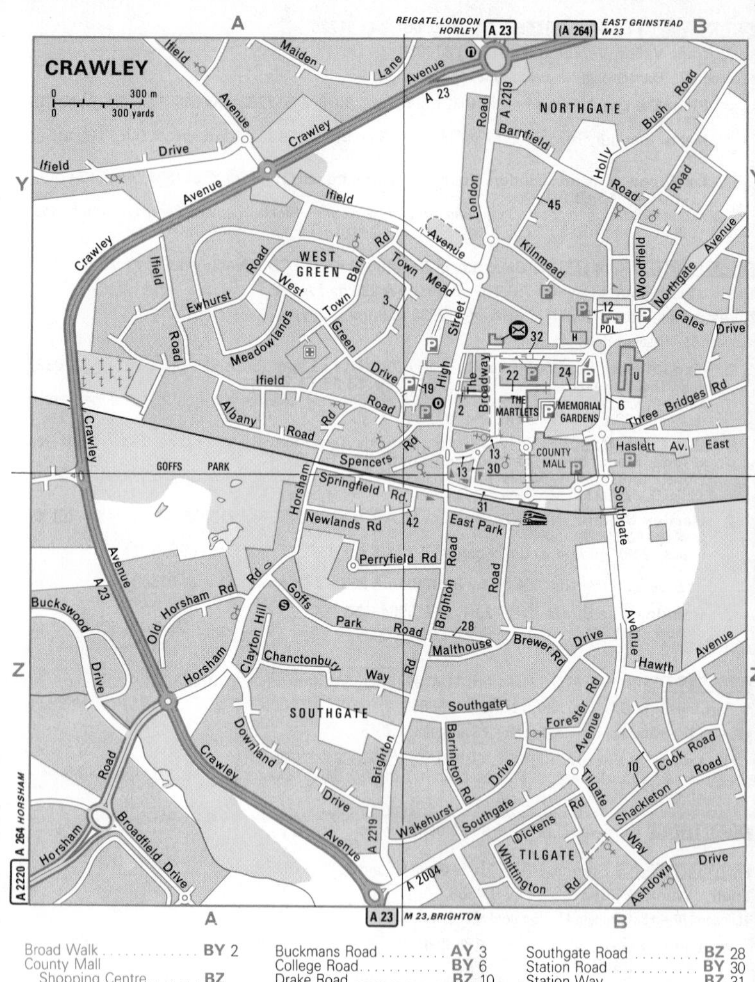

Broad Walk . . . . BY 2
County Mall Shopping Centre . . . . BZ
High Street . . . . BY
Queens Square . . . . BY 22
The Broadway . . . . BY
The Martlets . . . . BY

Buckmans Road . . . . AY 3
College Road . . . . BY 6
Drake Road . . . . BZ 10
Exchange Road . . . . BY 12
Haslett Av. West . . . . BY 13
Orchard Street . . . . BY 19
Queensway . . . . BY 24

Southgate Road . . . . BZ 28
Station Road . . . . BY 30
Station Way . . . . BZ 31
The Boulevard . . . . BY 32
Titmus Drive . . . . BZ 34
West Street . . . . ABZ 42
Woolborough Road . . . . . . BY 45

at Copthorne NE : 4 ½ m. on A 264 – BY – ✉ Copthorne – ☎ 01342 :

Copthorne London Gatwick, Copthorne Way, RH10 3PG, ☎ 714971, Telex 95500, Fax 717375, Lб, ≘s, park, squash – ⇔ rm ▤ rest TV ☎ P – 110. AE ⓓ VISA JCB

Lion D'Or **: Meals** *(closed Saturday lunch, Sunday and Bank Holidays)* 9.95/25.00 **st.** and a la carte 6.00 – ***Brasserie*** **: Meals** 15.00/20.00 6.00 **st.** and a la carte – ☐ 9.95 – **222 rm** 98.00/118.00 **st.**, 5 suites.

Copthorne Effingham Park, West Park Rd, RH10 3EU, on B 2028 ☎ 714994, Telex 95649, Fax 716039, ≤, Lб, ≘s, ☐, ⛳9, park – |‡| ⇔ rm ▤ rest TV ☎ ♿ P – 600 **119 rm**, 3 suites.

at Three Bridges E : 1 m. on Haslett Avenue East – BY – ✉ Crawley – ☎ 01293 :

Scandic Crown, Tinsley Lane South, RH11 1NP, N : ½ m. by Hazelwick Av. ☎ 561186, Telex 87485, Fax 561169, Lб, ≘s, ☐ – |‡| ⇔ rm ▤ TV ☎ ♿ P – 200 **149 rm**, 2 suites.
plan of Gatwick Y **n**

at Maidenbower E : 2½ m. by Haslett Av. and Worth Rd on B 2036 – BY – ✉ Crawley – ☎ 01293 :

Europa Gatwick, Balcombe Rd, RH10 7ZR, on B 2036 ☎ 886666, Group Telex 87531, Fax 886680, Ls, ≘s, ▢, ⚘ – |♦| ⇔ rm ▤ TV ☎ ♿ P – 🏔 150. AE ⓓ VISA. ✽
Mediterranee :* Meals** 7.95/12.95 **st.** and dinner a la carte 5.00 – (see also ***Silk Trader below) – ☐ 9.95 – **174 rm** 66.00/88.00 **st.**, 4 suites – SB. plan of Gatwick Z **a**

Silk Trader (at Europa Gatwick H.), Balcombe Rd, RH10 7ZR, on B 2036 ☎ 886666, Fax 886680, ⚘ – ▤ P. AE ⓓ VISA plan of Gatwick Z **a**
Meals - Chinese 18.00/19.95 **st.** and a la carte 5.00.

ATS Reynolds Rd, West Green ☎ 533151/2

CREWE Ches. 402 403 404 M 24 – pop. 59 097 – ECD : Wednesday – ☎ 01270.

Queen's Park Drive ☎ 666724.

♦London 174 – Chester 24 – ♦Liverpool 49 – ♦Manchester 36 – ♦Stoke-on-Trent 15.

Forte Travelodge without rest., Alsager Rd, Barthomley, CW2 5PT, SE : 5½ m. by A 5020 on A 500 at junction with M 6 ☎ 883157, Reservations (Freephone) 0800 850950 – TV ♿ P. AE VISA. ✽
42 rm 33.50 **t.**

ATS Gresty Rd ☎ 256285

CREWKERNE Somerset 403 L 31 **The West Country G.** – pop. 6 437 – ECD : Thursday – ☎ 01460.

Envir. : Forde Abbey★ *AC*, SW : 8 m. by B 3165 and B 3162 – Clapton Court Gardens★ *AC*, S : 3½ m. by B 3165.

Exc. : Montacute House★★ *AC*, NE : 7 m. by A 30 – Parnham House★★ *AC*, SE : 7½m. by A 356 and A 3066.

Windwhistle G. & C.C., Cricket St. Thomas, Chard ☎ 30231.

♦London 145 – Exeter 38 – ♦Southampton 81 – Taunton 20.

Broadview, 43 East St., TA18 7AG, ☎ 73424, ⚘ – ⇔ TV P
Meals (by arrangement) 12.00 – **3 rm** ☐ 30.00/46.00.

at Haselbury Plucknett NE : 2¾ m. by A 30 on A 3066 – ✉ Crewkerne – ☎ 01460 :

Oak House, North St., TA18 7RB, ☎ 73625, « 16C thatched cottage », ⚘ – ⇔ rest P
Easter-October – **Meals** (by arrangement) 10.50 **st.** – **7 rm** ☐ 21.00/48.00 **st.**

at North Perrot E : 3½ m. by A 30 on A 3066 – ✉ Crewkerne – ☎ 01460 :

Manor Arms, TA18 7SG, ☎ 72901, « 16C inn » – ⇔ TV P. VISA. ✽
Meals (in bar Sunday dinner and Monday) a la carte 10.50/14.40 **t.** 3.50 – ☐ 3.00 – **5 rm** 29.00/42.00 **t.** – SB.

at Misterton SE : 1½ m. on A 356 – ✉ Crewkerne – ☎ 01460 :

Yew Trees, Silver St., TA18 8NB, ☎ 77192, ⚘ – ⇔ P. ✽
closed Christmas – **Meals** (by arrangement) 12.00 – **3 rm** ☐ 19.00/38.00 **s.**

CRICK Northants. 403 404 Q 26 – see Rugby.

CRICKLADE Wilts 403 404 O 29 – pop. 4 680 – ECD : Wednesday and Saturday – ☎ 01793.

Cricklade Hotel, Common Hill ☎ 750751.

♦London 90 – ♦Bristol 45 – Gloucester 27 – ♦Oxford 34 – Swindon 6.

Cricklade H. & Country Club, Common Hill, SN6 6HA, SW : 1 m. on B 4040 ☎ 750751, Fax 751767, ←, Ls, ≘s, ▢, 9, park, ✗ – TV ☎ P – 🏔 120. AE VISA. ✽
Meals 13.00/19.00 **t.** and a la carte 5.75 – **46 rm** ☐ 70.00/95.00 **t.** – SB.

CROCKERTON Wilts. – see Warminster.

CROFT-ON-TEES Durham 402 P 20 – see Darlington.

CROMER Norfolk 404 X 25 – pop. 5 022 – ECD : Wednesday – ☎ 01263.

Royal Cromer, Overstrand Rd ☎ 512884.

Bus Station, Prince of Wales Rd, NR27 9HS ☎ 512497 (summer only).

♦London 132 – ♦Norwich 23.

Morden House, 20 Cliff Av., NR27 0AN, ☎ 513396, ⚘ – ⇔ rest. ⓓ. ✽
Meals 12.00 4.50 – **6 rm** ☐ 20.00/40.00 – SB.

Birch House, 34 Cabbell Rd, NR27 9HX, ☎ 512521 – ⇔ TV. VISA
Meals 6.50 **s.** 3.00 – **8 rm** ☐ 17.00/38.00 **s.** – SB.

Europe

If the name of the hotel
is not in bold type,
on arrival ask the hotelier his prices.

CRONDALL Hants. 404 R 30 – pop. 6 113 – ☎ 01252.
⛳18 Oak Park, Heath Lane ✆ 850880.
♦London 56 – Reading 21 – Winchester 30.

XX **Chesa,** Bowling Alley, GU10 5RJ, N : 1 m. ✆ 850328, Fax 850328 – Ⓟ. AE VISA
closed Sunday to Tuesday, first 3 weeks January and 3 weeks July-August – **Meals** (lunch by arrangement)/dinner 30.00 **t.** 5.45.

CRONTON Ches. 402 403 404 L 23 – see Widnes.

CROOK Durham 401 402 O 19 – pop. 6 390 – ✉ Bishop Auckland – ☎ 01388.
⛳18 Low Job's Hill ✆ 762429.
♦London 261 – ♦Carlisle 65 – ♦Middlesbrough 34 – ♦Newcastle upon Tyne 27.

Greenhead without rest., Fir Tree, DL15 8BL, SW : 3½ m. by A 689 off A 68 ✆ 763143, – TV Ⓟ. VISA.
7 rm 35.00/45.00 **s.**

CROSBY Mersey. 402 403 K 23 – see Liverpool.

CROSBY-ON-EDEN Cumbria 401 402 L 29 – see Carlisle.

CROWBOROUGH E. Sussex 404 U 30 – pop. 19 120 – ECD : Wednesday – ☎ 01892.
♦London 45 – ♦Brighton 25 – Maidstone 26.

Winston Manor, Beacon Rd, TN6 1AD, on A 26 ✆ 652772, Fax 665537, , , – TV ☎ Ⓟ – 250. AE VISA JCB
Meals 12.75/16.75 **t.** and a la carte 4.75 – **48 rm** 50.00/90.00 **t.** – SB.

ATS Church Rd ✆ 662100

Great Britain and *Ireland* are covered entirely
at a scale of 16 miles to 1 inch by our *map «Main roads»* 986.

CROWTHORNE Berks. 404 R 29 – pop. 19 166 – ECD : Wednesday – ☎ 01344.
♦London 42 – Reading 15.

Waterloo (Forte), Dukes Ride, RG11 7NW, on B 3348 ✆ 777711, Fax 778913 – TV ☎ Ⓟ – 50. AE VISA JCB.
Meals (bar lunch Monday to Saturday)/dinner 16.95 **st.** and a la carte 6.95 – 7.95 – **58 rm** 70.00/100.00 – SB.

XX **Beijing,** 103 Old Wokingham Rd, RG11 6LH, NE : ¾ m. by A 3095 ✆ 778802 – Ⓟ. AE VISA
closed Sunday lunch – **Meals** - Chinese 15.50/18.50 **t.** and a la carte.

CROXDALE Durham – see Durham.

CROYDE Devon 403 H 30 **The West Country G.** – ✉ Braunton – ☎ 01271.
♦London 232 – Barnstaple 10 – Exeter 50 – Taunton 61.

Kittiwell House, St. Mary's Rd, EX33 1PG, ✆ 890247, Fax 890469, « 16C thatched Devon longhouse » – rm TV ☎ Ⓟ. AE VISA
closed mid January-mid February – **Meals** (dinner only and Sunday lunch)/dinner 15.90 **t.** and a la carte 3.90 – **12 rm** (dinner included) 59.00/104.00 **st.** – SB.

Croyde Bay House , Moor Lane, Croyde Bay, EX33 1PA, NW : 1 m. by Baggy Point rd ✆ 890270, ← Croyde Bay, – rest TV Ⓟ. AE VISA
March-mid November – **Meals** (dinner only) 17.50 **st.** 3.85 – **7 rm** (dinner included) 59.00/98.00 **t.**

Whiteleaf, Hobbs Hill, EX33 1PN, ✆ 890266, – rest TV ☎ Ⓟ. VISA
closed 2 weeks May, 2 weeks July, 2 weeks October and December-February – **Meals** (dinner only) 18.50 **s.** 4.00 – **3 rm** 37.00/66.00 **s.**

CRUDWELL Wilts. 403 404 N 29 – see Malmesbury.

CUCKFIELD W. Sussex 404 T 30 – pop. 4 057 – ECD : Wednesday – ☎ 01444.
♦London 40 – ♦Brighton 15.

Ockenden Manor , Ockenden Lane, RH17 5LD, ✆ 416111, Fax 415549, « Part 16C manor », – TV ☎ Ⓟ – 50. AE VISA.
Meals 16.50/29.50 **t.** and a la carte 5.75 – 4.00 – **20 rm** 75.00/155.00, 2 suites – SB.

CULLOMPTON Devon 403 J 31 **The West Country G.** – pop. 7 159 – ☎ 01884.
See : Town★ – St. Andrew's Church★.
Envir. : Uffculme (Coldharbour Mill★★ *AC*) NE : 5½ m. by B 3181 and B 3391.
Exc. : Killerton★★, SW : 6½ m. by B 3181 and B 3185.
⛳9, ⛳18 Padbrook Park ✆ 38286.
♦London 197 – Exeter 15 – Taunton 29.

Lower Beers , Brithem Bottom, EX15 1NB, NW : 2 ¾ m. by B 3181 ✆ 32257, Fax 32257, « 16C farmhouse », – rest Ⓟ.
closed mid December-mid January – **Meals** (by arrangement) (communal dining) 25.00 **st.** 5.00 – **3 rm** 30.00/60.00 **st.**

CULWORTH Oxon. 404 Q 27 – ✉ Banbury – ☎ 01295.
◆London 84 – ◆Birmingham 48 – ◆Coventry 23 – ◆Oxford 31.

Fulford House, The Green, OX17 2BB, ☎ 760355, Fax 768304, « 17C house », – rm TV P.
closed mid December-mid February – **Meals** (by arrangement) (communal dining) 17.50 **st.** 5.00 – **3 rm** 30.00/56.00 **st.**

CURDWORTH W. Mids. – see Sutton Coldfield.

DALTON-IN-FURNESS Cumbria 402 K 21 – pop. 7 427 – ☎ 01229.
The Dunnerholme, Askham-in-Furness ☎ 462675.
◆London 283 – Barrow-in-Furness 3.5 – Kendal 30 – Lancaster 41.

Clarence House, Skelgate, LA15 8BQ, N : ¼ m. on A 595 ☎ 462508, Fax 467177, – TV ☎ P – 50. AE VISA.
Meals 8.75/30.00 **t.** and a la carte 8.50 – 6.50 – **17 rm** 60.00/80.00 **t.**

DARESBURY Ches. 402 403 404 M 23 – pop. 1 579 – ✉ Warrington – ☎ 01925.
◆London 197 – Chester 16 – ◆Liverpool 22 – ◆Manchester 25.

Lord Daresbury (De Vere), Chester Rd, WA4 4BB, on A 56 ☎ 267331, Fax 265615, , squash – rm TV ☎ P – 400. AE VISA
Meals *(closed lunch Saturday and Bank Holidays)* 14.00/22.00 **st.** and a la carte 5.00 – **140 rm** 95.00/125.00 **st.** – SB.

DARLEY ABBEY Derbs. 402 403 404 P 25 – see Derby.

En haute saison, et surtout dans les stations, il est prudent de retenir à l'avance.

DARLINGTON Durham 402 P 20 – pop. 98 906 – ECD : Wednesday – ☎ 01325.
18 Blackwell Grange, Briar Close ☎ 464464 – 18 Stressholme, Snipe Lane ☎ 363928.
Teesside Airport : ☎ 332811, E : 6 m. by A 67.
4 West Row, DL1 5PL ☎ 382698.
◆London 251 – ◆Leeds 61 – ◆Middlesbrough 14 – ◆Newcastle upon Tyne 35.

Blackwell Grange Moat House (Q.M.H.), Blackwell Grange, DL3 8QH, SW : 1 m. on A 167 ☎ 380888, Fax 380899, 18, – rm TV ☎ P – 300. AE VISA.
Meals 11.95/20.00 **st.** and a la carte – 8.95 – **99 rm** 80.00/98.00 **st.** – SB.

Swallow King's Head, Priestgate, DL1 1NW, ☎ 380222, Fax 382006 – rm TV ☎ P – 200. AE VISA
Meals 9.50/15.25 **st.** and a la carte 5.25 – **85 rm** 75.00/90.00 **st.**

Woodland House without rest., 63 Woodland Rd, DL3 7BQ, ☎ 461908 – TV
8 rm 20.00/40.00 **st.**

Sardis, 196 Northgate, DL1 1QU, ☎ 461222 – VISA
closed Sunday and Bank Holidays – **Meals** 11.00/16.00 **t.** and a la carte.

Sitar, 204 Northgate, DL1 1RB, ☎ 360787
Meals - Indian.

at Coatham Mundeville N : 4 m. on A 167 – ✉ Darlington – ☎ 01325 :

Hall Garth Country House, DL1 3LU, E : ¼ m. on Brafferton rd ☎ 300400, Fax 310083, 9, – TV ☎ P – 300
39 rm, 1 suite.

at Teesside Airport E : 5½ m. by A 67 – ✉ Darlington – ☎ 01325 :

St. George (Mt. Charlotte Thistle), DL2 1RH, ☎ 332631, Fax 333851, squash – TV ☎ P – 180. AE VISA
Meals *(closed Saturday lunch and Sunday dinner)* 8.50/15.50 **st.** and a la carte 4.95 – **58 rm** 74.00/84.00 **st.**, 1 suite.

at Croft-on-Tees S : 3½ m. on A 167 – ✉ Darlington – ☎ 01325 :

Clow Beck House without rest., Monk End Farm, DL2 2SW, W : ½ m. by South Parade ☎ 721075, « Working farm », park – TV P.
5 rm 25.00/47.00.

at Headlam NW : 6 m. by A 67 – ✉ Gainford – ☎ 01325 :

Headlam Hall, DL2 3HA, ☎ 730238, Fax 730790, « Part Jacobean and part Georgian manor house », park, – rest TV ☎ P – 150. AE VISA.
closed 25 December – **Meals** 11.00/22.50 **st.** 3.50 – **24 rm** 55.00/75.00 **st.**, 2 suites – SB.

at Heighington NW : 6 m. by A 68 off A 6072 – ✉ Darlington – ☎ 01325 :

The Dog, Cross Lanes, DL2 2TX, on A 68 ☎ 312152, – TV ☎ P
3 rm.

Eldon House without rest., East Green, DL5 6PP, ☎ 312270 – P
3 rm 25.00/40.00.

at Redworth NW : 7 m. by A 68 on A 6072 – ✉ Bishop Auckland – ☎ 01388 :

Redworth Hall ⑤, DL5 6NL, on A 6072 ☎ 772442, Fax 775112, « Part 18C and 19C manor house of Elizabethan origins », park, squash – rm rest – 300.
Crozier Conservatory* : Meals** 11.50/25.00 **t.** and a la carte (see also ***Blue Room below) – **96 rm** 95.00/110.00 **st.**, 4 suites – SB.

Blue Room (at Redworth Hall H.), DL5 6NL, on A 6072 ☎ 772442, Fax 775112, « Part 18C and 19C manor house of Elizabethan origins », park –
Meals (dinner only) a la carte 24.75/31.25 **t.**

ATS Albert St., off Neasham Rd ☎ 469271/469693

DARTFORD Kent 404 U 29 – ☎ 01322.

The Clocktower, Suffolk Rd, DA1 1EJ ☎ 343243.

♦London 20 – Hastings 51 – Maidstone 22.

Stakis Dartford Bridge, Masthead Close, Crossways Business Park, DA2 6QF, NE : 2 ½ m. by A 226, Cotton Lane and Crossways Boulevard ☎ 284444, Fax 911038, – rm – 240.
Meals *(closed lunch Saturday and Bank Holidays)* 15.00/18.50 **t.** and a la carte – 7.95 – **171 rm** 69.00/78.00 **st.**, 4 suites – SB.

Campanile, Dartford Bridge, Clipper Boulevard West, Edison's Park, Crossways, DA2 6QN, NE : 3 m. by A 226, Cotton Lane and Galleon Boulevard ☎ 278925 – – 30.
Meals 9.85 **st.** and a la carte 2.65 – 4.50 – **80 rm** 35.75 **st.**

DARTMOUTH Devon 403 J 32 **The West Country G.** – pop. 5 772 – ECD : Wednesday and Saturday – ☎ 01803.

See : Town★★ - Dartmouth Castle (≤★★★) *AC*.

Exc. : Start Point (≤★) S : 13 m. (including 1 m. on foot).

The Engine House, Mayors Avenue, TQ6 9YY ☎ 834224.

♦London 236 – Exeter 36 – ♦Plymouth 35.

Royal Castle, 11 The Quay, TQ6 9PS, ☎ 833033, Fax 835445, ≤ – rest
Meals (bar lunch Monday to Saturday)/dinner 20.50 **t.** and a la carte 4.95 – **25 rm** 45.00/108.00 **st.**

Dart Marina (Forte), Sandquay, TQ6 9PH, ☎ 832580, Fax 835040, ≤ –
Meals 20.00 **st.** (dinner) and a la carte 20.10/22.70 **st.** 6.95 – 8.50 – **35 rm** 75.00/98.00 **st.** – SB.

Ford House, 44 Victoria Rd, TQ6 9DX, ☎ 834047, –
closed January and February – **Meals** (residents only) (communal dining) (unlicensed) (dinner only and Sunday lunch)/dinner 22.50 **st.** – **3 rm** 40.00/60.00 **st.** – SB.

Wavenden House ⑤, Compass Cove, TQ6 0JN, S : 1 ¼ m. via Warfleet by Newcomen Rd, off Castle Rd ☎ 833979, ≤ River Dart and sea, –
closed Christmas-New Year – **Meals** (by arrangement) (communal dining) 15.00 **st.** – **3 rm** 25.00/38.00 **st.**

Wadstray House ⑤ without rest., Blackawton, TQ9 7DE, W : 4 ½ m. on A 3122 ☎ 712539, –
5 rm 30.00/45.00 **st.**

Three Feathers without rest., 51 Victoria Rd, TQ6 9RT, ☎ 834694 –
5 rm 35.00 **s.**

Carved Angel, 2 South Embankment, TQ6 9BH, ☎ 832465, ≤ Dart Estuary
closed Sunday dinner, Monday, 3 January-mid February and 24 to 26 December – **Meals** 25.50/47.50 **st.** and lunch a la carte 7.00.

Billy Budd's, 7 Foss St., TQ6 9DW, ☎ 834842 –
closed Sunday, Monday, 3 weeks February and 1 week November – **Meals** (booking essential) (light lunch)/dinner a la carte approx. 20.70 **t.**

at Stoke Fleming SW : 3 m. on A 379 – ✉ Dartmouth – ☎ 01803 :

Stoke Lodge, Cinders Lane, TQ6 0RA, ☎ 770523, Fax 770851, ≤, heated, –
Meals 9.25/16.95 **t.** and a la carte 5.25 – **24 rm** 41.25/80.00 **t.** – SB.

New Endsleigh, New Rd, TQ6 0NR, ☎ 770381 –
closed January – **Meals** 9.50 **t.** (dinner) and a la carte 4.50 – **12 rm** 29.00/60.00 **t.** – SB.

Plans de ville : *Les rues sont sélectionnées en fonction de leur importance pour la circulation et le repérage des établissements cités.*

Les rues secondaires ne sont qu'amorcées.

DAVENTRY Northants 404 Q 27 – pop. 15 934 – ECD : Thursday – 01327.

Norton Rd 702829 – Hellidon Lakes Hotel & C.C., Hellidon, Daventry 62550 – Staverton Park Hotel, Staverton 705911.

Moot Hall, Market Sq., NN11 4BH 300277.

London 79 – Coventry 23 – Northampton 13 – Oxford 46.

Daventry, Ashby Rd, NN11 5SG, N : 2¼ m. on A 361 301777, Fax 706313 – rm rest – 500.
Meals (bar lunch Monday to Saturday)/dinner 20.00 **st.** 6.50 – 8.25 – **136 rm** 80.00/105.00 **st.**, 2 suites – SB.

Britannia, London Rd, NN11 4EN, SE : ¾ m. on A 45 77333, Telex 312228, Fax 300420 – rm – 350.
Meals (carving rest.) (bar lunch Saturday) 8.95/20.00 **st.** and a la carte – **144 rm** 62.50/74.50 **st.**, 4 suites – SB.

at Badby S : 3½ m. by A 45 on A 361 – Daventry – 01327 :

Windmill Inn, Main St., NN11 6AN, 702363, Fax 311521 –
Meals a la carte 9.95/18.15 **t.** 5.00 – **8 rm** 37.50/59.00 **t.** – SB.

at Hellidon SW : 9½ m. by A 45 and A 361 on Hellidon rd – Daventry – 01327 :

Hellidon Lakes, NN11 6LN, SW : ¼ m. 62550, Fax 62559, park, – – 50.
Meals a la carte 16.00/26.50 **t.** – **23 rm** 85.00/110.00 **t.**, 2 suites – SB.

DAWLISH Devon 403 J 32 – pop. 11 929 – ECD : Thursday and Saturday – 01626.

Warren 862255.

The Lawn, EX7 9PW 863589.

London 215 – Exeter 13 – Plymouth 40 – Torquay 11.

Langstone Cliff, Dawlish Warren, EX7 0NA, N : 2 m. by A 379 865155, Fax 867166, heated, – – 400.
Meals 9.50/14.50 **st.** 4.00 – **68 rm** 40.00/70.00 **st.** – SB.

DEAL Kent 404 Y 30 – pop. 26 548 – ECD : Thursday – 01304.

Walmer & Kingsdown, The Leas, Kingsdown 373256.

Town Hall, High St., CT14 6BB 369576.

London 78 – Canterbury 19 – Dover 8.5 – Margate 16.

Sutherland House, 186 London Rd, CT14 9PT, 362853, Fax 361268 – rm
Meals 18.95 3.50 – **5 rm** 35.00/47.00 **st.** – SB.

at Kingsdown S : 2¾ m. by A 258 on B 2057 – Deal – 01304 :

Blencathra Country without rest., Kingsdown Hill, CT14 8EA, off Upper St. 373725, – rm
closed November – **7 rm** 17.00/38.00 **st.**

at Finglesham NW : 3½ m. by A 258 and Burgess Green on The Street – Deal – 01304 :

Finglesham Grange without rest., CT14 0NQ, NW : ¾ m. on Eastry rd 611314, –
3 rm 30.00/45.00 **s.**

ATS 40 Gilford Rd 361543

DEANSHANGER Bucks. 404 R 27 – see Stony Stratford.

DEDDINGTON Oxon. 403 404 Q 28 – pop. 2 319 – 01869.

London 72 – Birmingham 46 – Coventry 33 – Oxford 18.

Holcombe, High St., OX15 0SL, 338274, Fax 337167, – rm
Meals 13.95/25.00 **t.** and a la carte 6.25 – **16 rm** 50.00/115.00 **t.** – SB.

DEDHAM Essex 404 W 28 **Great Britain G.** – pop. 1 847 – ECD : Wednesday – Colchester – 01206.

Envir. : Stour Valley★ – Flatford Mill★, E : 6 m. by B 1029, A 12 and B 1070.

London 63 – Chelmsford 30 – Colchester 8 – Ipswich 12.

Maison Talbooth, Stratford Rd, CO7 6HN, W : ½ m. 322367, Fax 322752, –
Meals - (see *Le Talbooth* below) – 7.50 – **9 rm** 85.00/140.00 **st.**, 1 suite – SB.

XXX **Le Talbooth,** Gun Hill, CO7 6HP, W : 1 m. 323150, Fax 322309, « Part Tudor house in attractive riverside setting », –
Meals 15.00/19.50 **t.** and a la carte 23.50/36.00 **t.** 4.75.

XX **Fountain House & Dedham Hall** with rm, Brook St., CO7 6AD, 323027, – rest
Meals *(closed Sunday dinner and Monday)* (dinner only and Sunday lunch)/dinner 18.50 **st.** – **6 rm** 38.00/57.00 **st.** – SB.

DENMEAD Hants. 403 Q 31 – ☎ 01705.
♦London 70 – ♦Portsmouth 11 – Southampton 27.

XX **Barnard's,** Hambledon Rd, PO7 6NU, ℘ 257788, – AE VISA
closed Sunday, Monday, 2 weeks August and 1 week Christmas-New Year – **Meals** (dinner only) 14.50 **t.** and a la carte.

DENTON Gtr. Manchester 402 404 N 23 – pop. 35 813 – ☎ 0161.
Denton, Manchester Rd ℘ 336 3218.
♦London 196 – Chesterfield 41 – ♦Manchester 6.

Old Rectory, Meadow Lane, Haughton Green, M34 1GD, S : 2 m. by A 6017, Two Trees Lane and Haughton Green Rd ℘ 336 7516, Fax 320 3212, – rest rest – 80. AE VISA JCB.
Meals *(closed Saturday lunch)* 11.95/15.95 **t.** and a la carte 5.25 – **36 rm** 55.00/85.00 **t.** – SB.

DERBY Derbs. 402 403 404 P 25 **Great Britain G.** – pop. 218 802 – ECD : Wednesday – ☎ 01332.
See : City★ – Museum and Art Gallery★ (Collection of Derby Porcelain★) YZ **M1** – Royal Crown Derby Museum★ *AC* Z **M2**.
Envir. : Kedleston Hall★★ *AC*, NW : 4½m. by Kedleston Rd X.
Wilmore Rd, Sinfin ℘ 766323 – Mickleover, Uttoxeter Rd ℘ 513339 – Kedleston Park ℘ 840035 – , Breadsall Priory Hotel Moor Rd, Morley ℘ 832235 – Allestree Park, Allestree Hall ℘ 550616.
East Midlands Airport, Castle Donington : ℘ 810621, SE : 12 m. by A 6 X.
Assembly Rooms, Market Pl., DE1 3AH ℘ 255802.
♦London 132 – ♦Birmingham 40 – ♦Coventry 49 – ♦Leicester 29 – ♦Manchester 62 – ♦Nottingham 16 – ♦Sheffield 47 – ♦Stoke-on-Trent 35.

Plan opposite

Midland, Midland Rd, DE1 2SQ, ℘ 345894, Fax 293522, – rm – 150. AE VISA Z i
closed Christmas-New Year – **Meals** *(closed lunch Saturday and Bank Holidays)* 9.00/15.50 **st.** – 7.50 – **99 rm** 67.00/110.00 **st.** – SB.

La Gondola, 220 Osmaston Rd, DE23 8JX, ℘ 332895, Fax 384512 – – 70. AE VISA. X c
Meals - Italian (closed Sunday) (dancing Saturday) 8.15/12.50 **st.** and a la carte 6.00 – 4.50 – **19 rm** 45.00/56.00 **st.**, 1 suite.

Periquito, 119 London Rd, DE1 2QR, ℘ 340633, Fax 293502 – rm – 150
101 rm. Z o

Oast House (Premier), Foresters Leisure Park, 220 Osmaston Park Rd, DE3 8AG, ℘ 270027, Fax 270528 – rm – 40. AE VISA. X e
Meals (grill rest.) 7.25/16.00 **st.** and a la carte 4.25 – 3.45 – **26 rm** 39.50 **st.** – SB.

European Inn without rest., Midland Rd, DE1 2SL, ℘ 292000, Fax 293940 – – 100. AE VISA Z c
5.25 – **88 rm** 38.00 **st.**

XX **New Water Margin,** 72-74 Burton Rd, DE1 1TG, ℘ 364754, Fax 364754 – . AE VISA Z e
Meals - Chinese (Canton) 11.90/18.80 t. and a la carte 3.50.

X **G.C's,** 22 Iron Gate, DE1 3GP, ℘ 368732 – . AE VISA Y a
closed Sunday and Monday – **Meals** 6.95/12.95 **t.** and a la carte 5.10.

at Darley Abbey N : 1¾ m. on A 6 (Duffield Rd) – X – ✉ Derby – ☎ 01332 :

XX **Darleys on the River,** Darley Abbey Mills, DE22 1DZ, E : ½ m. by Mileash Lane and Old Lane ℘ 364987, Fax 364987, ← – . AE VISA
closed Sunday dinner – **Meals** 11.95 **t.** (lunch) and a la carte 18.40/26.80 **t.**

at Breadsall NE : 4 m. by A 52 off A 61 – X – ✉ Derby – ☎ 01332 :

Breadsall Priory H. Golf & Country Club (Country Club), Moor Rd, Morley, DE7 6DL, NE : 1¼ m. by Rectory Lane ℘ 832235, Fax 833509, , , , , , , squash – rest – 90. AE VISA.
Meals *(closed Saturday lunch)* 12.50/19.50 **t.** 5.75 – 9.00 – **91 rm** 90.00 **t.** – SB.

at Littleover SW : 2½ m. on A 5250 – ✉ Derby – ☎ 01332 :

La Villa, 222 Rykneld Rd, DE3 7AP, SW : 1¾ m. on A 5250 ℘ 510161, Fax 514010, – . AE VISA. by A 5250 X
Meals - Italian *(closed Monday lunch)* 9.25/14.95 **t.** and a la carte 4.75 – **16 rm** 45.00/75.00 **st.**

Forte Posthouse, Pastures Hill, DE23 7BA, ℘ 514933, Fax 518668, – rm – 65. AE VISA X a
Meals a la carte approx. 15.00 **t.** 5.50 – **60 rm** 56.00/69.50 **st.**, 2 suites.

at Mackworth NW : 2¾ m. by A 52 – X – ✉ Derby – ☎ 01332 :

Mackworth, Ashbourne Rd, DE22 4LY, on A 52 ℘ 824324, – . AE VISA
accommodation closed 25-26 December and 1 January – **Meals** (carving rest.) 5.95/6.95 **t.** and a la carte 4.95 – **14 rm** 44.50/67.50 **t.**

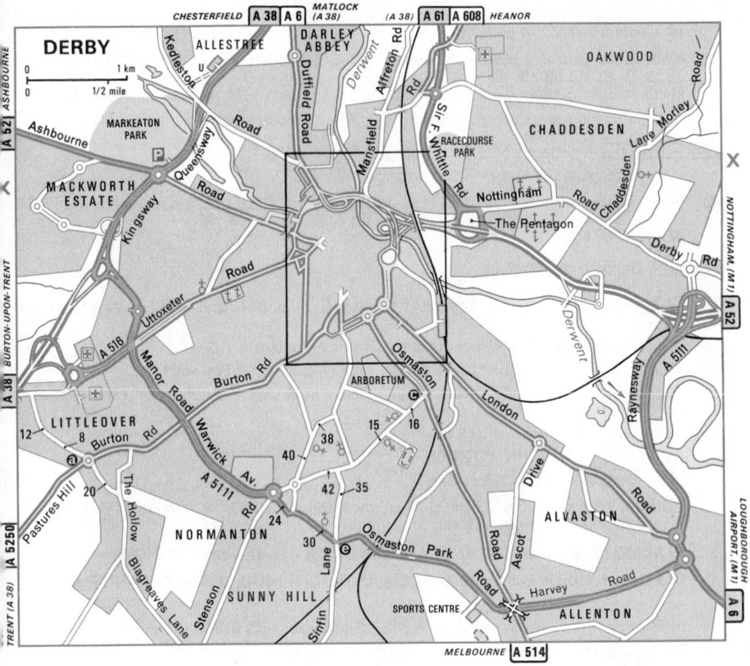

DERBY

Street	Grid	No.
Corn Market	Z	13
Iron Gate	Y	22
Eagle Shopping Centre	Z	
Victoria Street	Z	41
Albert Street	Z	2
Babington Lane	Z	3
Bold Lane	Y	4
Bradshaw Way	Z	5
Cathedral Road	Y	7
Chain Lane	X	8
Charnwood Street	Z	9
Corden Avenue	X	12
Corporation Street	YZ	14
Dairy House Road	X	15
Douglas Street	X	16
Duffield Road	Y	17
East Street	Z	18
Full Street	Y	19
Hillsway	X	20
Jury Street	Y	23
Kenilworth Avenue	X	24
King Street	Y	25
Leopold Street	Z	26
Market Place	YZ	27
Midland Road	Z	28
Mount Street	Z	29
Newdigate Street	X	30
Normanton Road	Z	31
Queen Street	Y	32
St. Mary's Gate	Y	33
St. Peter's Street	Z	34
St. Thomas Road	X	35
Sacheveral Street	Z	36
Stafford Street	Z	37
Stanhope Street	X	38
Upper Dale Road	X	40
Walbrook Road	X	42
Wardwick	Z	43

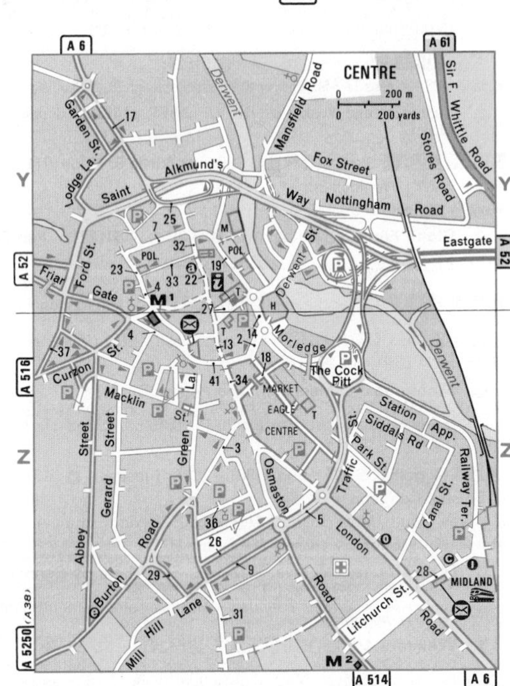

at Kedleston NW : 4 m. by Kedleston Rd – X – ✉ Derby – ☎ 01332 :

Kedleston Country House, Kedleston Rd, DE22 5JD, E : 2 m. ✆ 559202, Fax 558822 – TV ☎ ♿ P. AE VISA JCB
Meals *(closed Sunday dinner)* 6.50/16.95 **t.** and a la carte – **14 rm** 37.50/65.00 **t.** – SB.

ATS Gosforth Rd, off Ascot Drive ✆ 340854 ATS 67 Bridge St. ✆ 347327

DESBOROUGH Northants. 404 R 26 – pop. 7 351 – ☎ 01536.

♦London 83 – ♦Birmingham 52 – ♦Leicester 20 – Northampton 20.

Forte Travelodge without rest., Harborough Rd, NN14 2UG, N : 1½ m. on A 6 ✆ 762034, Reservations (Freephone) 0800 850950 – TV ♿ P. AE VISA.
32 rm 33.50 **t.**

DETHICK Derbs. – see Matlock.

DEVIZES Wilts. 403 404 O 29 **The West Country G.** – pop. 11 250 – ECD : Wednesday – ☎ 01380.

See : St. John's Church★★ – Market Place★ – Devizes Museum★ *AC.*

Envir. : Potterne (Porch House★★) S : 2½m. by A 360 – E : Vale of Pewsey★.

Exc. : Stonehenge★★★ *AC,* SE : 16 m. by A 360 and A 344 – Avebury★★ (The Stones★, Church★) NE : 7 m. by A 361.

18 Erlestoke Sands, Erlestoke ✆ 831069.

39 St. John's St., SN10 1BN ✆ 729408.

♦London 98 – ♦Bristol 38 – Salisbury 25 – Swindon 19.

Rathlin, Wick Lane, SN10 5DP, S : ¾ m. by A 360 ✆ 721999, – rest TV P.
closed 23 to 27 December – **Meals** (by arrangement) 8.00 **s.** – **3 rm** 25.00/40.00 **s.** – SB.

at Market Lavington S : 6 m. by A 360 on B 3098 – ✉ Devizes – ☎ 01380.

Old Coach House without rest., 21 Church St., SN10 4DU, ✆ 812879, – TV P
3 rm 21.00/39.00.

at Rowde NW : 2 m. by A 361 on A 342 – ✉ Devizes – ☎ 01380.

George & Dragon, SN10 2PN, on A 342 ✆ 723053, – P. VISA
closed Sunday, Monday, 25-26 December and 1 January – **Meals** (booking essential) 10.00 **t.** (lunch) and a la carte 14.00/27.00 **t.** 4.50.

DEWSBURY W. Yorks. 402 P 22 – ☎ 01924.

♦London 205 – ♦Leeds 9 – ♦Manchester 40 – ♦Middlesbrough 76 – ♦Sheffield 31.

Heath Cottage, Wakefield Rd, WF12 8ET, ✆ 465399, Fax 459405 – rm TV ☎ P – 80
27 rm.

DIDDLEBURY Shrops. 402 403 L 26 **Great Britain G.** – pop. 911 – ✉ Craven Arms – ☎ 01584.

Envir. : NW : Wenlock Edge★.

♦London 169 – ♦Birmingham 46.

Glebe Farm without rest., SY7 9DH, ✆ 841221, « Part Elizabethan house », – TV P.
March-November – **3 rm** 26.00/52.00 **s.**

DIDSBURY Gtr. Manchester 402 403 404 N 23 – see Manchester.

DISLEY Ches. 402 403 404 N 23 – pop. 4 590 – ECD : Wednesday – ✉ Stockport – ☎ 01663.

♦London 187 – Chesterfield 35 – ♦Manchester 12.

Moorside , Mudhurst Lane, Higher Disley, SK12 2AP, SE : 2 m. by Buxton Old Rd ✆ 764151, Fax 762794, ←, , , , , , squash – TV ☎ P – 300. AE VISA
Meals *(closed Saturday lunch)* 12.50/19.50 **st.** and a la carte 7.00 – **94 rm** 73.00/98.00 **st.**, 1 suite – SB.

DISS Norfolk 404 X 26 – pop. 6 301 – ECD : Tuesday – ☎ 01379.

18 Stuston Common ✆ 642847.

Meres Mouth, Mere St., IP22 3AG ✆ 650523 (summer only).

♦London 98 – ♦Ipswich 25 – ♦Norwich 21 – Thetford 17.

Malt House, Palgrave, IP22 1AE, SW : 1 m. by Denmark St. ✆ 642107, Fax 640315, « Gardens », – TV P. VISA.
closed 24 December-2 January – **Meals** (by arrangement)(communal dining) 15.00 **s.** – **3 rm** 23.00/54.00.

Weavers, Market Hill, IP22 3JZ, ✆ 642411 – VISA
closed Saturday lunch, Sunday, 2 weeks August-September, 1 week Christmas and Bank Holiday Mondays – **Meals** (light lunch)/dinner 10.00 **t.** and a la carte.

at Gissing NE : 5 m. by Burston rd – ✉ Diss – ☎ 01379 :

Old Rectory ⚘, Rectory Rd, IP22 3XB, ☎ 677575, Fax 674427, ≤, ▣, ⚘ – ⚘ TV P. VISA. ⚘
Meals (by arrangement) (communal dining) (unlicensed) 19.50 **st.** – **3 rm** ☐ 36.00/58.00 **st.**

at Scole E : 2½ m. by A 1066 on A 143 – ✉ Diss – ☎ 01379 :

Scole Inn, Main St., IP21 4DR, ☎ 740481, Fax 740762, « 17C inn » – ▤ rest TV ☎ P – 40. AE VISA
Meals 9.95/14.95 **st.** and a la carte 4.50 – **23 rm** ☐ 49.00/63.00 **st.** – SB.

at Brome (Suffolk) SE : 2¾ m. by A 143 on B 1077 – ✉ Eye – ☎ 01379 :

Oaksmere ⚘, IP23 8AJ, ☎ 870326, Fax 870051, « Part 16C house, topiary gardens », park – TV ☎ P – 40. AE VISA
Meals (in bar Sunday dinner) a la carte 18.45/26.15 **t.** 6.30 – **11 rm** ☐ 65.00/85.00 **st.** – SB.

at South Lopham W : 5½ m. on A 1066 – ✉ Diss – ☎ 01379 :

Malting Farm ⚘ without rest., Blo Norton Rd, IP22 2HT, ☎ 687201, ≤, « Working farm » – ⚘ P. ⚘
closed Christmas and New Year – **3 rm** ☐ 20.00/38.00 **s.**

at Fersfield NW : 7 m. by A 1066 – ✉ Diss – ☎ 01379 :

The Strenneth ⚘, Airfield Rd, IP22 2BP, ☎ 688182, Fax 688260, ⚘ – TV P. AE VISA
Meals (by arrangement) 13.00 **st.** 5.00 – **7 rm** ☐ 25.00/58.00 **s.** – SB.

ATS Shelfanger Rd ☎ 642861

DITTON PRIORS Shrops. 403 404 M 26 – pop. 680 – ✉ Bridgnorth – ☎ 01746.

London 154 – Birmingham 34 – Ludlow 13 – Shrewsbury 21.

Middleton Lodge ⚘ without rest., Middleton Priors, WV16 6UR, N : 1 m. ☎ 712228, « Part 17C hunting lodge », ⚘ – ⚘ TV P. ⚘
closed Christmas – **3 rm** ☐ 25.00/45.00.

Court House ⚘, South Rd, WV16 6SJ, ☎ 712554, ⚘ – ⚘ TV P
closed Christmas and January – **Meals** (by arrangement) 10.00 **st.** – **3 rm** ☐ 19.00/42.00 **st.** – SB.

Howard Arms, WV16 6SQ, ☎ 712200, ⚘ – P. VISA
closed Sunday dinner, Monday and 2 weeks September – **Meals** (dinner only and Sunday lunch)/dinner 24.00 **t.** 4.90.

DODDISCOMBSLEIGH Devon – see Exeter.

DONCASTER S. Yorks. 402 403 404 Q 23 – pop. 74 727 – ECD : Thursday – ☎ 01302.

18 Doncaster Town Moor, The Belle Vue Club ☎ 535286 – 18 Crookhill Park, Conisborough ☎ (01709) 862979 – 18 Wheatley, Amthorpe Rd ☎ 831655 – 9 Owston Park, Owston ☎ 330821.

Central Library, Waterdale, DN1 3JE ☎ 734309.

London 173 – Kingston-upon-Hull 46 – Leeds 30 – Nottingham 46 – Sheffield 19.

Doncaster Moat House (Q.M.H.), Warmsworth, DN4 9UX, SW : 2¾ m. on A 630 ☎ 310331, Fax 310197, ⚘, ⚘, ▣ – ⚘ ⚘ rm TV ☎ ♿ P – 350. AE VISA. ⚘
Meals *(closed lunch Saturday and Bank Holidays)* 9.95/14.95 **t.** and a la carte 4.75 – ☐ 8.00 – **98 rm** 77.50/99.50 **st.**, 2 suites – SB.

Danum Swallow, High St., DN1 1DN, ☎ 342261, Fax 329034 – ⚘ ⚘ rm TV ☎ P – 350.
64 rm, 2 suites.

Grand St. Leger, Racecourse Roundabout, Bennetthorpe, DN2 6AX, SE : 1½ m. on A 638 ☎ 364111, Fax 329865 – TV ☎ P – 60. AE VISA. ⚘
Meals 12.50/15.95 **t.** and a la carte 4.00 – **20 rm** ☐ 66.00/80.00 **st.** – SB.

Punch's (Toby), Bawtry Rd, Bessacarr, DN4 7BS, SE : 3 m. on A 638 ☎ 370037, Fax 532281 – ⚘ rm TV ☎ ♿ P – 40. AE VISA
Meals (grill rest.) 7.95 **st.** and a la carte 4.75 – **24 rm** ☐ 51.00/69.95 **st.** – SB.

Campanile, Doncaster Leisure Park, Bawtry Rd, DN4 7PD, SE : 2 m. on A 638 ☎ 370770, Fax 370813 – ⚘ rm TV ☎ ♿ P – 30. AE VISA
Meals 9.85 **st.** 4.65 – ☐ 4.25 – **51 rm** 35.75 **st.**

at Rossington SE : 6 m. on A 638 – ✉ Doncaster – ☎ 01302 :

Mount Pleasant, Great North Rd, DN11 0HP, on A 638 ☎ 868219, Fax 865130, ⚘, ⚘ – TV ☎ ♿ P – 60. AE VISA JCB. ⚘
Meals 7.95/10.95 **t.** and a la carte 4.00 – **30 rm** ☐ 44.00/65.00 **t.**, 1 suite – SB.

at Carcroft NW : 6½ m. on A 1 – ✉ Doncaster – ☎ 01302 :

Forte Travelodge without rest., Great North Rd, (northbound carriageway) ☎ 330841, Reservations (Freephone) 0800 850950 – TV ♿ P. AE VISA. ⚘
40 rm 33.50 **t.**

ATS Carr Hill, Balby ☎ 367337/366997

DORCHESTER Dorset 403 404 M 31 **The West Country G.** – pop. 15 037 – ECD : Thursday – ☎ 01305.

See : Town★ - Dorset County Museum★ *AC.*

Envir. : Maiden Castle★★ (≤★) SW : 2½ m. – Puddletown Church★, NE : 5½ m. by A 35.

Exc. : Moreton Church★★, E : 7½ m. – Bere Regis (St. John the Baptist Church★★) NE : 11 m. by A 35 – Athelhampton★ *AC,* NE : 6½ m. by A 35 - Cerne Abbas★, N : 7 m. by A 352.

Came Down ✆ 812531.

1 Acland Rd, DT1 1JW ✆ 267992.

London 135 – Bournemouth 27 – Exeter 53 – Southampton 53.

King's Arms, 30 High East St., DT1 1HF, ✆ 265353, Fax 260269 – ☎ – 100. AE VISA.
Meals a la carte 10.00/20.00 **t.** – 3.45 – **31 rm** 39.50/99.00 **t.**

Wessex Royale, 32 High West St., DT1 1UP, ✆ 262660, Fax 251941 – ☎ – 100. AE VISA
Meals 7.50/15.00 **st.** and dinner a la carte 4.50 – **23 rm** 39.95/59.95 **st.** – SB.

Casterbridge without rest., 49 High East St., DT1 1HU, ✆ 264043, Fax 260884, « Georgian town house » – ☎. AE VISA.
closed 25 and 26 December – **14 rm** 30.00/60.00 **st.**

Yalbury Cottage, Lower Bockhampton, DT2 8PZ, E : 2 ¼ m. by B 3150 and Bockhampton rd ✆ 262382, – . VISA.
closed January-mid February – **Meals** (dinner only) 15.00 **st.** and a la carte 4.00 – **8 rm** 40.00/60.00 **st.** – SB.

Westwood House without rest., 29 High West St., DT1 1UP, ✆ 268018, Fax 250282 – ☎. VISA.
7 rm 29.50/59.00 **st.**

Junction, 42 Great Western Rd, DT1 1UF, ✆ 268826 – – 60. VISA.
Meals *(closed dinner Friday to Sunday)* (in bar) 6.95 **t.** and a la carte 3.95 – 4.00 – **6 rm** 29.50/38.00 **t.**

XX **Mock Turtle,** 34 High West St., DT1 1UP, ✆ 264011 – VISA
closed 26-28 December – **Meals** *(closed lunch Saturday to Monday and Sunday dinner except Bank Holidays)* 12.50/20.95 **t.** 5.50.

XX **Shapla Tandoori,** 14 High East St., DT1 1HH, ✆ 269202 – . AE VISA
Meals - Indian a la carte 10.50/21.15 **st.** 4.50.

at Cerne Abbas N : 8 m. by B 3147 and A 37 off A 352 – ✉ Dorchester – ☎ 01300 :

Cerne Abbey without rest., DT2 7JQ, ✆ 341284, « Part 10C former Benedictine Abbey », heated, –
3 rm.

at Frampton NW : 6 m. by B 3147 and A 37 on A 356 – ✉ Dorchester – ☎ 01300 :

Hyde Farm House, DT2 9NG, NW : ½ m. on A 356 ✆ 320272, ≤, « Part 18C and 19C house », – rm .
Meals (dinner only) (unlicensed) 12.50 **st.** – **3 rm** 25.00/50.00 **st.**

ATS Unit 4, Great Western Ind. Centre ✆ 264756

DORCHESTER Oxon. 403 404 Q 29 **Great Britain G.** – pop. 1 5037 – ☎ 01865.

See : Town★.

Exc. : Ridgeway Path★★.

London 51 – Abingdon 6 – Oxford 8 – Reading 17.

White Hart, 26 High St., OX10 7HN, ✆ 340074, Fax 341082, « 17C coaching inn » – ☎
15 rm, 4 suites.

George, 23 High St., OX10 7HH, ✆ 340404, Fax 341620, – ☎ – 40. AE VISA
Meals a la carte 12.20/22.00 **t.** 6.00 – **18 rm** 55.00/85.00 **t.** – SB.

DORKING Surrey 404 T 30 – pop. 10 604 – ECD : Wednesday – ☎ 01306.

London 26 – Brighton 39 – Guildford 12 – Worthing 33.

Burford Bridge (Forte), Box Hill, RH5 6BX, N : 1 ½ m. on A 24 ✆ 884561, Fax 880386, heated, – ☎ – 300. AE VISA
Meals 16.95/22.50 **t.** and a la carte 6.50 – 9.95 – **48 rm** 85.00 **t.**

White Horse (Forte), High St., RH4 1BE, ✆ 881138, Fax 887241, heated – ☎ – 50. AE VISA JCB
Meals 10.50/17.95 **st.** and a la carte 6.00 – 8.50 – **68 rm** 75.00 **st.** – SB.

Forte Travelodge without rest., Reigate Rd, RH4 1QB, E : ½ m. on A 25 ✆ 740361, Reservations (Freephone) 0800 850950 – . AE VISA.
29 rm 33.50 **t.**

XX **Partners West Street,** 2-4 West St., RH4 1BL, ✆ 882826 – . AE VISA
closed Saturday lunch, and Sunday dinner – **Meals** 11.95/28.85 **st.** 5.50.

DORMINGTON Heref. and Worcs. – see Hereford.

DORRINGTON Shrops. 402 403 L 26 – see Shrewsbury.

DOULTING 403 404 M 30 – see Shepton Mallet.

DOVER Kent 404 Y 30 **Great Britain G.** – pop. 33 461 – ECD : Wednesday – ☎ 01304.

See : Castle★★ *AC* Y.

⛴ to France (Calais) (P & O European Ferries Ltd) (1 h 15), (Calais) (Hoverspeed Ltd) frequent services (35 mn) – to France (Calais) (Stena Sealink Line) frequent services (1 h 30 mn).

ℹ Townwall St., CT16 1JR ☎ 205108.

♦London 76 – ♦Brighton 84.

DOVER

Street	Grid	No.
Bench Street	Y	3
Biggin Street	Y	4
Cannon Street	Y	5
High Street	Y	
King Street	Y	13
Pencester Road	Y	
Castle Street	Y	6
Charlton Green	Y	7
Crabble Hill	Z	9
Eaton Road	Z	10
Ladywell, Park Street	Y	15
London Road	Y	17
Priory Road	Y	18
Priory Street	Y	19
Queen St.	Y	20
Sandwich Road	Z	21
Tower Street	Z	24
Worthington Street	Y	25

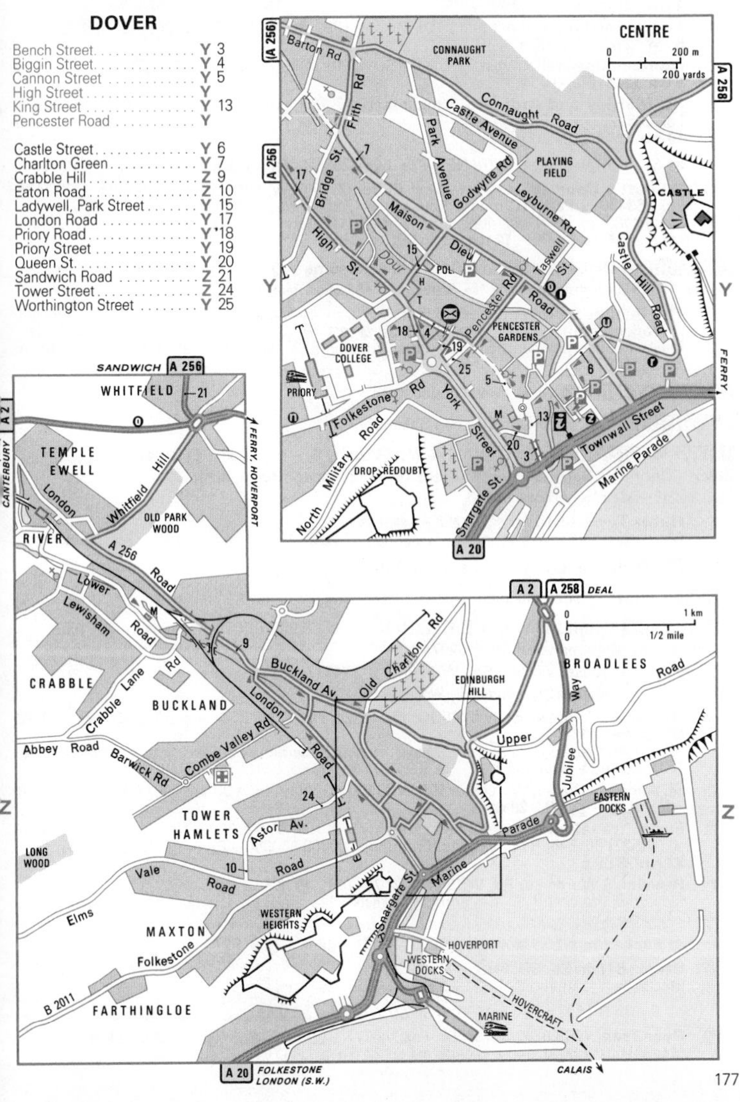

Forte Posthouse, Singledge Lane, Whitfield, CT16 3LF, NW : 3 ½ m. by A 256 on A 2 ✆ 821222, Fax 825576 – rm TV ☎ & P – 40. AE VISA. Z o
Meals a la carte approx. 15.00 **t.** 5.50 – **67 rm** 56.00 **st.**

Dover Moat House (Q.M.H.), Townwall St., CT16 1SZ, ✆ 203270, Telex 96458, Fax 213230, – rm TV ☎ – 80. AE VISA Y z
Meals 16.95 **st.** 5.45 – 8.95 – **79 rm** 61.00/96.00 **st.** – SB.

Travel Inn, Folkestone Rd, CT15 7AB, SW : 2 ½ m. on B 2011 ✆ 213339, Fax 214504 – rm TV & P. AE VISA. Z
closed 24 and 25 December – **Meals** (Beefeater grill) a la carte approx. 16.00 **t.** – 4.95 – **30 rm** 33.50 **st.**

Mildmay, 78 Folkestone Rd, CT17 9SF, ✆ 204278, Fax 215342 – rest TV ☎ P Y n
21 rm.

East Lee without rest., 108 Maison Dieu Rd, CT16 1RT, ✆ 210176, Fax 210176 – TV ☎. VISA. Y o
4 rm 30.00/40.00.

Penny Farthing without rest., 109 Maison Dieu Rd, CT16 1RT, ✆ 205563 – TV P. Y i
6 rm 22.00/40.00 **s.**

Number One without rest., 1 Castle St., CT16 1QH, ✆ 202007, – TV . Y u
5 rm 25.00/40.00 **s.**

St. Martins and Ardmore without rest., 17-18 Castle Hill Rd, CT16 1QW, ✆ 205938, Fax 208229 – TV. Y r
10 rm 30.00/45.00 **st.**

at St. Margaret's at Cliffe NE : 4 m. by A 258 – Z – on B 2058 – ✉ Dover – 01304 :

Wallett's Court with rm, West Cliffe, CT15 6EW, NW : ¾ m. on B 2058 ✆ 852424, Fax 853430, « Part 17C manor house », – rest TV ☎ P. VISA.
closed 23 to 27 December and 1 week January – **Meals** *(closed Sunday)* (dinner only) 25.00 **st.** 5.00 – **10 rm** 45.00/75.00 **st.** – SB.

DOVERIDGE Derbs. 402 403 404 O 25 – ✉ Ashbourne – 01889.
London 144 – Birmingham 32 – Derby 18 – Stafford 14 – Stoke-on-Trent 17.

The Beeches , Waldley, DE6 5LR, NE : 2 m. by Marston Lane ✆ 590288, Fax 590288, « Working farm », – TV ☎ P. AE VISA.
Meals (dinner only and Sunday lunch)/dinner a la carte 13.50/20.75 **t.** 3.95 – **10 rm** 38.50/50.00 **t.**

DOWN HATHERLEY Glos. – see Gloucester.

DOWNTON Wilts. 403 404 O 31 – see Salisbury.

DREWSTEIGNTON Devon 403 I 31 The West Country G. – pop. 668 – 01647.
Envir. : Dartmoor National Park★★ (Brent Tor ≤★★, Haytor Rocks ≤★).
London 216 – Exeter 15 – Plymouth 46

Hunts Tor, EX6 6QW, ✆ 281228 – rest
March-October – **Meals** (booking essential) 17.00 **st.** 4.35 – **4 rm** 27.00/55.00 **st.**

DRIFFIELD Humbs. 402 S 21 – see Great Driffield.

DRIFT Cornwall – see Penzance.

DROITWICH Heref. and Worcs. 403 404 N 27 – pop. 20 966 – ECD : Thursday – 01905.
18 Ombersley, Bishopswood Rd ✆ 620747.
St. Richard's House, Victoria Sq., WR9 8DS ✆ 774312.
London 129 – Birmingham 20 – Bristol 66 – Worcester 6.

Raven, St. Andrews St., WR9 8DU, ✆ 772224, Fax 772371, – TV ☎ P – 150. AE VISA.
closed August and Christmas – **Meals** *(closed Saturday lunch and Sunday dinner)* 10.00/16.00 **st.** and a la carte 5.00 – 9.95 – **71 rm** 49.95/109.95 **st.**, 1 suite.

St. Andrews House, Worcester Rd, WR9 8AL, S : ¼ m. by A 38 ✆ 779677, Fax 779752, – TV ☎ P – 80 – **29 rm.**

Forte Travelodge without rest., Rashwood Hill, WR9 8DA, NE : 1 ½ m. on A 38 ✆ (01527) 861545, Reservations (Freephone) 0800 850950 – TV & P. AE VISA.
32 rm 33.50 **t.**

Rossini, 6 Worcester Rd, WR9 8RB, ✆ 794799 – P. AE VISA
closed Sunday and 25 December – **Meals** - Italian 11.60 **t.** (lunch) and a la carte 14.20/24.50 **t.** 4.50.

at Feckenham E : 7 ¼ m. on B 4090 – ✉ Redditch – 01527 :

Steps, 6 High St., B96 6HS, ✆ 892678
Meals (by arrangement) 12.00 – **3 rm** 18.00/35.00 **s.**

at Smite S : 3 ¾ m. by B 4090, A 38 off A 4538 – ✉ Worcester – 01905 :

Pear Tree, WR3 8SY, ✆ 756565, Fax 756777 – TV ☎ & P – 30. AE VISA
Meals 8.50/17.50 **st.** and a la carte 4.95 **22 rm** 55.00/70.00 **st.**, 2 suites.

at Hadley Heath SW : 4 m. by Ombersley Way, A 4133 and Ladywood rd – ✉ Droitwich – ☎ 01905.

Hadley Bowling Green Inn, WR9 0AR, ☎ 620294, Fax 620771 – rest. –
Meals (bar lunch)/dinner 9.30 **st.** and a la carte – **14 rm** 45.00/57.00 **st.** – SB.

DRONFIELD Derbs. 402 403 404 P 24 – pop. 13 335 – ECD : Wednesday – ✉ Sheffield (S. Yorks.) – ☎ 01246.

♦ London 158 – Derby 30 – ♦ Nottingham 31 – ♦ Sheffield 6.

Manor House, 10-15 High St., S18 6PY, ☎ 413971 – – 25.
closed 25 and 26 December – **Meals** *(closed Monday dinner to non-residents, Monday lunch and Sunday dinner)* a la carte 18.20/23.45 **t.** 4.00 – **11 rm** 39.50/95.00 **t.** – SB.

Chantry, Church St., S18 6QB, ☎ 413014, Fax 413014, – .
Meals *(closed Sunday dinner and Monday to non-residents and 2 weeks July-August)* (bar lunch Monday to Saturday)/dinner 16.95 **t.** – **8 rm** 40.00/50.00 **st.**

Horsleygate Hall without rest., Horsleygate Lane, Holmesfield, S18 5WD, W : 3½ m. by B 5056 off B 6054 ☎ 890333, « Part Victorian, part Georgian house », –
3 rm 21.00/40.00 **t.**

DRYBROOK Glos. 403 404 M 28 – ☎ 01594.

♦London 149 – ♦Bristol 34 – Gloucester 12 – Newport 35.

Cider Press, The Cross, GL17 9EB, ☎ 544472 –
closed Tuesday and first 2 weeks January – **Meals** (by arrangement Sunday and Monday) a la carte 12.10/24.20 **t.**

DUDDENHOE END Essex 404 U 27 – see Saffron Walden.

DUDLEY W. Mids. 402 403 404 N 26 **Great Britain G.** – pop. 185 721 – ECD : Wednesday – ☎ 01384.

See : Black Country Museum★.

18, 9 Swindon, Bridgnorth Rd ☎ (01902) 897031 – 9 Sedgley, Sandyfields Rd ☎ (01902) 880503.

39 Churchill Shopping Centre, DY2 7BL, ☎ 250333.

♦London 132 – ♦Birmingham 10 – Wolverhampton 6.

Plan : see Birmingham p. 2

Copthorne Merry Hill, The Waterfront, Level St., Brierley Hill, DY5 1UR, SW : 2¼ m. by A 461 ☎ 482882, Fax 482773, – rm rest – 250. AU **z**
Meals 9.95/16.95 **st.** and a la carte 6.95 – 9.95 – **129 rm** 94.00/104.00 **st.**, 9 suites.

Ward Arms, Birmingham Rd, DY1 4RN, NE : ¾ m. on A 461 ☎ 458070, Fax 457502 – rm – 120.
Meals *(closed Saturday lunch)* a la carte 10.35/17.75 **t. 72 rm** 61.00 **t.**

Forte Travelodge without rest., Dudley Rd, Brierley Hill, DY5 1LQ, SW : 2 m. on A 461 ☎ 481579, Reservations (Freephone) 0800 850950 – . AU **c**
32 rm 33.50 **t.**

ATS Oakeywell St. ☎ 238047

DULVERTON Somerset 403 J 30 **The West Country G.** – pop. 1 870 – ECD : Thursday – ☎ 01398.

See : Village★.

Envir. : Tarr Steps★★, NW : 6 m. by B 3223.

♦London 198 – Barnstaple 27 – Exeter 26 – Minehead 18 – Taunton 27.

Ashwick House , TA22 9QD, NW : 4¼ m. by B 3223 ☎ 23868 (323868 from May), Fax 23868 (323868 from May), <, « Country house atmosphere », – rest
Meals (dinner only and Sunday lunch)/dinner 21.75 **t.** – **6 rm** (dinner included) 63.00/120.00 **t.** – SB.

at Brushford SW : 1¾ m. on B 3223 – ✉ Dulverton – ☎ 01398 :

Carnarvon Arms, TA22 9AE, ☎ 23302 (323302 from May), Fax 24022 (324022 from May), heated, , , park, – – 100.
Meals 10.50/27.50 **t.** and a la carte – **22 rm** 35.00/70.00 **t.**, 1 suite – SB.

DUNCHURCH Warks. 403 404 Q 26 – pop. 2 904 – ✉ Rugby – ☎ 01788.

♦London 90 – ♦Coventry 12 – ♦Leicester 24 – Northampton 26.

Forte Travelodge without rest., London Rd, Thurlaston, CV23 9LG, NW : 2½ m. on A 45 ☎ 521538, Reservations (Freephone) 0800 850950 – .
40 rm 33.50 **t.**

DUNSFORD Devon 403 I 31 – pop. 1212 – ☎ 01647.

♦London 206 – Exeter 6 – ♦Plymouth 35.

Dunsford Mills, EX6 7EF, SW : ½ m. on B 3212 (Moretonhampton rd) ☎ 52011, Fax 52988, « Converted 18C water mill », park – TV P. AE VISA
closed 2 to 16 January – **Meals** (bar lunch)/dinner 16.95 **t.** and a la carte 4.50 – **9 rm** 47.00/94.00 **t.** – SB.

DUNSLEY N. Yorks. – see Whitby.

DUNSTABLE Beds. 404 S 28 – pop. 48 436 – ECD : Thursday – ☎ 01582.

Tilsworth, Dunstable Rd ☎ (01525) 210721/210722.

The Library, Vernon Pl., LU5 4HA ☎ 471012.

♦London 40 – Bedford 24 – Luton 4.5 – Northampton 35.

Old Palace Lodge, Church St., LU5 4RT, ☎ 662201, Fax 696422 – rm rest TV ☎ P – 35. AE VISA
closed 26 to 30 December – **Meals** *(closed Saturday lunch)* 16.95/19.00 **t.** and a la carte – 8.75 – **49 rm** 73.50/83.50 **st.**

Highwayman, London Rd, LU6 3DX, SE : 1 m. on A 5 ☎ 661999, Fax 603812 – TV ☎ P – 40
53 rm.

at Hockliffe NW : 3¼ m. on A 5 – ✉ Dunstable – ☎ 01525 :

Forte Travelodge without rest., LU7 9LZ, ☎ 211177, Reservations (Freephone) 0800 850950 – TV P. AE VISA.
28 rm 33.50 **t.**

DUNSTER Somerset 403 J 30 **The West Country G.** – pop. 848 – ECD : Wednesday – ✉ Minehead – ☎ 01643.

See : Town★★ - Castle★★ *AC* (Upper rooms ≤★) – Dunster Water Mill★ *AC* – St. Georges Church★ – Dovecote★.

Envir. : Exmoor National Park★★ (Dunkery Beacon★★★, Watersmeet★, Valley of the Rocks★, Vantage Point★) – Cleeve Abbey★★ *AC*, SE : 5 m. by A 39 – Timberscombe (Church★) SW : 3½ m. by A 396.

♦London 184 – ♦Bristol 61 – Exeter 40 – Taunton 22.

Luttrell Arms (Forte), 36 High St., TA24 6SG, ☎ 821555, Fax 821567, « Part 15C inn », – TV ☎. AE VISA
Meals (bar lunch Monday to Saturday)/dinner 16.95 **t.** and a la carte 6.70 – 8.50 – **27 rm** 75.00/90.00 **t.** – SB.

Exmoor House, 12 West St., TA24 6SN, ☎ 821268, – TV. AE VISA
closed December and January – **Meals** (dinner only) 14.50 **st.** 4.10 – **7 rm** 36.50/57.00 **st.** – SB.

DURHAM Durham 401 402 P 19 **Great Britain G.** – pop. 38 105 – ECD : Wednesday – ☎ 0191.

See : City★★★ - Cathedral★★★ (Nave★★★, Chapel of the Nine Altars★★★, Sanctuary Knocker★) B – Oriental Museum★★ *AC* (at Durham University by A 167) B – City and Riverside (Prebends' Bridge ≤★★★ A , Framwellgate Bridge ≤★★ B) – Monastic Buildings (Cathedral Treasury★, Central Tower ≤★) B – Castle★ (Norman chapel★) *AC* B.

Mount Oswald, South Rd ☎ 386 7527.

Market Pl., DH1 3NJ ☎ 384 3720.

♦London 267 – ♦Leeds 77 – ♦Middlesbrough 23 – Sunderland 12.

Plan opposite

Royal County (Swallow), Old Elvet, DH1 3JN, ☎ 386 6821, Fax 386 0704, – rm rest TV ☎ P – 120. AE VISA — B a
County : **Meals** 14.00/21.00 **st.** 5.25 – *Bowes Brasserie* : **Meals** 7.50/16.00 **st.** 5.25 – **149 rm** 96.00/124.00 **st.**, 1 suite – SB.

Three Tuns Swallow, New Elvet, DH1 3AQ, ☎ 386 4326, Fax 386 1406 – rm TV ☎ P – 250. AE VISA — B e
Meals *(closed Saturday lunch)* 9.75/16.25 **st.** and a la carte – **46 rm** 86.00/99.00 **st.**, 1 suite – SB.

at Croxdale S : 3 m. by A 1050 on A 167 – B – ✉ Durham – ☎ 0191 :

Bridge Toby, DH1 3SP, ☎ 378 0524, Fax 378 9981 – rm TV ☎ P – 60. AE VISA
Meals (grill rest.) 7.95 **st.** and a la carte – **46 rm** 49.95/59.95 **st.** – SB.

ATS Finchale Rd, Newton Hall ☎ 384 1810 — ATS Mill Rd, Langley Moor ☎ 378 0262

DURHAM

Saddler Street . . . . B
Silver Street . . . . B 22

Alexander Crescent . . . . . A 2
Castle Chare . . . . A 3
Court Lane . . . . B 5
Elvet Bridge . . . . B 6
Elvet Crescent . . . . B 7

Flass Street . . . . A 8
Framwelgate Bridge . . . . B 9
Framwelgate Waterside . B 10
Gilesgate . . . . B 12
Grove Street . . . . A 13
Market Place . . . . B 14
Millburngate . . . . A 15
Neville Street . . . . A 16
Potters Bank . . . . A 18
Providence Row . . . . B 20
Sutton Street . . . . A 22

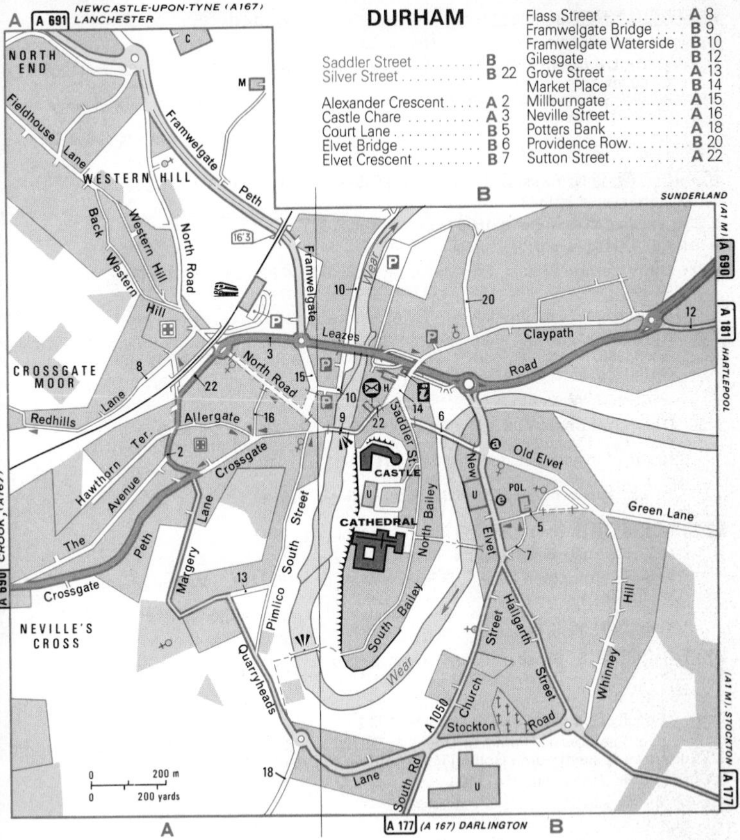

Don't confuse:

Comfort of hotels : 🏨🏨🏨 ... 🏠, ⛱, ⌂
Comfort of restaurants : XXXXX X
Quality of the cuisine : ✿✿✿, ✿✿, ✿, **Meals**

DUXFORD Cambs. 404 U 27 – see Cambridge.

EAGLESCLIFFE Cleveland 402 P 20 – see Stockton-on-Tees.

EARL'S COLNE Essex 404 W 28 – ✉ Colchester – ☎ 01787.

◆London 55 – ◆Cambridge 33 – Chelmsford 22 – Colchester 10.

⌂ **Elm House,** 14 Upper Holt St., CO6 2PG, on A 604 ☏ 222197, ⛱
Meals (by arrangement) (communal dining) 14.00 **s.** – **3 rm** ⊐ 19.00/50.00 **s.** – SB.

EARL SHILTON Leics. 403 404 Q 26 – pop. 16 484 – ECD : Wednesday – ✉ Leicester – ☎ 01455.

◆London 107 – ◆Birmingham 35 – ◆Coventry 16 – ◆Leicester 9 – ◆Nottingham 35.

🏠 Mill on the Soar, Coventry Rd, Sutton in the Elms, LE9 6QD, SE : 4 ½ m. by B 581 on A 4114 ☏ 282419, Fax 285937 – TV ☎ P – 🏃 40
20 rm.

EARL SOHAM Suffolk 404 X 27 – see Framlingham.

EARL STONHAM Suffolk 404 X 27 – ✉ Stowmarket – ☎ 01449.
♦London 81 – ♦Cambridge 47 – ♦Ipswich 10 – ♦Norwich 33.

XX ✿ **Mr. Underhill's** (Bradley), IP14 5DW, at junction of A 140 with A 1120 ✆ 711206 – **P**. AE VISA
closed Saturday lunch, Sunday dinner and Monday – **Meals** (lunch by arrangement) (booking essential)/dinner 28.00 **t.** 5.65
Spec. Warm escalope of smoked salmon with basil and ginger, Breast of Barbary duck with parslied sauce and sweetcorn pancakes, Hot chocolate tart.

EASINGWOLD N. Yorks. 402 Q 21 – pop. 3 545 – ✉ York – ☎ 01347.
18 Stillington Rd ✆ 821486.
Chapel Lane, YO6 3AE ✆ 821530 (summer only).
♦London 217 – ♦Middlesbrough 37 – York 14.

Old Vicarage without rest., Market Pl., YO6 3AL, ✆ 821015, – TV **P**
closed December and January – **5 rm** 22.50/42.00 **st.**

at Alne SW : 4 m. on Alne Rd – ✉ Aldwark – ☎ 01347 :

Aldwark Manor, Aldwark, YO6 2NF, SW : 3 ½ m. by Aldwark Bridge rd ✆ 838146, Fax 838867, ≤, 18, , park – rest TV ☎ **P** – 100. AE VISA JCB
Meals 9.50/17.50 **st.** 4.50 – **20 rm** 50.00/85.00 **t.** – SB.

at Raskelf W : 2 ¾ m. – ✉ York – ☎ 01347 :

Old Farmhouse, YO6 3LF, ✆ 821971, Fax 822392 – rest TV ☎ **P**
closed 23 December-31 January – **Meals** *(closed Sunday)* (dinner only) 16.00 **t.** 4.00 – **10 rm** (dinner included) 43.00/80.00 **t.** – SB.

To visit a town or region : use the ***Michelin Green Guides.***

EAST BARKWITH Lincs. 402 404 T 24 – ✉ Lincoln – ☎ 01673.
♦London 152 – Boston 30 – Great Grimsby 28 – Lincoln 13.

Grange, Torrington Lane, LN3 5RY, NW : ¾ m. ✆ 858249, « Working farm », , – TV **P**.
closed Christmas and New Year – **Meals** (by arrangement)(communal dining) 15.00 **s.** – **3 rm** 30.00/40.00 **s.**

EASTBOURNE E. Sussex 404 U 31 **Great Britain G.** – pop. 81 395 – ECD : Wednesday – ☎ 01323.
See : Seafront★.
Envir. : Beachy Head★★★, SW : 3 m. by B 2103 Z.
18, 9 Royal Eastbourne, Paradise Drive ✆ 729738 Z – 18 Eastbourne Downs, East Dean Rd ✆ 720827, Z – 9 Eastbourne Golfing Park, Lottbridge Drove ✆ 520400.
Cornfield Rd, BN21 4QL ✆ 411400.
♦London 68 – ♦Brighton 25 – ♦Dover 61 – Maidstone 49.

Plan opposite

Grand (De Vere), King Edward's Par., BN21 4EQ, ✆ 412345, Fax 412233, ≤, , , heated, , – rm TV ☎ **P** – 375. AE VISA Z x
Meals *(closed lunch Tuesday to Friday)* 25.00 **st.** and a la carte 5.75 – (see also **Mirabelle** below) – **149 rm** 91.50/160.00 **st.**, 15 suites – SB.

Cavendish (De Vere), 37-40 Grand Par., BN21 4DH, ✆ 410222, Fax 410941, ≤ – TV ☎ **P** – 200. AE VISA X r
Meals 6.95/17.50 **st.** and a la carte 4.75 – **108 rm** 70.00/130.00 **st.**, 4 suites – SB.

Queen's, Marine Par., BN21 3DY, ✆ 722822, Fax 731056, ≤ – TV ☎ **P** – 160. VISA. V e
Meals 6.95/11.00 **st.** – **106 rm** 32.00/74.00 **st.**, 2 suites – SB.

Lansdowne, King Edward's Par., BN21 4EE, ✆ 725174, Fax 739721, ≤ – TV ☎ – 130. AE VISA JCB Z z
closed 1 to 14 January – **Meals** 15.00 **st.** (dinner) and lunch a la carte 6.95/9.00 **st.** 5.00 – **125 rm** 49.00/94.00 **st.** – SB.

Langham, Royal Par., BN22 7AH, ✆ 731451, Fax 646623, ≤ – TV ☎. AE VISA Z e
closed mid November to mid February – **Meals** 6.75/13.50 **st.** 5.35 – **87 rm** (dinner included) 34.95/69.90 **st.** – SB.

Wish Tower, King Edward's Par., BN21 4EB, ✆ 722676, Fax 721474, ≤ – TV ☎ – 40. AE VISA Z r
Meals (bar lunch Monday to Saturday)/dinner 12.95 **st.** and a la carte – 7.50 – **65 rm** 55.00/130.00 **st.** – SB.

Brownings, 28 Upperton Rd, BN21 1JS, ✆ 724358, Fax 731288, heated – TV ☎ **P** – 40. AE VISA. Z a
Meals *(closed Sunday dinner)* (dinner only and Sunday lunch)/dinner 15.95 **t.** 4.95 – **11 rm** 35.00/60.00 **st.**

Oban, King Edward's Par., BN21 4DS, ✆ 731581, Fax 731581 – TV ☎. VISA X a
closed January and February – **Meals** (bar lunch)/dinner 10.00 **t.** 3.00 – **31 rm** 25.00/50.00 **t.** – SB.

EASTBOURNE

Arndale Centre V
Grove Road V
Seaside Rd V
South Street V
Terminus Road V

Ashford Road . . . . V 2
Bedfordwell Road . . . . V 3
Church Street . . . . Z 4
Cornfield Road . . . . V 5
Devonshire Place . . . . X 6
Gildredge Road . . . . V 7
Hailsham Road . . . . Y 8
High Street . . . . Z 9
Lewes Road . . . . Y 13
Lismore Road . . . . V 14

North Street . . . . V 15
Polegate By-Pass . . . . Y 18
St. Anthony's Avenue . . . . . Y 21
Station Road . . . . Y 24

Susan's Road . . . . V 25
The Goffs . . . . Z 26
Trinity Trees . . . . V 27
Upperton Road . . . . V, Z 28

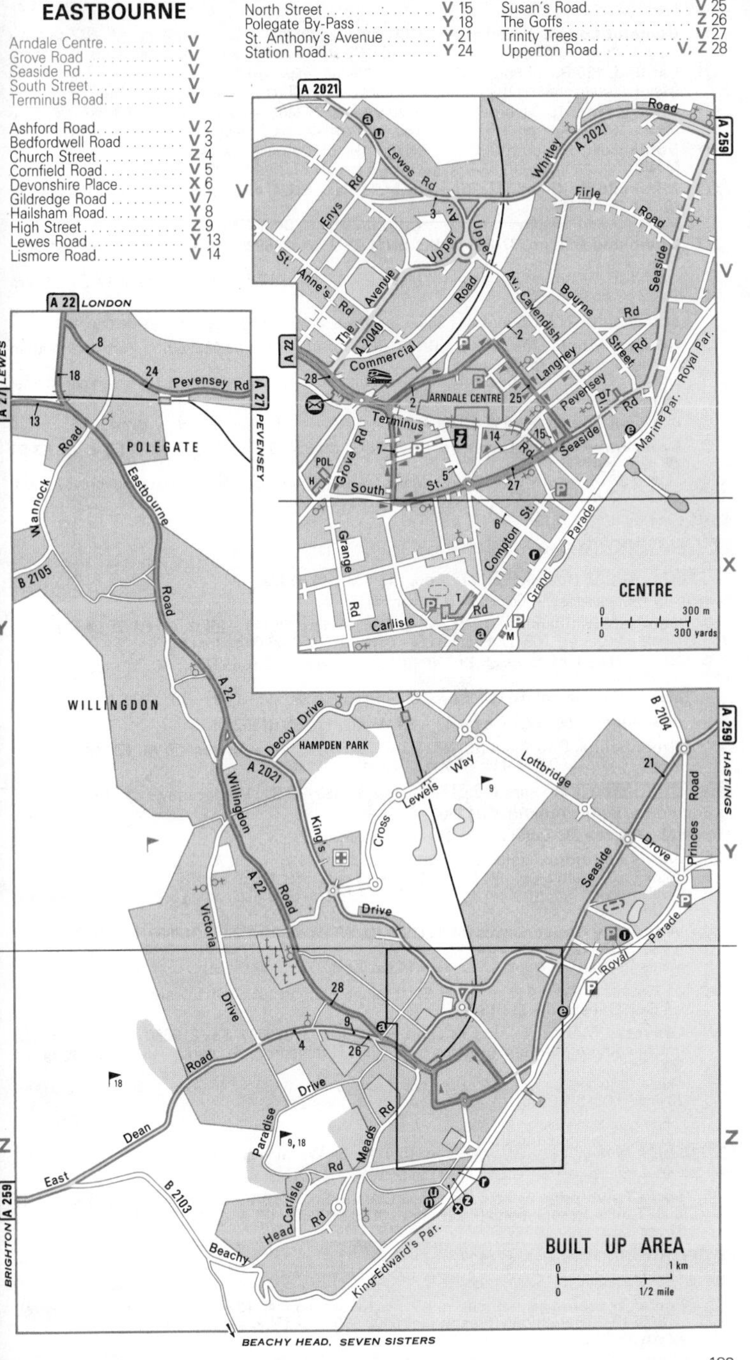

Camelot Lodge, 35 Lewes Rd, BN21 2BU, ☎ 725207 – rest. VISA. V a
April-October – Meals (by arrangement) 8.00 st. – 9 rm 21.00/42.00 st. – SB.

Far End, 139 Royal Par., BN22 7LH, ☎ 725666 – rest. Y i
May-October – Meals (by arrangement) 7.00 st. – 10 rm 17.00/34.00 – SB.

Cherry Tree, 15 Silverdale Rd, BN20 7AJ, ☎ 722406 – rest. VISA. Z u
Meals (by arrangement) 10.50 t. 3.50 – 10 rm 25.00/54.00 t. – SB.

Southcroft, 15 South Cliff Av., BN20 7AH, ☎ 729071 – Z n
Meals (by arrangement) 6.00 st. 2.50 – 6 rm 21.00/42.00 st.

XXXX **Mirabelle** (at Grand H.), King Edward's Par., BN21 4EQ, ☎ 410771, Fax 412233 – AE VISA Z x
Meals *(closed Sunday and Monday)* 15.50/28.50 st. and a la carte 5.75.

XX **Downland** with rm, 37 Lewes Rd, BN21 2BU, ☎ 732689 – AE VISA JCB. V u
closed 26 December-20 January – **Meals** (dinner only) 17.50 t. and a la carte 4.25 – **14 rm** 32.50/65.00 t. – SB.

at Jevington NW : 6 m. by A 259 – Z – on B 2105 – ✉ Polegate – ☎ 01323 :

XX **Hungry Monk**, The Street, BN26 5QF, ☎ 482178, Fax 483989, « Part Elizabethan cottages », – AE
closed 24 to 26 December and Bank Holiday Mondays – **Meals** (booking essential) (dinner only and Sunday lunch)/dinner 24.00 t. 5.80.

at Wilmington NW : 6½ m. by A 22 on A 27 – Y – ✉ Eastbourne – ☎ 01323 :

XX **Crossways** with rm, Lewes Rd, BN26 5SG, ☎ 482455, Fax 487811, – AE VISA JCB.
closed 23 December-24 January – **Meals** *(closed Sunday and Monday)* (dinner only) 23.95 t. 5.25 – **7 rm** 40.00/68.00 st. – SB.

ATS Langney Rise ☎ 761971

EAST BUCKLAND Devon 403 I 30 – see South Molton.

EAST DEREHAM Norfolk 404 W 25 – pop. 13 333 – ☎ 01362.

London 109 – Cambridge 57 – King's Lynn 27 – Norwich 16.

George, Swaffham Rd, NR19 2AZ, ☎ 696801, Fax 695711 – AE VISA
Meals a la carte 10.65/17.45 t. 3.50 – **7 rm** 40.00/48.00 t., 1 suite.

King's Head, 42 Norwich St., NR19 1AD, ☎ 693842, Fax 693776, – AE VISA
Meals 7.95/9.95 t. and a la carte 3.65 – **15 rm** 38.00/55.00 t. – SB.

at Wendling W : 5½ m. by A 47 – ✉ Wendling – ☎ 01362 :

Greenbanks, Swaffham Rd, NR19 2AR, ☎ 687742, – rest. VISA
Meals 10.00/23.00 st. 4.85 – **5 rm** 32.00/48.00 st. – SB.

EAST GRINSTEAD W. Sussex 404 T 30 – pop. 24 383 – ECD : Wednesday – ☎ 01342.

18 Copthorne, Borers Arm Rd ☎ 712508.

London 32 – Brighton 29 – Eastbourne 33 – Lewes 21 – Maidstone 32.

Jarvis Felbridge, London Rd, RH19 2BH, NW : 1½ m. on A 22 ☎ 326992, Fax 410778, heated, – 350. AE VISA
Meals *(closed Saturday lunch)* 10.50/15.00 st. and dinner a la carte 5.25 – 8.25 – **90 rm** 75.00/85.00 st. – SB.

Woodbury House, Lewes Rd, RH19 3UD, SE : ½ m. on A 22 ☎ 313657, Fax 314801, – AE VISA JCB.
Meals 15.95/19.95 t. and a la carte – **14 rm** 60.00/75.00 t. – SB.

at Gravetye SW : 4½ m. by B 2110 taking second turn left towards West Hoathly – ✉ East Grinstead – ☎ 01342 :

Gravetye Manor, Vowels Lane, RH19 4LJ, ☎ 810567, Fax 810080, « 16C manor house with gardens and grounds by William Robinson », park – rest. VISA.
Meals (booking essential) 22.00/28.00 s. and a la carte 23.70/40.30 s. 15.50 – 8.00 – **18 rm** 90.00/195.00 s.

ATS London Rd, North End ☎ 410740

EASTHAM Mersey. 402 403 L 24 – pop. 15 011 – ✉ Wirral – ☎ 0151.

London 209 – Birmingham 45 – Chester 13 – Liverpool 7.5 – Manchester 45.

Forte Travelodge without rest., New Chester Rd, L62 9AQ, at junction of M 53 with A 41 ☎ 327 2489, Reservations (Freephone) 0800 850950 – AE VISA.
31 rm 33.50 t.

EAST HORNDON Essex – ☎ 01277.

London 21 – Chelmsford 13 – Southend-on-Sea 17.

Forte Travelodge without rest., CM13 3LL, on A 127 (eastbound carriageway) ☎ 810819, Reservations (Freephone) 0800 850950 – AE VISA.
22 rm 33.50 t.

EASTLEIGH Devon 403 H 30 – see Bideford.

EASTLEIGH Hants. 403 P 31 – pop. 58 585 – ECD : Wednesday – ☏ 01703.

Fleming Park ✆ 612797 – Southampton (Eastleigh) Airport : ✆ 629600.

Town Hall Centre, Leigh Rd, SO5 4DE ✆ 641261.

London 74 – Winchester 8 – Southampton 4.

Forte Posthouse, Leigh Rd, SO5 5PG, ✆ 619700, Fax 643945, – rm rest TV ☎ & P – 250. AE VISA
Meals *(closed Saturday lunch)* a la carte approx. 15.00 **t.** 5.50 – **117 rm** 56.00 **t.**, 3 suites.

Forte Travelodge, Twyford Rd, SO5 4LF, N : 1m. on A 335 ✆ 616813, Reservations (Freephone) 0800 850950 – TV & P. AE VISA.
Meals (Harvester grill) a la carte approx. 16.00 **t.** – **32 rm** 33.50 **t.**

ATS Dutton Lane, Bishopstoke Rd ✆ 613027/613393

EASTLING Kent 404 W 30 – see Faversham.

EASTON CROSS Devon 403 I 31 – see Chagford.

EAST RETFORD Notts. 402 404 R 24 – pop. 20 6793 – ☏ 01777.

Amcott House Annexe, 40 Grove St., DN22 6JU ✆ 860780.

London 148 – Lincoln 23 – Nottingham 31 – Sheffield 27.

Old Plough, Top Street, North Wheatley, DN22 9DB, NE : 5 m. by A 620 ✆ (01427) 880916, ←, – TV P.
Meals (by arrangement) (communal dining) 12.50 **s.** – **3 rm** 25.00/50.00 **s.**

ATS Babworth Rd ✆ 706501

EAST WITTERING W. Sussex 404 R 31 – pop. 3 503 – ✉ Chichester – ☏ 01243.

London 74 – Brighton 37 – Portsmouth 25.

Clifford's Cottage, Bracklesham Lane, Bracklesham Bay, PO20 8JA, E : 1 m. by B 2179 on B 2198 ✆ 670250 – P. AE VISA
closed Sunday dinner, first week February and first 2 weeks November – **Meals** (dinner only and Sunday lunch)/dinner 16.50 **t.** and a la carte 4.25.

EAST WITTON N. Yorks. 402 O 21 – ✉ Leyburn – ☏ 01969.

London 238 – Leeds 45 – Middlesbrough 30 – York 39.

Blue Lion with rm, DL8 4SN, ✆ 24273, Fax 24189, « 19C inn », – TV ☎ P. VISA
Meals (in bar Tuesday to Saturday lunch, Sunday dinner and Monday) dinner a la carte 17.10/28.45 **t.** 6.85 – **9 rm** 40.00/70.00 **t.** – SB.

EBCHESTER Durham 401 402 O 19 – ✉ Consett – ☏ 01207.

Consett and District, Elmfield Rd, Consett ✆ 502186.

London 275 – Carlisle 64 – Newcastle upon Tyne 16.

Raven, Broomhill, DH8 6RY, SE : ¾ m. on B 6309 ✆ 560367, Fax 560262, ← – TV ☎ & P. AE VISA.
Meals *(closed Sunday dinner)* (bar lunch Monday to Saturday)/dinner 16.95 **st.** and a la carte 4.95 – **28 rm** 52.00/69.00 **st.** – SB.

ECCLESHALL Staffs. 402 403 404 N 25 – pop. 4 606 – ECD : Wednesday – ☏ 01785.

London 149 – Birmingham 33 – Derby 40 – Shrewsbury 26 – Stoke-on-Trent 12.

St. George, Castle St., ST21 6DF, ✆ 850300, Fax 851452 – TV ☎ P. AE VISA.
Meals *(closed Sunday dinner)* 8.95 **t.** (lunch) and a la carte 10.00/17.40 **t.** – **10 rm** 49.50/75.00 **t.** – SB.

Badger Inn, Green Lane, ST21 6BA, S : ¼ m. by A 519 ✆ 850564 – rest TV P. VISA.
Meals a la carte 7.00/13.70 **t.** 2.50 **4 rm** 25.00/40.00 **t.**

EDENBRIDGE Kent 404 U 30 **Great Britain G.** – pop. 7 581 – ☏ 01732.

Envir. : Hever Castle★ *AC*, E : 2½m. – Chartwell★ *AC*, N : 3 m. by B 2026.

18, 9 Crouch House Rd ✆ 867381.

London 35 – Brighton 36 – Maidstone 29.

Honours Mill, 87 High St., TN8 5AU, ✆ 866757, « Carefully renovated 18C mill » – AE VISA
closed Saturday lunch, Sunday dinner, Monday and 2 weeks Christmas-New Year – **Meals** 14.50/31.75 **st.** 5.50.

EGERTON Gtr. Manchester 402 ㉑ 403 ② 404 ⑨ – see Bolton.

Stadtpläne : *Die Auswahl der Straßen wurde unter Berücksichtigung des Verkehrs und der Zufahrt zu den erwähnten Häusern getroffen.*

Die weniger wichtigen Straßen wurden nur angedeutet.

EGHAM Surrey 404 S 29 – pop. 21 337 – ECD : Thursday – ☎ 01784.
♦London 29 – Reading 21.

Runnymede, Windsor Rd, TW20 0AG, on A 308 ☎ 436171, Fax 436340, Ls, ≘s, ▢, 🌳, 🎾 – |‡| ⚹ rm ▤ TV ☎ P – 🎤 350. VISA
Meals (bar lunch Saturday) (dancing Saturday evening) 16.95/30.00 **st.** 6.95 – ☕ 10.95 – **171 rm** 108.00/125.00 **st.** – SB.

Great Fosters, Stroude Rd, TW20 9UR, S : 1 ¼ m. by B 388 ☎ 433822, Fax 472455, « Elizabethan mansion, gardens », ≘s, heated, park, 🎾 – TV ☎ P – 🎤 65. VISA.
Meals 12.50/22.50 **t.** and a la carte 5.00 – **42 rm** ☕ 80.00/170.00 **t.**, 2 suites.

EGLINGHAM Northd. 401 402 O 17 – see Alnwick.

EIGHT ASH GREEN Essex 404 W 28 – see Colchester.

ELLAND W. Yorks. 402 O 22 – see Halifax.

ELSING Norfolk 404 X 25 – ✉ East Dereham – ☎ 01362.
♦London 118 – ♦Cambridge 66 – King's Lynn 33 – ♦Norwich 15.

Bartles Lodge ⛰, Church St., NR20 3EA, ☎ 637177, 🐟, 🌳 – TV P. VISA
Meals (by arrangement) 7.50 **st.** 3.95 – **7 rm** ☕ 25.00/44.00 **st.**

I prezzi	Per ogni chiarimento sui prezzi qui riportati, consultate le spiegazioni alle pagine dell'introduzione.

ELSLACK N. Yorks. 402 N 22 – see Skipton.

ELSTREE Herts. 404 T 29 – ☎ 0181 – 18 Watling St. ☎ 953 6115.
♦London 10 – Luton 22.

Plan : see Greater London (North West)

Edgwarebury (Country Club), Barnet Lane, WD6 3RE, ☎ 953 8227, Fax 207 3668, 🌳, park, 🎾 – ⚹ rm TV ☎ P – 🎤 80. VISA CT e
Meals *(closed Saturday lunch)* 15.95/21.50 **st.** and dinner a la carte 5.95 – ☕ 7.95 – **47 rm** 80.00 **st.**

ELTERWATER Cumbria – see Ambleside.

ELY Cambs. 404 U 26 **Great Britain G.** – pop. 11 345 – ECD : Tuesday – ☎ 01353.
See : Cathedral** *AC.*
18 Cambridge Rd ☎ 662751.
ℹ Oliver Cromwells House, 29 St. Mary's St., CB7 4HF ☎ 662062.
♦London 74 – ♦Cambridge 16 – ♦Norwich 60.

Lamb (Q.M.H.), 2 Lynn Rd, CB7 4EJ, ☎ 663574, Fax 666350 – TV ☎ P – 🎤 40. VISA
Meals (bar lunch Monday to Saturday)/dinner 14.50 **t.** and a la carte – ☕ 8.75 – **32 rm** 60.00/80.00 **t.** – SB.

Forte Travelodge without rest., Witchford Rd, CB6 3NN, W : 1 m. on A 10/A 142 roundabout, Ely by pass ☎ 668499, Reservations (Freephone) 0800 850950 – TV ♿ P. VISA.
39 rm 33.50 **t.**

Old Fire Engine House, 25 St. Mary's St., CB7 4ER, ☎ 662582, 🌳 – ⚹ P. VISA
closed Sunday dinner, 2 weeks Christmas-New Year and Bank Holidays – **Meals** - English (booking essential) a la carte 16.80/23.70 **t.**

at Littleport N : 5 ¾ m. on A 10 – ✉ Ely – ☎ 01353 :

Fen House, 2 Lynn Rd, CB6 1QG, ☎ 860645 – ⚹. VISA
closed Sunday and Monday – **Meals** (dinner only) 25.00 **st.** 6.00.

ATS 11 Broad St. ☎ 662758/662801

EMPINGHAM Leics. 402 404 S 26 – see Stamford (Lincs.).

EMSWORTH Hants. 404 R 31 – pop. 17 604 (inc. Southbourne) – ECD : Wednesday – ☎ 01243.
♦London 75 – ♦Brighton 37 – ♦Portsmouth 10.

Brookfield, 93-95 Havant Rd, PO10 7LF, ☎ 373363, Fax 376342, 🌳 – ▤ rest TV ☎ P – 🎤 50. VISA.
closed Christmas - New Year – **Meals** 13.95 **st.** and a la carte 4.50 – **41 rm** ☕ 49.00/69.00 **st.** – SB.

Forte Travelodge without rest., PO10 7RB, E : ½ m. on A 27 (eastbound carriageway) ☎ 370877, Reservations (Freephone) 0800 850950 – TV ♿ P. VISA
40 rm 33.50 **t.**

XXX **36 on the Quay,** 47 South St., The Quay, PO10 7EG, ✆ 375592 – AE VISA
closed lunch Monday and Saturday, Sunday, Tuesdays October-March and 2 weeks September-October – **Meals** 20.95/29.95 **t.** and dinner a la carte 6.95.

XX **Spencer's,** 36 North St., PO10 7DG, ✆ 372744 – AE VISA
closed Saturday lunch, Sunday, Monday and 25-26 December – **Meals** 21.00 **t.** (dinner) and lunch a la carte 12.55/18.20 **t.** 4.50.

ENNERDALE BRIDGE Cumbria 402 J 20 – ✉ Cleator – 01946.

London 315 – Carlisle 35 – Keswick 25 – Whitehaven 7.

Routen Llama Farm, Roughton, CA23 3AU, NE : 3½ m. on Croasdale rd ✆ 861270, < Ennerdale Water, « Working farm », park – TV P. VISA.
Meals (by arrangement) (communal dining) 14.00 **s.** 4.00 – **3 rm** 21.00/46.00 **s.** – SB.

ENSTONE Oxon. 403 404 P 28 – pop. 1 523 – ✉ Chipping Norton – 01608.

London 73 – Birmingham 48 – Gloucester 32 – Oxford 18.

Swan Lodge, Oxford Rd, OX7 4NE, on A 44 ✆ 678736, – TV P. VISA
closed 20 December-1 January – **Meals** (by arrangement) 14.00 **s.** 4.00 – **3 rm** 30.00/45.00 **st.** – SB.

EPSOM Surrey 404 ㉚ – pop. 67 007 (inc. Ewell) – ECD : Wednesday – 01372.

Longdown Lane South, Epsom Downs ✆ 721666 – Horton Park C.C., Hook Rd, Ewell ✆ (0181) 393 8400.

London 17 – Guildford 16.

Plan : see Greater London (South-West)

XX **Le Raj,** 211 Fir Tree Rd, Epsom Downs, KT19 3LB, SE : 2¼ m. by B 289 and B 284 on B 291 ✆ (01737) 371371 – AE VISA CZ
closed 25 and 26 December – **Meals** - Indian 15.00/20.00 **t.** and a la carte.

EPWORTH Humbs. 402 404 R 23 – ✉ Doncaster – 01427.

London 170 – Leeds 48 – Lincoln 31 – Sheffield 39.

X **Epworth Tap,** 9-11 Market Pl., DN9 1EU, ✆ 873333 – AE VISA
closed Sunday to Tuesday and 2 weeks Christmas – **Meals** (booking essential) (dinner only) 16.50 **t.** and a la carte **t.** 4.25.

ESCRICK N. Yorks. 402 Q 22 – see York.

ESHER Surrey 404 S 29 – pop. 46 688 (inc. Molesey) – ECD : Wednesday – 01372.

Thames Ditton & Esher, Portsmouth Rd ✆ (0181) 398 1551 BZ – Moore Place, Portsmouth Rd ✆ 463533 BZ – , Sandown Park, More Lane ✆ 65921 BZ.

London 20 – Portsmouth 58.

Plan : see Greater London (South-West)

XX **Good Earth,** 14-18 High St., KT10 9RT, ✆ 462489 – AE VISA BZ **e**
closed 24 to 27 December – **Meals** - Chinese 10.75/24.75 **t.** and a la carte 4.00.

X **La Orient,** 63 High St., KT10 9RQ, ✆ 466628 – AE VISA BZ **a**
Meals - South East Asian 16.50 **t.** (dinner) and a la carte 12.55/20.00 **t.** 3.75.

at Claygate SE : 1 m. by A 244 – ✉ Esher – 01372.

XXX **Les Alouettes,** 7 High St., KT10 0JW, ✆ 464882, Fax 465337 – AE VISA
closed Saturday lunch, Sunday dinner, 25 to 30 December and Bank Holidays – **Meals** - French 12.50/14.95 **t.** and a la carte 5.50. BZ **n**

X **Le Petit Pierrot,** 4 The Parade, KT10 0NU, ✆ 465105, Fax 467642 – AE VISA
closed Saturday lunch, and Sunday – **Meals** - French 9.95/18.95 **t.** 4.25. BZ **r**

ESKDALE GREEN Cumbria 402 K 20 **Great Britain G.** – pop. 316 – ECD : Wednesday and Saturday – ✉ Holmrook – 0194 67.

Exc. : Hard Knott Pass★★, E : 6 m. – Wrynose Pass★★, E : 8 m.

London 312 – Carlisle 59 – Kendal 60.

Bower House Inn, CA19 1TD, W : ¾ m. ✆ 23244, Fax 23308, – TV ☎ P.
24 rm.

ETTINGTON Warks. 403 404 P 27 – see Stratford-upon-Avon.

EVERCREECH Somerset 403 404 M 30 – see Shepton Mallet.

EVERSHOT Dorset 403 404 M 31 – pop. 225 – ✉ Dorchester – ☎ 01935.

♦London 149 – Bournemouth 39 – Dorchester 12 – Salisbury 53 – Taunton 30 – Yeovil 10.

Summer Lodge ⑤, Summer Lane, DT2 0JR, ☎ 83424, Fax 83005, « Part Georgian dower house, country house atmosphere », heated, – rest TV ☎ P. AE VISA
Meals 17.50/27.50 **st.** and dinner a la carte 30.00/45.00 **st.** 6.50 – **17 rm** 100.00/235.00 **st.** – SB.

Rectory House, Fore St., DT2 0JW, ☎ 83273, Fax 83273, – rest TV P. VISA.
closed December – **Meals** (by arrangement) 16.00 **t.** 3.50 – **6 rm** 30.00/60.00 **t.** – SB.

EVESHAM Heref. and Worcs. 403 404 O 27 – pop. 17 823 – ECD : Wednesday – ☎ 01386.

Almonry Museum, Abbey Gate, WR11 4BG ☎ 446944.

♦London 99 – ♦Birmingham 30 – Cheltenham 16 – ♦Coventry 32.

Evesham, Coopers Lane, WR11 6DA, off Waterside ☎ 765566, Fax 765443, Reservations (Freephone)0800 716969, – TV ☎ P. AE VISA
closed 25 and 26 December – **Meals** a la carte 11.40/18.50 **st.** – **40 rm** 55.00/84.00 **st.** – SB.

Waterside, 56-59 Waterside, WR11 6JZ, ☎ 442420, – TV ☎ P
17 rm.

Riverside ⑤, The Parks, Offenham Rd, WR11 5JP, NW : 2 m. by Waterside and B 4035 off B 4510 ☎ 446200, ≤, – rest TV ☎ P. VISA JCB
Meals *(closed Sunday dinner and Monday)* 15.95/21.95 **st.** and a la carte 6.95 – **7 rm** 60.00/80.00 **st.** – SB.

at Harvington N : 3¾ m. by A 4184 and A 435 off B 439 – ✉ Evesham – ☎ 01386 :

Mill at Harvington ⑤, Anchor Lane, WR11 5NR, SE : 1½ m. by B 439 ☎ 870688, Fax 870688, ≤, « 18C mill with riverside garden », heated, – TV ☎ P. AE VISA.
closed 24 to 29 December – **Meals** 13.95/23.00 **st.** 4.50 – **15 rm** 54.00/85.00 **st.** – SB.

at Abbot's Salford (Warks.) N : 4¾ m. by A 4184 and A 435 on B 439 – ✉ Evesham – ☎ 01386 :

Salford Hall, WR11 5UT, ☎ 871300, Fax 871301, « Tudor mansion with early 17C extension and gatehouse », – rest TV ☎ P – 50. AE VISA JCB.
closed 24 to 30 December – **Meals** 14.95/28.00 **t.** 7.65 – **34 rm** 75.00/120.00 **t.** – SB.

ATS Worcester Road ☎ 765313

EWEN Glos. 403 404 O 28 – see Cirencester.

EXEBRIDGE Somerset 403 J 30 – ✉ Dulverton – ☎ 01398.

♦London 194 – Exeter 23 – Minehead 19 – Taunton 23.

Anchor Inn, TA22 9AZ, ☎ 23433, « Riverside setting », – TV ☎ P. VISA
Meals (dinner only and Sunday lunch)/dinner 18.95 **t.** and a la carte 4.50 – **6 rm** 35.00/74.00 – SB.

EXETER Devon 403 J 31 **The West Country G.** – pop. 98 125 – ☎ 01392.

See : City★★ - Cathedral★★ Z – Maritime Museum★★ *AC* Z – Royal Albert Memorial Museum★ Y.

Exc. : Killerton★★ *AC*, NE : 7 m. by B 3181 V – Ottery St. Mary★ (St. Mary's★★) E : 12 m. by B 3183 – Y - A 30 and B 3174.

18 Downes Crediton, Hookway ☎ (01363) 773991.

Exeter Airport : ☎ 367433, E : 5 m. by A 30 V – **Terminal** : St. David's and Central Stations.

Civic Centre, Paris St., EX1 1JJ ☎ 265700 – Exeter Services, Sandygate (M 5), EX2 7NJ ☎ 437581/79088.

♦London 201 – Bournemouth 83 – ♦Bristol 83 – ♦Plymouth 46 – ♦Southampton 110.

Plans on following pages

Forte Crest, Southernhay East, EX1 1QF, ☎ 412812, Telex 42717, Fax 413549, – rm rest TV ☎ P – 150 Z a
109 rm, 1 suite.

Royal Clarence (Q.M.H.), Cathedral Yard, EX1 1HB, ☎ 58464, Fax 439423 – TV ☎ – 120. AE VISA. Y z
Meals 15.00/20.00 **t.** and lunch a la carte 6.50 – 8.95 – **55 rm** 81.00/115.00 **st.**, 1 suite – SB.

Buckerell Lodge, Topsham Rd, EX2 4SQ, ☎ 52451, Fax 412114, – rm TV ☎ P – 60. AE VISA X a
Meals 12.50/17.50 **t.** and a la carte 5.95 – 7.95 – **52 rm** 35.00/79.50 **t.** – SB.

St. Olaves Court, Mary Arches St., EX4 3AZ, ☎ 217736, Fax 413054, – TV ☎ P. AE VISA. Z e
Meals (see *Golsworthy's* below) – 4.00 – **17 rm** 65.00/80.00 **t.** – SB.

EXETER
BUILT UP AREA

Blackboy Road .... **V** 8	Hill Lane .... **V** 21	St. Andrew's Road .... **V** 48
Buddle Lane .... **X** 9	Marsh Barton Road .... **X** 25	Summer Lane .... **V** 51
Butts Road .... **X** 12	Mount Pleasant Road ...... **V** 29	Sweetbriar Lane .... **VX** 52
East Wonford Hill .... **X** 17	North Street HEAVITREE ... **X** 32	Trusham Road .... **X** 53
Heavitree Road .... **VX** 20	Old Tiverton Road .... **V** 35	Union Road .... **V** 54
	Polsloe Road .... **V** 39	Whipton Lane .... **X** 55
	Prince Charles Road ...... **V** 41	Wonford Road .... **X** 57
	Prince of Wales Road ..... **V** 42	Wonford Street .... **X** 58
		Woodwater Lane .... **X** 60

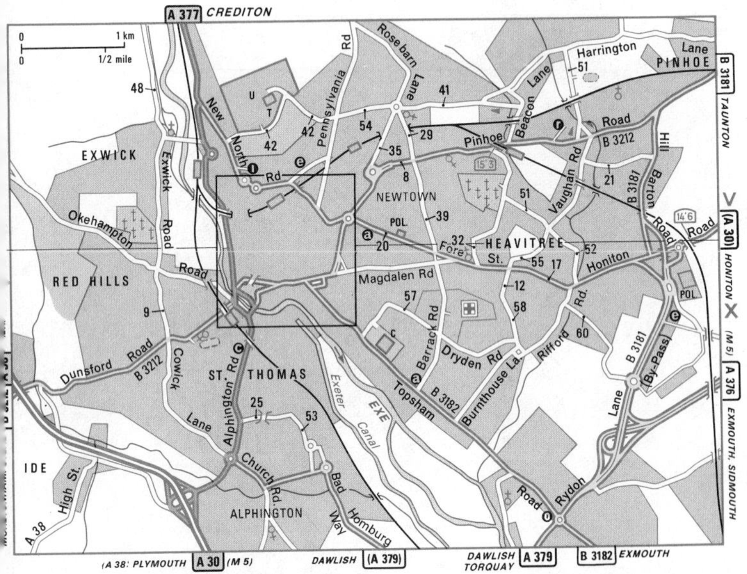

Rougemont Thistle (Mt. Charlotte Thistle), Queen St., EX4 3SP, ℘ 54982, Fax 420928 – lift rest TV ☎ P – 300. AE VISA — Y **x**
Meals 9.50/15.95 **st.** 4.60 – **88 rm** 69.00/79.00, 2 suites – SB.

Exeter Arms Toby, Rydon Lane, Middlemoor, EX2 7HL, E : 3 m. on B 3181 ℘ 435353, Fax 420826 – rm TV ☎ P – 80. AE VISA. — X **e**
Meals (grill rest.) 7.95 **t.** and a la carte – **37 rm** 48.00/58.00 **st.** – SB.

Devon Motel, Matford, EX2 8XU, S : 3 m. by A 377 on A 379 ℘ 59268, Fax 413142, – TV ☎ P – 80 — X
41 rm.

St. Andrews, 28 Alphington Rd, EX2 8HN, ℘ 76784, Fax 50249 – TV ☎ P. AE VISA. — X **c**
closed Christmas-New Year – **Meals** (bar lunch)/dinner a la carte 13.15/17.50 **st.** 4.35 – **16 rm** 39.00/55.00 **t.**

Edwardian without rest., 30-32 Heavitree Rd, EX1 2LQ, ℘ 76102 – TV ☎. AE VISA — V **a**
closed Christmas and New Year – **13 rm** 22.00/46.00 **st.**

Red House, 2 Whipton Village Rd, EX4 8AR, ℘ 56104, Fax 435708 – TV ☎ P. AE VISA — V **r**
Meals (in bar) 6.25/13.95 **t.** and a la carte 3.50 – **12 rm** 37.00/60.00 **st.** – SB.

Travel Inn, 398 Topsham Rd, EX2 6HE, ℘ 875441, Fax 876174 – rm TV P. AE VISA — X **o**
Meals a la carte approx 16.00 **t.** 4.95 – **45 rm** 33.50 **st.**

The Grange without rest., Stoke Hill, EX4 7JH, N : 1 ¾ m. by Old Tiverton Rd. ℘ 59723, ≤, heated, – TV P. — V
4 rm 18.00/36.00 **t.**

Raffles, 11 Blackall Rd, EX4 4HD, ℘ 70200 – TV. AE VISA — V **e**
Meals 12.00 **st.** 3.50 – **7 rm** 28.00/40.00 **st.** – SB.

Park View without rest., 8 Howell Rd, EX4 4LG, ℘ 71772, Fax 53047 – TV ☎ P. VISA — V **i**
15 rm 20.00/43.00 **t.**

EXETER CENTRE

Bedford St.	Y 6	Alphington Rd.	Z 2	New Bridge St.	Z 31
Fore St.	Z	Barnfield Rd	Z 3	Palace Gate	Z 36
Guildhall Shopping Centre	Y	Bartholomew Rd.	Z 5	Paul St.	Y 37
High St.	Y	Castle St.	Y 13	Preston St.	Z 40
		Cowick St.	Z 15	Princesshay	Y 44
		Edmund St.	Z 18	Quay Hill	Z 45
		King St.	Z 22	Queen's Terrace	Y 46
		Mary Arches St.	Z 26	St. Martin's Lane	Y 49
		Mint (The)	Z 28	Summerland	Y 50

XX **Golsworthy's** (at St. Olaves Court H.), Mary Arches St., EX4 3AZ, ✆ 217736, Fax 413054, ⛱ – Ⓟ. AE VISA
closed lunch Saturday and Sunday and dinner 25 December-3 January – **Meals** 13.50 and a la carte 🍷 6.00. Z **e**

X **Lamb's,** 15 Lower North St., EX4 3ET, ✆ 54269, Fax 431145 – 🚭. AE VISA Y **c**
Meals *(closed Saturday lunch, Sunday, Monday and Good Friday)* a la carte 15.30/23.00 **t.** 🍷 4.25.

at Pinhoe NE : 2 m. by A 30 – V – ✉ Exeter – ☎ 01392.

Gipsy Hill 🐎, Gipsy Hill Lane, via Pinn Lane, EX1 3RN, ✆ 465252, Fax 464302, ⛱ – TV ☎ Ⓟ – 🏛 120. AE VISA
closed 26 to 31 December – **Meals** 8.50/14.50 **t.** and a la carte 🍷 4.25 – **38 rm** ☕ 64.00/85.00 **st.** – SB.

at Huxham N : 5 m. by A 377 off A 396 – V – ✉ Exeter – ☎ 01392.

XX **Barton Cross** 🐎 with rm, Stoke Canon, EX5 4EJ, ✆ 841245, Fax 841942, « Part 17C thatched cottages », ⛱ – 🚭 TV ☎ Ⓟ. AE ⓓ VISA
Meals 18.50/22.50 **t.** and a la carte 🍷 5.50 – **7 rm** ☕ 63.50/95.00 **st.** – SB.

at Whimple NE : 9 m. by A 30 – V – ✉ Exeter – ☎ 01404 :

Woodhayes ⛺, EX5 2TD, ☎ 822237, « Georgian country house », 🌳, 🎾 – 🚭 rest TV ☎ P. AE VISA. 🚫
Meals (booking essential) 15.00/25.00 **st.** – **6 rm** ☕ (dinner included) 90.00/130.00 **st.**

at Clyst St. George SE : 5 m. on A 376 – X – ✉ Exeter – ☎ 01392 :

St. George and Dragon Toby, EX3 0QJ, ☎ 876121, Fax 876121, 🌳 – TV ☎ P – 80. AE VISA. 🚫
Meals (grill rest.) a la carte 10.40/16.35 **t.** – **13 rm** 60.00/70.00 **t.**

at Kennford S : 5 m. on A 38 – X – ✉ Exeter – ☎ 01392 :

Fairwinds, EX6 7UD, ☎ 832911, Fax 832911 – 🚭 TV ☎ P. VISA. 🚫
closed December – **Meals** (dinner only) 13.95 **st.** 3.95 – **8 rm** ☕ 25.00/48.00 **st.** – SB.

Gissons Arms, EX6 7UX, ☎ 832444 – TV ☎ P. VISA
Meals a la carte 9.00/16.00 **t.** 4.50 – **6 rm** ☕ 30.00/45.00 **t.**

at Doddiscombsleigh SW : 10 m. by B 3212 off B 3193 – X – ✉ Exeter – ☎ 01647 :

Nobody Inn ⛺, EX6 7PS, ☎ 52394, Fax 52978, ≤, « Part 16C inn », 🌳 – TV ☎ P. AE VISA. 🚫
closed 25 and 26 December – **Meals** *(closed Sunday and Monday except Bank Holidays)* (bar lunch)/dinner a la carte 10.45/18.45 **t.** 3.35 – **7 rm** ☕ 23.00/59.00 **t.**

at Ide SW : 3 m. by A 377 – X – ✉ Exeter – ☎ 01392 :

XX **Old Mill,** 20 High St., EX2 9RN, ☎ 59480 – P. AE VISA
closed Sunday and 26 to 29 December – **Meals** (lunch by arrangement)/dinner 14.00 **t.** and a la carte 3.50.

ATS 276/280 Pinhoe Road, Polsloe Bridge ☎ 55465

Prices — For full details of the prices quoted in the guide, consult the introduction.

EXETER SERVICE AREA Devon 403 J 31 – ✉ Exeter – ☎ 01392.

Granada, Moor Lane, Sandygate, EX2 4AR, M 5 Junction 30 ☎ 74044, Fax 410406 – 🚭 rm TV ☎ & P – 70. 🚫
Meals (grill rest.) – **76 rm.**

EXMOUTH Devon 403 J 32 **The West Country G.** – pop. 28 037 – ECD : Wednesday – ☎ 01395.

Envir. : A la Ronde★ *AC*, N : 2 m. by B 3180.

Alexandra Terr., EX8 1NZ ☎ 263744.

London 210 – Exeter 11.

Imperial (Forte), The Esplanade, EX8 2SW, ☎ 274761, Fax 265161, ≤, heated, 🌳, 🎾 – 🛗 🚭 TV ☎ P
57 rm.

Royal Beacon, The Beacon, EX8 2AF, ☎ 264886, Fax 268890, ≤, 🌳 – 🛗 TV ☎ 🚗 P – 70. AE VISA JCB
Meals 7.45/25.00 **t.** and a la carte 4.50 – **30 rm** ☕ 45.70/86.40 **t.** – SB.

Barn ⛺, Foxholes Hill, EX8 2DF, E : 1 m. ☎ 224411, Fax 224411, ≤, 🌳 – TV ☎ P – 60. VISA. 🚫
Meals (bar lunch Monday to Saturday)/dinner 13.00 **t.** 5.25 – **11 rm** ☕ 32.00/64.00 **t.** – SB.

at Lympstone N : 3 m. by A 376 – ✉ Exmouth – ☎ 01395.

XX **River House** with rm, The Strand, EX8 5EY, ☎ 265147, ≤ Exe Estuary – TV ☎. AE VISA
Meals *(closed Sunday dinner, Monday, 25 to 27 December and 1 January)* 23.95/27.50 **t.** and lunch a la carte 6.50 – ☕ 6.50 – **2 rm** 55.00/74.00 **t.**

EYAM Derbs. 402 403 404 O 24 – ✉ Sheffield – ☎ 01433.

London 163 – Derby 29 – Manchester 32 – Sheffield 12.

Miners Arms, Water Lane, S30 1RG, ☎ 630853 – TV P. 🚫
closed first 2 weeks January – **Meals** *(closed Sunday dinner and Monday)* (bar lunch Tuesday to Saturday)/dinner a la carte 8.85/16.15 **t.** 3.50 – **6 rm** ☕ 25.00/45.00 **st.**

EYE Suffolk 404 X 27 – pop. 1 741 – ☎ 01379.

London 94 – Ipswich 19 – Thetford 23.

Four Horseshoes, Thornham Magna, IP23 7HD, SW : 5 m. by B 1117 off A 140 ☎ 678777, Fax 678134, 🌳 – TV ☎ P. AE VISA
Meals 9.95/20.00 **t.** and a la carte 3.95 – **10 rm** ☕ 37.00/68.00 **st.** – SB.

EYTON Heref. and Worcs. – see Leominster.

FACCOMBE Hants. – see Hurstbourne Tarrant.

FAKENHAM Norfolk 404 W 25 – ☎ 01328.

♦London 111 – ♦Cambridge 64 – ♦Norwich 27.

Sculthorpe Mill, Lynn Rd, Sculthorpe, NR21 9QG, W : 2 ½ m. on A 148 ℘ 856161, Fax 856651, – TV ☎ P. AE VISA
Meals (bar lunch Monday to Saturday)/dinner 14.95 **t.** and a la carte 3.95 – **6 rm** 30.00/55.00 **t.** – SB.

FALFIELD Avon 403 404 M 29 – ☎ 01454.

♦London 132 – ♦Bristol 16 – Gloucester 22.

Gables, Bristol Rd, GL12 8DL, on A 38 ℘ 260502, Fax 261821, – rm TV ☎ P – 150. AE VISA.
Meals 13.00/22.00 **st.** and a la carte – 4.95 – **32 rm** 45.00/49.00 **t.**

*Benutzen Sie für weite Fahrten in Europa die **Michelin-Länderkarten** :*
970 Europa, 980 Griechenland, 984 Deutschland, 985 Skandinavien-Finnland,
986 Großbritannien-Irland, 987 Deutschland-Österreich-Benelux, 988 Italien,
989 Frankreich, 990 Spanien-Portugal, 991 Jugoslawien.

FALMOUTH Cornwall 403 E 33 **The West Country G.** – pop. 19 217 – ECD : Wednesday – ☎ 01326.

See : Town★ – Pendennis Castle★ (≤★★) *AC* B.

Envir. : Glendurgan Garden★★ *AC*, SW : 4½ m. by Swanpool Rd A – Mawnan Parish Church★ (≤★★) S : 4 m. by Swanpool Rd A – Cruise to Truro★ – Cruise along Helford River★.

Exc. : Trelissick Garden★★ (≤★★) NW : 13 m. by A 39 and B 3289 A – Carn Brea (≤★★) NW : 10 m. by A 393 A – Gweek (Setting★, Seal Sanctuary★) SW : 8 m. by A 39 and Treverva rd – Wendron (Poldark Mine★) *AC*, SW : 12½ m. by A 39 – A - and A 394.

18 Swanpool Rd ℘ 311262 A – 9 Budock Vean Hotel ℘ 250288.

28 Killigrew St., TR11 3PN ℘ 312300.

♦London 308 – Penzance 26 – ♦Plymouth 65 – Truro 11.

Plan opposite

Greenbank, Harbourside, TR11 2SR, ℘ 312440, Fax 211362, ≤ harbour, – rm TV ☎ P – 30. AE VISA A **a**
closed 25 December-13 January – ***Nightingales*** : **Meals** 9.95/18.50 **t.** and a la carte 5.20 – **61 rm** 63.50/145.00 **t.** – SB.

Royal Duchy, Cliff Rd, TR11 4NX, ℘ 313042, Fax 319420, ≤, – TV ☎ P. AE VISA. B **a**
Meals 8.95/15.50 **t.** and a la carte 4.50 – **44 rm** (dinner included) 58.00/107.00 **t.**, 2 suites – SB.

St. Michael's of Falmouth, Gyllyngvase Beach, Seafront, TR11 4NB, ℘ 312707, Fax 211772, ≤, – TV ☎ P – 60. AE VISA A **z**
Meals (bar lunch Monday to Saturday)/dinner 25.00 **st.** and a la carte 4.10 – **66 rm** 55.00/120.00 **st.** – SB.

Penmere Manor , Mongleath Rd, TR11 4PN, ℘ 211411, Fax 317588, heated, – rest TV ☎ P – 60. AE VISA A **e**
closed 24 to 27 December – **Meals** (bar lunch)/dinner 18.00 **s.** and a la carte – **39 rm** 57.00/112.00 **st.** – SB.

Broadmead, 66-68 Kimberley Park Rd, TR11 2DD, ℘ 315704, Fax 311048 – rest TV ☎ P. AE VISA A **u**
closed Christmas-New Year – **Meals** (bar lunch)/dinner 16.00 **st.** 4.25 – **12 rm** 26.00/56.00 **t.** – SB.

Carthion, Cliff Rd, TR11 4AP, ℘ 313669, Fax 212828, ≤, – TV ☎ P. AE VISA B **v**
Meals (bar lunch)/dinner 12.00 **t.** and a la carte 4.95 – **18 rm** (dinner included) 49.00/98.00 **t.** – SB.

Gyllyngvase House, Gyllyngvase Rd, TR11 4DJ, ℘ 312956, – rest TV ☎ P. B **s**
April-October – **Meals** 8.50 **st.** 4.80 – **15 rm** 19.00/42.00 **st.**

Trevaylor, 8 Pennance Rd, TR11 4EA, ℘ 313041, ≤ – rest TV P. A **r**
May-September – **Meals** 5.75 **st.** – **8 rm** 17.00/30.00.

Tresillian House, 3 Stracey Rd, TR11 4DW, ℘ 312425, – rest TV ☎ P. AE VISA. A **n**
March-October – **Meals** 11.50 **st.** 3.50 – **12 rm** (dinner included) 29.15/58.30 **st.** – SB.

Rosemullion, Gyllyngvase Hill, TR11 4DF, ℘ 314690 – rm TV P. B **c**
mid May-September – **Meals** 7.00 – **13 rm** 18.50/35.00 **s.**

Melvill House, 52 Melvill Rd, TR11 4DQ, ℘ 316645, Fax 211608 – TV P B **o**
closed Christmas and New Year – **Meals** (by arrangement) 7.50 – **7 rm** 17.50/38.00.

Esmond, 5 Emslie Rd, TR11 4BG, ℘ 313214 – TV. B **e**
closed 14 December-14 January – **Meals** (by arrangement) 7.50 **st.** 2.50 – **7 rm** 14.00/32.00 **st.**

FALMOUTH

Street	Grid	No.
Church Street	B	
High Street	A	
Market Street	A	33
Arwenack Street	B	2
Avenue Road	B	3
Beacon Road	A	4
Belmont Road	A	7
Berkeley Vale	A	8
Boscawen Road	A	9
Budock Terrace	A	13
Conway Road	A	14
De Pass Road	B	15
Emslie Road	B	18
Fenwick Road	A	19
Glasney Road	A	20
Grovehill Crescent	B	23
Gyllyngvase Hill	B	24
Gyllyngvase Road	B	25
Kimberley Place	A	28
Langton Road	A	29
Madeira Walk	A	30
Marlborough Crescent	A	34
Park Terrace	A	35
Pendennis Road	B	38
Swanpool Road	A	39
Symons Hill	A	40
Tredova Crescent	A	43
Trescobeas Road	A	44
Wellington Terrace	A	45
Windsor Terrace	A	48
Wodehouse Terrace	A	49

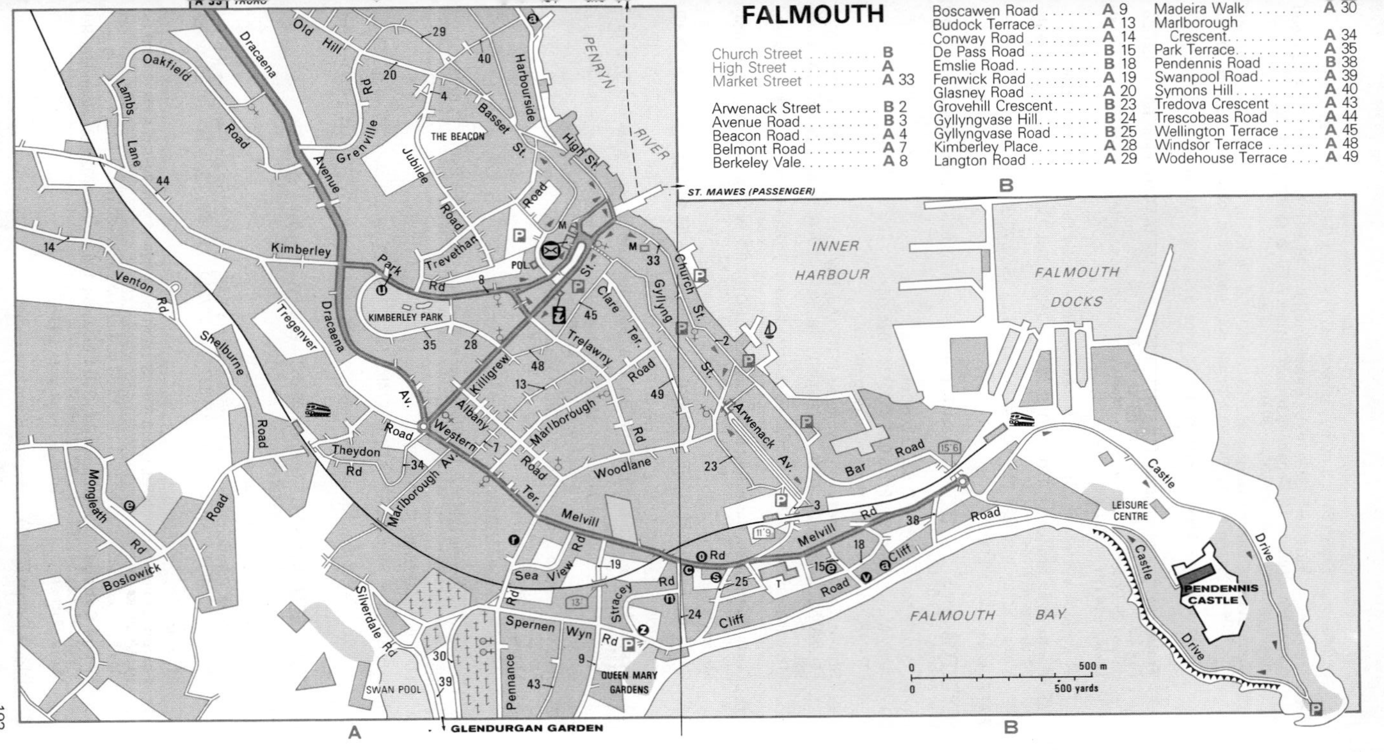

at Mawnan Smith SW : 5 m. by Trescobeas Rd – A – ✉ Falmouth – 01326 :

Meudon, TR11 5HT, E : ½ m. by Carwinion Rd 250541, Fax 250543, « ≤ Terraced gardens landscaped by Capability Brown », park – TV ☎ P. AE VISA
closed December and January – **30 rm**, 2 suites – SB.

Nansidwell Country House, TR11 5HU, SE : ¼ m. by Carwinion Rd 250340, Fax 250440, ≤, « Country house atmosphere, gardens », park – TV ☎ P. VISA
closed January – **Meals** 15.00/25.00 **t.** and dinner a la carte – **12 rm** 75.00/150.00 **st.** – SB.

Trelawne, Maenporth Rd, TR11 5HS, E : ¾ m. by Carwinion Rd 250226, Fax 250909, ≤, – rest TV ☎ P. AE VISA
closed 29 December-12 February – **Meals** (bar lunch Monday to Saturday)/dinner 25.50 **st.** 4.90 – **14 rm** 39.00/84.00 **st.** – SB.

at Budock Water W : 2 ¼ m. by Trescobeas Rd - A – ✉ Falmouth – 01326 :

Penmorvah Manor, TR11 5ED, S : ¾ m. 250277, Fax 250509, – rm TV ☎ P. AE VISA JCB.
Meals (bar lunch)/dinner 19.00 **st.** 4.75 – **27 rm** 35.00/70.00 **st.** – SB.

ATS Dracaena Av. 319233

FAREHAM Hants. 403 404 Q 31 **Great Britain G.** – **pop. 55 563 (inc. Portchester)** – ECD : Wednesday – 01329.

Envir. : Portchester castle★ *AC*, SE : 2½ m. by A 27.

Westbury Manor, West St., PO16 0JJ 221342/824896.

London 77 – Portsmouth 9 – Southampton 13 – Winchester 19.

Solent, Solent Business Park, Whiteley, PO15 7AJ, NW : 5 m. by A 27 (01489) 880000, Fax 880007, park, squash – rm TV ☎ P – 250. AE VISA
Meals (bar lunch Saturday) 11.95/20.00 **st.** and a la carte 6.95 – **81 rm** 82.00/112.00 **st.**, 7 suites – SB.

Forte Posthouse, Cartwright Drive, Titchfield, PO15 5RS, W : 2¾ m. on A 27 844644, Fax 844666, – rm TV ☎ P – 140. AE VISA
Meals a la carte approx. 15.00 **t.** 5.50 – **126 rm** 56.00/69.50 **t.**

Red Lion, East St., P016 0BP, 822640, Fax 823579, – TV ☎ P – 100. AE VISA.
Meals a la carte 9.00/19.70 **t.** – **42 rm** 55.00/70.00 **t.** – SB.

Lysses House, 51 High St., PO16 7BQ, 822622, Fax 822762, – rest TV ☎ P – 100. AE VISA.
closed 24 December-2 January – **Meals** *(closed Saturday lunch, Sunday and Bank Holidays)* 13.75/17.95 **st.** and a la carte 5.85 – **21 rm** 53.00/69.00 **st.**

Avenue House without rest., 22 The Avenue, PO14 1NS, W : ½ m. on A 27 232175, Fax 232196, – rm TV ☎ P. AE VISA
17 rm 39.50/54.00 **st.**

ATS Queens Rd 234941/280032

FARMBOROUGH Avon 403 M 29 **The West Country G.** – **pop. 1 084** – ✉ Bath – 01761.

Exc. : Bath★★★, NE : 7½ m. by A 39 and A 4.

London 137 – Bath 7.5 – Bristol 12 – Wells 13.

Streets, The Street, BA3 1AR, 471452, Fax 471452, heated, – TV ☎ P. AE VISA.
closed 23 December-1 January – **Meals** (residents only) (dinner only) 13.80 **st.** 4.60 – **8 rm** 42.00/52.00 **st.**

FARNBOROUGH Hants. 404 R 30 – **pop. 48 063** – ECD : Wednesday – 01252.

Southwood, Ively Rd 548700.

London 41 – Reading 17 – Southampton 44 – Winchester 33.

Forte Crest Farnborough, Lynchford Rd, GU14 6AZ, S : 1 ½ m. on Farnborough Rd (A 325) 545051, Group Telex 859637, Fax 377210, – rm TV ☎ P – 180
110 rm.

Falcon, 68 Farnborough Rd, GU14 6TH, S : ¾ m. on A 325 545378, Fax 522539 – TV ☎ P. AE VISA.
Meals *(closed Saturday Lunch)* 13.95/17.50 **st.** and a la carte – **30 rm** 67.95/77.95 **st.**

Wings Cottage, 32 Alexandra Rd, GU14 6DA, S : 1 ¼ m. by A 325 off Boundary Rd 544141, Fax 549361 – . AE VISA
Meals - Chinese 12.50/24.50 **st.** and a la carte 4.00.

FARNHAM Dorset 403 404 N 31 – see Blandford Forum.

FARNHAM Surrey 404 R 30 – pop. 36 284 – ECD : Wednesday – 01252.

Farnham Park,(Par Three) 715216 – Vernon House, 28 West St., GU9 7DR 715109.

London 45 – Reading 22 – Southampton 39 – Winchester 28.

Bush (Forte), The Borough, GU9 7NN, 715237, Fax 733530, – TV – 60.
Meals *(closed lunch Saturday and Bank Holidays)* 8.95/17.95 **st.** and a la carte 6.00 – 8.95 – **66 rm** 65.00/80.00 **st.** – SB.

Bishop's Table, 27 West St., GU9 7DR, 710222, Fax 733494, – TV .
closed 26 to 30 December – **Meals** *(closed Saturday lunch)* 16.50/27.50 **t.** 5.85 – **16 rm** 70.00/85.00 **t.** – SB.

Banaras, 40 Downing St., GU9 7PH, 734081 –
Meals - Indian 15.00/25.00 **t.** and a la carte 3.50.

at Churt S : 5¾ m. on A 287 – Churt – 01428 :

Pride of the Valley, Tilford Rd, GU10 2LE, E : 1 ½ m. by Hale House Lane 605799, Fax 605875, – TV
Meals - Italian – **11 rm.**

FARNINGHAM Kent 404 U 29 – Dartford – 01322.

London 18 – Hastings 46 – Maidstone 20.

Lion (Forte), High St., DA4 0DP, 866035, Fax 864357, – TV .
Meals (Harvester grill) a la carte 14.50/20.00 **t.** – 5.50 – **7 rm** 31.95/41.95 **st.**

FARRINGTON GURNEY Avon 403 404 M 30 **The West Country G.** – pop. 780 – Bristol – 01761.

Envir. : Downside Abbey★ (Abbey Church★) SE : 5 m. by A 37 and B 3139.

Exc. : Wells★★ - Cathedral★★★, Vicars' Close★, Bishop's Palace★ *AC* (≤★★) SW : 8 m. by A 39 – Chew Magna★ (Stanton Drew Stone Circles★ *AC*) NW : 9½m. by A 37 and B 3130.

London 132 – Bath 13 – Bristol 12 – Wells 8.

Country Ways, Marsh Lane, BS18 5TT, 452449, Fax 453360, – rest TV .
closed 1 week Christmas – **Meals** (lunch by arrangement) (residents only Sunday dinner) a la carte 18.60/21.95 **t.** 4.50 – **6 rm** 55.00/65.00 **t.** – SB.

FAR SAWREY Cumbria 402 L 20 – see Hawkshead.

FAUGH Cumbria – see Carlisle.

FAVERSHAM Kent 404 W 30 – pop. 17 070 – ECD : Thursday – 01795.

Fleur de Lys Heritage Centre, 13 Preston St., ME13 8NS 534542.

London 52 – Dover 26 – Maidstone 21 – Margate 25.

Read's (Pitchford), Painter's Forstal, ME13 0EE, SW : 2 ¼ m. by A 2 535344, Fax 591200, –
closed Sunday, Monday, last 2 weeks August and 26 December – **Meals** 14.50/23.50 **t.** and a la carte 32.00 **t.** 6.50
Spec. Hot soufflé of mature Montgomery cheddar cheese with Provence vegetables, Sesame duck breast, Oriental plum sauce and ginger stir-fried vegetables, Chocoholics anonymous.

at Boughton SE : 3 m. by A 2 – Faversham – 01227 :

White Horse Inn, The Street, ME13 9AX, 751343, Fax 751090 – TV .
Meals 9.75 **t.** and a la carte – **13 rm** 35.00/45.00 **t.** – SB.

at Eastling SW : 5 m. by A 2 – Faversham – 01795 :

Frith Farm House, Otterden, ME13 0DD, NW : 2 m. 890701, Fax 890009, –
TV .
Meals (by arrangement)(communal dining) 17.50 **s.** – **3 rm** 30.00/55.00 **s.**

ATS 20 North Lane 534039

FAWKHAM Kent – see Brands Hatch.

FECKENHAM Heref. and Worcs. 403 404 O 27 – see Droitwich.

FELIXSTOWE Suffolk 404 Y 28 – pop. 23 189 – ECD : Wednesday – 01394.

Felixstowe Ferry, Ferry Rd 286834.

to Belgium (Zeebrugge) (P & O European Ferries Ltd) 2 daily (5 h 45 mn).

to Harwich (Orwell & Harwich Navigation Co. Ltd) 5 daily (14 mn).

Leisure Centre, Undercliff Road West, IP11 8AB 276770.

London 84 – Ipswich 11.

Orwell Moat House (Q.M.H.), Hamilton Rd, IP11 7DX, 285511, Fax 670687, – 200.
Meals 13.50/17.50 **st.** and a la carte 6.00 – 8.75 – **56 rm** 60.00/70.00 **st.**, 1 suite – SB.

Waverley, Wolsey Gdns, IP11 7DF, 282811, Fax 670185, – 70.
Meals 14.95 **st.** (dinner) and a la carte 11.95/24.10 **st.** 3.75 – 7.50 – **20 rm** 48.50/66.95 **st.** – SB.

Marlborough, Sea Rd, IP11 8BJ, 285621, Fax 670724, – 100.
Meals (bar lunch Saturday) 8.95/13.00 **t.** and a la carte – **47 rm** 47.00/72.00 **t.** – SB.

ATS 4-8 Sunderland Rd, Carr Rd Ind. Est. 675604 ATS Crescent Rd 277596/277888

FELSTED Essex 404 V 28 – pop. 2 832 – Great Dunmow – 01371.

London 39 – Cambridge 31 – Chelmsford 9 – Colchester 24.

Rumbles Cottage, Braintree Rd, CM6 3DJ, 820996 –
closed Saturday lunch, Sunday dinner and Monday – **Meals** (lunch by arrangement)/dinner 12.50 **t.** and a la carte 4.00.

FENNY BRIDGES Devon 403 K 31 – Honiton – 01404.

London 166 – Exeter 12.

Greyhound Inn, EX14 0BJ, on A 30 850380, « 17C thatched inn », –
10 rm.

FERNDOWN Dorset 403 404 O 31 – pop. 23 921 – ECD : Wednesday – 01202.

London 108 – Bournemouth 6 – Dorchester 27 – Salisbury 23.

Dormy (De Vere), New Rd, BH22 8ES, on A 347 872121, Fax 895388, , , , , squash – rm – 250.
Meals *(closed Saturday lunch)* 15.95/21.50 **st.** and a la carte – **123 rm** 95.00/120.00 **st.**, 5 suites – SB.

Travel Inn, Ringwood Rd, Tricketts Cross, BH22 9BB, NE : 1 m. on A 348 874210 – rm .
Meals (Beefeater grill) a la carte approx. 16.00 **t.** – 4.95 – **32 rm** 33.50 **t.**

FERRYBRIDGE SERVICE AREA W. Yorks. – Leeds – 01977.

London 178 – Leeds 14 – Doncaster 14 – Rotherham 28 – York 28.

Granada Lodge without rest., WF11 0AF, at junction 33 of M 62 with A 1 670488, Reservations (Freephone) 0800 555300 – .
4.00 – **35 rm** 39.95 **st.**

FERSFIELD Norfolk – see Diss.

FINDON W. Sussex 404 S 31 – Worthing – 01903.

Findon Manor, High St., BN14 0TA, off A 24 872733, Fax 872733, « Part 16C stone and flint house », – – 40.
Meals *(closed Sunday dinner)* 12.50/14.95 **t.** **11 rm** 40.00/80.00 **t.**

FINGLESHAM Kent – see Deal.

FIVE ASHES E. Sussex. – see Mayfield.

For the quickest route use the Michelin Main Road Maps:
970 Europe, 980 Greece, 984 Germany, 985 Scandinavia-Finland,
986 Great Britain and Ireland, 987 Germany-Austria-Benelux, 988 Italy,
989 France, 990 Spain-Portugal and 991 Yugoslavia.

FLAMSTEAD Herts. 404 S 28 – pop. 1 399 – ✉ St. Albans – ☎ 01582.

♦London 32 – Luton 5.

Hertfordshire Moat House (Q.M.H.), London Rd, AL3 8HH, on A 5 ☏ 840840, Fax 842282, – rm TV ☎ P – 350. AE VISA
Meals *(closed Saturday lunch)* 16.95 **st.** and a la carte 5.75 – ☐ 9.50 – **89 rm** 49.50/59.50 **st.** – SB.

FLEET Hants. 404 R 30 – ☎ 01252.

♦London 40 – Basingstoke 11 – Reading 17.

Lismoyne, Church Rd, GU13 8NA, ☏ 628555, Fax 811761, – TV ☎ P – 100
44 rm.

FLEET SERVICE AREA Hants. – ✉ Basingstoke – ☎ 01252.

Forte Travelodge without rest., Hartley Witney, RG27 8BN, M3 between junctions 4a and 5 (southbound carriageway) ☏ 815587, Reservations (Freephone) 0800 850950 – TV P. AE VISA.
40 rm 33.50 **t.**

Halten Sie beim Betreten des Hotels oder des Restaurants
den Führer in der Hand.
Sie zeigen damit, daß Sie aufgrund dieser Empfehlung gekommen sind.

FLEETWOOD Lancs. 402 K 22 – pop. 27 899 – ECD : Wednesday – ☎ 01253.

18 Fleetwood, Golf House, Princes Way ☏ 873114.

to the Isle of Man (Douglas) (Isle of Man Steam Packet Co. Ltd) (summer only) (3 h 20 mn).

The Old Ferry Office, Ferry Dock, The Esplanade, FY7 6DL ☏ 773953.

♦London 245 – ♦Blackpool 10 – Lancaster 28 – ♦Manchester 53.

North Euston, The Esplanade, FY7 6BN, ☏ 876525, Fax 777842, ← – TV ☎ P – 180. AE VISA.
Meals *(closed Saturday lunch)* 10.00/16.00 **st.** and a la carte 5.25 – **55 rm** ☐ 46.50/66.00 **st.** – SB.

Payathai, 64 North Albert St., FY7 6AR, ☏ 872797
Meals - Thai (dinner only).

ATS 238 Dock St. ☏ 771211

FLITWICK Beds. 404 S 27 – pop. 11 283 – ☎ 01525.

♦London 45 – Bedford 13 – Luton 12 – Northampton 28.

Flitwick Manor, Church Rd, MK45 1AE, off Dunstable Rd ☏ 712242, Fax 718753, ←, « 18C manor house », park, – rest TV ☎ P. AE VISA
Meals 21.50/36.75 **t.** 6.45 – **15 rm** ☐ 88.00/190.00 **t.**

FOLKESTONE Kent 404 X 30 **Great Britain G.** – pop. 45 280 – ECD : Wednesday and Saturday – ☎ 01303.

See : The Leas★ (←★) Z.

to France (Boulogne) (Hoverspeed Ltd) 4-5 daily (55 mn).

Harbour St., CT20 1QN ☏ 258594 – Eurotunnel Exhibition Centre, St. Martins Plain, Cheriton High St., CT19 4QD ☏ 270547.

♦London 76 – ♦Brighton 76 – ♦Dover 8 – Maidstone 33.

Plan on next page

Clifton, The Leas, CT20 2EB, ☏ 851231, Fax 851231, ←, – TV ☎ – 100. AE VISA Z **r**
Meals 9.95/16.50 **t.** and a la carte 7.75 – ☐ 8.50 – **80 rm** ☐ 59.50/149.00 **st.** – SB.

Wards, 39 Earls Av., CT20 2HB, ☏ 245166, Fax 254480 – TV ☎ P – 50. AE VISA. X **c**
Meals a la carte 9.45/22.40 **t.** 3.75 – **10 rm** ☐ 45.00/85.00 **t.** – SB.

Banque without rest., 4 Castle Hill Av., CT20 2QT, ☏ 253797, – TV ☎. AE VISA Z **z**
12 rm ☐ 25.00/50.00.

Harbourside without rest., 14 Wear Bay Rd, CT19 6AT, ☏ 256528, Fax 241299, ←, – TV. AE. X **e**
6 rm ☐ 30.00/65.00 **s.**

La Tavernetta, Leaside Court, Clifton Gdns, CT20 2ED, ☏ 254955 – AE VISA Z **n**
closed Sunday and Bank Holidays – **Meals** - Italian 9.50 **t.** (lunch) and a la carte 14.50/24.70 **t.** 4.45.

Paul's, 2a Bouverie Rd West, CT20 2RX, ☏ 259697, Fax 226647 – VISA Z **e**
closed 3 days Christmas – **Meals** a la carte 15.65/16.30 **t.** 4.25.

ATS 318/324 Cheriton Rd ☏ 275198/275121

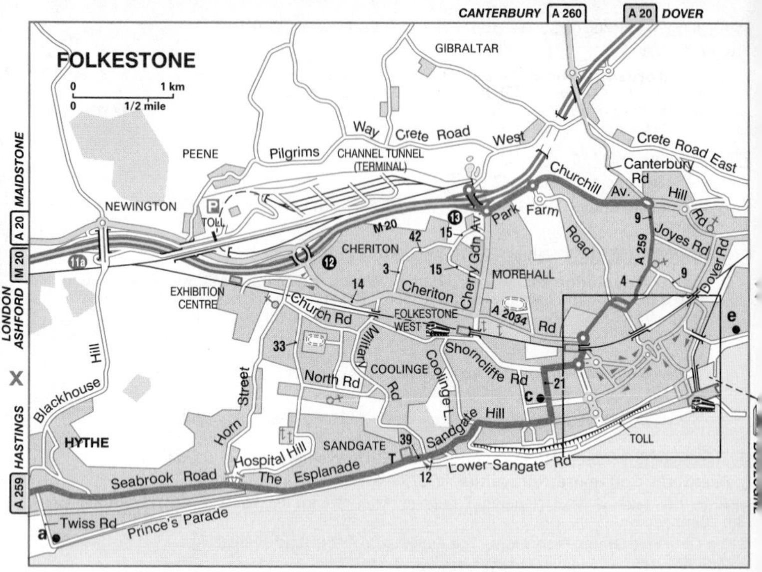

FOLKESTONE

CANTERBURY A 260 A 20 DOVER

0 1 km
0 1/2 mile

GIBRALTAR
PEENE
Pilgrims Way Crete Road West
CHANNEL TUNNEL (TERMINAL)
Crete Road East
Canterbury Rd
Hill Rd
Churchill Av.
Park Farm Road
Joyes Rd
Dover Rd
NEWINGTON
TOLL
M 20
CHERITON
MOREHALL
Cherry Gdn Av.
Cheriton A 2034 Rd
EXHIBITION CENTRE
Church Rd
FOLKESTONE WEST
Military Rd
COOLINGE
Coolinge L.
Shorncliffe Rd
North Rd
Horn Street
Blackhouse Hill
HYTHE
Hospital Hill
SANDGATE
Sandgate Hill
Seabrook Road
The Esplanade
Lower Sangate Rd
Twiss Rd
Prince's Parade
TOLL
LONDON ASHFORD M 20 A 20 MAIDSTONE
HASTINGS A 259

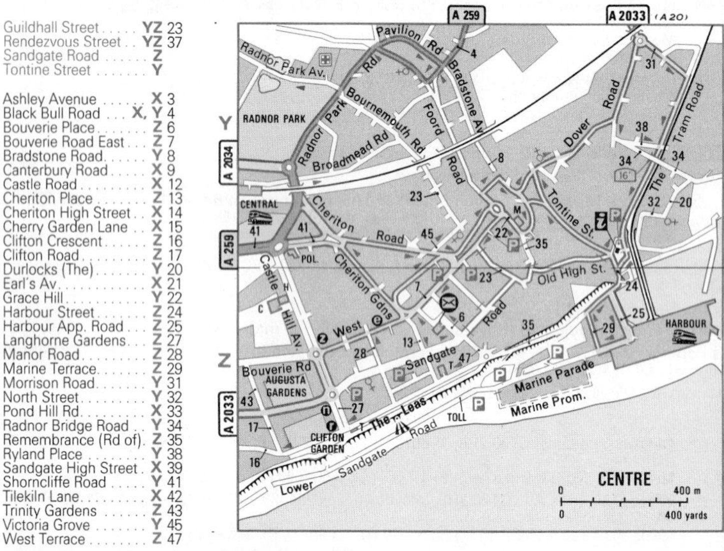

Guildhall Street . . . . . YZ 23
Rendezvous Street . . YZ 37
Sandgate Road . . . . . . Z
Tontine Street . . . . Y

Ashley Avenue . . . . . . X 3
Black Bull Road . . . X, Y 4
Bouverie Place . . . . . . Z 6
Bouverie Road East . . . Z 7
Bradstone Road. . . . . . Y 8
Canterbury Road . . . . . X 9
Castle Road . . . . X 12
Cheriton Place . . . . Z 13
Cheriton High Street . . X 14
Cherry Garden Lane . . X 15
Clifton Crescent . . . . . . Z 16
Clifton Road . . . . Z 17
Durlocks (The) . . . . Y 20
Earl's Av. . . . . X 21
Grace Hill . . . . Y 22
Harbour Street . . . . Z 24
Harbour App. Road . . . Z 25
Langhorne Gardens . . . Z 27
Manor Road . . . . Z 28
Marine Terrace . . . . Z 29
Morrison Road . . . . Y 31
North Street . . . . Y 32
Pond Hill Rd . . . . X 33
Radnor Bridge Road . . Y 34
Remembrance (Rd of). Z 35
Ryland Place . . . . Y 38
Sandgate High Street . X 39
Shorncliffe Road . . . . . Y 41
Tilekiln Lane . . . . X 42
Trinity Gardens . . . . . . Z 43
Victoria Grove . . . . Y 45
West Terrace . . . . Z 47

FONTWELL W. Sussex – ✉ Arundel – ☎ 01243.

ℹ Little Chef Complex, BN18 0SD ☎ 543269.

◆London 60 – Chichester 6 – Worthing 15.

🏨 **Forte Travelodge** without rest., BN18 0SB, at A 27/A 29 roundabout ☎ 543973, Reservations (Freephone) 0800 850950 – TV ♿ P. AE VISA.
32 rm 33.50 **t.**

FORD Wilts. – see Castle Combe.

FORDINGBRIDGE Hants. 403 404 O 31 – pop. 5 893 – ECD : Thursday – 01425.

Salisbury St., SP6 1AB 654560 (summer only).

London 101 – Bournemouth 17 – Salisbury 11 – Winchester 30.

XX **Hour Glass,** Salisbury Rd, Burgate, SP6 1LX, N : 1 m. on A 338 652348, « 14C thatched cottage », – P. VISA
closed Sunday dinner, Monday, 1 week February and 2 weeks November – **Meals** 8.95/17.95 **t.** 4.50.

at Woodgreen NE : 4 m. by B 3078 – ✉ Fordingbridge – 01725 :

Cottage Crest without rest., Castle Hill, SP6 2AX, 512009, <, – TV P.
3 rm 25.00/38.00 **st.**

at Stuckton SE : 1 m. by B 3078 – ✉ Fordingbridge – 01425 :

X **Three Lions,** Stuckton Rd, SP6 2HF, 652489, Fax 656144 – P. VISA
closed Sunday dinner, Monday, 3 weeks February-March, 2 weeks summer, 2 weeks autumn and Christmas-New Year – **Meals** (booking essential) a la carte 13.45/29.75 **t.** 5.25.

at Alderholt SW : 2 m. – ✉ Fordingbridge – 01425 :

XX **Moonacre,** SP6 3BB, 653142 – P. VISA
closed Sunday dinner, Monday and 1 to 21 March – **Meals** (dinner only and Sunday lunch)/dinner 11.00 **t.** and a la carte 3.75.

at Rockbourne NW : 4 m. by B 3078 – ✉ Fordingbridge – 01725 :

Shearings, SP6 3NA, 518256, Fax 518255, « Picturesque 16C thatched cottage », – P.
closed mid December-mid February – **Meals** (by arrangement) 20.00 **st.** – **3 rm** 24.00/48.00 **st.**

FOREST ROW E. Sussex 404 U 30 – pop. 4 762 – ECD : Wednesday – 01342.

Royal Ashdown Forest Hotel, Chapel Lane, 824866.

London 35 – Brighton 26 – Eastbourne 30 – Maidstone 32.

Brambletye, The Square, RH18 5EZ, 824144, Fax 824833 – TV P. AE VISA JCB.
Meals (carving lunch)/dinner 14.95 **t.** and a la carte 4.25 – **22 rm** 45.00/80.00 **st.** – SB.

Chequers Inn, The Square, RH18 5ES, 824394, Fax 825454 – TV P
25 rm.

at Wych Cross S : 2½ m. on A 22 – ✉ Forest Row – 01342 :

Ashdown Park, RH18 5JR, E : ¾ m. on Hartfield rd 824988, Fax 826206, <, « Part 19C manor house in extensive gardens », park, squash – TV P – 180. AE VISA.
Anderida : **Meals** 17.00/27.00 **st.** and a la carte 7.00 – **89 rm** 94.00/145.00 **st.**, 6 suites – SB.

Roebuck (Jarvis), RH18 5JL, 823811, Fax 824790, – rm TV P – 110. AE VISA
Meals 17.95 **t.** and a la carte – **30 rm** 75.00/95.00 – SB.

FORMBY Mersey. 402 K 23 – ✉ Southport – 01704.

London 213 – Liverpool 12 – Manchester 40 – Preston 27.

Tree Tops, Southport Old Rd, L37 0AB, 879651, Fax 879651, heated, – TV P – 200
Meals *(closed Saturday lunch)* (dancing Friday evening) – **11 rm.**

FORTON SERVICE AREA Lancs. – ECD : Wednesday – ✉ Forton – 01524.

(M 6) Forton, Bay Horse, LA2 9DU 792181.

Pavilion Lodge without rest., LA2 9DU, on M 6 792227, Fax 791703 – TV P
41 rm.

FOTHERINGHAY Northants. 404 S 26 – see Oundle.

FOULSHAM Norfolk – pop. 1 379 – ✉ East Dereham – 01362.

London 121 – Cambridge 69 – King's Lynn 31 – Norwich 18.

X **The Gamp,** Claypit Lane, NR20 5RW, 684114 – P. VISA
closed Sunday dinner, Monday and first 2 weeks January – **Meals** 9.95/10.95 **st.** and a la carte 3.60.

FOUR MARKS Hants. 403 404 Q 30 – pop. 2 814 – ✉ Alton – ☎ 01420.

♦London 58 – Guildford 24 – Reading 29 – ♦Southampton 24.

Forte Travelodge without rest., 156 Winchester Rd, GU34 5HZ, on A 31 ☎ 562659, Reservations (Freephone) 0800 850950 – TV ♿ P. VISA.
31 rm 33.50 **t.**

FOWEY Cornwall 403 G 32 **The West Country G.** – pop. 2 376 – ECD : Wednesday – ☎ 01726.

See : Town★★.

Envir. : Gribbin Head★★ (≤★★) 6 m. rtn on foot – Bodinnick (≤★★) - Lanteglos Church★, E : 5 m. by ferry – Polruan (≤★★) SE : 6 m. by ferry – Polkerris★, W : 2 m. by A 3082.

ℹ The Post Office, 4 Custom House Hill, PL23 1AA ☎ 833616.

♦London 277 – Newquay 24 – ♦Plymouth 34 – Truro 22.

Marina, 17 The Esplanade, PL23 1HY, ☎ 833315, Fax 833315, ≤ Fowey river and harbour, – rest TV ☎. AE VISA
Meals (dinner only) 17.00 **st.** and a la carte 4.00 – **11 rm** 45.00/84.00 **st.** – SB.

Carnethic House, Lambs Barn, PL23 1HQ, NW : 3/4 m. on A 3082 ☎ 833336, Fax 833336, heated, , – rest TV P. AE VISA.
closed December and January – **Meals** (bar lunch)/dinner 13.50 **st.** 3.25 – **8 rm** 30.00/60.00 **st.** – SB.

Ocean View without rest., 24 Tower Park, PL23 1JB, ☎ 832283, ≤, – .
May-September – **4 rm** 20.00/40.00 **s.**

Food for Thought, 4 Town Quay, PL23 1AT, ☎ 832221, Fax 832060, « Converted coastguard's cottage on quayside » – VISA
closed Sunday, January, February and Christmas – **Meals** (dinner only) 25.95 **t.** and a la carte 18.00/28.50 **t.**

at Golant N : 3 m. by B 3269 – ✉ Fowey – ☎ 01726 :

Cormorant, PL23 1LL, ☎ 833426, Fax 833426, ≤ River Fowey, , – TV ☎ P. AE VISA
closed January – ***Riverside*** : **Meals** (light lunch)/dinner 21.50 **t.** and a la carte 4.50 – **10 rm** 65.00/100.00 **t.** – SB.

at Bodinnick-by-Fowey E : 1/4 m. via car ferry – ✉ Fowey – ☎ 01726 :

Old Ferry Inn, PL23 1LX, ☎ 870237, ≤ Fowey Estuary and town, « Part 16C inn » – TV P. VISA
Meals *(closed November-March)* (bar lunch)/dinner 16.00 **t.** and a la carte – **12 rm** 27.50/74.00 **t.**

FOWLMERE Cambs. 404 U 27 – see Cambridge.

FOWNHOPE Heref. and Worcs. 403 404 M 27 – pop. 900 – ✉ Hereford – ☎ 01432.

♦London 132 – ♦Cardiff 46 – Hereford 6 – Gloucester 27.

Green Man Inn, HR1 4PE, ☎ 860243, Fax 860207, , – rest TV ☎ P. AE VISA.
Meals (bar lunch Monday to Saturday)/dinner a la carte approx. 13.80 **t.** 4.40 – **19 rm** 31.00/49.50 **t.** – SB.

Bowens Country House, HR1 4PS, on B 4224 ☎ 860430, Fax 860430, , – rest TV P. VISA.
Meals (by arrangement) 11.50 **t.** 3.50 – **12 rm** 20.00/40.00 – SB.

FRAMLINGHAM Suffolk 404 Y 27 – pop. 2 697 – ECD : Wednesday – ✉ Woodbridge – ☎ 01728.

♦London 92 – ♦Ipswich 19 – ♦Norwich 42.

Crown (Forte), Market Hill, IP13 9AN, ☎ 723521, Fax 724274, « 16C inn » – TV ☎ P. AE VISA
Meals 8.95/17.95 **t.** and a la carte – 8.50 – **14 rm** 70.00/120.00 **st.** – SB.

at Earl Soham W : 3 1/2 m. by B 1119 on A 1120 – ✉ Woodbridge – ☎ 01728 :

Abbey House, Monk Soham, IP13 7EN, NW : 2 1/2 m. by Kenton rd ☎ 685225, – P.
March-October – **Meals** (by arrangement) (communal dining) 13.00 **st.** – **3 rm** 22.00/44.00 **st.**

FRAMPTON Dorset 403 404 M 31 – see Dorchester (Dorset).

This Guide is not a comprehensive list of all hotels and restaurants,
nor even of all good hotels and restaurants in Great Britain and Ireland.

Since our aim is to be of service to all motorists,
we must show establishments in all categories and so we have made
a selection of some in each.

FRAMPTON-ON-SEVERN Glos. 403 404 M 28 – pop. 1 208 – ☎ 01452.
♦London 121 – ♦Bristol 48 – Gloucester 14.

XX **Savery's,** The Green, GL2 7EA, ℘ 740077 – VISA
closed Sunday, Monday, 2 weeks February and 25 December – **Meals** (dinner only) 26.95 **st.** 5.75.

FRANKLEY SERVICE AREA W. Mids. 403 404 ⑲ – ✉ Birmingham – ☎ 0121.

Granada Lodge without rest., B32 4AR, M5, between junctions 3 and 4 ℘ 550 3261, Fax 501 2880, Reservations (Freephone) 0800 555300 – rm TV ☎ & P. AE VISA. 4.00 – **60 rm** 39.95 **st.**

FRANT Kent 404 U 30 – see Royal Tunbridge Wells.

FRESHWATER BAY I.O.W. 403 404 P 31 – see Wight (Isle of).

FRIETH Bucks. – see Henley-on-Thames (Oxon.).

FRILFORD Oxon. 403 404 P 28-29 – see Abingdon.

Piante di città : *le vie sono selezionate in funzione della loro importanza per la circolazione e l'ubicazione degli edifici citati.*

Non indichiamo che l'inizio delle vie secondarie.

FRIMLEY Surrey 404 R 30 – pop. 44 674 (inc. Camberley) – ✉ Camberley – ☎ 01276.
♦London 39 – Reading 17 – ♦Southampton 47.

One Oak Toby, 114 Portsmouth Rd, GU15 1HS, NE : 1 m. on A 325 ℘ 691939, Fax 676088 – rm TV ☎ P – 30. AE VISA.
Meals (grill rest.) 7.95 **t.** and a la carte – **40 rm** 69.95/79.95 **t.**

FRINTON-ON-SEA Essex 404 X 28 – pop. 17 259 (inc. Walton) – ECD : Wednesday – ☎ 01255.
18, 9 1 The Esplanade ℘ 674618.
♦London 72 – Chelmsford 39 – Colchester 17.

Uplands, 41 Hadleigh Rd, CO13 9HQ, ℘ 674889, – P.
closed 23 to 30 December – **Meals** (by arrangement) 11.00 – **8 rm** 21.00/53.00.

FRITTENDEN Kent 404 V 30 – pop. 2 055 (inc. Sissinghurst) – ☎ 01580 80.
♦London 50 – Folkestone 34 – Hastings 23 – Maidstone 13.

Maplehurst , Mill Lane, TN17 2DT, NW : 1 m. ℘ 203, « Converted water mill », heated, – TV P. VISA.
Meals 17.00 4.50 – **3 rm** 37.00/54.00.

FRODSHAM Ches. 402 403 404 L 24 – pop. 8 903 – ✉ Warrington – ☎ 01928.
♦London 203 – Chester 11 – ♦Liverpool 21 – ♦Manchester 29 – ♦Stoke-on-Trent 42.

Forest Hills, Overton Hill, WA6 6HH, S : 1 ¾ m. by B 5152 ℘ 735255, Fax 735517, ←, , , , squash – rm TV ☎ P – 200. AE VISA JCB
Meals *(closed Saturday lunch)* (carving lunch Sunday) 9.95/16.95 **st.** and a la carte 5.50 – 8.00 – **57 rm** 75.00 **st.** – SB.

Heathercliffe Country House , Manley Rd, WA6 6HB, S : 1 ½ m. by B 5152 ℘ 733722, Fax 735667, ←, , park – rest TV ☎ P. AE VISA
Meals *(closed to non-residents Sunday dinner and Bank Holiday Mondays)* 9.95 **t.** and a la carte 5.95 – **9 rm** 38.00/75.00 **st.** – SB.

Old Hall, Main St., WA6 7AB, ℘ 732052, Fax 739046, – TV ☎ P – 30. AE VISA
Meals 6.95/16.50 **t.** and a la carte 5.95 – **20 rm** 55.75/69.00 **st.**, 1 suite – SB.

XX Chinese Delight, 15 Bridge Lane, WA6 7HJ, NE : ½ m. on A 56 ℘ 733383, Fax 739292 – P
Meals - Chinese.

ATS Brooklyn Garage, Chester Rd ℘ 733555

FULBROOK Oxon. 403 404 P 28 – see Burford.

GALMPTON Devon 403 J 32 – ✉ Brixham – ☎ 01803.
♦London 229 – ♦Plymouth 32 – Torquay 6.

Maypool Park , Maypool, TQ5 0ET, by Greenway Rd ℘ 842442, Fax 845782, ←, – TV ☎ P – 30. VISA.
closed February and November – **Meals** *(closed Sunday dinner to non-residents)* (dinner only) 18.50 **t.** 4.50 – **10 rm** 40.00/85.00 **t.**

GARFORTH W. Yorks. 402 P 22 – see Leeds.

GARSTANG Lancs. 402 L 22 – pop. 3 948 – ☎ 01995.

ℹ Discovery Centre Council Offices, High St., PR3 1FU ✆ 602125.

♦London 233 – ♦Blackpool 13 – Manchester 41.

Crofters, Cabus, PR3 1PH, W : ¾ m. on A 6 ✆ 604128, Fax 601646 – TV ☎ P – 200. VISA
Meals (dancing Saturday evening)(bar lunch Monday to Saturday)/dinner a la carte 11.60/22.70 **t.** 4.95 – **19 rm** 40.00/50.00 **t.** – SB.

Pickerings, Garstang Rd, Catterall, PR3 OHD, S : 1 ½ m. on B 6430 ✆ 602133, Fax 602100, – TV ☎ P – 25. VISA
Meals *(closed Monday lunch and Bank Holidays)* 12.50/18.50 **st.** 5.25 – **16 rm** 34.50/66.00 **st.** – SB.

at Bilsborrow S : 3¾ m. by B 6430 on A 6 – ✉ Preston – ☎ 01995 :

Guy's Thatched Hamlet, Canalside, St. Michaels Rd, PR3 ORS, off A 6 ✆ 640010, Fax 640141 – TV ☎ P. VISA JCB
Meals a la carte 9.10/18.00 **st.** 4.20 – 5.00 – **53 rm** 32.00 **st.** – SB.

Olde Duncombe House without rest., Garstang Rd, PR3 ORE, ✆ 640336 – TV ☎ P. VISA
10 rm 32.50/45.00 **st.**

GATESHEAD Tyne and Wear 401 402 P 19 **Great Britain G.** – pop. 91 429 – ECD : Wednesday – ☎ 0191.

Exc. : Beamish : North of England Open Air Museum★★ *AC*, SW : 6 m. by A 692 and A 6076 BX.

Ravensworth, Moss Heaps, Wrekenton ✆ 487 6014/487 2843 – Heworth, Gingling Gate ✆ 469 2137 BX.

ℹ Central Library, Prince Consort Rd, NE8 4LN ✆ 477 3478 BX – Metro Centre, 7 The Arcade, NE11 9YL ✆ 460 6345 AX.

♦London 282 – Durham 16 – ♦Middlesbrough 38 – ♦Newcastle upon Tyne 1 – Sunderland 11.

Plan : see Newcastle upon Tyne

Newcastle/Gateshead Marriott, Metro Centre, NE11 9XF, ✆ 493 2233, Fax 493 2030, – rm TV ☎ P – 400. VISA JCB AX **e**
Meals (bar lunch Saturday) 14.95/17.00 **st.** and dinner a la carte 8.00 – 10.50 – **150 rm** 89.00/108.00 **st.** – SB.

Swallow, High West St., NE8 1PE, ✆ 477 1105, Fax 478 1802, – rm TV ☎ P – 350. VISA BX **r**
Meals *(closed Saturday lunch)* (carving lunch) 7.50/19.50 **st.** and a la carte 6.75 – **99 rm** 78.00/105.00 **st.**, 4 suites – SB.

at Low Fell S : 2 m. by A 167 and Belle Vue Bank – BX – ✉ Gateshead – ☎ 0191 :

Eslington Villa, 8 Station Rd, NE9 6DR, ✆ 487 6017, Fax 482 2359, – rest TV ☎ P. VISA.
closed 24 to 31 December – **Meals** *(closed Saturday lunch, Sunday dinner and Bank Holidays)* 13.95/30.00 **t.** and a la carte 4.75 – **12 rm** 49.50/69.50 **t.** – SB.

ATS Earlsway/First Av., Team Valley Trading Est. ✆ 4910081

GATWICK AIRPORT W. Sussex 404 T 30 – ✉ Crawley – ☎ 01293.

✈ Gatwick Airport : ✆ 535353.

ℹ International Arrivals, Concourse, South Terminal, RH6 0NP ✆ 560108.

♦London 29 – ♦Brighton 28.

Plan opposite

London Gatwick Airport Hilton, South Terminal, RH6 0LL, ✆ 518080, Telex 877021, Fax 528980, – rm TV ☎ P – 500. VISA JCB Y **u**
Meals 10.95/18.95 **st.** and a la carte – 12.00 – **545 rm** 135.00 **st.**, 5 suites.

Ramada H. Gatwick, Povey Cross Rd, RH6 0BE, ✆ 820169, Telex 87440, Fax 820259, squash – rm TV ☎ P – 180. VISA Y **a**
Meals *(closed Saturday lunch)* 14.50/16.50 **st.** and a la carte – 8.50 – **250 rm** 95.00 **st.**, 5 suites.

Forte Crest, Gatwick Airport (North Terminal), RH6 0PH, ✆ 567070, Telex 87202, Fax 567739, – rm TV ☎ P – 370 Y **e**
454 rm, 14 suites.

Forte Posthouse, Povey Cross Rd, RH6 0BA, ✆ 771621, Fax 771054, heated – rm rest TV ☎ P – 120. VISA JCB Y **c**
Meals a la carte approx. 15.00 **t.** 5.50 – **210 rm** 56.00 **st.**

Travel Inn, Longbridge Way, Gatwick Airport (north Terminal), RH6 0NX, ✆ 568158 – rm rm TV P – 35. VISA. Y **s**
Meals (grill rest.) (dinner only) a la carte approx. 15.00 **t.** – 4.95 – **121 rm** 33.50 **t.**

ATS Building 238B, Perimeter Rd South ✆ 568333/568555

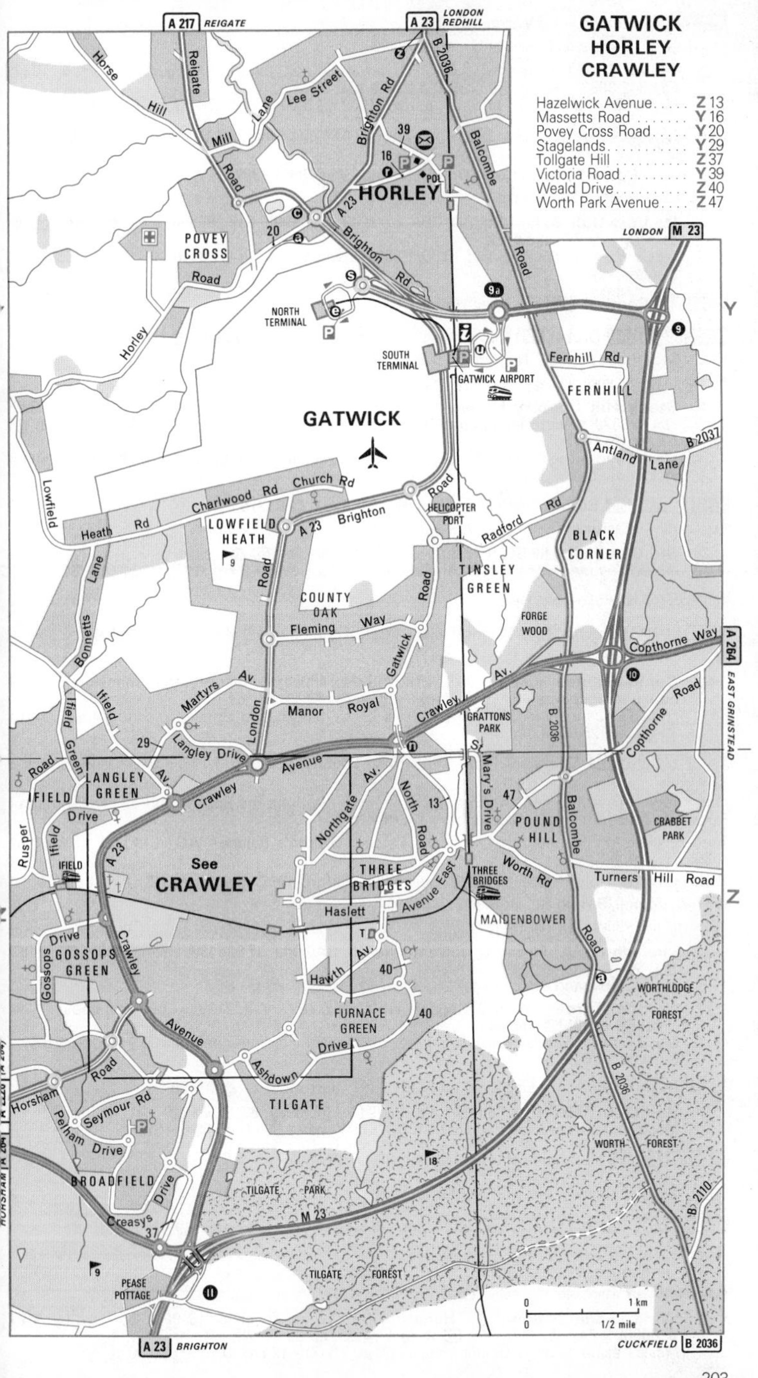
GATWICK
HORLEY
CRAWLEY
Hazelwick Avenue Z 13
Massetts Road Y 16
Povey Cross Road Y 20
Stagelands Y 29
Tollgate Hill Z 37
Victoria Road Y 39
Weald Drive Z 40
Worth Park Avenue Z 47
A 217 REIGATE
A 23 LONDON REDHILL
LONDON M 23
A 264 EAST GRINSTEAD
A 23 BRIGHTON
CUCKFIELD B 2036
HORLEY
POVEY CROSS
NORTH TERMINAL
SOUTH TERMINAL
GATWICK AIRPORT
GATWICK
FERNHILL
LOWFIELD HEATH
HELICOPTER PORT
BLACK CORNER
TINSLEY GREEN
COUNTY OAK
FORGE WOOD
GRATTONS PARK
LANGLEY GREEN
IFIELD
See CRAWLEY
THREE BRIDGES
POUND HILL
CRABBET PARK
MAIDENBOWER
GOSSOPS GREEN
FURNACE GREEN
TILGATE
WORTHLODGE FOREST
WORTH FOREST
BROADFIELD
TILGATE PARK
TILGATE FOREST
PEASE POTTAGE
Y
Z
1 km
1/2 mile

GAYTON Mersey. – ✉ Wirral – ☎ 0151.
◆London 206 – Birkenhead 12 – Chester 13 – ◆Liverpool 10.

Travel Inn, Chester Rd, L60 3FD, on A 540 at junction with A 551 ℘ 342 1982, Fax 342 8983 – rm ♿ P. AE VISA.
Meals (Beefeater grill) a la carte approx. 16.00 **t.** 5.60 – 4.95 – **37 rm** 33.50 **t.**

GERRARDS CROSS Bucks. 404 S 29 – pop. 19 447 (inc. Chalfont St.Peter) – ECD : Wednesday – ☎ 01753.
18 Denham Court, Denham Court Drive, Denham ℘ (01895) 835777.
◆London 22 – Aylesbury 22 – ◆Oxford 36.

De Vere Bull, Oxford Rd, SL9 7PA, on A 40 ℘ 885995, Fax 885504, – rm P – 200. AE VISA
Meals *(bar lunch Saturday)* 16.50/19.50 **st.** and a la carte – **93 rm** 110.00/160.00 **st.**, 2 suites – SB.

GILLAN Cornwall 403 E 33 – see Helford.

GILLINGHAM Dorset 403 404 N 30 The West Country G. – pop. 6 934 – ☎ 01747.
Exc. : Stourhead★★★ *AC*, N : 9 m. by B 3092, B 3095 and B 3092.
◆London 116 – Bournemouth 34 – ◆Bristol 46 – ◆Southampton 52.

Stock Hill Country House, Wyke, SP8 5NR, W : 1 ½ m. on B 3081 ℘ 823626, Fax 825628, « Victorian country house, antiques », park, – rest P. VISA.
Meals (booking essential) (lunch by arrangement)/dinner 30.00 **t.** 5.95 – **8 rm** (dinner included) 95.00/230.00 **t.**, 1 suite – SB.

GISLINGHAM Suffolk 404 X 27 – pop. 589 – ✉ Eye – ☎ 01379.
◆London 93 – ◆Cambridge 45 – ◆Ipswich 20 – ◆Norwich 30.

Old Guildhall, Mill St., IP23 8JT, ℘ 783361, – P
closed January – **Meals** (by arrangement) 10.00 **s.** 3.00 – **3 rm** 35.00/50.00 – SB.

GISSING Norfolk – see Diss.

GITTISHAM Devon 403 K 31 – pop. 602 – ECD : Thursday – ✉ Honiton – ☎ 01404.
◆London 164 – Exeter 14 – Sidmouth 9 – Taunton 21.

Combe House, EX14 0AD, ℘ 42756, Fax 46004, ≤, « Elizabethan mansion, country house atmosphere », park – P. AE VISA
closed 26 January - 10 February – **Meals** 13.00/19.50 **st.** and dinner a la carte 4.50 – **14 rm** 63.00/125.00 **st.**, 1 suite.

GLASTONBURY Somerset 403 L 30 The West Country G. – pop. 7 747 – ECD : Wednesday – ☎ 01458.
See : Town★★ - Abbey★★★ (Abbots Kitchen★) *AC* – St. John the Baptist Church★★ – Somerset Rural Life Museum★ *AC* – Glastonbury Tor★ (≤★★★).
Envir. : Wells★★ - Cathedral★★★, Vicars' Close★, Bishop's Palace★ *AC* (≤★★) NE : 5½ m. by A 39.
Exc. : Wookey Hole★★ (Caves★ *AC*, Papermill★, Fairground Collection★) NE : 8 m. by A 39.
The Tribunal, 9 High St., BA6 9DP ℘ 832954.
◆London 136 – ◆Bristol 26 – Taunton 22.

The Who'd 'A' Thought It, Northload St., BA6 9JJ, ℘ 834460, Fax 831039 – . VISA.
Meals 7.55 **t.** and a la carte 4.25 – **6 rm** 35.95/75.00 **t.** – SB.

XX **Number Three** with rm, 3 Magdalene St., BA6 9EW, ℘ 832129, « Georgian house », – P. VISA.
Meals *(closed Sunday to Tuesday)* (booking essential) (dinner only) 28.00 5.00 – 5.50 – **5 rm** 50.00/65.00.

at West Pennard E : 3½ m. on A 361 – ✉ Glastonbury – ☎ 01458 :

Red Lion, BA6 8NH, ℘ 832941, Fax 832941 – P. AE VISA.
Meals (in bar) a la carte 8.85/15.50 **t.** 3.50 – **7 rm** 30.00/45.00 **t.** – SB.

GLEWSTONE Heref. and Worcs. – see Ross-on-Wye.

GLOOSTON Leics. – see Market Harborough.

GLOSSOP Derbs. 402 403 404 O 23 – pop. 29 923 – ECD : Tuesday – ☎ 01457.
9 Sheffield Rd ℘ 865247.
The Gatehouse, Victoria St., SK13 8HT ℘ 855920.
◆London 194 – ◆Manchester 18 – ◆Sheffield 25.

Wind in the Willows, Hurst Rd, Derbyshire Level, SK13 9PT, E : 1 m. by A 57 ℘ 868001, Fax 853354, – P – 35. AE VISA.
Meals (residents only) (dinner only) 17.50 **st.** 5.00 – **12 rm** 52.00/90.00 **st.**

GLOUCESTER

Street	Grid	No.
Eastgate Shopping Centre	Y	
Eastgate Street	Y	10
Northgate Street	Y	16
Southgate Street	Y	
Barnwood By-Pass	Z	3
Black Dog Way	Y	5
Commercial Road	Y	6
Cotteswold Road	Z	8
Derby Road	Z	9
Great Western Road	Y	12
Heathville Road	Y	13
King Edward's Avenue	Z	14
Lower Westgate Street	Y	15
Parkend Road	Z	17
Parliament Street	Y	18
Pitt Street	Y	19
Quay Street	Y	20
Royal Oak Road	Y	21
St. Aldate Street	Y	22
St. Johns Lane	Y	23
Southern Avenue	Z	24
Spa Road	Y	26
Stroud Road	Z	28
Tredworth Road	Z	30
Worcester Street	Y	31

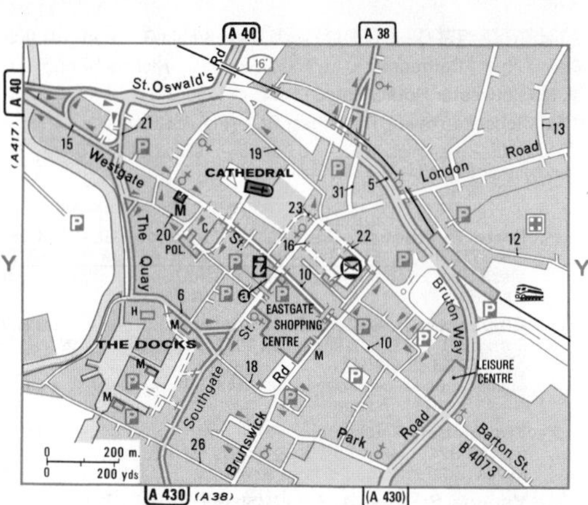

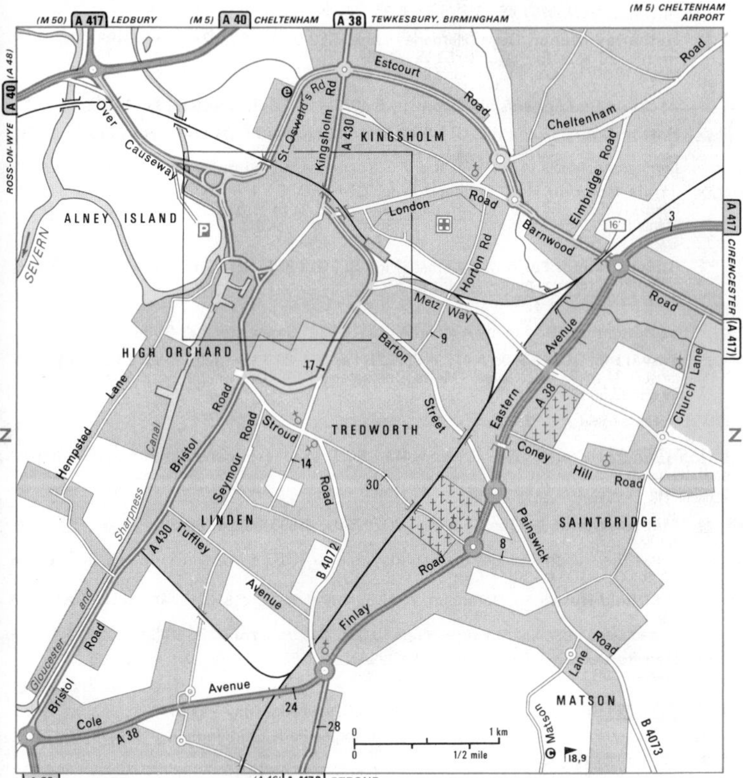

Benutzen Sie auf Ihren Reisen in Europa
die **Michelin-Länderkarten** 1 : 1 000 000.

GLOUCESTER Glos. 403 404 N 28 **Great Britain G.** – pop. 101 608 – ECD : Thursday – 01452.

See : City★ - Cathedral★★ Y – The Docks★ Y – Bishop Hooper's Lodging★ *AC* Y **M.**

18, 9 Gloucester Hotel, Matson Lane 525653.

St Michael's Tower, The Cross, GL1 1PD 421188.

London 106 – Birmingham 52 – Bristol 38 – Cardiff 66 – Coventry 57 – Northampton 83 – Oxford 48 – Southampton 98 – Swansea 92 – Swindon 35.

Plans on preceding page

Forte Posthouse, Crest Way, Barnwood, GL4 7RX, E : 3 m. by A 417 613311, Fax 371036, – rm – 100. Z
Meals (bar lunch Saturday) a la carte approx. 15.00 **t.** 5.50 – **122 rm** 56.00/69.50 **st.**, 1 suite.

Gloucester H. & Country Club (Jarvis), Robinswood Hill, Matson Lane, GL4 9EA, SE : 3 m. by B 4073 525653, Fax 307212, 18, 9, , squash – rm – 180. Z **c**
Meals *(closed Saturday lunch)* 11.00/14.50 **t.** and a la carte 4.95 – 8.50 – **102 rm** 65.00/85.00 **st.**, 5 suites – SB.

Travel Inn, Tewkesbury Rd, Longford, GL2 9BE, N : 1 ¾ m. on A 38 523519, Fax 300924 – rm . Z
Meals (Beefeater grill) a la carte approx. 16.00 **t.** – 4.95 – **40 rm** 33.50 **t.**

Yeungs, St. Oswald's Rd, Cattle Market, GL1 2SR, 309957 – . Z **e**
closed Monday lunch and Sunday – **Meals** - Chinese 12.00/22.50 **t.** and a la carte 4.00.

at Down Hatherley NE : 3¼ m. by A 38 – Z – Gloucester – 01452 :

Hatherley Manor, Down Hatherley Lane, GL2 9QA, 730217, Fax 731032, , – rest – 250.
Meals 10.50/15.00 **s.** and dinner a la carte 4.95 – **56 rm** 60.00/75.00 **st.** – SB.

at Upton St. Leonards SE : 3½ m. by B 4073 – Z – Gloucester – 01452 :

Hatton Court, Upton Hill, GL4 8DE, S : ¾ m. on B 4073 617412, Fax 612945, , , heated, – – 60.
Carringtons : **Meals** 14.50/19.95 **st.** and a la carte 4.50 – **45 rm** 85.00/110.00 **st.** – SB.

Jarvis Bowden Hall, Bondend Lane, GL4 8ED, E : 1 m. by Bondend rd 614121, Fax 611885, , , , , , park – rm – 85.
Meals (bar lunch Saturday)/dinner 15.95 **st.** and a la carte 5.25 – 7.50 – **72 rm** 85.00/102.00 **t.** – SB.

Bullens Manor Farm without rest., High St., GL4 8DL, SE : ½ m. 616463, Fax 371695, « Working farm », park – .
3 rm 20.00/40.00 **s.**

at Witcombe SE : 7 m. by A 40 on A 417 – Z – Gloucester – 01452 :

Travel Inn, GL3 4SS, on A 417 862521, Fax 864926 – rm .
closed 24 to 27 December – **Meals** (Beefeater grill) a la carte approx. 16.00 **t.** – 4.95 – **39 rm** 33.50 **t.**

ATS St. Oswalds Rd 527329

GOATHLAND N. Yorks. 402 R 20 – pop. 444 – ECD : Wednesday and Saturday – Whitby – 01947.

London 248 – Middlesbrough 36 – York 38.

Mallyan Spout , The Common, YO22 5AN, 896486, Fax 896327, , – .
Meals (bar lunch Monday to Saturday)/dinner 18.50 **t.** and a la carte 5.95 – **24 rm** 45.00/140.00 **t.** – SB.

Whitfield House , Darnholm, YO22 5LA, NW : ¾ m. 896215, – .
closed December and January – **Meals** 10.00 **t.** 4.25 – **8 rm** 25.00/50.00.

Heatherdene , The Common, YO22 5AN, 896334, , – rest .
Meals 11.75 **t.** 4.00 – **7 rm** 28.00/65.00 **t.** – SB.

GODALMING Surrey 404 S 30 – pop. 20 086 – ECD : Wednesday – 01483.

18 West Surrey, Enton Green 421275 – 9 Shillinglee Park, Chiddingfold (01428) 653237.

London 38 – Guildford 5 – Southampton 51.

Inn on the Lake, Ockford Rd, GU7 1RH, 415575, Fax 860445, – – 120.
Meals 17.50 **t.** – **17 rm** 75.00/85.00 **t.** – SB.

Kings Arms and Royal, High St., GU7 1EB, 421545, Fax 415403, – – 50.
accommodation closed 24-25 and 31 December – **Meals** *(closed 25 December)* a la carte 12.15/15.65 **t.** – **17 rm** 50.00/60.00 **t.**

at Hascombe SE : 3 ½ m. on B 2130 – ✉ Godalming – ☎ 01483.

X **White Horse,** GU8 4JA, ℘ 208258, Fax 208200, – AE VISA
closed 25 December – **Meals** (in bar Sunday dinner) 22.00 **t.** and a la carte.

ATS Meadrow ℘ 421845/422219

GODSTONE Surrey 404 T 30 – pop. 5 515 – ☎ 01342.
♦London 22 – ♦Brighton 36 – Maidstone 28.

XXX **La Bonne Auberge,** Tilburstow Hill, South Godstone, RH9 8JY, S : 2 ¼ m. ℘ 892318, Fax 893435, – P. AE VISA
closed Sunday dinner, Monday and 26 to 30 December – **Meals** - French 15.00/25.50 **st.** and a la carte 5.50.

GOLANT Cornwall 403 G 32 – see Fowey.

GOLCAR W. Yorks. – see Huddersfield.

GOLDEN GREEN Kent 404 U 30 – see Tonbridge.

GOMERSAL W. Yorks. 402 O 22 – see Bradford.

GOODWOOD W. Sussex 404 R 31 – see Chichester.

GOOSNARGH Lancs. 402 L 22 – ✉ Preston – ☎ 01772.
♦London 238 – ♦Blackpool 18 – Preston 6.

XX **Solo,** Goosnargh Lane, PR2 3BN, ℘ 865206 – AE VISA
Meals (dinner only and Sunday lunch)/dinner 22.50 **t.**

GORDANO SERVICE AREA Avon – ✉ Bristol – ☎ 01275.

Forte Travelodge without rest., BS20 9XG, M 5 : junction 19 ℘ 373709, Reservations (Freephone) 0800 850950 – TV P. AE VISA
40 rm 33.50 **t.**

GORING Berks 403 404 Q 29 **The West Country G.** – pop. 4 257 – ☎ 01491.
Exc. : Ridgeway Path★★.
♦London 56 – ♦Oxford 16 – Reading 12.

XX **Leatherne Bottel,** RG8 0HS, N : 1 ½ m. by B 4009 ℘ 872667, ←, « Thames-side setting » – P. AE VISA
Meals a la carte 22.20/29.95 **t.** 5.50.

GORLESTON-ON-SEA Norfolk 404 Z 26 – see Great Yarmouth.

GOSFORTH Cumbria 402 J 20 – pop. 1 568 – ✉ Seascale – ☎ 0194 67.
Seascale, The Banks ℘ 28202/28800.
♦London 317 – Kendal 55 – Workington 21.

Westlakes, Gosforth Rd, CA20 1HP, on A 595 ℘ 25221, Fax 25099, – TV ☎ P. AE VISA.
Meals *(closed Sunday lunch)* a la carte 12.70/21.00 **st.** 4.00 – **9 rm** 46.00/57.50 **st.**

GOSFORTH Tyne and Wear 401 402 P 18 – see Newcastle upon Tyne.

GOUDHURST Kent 404 V 30 **Great Britain G.** – pop. 2 498 – ECD : Wednesday – ✉ Cranbrook – ☎ 01580.
Envir. : Sissinghurst Castle★ *AC*, E : 5½m. by A 262.
♦London 45 – Hastings 22 – Maidstone 13.

Star and Eagle, High St., TN17 1AL, ℘ 211512, « 14C inn » – TV ☎ P. AE VISA
Meals a la carte 9.90/19.75 **t.** – **11 rm** 32.50/50.00 **t.**

GOVETON Devon 403 I 33 – see Kingsbridge.

GRAMPOUND Cornwall 403 F 33 **The West Country G.** – Truro – ☎ 01726.
Envir. : Trewithen★★★ *AC*, W : 2 m. by A 390 – Probus★ (tower★, Country Demonstration Garden★ *AC*) W : 2½m. by A 390.
♦London 287 – Newquay 16 – ♦Plymouth 44 – Truro 8.

XX **Eastern Promise,** 1 Moor View, TR2 4RT, ℘ 883033 – P. AE VISA JCB
closed Wednesday – **Meals** - Chinese (booking essential) (dinner only) 17.50 **st.** and a la carte 3.50.

GRANGE-IN-BORROWDALE Cumbria 402 K 20 – see Keswick.

GRANGE-OVER-SANDS Cumbria 402 L 21 **Great Britain G.** – pop. 3 867 – ECD : Thursday – ☎ 0153 95.

Envir. : Cartmel Priory★, NW : 3 m.

18 Meathop Rd ☎ 33180 – 9 Grange Fell, Fell Rd ☎ 32536.

Victoria Hall, Main St., LA11 6PT ☎ 34026 (summer only).

♦London 268 – Kendal 13 – Lancaster 24.

Netherwood, Lindale Rd, LA11 6ET, ☎ 32552, Fax 34121, ≤ Morecambe Bay, park – rest TV ☎ P – 150. VISA
Meals 11.75/24.50 **t.** and lunch a la carte 4.75 – **29 rm** 42.75/103.00 **t.** – SB.

Graythwaite Manor, Fernhill Rd, LA11 7JE, ☎ 32001, Fax 35549, ≤ gardens and Morecambe Bay, « Extensive flowered gardens », park, – TV ☎ P. VISA JCB.
closed 3 to 24 January – **Meals** 9.50/21.00 **t.** and a la carte 4.15 – **22 rm** 37.50/100.00 **st.** – SB.

Hampsfell House, Hampsfell Rd, LA11 6BG, ☎ 32567, – rest TV P. VISA
closed 25 and 26 December – **Meals** 7.50/16.50 **t.** and lunch a la carte **t.** 4.70 – **9 rm** 30.00/50.00 **t.** – SB.

at Lindale NE : 2 m. on B 5277 – ✉ Grange-over-Sands – ☎ 0153 95 :

Greenacres, LA11 6LP, ☎ 34578 – TV P. VISA.
closed December and first 2 weeks January – **Meals** (by arrangement) 13.50 **s.** – **5 rm** 30.00/56.00 **s.** – SB.

at Witherslack NE : 5 m. by B 5277 off A 590 – ✉ Witherslack – ☎ 0153 95 :

Old Vicarage, Church Rd, LA11 6RS, ☎ 52381, Fax 52373, « Part Georgian country house », – rest TV ☎ P. VISA JCB
Meals (booking essential) (dinner only and Sunday lunch)/dinner 22.50 **t.** 9.50 – **14 rm** 59.00/180.00 **t.** – SB.

at Cartmel NW : 3 m. – ✉ Cartmel – ☎ 0153 95 :

Aynsome Manor, LA11 6HH, NE : ¾ m. by Newby Bridge rd and Wood Broughton rd ☎ 36653, Fax 36016, – rest TV ☎ P. AE VISA
closed 2 to 27 January – **Meals** *(closed Sunday dinner to non-residents)* (dinner only and Sunday lunch)/dinner 18.50 **t.** 5.00 – **12 rm** (dinner included) 58.00/104.00 **t.** – SB.

XX **Uplands** with rm, Haggs Lane, LA11 6HD, E : 1 m. ☎ 36248, Fax 36248, ≤, – rest TV ☎ P. AE VISA
closed 1 January-23 February – **Meals** *(closed Monday)* (booking essential) 15.00/26.00 **t.** 4.00 – **5 rm** (dinner included) 75.00/140.00 **t.** – SB.

GRANTHAM Lincs. 402 404 S 25 **Great Britain G.** – pop. 30 700 – ECD : Wednesday – ☎ 01476.

See : St. Wulfram's Church★.

Envir. : Belton House★ *AC*, N : 2½ m. by A 607.

Exc. : Belvoir Castle★★ *AC*, W : 6 m. by A 607.

18, 9 Belton Park, Belton Lane, Londonthorpe Rd ☎ 67399 – 18 (2x), 9 Belton Woods ☎ 593200.

The Guildhall Centre, St. Peters Hill, NG31 6PZ ☎ 66444.

♦London 113 – ♦Leicester 31 – Lincoln 29 – ♦Nottingham 24.

De Vere Belton Woods, Belton, NG32 2LN, N : 2 m. on A 607 ☎ 593200, Fax 74547, 18, 9, park, squash – rm TV ☎ P – 275. AE VISA.
Manor : **Meals** (lunch by arrangement)/dinner 15.50/41.00 **st.** 6.50 – *Plus Fours* : **Meals** 13.50/20.00 **st.** 5.00 – **132 rm** 95.00/115.00 **st.**, 4 suites – SB.

Swallow, Swingbridge Rd, NG31 7XT, S : 1 ¼ m. at junction of A 607 with A 1 southbound sliproad ☎ 593000, Fax 592592, – TV ☎ P – 200. AE VISA
Meals 9.00/17.25 **st.** and a la carte – **88 rm** 85.00/98.00 **st.**, 1 suite – SB.

Angel and Royal (Forte), High St., NG31 6PN, ☎ 65816, Fax 67149, « Part 13C » – TV ☎ P – 30. AE VISA JCB.
Meals (bar lunch Monday to Saturday)/dinner 15.95 **st.** and a la carte 6.70 – 8.50 – **29 rm** 40.00/60.00 **st.** – SB.

at Hough-on-the-Hill N : 6¾ m. by A 607 on Hough Rd – ✉ Grantham – ☎ 01400 :

Brownlow Arms, NG32 2AZ, ☎ 50234, Fax 50772, « Part 17C inn », – TV ☎ P. VISA.
Meals *(closed Monday lunch and Sunday dinner)* (in bar) a la carte 11.70/18.15 **st.** – **5 rm** 30.00/47.00 **st.**

at Great Gonerby NW : 2 m. on B 1174 – ✉ Grantham – ☎ 01476 :

XX ✿ **Harry's Place** (Hallam), 17 High St., NG31 8JS, ☎ 61780 – VISA
closed Sunday, Monday and 25-26 December – **Meals** (booking essential) a la carte 28.50/38.00 **t.** 10.00
Spec. Lightly seared Orkney king scallops in a chilled spicy marinade, Loin of baby roe deer with a tarragon, white wine and Madeira sauce, Hot Bramley apple and Calvados soufflé.

at Grantham Service Area NW : 3 m on B 1174 at junction with A 1 – ✉ Grantham – ☎ 01476 :

Forte Travelodge without rest., NG32 2AB, ☎ 77500, Reservations (Freephone) 0800 850950 – TV & P. AE VISA. ✈
40 rm 33.50 **t.**

ATS East St. ☎ 590222 — ATS Elmer St. South ☎ 590444

GRASMERE Cumbria 402 K 20 **Great Britain G.** – ECD : Thursday – ☎ 0153 94.
See : Dove Cottage★ *AC* AY **A.**
Envir. : Lake Windermere★★, SE : by A 591 AZ.
Redbank Rd, LA22 9SW ☎ 35245 (summer only) – BZ.
♦London 282 – ♦Carlisle 43 – Kendal 18.

Plans : see Ambleside

Michaels Nook Country House, LA22 9RP, NE : ½ m. off A 591, turning by Swan H. ☎ 35496, Fax 35765, ≤ mountains and countryside, « Antiques and gardens » – rest TV ☎ P. AE VISA. — AY **n**
Meals (booking essential) 27.50/46.00 **t.** 6.95 – **12 rm** (dinner included) 112.00/270.00 **st.**, 2 suites – SB.

Wordsworth, Stock Lane, LA22 9SW, ☎ 35592, Fax 35765, ≘s, ⊠, – | rest ▤ rest TV ☎ P – 130. AE VISA. — BZ **s**
Prelude : **Meals** 17.50/29.50 **t.** and a la carte 6.50 – **35 rm** 59.00/145.00 **t.**, 2 suites – SB.

Swan (Forte), LA22 9RF, on A 591 ☎ 35551, Fax 35741, ≤, – TV ☎ P. AE VISA JCB — AY **r**
Meals 9.25/20.50 **t.** and a la carte 6.00 – 8.50 – **36 rm** 70.00/105.00 **t.** – SB.

White Moss House, Rydal Water, LA22 9SE, S : 1 ½ m. on A 591 ☎ 35295, Fax 35516, – rest TV ☎ P. VISA. — BY **v**
closed 5 December - 10 March – **Meals** *(closed Sunday)* (booking essential) (dinner only) 27.50 **t.** 4.95 – **6 rm** (dinner included) 83.00/174.00 **t.** – SB.

Rothay Garden, Broadgate, LA22 9RJ, ☎ 35334, Fax 35723, – rest TV ☎ P. VISA — AY **e**
Meals 16.95 **t.** (dinner) and lunch a la carte 9.25/13.85 **t.** – **25 rm** (dinner included) 47.50/135.00 **t.** – SB.

Oak Bank, Broadgate, LA22 9TA, ☎ 35217, Fax 35217, – rest TV ☎ P. VISA JCB — BZ **e**
closed January and 3 days Christmas – **Meals** (bar lunch)/dinner 18.00 4.00 – **15 rm** 30.00/120.00 **st.** – SB.

Grasmere, Broadgate, LA22 9TA, ☎ 35277, Fax 35277, – rest TV ☎ P. VISA JCB — BZ **r**
closed January – **Meals** (dinner only) 18.50 **t.** 5.50 – **12 rm** (dinner included) 35.00/104.00 **t.** – SB.

Lancrigg Vegetarian Country House, Easedale Rd, LA22 9QN, W : ½ m. on Easedale Rd ☎ 35317, ≤ Easedale Valley, , park – rest TV P — AY **u**
13 rm.

Bridge House, Stock Lane, LA22 9SN, ☎ 35425, – rest TV ☎ P. VISA JCB. — BZ **n**
closed 4 December-3 February – **Meals** (dinner only and Sunday lunch)/dinner 14.00 **t.** 4.70 – **12 rm** 30.00/70.00 **t.** – SB.

Rothay Lodge without rest., White Bridge, LA22 9RH, ☎ 35341, – TV P. — AY **o**
March-October – **6 rm** 22.00/44.00.

Banerigg without rest., Lake Rd, LA22 9PW, S : ¾ m. on A 591 ☎ 35204, ≤, – P. — AY **a**
March - November – **5 rm** 25.00/55.00 **st.**

GRASSENDALE Mersey 402 403 L 23 – see Liverpool.

GRASSINGTON N. Yorks. 402 O 21 – pop. 1 448 – ECD : Thursday – ✉ Skipton – ☎ 01756.
National Park Centre, Hebden Rd, BD23 5LB ☎ 752774 (summer only).
♦London 240 – Bradford 30 – Burnley 28 – ♦Leeds 37.

Ashfield House, BD23 5AE, ☎ 752584, – TV P. VISA.
closed mid December-mid February – **Meals** (by arrangement) 13.00 **st.** – **7 rm** 31.00/55.00 **st.** – SB.

Non dimenticate che in Gran Bretagna esistono limiti di velocità oltre a quelli indicati sui cartelli :
- 60 mph (= 96 km/ora) su strada
- 70 mph (= 112 km/ora) su strada a carreggiate separate e autostrada.

GRAVESEND Kent 404 V 29 – pop. 53 450 – ECD : Wednesday – ☎ 01474.

⛴ to Tilbury (White Horse Ferries Ltd) frequent services daily (5 mn).

ℹ 10 Parrock St., DA12 1ET ℘ 337600.

◆London 25 – ◆Dover 54 – Maidstone 16 – Margate 53.

- **Quality Manor,** Hever Court Rd, Singlewell, DA12 5UQ, SE : 2 ½ m. by A 227 off A 2 ℘ 353100, Fax 354978, ₺, ≘, ▣ – ⇔ rm ▤ rest ▣ ☎ ⓟ – 🏛 200. ▣ AE VISA. ✻
  Meals *(closed Sunday)* (light lunch)/dinner 25.00 **st.** and a la carte 6.00 – ▭ 7.95 – **39 rm** 55.50/150.00 **t.**
- **Overcliffe,** 15-16 Overcliffe, DA11 0EF, ℘ 322131, Fax 536737 – ▣ ☎ ⓟ. ▣ AE ⓓ VISA
  Meals (dinner only) a la carte approx. 15.00 **t.** 3.75 – **29 rm** ▭ 55.00/85.00 **t.** – SB.

GRAVETYE E. Sussex – see East Grinstead.

GRAYSHOTT Hants. 404 R 30 – ✉ Hindhead (Surrey) – ☎ 01428.

◆London 46 – ◆Portsmouth 31.

- **Woods Place,** Headley Rd, GU26 6LB, ℘ 605555, Fax 605555 – ▣ AE ⓓ VISA
  closed Sunday and Monday – **Meals** a la carte 16.80/22.50 **st.** 3.95.

GREASBY Mersey. 402 ㉜ 403 ⑫ – pop. 44 272 – ✉ Wirral – ☎ 0151.

◆London 220 – ◆Liverpool 9.

- Twelfth Man Lodge, Greasby Rd, L49 2PP, on B 5139 ℘ 677 5445, Fax 678 5085 – ▣ ☎ ♿ ⓟ
  30 rm.

GREAT AYTON N. Yorks. 402 Q 20 **Great Britain G.** – pop. 4 759 – ✉ Middlesbrough (Cleveland) – ☎ 01642.

See : Captain Cook Birthplace Museum★ *AC.*

ℹ High Green Car Park, TS9 6BJ ℘ 722835 (summer only).

◆London 245 – ◆Leeds 63 – ◆Middlesbrough 7 – York 48.

- **Ayton Hall** ⛰, Low Green, TS9 6BW, ℘ 723595, Fax 722149, ⛲ – ▣ ☎ ⓟ. ▣ AE ⓓ VISA. ✻
  Meals 11.95/25.00 **st.** and a la carte 6.50 – **9 rm** ▭ 75.00/125.00 **t.** – SB.

  at Ingleby Greenhow S : 3 ¾ m. by Easby rd on Ingleby rd – ✉ Middlesbrough (Cleveland) – ☎ 01642 :

- **Manor House Farm** ⛰, TS9 6RB, S : 1 m. via lane to manor, next to church ℘ 722384, ≤, ⛲ – ⇔ ⓟ. ✻
  closed 20 to 29 December – **Meals** 4.50 – **3 rm** ▭ (dinner included) 35.00/76.00 **st.** – SB.

GREAT BADDOW Essex 404 V 28 – see Chelmsford.

GREAT BARR W. Mids. 403 404 O 26 – see Birmingham.

GREAT BROUGHTON N. Yorks. 402 Q 20 – pop. 937 – ✉ Middlesbrough (Cleveland) – ☎ 01642.

◆London 241 – ◆Leeds 61 – ◆Middlesbrough 10 – York 54.

- **Wainstones,** 31 High St., TS9 7EW, ℘ 712268, Fax 711560 – ▣ ☎ ⓟ. ▣ AE VISA. ✻
  Meals a la carte 11.95/18.95 **t.** – **23 rm** ▭ 47.95/62.50 **t.** – SB.

GREAT DRIFFIELD Humbs. 402 S 21 **Great Britain G.** – pop. 8 970 – ECD : Wednesday – ✉ York – ☎ 01377.

Exc. : Burton Agnes Hall★ *AC*, NE : 6 m. by A 166 – Sledmere House★ *AC*, NW : 8 m. by A 166 and B 1252.

⛳18 Driffield, Sunderlandwick ℘ 253116 – ⛳9 Hainsworth Park, Brandesburton ℘ (01964) 542362.

◆London 201 – ◆Kingston-upon-Hull 21 – Scarborough 22 – York 29.

- **Star Inn,** Warter Rd, North Dalton, YO25 9UX, SW : 7 m. by A 164 and A 163 on B 1246 ℘ 217688 – ▣ ☎ ⓟ. ▣ VISA. ✻
  Meals *(closed Sunday dinner)* (bar lunch)/dinner a la carte 9.40/17.35 **t.** 3.50 – **7 rm** ▭ 29.50/39.50 **st.**

  at Lockington S : 9 ¾ m. by A 164 – ✉ Great Driffield – ☎ 01430.

- **Rockingham Arms,** YO25 9SH, ℘ 810607 – ⓟ. ▣ VISA
  closed Sunday, Monday, 25 to 26 December and Bank Holidays – **Meals** (dinner only) a la carte approx. 25.00 **t.** 4.75.

ATS 14 Westgate ℘ 252386/253628

GREAT DUNMOW Essex 404 V 28 – pop. 6 544 – ECD : Wednesday – ☎ 01371.

◆London 42 – ◆Cambridge 27 – Chelmsford 13 – Colchester 24.

- **Saracen's Head** (Forte), High St., CM6 1AG, ℘ 873901, Fax 875743 – ⇔ rest ▣ ☎ ⓟ – 🏛 40. ▣ AE ⓓ VISA JCB
  Meals 8.95/22.00 **t.** 6.25 – ▭ 8.50 – **24 rm** 70.00/105.00 **t.** – SB.

XXX **Starr** with rm, Market Pl., CM6 1AX, ✆ 874321, Fax 876337 – ⇔ TV ☎ Ⓟ. AE VISA. *closed 27 December and 2 to 10 January* – **Meals** *(closed Saturday lunch and Sunday dinner)* 22.50 **t.** (dinner) and lunch a la carte 15.75/32.45 **t.** 5.95 – **8 rm** 50.00/100.00 **st.**

GREAT GONERBY Lincs. 402 404 S 25 – see Grantham.

☛ *Michelin issues no plaques or signs to hotels and restaurants mentioned in this Guide.*

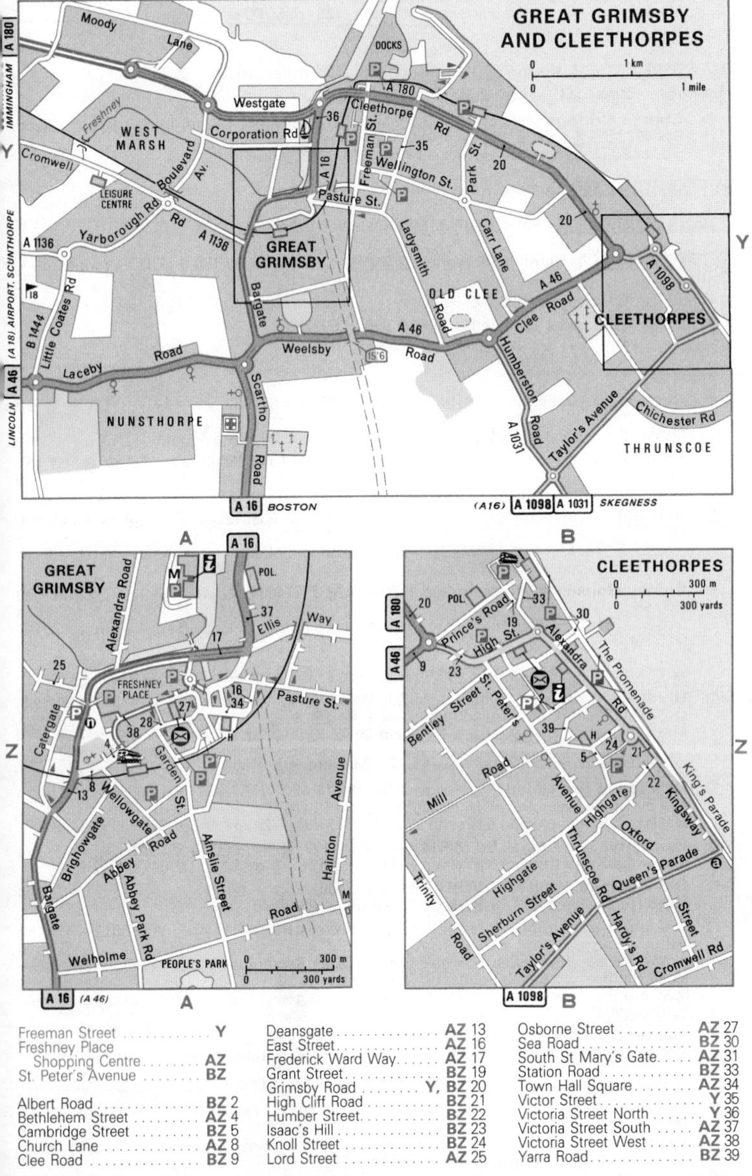

Freeman Street . . . . . Y
Freshney Place Shopping Centre . . . . . AZ
St. Peter's Avenue . . . . . BZ

Albert Road . . . . . BZ 2
Bethlehem Street . . . . . AZ 4
Cambridge Street . . . . . BZ 5
Church Lane . . . . . AZ 8
Clee Road . . . . . BZ 9
Deansgate . . . . . AZ 13
East Street . . . . . AZ 16
Frederick Ward Way . . . . . AZ 17
Grant Street . . . . . BZ 19
Grimsby Road . . . . . Y, BZ 20
High Cliff Road . . . . . BZ 21
Humber Street . . . . . BZ 22
Isaac's Hill . . . . . BZ 23
Knoll Street . . . . . BZ 24
Lord Street . . . . . AZ 25
Osborne Street . . . . . AZ 27
Sea Road . . . . . BZ 30
South St Mary's Gate . . . . . AZ 31
Station Road . . . . . BZ 33
Town Hall Square . . . . . AZ 34
Victor Street . . . . . Y 35
Victoria Street North . . . . . Y 36
Victoria Street South . . . . . AZ 37
Victoria Street West . . . . . AZ 38
Yarra Road . . . . . BZ 39

GREAT GRIMSBY Humbs. 402 404 T 23 – pop. 90 517 – ECD : Thursday – ☎ 01472.

Littlecoates Rd ✆ 342823 Y.

Humberside Airport : ✆ (01652) 688456, W : 13 m. by A 46 and A 18 Y.

The National Fishing Heritage, Alexandra Dock, DN31 1UF ✆ 342422 BZ.

London 172 – Boston 50 – Lincoln 36 – Sheffield 75.

Plan on preceding page

St. James (Forte), St. James Sq., DN31 1EP, ✆ 359771, Telex 527741, Fax 241427, – rm – 80. VISA. AZ **n**
Meals 8.00/22.00 **st.** and a la carte – 8.95 – **125 rm** 55.00 **st.** – SB.

ATS 2 Abbey Rd ✆ 358151

GREAT HOCKHAM Norfolk 404 W 26 – pop. 557 – ✉ Attleborough – ☎ 01953.

London 86 – Cambridge 41 – Norwich 23.

Church Cottage without rest., Breckles, NR17 1EW, N : 1 ½ m. by A 1075 ✆ 498286, Fax 498320, heated, – rm .
closed 20 December - 5 January – **3 rm** 17.00/34.00 **s.**

GREAT LANGDALE Cumbria – see Ambleside.

GREAT LONGSTONE Derbs. 402 403 404 O 24 – see Bakewell.

GREAT MALVERN Heref. and Worcs. 403 404 N 27 – pop. 30 153 – ECD : Wednesday – ☎ 01684.

Wood Farm, Malvern Wells ✆ 573905.

Winter Gdns Complex, Grange Rd, WR14 3HB ✆ 892289 B.

London 127 – Birmingham 34 – Cardiff 66 – Gloucester 24.

Plan opposite

Cotford, 51 Graham Rd, WR14 2HU, ✆ 574680, Fax 572952, – rest . VISA B **o**
Meals (dinner only) 16.00 **t.** 4.00 – **16 rm** 33.00/58.00 **st.** – SB.

Priory Park, 4 Avenue Rd, WR14 3AG, ✆ 565194, Fax 893603, – . VISA. B **x**
Meals (booking essential) 14.00/20.00 and a la carte – **6 rm** 38.00/68.00 **t.** – SB.

Red Gate, 32 Avenue Rd, WR14 3BJ, ✆ 565013, Fax 565013, – . VISA. B **r**
closed 2 weeks spring – **Meals** (residents only)(dinner only) 15.00 **st.** 4.00 – **7 rm** 27.00/54.00 **st.**

Sidney House, 40 Worcester Rd, WR14 4AA, ✆ 574994, ←, – rest . VISA. B **s**
closed Christmas and New Year – **Meals** (by arrangement) 15.00 **st.** – **8 rm** 20.00/59.00 **st.**

at Welland SE : 4½ m. by A 449 on A 4104 – A – ✉ Great Malvern – ☎ 01684 :

Holdfast Cottage , Marlbank Rd, WR13 6NA, W : ¾ m. on A 4104 ✆ 310288, Fax 311117, « 17C country cottage », – . VISA
Meals (dinner only) 17.00 **st.** 5.25 – **8 rm** 42.00/80.00 **st.** – SB.

at Malvern Wells S : 2 m. on A 449 – ✉ Malvern – ☎ 01684 :

Cottage in the Wood , Holywell Rd, WR14 4LG, ✆ 573487, Fax 560662, ← Severn and Evesham Vales, – rest . VISA A **z**
Meals 9.95 **st.** (lunch) and a la carte 22.00/25.50 7.50 – **20 rm** 60.00/97.00 **st.** – SB.

Essington , Holywell Rd, WR14 4LQ, ✆ 561177, ←, – . VISA A **e**
Meals (booking essential) (dinner only) 14.50 **t.** 5.50 – **9 rm** 35.00/64.00 **t.** – SB.

Old Vicarage, Hanley Rd, WR14 4PH, ✆ 572585, ←, – A **c**
Meals (by arrangement) 13.50 **st.** 4.50 – **6 rm** 28.00/46.00 **st.** – SB.

✿ **Croque-en-Bouche** (Marion Jones), 221 Wells Rd, WR14 4HF, ✆ 565612 – . VISA A **u**
closed Sunday to Tuesday, 1 week May, 2 weeks September and Christmas-New Year – **Meals** (booking essential) (dinner only) 33.50 **st.**
Spec. Japanese style selections, Roast leg of lamb with couscous, preserved lemon and pimiento, Salads and herbs from the garden.

Planters, 191-193 Wells Rd, WR14 9HB, ✆ 575065 – VISA A **a**
Meals - Oriental (booking essential)(dinner only) 19.50 **t.** and a la carte.

at Wynds Point S : 4 m. on A 449 – ✉ Malvern – ☎ 01684.

Malvern Hills, British Camp, WR13 6DW, ✆ 40237, Fax 40327, – . VISA A **s**
Meals *(closed Sunday dinner to non-residents)* (bar lunch Monday to Saturday)/dinner 15.00 **t.** 4.50 – **17 rm** 40.00/65.00 **t.** – SB.

GREAT MALVERN

Church Street	B	
Wells Road	B	
Albert Road South	B	3
Blackmore Park Road	A	5
Clerkenwell Crescent	B	6
Cockshot Road	B	8
Court Road	B	12
Croft Bank	A	13
Happy Valley off St. Ann's Road	B	15
Imperial Road	B	16
Jubilee Drive	A	17
Lygon Bank	B	18
Madresfield Road	B	20
Moorlands Road	B	22
North Malvern Road	B	23
Orchard Road	B	24
Richmond Road	B	26
Upper Welland Road	A	27
Walwyn Road	A	29
Wells Road	A	30
Zetland Road	B	31

Town plans
roads most used by traffic and those on which guide listed hotels and restaurants stand are fully drawn; the beginning only of lesser roads is indicated.

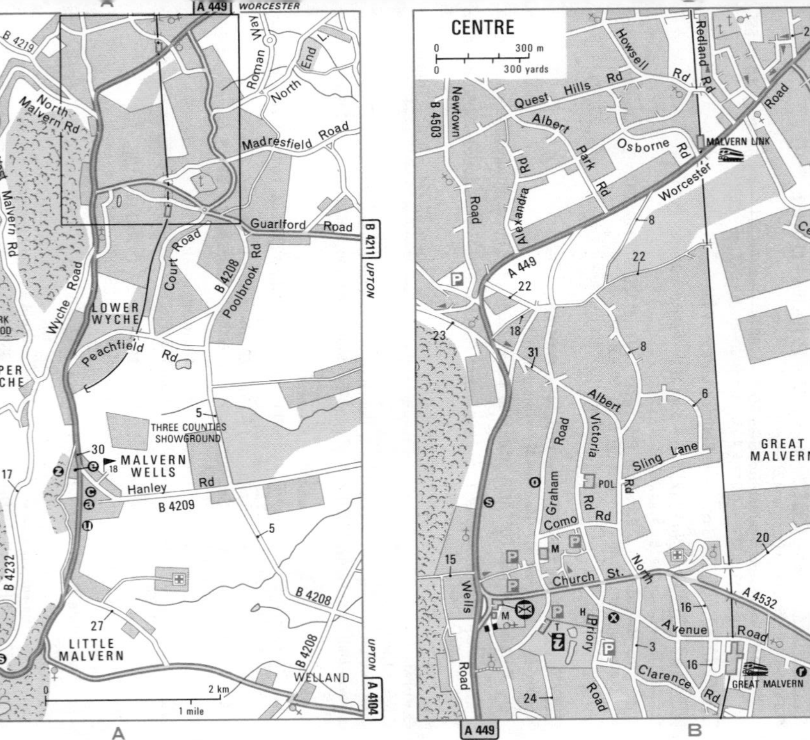

GREAT MILTON Oxon. 403 404 Q 28 – see Oxford.

GREAT MISSENDEN Bucks. 404 R 28 – pop. 7 429 (inc. Prestwood) – ECD : Thursday – ☎ 01494.

♦London 34 – Aylesbury 10 – Maidenhead 19 – ♦Oxford 35.

XX **La Petite Auberge,** 107 High St., HP16 0BB, ✆ 865370 – VISA
closed Sunday, 3 weeks Christmas and Bank Holidays – **Meals** - French (dinner only) a la carte 23.00/29.10 **t.**

GREAT OFFLEY Herts. 404 S 28 – pop. 1 365 – ✉ Hitchin – ☎ 01462.

♦London 40 – Bedford 14 – ♦Cambridge 29 – Luton 6.

Red Lion, Kings Walden Rd, SG5 3DZ, ✆ 768281, Fax 768281, – TV ☎ P. AE VISA
Meals 16.50 **st.** and a la carte 4.25 – **5 rm** 45.00/60.00 **st.** – SB.

GREAT RISSINGTON Glos. – see Bourton-on-the-Water.

GREAT SNORING Norfolk 404 W 25 – pop. 191 – ✉ Fakenham – ☎ 01328.

♦London 115 – ♦Cambridge 68 – ♦Norwich 28.

Old Rectory , Barsham Rd, NR21 0HP, ✆ 820597, Fax 820048, « Country house atmosphere », – rest TV ☎ P. AE ⓓ.
closed 24 to 27 December – **Meals** (booking essential) (dinner only) 23.00 **t.** – **6 rm** 68.00/88.00 **t.** – SB.

GREAT TEW Oxon. 403 404 P 28 – pop. 145 – ☎ 01608.

♦London 75 – ♦Birmingham 50 – Gloucester 42 – ♦Oxford 21.

Falkland Arms, OX7 4DB, ✆ 683653, Fax 683656, « 17C inn in picturesque village », – TV.
Meals *(closed Sunday and Monday)* (in bar) (lunch only) a la carte approx. 11.50 **st.** – **4 rm** 30.00/50.00 **st.**

GREAT YARMOUTH Norfolk 404 Z 26 **Great Britain G.** – pop. 87 724 – ECD : Thursday – ☎ 01493.

Envir. : The Broads★.

18 Gorleston, Warren Rd ✆ 661911 – 18 Beach House, Caister-on-Sea ✆ 720421.

Town Hall, Hall Quay, NR30 2PX ✆ 846345 – Marine Parade, NR30 2EJ ✆ 842195 (summer only).

♦London 126 – ♦Cambridge 81 – ♦Ipswich 53 – ♦Norwich 20.

Carlton, 1-5 Kimberley Terr., Marine Par., NR30 3JE, ✆ 855234, Fax 852220 – rm TV ☎ – 150. AE ⓓ VISA
Meals 8.95/13.95 **st.** and a la carte 4.25 – **88 rm** 56.00/150.00 **st.**, 2 suites – SB.

Dolphin, 14-15 Albert Sq., NR30 3JH, ✆ 855070, Fax 853798, , heated, – TV ☎ P – 140. AE ⓓ VISA
Meals 8.95/12.50 **st.** and a la carte 4.50 – **48 rm** 55.00/75.00 **st.**, 1 suite – SB.

Imperial, North Drive, NR30 1EQ, ✆ 851113, Fax 852229 – rest TV ☎ P – 150. AE ⓓ VISA
***Rambouillet* : Meals** 10.50/16.50 **st.** 6.00 – **39 rm** 55.00/70.00 **st.** – SB.

Embassy, Camperdown, NR30 3JB, ✆ 843135, Fax 331064 – TV ☎
24 rm.

Two Bears, Southtown Rd, NR31 0HV, on A 12 ✆ 603198, – TV ☎ P
11 rm.

at Gorleston-on-Sea S : 3 m. on A 12 – ✉ Great Yarmouth – ☎ 01493 :

Cliff, Cliff Hill, NR31 6DH, ✆ 662179, Fax 653617, – rm TV ☎ P – 170. AE ⓓ VISA.
Meals 14.50 **t.** and a la carte – **38 rm** 62.00/88.00 **t.**, 1 suite – SB.

ATS Suffling Rd ✆ 858211

GRENOSIDE S. Yorks. 402 403 404 P 23 – see Sheffield.

GRETA BRIDGE Durham 402 O 20 – ☎ 01833.

♦London 253 – ♦Carlisle 63 – ♦Leeds 63 – ♦Middlesbrough 32.

Morritt Arms, DL12 9SE, ✆ 627232, Fax 627392, , – rest TV ☎ P – 150. AE ⓓ VISA
Meals (bar lunch Monday to Saturday)/dinner 18.00 **st.** – **17 rm** 45.00/68.00 **st.** – SB.

GRIMSBY Humbs. 402 404 T 23 – see Great Grimsby.

GRIMSTON Norfolk – see King's Lynn.

GRINDLEFORD Derbs. 402 403 404 P 24 – ✉ Sheffield (S. Yorks.) – ☎ 01433.
◆London 165 – Derby 31 – ◆Manchester 34 – ◆Sheffield 10.

Maynard Arms, Main Rd, S30 1HP, ☎ 630321, Fax 630445, ≤, – rest TV ☎ P – 120. AE VISA.
Meals 10.95 **t.** (lunch) and a la carte 13.75/19.75 5.50 – **13 rm** 49.50/69.50 **t.** – SB.

GRINDLETON Lancs. 402 M 22 – pop. 1 446 (inc. West Bradford) – ✉ Bolton-by-Bowland – ☎ 01200.
◆London 241 – ◆Blackpool 38 – Lancaster 25 – ◆Leeds 45 – ◆Manchester 33.

Harrop Fold Country Farmhouse, Harrop Fold, BB7 4PJ, N : 2 ¾ m. by Slaidburn Rd ☎ 447600, ≤, « 17C longhouse », , park – TV ☎ P. VISA
closed January – **Meals** (dinner only) a la carte 12.40/15.50 **st.** 3.50 – **8 rm** 39.50/65.00 **st.** – SB.

GRINDON Staffs. – ✉ Leek – ☎ 01538.
◆London 118 – ◆Birmingham 70 – Derby 26 – ◆Manchester 42 – ◆Stoke-on-Trent 20.

Porch Farmhouse, ST13 7TP, ☎ 304545, « Part 17C », – rm TV P
Meals (by arrangement) (communal dining) – **3 rm** (dinner included) 40.00/80.00 **st.**

GRINGLEY Notts. 402 S 23 – ✉ Doncaster – ☎ 01777.
◆London 163 – ◆Leeds 43 – Lincoln 24 – ◆Nottingham 42 – ◆Sheffield 26.

Old Vicarage, DN10 4RF, on High St. ☎ 817248, Fax 817248, , – P. VISA.
closed Christmas – **Meals** (by arrangement)(communal dining) 16.00 **s.** 3.50 – **3 rm** 30.00/50.00 **s.**

GRIZEDALE Cumbria 402 K 20 – see Hawkshead.

GUILDFORD Surrey 404 S 30 – pop. 61 509 – ECD : Wednesday – ☎ 01483.
14 Tunsgate, GU1 3QT ☎ 444007 Y
◆London 33 – ◆Brighton 43 – Reading 27 – ◆Southampton 49.

Plan on next page

Forte Crest, Egerton Rd, GU2 5XZ, ☎ 574444, Fax 302960, , , , – rm TV ☎ P – 120 Z **v**
109 rm, 2 suites.

Angel Posting House and Livery, High St., GU1 3DP, ☎ 64555, Fax 33770, « 16C coaching inn with 13C vaulted cellar » – TV ☎ – 70. AE VISA Y **e**
Meals 10.95/18.00 **t.** and a la carte – 8.50 – **8 rm** 105.00/160.00 **t.**, 3 suites – SB.

Manor at Newlands, Newlands Corner, GU4 8SE, E : 5 ½ m. by A 246 on A 25 ☎ 222624, Fax 211389, – TV ☎ P – 150 by A 25 Z
19 rm.

Rumwong, 16-18 London Rd, GU1 2AF, ☎ 36092 – . VISA Y **a**
closed Monday and 2 weeks July-August – **Meals** - Thai 18.00 (dinner) and a la carte 12.00/22.00 4.75.

Café de Paris, 35 Castle St., GU1 3UQ, ☎ 34896 – AE VISA Y **u**
closed Saturday lunch, Sunday and Bank Holidays – **Meals** - French 11.80 **t.** and a la carte 4.25.

at Shere E : 6 ¾ m. by A 246 off A 25 – Z – ✉ Guildford – ☎ 01483 :

Kinghams, Gomshall Lane, GU5 9HB, ☎ 202168 – P. AE VISA
closed Sunday dinner and Monday – **Meals** 15.00 **t.** and a la carte 7.95.

at Albury E : 6 ¾ m. by A 25 – Z – on A 248 – ✉ Guildford – ☎ 01483 :

Drummond Arms, GU5 9AG, ☎ 202039, Fax 202039 – TV P. VISA.
Meals (in bar Sunday dinner and Monday) 14.95 **t.** and a la carte 4.20 – 6.00 – **7 rm** 38.00/50.00 **st.** – SB.

at Bramley S : 3 m. on A 281 – Z – ✉ Guildford – ☎ 01483 :

Bramley Grange, Horsham Rd, GU5 0BL, on A 281 ☎ 893434, Fax 893835, , – rm rest TV ☎ P – 100. AE VISA
Meals *(closed Saturday lunch)* 10.00/13.50 **st.** and a la carte 6.00 – **45 rm** 80.00/95.00 **st.** – SB.

GUILDFORD

Friary Centre . . . . Y
High Street . . . . Y
Market Street . . . . Y 18
North Street . . . . Y
Tunsgate
  Shopping Centre . . . . . . Y

Bedford Road . . . . Y 2
Bridge Street . . . . Y 3
Castle Street . . . . Y 5
Chertsey Street . . . . Y 6
Commercial Road . . . . Y 8
Eastgate Gardens . . . . Y 9
Friary Bridge . . . . Y 12
Ladymead . . . . Z 13
Leapale Lane . . . . Y 15
Leapale Road . . . . Y 16
Leas Road . . . . Y 17
Mary Road . . . . Y 19
Midleton Road . . . . Z 20
Millbrook . . . . Y 21
New Inn Lane . . . . Z 22
One Tree
  Hill Road . . . . Z 24
Onslow Street . . . . Y 25
Park Street . . . . Y 27
Quarry Street . . . . Y 28
Stoughton Road . . . . Z 30
Trood's Lane . . . . Z 31
Tungsgate . . . . Y 33
Warwick's Bench . . . . Y 34
Woodbridge Road . . . . Z 37

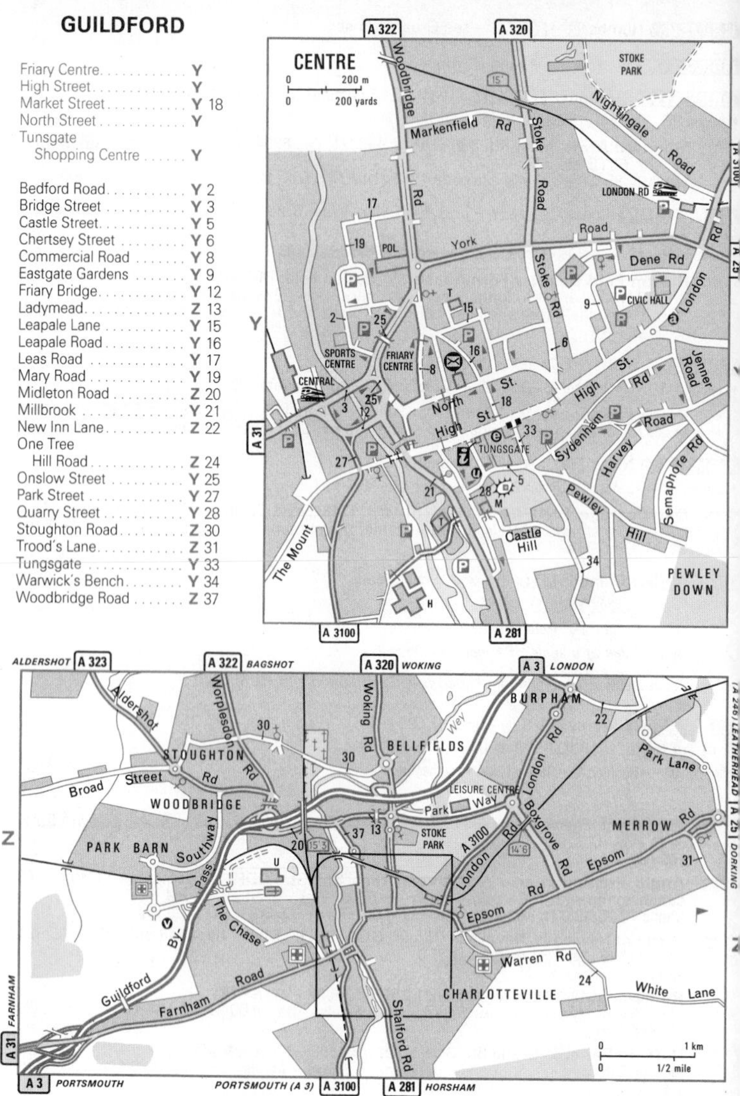

L'EUROPE en une seule feuille
Cartes Michelin n° 970 (routière, pliée) et n° 973 (politique, plastifiée).

GUITING POWER Glos. 403 404 O 28 – ✉ Cheltenham – ☎ 01451.
◆London 95 – ◆Birmingham 47 – Gloucester 30 – ◆Oxford 39.

Guiting Guest House, Post Office Lane, GL54 5TZ, ☎ 850470, Fax 850034, « 16C farmhouse » – ⇜ rm TV P
Meals (by arrangement) 16.00 **st.** – **3 rm** ☐ 26.00/42.00 **st.**

GULWORTHY Devon 403 H 32 – see Tavistock.

GUNTHORPE Notts. – ☎ 0115.
♦London 132 – Lincoln 32 – ♦Nottingham 12 – ♦Sheffield 40.

Unicorn, Gunthorpe Bridge, NG14 7FB, SE : 1½ m. by A 6097 and Gunthorpe (riverside) rd ☏ 966 3612, Fax 966 4801, – rest TV ☎ P. AE VISA
closed 25 December – **Meals** (grill rest.) a la carte 8.20/17.60 **st.** 4.50 – **16 rm** 47.50/62.50 **t.**

HACKNESS N. Yorks. 402 S 21 – see Scarborough.

HADLEIGH Suffolk 404 W 27 – pop. 6 595 – ☎ 01473.
Toppesfield Hall, IP7 5DN ☏ 822922.
♦London 72 – ♦Cambridge 49 – Colchester 17 – ♦Ipswich 10.

Edgehill, 2 High St., IP7 5AP, ☏ 822458, – TV P
closed 24 December-1 January – **Meals** (by arrangement) 15.00 **st.** 4.50 – **9 rm** 35.00/65.00 **st.** – SB.

Gables, 63-67 Angel St., IP7 5EY, ☏ 827169, – TV ☎ P
4 rm.

Odds and Ends House without rest., 131 High St., IP7 5EG, ☏ 822032, – TV P
9 rm 20.00/40.00 **st.**

HADLEY HEATH Heref. and Worcs. – see Droitwich.

HAGLEY W. Mids. 403 404 N 26 – see Stourbridge.

HAILEY Oxon. 403 404 P 28 – see Witney.

HAILSHAM E. Sussex 404 U 31 – pop. 14 906 – ECD : Thursday – ☎ 01323.
18 Wellshurst G. & C.C., North St., Hellingly ☏ (0142) 863636.
The Library, Western Rd, BN27 3DN ☏ 840604.
♦London 57 – ♦Brighton 23 – Eastbourne 7 – Hastings 20.

Boship Farm, Lower Dicker, BN27 4AT, NW : 3 m. by A 295 on A 22 ☏ 844826, Fax 843945, heated, – rm TV ☎ P – 120. AE VISA
Meals *(closed Saturday lunch)* 6.95/15.75 **st.** and a la carte 5.50 – **44 rm** 42.95/69.90 **t.**, 2 suites – SB.

Forte Travelodge without rest., Boship Roundabout, Lower Dicker, BN27 4DT, NW : 3 m. by A 295 on A 22 ☏ 844556, Reservations (Freephone) 0800 850950 – TV P. AE VISA
40 rm 33.50 **t.**

at Magham Down NE : 2 m. by A 295 on A 271 – ✉ Hailsham – ☎ 01323 :

Olde Forge, BN27 1PN, ☏ 842893, Fax 842893 – TV ☎ P. AE VISA
Meals (dinner only) 12.50 **t.** and a la carte – **7 rm** 38.00/60.00 **st.** – SB.

HALE Gtr. Manchester 402 403 404 M 23 – see Altrincham.

HALEBARNS Gtr. Manchester – see Altrincham.

HALFORD Warks. 403 404 P 27 – ✉ Shipston-on-Stour – ☎ 01789.
♦London 88 – ♦Birmingham 36 – Gloucester 42.

Sykes House, CV36 5BT, ☏ 740976, « 16C house », – P. VISA
closed Sunday to Tuesday and 27 to 30 December – **Meals** (by arrangement) (booking essential) (dinner only) 32.50 **t.**

HALIFAX W. Yorks. 402 O 22 – pop. 76 675 – ECD : Thursday – ☎ 01422.
18 Halifax Bradley Hall, Holywell Green ☏ 374108 – 18 West End, Highroad Well ☏ 353608, 18 Union Lane, Ogden ☏ 244171 – 9 Ryburn, Norland, Sowerby Bridge ☏ 831355 – 9 Elland, Hammerstones Leach Lane, Hullen Edge ☏ 372505 – 9 Lightcliffe, Knowle Top Rd ☏ 202459.
Piece Hall, HX1 1RE ☏ 368725.
♦London 205 – Bradford 8 – Burnley 21 – ♦Leeds 15 – ♦Manchester 28.

Holdsworth House, Holdsworth Rd, Holmfield, HX2 9TG, N : 3 m. by A 629 and Shay Lane ☏ 240024, Fax 245174, « Part 17C house », – TV ☎ P – 80. AE VISA
closed 24 to 30 December – **Meals** *(closed lunch Saturday and Sunday)* 12.50/19.50 **st.** and a la carte – 5.00 – **36 rm** 69.90/90.00 **st.**, 4 suites – SB.

Hilton National Huddersfield, Ainley Top, HD3 3RH, S : 5¾ m. at junction of A 629 with A 643 ☏ 375431, Fax 310067, – rm rest TV ☎ P – 400. AE VISA JCB
Meals (carving lunch) 12.75/16.95 **st.** and a la carte – 10.25 – **117 rm** 78.00 **st.**, 1 suite.

Imperial Crown, 42-46 Horton St., HX1 1BR, ☏ 342342, Fax 349866 – rm TV ☎ P – 150. AE VISA
Meals *(closed Sunday dinner)* 9.75/13.75 **t.** and dinner a la carte – **39 rm** 63.50/74.50 **st.**, 2 suites – SB.

Imperial Crown Lodge without rest., 31 Square Rd, HX1 1QG, ☏ 342342, Fax 349866 – TV P. AE VISA
6.95 – **15 rm** 42.50 **t.**

at Luddenden Foot W : 4 ¼ m. on A 646 – ✉ Halifax – ☎ 01422 :

Collyers, Burnley Rd, HX2 6AH, on A 646 ☎ 882624, Fax 883897 rm TV ☎ P. AE ① VISA
Meals (booking essential Sunday) a la carte 14.15/16.75 **st.** 4.80 – **6 rm** 24.00/56.50 **st.** – SB.

at Elland S : 3 ½ m. by A 629 – ✉ Halifax – ☎ 01422 :

Berties Bistro, 7-10 Town Hall Buildings, HX5 OEU, ☎ 371724, Fax 372830 – ▤. VISA
closed Monday and Bank Holidays – **Meals** (dinner only) 9.50/15.50 **t.** and a la carte 4.50.

ATS Hope St. ☎ 365892/360819

HALLAND E. Sussex 404 U 31 – ECD : Wednesday – ✉ Lewes – ☎ 01825.
♦London 48 – ♦Brighton 16 – Eastbourne 16 – Royal Tunbridge Wells 19.

Halland Forge, BN8 6PW, on A 22 ☎ 840456, Fax 840773, park – TV ☎ P. AE ① VISA JCB.
Meals 12.50/18.00 **t.** and a la carte – 8.00 – **20 rm** 46.00/58.00 **t.** – SB.

HALL GREEN W. Mids. 402 403 404 O 26 – see Birmingham.

HALNAKER W. Sussex – see Chichester.

HALTWHISTLE Northd 401 402 M 19 **Great Britain G.** – pop. 3 773 – ☎ 01434.
Envir. : Hadrian's Wall★★, N : 4½ m. by A 6079 – Housesteads★★ *AC*, NE : 6 m. by B 6318 – Roman Army Museum★ *AC*, NW : 5 m. by A 69 and B 6318 – Vindolanda (Museum★) *AC*, NE : 5 m. by A 69 – Steel Rig (≤★) NE : 5½ m. by B 6318.
9 Greenhead ☎ (016977) 47367.
Church Hall, Main St., NE49 0BE ☎ 322002.
♦London 335 – ♦Carlisle 22 – ♦Newcastle upon Tyne 37.

Bellister Castle, NE49 0HZ, S : 1 m. by A 69 on Alston rd ☎ 320391, Fax 320391, « Castellated manor house of 17C origins », – P
Meals (by arrangement) (communal dining) 19.50 **st.** – **3 rm** 64.00 **st.** – SB.

Ashcroft without rest., Lantys Lonnen, NE49 0DA, ☎ 320213, « Gardens » – P.
closed 22 December-5 January – **8 rm** 16.00/36.00.

HAMBLETON Leics. – see Oakham.

HAMBROOK Avon 403 404 M 29 – see Bristol.

HAMPTON LOADE Shrops. 402 403 404 M 26 – see Bridgnorth.

HAMSTEAD MARSHALL Berks. 403 404 P29 – see Newbury.

HAMSTERLEY Durham 401 402 O 19 – pop. 397 – ✉ Bishop Auckland – ☎ 01388.
♦London 260 – ♦Carlisle 75 – ♦Middlesbrough 30 – ♦Newcastle upon Tyne 22.

Grove House, Hamsterley Forest, DL13 3NL, W : 3¾ m. via Bedburn ☎ 488203, – P.
Meals 14.00 **t.** – **3 rm** 25.00/50.00 **s.**

HANDFORTH Ches. 402 403 404 N 23 – see Wilmslow.

HANSLOPE Bucks. 404 R 27 – see Milton Keynes.

HANWOOD Shrops. 402 403 L 25 – see Shrewsbury.

HAREWOOD W. Yorks. 402 P 22 – pop. 3 222 – ✉ Leeds – ☎ 0113.
♦London 214 – Harrogate 9 – ♦Leeds 10 – York 20.

Harewood Arms, Harrogate Rd, LS17 9LH, on A 61 ☎ 288 6566, Fax 288 6064, – TV ☎ P. AE ① VISA.
Meals 15.50 **t.** (dinner) and a la carte 16.25/21.10 **t.** – **24 rm** 65.00/78.00 **t.** – SB.

HARLOW Essex 404 U 28 – pop. 74 629 – ECD : Wednesday – ☎ 01279.
18 Nazeing, Middle St. ☎ (01992) 893798.
♦London 22 – ♦Cambridge 37 – ♦Ipswich 60.

Churchgate Manor, Churchgate St., Old Harlow, CM17 OJT, E : 3 ¼ m. by A 414 and B 183 ☎ 420246, Fax 437720, , , , – TV ☎ P – 170. AE ① VISA JCB
Meals *(closed Saturday lunch)* 10.95/25.00 **t.** and a la carte – 8.25 – **82 rm** 67.00/82.00 **t.**, 3 suites – SB.

Harlow Moat House (Q.M.H.), Southern Way, CM18 7BA, SE : 2 ¼ m. by A 1025 on A 414 ☏ 422441, Telex 81658, Fax 635094 – rm – 150.
Meals (bar lunch Saturday and Bank Holidays) 15.00 **st.** and a la carte – 9.50 – **118 rm** 65.00 **st.** – SB.

Green Man (Forte), Mulberry Green, Old Harlow, CM17 0ET, E : 2 ¼ m. by A 414 and B 183 ☏ 442521, Fax 626113 – rm – 60.
Meals *(closed Saturday lunch)* 11.25/27.95 **st.** and a la carte 5.55 – 8.95 – **55 rm** 65.00/75.00 **st.** – SB.

Travel Inn, Cambridge Rd, Old Harlow, CM20 2EP, NE : 3 ¼ m. by A 414 on A 1184 ☏ 442545, Fax 452169 – rm.
Meals (Beefeater grill) a la carte approx. 16.00 **t.** – 4.95 – **38 rm** 33.50 **t.**

ATS 14 Burnt Mill ☏ 421965

HARNHAM Wilts. 403 404 O 30 – see Salisbury.

HAROME N. Yorks. – see Helmsley.

HARPENDEN Herts. 404 S 28 – pop. 27 294 – ECD : Wednesday – 01582.

London 32 – Luton 6.

Harpenden Moat House (Q.M.H.), 18 Southdown Rd, AL5 1PE, ☏ 764111, Fax 769858, – rm – 100.
51 rm, 2 suites – SB.

Glen Eagle, 1 Luton Rd, AL5 2PX, ☏ 760271, Fax 460819, – rest – 35.
Meals *(closed Saturday lunch and Sunday dinner)* 17.50 **st.** and a la carte 7.50 – 8.75 – **50 rm** 69.50/79.50 **st.**

Chef Peking, 5-6 Church Green, AL5 2TP, ☏ 769358 –.
Meals - Chinese (Peking, Szechuan) 15.00/24.00 **st.** and a la carte 4.00.

HARROGATE N. Yorks. 402 P 22 **Great Britain G.** – pop. 63 637 – ECD : Wednesday – 01423.

See : Town★.

Exc. : Fountains Abbey★★★ *AC* : Studley Royal★★ *AC* (≤★ from Anne Boleyn's Seat) - Fountains Hall (Façade★), N : 13 m. by A 61 and B 6265 AY – Harewood House★★ (The Gallery★) *AC*, S : 7½m. by A 61 BZ.

18 Forest Lane Head ☏ 863158 – 18 Follifoot Rd, Pannal ☏ 871641 – 18 Oakdale ☏ 567162 – 9 Crimple Valley, Hookstone Wood Rd ☏ 883485.

Royal Baths Assembly Rooms, Crescent Rd, HG1 2RR ☏ 525666.

London 211 – Bradford 18 – Leeds 15 – Newcastle Upon Tyne 76 – York 22.

Plan on next page

Nidd Hall, Nidd, HG3 3BN, N : 4 ¼ m. by A 61 on B 6165 ☏ 771598, Fax 770931, ≤, « 19C manor house », park, squash – – 250. AY
Meals (light lunch Saturday) 18.50 **st.** and a la carte 6.25 – **56 rm** 95.00/150.00 **st.**, 3 suites – SB.

Majestic (Forte), Ripon Rd, HG1 2HU, ☏ 568972, Fax 502283, squash – rm – 300. AY c
Meals (bar lunch)/dinner 23.95 **st.** and a la carte 7.10 – 9.95 – **146 rm** 75.00/110.00 **st.**, 10 suites – SB.

Old Swan, Swan Rd, HG1 2SR, ☏ 500055, Fax 501154, – rest – 350. AY e
Meals 12.50/20.00 **st.** and a la carte – **125 rm** 85.00/130.00 **st.**, 10 suites – SB.

Moat House International (Q.M.H.), Kings Rd, HG1 1XX, ☏ 500000, Telex 57575, Fax 524435, ≤ – rm rest – 350. BY x
***Abbey* : Meals** (carving rest.) (dinner only) 14.95/16.00 **st.** 6.00 – ***Boulevard* : Meals** *(closed Sunday dinner and Monday)* 5.00/19.95 **st.** and a la carte 6.00 – 9.00 – **205 rm** 100.00/130.00 **st.**, 9 suites – SB.

St. George (Swallow), 1 Ripon Rd, HG1 2SY, ☏ 561431, Fax 530037, – rm – 150. AY o
Meals (buffet lunch)/dinner 17.50 **st.** and dinner a la carte – **92 rm** 85.00/105.00 **st.**, 1 suite – SB.

Crown (Forte), Crown Pl., HG1 2RZ, ☏ 567755, Fax 502284 – – 300. AZ i
Meals (bar lunch Monday to Saturday)/dinner 17.95 **t.** and a la carte 6.95 – 8.95 – **116 rm** 68.00/78.00 **st.**, 5 suites – SB.

Balmoral, Franklin Mount, HG1 5EJ, ☏ 508208, Fax 530652, « Antique furnishings » – rest. BY v
Meals (dinner only) 17.50 **st.** and a la carte 4.50 – 7.50 – **19 rm** 67.00/90.00 **st.**, 1 suite – SB.

Grants, Swan Rd, HG1 2SS, ☏ 560666, Fax 502550 – rest – 70. AY s
Meals 9.75/17.50 **t.** 6.25 – **41 rm** 90.00/139.00 **t.**, 1 suite – SB.

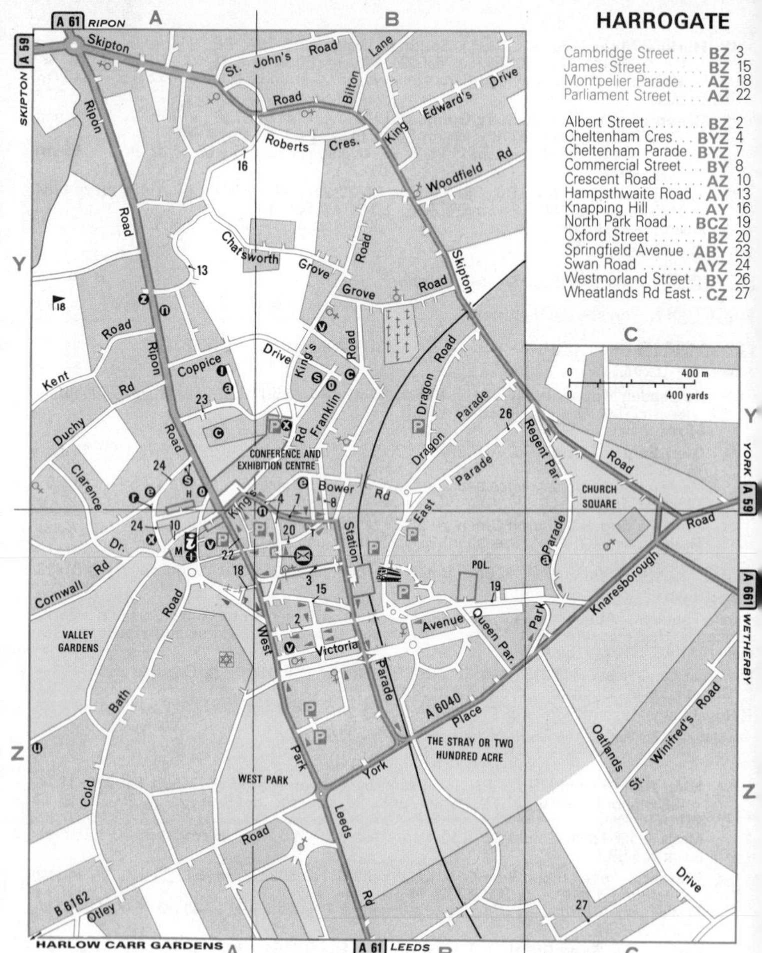

Studley, 28 Swan Rd, HG1 2SE, ☎ 560425, Fax 530967 – |‡| TV ☎ P. AE VISA. AZ **x**
closed 25 and 26 December – **Meals** 16.00 **t.** (dinner) and a la carte 17.75/22.00 **t.** 4.25 – **34 rm** 69.50/100.00 **t.**, 2 suites – SB.

Hospitality Inn (Mt. Charlotte Thistle), Prospect Pl., West Park, HG1 1LB, ☎ 564601, Telex 57530, Fax 507508 – |‡| TV ☎ P – 150. AE VISA JCB. BZ **v**
Meals (bar lunch Monday to Saturday)/dinner 17.50 **st.** and a la carte – 8.50 – **66 rm** 65.00/90.00 **st.**, 5 suites – SB.

Ruskin, 1 Swan Rd, HG1 2SS, ☎ 502045, Fax 506131, – TV P. VISA. AY **s**
Meals (dinner only) 16.95 **st.** 4.95 – **7 rm** 39.00/70.00 **st.** – SB.

White House, 10 Park Par., HG1 5AH, ☎ 501388, Fax 527973, – rest TV ☎ P. AE VISA. CZ **a**
Meals (booking essential) 14.50 **t.** (lunch) and a la carte 16.25/21.70 **t.** 4.85 – **9 rm** 68.50/125.00 **t.**, 1 suite – SB.

Britannia Lodge, 16 Swan Rd, HG1 2SA, ☎ 508482, Fax 526840 – rest TV ☎ P. AE VISA. AYZ **r**
Meals 10.50/12.50 **t.** 4.50 – **12 rm** 45.00/60.00 **t.** – SB.

Alexa House, 26 Ripon Rd, HG1 2JJ, ✆ 501988, Fax 504086 – ⇔ rest TV ☎ P. VISA AY n
Meals (lunch by arrangement)/dinner 9.95 **t.** 3.95 – **13 rm** 35.00/55.00 **st.** – SB.

Abbey Lodge, 29-31 Ripon Rd, HG1 2JL, ✆ 569712, Fax 530570 – TV ☎ P. AE VISA AY z
closed 25 to 30 December – **Meals** (dinner only) 16.00 **t.** 6.25 – **17 rm** 28.00/59.00 **t.** – SB.

Brookfield House without rest., 5 Alexandra Rd, HG1 5JS, ✆ 506646, Fax 523151 – ⇔ TV ☎ P. VISA BY s
6 rm 30.00/46.00 **st.**

Alexandra Court without rest., 8 Alexandra Rd, HG1 5JS, ✆ 502764, Fax 523151 – ⇔ TV ☎ P. VISA. BY o
closed 31 December – **13 rm** 38.00/55.00.

Garden House, 14 Harlow Moor Drive, HG2 0JX, ✆ 503059 – ⇔ rest TV. AE VISA. AZ u
Meals (by arrangement) 10.00 **st.** 4.00 – **7 rm** 22.00/44.00 **st.** – SB.

Arden House, 69-71 Franklin Rd, HG1 5EH, ✆ 509224, Fax 561170 – ⇔ rest TV ☎ P. AE VISA BY c
closed 1 week Christmas – **Meals** 15.00 **st.** – **14 rm** 26.00/55.00 **st.** – SB.

Knabbs Ash without rest., Felliscliffe, HG3 2LT, NW : 5 ½ m. by A 61 Y on A 59 ✆ 771040, Fax 771515, ≤, – ⇔ TV P.
3 rm 25.00/40.00 **t.**

Stoney Lea without rest., 13 Spring Grove, HG1 2HS, ✆ 501524 – TV. AY i
closed Christmas-New Year – **7 rm** 26.00/40.00.

Ashwood House without rest., 7 Spring Grove, HG1 2HS, ✆ 560081, Fax 527928 – ⇔ TV. AY a
closed 24 December-2 January – **9 rm** 21.00/48.00.

Knox Mill House without rest., Knox Mill Lane, HG3 2AE, N : 1 ½ m. by A 61 AY ✆ 560650, ≤ – P.
closed Christmas - New Year – **3 rm** 34.00/38.00 **st.**

Millers, The Bistro, 1 Montpellier Mews, HG1 2TG, ✆ 530708 – AE VISA AZ v
closed Sunday, Monday, 2 weeks August and 1 week Christmas – **Meals** a la carte 9.50/20.50 **t.**

Grundy's, 21 Cheltenham Cres., HG1 1DH, ✆ 502610 – AE VISA BYZ n
closed Sunday, 2 weeks January-February, 2 weeks July-August and Bank Holidays – **Meals** (dinner only) 13.95 **t.** and a la carte.

La Bergerie, 11-13 Mount Par., HG1 1BX, ✆ 500089. VISA AY e
closed Sunday – **Meals** - French (dinner only) 16.50 **t.** 4.00.

Drum and Monkey, 5 Montpellier Gdns, HG1 2TF, ✆ 502650 – VISA AZ v
closed Sunday and 24 December-2 January – **Meals** - Seafood (booking essential) a la carte 10.35/22.60 **t.** 3.35 :

at Burn Bridge S : 4 m. by A 61 BZ – ✉ Harrogate – ☎ 01423 :

Lockwoods, 55 Burn Bridge Rd, HG3 1PB, ✆ 879933 – P. AE VISA
closed Sunday dinner, Monday, 24 December and 1 January – **Meals** (dinner only and Sunday lunch)/dinner 13.95 **t.** and a la carte.

at Beckwithshaw SW : 2 ¾ m. on B 6162 AZ – ✉ Harrogate – ☎ 01423 :

Sandringham, Otley Rd, HG2 0NN, ✆ 500722, Fax 530509, « Antiques and memorabilia » – ⇔ rest TV ☎ P. AE VISA.
Meals *(closed Monday lunch, Sunday dinner and Bank Holidays)* (by arrangement to non-residents) 16.00/26.00 **t.** 6.00 – **6 rm** 55.00/80.00 **t.**, 1 suite – SB.

at Markington NW : 8 ¾ m. by A 61 – AY – ✉ Harrogate – ☎ 01423 :

Hob Green, HG3 3PJ, SW : ½ m. ✆ 770031, Fax 771589, ≤, « Country house in extensive parkland », – TV ☎ P
11 rm, 1 suite.

ATS Leeds Rd, Pannal ✆ 879194

HARTFIELD E. Sussex 404 U 30 – pop. 2 2026 – ☎ 01892.

London 47 – Brighton 28 – Maidstone 25.

Bolebroke Mill without rest., Edenbridge Rd, TN7 4JP, N : 1 ¼ m. by B 2026 on unmarked rd ✆ 770425, « Part early 17C cornmill, original features », – ⇔ TV P
5 rm.

HARTFORD Ches. 402 403 404 M 24 – pop. 4 605 – ☎ 01606.

London 188 – Chester 15 – Liverpool 31 – Manchester 25.

Hartford Hall, 81 School Lane, CW8 1PW, ✆ 75711, Fax 782285, – TV ☎ P – 35. AE VISA
Meals *(closed Bank Holidays except Christmas to non residents)* 16.95 **st.** 6.35 – **19 rm** 64.50/72.50 **st.**, 1 suite.

HARTINGTON Derbs. 402 403 404 O 24 – pop. 1 604 – ✉ Buxton – ☎ 01298.

♦London 168 – Derby 36 – ♦Manchester 40 – ♦Sheffield 34 – Stoke-on-Trent 22.

Biggin Hall ≫, Biggin, SK17 0DH, SE : 2 m. by B 5054 ℘ 84451, Fax 84681, ≤, « 17C hall », ⌘ – ⇔ rest TV P. AE VISA. ⚹
Meals 14.50 **st.** ₰ 4.50 – ☐ 3.50 – **14 rm** 30.00/80.00 **st.** – SB.

HARTLEBURY Heref. and Worcs. 403 N 26 – pop. 2 253 – ☎ 01299.

♦London 135 – ♦Birmingham 20 – Worcester 11.

Forte Travelodge without rest., Crossway Green, DX11 6DR, S : 2 ½ m. by B 4193 on A 449 (southbound carriageway) ℘ 250553, Reservations (Freephone) 0800 850950 – TV & P. AE VISA. ⚹
32 rm 33.50 **t.**

HARTLEPOOL Cleveland 402 Q 19 – pop. 91 749 – ECD : Wednesday – ☎ 01429.

18 Seaton Carew, Tees Rd ℘ 266249/261040 – 18 Castle Eden and Peterlee ℘ 836220 – 18 Hart Warren ℘ 274398.

✈ Teesside Airport : ℘ (01325) 332811, SW : 20 m. by A 689, A 1027, A 135 and A 67.

ℹ Civic Centre, Victoria Rd, TS24 8AY ℘ 266522 ext : 2408.

♦London 263 – Durham 19 – ♦Middlesbrough 9 – Sunderland 21.

Grand, Swainson St., TS24 8AA, ℘ 266345, Fax 265217 – |$| TV ☎ – 150. AE VISA
Meals (carving rest.) (bar lunch Monday to Saturday)/dinner 8.95 **st.** and a la carte ₰ 4.00 – **46 rm** ☐ 44.95/75.00 **st.**, 1 suite.

York, 185-187 York Rd, TS26 9EE, ℘ 867373, Fax 867220 – TV ☎. AE. ⚹
Meals *(closed Sunday dinner)* (dinner only and Sunday lunch)/dinner 10.95 **t.** and a la carte ₰ 4.95 – **13 rm** ☐ 25.00/48.00 **t.** – SB.

at Seaton Carew SE : 2 m. on A 178 – ☎ 01429 :

Marine, 5-7 The Front, TS25 1BS, ℘ 266244, Fax 864144, ≤ – TV ☎ P. AE VISA. ⚹
closed 25 December – **Meals** (carving rest.) (bar lunch Saturday) 6.95/8.50 **st.** and a la carte ₰ 4.75 – **25 rm** ☐ 45.00/65.00 **st.**

Krimo's, 8 The Front, TS25 1BS, ℘ 266120 – VISA
closed Saturday lunch, Sunday, Monday, first 2 weeks August, 24-26 December and 1 January – **Meals** 9.40 **st.** (lunch) and a la carte 11.80/21.10 **st.** ₰ 3.95.

ATS York Rd ℘ 275552

HARTSHEAD MOOR SERVICE AREA W. Yorks. 402 O 22 – ✉ Brighouse – ☎ 01274.

♦London 213 – Bradford 8 – Burnley 31 – ♦Manchester 35 – ♦Sheffield 39.

Forte Travelodge without rest., Clifton, HD6 4RJ, M 62 : between junctions 25 and 26 (eastbound carriageway) ℘ 851706, Reservations (Freephone) 0800 850950 – TV & P. AE VISA
40 rm 33.50 **t.**

HARVINGTON Heref. and Worcs. 403 404 027 – see Evesham.

HARWELL Oxon. 403 404 Q 29 – ☎ 01235.

♦London 64 – ♦Oxford 16 – Reading 18 – Swindon 22.

Kingswell, Reading Rd, OX11 0LZ, S : ¾ m. on A 417 ℘ 833043, Telex 83173, Fax 833193 – TV ☎ P – 30. AE VISA. ⚹
Meals 14.50/17.50 **st.** and a la carte ₰ 5.25 – **19 rm** ☐ 72.50/95.00 **st.** – SB.

HARWICH and DOVERCOURT Essex 404 X 28 – pop. 15 374 (Harwich) – ECD : Wednesday – ☎ 01255.

9 Station Rd, Parkeston ℘ 503616.

to Germany (Hamburg) (Scandinavian Seaways) 1 daily (19 h 30 mn) – to Denmark (Esbjerg) (Scandinavian Seaways) (18 h 30 mn) – to The Netherlands (Hook of Holland) (Stena Sealink Line) 2 daily (6 h 30 mn) day, (9 h 30 mn) night – to Sweden (Gothenburg) (Scandinavian Seaways) (24 h).

to Felixstowe (Orwell & Harwich Navigation Co. Ltd) 5 daily (14 mn).

ℹ Essex County Council, Parkeston Quay, CO12 4SP ℘ 506139.

♦London 78 – Chelmsford 41 – Colchester 20 – ♦Ipswich 23.

XX **Pier at Harwich** with rm, The Quay, CO12 3HH, ℘ 241212, Fax 551922, ≤ – TV ☎ P. AE VISA. ⚹
Meals - Seafood 9.00/16.00 **t.** and a la carte ₰ 6.75 – ☐ 4.00 – **6 rm** 45.00/72.50 **t.** – SB.

ATS 723 Main Rd, Dovercourt ℘ 508314

HASCOMBE Surrey – see Godalming.

HASELBURY PLUCKNETT Somerset 403 L 31 – see Crewkerne.

HASLEMERE Surrey 404 R 30 – pop. 7 326 – ECD : Wednesday – 01428.

◆London 47 – ◆Brighton 46 – ◆Southampton 44.

Lythe Hill, Petworth Rd, GU27 3BQ, E : 1 ½ m. on B 2131 ℘ 651251, Fax 644131, ⩽, park, – 60. AE VISA JCB
Meals *(closed Saturday dinner and Sunday lunch)* 17.50 **st.** and a la carte 7.25 ***Auberge de France* : Meals** - French (closed Monday) (dinner only and Sunday lunch)/dinner 17.50 **st.** and a la carte 27.50/36.50 **st.** 7.25 – 8.00 – **28 rm** 74.00/95.00 **st.**, 12 suites – SB.

Georgian, High St., GU27 2JY, ℘ 651555, Fax 661304, squash – AE VISA
Meals 12.50/15.95 **t.** and a la carte 6.95 – **24 rm** 60.00/75.00 **t.**, 1 suite – SB.

HASSOP Derbs. – see Bakewell.

Es ist empfehlenswert, ***in der Hauptsaison*** *und vor allem in Urlaubsorten, Hotelzimmer im voraus zu bestellen. Benachrichtigen Sie sofort das Hotel, wenn Sie ein bestelltes Zimmer nicht belegen können.*

Wenn Sie an ein Hotel im Ausland schreiben, fügen Sie Ihrem Brief einen internationalen Antwortschein bei (im Postamt erhältlich).

HASTINGS and ST. LEONARDS E. Sussex 404 V 31 – pop. 80 820 – 01424.

18 Beauport Park, Battle Rd, St. Leonards, ℘ 852977.

4 Robertson Terr., TN34 1EA ℘ 718888 – Fishmarket, The Stade, TN34 1EZ ℘ 718888 (summer only).

◆London 65 – ◆Brighton 37 – Folkestone 37 – Maidstone 34.

Plan on next page

Royal Victoria, Marina, TN38 0BD, ℘ 445544, Fax 721995, ⩽ – rm – 70. AE VISA AY **e**
Meals (bar lunch Monday to Saturday)/dinner 16.00 **t.** and a la carte 4.50 – **50 rm** 65.00/90.00 **t.** – SB.

Beauport Park, Battle Rd, TN38 8EA, NW : 3½ m. at junction of A 2100 with B 2159 ℘ 851222, Fax 852465, ⩽, « Formal garden », heated, 18, park, – rest – 60. AE VISA JCB AY
Meals 15.00/16.50 **t.** and a la carte 5.00 – **23 rm** 62.00/85.00 **st.** – SB.

Cinque Ports, Summerfields, Bohemia Rd, TN34 1ET, ℘ 439222, Fax 437277 – 250. AE VISA JCB. AZ **a**
40 rm.

Tower House, 26-28 Tower Rd West, TN38 0RG, ℘ 427217, – AE VISA. AY **c**
Meals (dinner only) 10.50 **st.** 4.50 – **12 rm** 25.00/47.50 **st.**

Eagle House, 12 Pevensey Rd, TN38 0JZ, ℘ 430535, Fax 437771 – AE VISA
Meals (dinner only) 18.95 **st.** 3.00 – **19 rm** 31.60/49.00 **st.** AZ **c**

Parkside House without rest., 59 Lower Park Rd, TN34 2LD, ℘ 433096, Fax 421431, – VISA. BY **e**
5 rm 25.00/58.00 **st.**

Norton Villa without rest., Hill St., Old Town, TN34 3HU, ℘ 428168, ⩽, – BY **n**
4 rm 22.00/40.00 **s.**

Chimes, 1 St. Matthews Gdns, Silverhill, TN38 0TS, ℘ 434041, – AY **a**
Meals (by arrangement) 9.00 **s.** 3.00 – **9 rm** 19.00/40.00 **s.**

Filsham Farmhouse, 111 Harley Shute Rd, TN38 8BY, ℘ 433109, Fax 461061, « Part 17C », – rm AY **u**
closed 1 to 14 January – **Meals** (by arrangement) 12.50 **s.** – **3 rm** 25.00/50.00 **s.** – SB.

Röser's, 64 Eversfield Pl., TN37 6DB, ℘ 712218 – AE VISA BZ **i**
closed Saturday lunch, Sunday, Monday, first week January and 2 weeks August – **Meals** 15.95/18.95 **st.** and a la carte 22.85/30.85 **st.** 4.95.

ATS Menzies Rd, Pondswood Ind. Est., St. Leonards-on-Sea ℘ 427780/424567

HASTINGS AND ST. LEONARDS

King's Road . . . . **AZ** 22
London Road . . . . **AZ**
Norman Road . . . . **AZ**
Queen's Road . . . . **BZ**
Robertson Street . . . . **BZ** 27
Wellington Place . . . . **BZ** 35

Bourne (The) . . . . **BY** 4
Cambridge Gardens . . . . . . **BZ** 5
Castle Street . . . . **BZ** 7
Castle Hill Road . . . . **BZ** 8
Cornwallis Gardens . . . . . . **BZ** 9
Cornwallis Terrace . . . . **BZ** 10
Denmark Place . . . . **BZ** 13
Dorset Place . . . . **BZ** 15
Gensing Road . . . . **AZ** 16
George Street . . . . **BY** 18

Grosvenor Crescent . . . . . . **AY** 19
Harold Place . . . . **BZ** 20
Marine Court . . . . **AZ** 23
Rock-a-Nore Road . . . . **BY** 30
St. Helen's Park Road . . . . **BY** 31
Sedlescombe Road South . **AY** 32
Silchester Road . . . . **AZ** 33
Warrior Square . . . . **AZ** 34
Wellington Square . . . . **BZ** 36
White Rock Road . . . . **BZ** 38

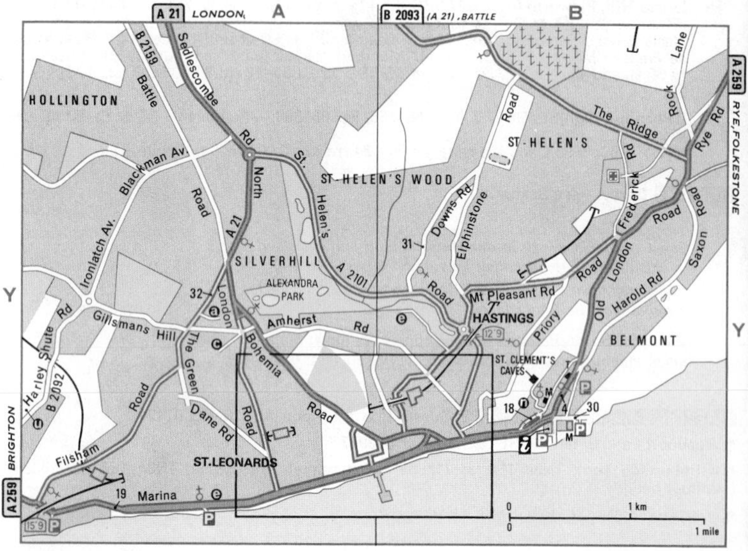

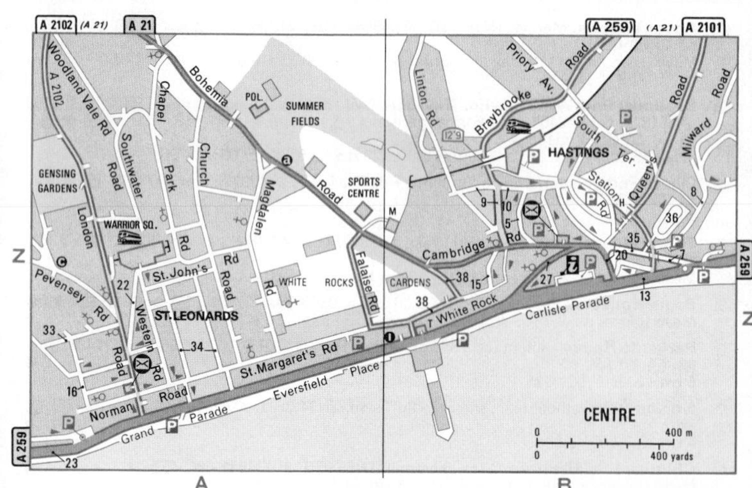

Don't confuse:

Comfort of hotels	: 🏨🏨 ... 🏠, 🏠, 🏠
Comfort of restaurants	: XXXXX X
Quality of the cuisine	: ✿✿✿, ✿✿, ✿, **Meals**

HATCH BEAUCHAMP Somerset 403 K 30 – see Taunton.

HATFIELD Herts. 404 T 28 **Great Britain G.** – pop. 24 238 – ECD : Monday and Thursday – 01707.

See : Hatfield House★★ *AC*.

Hatfield London, Bedwell Park, Essendon 642624.

London 27 – Bedford 38 – Cambridge 39.

Hatfield Oak, Roehyde Way, AL10 9AF, S : 2 m. by B 6426 on A 1001 275701, Fax 266033 – rm – 120. VISA
Meals 15.25 **st.** (dinner) and a la carte 11.50/15.00 **st.** – **76 rm** 62.50/75.00 **st.** – SB.

Jarvis Comet, 301 St. Albans Rd West, AL10 9RH, W : 1 m. by B 6426 on A 1057 at junction with A 1001 265411, Fax 264019 – rm – 120. VISA.
Meals *(closed Saturday lunch)* (carving rest.) 8.75/13.95 **st.** and a la carte 6.25 – 8.00 – **55 rm** 79.00/89.00 **st.** – SB.

HATFIELD HEATH Essex. 404 U 28 – see Bishop's Stortford (Herts.).

HATHERLEIGH Devon 403 H 31 – pop. 1 542 – ECD : Wednesday – Okehampton – 01837.

London 230 – Exeter 29 – Plymouth 38.

The Tally Ho, 14 Market St., EX20 3JN, 810306, « Part 16C inn », – rm . VISA.
Meals *(in bar Sunday, Wednesday and Thursday)* (bar lunch)/dinner 16.50 **st.** and a la carte 3.75 – 2.75 – **3 rm** 28.00/40.00 **st.**

at Sheepwash NW : 5½ m. by A 3072 – Beaworthy – 01409 :

Half Moon Inn, The Square, EX21 5NE, 231376, Fax 231673, « 17C inn », – . VISA
closed January – **Meals** (bar lunch)/dinner 17.75 **t.** 4.50 – **14 rm** 33.00/66.00 **t.**

HATHERSAGE Derbs. 402 403 404 P 24 – pop. 2 858 – ECD : Wednesday – Sheffield (S. Yorks.) – 01433.

Sickleholme, Bamford 651306.

London 165 – Manchester 33 – Sheffield 10.

George, Main Rd, S30 1BB, 650436, Fax 650099 – – 30. VISA.
Meals 6.00/18.00 **t.** and a la carte 5.50 – **18 rm** 59.50/80.00 **t.** – SB.

Highlow Hall, S30 1AX, S : 1½ m. by B 6001 on Abney rd 650393, park –
Meals (by arrangement) 15.95 **st.** 4.50 – **6 rm** 18.00/55.00 **st.** – SB.

HATTON Warks. – see Warwick.

HAVANT Hants. 404 R 31 – pop. 50 098 – ECD : Wednesday – 01705.

1 Park Rd South, PO9 1HA 480024.

London 70 – Brighton 39 – Portsmouth 9 – Southampton 22.

Bear, 15 East St., PO9 1AA, 486501, Fax 470551 – rm – 100
42 rm.

ATS 60-62 Bedhampton Rd 483018/451570

HAWES N. Yorks. 402 N 21 – pop. 1 315 – 01969.

Dales Countryside Museum, Station Yard, DL8 3NT 667450 (summer only).

London 253 – Kendal 27 – Leeds 72 – York 65.

Simonstone Hall, Simonstone, DL8 3LY, N : 1 ½ m. on Muker rd 667255, Fax 667741, – rest . VISA
Meals (bar lunch Monday to Saturday)/dinner 19.75 **t.** 6.50 – **10 rm** 55.00/100.00 **t.** – SB.

Stone House, Sedbusk, DL8 3PT, N : 1 m. by Muker rd on Askrigg rd 667571, Fax 667720, « Collections of ornaments and curios », – rest . VISA
closed January – **Meals** (dinner only) 15.50 **t.** 3.95 – **18 rm** 30.50/74.00 **t.** – SB.

Rookhurst Georgian Country House, Gayle, DL8 3RT, S : ½ m. by Gayle rd 667454, – . VISA.
closed 16 December-31 January – **Meals** (booking essential) (residents only) (dinner only) 20.00 **t.** and a la carte 12.00/20.00 **t.** 6.75 – **5 rm** (dinner included) 45.00/112.00 **t.** – SB.

Cockett's, Market Pl., DL8 3RD, 667312, Fax 667162, – . VISA.
closed 28 November-27 December – **Meals** *(closed Friday lunch)* 15.00 **st.** (dinner) and a la carte 8.95/23.40 **st.** 5.60 – **8 rm** 30.00/54.00 **st.** – SB.

Herriot's, Main St., DL8 3QU, 667536 – . VISA
April-October – **Meals** (bar lunch)/dinner a la carte 11.85/14.65 **t.** 3.95 – **6 rm** 29.00/46.00 **t.** – SB.

Brandymires, Muker Rd, DL8 3PR, 667482 –
February-mid October – **Meals** (by arrangement) 10.50 3.50 – **4 rm** 25.50/35.00 **st.**

HAWKHURST Kent 404 V 30 **Great Britain G.** – pop. 4 217 – ECD : Wednesday – ☎ 01580.

Envir. : Bodiam Castle★★ *AC*, SE : 3½ m. by B 2244.

♦London 47 – Folkestone 34 – Hastings 14 – Maidstone 19.

- **Tudor Court**, Rye Rd, TN18 5DA, E : ¾ m. on A 268 ℘ 752312, Fax 753966, ≤, « Gardens », – ⇔ rest TV ☎ P – 60. VISA JCB
  Meals *(closed Monday lunch)* 12.95/14.95 **t.** and dinner a la carte 4.25 – **18 rm** 49.00/80.00 **t.** – SB.

HAWKRIDGE Somerset 403 J 30 **The West Country G.** – ✉ Dulverton – ☎ 0164 385.

Envir. : Tarr Steps★★, NE : 2½ m.

Exc. : Exmoor National Park★★.

♦London 203 – Exeter 32 – Minehead 17 – Taunton 32.

- Tarr Steps, TA22 9PY, NE : 1½ m. ℘ 293, ≤, , park – P
  13 rm.

Michelin issues no plaques or signs to hotels and restaurants mentioned in this Guide.

HAWKSHEAD Cumbria 402 L 20 **Great Britain G.** – pop. 570 – ECD : Thursday – ✉ Ambleside – ☎ 0153 94.

See : Village★.

Envir. : Lake Windermere★★ – Coniston Water★ (Brantwood★, on east side), SW : by B 5285.

Main Car Park, LA22 0NT ℘ 36525 (summer only).

♦London 283 – ♦Carlisle 52 – Kendal 19.

- **Highfield House**, Hawkshead Hill, LA22 0PN, W : ½ m. on B 5285 (Coniston rd) ℘ 36344, Fax 36793, ≤ Kirkstone Pass and Fells, – ⇔ rest TV P. VISA
  closed 3 to 27 January and 22 to 26 December – **Meals** (light lunch)/dinner 17.50 **st.** – **11 rm** 33.50/62.00 **st.** – SB.
- **Queen's Head**, Main St., LA22 0NS, ℘ 36271, Fax 36722 – TV ☎. VISA.
  Meals (bar lunch)/dinner a la carte 14.00/24.00 **t.** 4.75 – **14 rm** 45.00/59.50 **t.**
- **Rough Close**, LA22 0QF, S : 1½ m. on Newby Bridge rd ℘ 36370, – ⇔ P. VISA.
  April-October – 4.50 – **5 rm** (dinner included) 42.50/75.00 **t.**
- **Ivy House**, Main St., LA22 0NS, ℘ 36204 – ⇔ rest P
  March-October – **Meals** 10.50 **t.** – **11 rm** 25.50/55.00 **t.** – SB.

at ***Near Sawrey*** SE : 2 m. on B 5285 – ✉ Ambleside – ☎ 0153 94.

- **Ees Wyke**, LA22 0JZ, ℘ 36393, Fax 36393, ≤ Esthwaite Water and Grizedale Forest, – ⇔ rest TV P.
  closed January and February – **Meals** (booking essential) (dinner only) 18.00 **st.** – **8 rm** (dinner included) 58.00/100.00 **st.** – SB.
- Garth Country House, LA22 0JZ, ℘ 36373, ≤, – TV P
  7 rm.

at ***Far Sawrey*** SE : 2½ m. on B 5285 – ✉ Ambleside – ☎ 0153 94.

- **West Vale**, LA22 0LQ, ℘ 42817, ≤ – ⇔ rest P.
  March-October – **Meals** 10.00 **t.** 3.50 – **8 rm** 21.50/43.00 **t.**

at ***Grizedale*** SW : 2¾ m. – ✉ Ambleside – ☎ 0153 94.

- **Grizedale Lodge**, LA22 0QL, ℘ 36532, Fax 36572 – ⇔ TV P. VISA.
  closed 2 January-10 February – **Meals** (bar lunch)/dinner 17.95 **t.** 4.50 – **9 rm** (dinner included) 60.00/104.00 **t.** – SB.

HAWNBY N. Yorks 402 Q 21 – see Helmsley.

HAWORTH W. Yorks. 402 O 22 **Great Britain G.** – pop. 5 041 – ECD : Tuesday – ✉ Keighley – ☎ 01535.

See : Haworth Parsonage and the Brontës★ *AC*.

2-4 West Lane, BD22 8EF ℘ 642329.

♦London 213 – Burnley 22 – ♦Leeds 22 – ♦Manchester 34.

- **Old White Lion**, 6 West Lane, BD22 8DU, ℘ 642313, Fax 646222 – TV ☎ P – 70. VISA.
  Meals (bar lunch Monday to Saturday)/dinner 11.00 **st.** and a la carte – **14 rm** 35.00/46.00 **st.** – SB.
- **Ferncliffe**, Hebden Rd, BD22 8RS, on A 6033 ℘ 643405, ≤ – TV P. VISA
  closed 26 to 30 December – **Meals** (by arrangement) 10.95 **st.** 3.75 – **6 rm** 19.50/39.00 **st.**
- XX **Weaver's** with rm, 15 West Lane, BD22 8DU, ℘ 643822, « Converted weavers cottages » – ⇔ rest TV ☎. VISA.
  closed first 2 weeks January and last 2 weeks July – **Meals** *(closed Sunday and Monday)* (dinner only) 12.95 **t.** and a la carte 4.15 – **4 rm** 47.50/67.50 **t.** – SB.

HAYDOCK Mersey. 402 403 404 M 23 – pop. 10 965 – ✉ St Helens – ☎ 01942.

♦London 198 – ♦Liverpool 17 – ♦Manchester 18.

Haydock Thistle (Mt. Charlotte Thistle), Penny Lane, WA11 9SG, NE : ½ m. on A 599 ✆ 272000, Fax 711092, – rm rest – 250.
Meals (bar lunch Saturday) 12.00/18.50 **st.** and a la carte – 8.95 – **135 rm** 79.00/89.00 **st.**, 4 suites – SB.

Forte Posthouse, Lodge Lane, WA12 0JG, NE : 1 m. on A 49 ✆ 717878, Fax 718419, – rm rest – 180.
Meals a la carte approx. 15.00 **t.** 5.50 – **136 rm** 56.00/69.50 **st.**

Forte Travelodge without rest., Piele Rd, WA11 9TL, on A 580 ✆ 272055, Reservations (Freephone) 0800 850950 – – **40 rm** 33.50 **t.**

ATS Legh Rd, ✆ (0744) 750551

HAYDON BRIDGE Northd. 401 402 N 19 – ✉ Hexham – ☎ 01434.

♦London 344 – Carlisle 31 – ♦Newcastle-upon-Tyne 27.

Geeswood House, Whittis Rd, NE47 6AQ, ✆ 684220, –
closed Christmas – **Meals** (communal dining) 10.00 **st.** – **3 rm** 20.00/34.00 **st.** – SB.

HAYFIELD Derbs. 402 403 404 O 23 – ✉ Stockport (Ches.) – ☎ 01663.

♦London 191 – ♦Manchester 22 – ♦Sheffield 29.

Waltzing Weasel, New Mills Rd, Birch Vale, SK12 5BT, W : ½ m. on A 6015 ✆ 743402, Fax 743402, –
closed Christmas Day – **Meals** (carving lunch) 15.00/23.75 **t.** and lunch a la carte 4.50 – **8 rm** 45.00/95.00 **st.**

Old Bank House, SK12 5EP, off Church St. ✆ 747354 – .
Meals (by arrangement) 11.50 – **3 rm** 20.00/38.00 **s.** – SB.

Bridge End, 7 Church St., SK12 5JE, ✆ 747321, Fax 742121 – .
Meals (dinner only and Sunday lunch)/dinner a la carte 18.10/25.45 **t.** 4.75.

HAYLING ISLAND Hants. 404 R 31 – pop. 16 016 – ECD : Wednesday – ☎ 01705.

Links Lane ✆ 463712/463777 – Beachlands Seafront, PO11 OAG ✆ 467111 (summer only).

♦London 77 – ♦Brighton 45 – ♦Southampton 28.

Cockle Warren Cottage, 36 Seafront, PO11 9HL, ✆ 464961, heated – .
closed 1 week June and 1 week October – **Meals** (by arrangement) 26.50 **st.** 4.25 – **5 rm** 45.00/84.00 **st.** – SB.

HAYTOR Devon – see Bovey Tracey.

HAYTOR VALE Devon – see Bovey Tracey.

HAYWARDS HEATH W. Sussex 404 T 31 – ☎ 01444.

Paxhill Park, Lindfield ✆ 484467.

♦London 41 – ♦Brighton 16.

Birch, Lewes Rd, RH17 7SF, E : ¾ m. on A 272 ✆ 451565, Fax 440109 – rm – 60.
Meals (bar lunch Saturday) 10.95/15.95 and a la carte 4.50 – **53 rm** 58.00/72.00 – SB.

ATS Gower Rd ✆ 412640/454189

HEADLAM Durham – see Darlington.

HEATHFIELD E. Sussex 404 U 31 – pop. 6 280 – ☎ 01435.

♦London 51 – ♦Brighton 23 – Eastbourne 16.

Risingholme without rest., 38 High St., TN21 8LS, ✆ 864645, – .
closed January and February – **4 rm** 25.00/40.00 **s.**

HEATHROW AIRPORT Middx. – see Hillingdon (Greater London).

HEBDEN BRIDGE W. Yorks. 402 N 22 – pop. 4 167 – ECD : Tuesday – ✉ Halifax – ☎ 01422 – Hebden Bridge, Wadsworth ✆ 842896 – 1 Bridge Gate, HX7 8EX ✆ 843831.

♦London 223 – Burnley 13 – ♦Leeds 24 – ♦Manchester 25.

Carlton, Albert St., HX7 8ES, ✆ 844400, Fax 843117 – – 100.
Meals 7.25/11.00 **st.** and a la carte – **18 rm** 59.00/79.00 **st.** – SB.

Redacre Mill, Mytholmroyd, HX7 5DQ, SE : 1 ½ m. by A646 off Westfield Terr. ✆ 885563, « Converted canalside warehouse », – .
closed weekends November-February – **Meals** (bar lunch)/dinner 10.50 **st.** – **5 rm** 35.00/50.00 **st.** – SB.

Kitties, 52 Market St., HX7 6AA, ✆ 842956.
closed Monday, Tuesday and 25 December - 31 January – **Meals** (dinner only) a la carte 16.50/28.00 **t.** 4.95.

HEDON Humbs. 402 T 22 – see Kingston-upon-Hull.

HEIGHINGTON Durham 402 P20 – see Darlington.

HELFORD Cornwall 403 E 33 **The West Country G.** – ✉ Helston – ☎ 01326.

Envir. : Lizard Peninsula★.

Exc. : Helston (Flora Day Furry Dance★★) (May) W : 11 m.

♦London 324 – Falmouth 15 – Penzance 22 – Truro 27.

XX **Riverside** with rm, TR12 6JU, ☎ 231443, Fax 231103, ≤, « Converted cottages in picturesque setting », – TV P.
March-October – **Meals** (dinner only) 30.00 **st.** 5.00 – **6 rm** 60.00/120.00 **st.**

at Gillan SE : 3 m. – ✉ Helston – ☎ 01326 :

Tregildry, TR12 6HG, ☎ 231378, Fax 231561, ≤ Gillan Creek, sea, – TV P. VISA
mid March-mid October – **Meals** (bar lunch)/dinner 17.00 **t.** 4.25 – **10 rm** 31.50/62.00 – SB.

HELLIDON Northants. 404 Q 27 – see Daventry.

HELMSLEY N. Yorks. 402 Q 21 **Great Britain G.** – pop. 1 833 – ECD : Wednesday – ☎ 01439.

Envir. : Rievaulx Abbey★★ *AC*, NW : 2½ m. by B 1257.

Ampleforth College, 56 High St. ☎ 770678.

Town Hall, Market Pl., YO6 5BL ☎ 770173 (summer only).

♦London 234 – ♦Middlesbrough 29 – York 24.

Black Swan (Forte), Market Pl., YO6 5BJ, ☎ 770466, Fax 770174, « Part 16C inn », – TV ☎ P. AE VISA JCB
Meals 15.00/26.00 **st.** and a la carte 7.00 – 9.50 – **44 rm** 85.00/170.00 **st.** – SB.

Feathers, Market Pl., YO6 5BH, ☎ 770275, Fax 771101, – TV P. AE VISA
closed 1 week Christmas and 27 January - 9 February – **Meals** (bar lunch)/dinner a la carte 9.20/17.25 **t.** 4.00 – **17 rm** 22.00/53.00 **t.** – SB.

Laskill Farm, YO6 5BN, NW : 6 ¼ m. by B 1257 ☎ 798268, « Working farm », – rest TV P
Meals (by arrangement) (communal dining) 11.00 3.50 – **8 rm** 17.50/40.00 **st.**

at Harome E : 2¾ m. by A 170 – ✉ York – ☎ 01439 :

Pheasant, YO6 5JG, ☎ 771241, – rest TV ☎ P
closed January, February and Christmas – **Meals** (bar lunch)/dinner 18.50 **t.** 2.60 – **12 rm** (dinner included) 57.50/120.00 **t.**, 2 suites – SB.

at Nawton E : 3¼ m. on A 170 – ✉ York – ☎ 01439 :

Plumpton Court, High St., YO6 5TT, ☎ 771223, – P.
mid March-October – **Meals** (by arrangement) 10.50 **st.** 3.10 – **8 rm** 31.00/48.00 **st.**

at Nunnington SE : 6¼ m. by A 170 off B 1257 – ✉ York – ☎ 01439 :

XX **Ryedale Lodge** with rm, YO6 5XB, W : 1 m. ☎ 748246, Fax 694633, ≤, « Converted railway station », – rest TV ☎ P. VISA
Meals (dinner only) 26.75 **t.** 5.00 – **7 rm** 47.50/81.00 **t.** – SB.

at Old Byland NW : 5 m. by B 1257 – ☎ 01439 :

Valley View Farm, YO6 5LG, ☎ 798221, « Working farm », , park – TV P. VISA
Meals 12.00 **s.** 3.00 – **4 rm** 25.00/50.00 **s.** – SB.

at Hawnby NW : 6¼ m. by B 1257 – ✉ Helmsley – ☎ 01439 :

Hawnby, YO6 5QS, ☎ 798202, Fax 798417, – TV ☎ P. VISA.
closed January and February – **Meals** *(closed Tuesday)* (dinner only) 20.00 **t.** 4.25 – **6 rm** 50.00/70.00 **t.** – SB.

HEMEL HEMPSTEAD Herts. 404 S 28 – pop. 80 110 – ECD : Wednesday – ☎ 01442.

Little Hay, Box Lane, Bovington ☎ 833798 – Boxmoor, 18 Box Lane ☎ 242434.

Dacorum Information Centre, HP1 1HA ☎ 64451/60161.

♦London 30 – Aylesbury 16 – Luton 10 – Northampton 46.

Forte Posthouse, Breakspear Way, HP2 4UA, E : 2 ½ m. on A 414 ☎ 251122, Fax 211812, – rm TV ☎ P – 60. AE VISA JCB
Meals a la carte approx. 15.00 **t.** 5.50 – **146 rm** 53.50/69.50 **st.**

Boxmoor Lodge, London Rd, HP1 2RA, W : 1 m. on A 41 ☎ 230770, Fax 252230 – TV ☎ P. AE VISA
Meals *(closed Monday lunch and Sunday)* 9.95/15.75 **t.** and a la carte 4.95 – **18 rm** 48.00/65.00 **t.**

at Bourne End W : 2 1/4 m. on A 4251 – ✉ Hemel Hempstead – ☎ 01442 :

Hemel Hempstead Moat House (Q.M.H.), London Rd, HP1 2RJ, ℘ 871241, Fax 866130 – rm – 100
61 rm.

Travel Inn, Story Lane, HPI 2S8, ℘ 879149, Fax 879147 – rm. AE VISA.
Meals (grill rest.) a la carte approx. 16.00 **t.** – 4.95 – **60 rm** 33.50 **t.**

HENFIELD W. Sussex 404 T 31 – ☎ 01903.

London 47 – Brighton 10 – Worthing 11.

Tottington Manor, Edburton, BN5 9LJ, SE : 3 1/2 m. by A 2037 on Fulking rd ℘ 815757, Fax 879331, –. AE VISA.
Meals 19.00 **t.** (dinner) and a la carte 18.55/24.15 **t.** 5.00 – **6 rm** 40.00/90.00 **t.** – SB.

at Wineham NE : 3 1/2 m. by A 281, B 2116 and Wineham Lane – ✉ Henfield – ☎ 01403.

Frylands without rest., BN5 9BP, W : 1/4 m. taking left turn at telephone box ℘ 710214, Fax 711449, « Part Elizabethan farmhouse », heated, , park –.
closed 23 December-1 January – **3 rm** 16.00/35.00.

HENLEY-IN-ARDEN Warks. 403 404 O 27 – pop. 1 814 – ECD : Thursday – ☎ 01564.

London 104 – Birmingham 15 – Stratford-upon-Avon 8 – Warwick 8.5.

Ashleigh House without rest., Whitley Hill, B95 5DL, E : 1 3/4 m. on Warwick Rd ℘ 792315, Fax 794133, –. VISA.
10 rm 40.00/50.00 **st.**

HENLEY-ON-THAMES Oxon. 404 R 29 – pop. 10 558 – ECD : Wednesday – ☎ 01491.

Huntercombe, Nuffield ℘ 641207 – Town Hall, Market Place, RG9 2AQ ℘ 578034.

London 40 – Oxford 23 – Reading 9.

Shepherds without rest., Rotherfield Greys, RG9 4QL, W : 3 1/2 m. by Peppard rd on Shepherds Green rd ℘ 628413, –.
closed Christmas and New Year – **4 rm** 23.00/48.00 **st.**

Villa Marina, 18 Thameside, RG9 1BH, ℘ 575262, Fax 411394 – AE VISA
Meals - Italian 6.00 **t.** (lunch) and a la carte 15.80/23.90 **t.** 4.00.

Slow Boat, 25 Duke St., RG9 1UR, ℘ 410001 – AE VISA
closed 25 to 28 December – **Meals** - Chinese (Peking) 5.50/18.00 **st.** and a la carte.

at Stonor N : 4 m. by A 4130 on B 480 – ✉ Henley-on-Thames – ☎ 01491.

Stonor Arms with rm, RG9 6HE, ℘ 638345, Fax 638863, –. AE VISA.
***Stonor* : Meals** *(closed Sunday)* (dinner only) 29.50/34.00 **t.** – **8 rm** 82.50/92.50 **t.**, 1 suite – SB.

Blades, – **Meals** a la carte 15.05/25.70 **t.**

at Frieth (Bucks.) NE : 7 1/2 m. by A 4155 – ✉ Henley-on-Thames – ☎ 01494.

Yew Tree, RG9 6RJ, ℘ 882330 –. AE VISA
Meals 13.95/18.95 **t.** and a la carte 4.95.

HEREFORD Heref. and Worcs. 403 L 27 **Great Britain G.** – pop. 50 234 – ECD : Thursday – ☎ 01432.

See : City★ - Cathedral★★ (Mappa Mundi★) A **A** – Old House★ A **B.**

Exc. : Kilpeck (Church of SS. Mary and David★★) SW : 8 m. by A 465 B.

Ravens Causeway, Wormsley ℘ 830219 – Belmont House, Belmont ℘ 352666 – , Hereford Municipal,Holmer Rd ℘ 278178 B – 1 King Street, HR4 9BW ℘ 268430.

London 133 – Birmingham 51 – Cardiff 56.

Plan on next page

Green Dragon (Forte), Broad St., HR4 9BG, ℘ 272506, Fax 352139 – – 200. AE VISA — A **e**
Meals 7.95/24.45 **t.** and dinner a la carte 5.25 – 8.50 – **84 rm** 65.00/75.00 **t.**, 3 suites – SB.

Hereford Moat House (Q.M.H.), Belmont Rd, HR2 7BP, SW : 1 1/2 m. on A 465 ℘ 354301, Fax 275114 – – 300. AE VISA — B **c**
Meals *(closed Saturday lunch)* (carving lunch)/dinner 20.00 **st.** and a la carte 5.00 – 8.75 – **60 rm** 55.00/75.00 **st.** – SB.

Castle Pool, Castle St., HR1 2NR, ℘ 356321, Fax 356321, –. AE VISA
Meals 7.90/15.00 **st.** and a la carte 4.00 – **26 rm** 35.00/82.00 **st.** – SB. — A **a**

Travel Inn, Holmer Rd, Holmer, HR4 9RS, N : 1 3/4 m. on A 49 ℘ 274853, Fax 343003 – rm. AE VISA. — B
Meals (Beefeater grill) a la carte approx. 16.00 **t.** – 4.95 – **39 rm** 33.50 **st.**

Merton, 28 Commercial Rd, HR1 2BD, ℘ 265925, Fax 354983, –. AE VISA. — A **n**
Meals *(closed Sunday)* (bar lunch)/dinner a la carte 11.40/21.50 **t.** 5.00 – **17 rm** 40.00/65.00 **st.** – SB.

HEREFORD

Broad Street . . . . A 7
Commercial Street . . . A 13
High Street . . . . A 19
High Town. . . . . A 20
Maylord Orchards Shopping Centre. . . A

Aubrey St. . . . . A 3
Berrington St. . . . . A 5

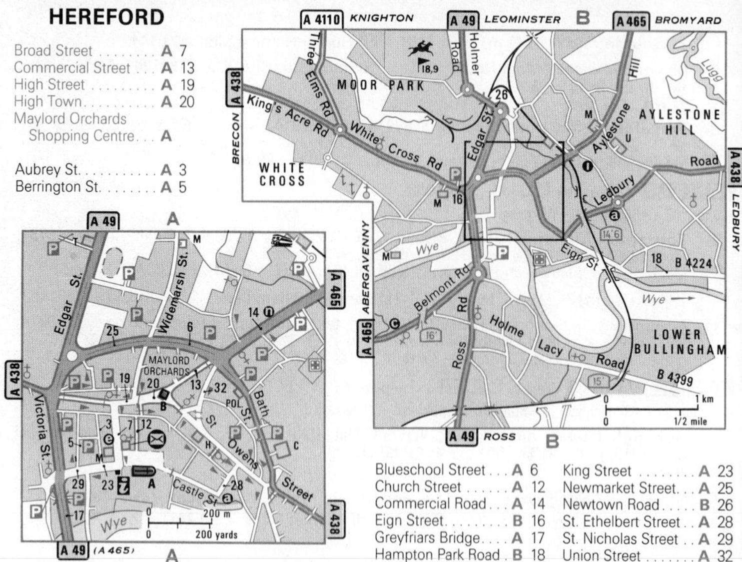

Blueschool Street . . . A 6
Church Street . . . . . . A 12
Commercial Road . . . A 14
Eign Street. . . . . B 16
Greyfriars Bridge. . . . A 17
Hampton Park Road . B 18
King Street . . . . A 23
Newmarket Street. . . A 25
Newtown Road. . . . . B 26
St. Ethelbert Street . . A 28
St. Nicholas Street . . A 29
Union Street . . . . A 32

Somerville, 12 Bodenham Rd, HR1 2TS, ℘ 273991, Fax 265862, – TV ☎ P. AE VISA — B i
Meals 11.50 **t.** 4.40 – **10 rm** 26.00/51.00 **t.** – SB.

Ferncroft, 144 Ledbury Rd, HR1 2TB, ℘ 265538, – TV P. VISA. — B a
closed 2 weeks December-January – **Meals** (by arrangement) 15.00 **st.** 3.75 – **11 rm** 21.00/45.00 **st.**

Ramblers Court, Whitestone, HR1 3SD, NE : 4 m. by A 465 B on A 4103 ℘ 850128, – rest TV P
Meals 11.50 **st.** – 5.00 – **5 rm** 25.00/30.00.

at Marden N : 5 ¾ m. by A 49 – B – ✉ Hereford – 01568 :

The Vauld Farm, HR1 3HA, NE : 1 ½ m. by Urdimarsh rd ℘ 797898, « 16C timbered farmhouse », – P.
Meals (by arrangement) (communal dining) 15.00 **s.** – **4 rm** 20.00/50.00 **s.**, 1 suite.

at Canon Pyon N : 7 m. on A 4110 – B – ✉ Hereford – 01432 :

Hermitage Manor without rest., HR4 8NR, S : 1 m. on A 4110 ℘ 760317, ≤ Vale of Hereford, – TV P.
Easter-November – **3 rm** 30.00/50.00.

at Dormington E : 5 ¼ m. on A 438 – B – ✉ Hereford – 01432 :

Dormington Court, HR1 4DA, ℘ 850370, Fax 850370, – rest TV P. VISA
Meals (dinner only) 16.50 **st.** 5.00 – **8 rm** 34.00/60.00 **st.** – SB.

at Much Birch S : 5 ½ m. on A 49 – B – ✉ Hereford – 01981 :

Pilgrim, Ross Rd, HR2 8HJ, ℘ 540742, Fax 540620, ≤, – TV ☎ P – 45. AE VISA.
Meals (bar lunch)/dinner 19.50 **st.** and a la carte 4.95 – **20 rm** 49.50/59.50 **st.** – SB.

at Ruckhall W : 5 m. by A 49 off A 465 – B – ✉ Eaton Bishop – 01981 :

Ancient Camp Inn, HR2 9QX, ℘ 250449, ≤ River Wye and countryside – TV ☎ P. VISA.
Meals *(closed Sunday dinner and Monday)* a la carte 15.00/17.50 **t.** 5.20 – **5 rm** 35.00/58.00 **t.**

at Byford W : 7 ½ m. by A 438 B – ✉ Hereford – 01981.

Old Rectory, HR4 7LD, on A 438 ℘ 22218 (590218 from June), Fax 22499 (590499 from June), – TV P.
March-November – **Meals** (by arrangement) 12.50 **s.** – **3 rm** 25.00/37.00 **s.**

ATS 6 Kyrle St. ℘ 265491

HERMITAGE Dorset - see Sherborne.

HERNE BAY Kent 404 X 29 – pop. 26 523 – ECD : Thursday – ☎ 01227.

Herne Bay, Eddington ✆ 374097 – 🛈 12 William Street, CT6 5EJ ✆ 361911.

♦London 63 – ♦Dover 24 – Maidstone 32 – Margate 13.

Northdown without rest., 14 Cecil Park, CT6 6DL, ✆ 372051, Fax 372051, – TV ☎ P. VISA.
5 rm 19.00/42.00 **st.**

HERSTMONCEUX E. Sussex 404 U 31 – pop. 3 898 – ☎ 01323.

♦London 63 – Eastbourne 12 – Hastings 14 – Lewes 16.

XX **Sundial,** Gardner St., BN27 4LA, ✆ 832217, « Converted 16C cottage », – P. AE VISA
closed Sunday dinner, Monday, 6 August-3 September and Christmas-20 January – **Meals** - French 15.50/24.50 **t.** and a la carte 5.50.

HERTFORD Herts. 404 T 28 – pop. 22 176 – ☎ 01992.

🛈 The Castle, SG14 1HR ✆ 584322.

♦London 24 – ♦Cambridge 35 – Luton 26.

Hall House , Broad Oak End, SG14 2JA, NW : 1 ¾ m. by A 119 and Bramfield Rd ✆ 582807, – TV P. VISA.
closed Christmas and New Year – **Meals** (by arrangement) 20.00 **s.** – **3 rm** 48.00/60.00 **s.**

HERTINGFORDBURY Herts. 404 T 28 – pop. 633 – ✉ Hertford – ☎ 01992.

♦London 26 – Luton 18.

White Horse (Forte), Hertingfordbury Rd, SG14 2LB, ✆ 586791, Fax 550809, – TV ☎ P – 50. AE VISA JCB
Meals *(closed Saturday lunch)* 10.25/18.95 **t.** and a la carte 6.00 – 8.50 – **42 rm** 70.00/95.00 **st.** – SB.

HETHERSETT Norfolk 404 X 26 – see Norwich.

HETTON N. Yorks. 402 N 21 – pop. 115 – ✉ Skipton – ☎ 01756.

♦London 237 – Burnley 25 – ♦Leeds 33.

XXX **Angel Inn,** BD23 6LT, ✆ 730263, Fax 730363, « Attractive 18C inn » – P. VISA
closed Sunday dinner – **Meals** (bar lunch Monday to Saturday)/dinner 22.95 **t.** 4.50.

HEVERSHAM Cumbria 402 L 21 – ✉ Milnthorpe – ☎ 0153 95.

♦London 270 – Kendal 7 – Lancaster 18 – ♦Leeds 72.

Blue Bell, Princes Way, LA7 7EE, on A 6 ✆ 62018, Fax 62455, – TV ☎ P. AE VISA
Meals 10.95/15.95 **t.** and a la carte 4.95 – **21 rm** 34.50/64.00 **st.** – SB.

HEXHAM Northd. 401 402 N 19 **Great Britain G.** – pop. 11 342 – ECD : Thursday – ☎ 01434.

See : Abbey★ (Saxon Crypt★★, Leschman chantry★).

Envir. : Hadrian's Wall★★, N : 4½ m. by A 6079.

Exc. : Housesteads★★, NW : 12½ m. by A 6079 and B 6318.

Spital Park ✆ 602057 – Slaley Hall, Slaley ✆ 673350 – Tynedale, Tyne Green ✆ 608154.

🛈 The Manor Office, Hallgate, NE46 1XD ✆ 605225.

♦London 304 – ♦Carlisle 37 – ♦Newcastle upon Tyne 21.

Beaumont, Beaumont St., NE46 3LT, ✆ 602331, Fax 602331 – TV ☎ – 80. AE VISA JCB.
closed 25 and 26 December – **Meals** a la carte 12.50/24.00 **t.** 3.75 – **23 rm** 50.00/80.00 **t.** – SB.

County, Priestpopple, NE46 1PS, ✆ 602030 – TV ☎. AE VISA
Meals a la carte 5.75/11.30 **t.** 4.00 – **9 rm** 42.00/55.00 **t.** – SB.

Middlemarch without rest., Hencotes, NE46 2EB, ✆ 605003 – TV P.
3 rm 26.00/48.00 **st.**

West Close House without rest., Hextol Terr., NE46 2AD, by Allendale Rd ✆ 603307, – P
4 rm 18.50/46.00 **st.**

XX **Black House,** Dipton Mill Rd, NE46 1RZ, S : 1 ¼ m. by B 6306 and Whitley Chapel rd ✆ 604744 – P. VISA
closed Sunday and Monday – **Meals** (dinner only) 25.95 **t.** and a la carte **t.** 5.40.

ATS Haugh Lane ✆ 602394

HEYTESBURY Wilts. 403 404 N 30 – see Warminster.

HICKSTEAD W. Sussex – ☎ 01444.

Forte Travelodge without rest., Jobs Lane, RH17 5N7, off A 23 ✆ 881377, Reservations (Freephone) 0800 850950 – TV P. AE VISA.
40 rm 33.50 **t.**

HIGHAM Suffolk 404 W 28 – pop. 119 – ✉ Colchester – ☎ 01206.
◆London 55 – Colchester 10 – ◆Ipswich 11.

- **Old Vicarage** without rest., CO7 6JY, ☎ 337248, ≤, « 16C former vicarage », heated, –
  3 rm 25.00/54.00 **st.**

HIGH WYCOMBE Bucks. 404 R 29 – pop. 69 575 – ECD : Wednesday – ☎ 01494.
Penn Rd, Hazlemere ☎ 714722 – Wycombe Heights, Rayners Av., Loudwater ☎ 816686.
6 Cornmarket, HP11 2BW ☎ 421892.
◆London 34 – Aylesbury 17 – ◆Oxford 26 – Reading 18.

- **Forte Posthouse,** Handy Cross, HP11 1TL, SW : 1 ½ m. by A 404 ☎ 442100, Fax 439071 – rm rest – 100. AE VISA
  Meals a la carte approx. 15.00 **t.** 5.50 – **106 rm** 59.50/69.50 **st.**
- **Alexandra,** Queen Alexandra Rd, HP11 2JX, ☎ 463494, Fax 463560 – . AE VISA.
  closed 24 to 27 December – **Meals** *(closed Bank Holidays)* (dinner only) 8.95 **st.** and a la carte 4.00 – 7.90 – **29 rm** 54.00 **st.**, 1 suite.

ATS Copyground Lane ☎ 525101/438019

HILLSFORD BRIDGE Devon – see Lynton.

HILMARTON Wilts. 403 404 O 29 – ✉ Calne – ☎ 01249.
◆London 94 – ◆Bristol 36 – Salisbury 39 – Swindon 14.

- **Burfoots,** 1 The Close, SN11 8TQ, ☎ 760492, Fax 760609, heated, – .
  Meals (by arrangement) 11.50 – **3 rm** 17.50/40.00 **st.**

HILPERTON Wilts. 403 404 N 30 – see Trowbridge.

HILTON PARK SERVICE AREA W. Mids. – ✉ Wolverhampton – ☎ 01922.

- Pavilion Lodge without rest., WV11 2DR, M 6 between junctions 10 A and 11 ☎ 414100, Fax 418762 –
  64 rm.

HINCKLEY Leics. 402 403 404 P 26 – pop. 35 510 – ECD : Thursday – ☎ 01455.
Hinckley Library, Lancaster Rd, LE10 0AT ☎ 635106.
◆London 103 – ◆Birmingham 31 – ◆Coventry 12 – ◆Leicester 14.

- **Sketchley Grange,** Sketchley Lane, LE10 3HU, S : 1 ½ m. by B 4109 (Rugby Rd) ☎ 251133, Fax 631384, – rm – 300. AE VISA
  Meals *(closed Sunday dinner)* 10.95/18.95 **t.** and a la carte 5.75 – **38 rm** 57.00/89.00 **st.** – SB.

ATS 5 Leicester Rd ☎ 632022/635835

HINDON Wilts. 403 404 N 30 – pop. 489 – ECD : Saturday – ✉ Salisbury – ☎ 01747.
◆London 107 – Bath 28 – Bournemouth 40 – Salisbury 15.

- **Lamb at Hindon,** SP3 6DP, ☎ 820573, Fax 820605 – rest . AE VISA.
  Meals 13.50/25.50 **st.** and a la carte 4.95 – **13 rm** 38.00/55.00 **st.** – SB.

HINTLESHAM Suffolk 404 X 27 – see Ipswich.

HINTON CHARTERHOUSE Avon – see Bath.

HITCHIN Herts. 404 T 28 – pop. 33 480 – ECD : Wednesday – ☎ 01462.
Hitchin Library, Paynes Park, SG5 1EW ☎ 434738/450133.
◆London 40 – Bedford 14 – ◆Cambridge 26 – Luton 9.

- **Lord Lister,** Park St., SG4 9AH, ☎ 432712, Fax 438506 – . AE VISA
  Meals (by arrangement)(dinner only) 8.95 **st.** 2.75 – **20 rm** 46.00/60.00 **st.** – SB.

at Little Wymondley SE : 2½ m. by A 602 – ✉ Hitchin – ☎ 01438 :

- **Blakemore Thistle** (Mt. Charlotte Thistle), Blakemore End Rd, SG4 7JJ, ☎ 355821, Fax 742114, heated, – rm – 150. AE VISA
  Meals *(closed Saturday lunch)* 10.25/17.25 **st.** and a la carte – 8.50 – **80 rm** 65.00/75.00 **st.**, 2 suites – SB.
- XX **Redcoats Farmhouse** with rm, Redcoats Green, SG4 7JR, S : ½ m. by A 602 ☎ 729500, Fax 723322, « Part 15C farmhouse », – . AE VISA.
  closed 1 week Christmas – **Meals** *(closed Saturday lunch, Sunday dinner and Bank Holiday Mondays)* 12.00/15.00 **t.** and a la carte 4.50 – **14 rm** 53.00/93.00 **st.** – SB.

HOCKLEY HEATH Warks. 403 404 O 26 – pop. 3 507 – ✉ Solihull – ☎ 01564.
◆London 117 – ◆Birmingham 11 – ◆Coventry 17.

- **Nuthurst Grange,** Nuthurst Grange Lane, B94 5NL, S : ¾ m. by A 3400 ☎ 783972, Fax 783919, – – 40. AE VISA.
  Meals (see below) – 8.90 – **15 rm** 89.00/125.00 **t.** – SB.

XXX **Nuthurst Grange,** Nuthurst Grange Lane, B94 5NL, S : ¾ m. by A 3400 ℘ 783972, Fax 783919, ⛱ – ⇔ P. AE ① VISA
Meals *(closed Saturday lunch)* 16.50/45.00 **t.** 6.90.

HOCKLIFFE Beds. 404 S 28 – see Dunstable.

HOO GREEN Ches. – see Knutsford.

HODNET Shrops. 402 403 404 M 25 – pop. 1 405 – ☎ 01630.
♦London 166 – ♦Birmingham 50 – Chester 32 – ♦Stoke-on-Trent 22 – Shrewsbury 14.

Bear, Shrewsbury St., TF9 3NH, ℘ 685214, Fax 685787 – TV ☎ P. VISA.
Meals a la carte 9.80/20.00 **t.** 4.25 – **6 rm** 30.00/55.00 **t.** – SB.

at Stoke-on-Tern E : 2 ¼ m. by A 442 on Stoke-on-Tern rd – ✉ Market Drayton – ☎ 01630.

Stoke Manor without rest., TF9 2DU, E : ½ m. on Wistanswick rd ℘ 685222, Fax 685666, « Working farm with vintage tractor collection », ⛱ – ⇔ TV P.
closed December – **3 rm** 25.00/50.00 **st.**

HOLBETON Devon 403 I 32 – pop. 541 – ☎ 01752.
♦London 236 – Exeter 40 – ♦Plymouth 10 – Torquay 26.

Alston Hall, Alston, PL8 1HN, SW : 2½ m. ℘ 830555, Fax 830494, ≤, ⛱, ⛱ – ⇔ rest TV ☎ P – 80. AE ① VISA
Meals 12.50/22.00 **t.** and dinner a la carte 5.00 – **20 rm** 65.00/130.00 **t.** – SB.

HOLDENBY Northants. – ✉ Northampton – ☎ 01604.
♦London 77 – ♦Birmingham 58 – ♦Leicester 26 – Northampton 6.

XXX **Lynton House** with rm, NN6 8DJ, SE :¼ m. ℘ 770777, Fax 770777, ⛱ – TV ☎ P. AE VISA.
closed 1 week May, 1 week August and 4 days Christmas – **Meals** - Italian (closed Monday and Saturday lunch, Sunday and Bank Holidays) 11.50/19.75 **t.** and a la carte 6.75 – **5 rm** 49.00/55.00 **t.** – SB.

HOLFORD Somerset 403 K 30 **Great Britain G.** – pop. 307 – ✉ Bridgwater – ☎ 01278.
Envir. : Stogursey Priory Church★★, W : 4½m..
♦London 171 – ♦Bristol 48 – Minehead 15 – Taunton 22.

Combe House, Holford Combe, TA5 1RZ, S : 1 m. ℘ 741382, « Country house atmosphere », ⛱ – ⇔ rest TV ☎ P. AE VISA
mid March-October – **Meals** (bar lunch)/dinner 15.75 **st.** 4.70 – **19 rm** 39.00/98.00 **st.** – SB.

HOLMES CHAPEL Ches. 402 403 404 M 24 – pop. 5 369 – ☎ 01477.
♦London 181 – Chester 25 – ♦Liverpool 41 – ♦Manchester 24 – ♦Stoke-on-Trent 20.

Old Vicarage, Knutsford Rd, Cranage, CW4 8EF, NW : ½ m. on A 50 ℘ 532041, Fax 535728 – TV ☎ & P – 30. AE VISA.
***Church's Brasserie* : Meals** a la carte 12.90/18.25 **t.** 4.95 – **25 rm** 65.00/77.00 **st.** – SB.

Holly Lodge, 70 London Rd, CW4 7AS, on A 50 ℘ 537033, Fax 535823 – ⇔ rm TV ☎ P – 140. AE ① VISA
***Truffles* : Meals** (closed Saturday lunch and Bank Holidays) (dancing Friday night in winter) 8.60/13.95 **t.** – **33 rm** 64.00/75.00 **t.** – SB.

Cottage Rest. and Lodge, London Rd, Allostock, WA16 9LU, N : 3 m. on A 50 ℘ (01565) 722470, Fax 722749 – ⇔ rm TV ☎ P. AE VISA.
Meals *(closed Sunday to non-residents)* 9.95/16.00 **t.** and a la carte – **12 rm** 56.00/60.00 **t.** – SB.

HOLMFIRTH W. Yorks. 402 404 O 23 – pop. 21 148 – ECD : Tuesday – ✉ Huddersfield – ☎ 01484.
49-51 Huddersfield Rd, HD7 1JP ℘ 687603.
♦London 195 – ♦Leeds 23 – ♦Manchester 25 – ♦Sheffield 22.

Holme Castle, Holme, HD7 1QG, ℘ 686764, Fax 687775, ≤ – ⇔ TV P. AE VISA.
Meals (by arrangement) 19.00 **t.** 5.40 – **8 rm** 30.00/65.00 **t.**

HOLNE Devon 403 I 32 – see Ashburton.

HOLT Norfolk 404 X 25 – pop. 2 972 – ECD : Thursday – ☎ 01263.
♦London 124 – King's Lynn 34 – ♦Norwich 22.

XX **Yetman's,** 37 Norwich Rd, NR25 6SA, ℘ 713320 – ⇔
closed Monday and Tuesday – **Meals** (dinner only and lunch Saturday and Sunday) 19.50/29.50 **t.**

ATS Hempstead Rd Ind. Est. ℘ 712015

HOLYWELL Cambs. 404 T 27 – see St. Ives (Cambs.).

HONILEY Warks. – see Warwick

HONITON Devon 403 K 31 **The West Country G.** – pop. 6 490 – ECD : Thursday – ☎ 01404 :

See : All Hallows Museum★ *AC*.

Envir. : Ottery St. Mary★ (St. Mary's★) SW : 5 m. by A 30 and B 3177.

Exc. : Faraway Countryside Park (≤★) *AC*, SE : 6½ m. by A 375 and B 3174.

ℹ Dowell Street, East Car Park, EX14 8LT ☎ 43716 (summer only).

♦London 186 – Exeter 17 – ♦Southampton 93 – Taunton 18.

Deer Park ⛰, Buckerell Village, Weston, EX14 0PG, W : 2½ m. by A 30 ☎ 41266, Fax 46598, ≤, ≘s, ⛱ heated, ↝, ⛲, park, ⚔, squash – TV ☎ P – 🏛 60. ⊠ AE ⊙ VISA. ⚘
Meals 12.00/35.00 **st.** and a la carte 🍷 4.50 – **30 rm** ⊑ 33.00/120.00 **st.** – SB.

at Wilmington E : 3 m. on A 35 – ✉ Honiton – ☎ 01404 :

Home Farm, EX14 9JR, on A 35 ☎ 831278, Fax 831411, « Part 16C thatched farm », ⛲ – TV ☎ P. ⊠ AE VISA
Meals 12.00 **t.** and a la carte 🍷 5.85 – **13 rm** ⊑ 30.00/56.00 **t.** – SB.

at Payhembury NW : 7½ m. by A 30 – ✉ Honiton – ☎ 01404 :

Cokesputt House ⛰, EX14 0HD, ☎ 841289, ≤, « Part 17C and 18C house », ⛲ – ⊁ P. ⊠ AE VISA. ⚘
closed Christmas – **Meals** (booking essential) (residents only) (communal dining) 17.00 **s.** – **3 rm** ⊑ 29.00/58.00 **s.**

HOOK Hants. 404 R 30 – pop. 6 003 – ECD : Thursday – ✉ Basingstoke – ☎ 01256.

♦London 47 – Reading 13 – ♦Southampton 35.

Basingstoke Country, London Rd, Nately Scures, RG27 9JS, W : 1 m. on A 30 ☎ 764161, Fax 768341, Ⅎ₆, ≘s, ⛱, ⛲ – |‡| ▤ rest TV ☎ ♿ P – 🏛 170. ⊠ AE ⊙ VISA. ⚘
Meals *(closed Saturday lunch)* 11.75/19.50 **st.** and a la carte 🍷 5.25 – ⊑ 8.75 – **70 rm** 74.25 **st.** – SB.

Raven, Station Rd, RG27 9HS, ☎ 762541, Fax 768677, ≘s – ⊁ rm TV ☎ P – 🏛 90. ⊠ AE ⊙ VISA. ⚘
Meals 15.00 **t.** (dinner) and a la carte 13.00/24.00 **t.** – **38 rm** ⊑ 60.00/70.00 **t.**

White Hart, London Rd, RG27 9DZ, on A 30 ☎ 762462, Fax 768351, ⛲ – TV ☎ P. ⊠ AE VISA
Meals a la carte 10.05/18.75 **st.** – **22 rm** ⊑ 57.00/64.00 **st.**

Hook House without rest., London Rd, RG27 9EQ, W : ½ m. on A 30 ☎ 762630, Fax 760232, « Part Georgian house », ⛲ – ⊁ TV ☎ P. ⊠ AE VISA. ⚘
6 rm ⊑ 45.00 **t.**

at Rotherwick N : 2 m. by A 30 and B 3349 on Rotherwick rd – ✉ Basingstoke – ☎ 01256 :

Tylney Hall ⛰, RG27 9AJ, S : 1½ m. by Newnham rd on Ridge Lane ☎ 764881, Fax 768141, « 19C mansion in extensive gardens by Gertrude Jekyll », Ⅎ₆, ≘s, ⛱ heated, ⛱, park, ⚔ – TV ☎ P – 🏛 100. ⊠ AE ⊙ VISA JCB. ⚘
Meals 19.75/28.00 **st.** and a la carte 🍷 6.75 – **82 rm** ⊑ 102.00/132.00 **st.**, 9 suites – SB.

HOOK Wilts. – see Swindon.

HOPE Derbs. 402 403 404 O 23 – ✉ Sheffield – ☎ 01433.

♦London 180 – Derby 50 – ♦Manchester 31 – ♦Sheffield 15 – ♦Stoke-on-Trent 40.

Underleigh ⛰, S30 2RF, N : 1 m. by Edale rd ☎ 621372, Fax 621372, ≤, ⛲ – ⊁ rest TV P. ⊠ VISA. ⚘
Meals (communal dining) 14.50 🍷 3.50 – **6 rm** ⊑ 30.00/50.00 **t.** – SB.

HOPE COVE Devon 403 I 33 – see Salcombe.

HOPTON CASTLE Shrops. 403 L 26 – see Leintwardine.

HOPTON WAFERS Shrops. 403 404 M 26 – pop. 972 – ✉ Kidderminster – ☎ 01299.

♦London 150 – ♦Birmingham 32 – Shrewsbury 38.

Crown Inn, DY14 0NB, on A 4117 ☎ 270372, Fax 271127 – TV ☎ P. ⊠ AE VISA. ⚘
Meals *(closed Sunday dinner and Monday)* (bar lunch Monday to Saturday)/dinner 22.50 **st.** 🍷 4.50 – **8 rm** ⊑ 40.00/70.00 **st.** – SB.

HOPWOOD W. Mids. – ✉ Birmingham – ☎ 0121.

♦London 131 – ♦Birmingham 8.

Westmead (Country Club), Redditch Rd, B48 7AL, on A 441 ☎ 445 1202, Fax 445 6163, ≘s – ⊁ rm ▤ rest TV ☎ P – 🏛 250. ⊠ AE ⊙ VISA. ⚘
Meals 11.95/25.00 **st.** and a la carte 🍷 5.95 – ⊑ 7.50 – **58 rm** 63.00/73.00 **st.** – SB.

HORLEY Surrey 404 T 30 – pop. 19 267 – ECD : Wednesday – 01293.
♦London 27 – ♦Brighton 26 – Royal Tunbridge Wells 22.

Plan : see Gatwick

Chequers Thistle (Mt. Charlotte Thistle), Brighton Rd, RH6 8PH, on A 23 ✆ 786992, Fax 820625, – rm – 60. Y z
Meals *(closed Saturday lunch)* 11.25/17.00 **t.** – 8.50 – **78 rm** 79.00/89.00 **t.** – SB.

Langshott Manor, Langshott, RH6 9LN, by Ladbroke Rd ✆ 786680, Fax 783905, « Part Elizabethan manor house », – rm . Y
closed 23 to 30 December – **Meals** (booking essential) 22.50/25.00 **t.** 6.00 – 8.00 – **7 rm** 75.00/115.00 **t.**

Lawn without rest., 30 Massetts Rd, RH6 7DE, ✆ 775751, Fax 821803, – . Y r
closed Christmas and New Year – **7 rm** -/42.00 **s.**

HORNCASTLE Lincs. 402 404 T 24 – 01507.
♦London 140 – Boston 19 – Great Grimsby 31 – Lincoln 21.

Admiral Rodney, North St., LN9 5DX, ✆ 523131, Fax 523104 – rm – 120. .
Meals *(closed Sunday dinner)* (carving lunch) 7.15 **t.** and dinner a la carte 8.60/11.85 **t.** 4.25 – **32 rm** 37.50/75.00 **t.** – SB.

HORNING Norfolk 404 Y 25 **Great Britain G.** – pop. 1 070 – ECD : Wednesday – ✉ Norwich – 01692.
Envir. : The Broads★.
♦London 122 – Great Yarmouth 17 – ♦Norwich 11.

Petersfield House , Lower St., NR12 8PF, ✆ 630741, Fax 630745, – .
Meals (dancing Saturday evening) 13.00/15.50 **t.** and a la carte 4.75 – **18 rm** 58.00/82.00 **t.** – SB.

HORNINGSHAM Wilts. 403 404 N 30 – see Warminster.

HORNS CROSS Devon 403 H 31 **The West Country G.** – ECD : Wednesday – ✉ Bideford – 01237.
Exc. : Clovelly★★, NW : 7 m. by A 39 and B 3237.
♦London 237 – Barnstaple 15 – Exeter 48.

Foxdown Manor , Foxdown, EX39 5PJ, S : 1 m. ✆ 451325, Fax 451525, , , heated, , park, – rest .
Meals (bar lunch Monday to Saturday)/dinner 19.95 **st.** and a la carte 4.30 – **7 rm** (dinner included) 70.00/130.00 **st.**, 1 suite – SB.

Penhaven Country , Parkham, EX39 5PL, S : 2 m. ✆ 451711, Fax 451878, , park – rest .
Meals (dinner only and Sunday lunch November-May)/dinner 12.95 **t.** and a la carte 4.75 – **12 rm** 55.95/120.00 **st.** – SB.

Old Rectory , Parkham, EX39 5PL, S : 2 m. ✆ 451443, – .
Meals 25.00 **s.** 4.00 – **3 rm** 50.00/78.00 **s.** – SB.

HORSFORTH W. Yorks. 402 P 22 – see Leeds.

HORSHAM W. Sussex 404 T 30 – pop. 38 356 – ECD : Monday and Thursday – 01403.
Mannings Heath, Goldings Lane ✆ 210168.
9 Causeway, RH12 1HE ✆ 211661.
♦London 39 – ♦Brighton 23 – Guildford 20 – Lewes 25 – Worthing 20.

South Lodge , Brighton Rd, Lower Beeding, RH13 6PS, SE : 5 m. on A 281 ✆ 891711, Fax 891766, , « Victorian mansion, gardens », , , park, – rest – 80. .
Meals 16.00/32.00 **t.** and a la carte 8.00 – 10.00 – **37 rm** 90.00/175.00 **t.**, 2 suites – SB.

Cisswood House, Sandygate Lane, Lower Beeding, RH13 6NF, SE : 3 ¾ m. on A 281 ✆ 891216, Fax 891621, , – – 150. .
closed Christmas and New Year – **Meals** *(closed Sunday, Easter and last week August)* 17.00/21.00 **t.** 5.50 – 4.50 – **30 rm** 65.00/90.00 **st.**, 2 suites – SB.

Travel Inn, The Station, 57 North St., RH12 1RB, ✆ 250141, Fax 270797 – rm .
Meals (Beefeater grill) a la carte approx. 16.00 **t.** 4.95 – **40 rm** 33.50 **t.**

Jeremy's (at the Crabtree), Brighton Rd, Lower Beeding, RH13 6PT, SE : 5¼ m. on A 281 ✆ 891257, Fax 891606 – .
closed dinner Sunday and Monday – **Meals** 24.00 **t.** (dinner) and lunch a la carte approx. 14.50 **t.**

at Slinfold W : 4 m. by A 281 off A 264 – ✉ Horsham – 01403 :

Random Hall, Stane St., RH13 7QX, W : ½ m. on A 29 ✆ 790558, Fax 791046, « Part 16C farmhouse » – .
Meals 9.50/17.35 **st.** and a la carte 4.90 – 7.50 – **15 rm** 60.00/75.00 **st.** – SB.

ATS Rear of Brighton Rd Filling Station ✆ 267491/251736

HORSHAM ST. FAITH Norfolk 404 X 25 – see Norwich.

HORTON Dorset 403 404 O 31 – see Wimborne Minster.

HORTON Northants. 404 R 27 – pop. 500 – ✉ Northampton – ☎ 01604.

♦London 66 – Bedford 18 – Northampton 6.

XX **French Partridge,** Newport Pagnell Rd, NN7 2AP, ✆ 870033, Fax 870032 – P
closed Sunday, Monday, 2 weeks Easter, 3 weeks August and 2 weeks Christmas – **Meals** (booking essential) (dinner only) 24.00 **st.** 5.50.

HORTON-CUM-STUDLEY Oxon. 403 404 Q 28 – pop. 453 – ECD : Wednesday – ✉ Oxford – ☎ 01865.

♦London 57 – Aylesbury 23 – ♦Oxford 7.

Studley Priory , OX33 1AZ, ✆ 351203, Fax 351613, ≤, « Elizabethan manor house in park », – TV ☎ P – 25. AE VISA JCB.
Meals 19.50/25.00 **st.** and a la carte – **18 rm** 88.00/150.00 **st.**, 1 suite – SB.

HORWICH Lancs. 402 404 M 23 – pop. 16 656 – ✉ Bolton – ☎ 01204.

♦London 214 – Liverpool 32 – ♦Manchester 18 – Preston 19.

Swallowfield, Chorley New Rd, BL6 6HN, SE : ¾ m. on A 673 ✆ 697914, Fax 68900 – TV ☎ P – 25. AE VISA
closed 20 December - 3 January – **Meals** *(closed Friday to Sunday)* (bar lunch)/dinner 12.00 **st.** and a la carte 3.50 – **32 rm** 43.00/55.00 **st.**

ATS 101 Chorley New Rd ✆ 68077/68806

HOTHFIELD Kent 404 W 30 – see Ashford.

HOUGH-ON-THE-HILL Lincs. – see Grantham.

HOUGHTON CONQUEST Beds. 404 S 27 – see Bedford.

HOVE E. Sussex 404 T 31 – see Brighton and Hove.

HOVINGHAM N. Yorks. 402 R 21 – pop. 310 – ECD : Thursday – ✉ York – ☎ 01653.

♦London 235 – ♦Middlesbrough 36 – York 25.

Worsley Arms, YO6 4LA, ✆ 628234, Fax 628130, « Part 19C coaching inn », – TV ☎ P – 25. AE VISA
Meals (bar lunch Monday to Saturday) 12.50/21.50 **t.** 4.50 – **22 rm** 62.00/106.00 **t.** – SB.

HOWTOWN Cumbria – see Ullswater.

HUDDERSFIELD W. Yorks. 402 404 O 23 – pop. 147 825 – ECD : Wednesday – ☎ 01484.

18, 9 Bradley Park, Bradley Rd ✆ 539988 – 18 Woodsome Hall, Fenay Bridge ✆ 602971 – 18 Outlane, Slack Lane ✆ (01422) 374762 – 18 Meltham, Thick Hellins Hall ✆ 850227 – 18 Fixby Hall, Lightbridge Rd ✆ 420110, - 18 Crosland Heath ✆ 653216.

High Street Building, 3-5 Albion St., HD1 2NW ✆ 430808.

♦London 191 – Bradford 11 – ♦Leeds 15 – ♦Manchester 25 – ♦Sheffield 26.

George, St. George's Sq., HD1 1JA, ✆ 515444, Fax 435056 – rm TV ☎ P – 150. AE VISA.
Meals 9.25/14.95 **t.** and a la carte – **59 rm** 75.00/85.00 **t.**, 1 suite – SB.

Lodge, 48 Birkby Lodge Rd, Birkby, HD2 2BG, N : 1 ½ m. by A 629 and Blacker Rd ✆ 431001, Fax 421590, – TV ☎ P – 35. AE VISA
closed 25 to 27 December – **Meals** *(closed Sunday dinner)* 6.25/23.50 **t.** and lunch a la carte 5.00 – **11 rm** 50.00/60.00 **t.** – SB.

Briar Court, Halifax Rd, Birchencliffe, HD3 3NT, NW : 2 m. on A 629 ✆ 519902, Fax 431812 – rm TV ☎ P – 90. AE VISA JCB
Meals 12.95 **st.** (dinner) and a la carte 10.45/19.95 **st.** 4.00 – **44 rm** 54.50/68.00 **st.**, 3 suites.

Wellfield House, 33 New Hey Rd, Marsh, HD3 4AL, W : 1 ½ m. on A 640 ✆ 425776, Fax 532122, « Victorian house », – rest TV ☎ P. AE VISA.
closed 24 December-2 January – **Meals** (residents only) (dinner only) 15.00 **st.** 3.95 – **5 rm** 40.00/55.00 **st.**

Huddersfield, 37-47 Kirkgate, HD1 1QT, ✆ 512111, Fax 435262, – TV ☎ P. AE VISA
Meals 10.00/15.00 **st.** and a la carte 4.00 – **46 rm** 46.00/70.00 **st.** – SB.

Elm Crest, 2 Queens Rd, HD2 2AG, off Edgerton Rd (A 629) ✆ 530990, Fax 516227 – TV ☎ P. AE VISA.
Meals (by arrangement) 16.00 **st.** 4.50 – **8 rm** 32.00/58.00 **st.**

The Mallows without rest., 55 Spring St., Springwood, HD1 4AZ, ✆ 544684 – TV P.
closed 20 December - 3 January – **6 rm** 15.00/35.00 **st.**

at Golcar W : 3 ½ m. by A 62 on B 6111 – ✉ Huddersfield – ☎ 01484 :

XX **Weaver's Shed,** Knowl Rd, via Scar Lane, HD7 4AN, ☎ 654284, Fax 654284, « Converted 18C woollen mill » – P. AE VISA
closed Saturday lunch, Sunday, Monday, first 2 weeks January, 2 weeks July-August and Bank Holidays – **Meals** 10.95 **t.** (lunch) and a la carte 16.45/22.45 **t.**

at Outlane NW : 4 m. on A 640 – ✉ Huddersfield – ☎ 01422 :

Old Golf House (Country Club), New Hey Rd, HD3 3YP, ☎ 379311, Fax 372694 – rm rest TV ☎ P – 100. AE VISA.
Meals *(closed Saturday lunch)* 9.95/14.95 **st.** and a la carte 5.00 – 7.50 – **49 rm** 59.00/69.00 **st.** – SB.

ATS Leeds Rd ☎ 534441

HULL Humbs. 402 S 22 – see Kingston-upon-Hull.

Michelin n'accroche pas de panonceau aux hôtels et restaurants qu'il signale.

HUNGERFORD Berks. 403 404 P 29 **The West Country G.** – pop. 6 174 – ECD : Thursday – ☎ 01488.

Envir. : Littlecote★★ (arms and armour★, Roman mosaic floor★) *AC*, NW : 2 m. by A 4 and B 4192.

Exc. : Savernake Forest★★ (Grand Avenue★★★) W : 7 m. by A 4.

London 74 – Bristol 57 – Oxford 28 – Reading 26 – Southampton 46.

Jarvis Bear, 17 Charnham St., RG17 0EL, on A 4 ☎ 682512, Fax 684357 – rm TV ☎ P – 85. AE VISA.
Meals 11.50/15.50 **t.** and a la carte 6.75 – 8.25 – **41 rm** 65.00/85.00 **t.** – SB.

Three Swans, High St., RG17 0DL, ☎ 682721, Fax 681708 – rm TV ☎ P – 70. AE VISA
Meals 10.95 **t.** and a la carte 4.95 – **15 rm** 55.00/70.00 **t.** – SB.

Marshgate Cottage, Marsh Lane, RG17 0QX, W : ¾ m. by Church St. ☎ 682307, Fax 685475, ≤, – rm TV ☎ P. AE VISA.
closed 24 December-15 January – **Meals** (by arrangement) 15.50 **st.** – **9 rm** 35.50/48.50 **st.**

X **Just William's,** 50 Church St., RG17 0JH, ☎ 681199 – VISA
closed Monday dinner, Sunday and Bank Holidays – **Meals** a la carte 11.20/16.95 **t.**

HUNSTANTON Norfolk 402 404 V 25 – pop. 4 799 – ECD : Thursday – ☎ 01485.

18 Golf Course road, ☎ 532811.

The Green, PE36 5AH ☎ 532610.

London 120 – Cambridge 60 – Norwich 45.

Le Strange Arms, Golf Course Rd, PE36 6JJ, N : 1 m. by A 149 ☎ 534411, Fax 534724, ≤, – TV ☎ P – 120. AE VISA
Meals (dinner only and Sunday lunch)/dinner 15.00 **t.** and a la carte – **38 rm** 48.00/80.00 **t.** – SB.

Claremont without rest., 35 Greevegate, PE36 6AF, ☎ 533171 – TV. VISA
7 rm 22.00/44.00 **s.**

Fieldsend without rest., 26 Homefields Rd, PE36 5HL, ☎ 532593 – TV P.
3 rm 20.00/32.00 **st.**

Pinewood without rest., 26 Northgate, PE36 6AP, ☎ 533068 – rest TV P. AE VISA
closed November and Christmas-New Year – **8 rm** 25.00/50.00 **st.**

HUNSTRETE Avon 403 404 M 29 – see Bristol.

HUNTINGDON Cambs. 404 T 26 – pop. 15 424 – ECD : Wednesday – ☎ 01480.

18 Brampton Park, Buckden Rd ☎ 434700 – 9 Hemingford Abbots, New Farm Lodge, Cambridge Rd ☎ 495000.

The Library, Princes St., PE18 6PH ☎ 425831.

London 69 – Bedford 21 – Cambridge 16.

Old Bridge, 1 High St., PE18 6TQ, ☎ 452681, Fax 411017 – TV ☎ P – 40. AE VISA
Meals a la carte 14.90/25.85 **st.** 4.95 – **26 rm** 69.50/120.00 **st.**

George (Forte), George St., PE18 6AB, ☎ 432444, Fax 453130 – TV ☎ P – 150. AE VISA JCB
Meals (bar lunch Monday to Saturday)/dinner 20.00 **st.** and a la carte 6.95 – 8.75 – **24 rm** 60.00/75.00 **st.** – SB.

Forte Travelodge without rest., SE : 5 ½ m. on A 14 (eastbound carriageway) ☎ (01954) 30919, Reservations (Freephone) 0800 850950 – TV P. AE VISA.
40 rm 33.50 **t.**

ATS Nursery Rd ☎ 451031/451515

HURLEY-ON-THAMES Berks. 404 R 29 – pop. 2 068 – ECD : Wednesday – ✉ Maidenhead – ☎ 01628.

♦London 38 – ♦Oxford 26 – Reading 12.

Ye Olde Bell (Jarvis), High St., SL6 5LX, ☎ 825881, Fax 825939, « Part 12C inn », – TV ☎ P – 140. AE VISA
Meals 14.95/19.95 **t.** and a la carte 5.00 – 8.50 – **35 rm** 82.50/92.50 **t.**, 1 suite – SB.

HURSTBOURNE TARRANT Hants. 403 404 P 30 – pop. 700 – ✉ Andover – ☎ 01264.

♦London 77 – ♦Bristol 77 – ♦Oxford 38 – ♦Southampton 33.

Esseborne Manor, SP11 0ER, NE : 1½ m. on A 343 ☎ 736444, Fax 736473, – TV ☎ P. AE VISA.
Meals 9.95/17.50 and dinner a la carte 6.00 – **12 rm** 85.00/99.00 **t.** – SB.

at Faccombe N : 3½ m. by A 343 – ✉ Andover – ☎ 01264.

Jack Russell, SP11 0DS, ☎ 737315 – TV P
3 rm.

HURST GREEN Lancs. 402 M 22 – ✉ Clitheroe – ☎ 01254.

♦London 236 – Blackburn 12 – Burnley 13 – Preston 12.

Shireburn Arms, Whalley Rd, BB7 9QJ, on B 6243 ☎ 826518, Fax 826208, – TV ☎ P. AE VISA
Meals (bar lunch Saturday) 7.80/10.95 **t.** and dinner a la carte 5.00 – **16 rm** 39.00/49.00 **t.** – SB.

HUSBANDS BOSWORTH Leics. 403 404 Q 26 – pop. 912 – ✉ Lutterworth – ☎ 01858.

♦London 88 – ♦Birmingham 40 – ♦Leicester 14 – Northampton 17.

Fernie Lodge, Berridges Lane, LE17 6LE, by Bell Lane ☎ 880551, Fax 880014 – rest rest TV ☎ P – 50
17 rm, 1 suite.

HUTTON-LE-HOLE N. Yorks. 402 R 21 – ☎ 01751.

♦London 244 – Scarborough 27 – York 33.

Burnley House, YO6 6UA, ☎ 417548, Fax 417174, – TV P.
Easter-November – **Meals** (by arrangement) 15.00 **st.** 3.50 – **7 rm** 39.00/65.00 **st.**

Hammer and Hand, YO6 6UA, ☎ 417300 – TV P
Meals (by arrangement) 11.00 **st.** 4.25 – **3 rm** 30.00/44.00 **st.** – SB.

HUXHAM Devon – see Exeter.

HUYTON Mersey. 402 403 L 23 – see Liverpool.

HYDE Gtr. Manchester 402 403 404 N 23 – ☎ 0161.

♦London 202 – ♦Manchester 10.

Village H. & Leisure Club, Captain Clarke Rd, Dunkinfield, SK14 4QG, NW : 1¼ m. by A 627 ☎ 368 1456, squash – TV ☎ P – 150
Meals (grill rest.) – **89 rm.**

HYTHE Kent 404 X 30 – pop. 13 751 – ECD : Wednesday – ☎ 01303.

18 Sene Valley, Sene, Folkestone ☎ 268513.

Prospect Rd Car Park, CT21 5NH ☎ 267799 (summer only).

♦London 68 – Folkestone 6 – Hastings 33 – Maidstone 31.

Plan : see Folkestone

Hythe Imperial, Prince's Par., CT21 6AE, ☎ 267441, Fax 264610, 9, squash – rest TV ☎ P – 200. AE VISA. X a
Meals 15.00/19.00 **st.** and a la carte 6.50 – **98 rm** 85.00/105.00 **st.**, 2 suites – SB.

Stade Court, West Par., CT21 6DT, ☎ 268263, Fax 261803, – rm TV ☎ P – 35. AE VISA
Meals 10.95/17.50 **t.** and a la carte – **42 rm** 60.00/82.50 **t.** – SB.

IBSTONE Bucks – pop. 254 – ✉ High Wycombe – ☎ 01491.

♦London 39 – ♦Oxford 20 – Reading 19.

Fox of Ibstone Country, HP14 3GG, ☎ 638722, Fax 638873, – TV ☎ P. AE VISA.
Meals 8.50/25.00 **t.** and a la carte – **9 rm** 58.00/76.00 **t.** – SB.

IDE Devon 403 J 31 – see Exeter.

IFFLEY Oxon – see Oxford.

ILKLEY W. Yorks. 402 O 22 – pop. 13 530 – ECD : Wednesday – 01943.

Myddleton 607277.

Station Rd, LS29 8HA 602319.

London 210 – Bradford 13 – Harrogate 17 – Leeds 16 – Preston 46.

Rombalds, 11 West View, Wells Rd, LS29 9JG, 603201, Fax 816586 – – 70. AE VISA
closed 27 to 30 December – **Meals** 9.95/14.95 **t.** and a la carte 6.50 – **11 rm** 72.00/100.00 **st.**, 4 suites – SB.

Grove, 66 The Grove, LS29 9PA, 600298 – rest . AE VISA.
closed 23 December-3 January – **Meals** (bar lunch)/dinner 13.00 **st.** 3.50 – **6 rm** 39.00/54.00 **st.**

Box Tree, 37 Church St., LS29 9DR, 608484, Fax 607186 – AE VISA
closed Sunday dinner, Monday, and last 2 weeks January – **Meals** 22.50/29.50 **st.** 4.95.

ILLOGAN Cornwall 403 E 33 **The West Country G.** – pop. 13 095 – Redruth – 01209.

Envir. : Portreath★, NW : 2 m. by B 3300 – Hell's Mouth★, SW : 5 m. by B 3301.

London 305 – Falmouth 14 – Penzance 17 – Truro 11.

Aviary Court, Mary's Well, TR16 4QZ, NW : 3/4 m. by Alexandra Rd 842256, Fax 843744, – . AE VISA.
Meals (dinner only and Sunday lunch)/dinner 12.00 **t.** and a la carte 5.00 – **6 rm** 42.00/58.00 **t.**

ILMINSTER Somerset 403 L 31 **The West Country G.** – pop. 4 162 – 01460.

See : Town★ - St. Mary's★★.

Envir. : Barrington Court Gardens★ *AC*, NE : 3½m. by B 3168.

London 145 – Taunton 12 – Yeovil 17.

Forte Travelodge without rest., Southfield Roundabout, Horton Cross, TA19 9PT, NW : 1½ m. at junction of A 303 with A 358 53748, Reservations (Freephone) 0800 850950 – . AE VISA.
32 rm 33.50 **t.**.

IMPINGTON Cambs. – see Cambridge.

INGATESTONE Essex 404 V 28 – pop. 4 815 – ECD : Wednesday – Chelmsford – 01277.

London 27 – Chelmsford 6.

Ivy Hill, Writtle Rd, Margaretting, CM4 0EW, NE : 2¼ m. by A 12 353040, Fax 355038, heated, , – – 200. AE VISA.
Meals *(closed Saturday lunch and Sunday dinner)* 18.95 **st.** 6.50 – 6.95 – **34 rm** 65.00/90.00 **st.**

INGLEBY GREENHOW N. Yorks. 402 Q 20 – see Great Ayton.

INGLETON N. Yorks. 402 M 21 – pop. 1 979 – Carnforth – 0152 42.

Community Centre Car Park, LA6 3HJ 41049 (summer only).

London 266 – Kendal 21 – Lancaster 18 – Leeds 53.

Moorgarth Hall Country House, New Rd, LA6 3DN, SE : ¼ m. on A 65 41946, Fax 42252, – . VISA.
closed Christmas-New Year – **Meals** (by arrangement)(dinner only) 20.00 – **8 rm** 27.50/60.00.

Pines Country House, New Rd, LA6 3HN, NW : ¼ m. on A 65 41252, – .
VISA
Meals (by arrangement) 10.50 **t.** 3.00 – **5 rm** 24.00/38.00 **st.** – SB.

INSTOW Devon 403 H 30 – see Bideford.

IPSWICH Suffolk 404 X 27 **Great Britain G.** – pop. 116 956 – ECD : Monday and Wednesday – 01473.

See : Christchurch Mansion (collection of paintings★) X **B.**

Rushmere Heath 727109 – , Purdis Heath, Bucklesham Rd 727474 – Fynn Valley, Witnesham 785463.

Ipswich Airport : 720111, Z.

St Stephen Church, St Stephen Lane, IP1 1DP 258070.

London 76 – Norwich 43.

IPSWICH

Buttermarket Schopping Centre .... X 9
Carr Street .... X 10
Corn Hill .... X 16
Tavern Street X
Westgate Street .... X 52

Argyle Street .... X 2
Back Hamlet .... Z 3
Birkfield Drive .... Z 5
Bond Street .... X 6
Bridgwater Road .... Z 7
Chevallier Street .... Y 13
College Street .... X 15
Dogs Head Street .... X 18
Ellenbrook Road .... Z 19
Falcon Street .... X 21
Fore Hamlet .... Z 22
Franciscan Way .... X 24
Friars Street .... X 25
Grey Friars Road .... X 26
Grove Lane .... YZ 28
Handford Road ...... X, Y 30
Lloyds Avenue .... X 31
Lower Orwell Street .... X 32
Northgate Street .... X 33
Orwell Place .... X 34
Queen Street .... X 37
St. Helen's Street .... X, Y 39
St. Margarets Street .... X 40
St. Nicholas Street .... X 41
St. Peter's Street .... X 42
Salthouse Street .... X 43
Silent Street .... X 46
Upper Orwell Street .... X 49
Waterworks Street .... X 51
Yarmouth Road .... Y 54

CENTRE
CHRISTCHURCH PARK
CIVIC CENTRE
Fonnereau Rd
Charles Street
Crown Street
St. Matthew's St.
Berners Street
St. George's St.
High St.
Museum St.
Tower Ramparts
Tavern St.
Woodbridge Rd
Christchurch Street
Hervey Street
Bolton Lane
Elm St.
Civic Drive
Portman Road
Princes St.
Wolsey St.
Tacket St.
Rope Walk
Fore St.
Grimwade St.
Upper Brook St.
Lower Brook St.
Foundation St.
Star Lane
Key Street
Commercial Road
Bridge St.
Burrell Road
A 1156
A 1071
A 1214
A 137
(A 12)
(A 45)
X
300 m
300 yards

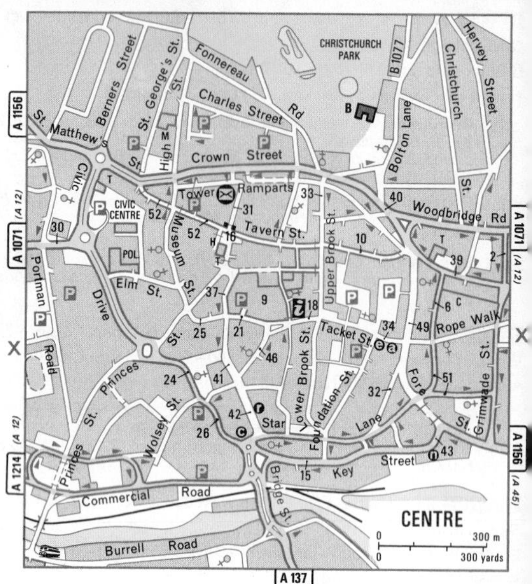

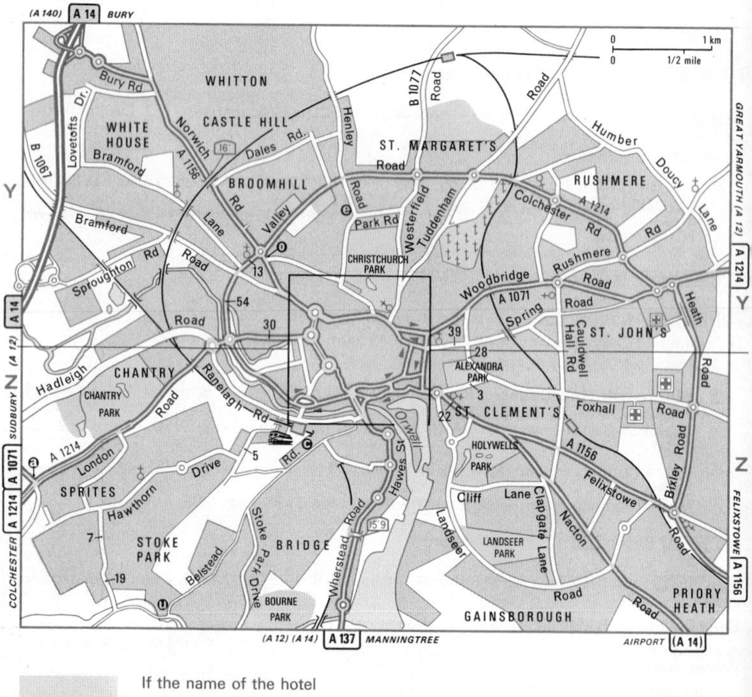

(A 140) A 14 BURY
WHITTON
CASTLE HILL
WHITE HOUSE
BROOMHILL
ST. MARGARET'S
RUSHMERE
CHRISTCHURCH PARK
CHANTRY
CHANTRY PARK
ALEXANDRA PARK
ST. JOHN'S
ST. CLEMENT'S
HOLYWELLS PARK
SPRITES
STOKE PARK
BRIDGE
BOURNE PARK
LANDSEER PARK
GAINSBOROUGH
PRIORY HEATH
Bury Rd
Lovetofts Dr.
Norwich Rd
Bramford Lane
Bramford Road
Sproughton Rd
Dales Rd.
Valley Rd
Henley Road
Park Rd
Westerfield Road
Tuddenham
Colchester Rd
Humber Doucy Lane
Woodbridge Road
Rushmere Road
Spring Road
Cauldwell Hall Rd
Heath Road
Foxhall Road
Bixley Road
Hadleigh Road
Ranelagh Rd
London Road
Hawthorn Drive
Belstead
Stoke Park Drive
Wherstead Road
Hawes St
Orwell
Landseer
Cliff Lane
Clapgate Lane
Nacton Road
Felixstowe Road
A 1214
A 1071
A 1156
B 1067
B 1077
A 14
Y
Z
GREAT YARMOUTH (A 12)
FELIXSTOWE
SUDBURY (A 12)
COLCHESTER
(A 12) (A 14) A 137 MANNINGTREE
AIRPORT (A 14)
1 km
1/2 mile

Europe

If the name of the hotel
is not in bold type,
on arrival ask the hotelier his prices.

Belstead Brook, Belstead Rd, IP2 9HB, SW : 2 ½ m. ✆ 684241, Fax 681249, – rm – 60. VISA Z u
Meals *(closed Saturday lunch)* 10.00/16.00 **st.** and a la carte 5.70 – 7.00 – **74 rm** 65.50/75.50 **st.**, 2 suites – SB.

Suffolk Grange (Country Club), The Havens, Ransomes Europark, IP3 9SJ, SE : 3 ½ m. by A 1156 and Nacton Rd at junction with A 45 ✆ 272244, Fax 272484, – rm rest – 180. VISA Y
Meals *(closed Saturday lunch)* 12.50/15.50 **st.** and a la carte – 7.50 – **60 rm** 59.00/79.00 **t.** – SB.

Marlborough, Henley Rd, IP1 3SP, ✆ 257677, Fax 226927, – – 45. VISA Y e
Meals 13.50/23.00 **t.** and a la carte 4.50 – **21 rm** 59.00/69.00 **t.**, 1 suite – SB.

Novotel, Greyfriars Rd, IP1 1UP, ✆ 232400, Telex 987684, Fax 232414 – rm – 200. VISA JCB X c
Meals 12.50 **st.** and dinner a la carte 4.95 – 7.50 – **100 rm** 49.50 **st.** – SB.

Constable Country, London Rd, IP2 0UA, SW : 2 ¼ m. on A 1214 ✆ 690313, Fax 680412, heated – rm – 110. Z a
112 rm.

Bentley Tower, 172 Norwich Rd, IP1 2PY, ✆ 212142, Fax 212142 – . VISA JCB. Y o
closed 24 December-4 January – **Meals** (bar lunch)/dinner 13.50 **st.** and a la carte 4.50 – **13 rm** 35.00/48.00 **st.** – SB.

Highview House, 56 Belstead Rd, IP2 8BE, ✆ 688659, – Z c
11 rm.

Orwell House, 4 Orwell Pl., IP4 1BB, ✆ 230254 – VISA X e
closed Sunday and Monday – **Meals** 9.95/15.00 **t.** and a la carte 4.50.

Bombay, 6 Orwell Pl., IP4 1BB, ✆ 251397 X a
Meals - Indian 7.50 **t.** and a la carte 3.50.

St. Peter's, 35-37 St Peter's St., IP1 1XF, ✆ 210810, Fax 210810 – . VISA
closed Sunday and Monday – **Meals** a la carte 14.15/15.45 **t.** 5.25. X r

Mortimer's on the Quay, Wherry Quay, IP4 1AS, ✆ 230225 – VISA JCB X n
closed Saturday lunch, Sunday, 2 weeks August-September, 24 December-6 January and Bank Holidays – **Meals** - Seafood a la carte 11.85/23.30 **t.** 2.90.

at Copdock SW : 4 m. by A 1214 off A 1071 – Z – ✉ Ipswich – 01473 :

Ipswich Moat House (Q.M.H.), Old London Rd, IP8 3JD, ✆ 730444, Fax 730801, – rm – 400. VISA
Meals (carving lunch)/dinner 13.50 **st.** and a la carte 4.50 – 8.25 – **74 rm** 57.50/85.00 **st.** – SB.

at Burstall W : 4 ½ m. by A 1214 off A 1071 – Y – ✉ Ipswich – 01473 :

Mulberry Hall , IP8 3DP, ✆ 652348, , – .
closed Christmas – **Meals** (by arrangement) (communal dining) 14.00 – **3 rm** 16.50/35.00 **st.**

at Hintlesham W : 5 m. by A 1214 on A 1071 – Y – ✉ Ipswich – 01473 :

Hintlesham Hall , IP8 3NS, ✆ 652268, Fax 652463, , « Georgian country house of 16C origins », , , heated, 18, , , park, – rest – 30. VISA
Meals (residents only Saturday lunch) 18.50/24.00 **st.** and a la carte 26.40/43.45 **st.** 6.25 – **29 rm** 85.00/180.00 **st.**, 4 suites – SB.

ATS White Elm St. ✆ 217157

IRON BRIDGE Shrops. 403 404 M 26 **Great Britain G.** – pop. 2 583 – 01952.

See : Ironbridge Gorge Museum★★ *AC* (The Iron Bridge★★, Coalport China Museum★★, Blists Hill Open Air Museum★★, Museum of the River and visitors centre★).

4 The Wharfage, TF8 7AW ✆ 432166.

London 135 – Birmingham 36 – Shrewsbury 18.

Valley, Buildwas Rd, TF8 7DW, on B 4380 ✆ 432247, Fax 432308, – rest – 250. VISA.
Meals 12.50/22.00 **st.** and a la carte – **34 rm** 62.00/72.00 **st.** – SB.

Severn Lodge without rest., New Rd, TF8 7AS, ✆ 432148, Fax 432148, –
3 rm 37.00/48.00 **st.**

Bridge House without rest., Buildwas, TF8 7BN, W : 2 m. on B 4380 ✆ 432105, « 17C cottage », – .
closed Christmas and New Year – **4 rm** 25.00/48.00 **s.**

ISLEY WALTON Leics. – see Castle Donington.

IVINGHOE Bucks. 404 S 28 – pop. 2 817 (inc. Pitstone) – ✉ Leighton Buzzard – ☎ 01296.
Wellcroft ✆ 668696.
♦London 42 – Aylesbury 9 – Luton 11.

XX **King's Head,** Station Rd, LU7 9EB, ✆ 668388, Fax 668107 – ▤ Ⓟ. AE VISA
Meals 12.50/20.25 **st.** and a la carte 6.85.

IVY HATCH Kent – see Sevenoaks.

IXWORTH Suffolk 404 W 27 – pop. 2 720 – ✉ Bury St. Edmunds – ☎ 01359.
♦London 85 – ♦Cambridge 35 – ♦Ipswich 25 – ♦Norwich 36.

XX **Theobalds,** 68 High St., IP31 2HJ, ✆ 231707 – VISA
closed Saturday lunch, Sunday dinner, Monday and Bank Holidays – **Meals** 16.25/26.00 **t.** and a la carte.

at Pakenham S : 3¼ m. by A 1088 – ✉ Bury St. Edmunds – ☎ 01359 :

Hamling House, Bull Rd, IP31 2LW, ✆ 230934, Fax 232298, – rest TV Ⓟ. AE VISA
Meals *(closed Sunday dinner)* 11.50/16.50 **st.** 3.00 – **7 rm** 48.00/64.00 **t.** – SB.

JERVAULX ABBEY N. Yorks. – see Masham.

JEVINGTON E. Sussex 404 U 31 – see Eastbourne.

KEDLESTON Derbs. 402 403 404 P 25 – see Derby.

KEIGHLEY W. Yorks. 402 O 22 – ☎ 01535.
Branshaw, Branshaw Moor, Oakworth ✆ 643235 – Riddlesden, Howden Rough ✆ 602148.
♦London 200 – Bradford 10 – Burnley 20.

Beeches (Toby), Bradford Rd, BD21 4BB, ✆ 610611, Fax 610037 – rm TV Ⓟ – 35. AE VISA
Meals (grill rest.) 7.95/25.00 **st.** and a la carte – **43 rm** 60.00/70.00 **st.** – SB.

Dalesgate, 406 Skipton Rd, Utley, BD20 6HP, ✆ 664930, Fax 611253 – TV Ⓟ. AE VISA
Meals *(closed Sunday)* (dinner only) 15.50 **st.** and a la carte – **21 rm** 42.00/51.00 **st.** – SB.

ATS 69-73 Bradford Rd, Riddlesden ✆ 607533/607933

KEMBLE Glos. 403 404 N 28 – see Cirencester.

KEMERTON Glos. – see Tewkesbury.

KENDAL Cumbria 402 L 21 **Great Britain G.** – pop. 14 061 – ECD : Thursday – ☎ 01539.
Envir. : Levens Hall and Garden★ *AC*, S : 4½ m. by A 591, A 590 and A 6.
Exc. : Lake Windermere★★, NW : 8 m. by A 5284 and A 591.
The Heights ✆ 724079.
Town Hall, Highgate, LA9 4DL ✆ 725758.
♦London 270 – Bradford 64 – Burnley 63 – ♦Carlisle 49 – Lancaster 22 – ♦Leeds 72 – ♦Middlesbrough 77 – ♦Newcastle upon Tyne 104 – Preston 44 – Sunderland 88.

Woolpack, Stricklandgate, LA9 4ND, ✆ 723852, Fax 728608 – rm TV Ⓟ – 100
54 rm.

Garden House, Fowl-Ing Lane, LA9 6PH, NE : ½ m. by A 685 ✆ 731131, Fax 731131, – TV Ⓟ. AE VISA JCB
Meals 7.50/19.50 **st.** and a la carte 5.50 – **10 rm** 45.00/70.00 **st.** – SB.

Lane Head House, Helsington, LA9 5RJ, S : 1 ¾ m. on A 6 ✆ 731283, ←, – rest TV Ⓟ. AE VISA JCB.
closed November – **Meals** *(closed Sunday)* (dinner only) 16.50 **s.** – **7 rm** 35.00/60.00 **s.** – SB.

at Selside N : 6 m. on A 6 – ✉ Kendal – ☎ 01539 :

Low Jock Scar, LA8 9LE, off A 6 ✆ 823259, – Ⓟ
March-October – **Meals** (by arrangement) 14.00 **st.** 3.75 – **5 rm** 27.00/50.00 **st.**

ATS Mintsfeet Est. ✆ 721559/723802

KENILWORTH Warks. 403 404 P 26 **Great Britain G.** – pop. 18 782 – ☎ 01926.
See : Castle★ *AC*.
The Library, 11 Smalley Pl., CV8 1QG ✆ 52595/50708.
♦London 102 – ♦Birmingham 19 – ♦Coventry 5 – Warwick 5.

De Montfort (De Vere), The Square, CV8 1ED, ✆ 55944, Fax 57830 – rm TV Ⓟ – 300. AE VISA
Meals 8.95/15.50 **st.** 4.75 – **96 rm** 75.00/95.00 **st.** – SB.

Periquito Chesford Grange, Chesford Bridge, CV8 2LD, SE : 1 3/4 m. on A 452 ℘ 59331, Fax 59075, park – rm – 800
129 rm, 1 suite.

Victoria Lodge, 180 Warwick Rd, CV8 1HU, ℘ 512020, Fax 58703, AE VISA
closed 24 December - 2 January – **Meals** (residents only) (lunch by arrangement)/dinner a la carte 9.00/15.25 **st.** 2.75 – **7 rm** 32.00/47.00 **st.**

Castle Laurels, 22 Castle Rd, CV8 1NG, ℘ 56179, Fax 54954 – VISA
closed 24 December-2 January – **Meals** (dinner only) a la carte approx. 11.50 **t.** 7.95 – **12 rm** 29.50/47.00 **st.**

Abbey without rest., 41 Station Rd, CV8 5JD, ℘ 512707, Fax 59148 –
7 rm 19.00/40.00.

Simpson's, 101-103 Warwick Rd, CV8 1HL, ℘ 864567 – VISA JCB
closed Saturday lunch, Sunday, 25 to 26 December and Bank Holidays – **Meals** 11.95/ 17.95 **st.** 6.95.

Bosquet, 97a Warwick Rd, CV8 1HP, ℘ 52463 – AE VISA
closed Sunday, Monday, 3 weeks August and 1 week Christmas – **Meals** - French 19.80 **t.** and a la carte 5.40.

Diment, 121-123 Warwick Rd, CV8 1HP, ℘ 53763 – AE VISA
closed Saturday lunch, Sunday, Monday, 1 week Easter, first 3 weeks August and Bank Holidays – **Meals** 13.20 **t.** (lunch) and a la carte 17.15/24.15 **t.** 4.75.

KENNFORD Devon 403 J 32 – see Exeter.

KERNE BRIDGE Heref. and Worcs. – see Ross-on-Wye.

KESSINGLAND Suffolk 404 Z 26 – 01502.

London 112 – Ipswich 39 – Norwich 32.

Old Rectory without rest., 157 Church Rd, NR33 7SQ, ℘ 740020,
Easter - September – **3 rm** 24.00/44.00 **st.**

KESWICK Cumbria 402 K 20 **Great Britain G.** – pop. 4 836 – ECD : Wednesday – 0176 87.

Envir. : Derwentwater★ Y – Thirlmere (Castlerigg Stone Circle★), E : 1 1/2 m. Y **A.**

Threlkeld Hall ℘ 79324.

Moot Hall, Market Sq., CA12 5JR ℘ 72645 – at Seatoller, Seatoller Barn, Borrowdale Keswick, CA12 5XN ℘ 77294 (summer only).

London 294 – Carlisle 31 – Kendal 30.

Plan on next page

Underscar Manor, Applethwaite, CA12 4PH, N : 1 3/4 m. by A 591 on Underscar rd ℘ 75000, Fax 74904, Derwent Water, « Italianate Victorian country house », park – rest AE VISA Y
Meals 14.00/25.00 **st.** and a la carte 6.50 – **11 rm** (dinner included) 75.00/250.00 **st.** – SB.

Brundholme Country House, Brundholme Rd, CA12 4NL, ℘ 74495, Fax 73536, – rest AE VISA Y **e**
closed December and January – **Meals** (dinner only) 22.00 **t.** and a la carte 6.00 – **11 rm** 40.00/100.00 **t.** – SB.

Lyzzick Hall, Underskiddaw, CA12 4PY, NW : 2 1/2 m. on A 591 ℘ 72277, Fax 72278, heated, – rest AE VISA Y
closed February – **Meals** 10.00/22.50 **t.** and a la carte 3.95 – **25 rm** 35.00/70.00 **t.** – SB.

Grange Country House, Manor Brow, Ambleside Rd, CA12 4BA, ℘ 72500, – VISA Y **u**
mid March-mid November – **Meals** (light lunch)/dinner 17.50 **st.** 4.25 – **10 rm** (dinner included) -/98.00 **st.**

Dale Head Hall, Thirlmere, CA12 4TN, SE : 5 3/4 m. by A 591 ℘ 72478, Lake Thirlmere, – VISA JCB Y
Meals (dinner only) 19.00 **st.** 6.00 – **9 rm** (dinner included) 69.00/150.00 **st.** – SB.

Applethwaite Country House, Underskiddaw, CA12 4PL, NW : 1 3/4 m. on Ormathwaite rd ℘ 72413, – rest VISA Y
closed Christmas and New Year – **Meals** (dinner only) 15.50 **st.** 3.25 – **12 rm** 29.00/ 58.00 **st.** – SB.

Chaucer House, Ambleside Rd, CA12 4DR, ℘ 72318, Fax 75551 – rest AE VISA JCB Z **a**
closed December and January – **Meals** (lunch by arrangement)/dinner 14.50 **t.** and a la carte 4.80 – **35 rm** 33.70/64.40 **t.** – SB.

Crow Park, The Heads, CA12 5ER, ℘ 72208, Fax 74776, – VISA Z **e**
closed January – **Meals** (dinner only) 14.00 **st.** – **28 rm** 27.50/53.00 – SB.

Lairbeck, Vicarage Hill, CA12 5QB, ℘ 73373, – rm VISA Y **a**
Meals (dinner only) 13.00 **st.** 3.25 – **14 rm** (dinner included) 24.00/62.00 **st.** – SB.

KESWICK

Main Street . . . . Z
Pack Horse Yard . . . Z 21
Station Street . . . . . Z 26

Bank Street . . . . Z 2
Borrowdale Road . . Z 3
Brackenrigg Drive . . Z 5
Brundholme Road . Y 6
Chestnut Hill . . . . . . Y 8
Church Street . . . . . Z 10
Crosthwaite Road . . Y 12
Derwent Street . . . . Z 13
High Hill . . . . Z 14
Manor Brow . . . . . . Y 17
Market Square . . . . Z 18
Otley Road . . . . Z 20
Police Station Court . . . . Z 22
Ratcliffe Place . . . . . Z 23
St. Herbert Street . . . . Z 24
Standish Street . . . . Z 25
The Crescent . . . . . . Z 27
The Hawthorns . . . . Y 29
The Headlands . . . . Z 31
Tithebarn Street . . . Z 32

North is at the top on all town plans.

Les plans de villes sont disposés le Nord en haut.

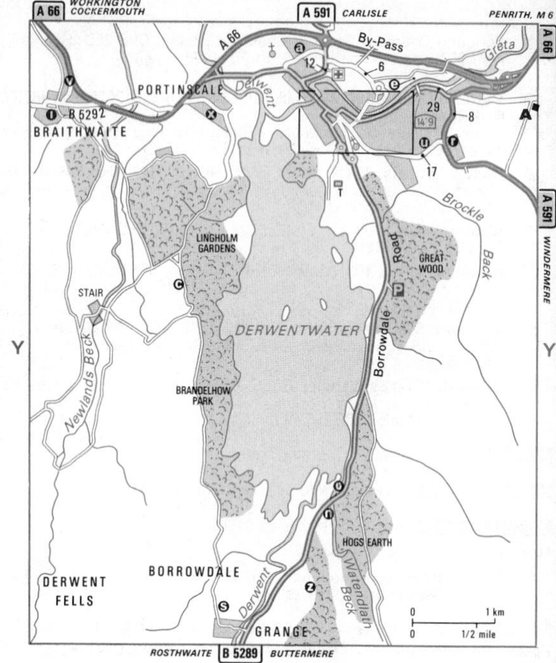

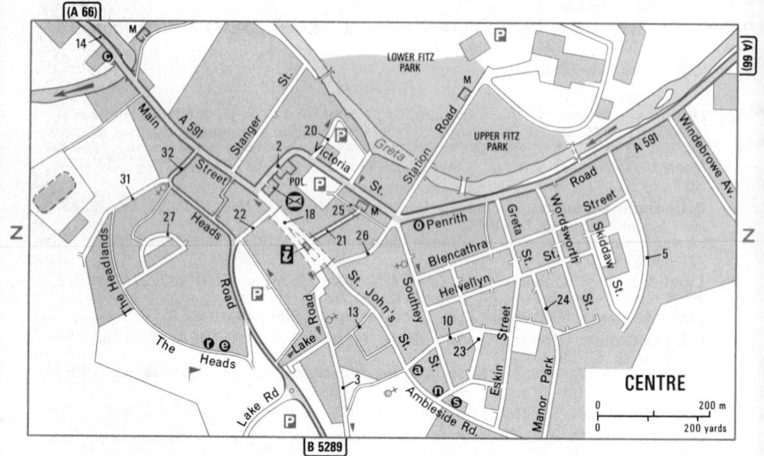

Acorn House without rest., Ambleside Rd, CA12 4DL, ☎ 72553 – ⇔ TV P. VISA. Z s
closed December and January – **10 rm** 25.00/45.00 **st.**

Brackenrigg Country House, Thirlmere, CA12 4TF, SE : 3 m. on A 591 ☎ 72258, – rest P. Y
Easter-October – **Meals** (by arrangement) 15.00 **s.** – **6 rm** 22.50/49.00 **s.** – SB.

Claremont House, Chestnut Hill, CA12 4LT, ☎ 72089, ≤, – P. Y r
Meals (by arrangement) 16.50 **s.** 5.50 – **6 rm** 22.00/50.00 **s.**

Greystones, Ambleside Rd, CA12 4DP, ☎ 73108 – TV P. Z n
mid February - mid November – **Meals** (by arrangement) 12.50 **st.** – **9 rm** 21.00/43.00 **st.**

Linnett Hill, 4 Penrith Rd, CA12 4HF, ℘ 73109 – rest TV P. VISA JCB. Z **o**
Meals 12.00 **t.** – **10 rm** 23.50/43.00 **t.** – SB.

Highfield, The Heads, CA12 5ER, ℘ 72508, ← – rest TV P Z **r**
Easter-October – **Meals** (by arrangement) 12.00 **t.** 4.50 – **19 rm** 17.50/50.00 **t.**

La Primavera, Greta Bridge, High Hill, CA12 5NX, ℘ 74621 – P. VISA Z **c**
closed 15 January - 4 March – **Meals** - Italian (closed Monday except Bank Holidays) 10.25/18.25 **t.** and a la carte 4.75.

at Threlkeld E : 4 m. by A 591 off A 66 – Y – ✉ Keswick – ☎ 0176 87 :

Scales Farm, CA12 4SY, NE : 1 ¾ m. on A 66 ℘ 79660, – rest TV P
Meals (by arrangement) 15.00 – **5 rm** 25.00/40.00 – SB.

at Borrowdale S : 3 ¼ m. on B 5289 – ✉ Keswick – ☎ 0176 87 :

Stakis Keswick Lodore, CA12 5UX, ℘ 77285, Fax 77343, ←, , , heated, , , park, , squash – rest TV ☎ P – 80. AE VISA JCB. Y **n**
Meals (bar lunch Monday to Saturday)/dinner 19.50 **t.** and a la carte – **67 rm** 75.00/150.00 **t.**, 1 suite – SB.

Mary Mount, CA12 5UU, ℘ 77223, ←, – TV P. VISA Y **o**
Meals a la carte 11.95/15.25 **t.** 4.20 – **14 rm** 26.00/52.00 **t.**

Greenbank, CA12 5UY, ℘ 77215, ←, – P. Y **z**
closed December and January – **Meals** (dinner only) 12.00 **s.** 3.00 – **10 rm** (dinner included) 37.00/74.00 **st.** – SB.

at Grange-in-Borrowdale S : 4 ¾ m. by B 5289 – Y – ✉ Keswick – ☎ 0176 87 :

Borrowdale Gates Country House, CA12 5UQ, ℘ 77204, Fax 77254, ←, – rest TV ☎ P. VISA. Y **s**
closed 2 to 31 January and 4 to 16 December – **Meals** (bar lunch Monday to Saturday)/dinner 20.00 **t.** 5.25 – **22 rm** (dinner included) 62.50/130.00 **t.**

at Rosthwaite S : 6 m. on B 5289 – Y – ✉ Keswick – ☎ 0176 87 :

Hazel Bank, CA12 5XB, ℘ 77248, ←, – TV P. VISA
Easter-October – **Meals** (dinner only) 3.80 – **6 rm** (dinner included) 43.00/86.00 **st.**

at Seatoller S : 8 m. on B 5289 – Y – ✉ Keswick – ☎ 0176 87 :

Seatoller House, CA12 5XN, ℘ 77218, ← Borrowdale, – P
mid March-mid November – **Meals** (by arrangement) (communal dining) 5.50 – **9 rm** (dinner included) 33.50/64.00 **t.**

at Portinscale W : 1 ½ m. by A 66 – ✉ Keswick – ☎ 0176 87 :

Swinside Lodge, Newlands, CA12 5UE, S : 1 ½ m. on Grange Rd ℘ 72948, ← Catbells and Newlands Valley, – TV P. Y **c**
closed December-mid February – **Meals** (unlicensed) (dinner only) 27.50 **t.** – **9 rm** (dinner included) 60.00/135.00 **t.** – SB.

Derwent Cottage, CA12 5RF, ℘ 74838, – TV P. VISA. Y **x**
March-mid November – **Meals** (residents only) (dinner only) 15.00 **st.** 3.00 – **5 rm** 38.00/64.00 **st.** – SB.

at Braithwaite W : 2 m. by A 66 on B 5292 – ✉ Keswick – ☎ 0176 87 :

Ivy House, CA12 5SY, ℘ 78338, Fax 78113 – rest TV ☎ P. AE VISA. Y **i**
closed January – **Meals** (dinner only) 18.95 **t.** 3.70 – **12 rm** (dinner included) 46.00/92.00 **t.** – SB.

Middle Ruddings, CA12 5RY, on A 66 ℘ 78436, Fax 78438, – rest TV ☎ P. VISA Y **v**
Meals (bar lunch)/dinner a la carte approx. 14.00 **t.** 3.60 – **13 rm** 32.00/64.00 **t.** – SB.

Cottage in The Wood, Whinlatter Pass, CA12 5TW, NW : 1 ¾ m. on B 5292 ℘ 78409, ←, – P Y
mid March-mid November – **Meals** (dinner only) 17.50 **st.** – **7 rm** (dinner included) 55.00/84.00 **st.** – SB.

at Thornthwaite W : 3 ½ m. by A 66 – Y – ✉ Keswick – ☎ 0176 87 :

Thwaite Howe, CA12 5SA, ℘ 78281, ← Skiddaw and Derwent Valley, – rest TV ☎ P
March - October – **Meals** (dinner only) 15.00 **st.** 4.00 – **8 rm** (dinner included) 56.50/83.00 **st.** – SB.

Ne confondez pas :

Confort des hôtels : ...
Confort des restaurants : XXXXX X
Qualité de la table : ✿✿✿, ✿✿, ✿, Meals

KETTERING Northants. 404 R 26 – 01536.

The Coach House, Sheep St., NN16 0AN 410266/410333.

London 88 – Birmingham 54 – Leicester 16 – Northampton 24.

Kettering Park, Kettering Parkway, NN15 6XT, S : 2¼ m. by A 509 (Wellingborough rd) at junction with A 14 416666, Fax 416171, squash – rm – 200.
Meals (bar lunch Saturday) 11.95/20.00 **st.** and a la carte 6.95 – **85 rm** 90.00/110.00 **st.**, 3 suites – SB.

Periquito, Market Pl., NN16 0AJ, 520732, Fax 411036 – – 150
40 rm, 1 suite.

ATS Northfield Av. 512832

KETTLEWELL N. Yorks. 402 N 21 – pop. 297 (inc. Starbotton) – ECD : Tuesday and Thursday – Skipton – 01756.

London 237 – Bradford 33 – Leeds 40.

Racehorses, BD23 5QZ, 760233 –
11 rm.

Cam Lodge, BD23 5QU, 760276, –
April-October – **Meals** 12.00 **st.** – **4 rm** 20.00/40.00 **st.**

at Starbotton NW : 1¾ m. on B 6160 – Skipton – 01756 :

Hilltop Country, BD23 5HY, 760321, « 17C stone built house », park –
mid March-mid November – **Meals** (by arrangement) 15.00 **st.** 4.60 – **5 rm** 42.00/58.00 **st.** – SB.

KEXBY N. Yorks. – see York.

KEYSTON Cambs. 404 S 26 – pop. 257 (inc. Bythorn) – Huntingdon – 01832.

London 75 – Cambridge 29 – Northampton 24.

Pheasant Inn, Village Loop Rd, PE18 0RE, 710241, Fax 710340 –
Meals a la carte 15.20/26.40 **t.**

KIDDERMINSTER Heref. and Worcs. 403 404 N 26 – pop. 50 385 – ECD : Wednesday – 01562.

Severn Valley Railway Station, Comberton Hill, DY10 1QX 829400 (summer only).

London 139 – Birmingham 17 – Shrewsbury 34 – Worcester 15.

Stone Manor, Stone, DY10 4PJ, SE : 2½ m. on A 448 777555, Fax 777834, park, – rm – 150.
Meals 10.95/16.50 **t.** and a la carte 6.50 – 6.50 – **51 rm** 62.50 **t.**, 1 suite – SB.

Gainsborough House, Bewdley Hill, DY11 6BS, 820041, Fax 66179 – – 250
42 rm.

Collingdale, 197 Comberton Rd, DY10 1VE, 515460 –
Meals (by arrangement) 7.50 **st.** 3.00 – **9 rm** 17.50/35.00 **st.**

at Chaddesley Corbett SE : 4½ m. by A 448 – Kidderminster – 01562 :

Brockencote Hall, DY10 4PY, on A 448 777876, Fax 777872, « Part 19C mansion in park », – rest – 30.
Meals *(closed Saturday lunch)* 17.50/22.50 **st.** and a la carte 22.80/47.00 **st.** 5.95 – **17 rm** 80.00/135.00 **st.** – SB.

ATS Park St. 744668/744843

KIDLINGTON Oxon. 403 404 Q 28 – see Oxford.

KILSBY Northants. 403 404 Q 26 – see Rugby (Warks.).

KILVE Somerset 403 K 30 – pop. 344 – Bridgewater – 01278.

London 172 – Bristol 49 – Minehead 13 – Taunton 23.

Hood Arms, TA5 1EA, 741210, – rest
closed Christmas Day – **Meals** 10.00/16.50 **t.** and a la carte 3.30 – **5 rm** 38.00/64.00 **t.** – SB.

KINGHAM Oxon. 403 404 P 28 – pop. 1 434 – ECD : Wednesday – 01608.

London 81 – Gloucester 32 – Oxford 25.

Mill House, OX7 6UH, 658188, Fax 658492, – – 50.
Meals 13.95/25.90 **t.** and a la carte 5.00 – **21 rm** 45.00/96.00 **t.** – SB.

KINGSBRIDGE Devon 403 I 33 **The West Country G.** – pop. 5 081 – ECD : Thursday – ☎ 01548.

See : Town★ – Boat Trip to Salcombe★★ *AC*.

Exc. : Prawle Point (≤★★★) SE : 10 m. around coast by A 379.

Thurlestone ☎ 560405.

The Quay, TQ7 1HS ☎ 853195.

♦London 236 – Exeter 36 – ♦Plymouth 20 – Torquay 21.

Kings Arms, Fore St., TQ7 1AB, ☎ 852071, Fax 852977, – – 30
11 rm.

at Goveton NE : 2½ m. by A 381 – ✉ Kingsbridge – ☎ 01548 :

Buckland-Tout-Saints, TQ7 2DS, ☎ 853055, Fax 856261, ≤, « Queen Anne mansion », park – rest . VISA
Meals (booking essential) 14.50/28.00 **t.** 6.50 – **13 rm** 50.00/140.00 **t.**

at Chillington E : 5 m. on A 379 – ✉ Kingsbridge – ☎ 01548 :

White House, TQ7 2JX, ☎ 580580, Fax 581124, – rest . VISA
April-December – **Meals** (bar lunch)/dinner 12.00 **st.** 4.20 – **7 rm** (dinner included) 52.00/108.00 **st.** – SB.

at Torcross E : 7 m. on A 379 – ✉ Kingsbridge – ☎ 01548 :

The Venture without rest., TQ7 2TQ, ☎ 580314, ≤ – .
mid February-September – **3 rm** 18.00/36.00 **s.**

at Thurlestone W : 4 m. by A 381 – ✉ Kingsbridge – ☎ 01548 :

Thurlestone, TQ7 3NN, ☎ 560382, Fax 561069, ≤, heated, , , , squash – rest rest – 100. VISA
Meals 9.50/25.00 **st.** and lunch a la carte 5.50 – **68 rm** 55.00/140.00 **st.** – SB.

at Bantham W : 5 m. by A 379 – ✉ Kingsbridge – ☎ 01548 :

Sloop Inn, TQ7 3AJ, ☎ 560489, Fax 560489 –
closed mid December-31 January – **Meals** a la carte 11.20/14.25 **t.** – **5 rm** 30.00/55.00 **t.** – SB.

ATS Union Rd ☎ 853247/852699

KINGSDOWN Kent 404 Y 30 – see Deal.

KINGSKERSWELL Devon 403 J 32 – pop. 4 210 – ✉ Torquay – ☎ 01803.

♦London 219 – Exeter 21 – ♦Plymouth 33 – Torquay 4.

Pitt House, 2 Church End Rd, TQ12 5DS, ☎ 873374, « 15C thatched dower house », – . VISA
closed Sunday dinner, Monday and January – **Meals** (light lunch)/dinner 14.50 **st.** and a la carte.

KINGS LANGLEY Herts 404 S 28 – ☎ 01923.

♦London 26 – Luton 14.

Langleys, Hempstead Rd, WD4 8BR, ☎ 263150, Fax 264061 – rm
Meals (grill rest.) – **40 rm.**

KING'S LYNN Norfolk 402 404 V 25 **Great Britain G.** – pop. 37 323 – ECD : Wednesday – ☎ 01553.

Exc. : Houghton Hall★★ *AC*, NE : 14½m. by A 148 – Four Fenland Churches★ (Terrington St. Clement, Walpole St. Peter, West Walton, Walsoken) SW : by A 47.

Eagles, School Rd, Tylney All Saints ☎ 827147 – Granary Hotel, Little Dunham ☎ (01328) 701310.

The Old Gaol House, Saturday Market Pl., PE30 5DQ ☎ 763044.

♦London 103 – ♦Cambridge 45 – ♦Leicester 75 – ♦Norwich 44.

Knights Hill, Knights Hill Village, South Wootton, PE30 3HQ, NE : 4½ m. on A 148 at junction with A 149 ☎ 675566, Fax 675568, , , , – – 300. VISA
Meals (bar lunch Monday to Saturday)/dinner 15.50 **t.** and a la carte – 7.00 – **52 rm** 65.00/175.00 **t.** – SB.

Duke's Head (Forte), Tuesday Market Pl., PE30 1JS, ☎ 774996, Fax 763556 – – 240. VISA
Meals 16.95 **st.** (dinner) and a la carte 19.30/20.85 **st.** 6.70 – 8.50 – **71 rm** 60.00/70.00 **st.** – SB.

Butterfly, Beveridge Way, PE30 4NB, S : 2¼ m. by Hardwick Rd at junction of A 10 with A 47 ☎ 771707, Fax 768027 – rm – 40. VISA
Meals 10.85/11.95 **t.** and a la carte 4.50 – 6.50 – **50 rm** 49.00 **t.** – SB.

Russet House, 53 Goodwins Rd, PE30 5PE, ☎ 773098, Fax 773098, – rest.
closed Christmas-New Year – **Meals** (booking essential)(dinner only) 12.50 **t.** 2.80 – **12 rm** 34.50/70.00 **t.**

Fairlight Lodge, 79 Goodwins Rd, PE30 5PE, ☎ 762234, Fax 770280, –
closed 24 to 26 December – **Meals** (by arrangement) 15.00 **st.** – **7 rm** 16.00/36.00 **st.**

Rococo, 11 Saturday Market Pl., PE30 5DQ, ☎ 771483 – AE VISA
closed Monday lunch and Sunday – **Meals** 12.00/24.50 **t.**

at Grimston NE : 6 ¼ m. by A 148 – ✉ King's Lynn – 01485 :

Congham Hall , Lynn Rd, PE32 1AH, ☎ 600250, Fax 601191, ≤, « Part Georgian manor house, herb garden », heated, park, – rest – 25. AE VISA.
Meals *(closed Saturday lunch)* 15.00/32.00 **t.** 6.00 – **12 rm** 65.00/125.00 **t.**, 2 suites – SB.

at Tottenhill S : 5 ¼ m. on A 10 – ✉ King's Lynn – 01553 :

Oakwood House, PE33 0RH, N : ½ m. on A 10 ☎ 810256, – VISA.
Meals (dinner only) a la carte 9.00/13.10 **st.** 4.15 – **10 rm** 30.00/40.00 **st.** – SB.

ATS 4 Oldmedow Rd, Hardwick Rd Trading Est. ☎ 774035

KINGSTEIGNTON Devon 403 J 32 – pop. 8 913 – ECD : Thursday – ✉ Newton Abbot – 01626.

♦London 223 – Exeter 17 – ♦Plymouth 33 – Torquay 7.

Passage House, Hackney Lane, TQ12 3QH, S : ½ m. ☎ 55515, Fax 63336, ≤, – – 150. AE VISA.
Meals 8.50/16.95 **t.** and a la carte **38 rm** 59.00/75.00 **t.**, 1 suite – SB.

KINGSTON Devon 403 I 33 – pop. 364 – ✉ Kingsbridge – 01548.

♦London 237 – Exeter 41 – ♦Plymouth 11.

Trebles Cottage , TQ7 4PT, ☎ 810268, Fax 810268, – rm. AE VISA
Meals 14.00 **st.** 5.50 – **5 rm** 30.00/60.00 **st.** – SB.

KINGSTON-UPON-HULL Humbs. 402 S 22 **Great Britain G.** – pop. 254 117 – ECD : Monday and Thursday – 01482.

Exc. : Burton Constable★ *AC*, NE : 9 m. by A 165 and B 1238 – Z.

Springhead Park, Willerby Rd ☎ 656309 – Sutton Park, Salthouse Rd ☎ 74242.

Humberside Airport : ☎ (01652) 688456, S : 19 m. by A 63 – **Terminal** : Coach Service.

to The Netherlands (Rotterdam) (North Sea Ferries) (13 h 30 mn) – to The Netherlands (Zeebrugge) (North Sea Ferries) (13 h 45 mn).

Central Library, Albion St., HU1 3TF ☎ 223344 – King George Dock, Hedon Rd, HU9 5PR ☎ 702118 – 75-76 Carr Lane, HU1 3RQ ☎ 223559.

♦London 183 – ♦Leeds 61 – ♦Nottingham 94 – ♦Sheffield 68.

Plan opposite

Forte Crest, Castle St., HU1 2BX, ☎ 225221, Fax 213299, – rm – 120 Y **n**
99 rm.

Royal (Friendly), Ferensway, HU1 3UF, ☎ 25087, Fax 23172, – rm rest – 450. AE VISA. Y **a**
Meals 13.50 **st.** and a la carte 5.50 – 6.75 – **155 rm** 57.75/94.00 **st.** – SB.

Travel Inn, Ferriby Rd, Hessle, HU13 0JA, W : 7 m. by A 63 and A 164 ☎ 645285, Fax 645299 – rm. AE VISA. Z
Meals (grill rest.) a la carte approx. 16.00 **t.** – 4.95 – **40 rm** 33.50 **t.**

Campanile, Beverley Rd, Freetown Way, HU2 9AN, ☎ 25530, Fax 587538 – rm – 35. AE VISA. X **a**
Meals 9.85 **t.** 4.65 – 4.25 – **47 rm** 35.75 **t.**

Roseberry, 86 Marlborough Av., HU5 3JT, ☎ 445256 – VISA. Z **a**
Meals 9.00 **s.** – **5 rm** 20.00/42.00 **st.**

Earlsmere, 76-78 Sunnybank, off Spring Bank West, HU3 1LQ, ☎ 41977, Fax 473714 – VISA Z **i**
closed Christmas – **Meals** (by arrangement) 12.50 **st.** 3.00 – **15 rm** 18.80/41.10 **st.** – SB.

Cerutti's, 10 Nelson St., HU1 1XE, ☎ 28501, Fax 587597 – VISA Y **o**
closed Saturday lunch, Sunday, 1 week Christmas and Bank Holidays – **Meals** - Seafood a la carte 15.50/23.75 **t.** 5.40.

at Hedon E : 6½ m. by A 63 on A 1033 – Z – ✉ Kingston-upon-Hull – 01482 :

Kingstown, Hull Rd, HU12 8DJ, W : 1 m. on A 1033 ☎ 890461, Fax 890713 – AE VISA.
Meals (in bar Monday to Saturday lunch and Sunday)/dinner 14.95 **st.** 4.75 – **34 rm** 62.00/85.00 **st.** – SB.

KINGSTON-UPON-HULL

Carr Lane . . . . Y
George Street X
Jameson Street . . . . Y 17
King Edward Street . . . . . Y 19
Paragon Street . . . . Y 29
Princes Quay Shopping Centre . . . . . Y
Prospect Shopping Centre X
Prospect Street X
Whitefriargate . . . . Y 49

Bond Street . . . . X 3
Commercial Road . . . . . . Y 8
County Road North . . . . . Z 9
Dock Office Row . . . . X 10
Dock Street . . . . X 12
Fairfax Avenue . . . . Z 13
Ferensway . . . . XY 14
Grimston Street . . . . X 15
Humber Dock Street . . . . Y 16
Jarratt Street . . . . X 18
Lowgate . . . . Y 23
Market Place . . . . Y 24
Maybury Road . . . . Z 25
Prince's Avenue . . . . Z 31
Prince's Dock Street . . . . Y 32
Queen's Road . . . . Z 33
Queen Street . . . . Y 35
Queen's Dock Avenue . . X 36
Reform Street . . . . X 37
Sculcoates Bridge . . . . . . X 42
Southcoates Avenue . . . . Z 43
Southcoates Lane . . . . . . Z 44
Waterhouse Lane . . . . . . Y 47
Wilberforce Drive . . . . . . X 50
Worship Street . . . . X 52

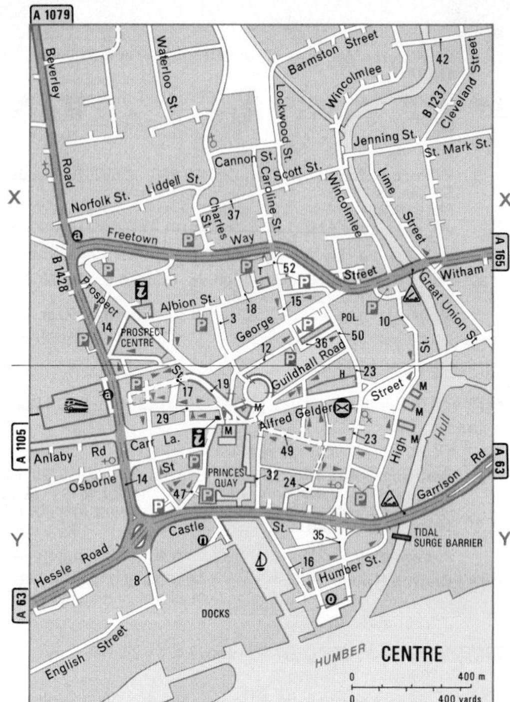

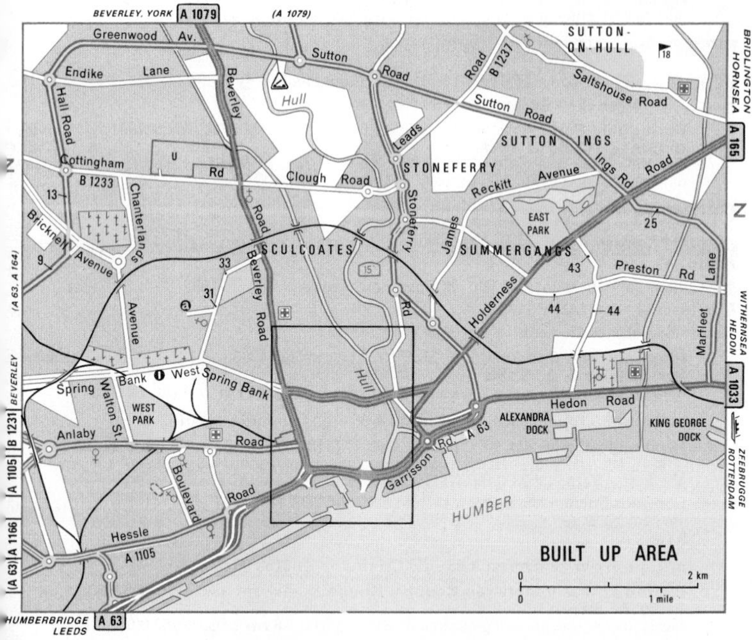

BEVERLEY, YORK A 1079 (A 1079)

Greenwood Av.
Endike Lane
Hall Road
Cottingham Rd
B 1233
Beverley Road
Sutton Road
Hull
SUTTON-ON-HULL
Saltshouse Road
Sutton Road
B 1237
Leads Road
SUTTON INGS
Ings Rd
STONEFERRY
Clough Road
Reckitt Avenue
Chanterlands Avenue
Bricknell Avenue
SCULCOATES
Stoneferry Rd
James Reckitt Avenue
EAST PARK
SUMMERGANGS
Preston Rd
Marfleet Lane
Holderness Road
Spring Bank West
Spring Bank
Walton St.
WEST PARK
Anlaby Road
Boulevard
Hedon Road
ALEXANDRA DOCK
KING GEORGE DOCK
Garrisson Rd.
A 63
HUMBER
Hessle Road
A 1105
BRIDLINGTON HORNSEA A 165
WITHERNSEA HEDON A 1033
ZEEBRUGGE ROTTERDAM
(A 63, A 164)
BEVERLEY B 1231
A 1105
A 1166
(A 63)
HUMBERBRIDGE LEEDS A 63
Z

BUILT UP AREA

0 2 km
0 1 mile

at Willerby W : 5 m. by A 1079 – Z – and Willerby Rd – ✉ Kingston-upon-Hull – ☎ 01482 :

Grange Park, Main St., HU10 6EA, N : 1 m. by Beverley Rd ☎ 656488, Fax 655848, ⛨, ☐, ⛬ – 🛗 ⚝ rm ▤ rest TV ☎ ♿ P – 🔔 350. ☐ AE ◑ VISA by Spring Bank Z
Meals 15.95 **st.** (dinner) and a la carte 14.40/20.50 **st.** 🌡 4.60 – ☐ 8.00 **100 rm** 59.50/69.50 **st.**, 4 suites – SB.

Willerby Manor, Well Lane, HU10 6ER, ☎ 652616, Fax 653901, ⛬ – TV ☎ P – 🔔 500. ☐ VISA. ⚝
Meals *(closed Saturday lunch, Sunday dinner and Bank Holidays)* 12.00/14.00 **st.** and a la carte 🌡 4.90 – ☐ 7.25 – **32 rm** 59.00/82.00 **st.**

at North Ferriby W : 7 m. on A 63 – Z – ✉ Kingston-upon-Hull – ☎ 01482 :

Forte Posthouse, Ferriby High Rd, HU14 3LG, ☎ 645212, Fax 643332 – ⚝ rm ▤ rest TV ☎ P – 🔔 100. ☐ AE ◑ VISA
Meals a la carte approx. 15.00 **t.** 🌡 5.50 – **95 rm** 56.00 **st.**

ATS Great Union St. ☎ 29044 ATS Scott St. ☎ 29370/225502

KINGSTOWN Cumbria – see Carlisle.

KINGTON Heref. and Worcs. 403 K 27 – pop. 2 197 – ECD : Wednesday – ☎ 01544.
⛳18 Bradnor Hill ☎ 230340.
♦London 152 – ♦Birmingham 61 – Hereford 19 – Shrewsbury 54.

Penrhos Court, HR5 3LH, E : 1½ m. on A 44 ☎ 230720, Fax 230754, « Part 15C and 16C house with medieval cruck hall », ⛬ – ⚝ TV ☎ P – 🔔 25. AE. ⚝
closed February – **Meals** (dinner only)(booking essential) 25.00 **t.** and a la carte 🌡 6.00 – **11 rm** ☐ 75.00/140.00 **st.** – SB.

at Lyonshall E : 2½ m . by A 44 on A 480 – ✉ Kington – ☎ 01544 :

Church House, HR5 3HR, on A 44 ☎ 340350, ⛬ – ⚝ P. ⚝
closed 24 December-2 January – **Meals** (by arrangement) 9.00 – **3 rm** 20.00/36.00 – SB.

ATS 20-22 Bridge St. ☎ 230350

KINTBURY Berks. 403 404 P 29 – pop. 2 472 – ✉ Newbury – ☎ 01488.
♦London 73 – Newbury 6 – Reading 23.

Dundas Arms with rm, 53 Station Rd, RG15 0UT, ☎ 658263, Fax 658568, ←, « Canal and riverside setting », ⛬ – TV ☎ P. ☐ AE VISA
closed Christmas - New Year – **Meals** *(closed Monday lunch and Sunday)* 18.50 **t.** (lunch) and dinner a la carte 23.45/26.95 **t.** 🌡 5.00 – **5 rm** ☐ 55.00/65.00 **t.**

KINVER Staffs. 403 404 N 26 – see Stourbridge (W. Mids).

KIRKBURTON W. Yorks. 402 404 O 23 ⑳ – ✉ Huddersfield – ☎ 01484.
♦London 195 – ♦Leeds 20 – ♦Manchester 32 – ♦Sheffield 22.

Springfield Park, Penistone Rd, HD8 0PE, on A 629 ☎ 607788, Fax 607961 – ⚝ rm TV ☎ P – 🔔 140. ☐ AE ◑ VISA
Old Mill : **Meals** a la carte 11.30/23.05 **t.** 🌡 5.90 – ***Topo's :*** **Meals** - Italian (closed Monday dinner) a la carte 8.40/17.85 **t.** 🌡 5.90 – **43 rm** ☐ 53.50/100.00 **st.**

KIRBY HILL N. Yorks. – see Richmond.

KIRKBY LONSDALE Cumbria 402 M 21 – pop. 2 076 – ECD : Wednesday – ✉ Carnforth – ☎ 0152 42.
⛳18 Scaleber Lane, Barbon ☎ 36365 – ⛳9 Casterton, Sedbergh Rd ☎ 71592.
🅸 24 Main St., LA6 2AE ☎ 71437.
♦London 259 – ♦Carlisle 62 – Kendal 13 – Lancaster 17 – ♦Leeds 58.

Pheasant Inn, Casterton, LA6 2RX, NE : 1 ¼ m. on A 683 ☎ 71230, Fax 71230, ⛬ – ⚝ rest TV ☎ ♿ P. ☐ VISA
Meals (bar lunch)/dinner a la carte 13.75/20.50 **t.** 🌡 5.00 – **10 rm** ☐ 40.00/64.00 **t.**

at Cowan Bridge (Lancs) SE : 2 m. on A 65 – ✉ Carnforth – ☎ 0152 42 :

Hipping Hall, LA6 2JJ, SE : ½ m. on A 65 ☎ 71187, Fax 72452, ⛬ – TV ☎ P. ☐ VISA
closed January and February – **Meals** (residents only) (communal dining) (dinner only) 20.00 **st.** – **5 rm** ☐ 62.00/88.00 **st.**, 2 suites – SB.

Cobwebs Country House ⛬ with rm, Leck, LA6 2HZ, NE : ¼ m. ☎ 72141, Fax 72141, ⛬ – ⚝ rest TV ☎ P
5 rm.

at Lupton NW : 3¾ m. on A 65 – ✉ Carnforth – ☎ 0153 95 :

Lupton Tower Vegetarian Country House ⛬ with rm, LA6 2PR, ☎ 67400, ←, ⛬ – ⚝ P. ☐ VISA
Meals (dinner only)(booking essential) 18.00 **t.** 🌡 5.00 – **6 rm** ☐ 30.00/62.00 **t.** – SB.

KIRKBYMOORSIDE N. Yorks. 402 R 21 – pop. 3 825 – ECD : Thursday – 01751.
Manor Vale 431525.
London 244 – Scarborough 26 – York 33.

George and Dragon, 17 Market Pl., YO6 6AA, 433334, Fax 433334, « Part 17C coaching inn », – rest . VISA
Meals (bar lunch)/dinner a la carte 11.40/20.35 **st.** 5.00 – **19 rm** 44.00/72.00 **st.** – SB.

KIRKBY STEPHEN Cumbria 402 M 20 – pop. 2 209 – ECD : Thursday – 0176 83.
Market St., CA17 4QN 71199 (summer only).
London 285 – Carlisle 48 – Kendal 24.

Town Head House, High St., CA17 4SH, 71044, Fax 72128, – . VISA
Meals (dinner only) a la carte 14.50/19.90 **st.** 3.50 – **6 rm** 40.00/73.00 **st.** – SB.

Ing Hill Lodge , Mallerstang Dale, CA17 4JT, S : 4 ½ m. on B 6259 71153, Fax 71153, Mallerstang Dale, –
Meals 12.50 **st.** 3.50 – **4 rm** 25.00/50.00 **st.** – SB.

KIRKCAMBECK Cumbria 401 402 L 18 – see Brampton.

KIRKHAM Lancs. 402 L 22 – pop. 6 311 – Preston – 01772.
London 240 – Blackpool 9 – Preston 7.

Cromwellian, 16 Poulton St., PR4 2AB, 685680, Fax 685680 – AE VISA
closed Sunday and Monday – **Meals** (dinner only) a la carte 13.95/19.95 **st.** 5.25.

KIRKOSWALD Cumbria 401 402 L 19 – pop. 1 281 – Penrith – 01768.
London 300 – Carlisle 23 – Kendal 41 – Lancaster 58.

Prospect Hill , CA10 1ER, N : ¾ m. 898500, , « Converted 18C farm buildings », – .
11 rm.

KIRKWHELPINGTON Northd. 401 402 N/O 18 **Great Britain G.** – pop. 353 – Morpeth – 01830.
Envir. : Wallington House★ *AC*, E : 3½ m. by A 696 and B 6342.
London 305 – Carlisle 46 – Newcastle upon Tyne 20.

Shieldhall , Wallington, NE61 4AQ, SE : 2 ½ m. by A 696 on B 6342 540387, Fax 540387, – . VISA.
April-September – **Meals** (by arrangement) 13.50 4.50 – **6 rm** 30.00/46.00.

KNARESBOROUGH N. Yorks. 402 P 21 – pop. 13 848 – ECD : Thursday – 01423.
Boroughbridge Rd 863219.
35 Market Place, HG5 8AL 866886 (summer only).
London 217 – Bradford 21 – Harrogate 3 – Leeds 18 – York 18.

Dower House, Bond End, HG5 9AL, 863302, Fax 867665, , , , – rm – 65.
Meals (bar lunch Monday to Saturday)/dinner 18.50 **t.** and a la carte – **31 rm** 53.00/94.00 **st.**, 1 suite – SB.

KNIGHTWICK Heref. and Worcs. 403 404 M 27 – pop. 87 – ECD : Wednesday – Worcester – 01886.
London 132 – Hereford 20 – Leominster 18 – Worcester 8.

Talbot, WR6 5PH, on B 4197 821235, Fax 821060, , , squash – . VISA
Meals (restricted dinner Sunday) a la carte 11.00/23.85 **t.** 3.20 – **10 rm** 31.00/56.50 **t.**

KNOWLE W. Mids. 403 404 O 26 – pop. 11 203 – ECD : Thursday – Solihull – 01564.
London 108 – Birmingham 9 – Coventry 10 – Warwick 11.

Bridgewater, 2110 Warwick Rd, B93 0EE, S : 1 ½ m. on A 4141 771177, Fax 770141, – rest . AE VISA
Meals a la carte 9.95/22.95 **st.** 4.50 – **20 rm** 57.50/75.00 **st.** – SB.

Greswolde Arms, 1657 High St., B93 0LL, 772711, Fax 770354 – rm – 150
36 rm.

KNOWL HILL Berks. 404 R 29 – Twyford – 01628.
9, 18, Hennerton, Crazies Hill Rd, Wargrave (01734) 401000.
London 38 – Maidenhead 5 – Reading 8.

Bird in Hand, Bath Rd, RG10 9UP, 826622, Fax 826748, – . AE VISA
accommodation closed 25 and 26 December – **Meals** 9.95/15.00 **t.** and a la carte 5.50 – **15 rm** 67.50/90.00 **st.** – SB.

KNOWSLEY Mersey. 402 403 L 23 – see Liverpool.

KNUTSFORD Ches. 402 403 404 M 24 – pop. 13 352 – ECD : Wednesday – ☎ 01565.
Council Offices, Toft Rd, WA16 6TA ☎ 632611/632210.
♦London 187 – Chester 25 – ♦Liverpool 33 – ♦Manchester 18 – ♦Stoke-on-Trent 30.

Cottons, Manchester Rd, WA16 0SU, NW : 1 ½ m. on A 50 ☎ 650333, Fax 755351, , , , – rm – 200.
Magnolia : **Meals** (bar lunch Saturday) 11.95/18.00 **st.** and a la carte 6.95 – **73 rm** 79.00/124.00 **st.**, 9 suites – SB.

Longview, 55 Manchester Rd, WA16 0LX, ☎ 632119, Fax 652402 – .
closed 24 December-2 January – **Meals** *(closed Sunday and Bank Holidays)* (lunch by arrangement)/dinner 22.50 **t.** and a la carte 5.50 – **23 rm** 50.00/75.00 – SB.

Forte Travelodge without rest., Chester Rd, Tabley, WA16 0PP, NW : 2 ¾ m. by A 5033 on A 556 ☎ 652187, Reservations (Freephone) 0800 850950 – .
32 rm 33.50 **t.**

Belle Epoque Brasserie with rm, 60 King St., WA16 6DT, ☎ 633060, Fax 634150, « Art Nouveau », – – 100.
closed first week January and Bank Holidays – **Meals** *(closed Sunday)* a la carte 14.95/23.40 **st.** 4.50 – 5.50 – **7 rm** 40.00/50.00 **st.**

Treasure Village, 84 King St., WA16 6EG, ☎ 651537 –
Meals - Chinese.

Est, Est, Est !, 81 King St., WA16 6DX, ☎ 755487, Fax 651151 – .
closed Saturday lunch and 25-26 December – **Meals** - Italian 9.95 **t.** and a la carte.

at Mobberley NE : 2 ½ m. by A 537 on B 5085 – ✉ Knutsford – ☎ 01565 :

Laburnum Cottage without rest., Knutsford Rd, WA16 7PU, W : ¾ m. on B 5085 ☎ 872464, Fax 872464, « Gardens » – .
5 rm 38.00/48.00 **st.**

Hinton, Town Lane, WA16 7HH, on B 5085 ☎ 873484, Fax 873484, – .
Meals (by arrangement) 9.50 – **4 rm** 30.00/48.00 **s.**

at Over Peover SE : 5 m. by A 50 and Stocks Lane – ✉ Knutsford – ☎ 01625 :

The Dog, Wellbank Lane, Peover Heath, WA16 8UP, ☎ 861421, Fax 861421 – .
Meals (in bar) 12.15/15.30 **t.** 3.75 – **3 rm** 45.00/68.00 **t.**

at Hoo Green NW : 3 ½ m. on A 50 – ✉ Knutsford – ☎ 01565 :

Kilton Inn (Premier), Warrington Rd, WA16 0PZ, ☎ 830420, Fax 830411 – .
Meals (grill rest.) 10.00 **st.** and a la carte 3.75 – 3.45 – **28 rm** 39.50 **st.** – SB.

at Bucklow Hill NW : 3 ½ m. at junction A 556 and A 5034 – ✉ Knutsford – ☎ 01565 :

Swan (Premier), Bucklow Hill, Chester Rd, WA16 6RD, ☎ 830295, Fax 830614 – rm – 50
70 rm.

ATS Malt St. ☎ 652224

LACOCK Wilts. 403 404 N 29 **The West Country G.** – pop. 1 068 – ✉ Chippenham – ☎ 01249.
See : Village★ - Lacock Abbey★ *AC* – High St.★, St. Cyriac★, Fox Talbot Museum of Photography★ *AC*.
♦London 109 – Bath 16 – ♦Bristol 30 – Chippenham 3.

Sign of the Angel, 6 Church St., SN15 2LA, ☎ 730230, Fax 730527, « Part 14C and 15C former wool merchant's house in National Trust village », –
Meals - English **9 rm.**

LANCASTER Lancs. 402 L 21 **Great Britain G.** – pop. 43 902 – ECD : Wednesday – ☎ 01524.
See : Castle★ *AC*.
18 Ashton Hall, Ashton-with-Stodday ☎ 752090 – 9 Lansil, Caton Rd ☎ 39269 – 9 Robin Lane, Bentham ☎ (015242) 61018.
29 Castle Hill, LA1 1YN ☎ 32878.
♦London 252 – ♦Blackpool 26 – Bradford 62 – Burnley 44 – ♦Leeds 71 – ♦Middlesbrough 97 – Preston 26.

Lancaster House, Green Lane, LA1 4GJ, S : 3 ¼ m. by A 6 ☎ 844822, Fax 844766, , , – rm – 120.
Gressingham : **Meals** 10.95/25.50 **st.** and a la carte 5.00 – **80 rm** 79.00/89.00 **st.** – SB.

Forte Posthouse, Waterside Park, Caton Rd, LA1 3RA, NE : 1 ½ m. on A 683 ☎ 65999, Fax 841265, , , , – rm – 120.
Meals a la carte approx. 15.00 **t.** 5.50 – **115 rm** 53.50/69.50 **st.**

Edenbreck House without rest., Sunnyside Lane, off Ashfield Av., LA1 5ED, by Westbourne Rd, near the station ☎ 32464, –
closed Christmas – **5 rm** 25.00/50.00.

at Carnforth N : 6 ¼ m. on A 6 – ✉ Lancaster – ☎ 01524 :

New Capernwray Farm ⑤, Capernwray, LA6 1AD, NE : 3 m. by B 6254 ✆ 734284, Fax 734284, ≤, ⛰ – ⇔ TV P. VISA
Meals (communal dining) 17.50 **s.** – **3 rm** ☐ 34.00/58.00 **s.**

at Claughton NE : 6 ¾ m. on A 683 – ✉ Kirkby Lonsdale – ☎ 0152 42 :

Old Rectory, LA2 9LA, on A 683 ✆ 21455, Fax 21791, ⛰ – ⇔ rest TV ☎ P. VISA. ✂
Meals *(closed Sunday)* (dinner only) 14.95 **t.** and a la carte 24.45/36.95 **t.** 4.50 – **12 rm** ☐ 25.00/50.00 **t.** – SB.

LANERCOST Cumbria 401 402 L 19 – see Brampton.

LANGHO Lancs. 402 M 22 - see Blackburn.

LANREATH Cornwall 403 G 32 – pop. 504 – ✉ Looe – ☎ 01503.
◆London 269 – ◆Plymouth 26 – Truro 34.

Punch Bowl Inn, PL13 2NX, ✆ 220218, ⛰ – TV P. VISA
Meals (bar lunch)/dinner 10.00 **st.** and a la carte 3.00 – **14 rm** ☐ 30.00/70.00 **t.** – SB.

If you find you cannot take up a hotel booking you have made, please let the hotel know immediately.

LANSALLOS Cornwall 403 G 32 – pop. 1 625 – ✉ Fowey – ☎ 01726.
◆London 273 – ◆Plymouth 30.

Carneggan House ⑤, Lanteglos-by-Fowey, PL23 1NW, NW : 2 m. on Polruan rd ✆ 870327, ≤, ⛰, ✂ – TV P. AE VISA. ✂
closed January – **Meals** 25.00 **st.** 3.50 – **3 rm** ☐ 25.00/54.00 **st.**

LARKFIELD Kent 404 V 30 – see Maidstone.

LASTINGHAM N. Yorks. 402 R 21 – pop. 87 – ECD : Wednesday – ✉ York – ☎ 01751.
◆London 244 – Scarborough 26 – York 32.

Lastingham Grange ⑤, YO6 6TH, ✆ 417345, ≤, « Country house atmosphere », ⛰, park – ⇔ rest TV ☎ P. ✂
March-November – **Meals** (light lunch Monday to Saturday)/dinner 23.50 **t.** 3.50 – **12 rm** ☐ 62.50/115.50 – SB.

LAUNCESTON Cornwall 403 G 32 – ☎ 01566.
◆London 273 – Exeter 50 – Plymouth 30 – Truro 33.

Randells, Prospect House, 11 Western Rd, PL15 7AS, ✆ 776484.

ATS Pennygillam Ind. Est. ✆ 773066

LAVENHAM Suffolk 404 W 27 **Great Britain G.** – pop. 1 693 – ECD : Wednesday – ✉ Sudbury – ☎ 01787.
See : Town★★ – Church of SS. Peter and Paul★.
Lady St., CO10 9RA ✆ 248207 (summer only).
◆London 66 – ◆Cambridge 39 – Colchester 22 – ◆Ipswich 19.

Swan (Forte), High St., CO10 9QA, ✆ 247477, Fax 248286, « Part 14C timbered inn », ⛰ – ⇔ TV ☎ P – 35. AE VISA JCB
Meals 12.95/21.95 **t.** and a la carte 6.50 – ☐ 8.50 – **45 rm** 75.00/120.00 **t.**, 2 suites – SB.

Angel, Market Pl., CO10 9QZ, ✆ 247388, Fax 247057, « 15C inn », ⛰ – TV ☎ P. VISA. ✂
closed Christmas Day – **Meals** a la carte 10.45/15.95 **t.** 3.00 – **8 rm** ☐ 37.50/60.00 **t.** – SB.

Angel Corner, 17 Market Pl., CO10 9QZ, ✆ 247168, Fax 247905, « 15C former wool-merchant's house », ⛰ – ✂
March-October – **Meals** (by arrangement) (communal dining) 15.00 – **3 rm** ☐ 23.00/39.00.

Great House with rm, Market Pl., CO10 9QZ, ✆ 247431, Fax 248080, « Part 14C timbered house » – TV ☎. VISA
closed 3 weeks January – **Meals** - French (closed Sunday dinner and Monday except Bank Holidays) 15.95 **t.** (dinner) and a la carte 12.40/25.25 **t.** 6.90 – **1 rm** ☐ 50.00/68.00 **t.**, **3 suites** 60.00/80.00 **t.** – SB.

at Brent Eleigh SE : 2 ½ m. by A 1141 – ✉ Sudbury – ☎ 01787 :

Street Farm without rest., CO10 9NU, ✆ 247271, ⛰ – ⇔ P. ✂
March - November – **3 rm** ☐ 20.00/40.00.

LEA Lancs. – see Preston.

LEAMINGTON SPA Warks. 403 404 P 27 – see Royal Leamington Spa.

LEDBURY Heref. and Worcs. 403 404 M 27 – pop. 5 119 – ECD : Wednesday – ☎ 01531.
1 Church Lane, HR8 1EA ℘ 636147.
♦London 119 – Hereford 14 – Newport 46 – Worcester 16.

Feathers, High St., HR8 1DS, ℘ 635266, Fax 632001, « Timbered 16C inn », squash – TV ☎ P – 120. AE VISA
Meals a la carte 12.15/24.95 **t.** – **11 rm** 59.50/78.50 – SB.

Wall Hills, Hereford Rd, HR8 2PR, ℘ 632833, ←, – P. VISA.
closed 23 December-2 January – **Meals** 16.75 **st.** 4.50 – **3 rm** 35.00/52.00 **st.** – SB.

Barn House, New St., HR8 2DX, ℘ 632825, « Part 17C House », – P – 30. VISA
closed 25 December – **Meals** (by arrangement) – **3 rm** 40.00/56.00 **t.**

at Wellington Heath N : 2 m. by B 4214 – ✉ Ledbury – ☎ 01531 :

Hope End, Hope End, HR8 1JQ, N : ¾ m. ℘ 633613, Fax 636366, « 18C house, restored Georgian gardens », park – rest ☎ P. VISA.
closed mid December-first week February – **Meals** (booking essential) (dinner only) 30.00 **t.** 4.50 – **9 rm** 85.00/140.00 **t.** – SB.

at Bishops Frome NW : 8 m. on B 4214 – ✉ Worcester – ☎ 01531 :

Five Bridges, WR6 5BX, SW : 1 ¼ m. on A 4103 ℘ 640340 – P. VISA
closed Sunday dinner and Monday – **Meals** a la carte 13.15/22.80 **st.** 4.25.

LEEDS W. Yorks. 402 P 22 **Great Britain G.** – pop. 680 722 – ECD : Wednesday – ☎ 0113.
See : City★ - City Art Gallery★ *AC* DZ **M.**
Envir. : Kirkstall Abbey★ *AC*, NW : 3 m. by A 65 BV – Templenewsam★ (decorative arts★) *AC*, E : 5 m. by A 64 and A 63 CX **D.**
Exc. : Harewood House★★ (The Gallery★) *AC*, N : 8 m. by A 61 CV.
18, 18 Temple Newsam, Temple Newsam Rd, Halton ℘ 2645624 CV – 18 Gotts Park, Armley Ridge Rd, ℘ 2342019 BV – 18 Middleton Park, Ring Rd, Beeston Park, Middleton ℘ 2709506 CX – 18, 9 Moor Allerton, Coal Rd, Wike ℘ 2661154 – 18 Howley Hall, Scotchman Lane, Morley ℘ (01924) 472432 – 9 Roundhay, Park Lane ℘ 2662695, CV.
Leeds - Bradford Airport : ℘ 250 9696, NW : 8 m. by A 65 and A 658 BV.
The Arcade, City Station, LS1 4DG ℘ 247 8301.
♦London 204 – ♦Liverpool 75 – ♦Manchester 43 – ♦Newcastle upon Tyne 95 – ♦Nottingham 74.

Plans on following pages

Oulton Hall (De Vere), Rothwell Lane, Oulton, LS26 8HN, SE : 5½ m. by A 61 and A 639 ℘ 282 1000, Fax 282 8066, ←, , , , , squash – rest TV ☎ P – 330. AE VISA CX **a**
Bronte : **Meals** *(closed Saturday lunch)* 11.00/19.95 **st.** and a la carte – **150 rm** 105.00/115.00 **st.**, 2 suites – SB.

Leeds Marriott, 4 Trevelyan Sq., Boar Lane, LS1 6ET, ℘ 236 6366, Fax 236 6367, , , – rm TV ☎ P – 350. AE VISA JCB DZ **x**
Dyson's : **Meals** 12.95 **t.** and a la carte 14.25/22.00 **t.** 5.50 – 10.25 – **241 rm** 110.00/120.00 **st.**, 3 suites – SB.

42 The Calls, 42 The Calls, LS2 7EW, ℘ 244 0099, Fax 234 4100, ←, « Converted riverside grain mill » – rm TV ☎ . AE VISA. DZ **z**
closed 5 days at Christmas – **Meals** - (see ***Brasserie Forty Four*** below) – 10.00 – **38 rm** 95.00/140.00 **st.**, 3 suites – SB.

Holiday Inn, Wellington St., LS1 4DL, ℘ 244 2200, Fax 244 0460, , , – rm TV ☎ P – 200. AE VISA JCB. CZ **c**
Meals *(closed Saturday lunch)* 15.95 **st.** and a la carte 8.95 – 10.95 – **120 rm** 110.00 **st.**, 5 suites – SB.

Hilton National Leeds, Neville St., LS1 4BX, ℘ 244 2000, Telex 557143, Fax 243 3577, , , – rm TV ☎ P – 300. AE VISA JCB DZ **r**
Meals *(closed Saturday lunch)* 11.95/14.95 **st.** and a la carte 6.55 – 10.50 – **186 rm** 89.00 **st.**, 20 suites – SB.

Queen's (Forte), City Sq., LS1 1PL, ℘ 243 1323, Telex 55161, Fax 242 5154 – rm TV ☎ P – 600 DZ **a**
182 rm, 6 suites.

Weetwood Hall, Otley Rd, LS16 5PS, NW : 4 m. on A 660 ℘ 230 6000, Fax 230 6095, – rest TV ☎ P – 150. AE VISA BV **c**
Meals (carving lunch) 11.50/13.95 **st.** – 7.50 – **108 rm** 67.50/129.00 **st.** – SB.

Haley's, Shire Oak Rd, Headingley, LS6 2DE, NW : 2 m. off Otley Rd (A 660) ℘ 278 4446, Fax 275 3342 – TV ☎ P – 25. AE VISA. CV **s**
closed 26 to 30 December – **Meals** *(closed Sunday dinner)* (dinner only and Sunday lunch)/dinner 22.85 **st.** and a la carte 5.25 – **22 rm** 85.00/102.00 **st.** – SB.

Metropole, King St., LS1 2HQ, ℘ 245 0841, Fax 242 5156 – rm TV ☎ P – 200. AE VISA. CZ **e**
closed 25 to 30 December – **Meals** (bar lunch Monday to Saturday)/dinner 17.95 **st.** and a la carte 5.95 – 7.95 – **81 rm** 75.00/95.00 **st.** – SB.

Merrion Thistle (Mt. Charlotte Thistle), Merrion Centre, 17 Wade Lane, LS2 8NH, ✆ 243 9191, Telex 55459, Fax 242 3527 – rest – 80. AE VISA JCB DZ **e**
Meals 14.75 **t.** and a la carte 5.40 – 8.75 – **108 rm** 75.00/95.00 **t.**, 1 suite – SB.

Golden Lion (Mt. Charlotte Thistle), 2 Lower Briggate, LS1 4AE, ✆ 243 6454, Fax 242 9327 – rm – 120. AE VISA JCB DZ **v**
Meals *(closed Sunday lunch)* (bar lunch Saturday) 12.95/15.95 **st.** and a la carte 4.65 – **89 rm** 75.00/85.00 **st.** – SB.

Aragon, 250 Stainbeck Lane, LS7 2PS, ✆ 275 9306, Fax 275 7166, – . AE VISA CV **c**
Meals (bar lunch)/dinner 9.80 **st.** – **14 rm** 25.10/46.90 **st.** – SB.

Pinewood, 78 Potternewton Lane, LS7 3LW, ✆ 262 2561, Fax 262 2561, – rest . AE VISA. AY **a**
Meals (by arrangement) 9.50 **t.** 5.00 – **10 rm** 34.00/40.00 **t.** – SB.

Ash Mount without rest., 22 Wetherby Rd, Oakwood, LS8 2QD, ✆ 265 8164, Fax 265 8164, – . VISA CV **u**
11 rm 20.00/44.00 **st.**

Leodis Brasserie, Victoria Mill, Sovereign St., LS1 4BJ, ✆ 242 1010, Fax 243 0432 – . AE VISA AZ **e**
closed Saturday lunch and Sunday – **Meals** 11.95 **t.** and a la carte 14.55/25.55 **t.** 5.50.

Brasserie Forty Four, 42-44 The Calls, LS2 8AQ, ✆ 234 3232, Fax 234 3332 – . AE VISA DZ **z**
closed Saturday lunch, Sunday, 5 days at Christmas and Bank Holidays – **Meals** 11.25 **st.** (lunch) and a la carte 13.35/26.95 **t.** 5.95.

Maxi's, 6 Bingley St., LS3 1LX, off Kirkstall Rd ✆ 244 0552, Fax 234 3902, « Pagoda, ornate decor » – . AE VISA AZ **a**
Meals - Chinese (Canton, Peking) 16.00 **st.** (dinner)and a la carte approx. 12.70.

Lucky Dragon, Templar Lane, LS2 7LP, ✆ 245 0520 – DZ **u**
Meals - Chinese (Cantonese).

Hereford Beefstouw, Calls Landing, 38 The Calls, LS2 7EW, ✆ 245 3870, Fax 243 9035, « Converted riverside warehouse » – . AE VISA DZ **c**
Meals (grill rest.) a la carte 13.00/28.00 **st.** 5.25.

Sous le nez en ville, Quebec House, Quebec St., LS1 2HA, ✆ 244 0108, Fax 245 0240 – AE VISA CZ **a**
closed Saturday lunch, Sunday and Bank Holidays – **Meals** 13.95 **st.** (dinner) and a la carte 12.65/20.95 **st.**

La Grillade, 31-33 East Par., LS1 5PS, ✆ 245 9707, Fax 242 6112 – . AE VISA
closed Sunday – **Meals** - French Brasserie 8.95 **t.** and a la carte 3.90. CZ **n**

at Seacroft NE : 5 ½ m. at junction of A 64 with A 6120 – ✉ Leeds – 0113 :

Stakis Leeds, Ring Rd, LS14 5QP, ✆ 273 2323, Fax 232 3018 – rm rest – 250. AE VISA CV **a**
Meals 9.50/15.25 **st.** and dinner a la carte 5.00 – 8.50 – **100 rm** 72.00/88.00 **st.** – SB.

at Garforth E : 6 m. by A 63 – CV at junction with A 642 – ✉ Leeds – 0113 :

Hilton National, Wakefield Rd, LS25 1LH, ✆ 286 6556, Fax 286 8326, – rm rest – 350. AE VISA JCB
Meals *(closed Saturday lunch)* (carving lunch) 14.50/17.95 **t.** and dinner a la carte 5.95 – 10.25 – **144 rm** 69.00/84.00 **t.** – SB.

Aagrah, Aberford Rd, LS25 2HF, on A 642 ✆ 287 6606 –
Meals - Indian.

at Pudsey W : 5 ¾ m. by A 647 – ✉ Leeds – 01274 :

Aagrah, 483 Bradford Rd, LS28 8ED, on A 647 ✆ 668818 – . AE VISA BV **e**
closed 25 December – **Meals** - Indian (dinner only and Sunday lunch)/dinner 17.85 **t.** and a la carte 4.00.

at Horsforth NW : 5 m. by A 65 off A 6120 – ✉ Leeds – 0113 :

Paris, 36A Town St., LS18 4RJ, ✆ 258 1885, Fax 258 5329. AE VISA BV **a**
closed 25-26 December and 1 January – **Meals** (dinner only) 12.95 **t.** and a la carte 4.25.

at Bramhope NW : 8 m. on A 660 – BV – ✉ Leeds – 0113 :

Jarvis Parkway, Otley Rd, LS16 8AG, S : 2 m. on A 660 ✆ 267 2551, Fax 267 4410, – rm – 250. AE VISA
Meals *(closed Saturday lunch)* 9.50/16.85 **st.** and a la carte – 8.95 – **105 rm** 89.00/109.00 **st.** – SB.

Forte Crest, Leeds Rd, LS16 9JJ, ✆ 284 2911, Telex 556367, Fax 284 3451, park – rm – 160
123 rm, 1 suite.

ATS Cross Green Lane ✆ 245 9423 ATS 2 Regent St. ✆ 243 0652

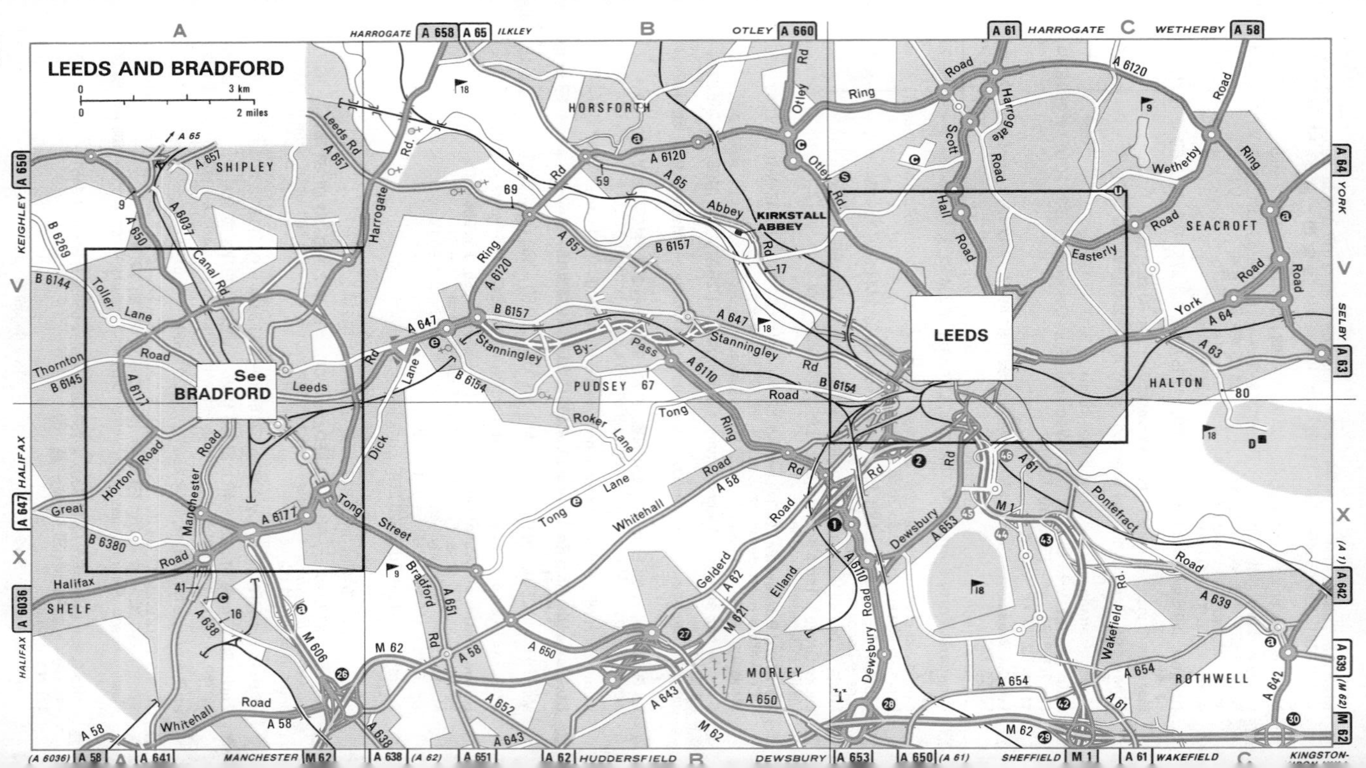
LEEDS AND BRADFORD
0 3 km
0 2 miles
LEEDS
See BRADFORD
HORSFORTH
SHIPLEY
KIRKSTALL ABBEY
PUDSEY
SEACROFT
HALTON
ROTHWELL
MORLEY
SHELF
HARROGATE A 658 A 65 ILKLEY
OTLEY A 660
A 61 HARROGATE
WETHERBY A 58
A 64 YORK
SELBY A 63
(A 1) A 642
A 639 (M 62) M 62
KEIGHLEY A 650
HALIFAX A 647
HALIFAX A 6036
(A 6036) A 58
A 641
MANCHESTER M 62
A 638 (A 62)
A 651
A 62 HUDDERSFIELD
DEWSBURY A 653
A 650 (A 61)
SHEFFIELD M 1
A 61 WAKEFIELD

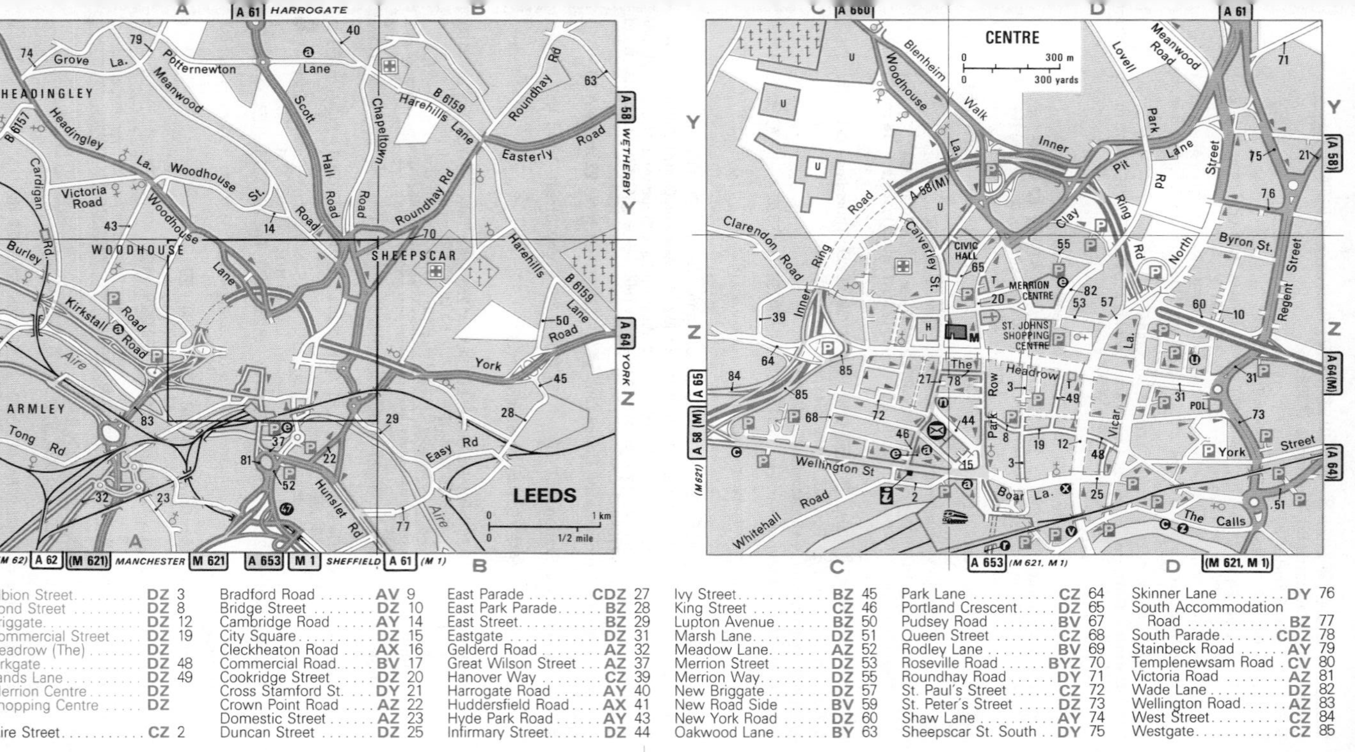

Street	Grid	No.
Albion Street	DZ	3
Bond Street	DZ	8
Briggate	DZ	12
Commercial Street	DZ	19
Headrow (The)	DZ	
Kirkgate	DZ	48
Lands Lane	DZ	49
Merrion Centre Shopping Centre	DZ	
Aire Street	CZ	2
Bradford Road	AV	9
Bridge Street	DZ	10
Cambridge Road	AY	14
City Square	DZ	15
Cleckheaton Road	AX	16
Commercial Road	BV	17
Cookridge Street	DZ	20
Cross Stamford St.	DY	21
Crown Point Road	AZ	22
Domestic Street	AZ	23
Duncan Street	DZ	25
East Parade	CDZ	27
East Park Parade	BZ	28
East Street	BZ	29
Eastgate	DZ	31
Gelderd Road	AZ	32
Great Wilson Street	AZ	37
Hanover Way	CZ	39
Harrogate Road	AY	40
Huddersfield Road	AX	41
Hyde Park Road	AY	43
Infirmary Street	DZ	44
Ivy Street	BZ	45
King Street	CZ	46
Lupton Avenue	BZ	50
Marsh Lane	DZ	51
Meadow Lane	AZ	52
Merrion Street	DZ	53
Merrion Way	DZ	55
New Briggate	DZ	57
New Road Side	BV	59
New York Road	DZ	60
Oakwood Lane	BY	63
Park Lane	CZ	64
Portland Crescent	DZ	65
Pudsey Road	BV	67
Queen Street	CZ	68
Rodley Lane	BV	69
Roseville Road	BYZ	70
Roundhay Road	DY	71
St. Paul's Street	CZ	72
St. Peter's Street	DZ	73
Shaw Lane	AY	74
Sheepscar St. South	DY	75
Skinner Lane	DY	76
South Accommodation Road	BZ	77
South Parade	CDZ	78
Stainbeck Road	AY	79
Templenewsam Road	CV	80
Victoria Road	AZ	81
Wade Lane	DZ	82
Wellington Road	AZ	83
West Street	CZ	84
Westgate	CZ	85

LEEK Staffs. 402 403 404 N 24 – pop. 19 850 – ECD : Thursday – ☎ 01538.

Westwood, Newcastle Rd, Wallbridge ✆ 398385.

Market Pl., ST13 5HH ✆ 381000.

♦London 122 – Derby 30 – ♦Manchester 39 – ♦Stoke-on-Trent 12.

Bank End Farm Motel, Leek Old Rd, Longsdon, ST9 9QJ, SW : 2 ½ m. by A 53 ✆ 383638, « Working farm », – . VISA
Meals (dinner only) 17.50 **st.** and a la carte 4.95 – **9 rm** 27.00/50.00 **st.**

Pethills Bank Cottage without rest., Bottom House, ST13 7PF, SE : 6 m. by A 523 ✆ 304277, Fax 304575, – .
closed Christmas-28 February – **3 rm** 30.00/44.00.

Country Cottage, Back Lane Farm, Winkhill, ST13 7PJ, SE : 5 ½ m. by A 523 ✆ 308273, Fax 308098, , park –
Meals 11.50 **st.** – **4 rm** 19.00/36.00 **st.**

at Butterton E : 8 m. by A 523 off B 5053 – ✉ Leek – ☎ 01538 :

Black Lion Inn, ST13 7ST, ✆ 304232, « 18C inn », – . AE VISA.
Meals (meals in bar except Friday and Saturday dinner and Sunday lunch) 8.45 **st.** (lunch) and a la carte approx. 13.65 **st.** 3.95 – **3 rm** 29.40/47.00 **st.**

LEEMING BAR N. Yorks. 402 P 21 – pop. 1 824 – ECD : Wednesday – ✉ Northallerton – ☎ 01677.

♦London 235 – ♦Leeds 44 – ♦Middlesbrough 30 – ♦Newcastle upon Tyne 52 – York 37.

White Rose, DL7 9AY, ✆ 422707, Fax 425123 – . AE VISA
Meals (bar lunch Monday to Saturday)/dinner 12.95 **t.** and a la carte – **18 rm** 29.50/43.00 **t.**

LEE-ON-THE-SOLENT Hants. 403 404 Q 31 – pop. 7 259 – ECD : Thursday – ☎ 01705.

Gosport & Stokes Bay, Fort Rd, Haslar, Gosport ✆ 851625.

♦London 81 – ♦Portsmouth 13 – ♦Southampton 15 – Winchester 23.

Belle Vue, 39 Marine Par. East, PO13 9BW, ✆ 550258, Fax 552624, – . AE VISA.
closed 25 and 26 December – **Meals** a la carte 9.95/19.95 **st.** 5.50 – 7.00 – **27 rm** 37.50/55.00 **st.** – SB.

LEICESTER Leics. 402 403 404 Q 26 **Great Britain G.** – pop. 270 493 – ☎ 0116.

See : Guildhall★ BY **B** – Museum and Art Gallery★ CY **M2** – St. Mary de Castro Church★ BY **A.**

Leicestershire, Evington Lane ✆ 2736035, AY – Western Park, Scudamore Rd ✆ 2876158/2872339 – Humberstone Heights, Gypsy Lane ✆ 2761905, AX – Oadby, Leicester Road Racecourse ✆ 2700215/2709052, AY.

East Midlands Airport, Castle Donington : ✆ (01332) 810621 NW : 22 m. by A 50 – AX - and M1.

St. Margaret's Bus Station, LE1 3TY ✆ 251 1301 – 7-9 Everly Street, Town Hall Square, LE1 6AG ✆ 265 0555.

♦London 107 – ♦Birmingham 43 – ♦Coventry 24 – ♦Nottingham 26.

Plans on following pages

Holiday Inn, 129 St. Nicholas Circle, LE1 5LX, ✆ 253 1161, Telex 341281, Fax 251 3169, – rm – 250. AE VISA JCB — BY **c**
Meals a la carte 15.00/34.50 **st.** 5.75 – 9.95 – **187 rm** 84.00/109.00 **st.**, 1 suite – SB.

Grand (Jarvis), 73 Granby St., LE1 6ES, ✆ 255 5599, Fax 254 4736 – rm – 450. AE VISA — CY **o**
Meals *(closed Saturday lunch)* 11.95/14.95 **st.** and a la carte 4.85 – 8.50 – **91 rm** 79.00/89.00 **st.**, 1 suite – SB.

Belmont House, De Montfort St., LE1 7GR, ✆ 254 4773, Fax 247 0804 – rm – 100. AE VISA — CY **c**
closed 24 to 28 December – **Meals** *(closed lunch Saturday and Bank Holiday Mondays)* 11.95/17.50 **t.** and a la carte 6.00 – 8.50 – **65 rm** 65.00/85.00 **st.** – SB.

Spindle Lodge, 2 West Walk, LE1 7NA, ✆ 255 1380, Fax 254 3076 – . VISA — CY **r**
closed 23 December-1 January – **Meals** (by arrangement) 11.60 **st.** – **13 rm** 27.50/59.50 **st.**

Scotia, 10 Westcotes Drive, LE3 0QR, ✆ 254 9200 – — AY **c**
Meals (by arrangement) 8.45 3.95 – **11 rm** 20.00/45.00 **t.** – SB.

Seaforth without rest., 12 Westcotes Drive, LE3 0QR, ✆ 255 4895 – . — AY **c**
4 rm.

XX **Welford Place**, 9 Welford Place, LE1 6ZH, ✆ 247 0758, Fax 247 1843 – AE VISA — CY **s**
Meals 10.50/14.00 **st.** and a la carte 4.95.

XX Man Ho, 14-16 King St., LE1 6RJ, ✆ 255 7700, Fax 254 5629 — CY **u**
Meals - Chinese.

XX **Curry House**, 64 London Rd, LE2 0QD, ✆ 255 0688. AE VISA — CY **e**
closed Sunday – **Meals** - Indian 10.00/30.00 **t.** and a la carte 3.65.

LEICESTER

BUILT UP AREA

Asquith Way . . . . AY 2
Belgrave Road . . . . AX 4
Braunstone Avenue . . . . . . AY 10
Braunstone Lane East . . . . AY 13
Braunstone Way . . . . AY 14
Checketts Road . . . . AX 17
Fosse Road North . . . . AX 22
Fullhurst Avenue . . . . AY 23
Glenfrith Way . . . . AX 24
Henley Road . . . . AX 29
Humberstone Road . . . . . . AX 34
King Richards Road . . . . . . AY 37
Knighton Road . . . . AY 38
Loughborough Road . . . . . AX 40
Marfitt Street . . . . AX 41
Middleton Street . . . . AY 44
Stoughton Road . . . . AY 66
Upperton Road . . . . AY 68
Walnut Street . . . . AY 69
Wigston Lane . . . . AY 75
Woodville Road . . . . AY 76
Wyngate Drive . . . . AY 78

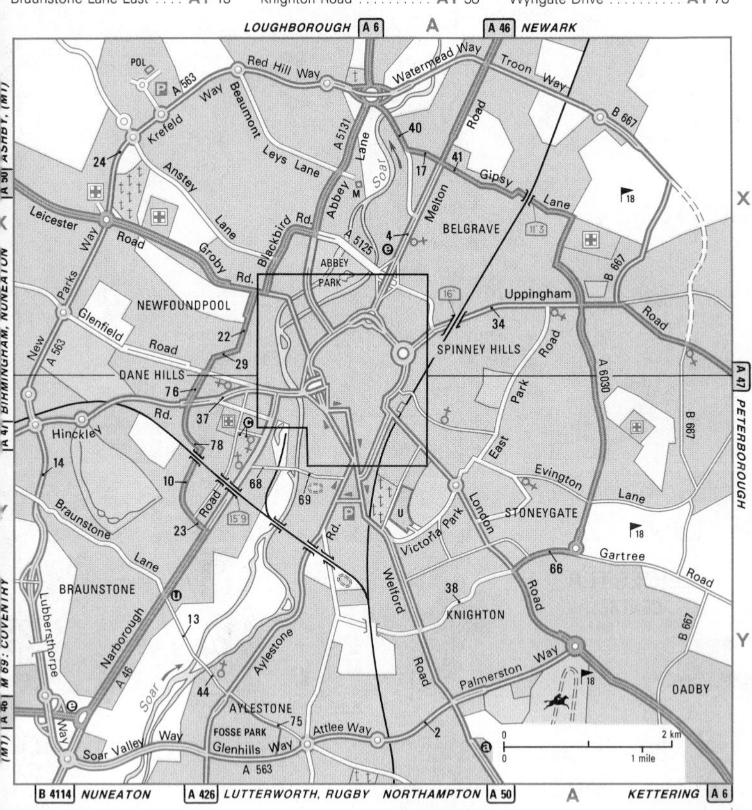

XX **Curry Pot,** 78-80 Belgrave Rd, LE4 5AS, ☎ 253 8256, Fax 262 5125 – AE VISA AX **e**
closed Sunday – **Meals** - Indian a la carte 13.95/23.60 **t.**

XX **Water Margin,** 76-78 High St., LE1 5YP, ☎ 251 6422 – AE VISA BY **x**
Meals - Chinese (Canton) 5.50/20.00 **t.** and a la carte.

X **Casa Romana,** 5 Albion St., LE1 6GD, ☎ 254 1174 – VISA CY **a**
closed Saturday lunch, Sunday and Bank Holidays – **Meals** - Italian (booking essential) a la carte 12.90/18.90 **t.** 3.80.

at Rothley N : 5 m. by A 6 – AX – on B 5328 – ✉ Leicester – 0116.

Rothley Court (Forte), Westfield Lane, LE7 7LG, W : ½ m. on B 5328 ☎ 237 4141, Fax 237 4483, ≤, « Part 13C house and 11C chapel », – rm – 100. AE VISA JCB
Meals *(closed Saturday lunch)* 10.95/19.95 **st.** and dinner a la carte 7.45 – 8.50 – **35 rm** 75.00/85.00 **st.**, 1 suite – SB.

Limes, 35 Mountsorrel Lane, LE7 7PS, ☎ 230 2531 – AE VISA.
closed 23 December-1 January – **Meals** (dinner only) a la carte 7.45/16.00 **st.** 4.95 – **11 rm** 40.00/65.00 **st.**

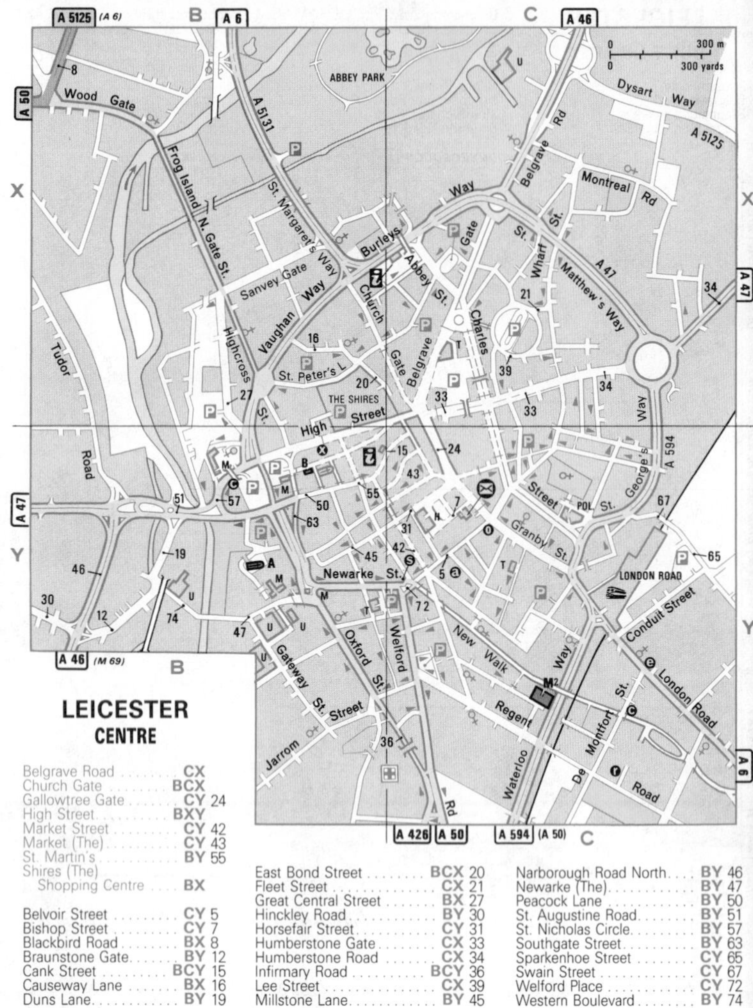

LEICESTER
CENTRE

Belgrave Road CX
Church Gate . . . . BCX
Gallowtree Gate . . . . CY 24
High Street . . . . BXY
Market Street . . . . CY 42
Market (The) . . . . CY 43
St. Martin's . . . . BY 55
Shires (The) Shopping Centre . . . . BX

Belvoir Street . . . . CY 5
Bishop Street . . . . CY 7
Blackbird Road . . . . BX 8
Braunstone Gate . . . . . . BY 12
Cank Street . . . . BCY 15
Causeway Lane . . . . BX 16
Duns Lane . . . . BY 19
East Bond Street . . . . BCX 20
Fleet Street . . . . CX 21
Great Central Street . . . . . . BX 27
Hinckley Road . . . . BY 30
Horsefair Street . . . . CY 31
Humberstone Gate . . . . CX 33
Humberstone Road . . . . . . CX 34
Infirmary Road . . . . BCY 36
Lee Street . . . . CX 39
Millstone Lane . . . . BY 45
Narborough Road North . . . . BY 46
Newarke (The) . . . . BY 47
Peacock Lane . . . . BY 50
St. Augustine Road . . . . BY 51
St. Nicholas Circle . . . . BY 57
Southgate Street . . . . BY 63
Sparkenhoe Street . . . . CY 65
Swain Street . . . . CY 67
Welford Place . . . . CY 72
Western Boulevard . . . . BY 74

at Thrussington NE : 10 m. by A 46 – AX – ✉ Leicester – ☎ 01664 :

Forte Travelodge without rest., Green Acres Filling Station, LE7 8TF, on A 46 (southbound carriageway) ☎ 424525, Reservations (Freephone) 0800 850950 – TV ♿ P. AE VISA.
32 rm 33.50 **t.**

at Oadby SE : 3½ m. on A 6 – AY – ✉ Leicester – ☎ 0116 :

Leicestershire Moat House (Q.M.H.), Wigston Rd, LE2 5QE, on B 582 ☎ 271 9441, Fax 272 0559 – TV ☎ ♿ P – 250. AE VISA
Meals *(closed Saturday lunch and Bank Holidays)* (carving rest.) 10.60/14.75 **t.** – 8.75 – **57 rm** 68.00/79.00 **st.** – SB.

at Wigston Fields SE : 3¼ m. on A 50 – ✉ Leicester – ☎ 0116 :

Stage, 299 Leicester Rd, LE18 1JW, ☎ 288 6161, Fax 281 1874, – rm TV ☎ ♿ P – 200. AE VISA JCB. AY **a**
Meals *(closed Saturday lunch)* 7.95/14.95 **st.** and a la carte – **71 rm** 62.00/79.00 **st.** – SB.

at Braunstone SW : 2 m. on A 46 – ✉ Leicester – ☎ 0116 :

Stakis Leicester, LE3 2WQ, SW : 1 ¾ m. by A 46 ✆ 263 0066, Fax 263 0627, ‹Fitness›, ‹Sauna›, ‹Pool›, ‹Garden› – ‹Non-smoking› rm ‹A/c› rest ‹TV› ☎ ‹Disabled› ‹Parking› – ‹Conference› 80. ‹S› ‹AE› ‹D› ‹VISA› ‹JCB› AY **e**
Meals (bar lunch Saturday and Bank Holidays) 11.95/18.95 **t.** and a la carte – ‹Breakfast› 9.00 – **131 rm** 90.00/100.00 **t.**, 10 suites – SB.

Forte Posthouse, Braunstone Lane East, LE3 2FW, ✆ 263 0500, Fax 282 3623 – ‹Lift› ‹Non-smoking› rm ‹A/c› rest ‹TV› ☎ ‹Parking› – ‹Conference› 80. ‹S› ‹AE› ‹D› ‹VISA› AY **u**
Meals a la carte approx. 15.00 **t.** ‹Wine› 5.50 – **170 rm** 56.00 **st.**

at Leicester Forest East W : 3 m. on A 47 – AY – ✉ Leicester – ☎ 0116 :

Red Cow, Hinckley Rd, LE3 3PG, ✆ 238 7878, Fax 238 7878 – ‹Non-smoking› rm ‹TV› ☎ ‹Disabled› ‹Parking›. ‹S› ‹AE› ‹VISA›. ‹No dogs›
Meals (grill rest.) 7.95 and a la carte – ‹Breakfast› 4.95 – **31 rm** 39.50 **t.**

ATS 16 Wanlip St. ✆ 262 4281 ATS 31 Woodgate ✆ 262 5611

LEIGH DELAMERE SERVICE AREA Wilts. – ✉ Chippenham – ☎ 01666.

Granada Lodge without rest., SN14 6LB, M 4 between junctions 18 and 17 (eastbound carriageway) ✆ 837097, Fax 837112, Reservations (Freephone) 0800 555300 – ‹Non-smoking› ‹TV› ☎ ‹Disabled› ‹Parking›. ‹S› ‹AE› ‹VISA›. ‹No dogs›
‹Breakfast› 4.00 – **35 rm** 39.95 **st.**

LEIGHTON BUZZARD Beds. 404 S 28 – pop. 32 610 – ECD : Thursday – ☎ 01525.

‹Golf 18› Plantation Rd ✆ 373811/373812 – ‹Golf 18› Aylesbury Vale, Wing ✆ 240196 – ‹Golf 9› Wellcroft ✆ 668696.
♦London 47 – Bedford 20 – Luton 12 – Northampton 30.

Swan, High St., LU7 7EA, ✆ 372148, Fax 370444 – ‹TV› ☎ ‹Parking› – ‹Conference› 40. ‹S› ‹AE› ‹D› ‹VISA›
Meals (dinner only and Sunday lunch)/dinner 13.95 **st.** and a la carte ‹Wine› 4.25 – ‹Breakfast› 7.50 – **38 rm** 55.00/71.00 **st.** – SB.

ATS Unit C, Camden Ind. Est., 83 Lake St. ✆ 376158/379238

LEINTWARDINE Shrops. 403 L 26 – ✉ Craven Arms – ☎ 01547.

♦London 156 – ♦Birmingham 55 – Hereford 24 – Worcester 40.

Upper Buckton Farm ‹Quiet›, Buckton, SY7 0JU, W : 2 m. by A 4113 and Buckton rd ✆ 540634, ‹View›, « Working farm », ‹Garden› – ‹Non-smoking› ‹Parking›
Meals (by arrangement) 14.00 **s.** – **3 rm** ‹Breakfast› 20.00/40.00 – SB.

at Hopton Castle NW : 4½ m. by Craven Arms rd, B 4367 and B 4385 – ✉ Craven Arms – ☎ 015474 :

Upper House Farm ‹Quiet›, SY7 0QF, ✆ 319, « Working farm », ‹Garden› – ‹TV› ‹Parking›
Meals (by arrangement) – **3 rm.**

LENHAM Kent 404 W 30 – ✉ Maidstone – ☎ 01622.

♦London 45 – Folkestone 28 – Maidstone 9.

Lime Tree, 8-10 The Limes, The Square, ME17 2PQ, ✆ 859509, Fax 850096 – ‹TV› ☎. ‹S› ‹D› ‹VISA›. ‹No dogs›
Meals 10.95/18.95 and a la carte – **7 rm** ‹Breakfast› 37.50/47.50 **st.** – SB.

LEOMINSTER Heref. and Worcs. 403 L 27 Great Britain G. – pop. 8 637 – ECD : Thursday – ☎ 01568.

Envir. : Berrington Hall★ *AC*, N : 3 m. by A 49.
‹Golf 18› Ford Bridge ✆ 612863.
‹Tourist info› 1 Corn Square, HR6 8AA ✆ 616460 (summer only).
♦London 141 – ♦Birmingham 47 – Hereford 13 – Worcester 26.

Talbot, West St., HR6 8EP, ✆ 616347, Fax 616347 – ‹TV› ☎ ‹Parking› – ‹Conference› 120. ‹S› ‹AE› ‹D› ‹VISA› ‹JCB›
Meals 10.00/16.00 **t.** and a la carte – **20 rm** ‹Breakfast› 45.00/72.00 **t.** – SB.

Heath House ‹Quiet›, Humber, Stoke Prior, HR6 0NF, SE : 3 ¾ m. by A 44 on Risbury rd ✆ 760385 – ‹Parking›. ‹No dogs›
March-November – **Meals** (by arrangement)(communal dining) 17.00 **st.** ‹Wine› 3.00 – **3 rm** ‹Breakfast› 16.00/40.00 **st.** – SB.

at Bodenham E : 1 ¼ m. on A 417 – ✉ Hereford – ☎ 0156 884 :

Maund Court, HR1 3JA, E : 1 ¼ m. on A 417 ✆ 282, ‹Outdoor pool› heated, ‹Garden› – ‹TV› ‹Parking›. ‹No dogs›
March-November – **Meals** (by arrangement) 12.00 **st.** – **4 rm** ‹Breakfast› 17.00/34.00 **st.**

at Eyton NW : 2 m. by B 4361 – ✉ Leominster – ☎ 01568 :

The Marsh ‹Quiet›, HR6 0AG, ✆ 613952, « Part 14C timbered house », ‹Garden› – ‹Non-smoking› ‹TV› ☎ ‹Parking›. ‹S› ‹AE› ‹D› ‹VISA›. ‹No dogs›
closed 24 December to 30 December – **Meals** (booking essential) (lunch by arrangement) 19.50/22.50 **st.** ‹Wine› 6.75 – **5 rm** ‹Breakfast› 80.00/110.00 **st.** – SB.

ATS Market Mill, Dishley St. ✆ 612679/614114

LETCHWORTH Herts. 404 T 28 – pop. 20 626 – ECD : Wednesday – ✆ 01462.

♦London 40 – Bedford 22 – ♦Cambridge 22 – Luton 14.

Broadway Toby, The Broadway, SG6 3NZ, ✆ 480111, Fax 481563 – |$| TV ☎ P – 180
35 rm.

ATS Unit 21, Jubilee Trade Centre, Works Rd ✆ 670517

LEW Oxon – ✉ Oxford – ✆ 01993.

Farmhouse, University Farm, OX18 2AU, ✆ 850297, Fax 850965, – TV ☎ ♿ P. VISA.
closed Christmas and New Year – **Meals** *(closed Sunday)* (residents only Monday to Thursday) (dinner only) 18.50 **st.** 4.25 – **6 rm** 39.00/52.00 **st.** – SB.

LEWDOWN Devon 403 H 32 **The West Country G.** – ✆ 01566.

Envir. : Lydford★★ (Lydford Gorge★★) E : 4 m.

Exc. : Launceston★ - Castle★ (<★) St. Mary Magdalene★, South Gate★, W : 8 m. by A 30 and A 388.

♦London 238 – Exeter 37 – ♦Plymouth 22.

Lewtrenchard Manor , EX20 4PN, S : 3/4 m. by Lewtrenchard rd ✆ 783256, Fax 783332, « 17C manor house and gardens », , park – rest TV ☎ P. AE VISA
Meals (lunch by arrangement Monday to Saturday)/dinner 25.00 **t.** and a la carte 5.00 – **8 rm** 75.00/135.00 **t.**

Wenn Sie ein ruhiges Hotel suchen,
benutzen Sie zuerst die Karte in der Einleitung
oder wählen Sie im Text ein Hotel mit dem Zeichen oder .

LEWES E. Sussex 404 U 31 **Great Britain G.** – pop. 15 376 – ECD : Wednesday – ✆ 01273.

See : Town★ (High Street★, Keere Street★) – Castle (<★) *AC.*

Exc. : Sheffield Park Garden★ *AC*, N : 9 1/2 m. by A 275.

18 Chapel Hill ✆ 473245.

Lewes House, 187 High St., BN7 2DE ✆ 483448.

♦London 53 – Brighton 8 – Hastings 29 – Maidstone 43.

Millers without rest., 134 High St., BN7 1XS, ✆ 475631, – TV.
closed 4 November and 20 December-5 January – **3 rm** 40.00/46.00 **s.**

Hillside without rest., Rotten Row, BN7 1TN, ✆ 473120, – .
3 rm 18.00/38.00 **s.**

Pailin, 20 Station St., BN7 2DB, ✆ 473906 – AE VISA JCB
closed Sunday lunch – **Meals** - Thai a la carte 8.85/12.90 **t.**

ATS 18 North St. ✆ 477972/3

LICHFIELD Staffs. 402 403 404 O 25 **Great Britain G.** – pop. 25 408 – ECD : Wednesday – ✆ 01543.

See : City★ - Cathedral★★ *AC.*

18 Seedy Mill, Elmhurst ✆ 417333.

Donegal House, Bore St., WS13 6NE ✆ 252109.

♦London 128 – ♦Birmingham 16 – Derby 23 – ♦Stoke-on-Trent 30.

Little Barrow, Beacon St., WS13 7AR, ✆ 414500, Fax 415734 – TV ☎ P – 100. AE VISA.
Meals 8.00/18.00 **st.** and a la carte 4.25 – **24 rm** 45.00/60.00 **st.** – SB.

Thrales, 40-44 Tamworth St., WS13 6JJ, (corner of Backcester Lane) ✆ 255091 – VISA
closed Sunday dinner and Bank Holiday Mondays – **Meals** 9.95 **t.** (lunch) and a la carte 18.95/25.00 **t.**

ATS Eastern Av. ✆ 414200

LIFTON Devon 403 H 32 **The West Country G.** – pop. 964 – ECD : Tuesday – ✆ 01566.

Envir. : Launceston★ - Castle★ (<★) St. Mary Magdalene★, South Gate★, W : 4 1/2m . by A 30 and A 388.

♦London 238 – Bude 24 – Exeter 37 – Launceston 4 – ♦Plymouth 32.

Arundell Arms, Fore St., PL16 0AA, on A 30 ✆ 784666, Fax 784494, , – rest TV ☎ P – 100. AE VISA
closed 24 to 26 December – **Meals** 16.50/28.50 **t.** 6.25 – **29 rm** 38.00/93.00 **t.** – SB.

Thatched Cottage , Sprytown, PL16 0AY, E : 1 1/4 m. by A 30 ✆ 784224, Fax 784334, – TV P. AE VISA.
Meals 21.50 **st.** (dinner) and lunch a la carte 9.95/13.90 **st.** 5.95 – **5 rm** 35.00/90.00 **st.** – SB.

LIMPLEY STOKE Avon – see Bath.

LINCOLN Lincs. 402 404 S 24 **Great Britain G.** – pop. 81 987 – ECD : Wednesday – 01522.

See : City★★ - Cathedral and Precincts★★★ *AC* Y – High Bridge★★ Z **9** – Usher Gallery★★ *AC* YZ **M1** – Jew's House★ Y – Castle★ *AC* Y.

Envir. : Doddington Hall★ *AC*, W : 6 m. by B 1003 – Z – and B 1190.

Exc. : Gainsborough Old Hall★ *AC*, NW : 19 m. by A 57 – Z – and A 156.

Carholme ℘ 523725.

Humberside Airport : ℘ (01652) 688456, N : 32 m. by A 15 – Y – M 180 and A 18.

9 Castle Hill, LN1 3AA ℘ 529828 – 21 The Cornhill, LN5 7HB ℘ 512971.

London 140 – Bradford 81 – ◆Cambridge 94 – ◆Kingston-upon-Hull 44 – ◆Leeds 73 – ◆Leicester 53 – ◆Norwich 104 – ◆Nottingham 38 – ◆Sheffield 48 – York 82.

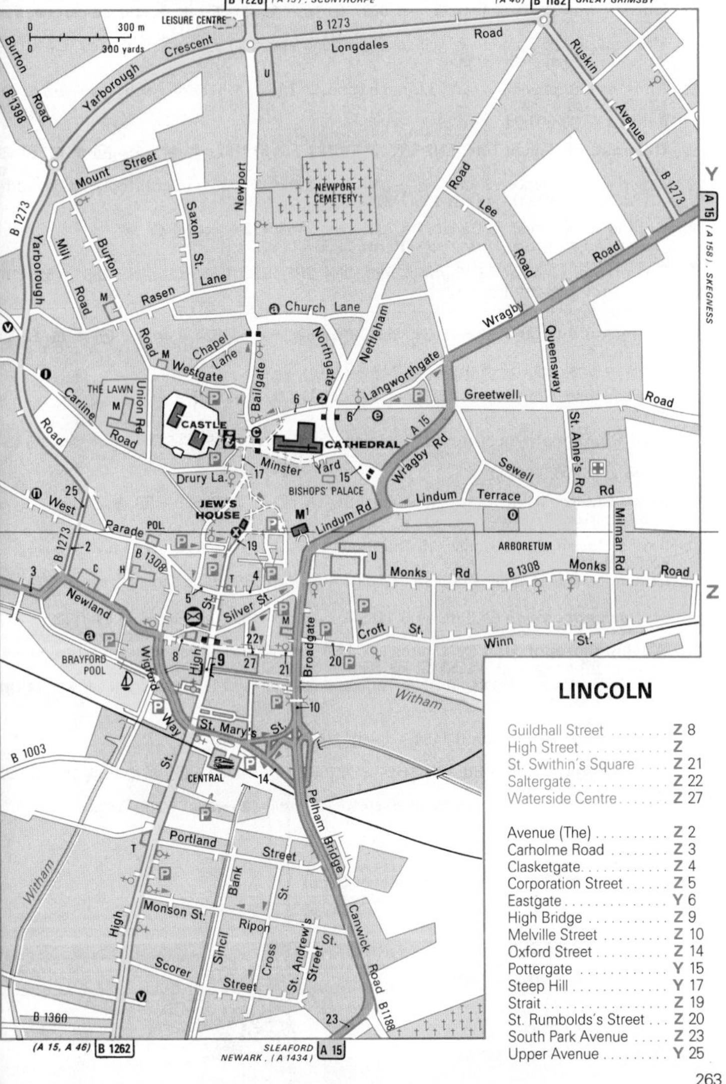

White Hart (Forte), Bailgate, LN1 3AR, ☎ 526222, Fax 531798, « Antique furniture » – lift – rm TV ☎ – P – 70. AE VISA Y c
Meals 8.95/19.95 **t.** and a la carte 6.25 – 8.95 – **37 rm** 80.00/115.00 **st.**, 13 suites – SB.

Courtyard by Marriott, Brayford Side North, LN1 1YW, ☎ 544244, Fax 560805, – lift – rm TV ☎ P – 30. AE VISA JCB Z a
Meals 10.00/12.00 **st.** and a la carte 5.50 – 8.50 – **95 rm** 61.00 **st.** – SB.

Forte Posthouse, Eastgate, LN2 1PN, ☎ 520341, Fax 510780 – lift rm TV ☎ P – 90. AE VISA JCB. Y z
Meals a la carte approx. 15.00 **t.** 5.50 – **70 rm** 56.00 **t.**

D'Isney Place without rest., Eastgate, LN2 4AA, ☎ 538881, Fax 511321, – TV ☎. AE VISA Y e
17 rm 50.00/124.00 **t.**

Damons Motel, 997 Doddington Rd, LN6 3SE, SW : 4 ¼ m. by A 15 on B 1190 at junction with A 46 ☎ 500422, Fax 689719, – rm TV ☎ P. AE VISA Z
Meals *(closed 25 December)* (grill rest.) (booking essential) a la carte 9.05/16.90 **t.** 4.15 – 2.50 – **47 rm** 34.00/37.00 **t.**

Minster Lodge without rest., 3 Church Lane, LN2 1QJ, ☎ 513220, Fax 513220 – TV ☎ P. AE VISA Y a
6 rm 43.50/50.00 **t.**

Hillcrest, 15 Lindum Terr., LN2 5RT, ☎ 510182, Fax 510182, ←, – TV ☎ P. AE VISA Y o
closed 23 December-2 January – **Meals** *(closed Sunday)* (dinner only) a la carte 12.20/16.95 **t.** 4.00 – **17 rm** 47.00/65.00 **t.** – SB.

Carline without rest., 3 Carline Rd, LN1 1HL, ☎ 530422 – TV P. Y i
closed Christmas and New Year – **10 rm** 30.00/38.00 **t.**

Travel Inn, Lincoln Rd, Canwick Hill, LN4 2RF, SE : 1 ¾ m. on B 1188 ☎ 525216, Fax 542521 – rm TV P Z
Meals (Beefeater grill) a la carte approx. 16.00 **t.** – 4.95 – **40 rm** 33.50 **t.**

Tennyson, 7 South Park Av., LN5 8EN, ☎ 521624, Fax 521624 – rest TV ☎ P. AE VISA. by A 158 Z
Meals 13.25 **st.** 4.25 – **8 rm** 26.00/40.00 **st.** – SB.

Ashlin House without rest., 132 West Par., LN1 1LD, ☎ 531307 – TV P Y n
9 rm.

ABC Charisma without rest., 126 Yarborough Rd, LN1 1HP, ☎ 543560, ← – TV P. Y v
11 rm 18.00/38.00 **st.**

Rowan Lodge without rest., 58 Pennell St., LN5 7TA, ☎ 529589 – TV P. Z v
3 rm 16.00/28.00 **t.**

Jew's House, Jew's House, 15 The Strait, LN2 1JD, ☎ 524851, « 12C town house » – AE VISA YZ x
closed Sunday, Monday and Bank Holidays – **Meals** 9.95/18.50 **t.** and a la carte 5.00.

at Washingborough E : 3 m. by B 1188 – Z – on B 1190 – ✉ Lincoln – ☎ 01522 :

Washingborough Hall ⑤, Church Hill, LN4 1BE, ☎ 790340, Fax 792936, heated, – rm TV ☎ P – 45. AE VISA
closed Christmas – **Meals** (lunch by arrangement)/dinner 21.00 **t.** and a la carte – **12 rm** 49.00/88.00 **t.** – SB.

at Branston SE : 3 m. on B 1188 – Z – ☎ 01522 :

Moor Lodge, Sleaford Rd, LN4 1HU, ☎ 791366, Fax 794389 – TV ☎ P – 150. AE VISA
Meals (bar lunch Saturday) 9.75/16.30 **t.** and a la carte – **25 rm** 50.00/80.00 **t.** – SB.

ATS Crofton Rd, Allenby Rd Trading Est. ☎ 527225

LINDALE Cumbria 402 L 21 – see Grange-over-Sands.

LISKEARD Cornwall 403 G 32 The West Country G. – pop. 7 657 – ECD : Wednesday – ☎ 01579.

See : Church★.

Exc. : Lanhydrock★★, W : 11½ m. by A 38 and A 390 – NW : Bodmin Moor★★ - St. Endellion Church★★ - Altarnun Church★ - St. Breward Church★ - Blisland★ (church★) - Camelford★ - Cardinham Church★ - Michaelstow Church★ - St. Kew★ (church★) - St. Mabyn Church★ - St. Neot★ (Parish Church★★) - St. Sidwell's, Laneast★ - St. Teath Church★ - St. Tudy★.

♦London 261 – Exeter 59 – ♦Plymouth 18 – Truro 37.

Well House ⛰, St. Keyne, PL14 4RN, S : 3 ½ m. on St. Keyne Well rd ✆ 342001, Fax 343891, ≤, heated, park, tennis – TV ☎ P. VISA
Meals (booking essential) 24.95 (dinner) **t.** 4.25 – **7 rm** 60.00/105.00 **t.**

Old Rectory ⛰, Duloe Rd, St. Keyne, PL14 4RL, S : 3 ¼ m. on B 3254 ✆ 342617, park – rest TV P. VISA
closed Christmas – **Meals** (residents only) (dinner only) a la carte 12.70/16.75 **st.** – **8 rm** 25.00/60.00 **st.** – SB.

ATS 10 Dean St. ✆ 345489/345247

LITTLEBURY GREEN Essex 404 O 27 – see Saffron Walden.

LITTLE CHALFONT Bucks. 404 S 29 – pop. 3 991 – ☎ 01494.

Lodge Lane, Amersham ✆ 764877.

♦London 31 – Luton 20 – ♦Oxford 37.

Chalfont Dynasty, 9 Nightingales Corner, HP7 9PZ, ✆ 764038 – AE VISA
Meals - Chinese (Peking) 6.95/10.00 **t.** and a la carte 5.75.

LITTLEHAMPTON W. Sussex 404 S 31 – ☎ 01903.

♦London 64 – ♦Brighton 18 – ♦Portsmouth 31.

Bailiffscourt ⛰, Climping St., Climping, BN17 5RW, W : 2 ¾ m. by A 259 ✆ 723511, Fax 723107, « Reconstructed medieval house », park, tennis – rest TV ☎ P – 35. AE VISA
Meals 17.50/29.50 **t.** 6.25 – **23 rm** 80.00/105.00 **t.** – SB.

Amberley Court without rest., Crookthorn Lane, Climping, BN17 5QU, W : 1 ¾ m. by B 2187 off A 259 ✆ 725131, – TV P.
3 rm 30.00/50.00 **st.**

ATS Church St. ✆ 713085/716919

LITTLE LANGDALE Cumbria 402 K 20 – see Ambleside.

LITTLE LANGFORD Wilts. - see Salisbury.

LITTLEOVER Derbs. 402 403 404 P 25 – see Derby.

LITTLE PETHERICK Cornwall 403 F 32 – see Padstow.

LITTLEPORT Cambs 404 U 26 – see Ely.

LITTLE RISSINGTON Glos. 403 404 O 28 – see Bourton-on-the-Water.

LITTLE SINGLETON Lancs. – see Blackpool.

LITTLE SUTTON Ches. – ✉ South Wirral – ☎ 0151.

♦London 208 – Chester 12 – ♦Liverpool 9 – ♦Manchester 48.

Woodhey, Berwick Rd, L66 4PS, at junction with A 550 ✆ 339 5121, Fax 339 3214, – rest TV ☎ P – 200. AE VISA
Meals (bar lunch) (dancing Saturday evening)/dinner 14.45 **t.** and a la carte 13.55/20.95 **t.** 4.95 – **53 rm** 60.00/75.00 **t.** – SB.

LITTLE THORNTON Lancs. 402 L 22 – see Blackpool.

Pleasant hotels and restaurants are shown in the Guide by a red sign.
Please send us the names of any where you have enjoyed your stay.
Your Michelin Guide will be even better.

XXXXX ... X

LITTLE WALSINGHAM Norfolk 404 W 25 – pop. 525 – ✉ Walsingham – ☎ 01328.

♦London 117 – ♦Cambridge 67 – Cromer 21 – ♦Norwich 32.

- **White Horse Inn,** Fakenham Rd, East Barsham, NR21 0LH, S : 2 ¼ m. on B 1105 ✆ 820645, Fax 820645 – TV P. VISA
  Meals 6.35/17.85 **t.** and a la carte 3.25 – **3 rm** 30.00/48.00 **t.**

- **Old Bakehouse** with rm, 33-35 High St., NR22 6BZ, ✆ 820454 – TV. VISA
  closed 2 weeks January-February, 1 week June and 1 week November – **Meals** *(closed Sunday, Monday and Tuesday November-Easter)* (dinner only) 23.50 **t.** and a la carte 4.50 – **3 rm** 22.50/40.00 **t.**

LITTLE WEIGHTON Humbs. 402 S 22 – ✉ Cottingham – ☎ 01482.

♦London 184 – ♦Kingston-upon-Hull 8 – ♦Leeds 45 – York 31.

- **Rowley Manor**, HU20 3XR, SW : ½ m. by Rowley Rd ✆ 848248, Fax 849900, ≤, « Georgian manor house », – TV ☎ P – 100. AE VISA
  Meals a la carte 16.45/26.15 **t.** 5.15 – **16 rm** 55.00/85.00 **t.** – SB.

LITTLEWICK GREEN Berks. 404 R 29 – see Maidenhead.

LITTLE WITLEY Heref. and Worcs. 403 404 M 27 – see Abberley.

LITTLE WYMONDLEY Herts. 404 T 28 – see Hitchin.

LIVERPOOL Mersey. 402 403 L 23 **Great Britain G.** – pop. 452 450 – ECD : Wednesday – 0151.

See : City★ – Walker Art Gallery★★ DY **M2** – Liverpool Cathedral★★ (Lady Chapel★) EZ – Metropolitan Cathedral of Christ the King★★ EY – Albert Dock★ CZ (Merseyside Maritime Museum★ *AC* **M1** - Tate Gallery Liverpool★).

Exc. : Speke Hall★ *AC*, SE : 8 m. by A 561 BX.

Allerton Park, Allerton Road 428 1046/7490 – Liverpool Municipal, Ingoe Lane, Kirkby 546 5435, BV – Bowring, Bowring Park, Roby Rd, Huyton 489 1901.

Liverpool Airport : 486 8877, SE : 6 m. by A 561 BX – **Terminal** : Pier Head.

to Isle of Man (Douglas) (Isle of Man Steam Packet Co. Ltd) (4 h) – to Northern Ireland (Belfast) (Norse Irish Ferries Ltd) (11 h).

to Birkenhead (Mersey Ferries) (10 mn) – to Wallasey (Mersey Ferries) (20 mn).

Merseyside Welcome Centre, Clayton Square Shopping Centre, L1 1QR 709 3631.

♦London 219 – ♦Birmingham 103 – ♦Leeds 75 – ♦Manchester 35.

Town plans : Liverpool pp. 2-5

Liverpool Moat House (Q.M.H.), Paradise St., L1 8JD, 709 0181, Fax 709 2706, , – rm – 400. VISA DZ **n**
Meals 18.25 (dinner) and a la carte 13.75/30.75 **t.** 5.00 – 8.75 – **244 rm** 95.00 **st.**, 7 suites – SB.

Atlantic Tower (Mt. Charlotte Thistle), 30 Chapel St., L3 9RE, 227 4444, Fax 236 3973, – rm – 100. VISA JCB CY **r**
Meals *(closed Saturday lunch)* 12.95/23.00 **t.** and a la carte 4.90 – **223 rm** 85.00/99.00 **st.**, 3 suites – SB.

Campanile, Wapping and Chaloner St., L3 4AJ, 709 8104, Fax 709 8725 – rm – 30. VISA CZ **a**
Meals 9.85 **st.** and a la carte 4.65 – 4.25 – **80 rm** 35.75 **st.**

Dolby, 36-42 Chaloner St., Queens Dock, L3 4DE, 708 7272, – . VISA. DZ **c**
Meals (dinner only) a la carte 8.25 **t.** 4.50 – 4.00 – **64 rm** 29.50 **t.**

Travel Inn, Queens Dr., West Derby, L13 0DL, E : 4 m. on A 5058 (Ringroad) 228 4724, Fax 220 7610 – rm BV **a**
Meals (Beefeater grill) a la carte approx. 16.00 **t.** – 4.95 – **40 rm** 33.50 **t.**

XXX **Ristorante Del Secolo,** 36-40 Stanley St., L1 6AL, 236 4004 – VISA DY **e**
closed Saturday lunch, Sunday and Bank Holidays – **Meals** - Italian a la carte 17.85/26.85 **t.** 5.95.

X **Est, Est, Est !,** Unit 6, Edward Pavilion, Albert Dock, L3 4AA, 708 6969 – VISA CZ **e**
Meals - Italian a la carte 14.75/18.55 **t.** 4.75.

at Netherton N : 6 m. by A 5038 off A 5036 – AV – ✉ Liverpool – 0151 :

Park (Premier), Park Lane West, L30 3SU, on A 5036 525 7555, Fax 525 2481 – – 100. VISA.
Meals 5.95/7.25 **st.** and a la carte 4.25 – 3.45 – **62 rm** 39.50 **st.** – SB.

at Crosby N : 5½ m. on A 565 – AV – 0151 :

Blundellsands, The Serpentine, Blundellsands, L23 6TN, W : 1¼ m. via College Rd, Mersey Rd and Agnes Rd 924 6515, Fax 931 5364 – rm – 200. VISA
Meals *(closed Saturday lunch)* 7.50/12.50 **t.** and a la carte 6.95 – **41 rm** 59.50/95.00 **t.**

at Woolton SE : 6 m. by A 562 – BX – A 5058 and Woolton Rd – ✉ Liverpool – 0151 :

Woolton Redbourne, Acrefield Rd, L25 5JN, 428 2152, Fax 724 6114, « Victorian house, antiques », – . VISA
Meals (residents only) 18.95 **t.** 5.95 – **18 rm** 58.00/82.00 **t.** – SB.

at Huyton E : 8¼ m. by A 5047 and A 5080 on B 5199 – ✉ Liverpool – 0151.

Logwood Mill, Fallows Way, L35 1RZ, SE : 3¼ m. by A 5080 off Windy Arbor Rd 449 2341, Fax 449 3832, , – – 200. VISA.
Meals *(closed lunch Saturday and Bank Holidays)* 12.15/15.75 **st.** and a la carte – **63 rm** 69.50/99.50 **st.** – SB.

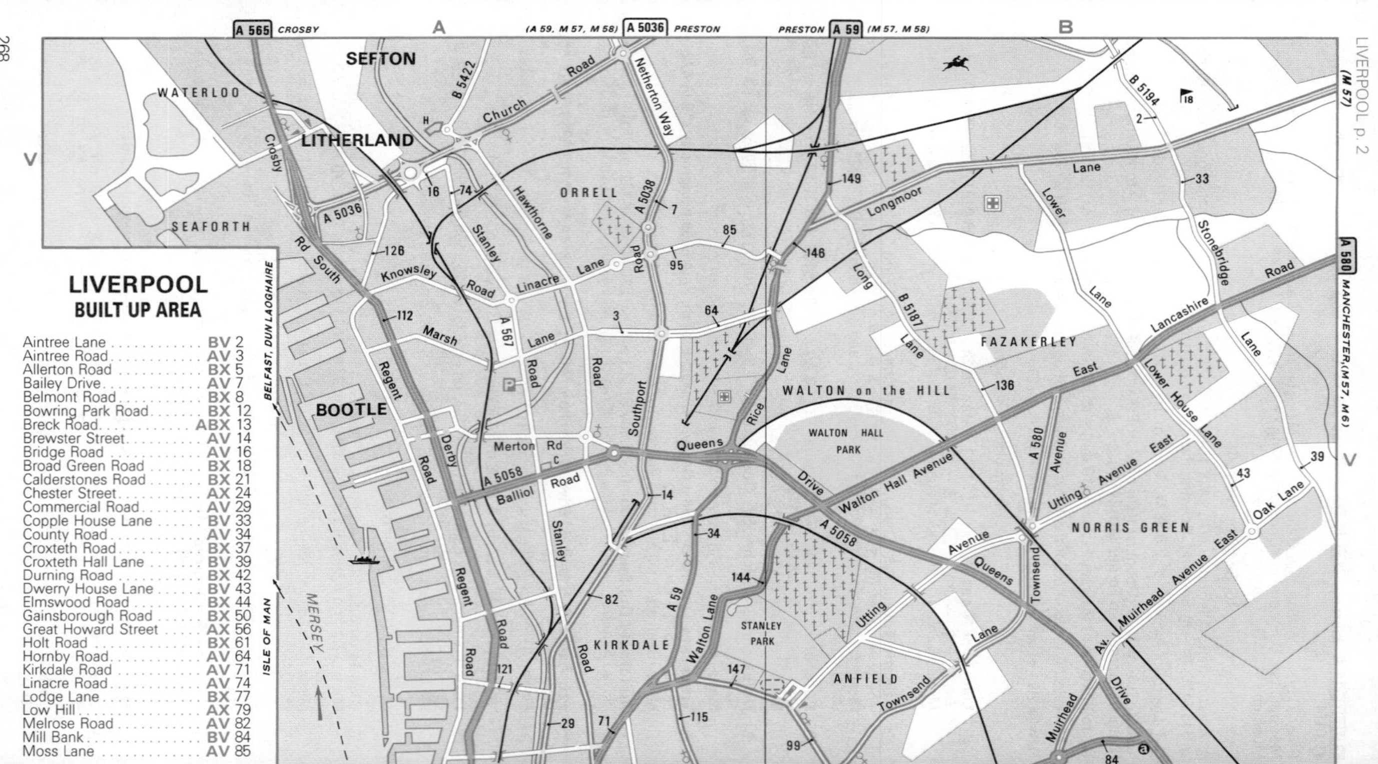

LIVERPOOL
BUILT UP AREA

Aintree Lane . . . . BV 2
Aintree Road . . . . AV 3
Allerton Road . . . . BX 5
Bailey Drive . . . . AV 7
Belmont Road . . . . BX 8
Bowring Park Road . . . . BX 12
Breck Road . . . . ABX 13
Brewster Street . . . . AV 14
Bridge Road . . . . AV 16
Broad Green Road . . . . BX 18
Calderstones Road . . . . BX 21
Chester Street . . . . AX 24
Commercial Road . . . . AV 29
Copple House Lane . . . . BV 33
County Road . . . . AV 34
Croxteth Road . . . . BX 37
Croxteth Hall Lane . . . . BV 39
Durning Road . . . . BX 42
Dwerry House Lane . . . . BV 43
Elmswood Road . . . . BX 44
Gainsborough Road . . . . BX 50
Great Howard Street . . . . AX 56
Holt Road . . . . BX 61
Hornby Road . . . . AV 64
Kirkdale Road . . . . AV 71
Linacre Road . . . . AV 74
Lodge Lane . . . . BX 77
Low Hill . . . . AX 79
Melrose Road . . . . AV 82
Mill Bank . . . . BV 84
Moss Lane . . . . AV 85

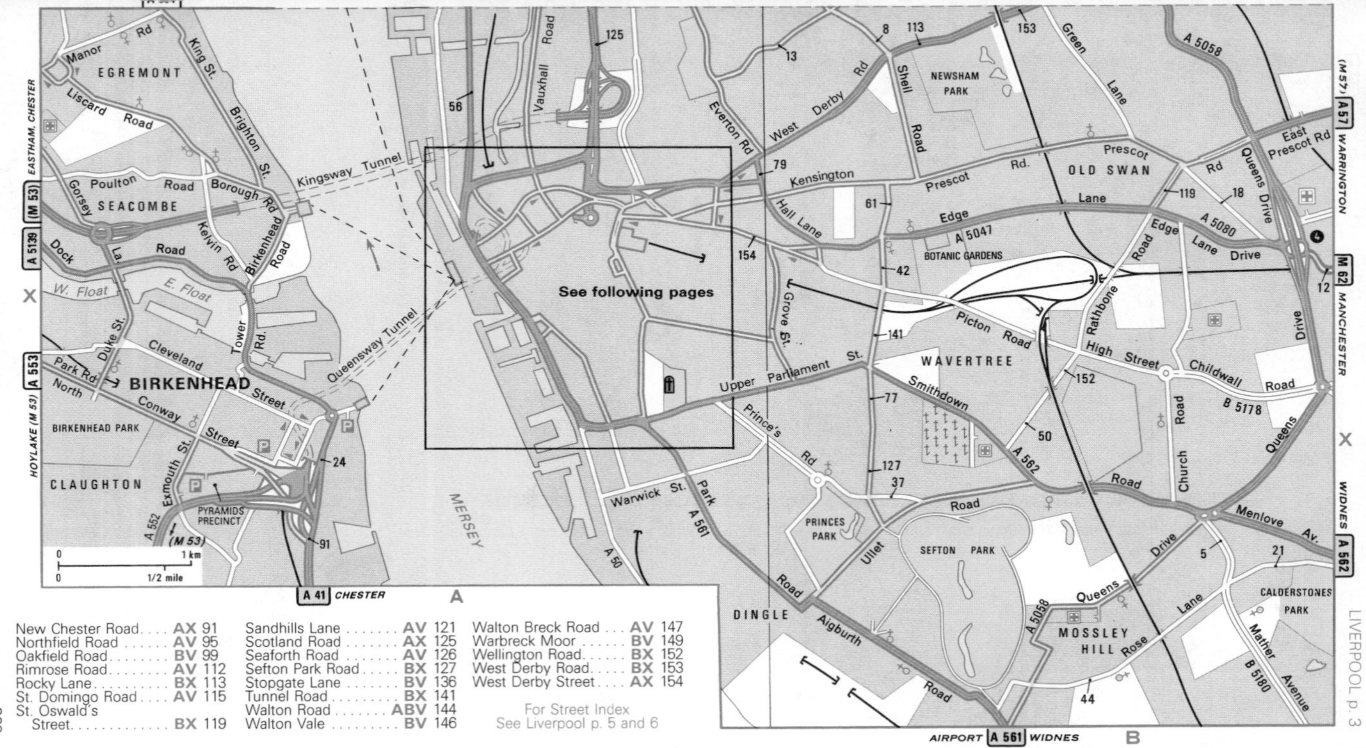

New Chester Road .... AX 91
Northfield Road ...... AV 95
Oakfield Road .... BV 99
Rimrose Road .... AV 112
Rocky Lane .... BX 113
St. Domingo Road .... AV 115
St. Oswald's Street .... BX 119
Sandhills Lane .... AV 121
Scotland Road .... AX 125
Seaforth Road .... AV 126
Sefton Park Road ..... BX 127
Stopgate Lane .... BV 136
Tunnel Road .... BX 141
Walton Road .... ABV 144
Walton Vale .... BV 146
Walton Breck Road ... AV 147
Warbreck Moor ...... BV 149
Wellington Road ...... BX 152
West Derby Road ..... BX 153
West Derby Street .... AX 154

For Street Index
See Liverpool p. 5 and 6

LIVERPOOL
CENTRE

Street	Grid	No.
Argyle St.	DZ	6
Blackburne Pl.	EZ	11
Brunswick Rd.	EY	19
Canning Pl.	CZ	23
Churchill Way	DY	25
Clarence St.	EYZ	26
College Lane	DZ	28
Commutation Row	DY	30
Cook St.	CY	32
Crosshall St.	DY	36
Daulby St.	EY	40
Erskine St.	EY	45
Fontenoy St.	DY	48
Forrest St.	DZ	49
George's Dock Gate	CY	51
Grafton St.	DZ	53
Great Charlotte St.	DY	54
Great Howard St.	CY	56
Hatton Garden	DY	57
Haymarket	DY	58
Hood St.	DY	62
Houghton St.	DY	65
Huskisson St.	EZ	66
James St.	CY	68
King Edward St.	CY	69
Knight St.	EZ	72
Leece St.	EZ	73
Liver St.	CZ	76
Mansfield St.	DEY	80
Mathew St.	CDY	81
Moss St.	EY	86
Mount St.	EZ	88
Myrtle St.	EZ	89
Newington	DZ	92
New Quay	CY	93
North John St.	CY	96
Norton St.	DY	97
Parker St.	DY	103
Prescot St.	EY	105
Prince's Rd	EZ	107
Ranelagh St.	DY	108
Richmond St.	DY	109
Roe St.	DY	114
St. James Pl.	EZ	117
St. John's Lane	DY	118
School Lane	DYZ	122
Scotland Pl.	DY	123
Sefton St.	DZ	129
Seymour St.	EY	130
Skelhorne St.	DY	133
Stanley St.	CDY	135
Suffolk St.	DZ	137
Tarleton St.	DY	139
Victoria St.	DY	143
Water St.	CY	150
William Brown St.	DY	156
York St.	DZ	157

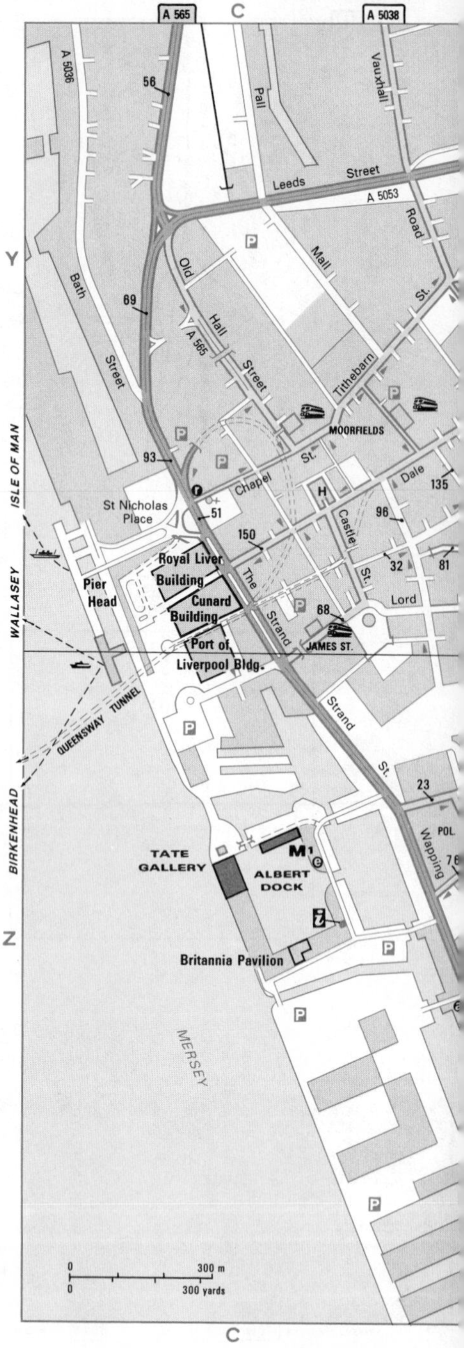

GREEN TOURIST GUIDES

Picturesque scenery, buildings
Attractive routes
Touring programmes
Plans of towns and buildings.

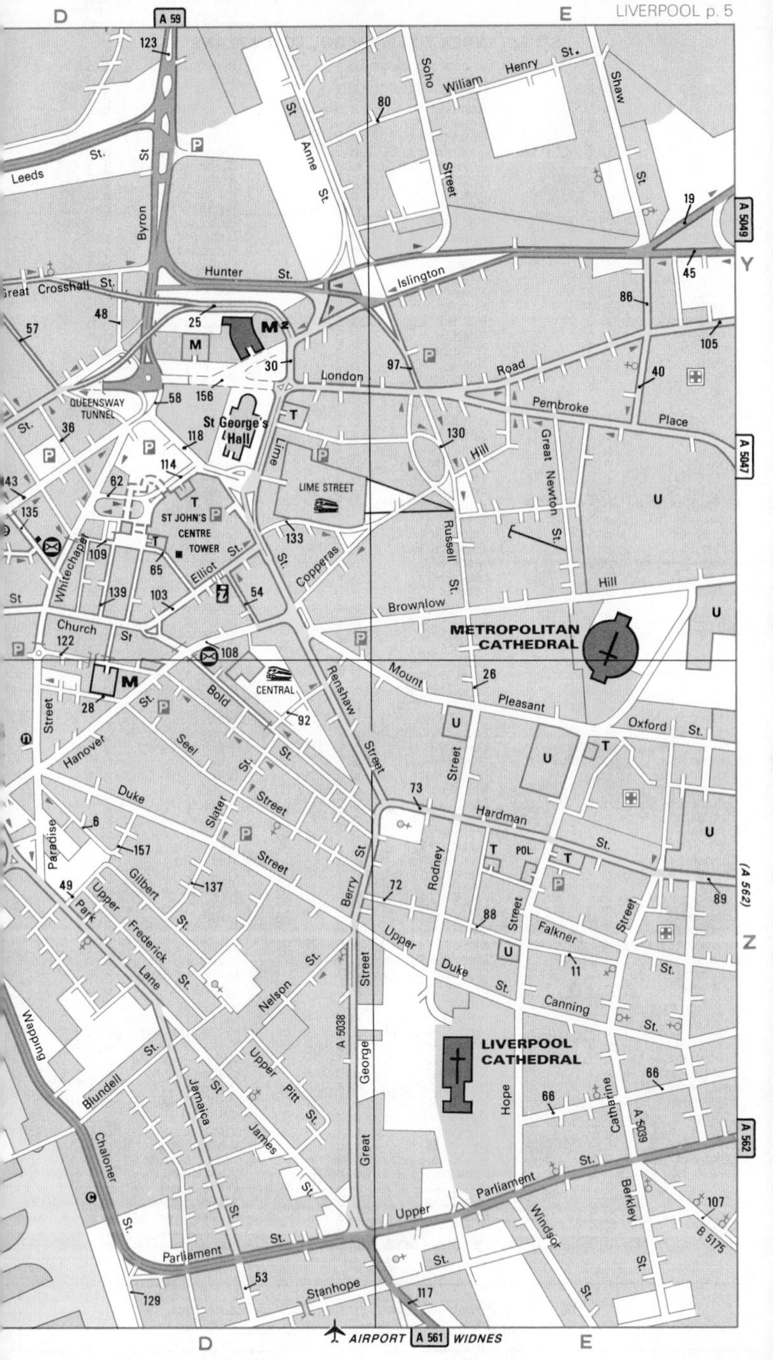
D
E
A 59
Y
Z
A 5049
A 5047
(A 562)
A 562
Leeds St.
Byron St
Anne St.
Soho Street
William Henry St.
Shaw St.
Hunter St.
Islington
Great Crosshall St.
London Road
Pembroke Place
QUEENSWAY TUNNEL
St George's Hall
Lime St.
LIME STREET
Great Newton St.
Russell St.
Hill
ST JOHN'S CENTRE
TOWER
Elliot St.
Copperas Hill
Whitechapel
Brownlow Hill
Church St
METROPOLITAN CATHEDRAL
Mount Pleasant
CENTRAL
Bold St.
Renshaw Street
Oxford St.
Hanover St.
Seel St.
Duke Street
Slater Street
Hardman St.
POL.
Paradise Street
Gilbert St.
Berry St
Rodney Street
Falkner Street
Upper Frederick St.
Park Lane
Upper Duke St.
Nelson St.
Canning St.
A 5038
Great George Street
Wapping
Blundell St.
Jamaica St
Upper Pitt St.
James St.
LIVERPOOL CATHEDRAL
Hope Street
Catharine
A 5039
Chaloner St.
Upper Parliament St.
Parliament St.
Windsor St.
Berkley St.
B 5175
Stanhope St.
AIRPORT
A 561
WIDNES

STREET INDEX TO LIVERPOOL TOWN PLANS

Street	Page	Grid	No.
Bold St.	p. 5	DZ	
Church St.	p. 5	DY	
Lime St.	p. 5	DY	
London Rd	p. 5	DEY	
Lord St.	p. 4	CDY	
Parker St.	p. 5	DY	103
Ranelagh St.	p. 5	DY	108
Renshaw St.	p. 5	DEZ	
St. Johns Centre	p. 5	DY	
Aigburth Rd	p. 3	BX	
Aintree Lane	p. 2	BV	2
Aintree Rd	p. 2	AV	3
Allerton Rd.	p. 3	BX	5
Argyle St.	p. 5	DZ	6
Bailey Drive	p. 2	AV	7
Balliol Rd	p. 2	AV	
Bath St.	p. 4	CY	
Belmont Rd	p. 3	BX	8
Berkley St.	p. 5	EZ	
Berry St.	p. 5	DZ	
Birkenhead Rd	p. 3	AX	
Blackburne Pl.	p. 5	EZ	11
Blundell St.	p. 5	DZ	
Bold St.	p. 5	DZ	
Borough Rd	p. 3	AX	
Bowring Park Rd	p. 3	BX	12
Breck Rd	p. 3	ABX	13
Brewster St.	p. 2	AV	14
Bridge Rd.	p. 2	AV	16
Brighton St.	p. 3	AX	
Broad Green Rd	p. 3	BX	18
Brownlow Hill	p. 5	DEY	
Brunswick Rd	p. 5	EY	19
Byron St.	p. 5	DY	
Calderstones Rd	p. 3	BX	21
Canning Pl.	p. 4	CZ	23
Canning St.	p. 5	EZ	
Castle St.	p. 4	CY	
Catharine St.	p. 5	EZ	
Chaloner St.	p. 5	DZ	
Chapel St.	p. 4	CY	
Chester St.	p. 3	AX	24
Childwall Rd	p. 3	BX	
Church Rd	p. 3	BX	
Church Rd LITHERLAND	p. 2	AV	
Church St.	p. 5	DY	
Churchill Way	p. 5	DY	25
Clarence St.	p. 5	EYZ	26
Cleveland St.	p. 3	AX	
College Lane	p. 5	DZ	28
Commercial Rd	p. 2	AV	29
Commutation Row	p. 5	DY	30
Conway St.	p. 3	AX	
Cook St.	p. 4	CY	32
Copperas Hill	p. 5	DE	
Copple House La.	p. 2	BV	33
County Rd	p. 2	AV	34
Crosby Rd South	p. 2	AV	
Crosshall St.	p. 5	DY	36
Croxteth Rd	p. 3	BX	37
Croxteth Hall Lane	p. 2	BV	39
Dale St.	p. 4	CDY	
Daulby St.	p. 5	EY	40
Derby Rd	p. 2	AV	
Duke St.	p. 5	DZ	
Duke St. BIRKENHEAD	p. 3	AX	
Durning Rd	p. 3	BX	42
Dwerry House Lane	p. 2	BV	43
East Lancashire Rd	p. 2	BV	
East Prescot Rd	p. 3	BX	
Edge Lane	p. 3	BX	
Edge Lane Drive	p. 3	BX	
Elliot St.	p. 5	DY	
Elmswood Rd	p. 3	BX	44
Erskine St.	p. 5	EY	45
Everton Rd.	p. 3	AX	
Exmouth St.	p. 3	AX	
Fontenoy St.	p. 5	DY	48
Forrest St.	p. 5	DZ	49
Freeman St.	p. 3	AX	
Gainsborough Rd	p. 3	BX	50
George's Dock Lane	p. 4	CY	51
Gilbert St.	p. 5	DZ	
Gorsey Lane	p. 3	AX	
Grafton St.	p. 5	DZ	53
Great Charlotte St.	p. 5	DY	54
Great Crosshall St.	p. 5	DY	
Great George St.	p. 5	DY	
Great Howard St.	p. 4	CY	56
Great Newton St.	p. 5	EY	
Green Lane	p. 3	BX	
Grove St.	p. 3	BX	
Hall Lane	p. 3	BX	
Hannover St.	p. 5	DZ	
Hardman St.	p. 5	EZ	
Hatton Garden	p. 5	DY	57
Haymarket	p. 5	DY	58
Hawthorne Rd	p. 2	AV	
High St.	p. 3	BX	
Holt Rd	p. 3	BX	61
Hood St.	p. 5	DY	62
Hope St.	p. 5	EZ	
Hornby Rd	p. 2	AV	64
Houghton St.	p. 5	DY	65
Hunter St.	p. 5	DY	
Huskisson St.	p. 5	EZ	66
Islington	p. 5	EY	
Jamaica St.	p. 5	DZ	
James St.	p. 4	CY	68
Kelvin Rd	p. 3	AX	
Kensington	p. 3	BX	
King St.	p. 3	AX	
King Edward St.	p. 4	CY	69
Kirkdale Rd.	p. 2	AV	71
Knight St.	p. 5	EZ	72
Knowsley Rd	p. 2	AV	
Leece St.	p. 5	EZ	73
Leeds St.	p. 4	CY	
Lime St.	p. 5	DY	
Linacre Rd	p. 2	AV	74
Linacre Lane	p. 2	AV	
Liscard Rd	p. 3	AX	
Liver St.	p. 5	CZ	76
Lodge Lane	p. 3	BX	77
London Rd	p. 5	DEY	
Long Lane	p. 2	BV	
Longmoor Lane	p. 2	BV	
Lord St.	p. 4	CDY	
Lower House Lane	p. 2	BV	
Lower Lane	p. 2	BV	
Low Hill	p. 3	ABX	79
Manor Rd	p. 2	AX	
Mansfield St.	p. 5	DEY	80
Marsh Lane	p. 2	AV	
Mather Av.	p. 3	BX	
Mathew St.	p. 4	CDY	81
Melrose Rd	p. 2	AV	82
Menlove Av.	p. 3	BV	
Merton Rd	p. 2	AV	
Mill Bank	p. 2	BV	84
Moss Lane	p. 2	AV	85
Moss St.	p. 5	EY	86
Mount Pleasant	p. 5	EZ	
Mount St.	p. 5	EZ	88
Muirhead Av.	p. 2	BV	
Muirhead Av. East	p. 2	BV	
Myrtle St.	p. 5	EZ	89
Nelson St.	p. 5	DZ	
Netherton Way	p. 2	AV	
New Chester Rd	p. 3	AX	91
Newington	p. 5	DZ	92
New Quay	p. 4	CY	93
Northfield Rd	p. 2	AV	95
North John St.	p. 4	CY	96
Norton St.	p. 5	EY	97
Oakfield Rd	p. 2	BV	99
Old Hall St.	p. 4	CY	
Oxford St.	p. 5	EZ	
Pall Mall	p. 4	CY	
Paradise St.	p. 5	DZ	
Parker St.	p. 5	DY	103
Park Lane	p. 5	DZ	
Park Rd.	p. 3	AX	
Park Rd North	p. 3	AX	
Parliament St.	p. 5	DZ	
Pembroke Pl.	p. 5	EY	
Picton Rd	p. 3	BX	
Poulton Rd	p. 3	AX	
Prescot Rd	p. 3	BX	
Prescot St.	p. 5	EY	105
Prince's Rd	p. 5	EZ	107
Queens Drive	p. 3	BX	
Queensway	p. 3	AX	
Ranelagh St.	p. 5	DY	108
Rathbone Rd	p. 3	BX	
Renshaw Rd.	p. 5	DZ	
Rice Lane	p. 2	AV	
Richmond St.	p. 5	DY	109
Rimrose Rd	p. 2	AV	112
Rocky Lane	p. 3	BX	113
Rodney St.	p. 5	EZ	
Roe St.	p. 5	DY	114
Rose Lane	p. 3	BX	
Russel St.	p. 5	EY	
St. Anne St.	p. 5	DY	
St. Domingo Rd.	p. 2	AV	115
St. James Pl.	p. 5	EZ	117
St. James St.	p. 5	DZ	
St. John's Lane	p. 5	DY	118
St. Johns Centre	p. 5	DY	
St. Nicholas Pl.	p. 4	CY	
St. Oswald's St.	p. 3	BX	119
Sandhills Lane	p. 2	AV	121
School Lane	p. 5	DYZ	122
Scotland Pl.	p. 5	DY	123
Scotland Rd	p. 3	AX	125
Seaforth Rd	p. 2	AV	126
Seel St.	p. 5	DZ	
Sefton Park Rd.	p. 3	BX	127
Sefton St.	p. 3	DZ	129
Seymour St.	p. 5	EY	130
Shaw St.	p. 5	EY	
Sheil Rd	p. 3	BX	
Skelhorne St.	p. 5	EY	133
Slater St.	p. 5	DZ	
Smithdown Rd.	p. 3	BX	
Soho St.	p. 5	EY	
South John St.	p. 4	CYZ	
Southport Rd	p. 2	AV	
Stanhope St.	p. 5	DZ	
Stanley Rd	p. 2	AV	
Stanley St.	p. 4	CDY	135
Stonebridge Lane	p. 2	BV	
Stopgate Lane	p. 2	BV	136
Strand St.	p. 4	CZ	
Strand (The)	p. 4	CY	
Suffolk St.	p. 5	DZ	137
Tarleton St.	p. 5	DY	139
Tithebarn St.	p. 4	CY	
Townsend Av.	p. 2	BV	
Townsend Lane	p. 2	BV	
Tunnel Rd.	p. 3	BX	141
Ullet Rd	p. 3	BX	
Upper Duke St.	p. 5	EZ	
Upper Frederick St.	p. 5	DZ	
Upper Parliament St.	p. 5	EZ	
Upper Pitt	p. 5	DZ	
Utting Av.	p. 2	AV	
Utting Av. East	p. 2	BV	
Vauxhall Rd	p. 4	CY	
Victoria St.	p. 5	DY	143
Walton Lane	p. 2	AV	
Walton Rd	p. 2	ABV	144
Walton Vale	p. 2	BV	146
Walton Breck Rd	p. 2	AV	147
Walton Hall Av.	p. 2	BV	
Wapping	p. 4	CDZ	
Warbreck Moor	p. 2	BV	149
Warwick	p. 3	AX	
Water St.	p. 4	CY	150
Wellington Rd	p. 3	BX	152
West Derby Rd	p. 3	BX	153
West Derby St.	p. 3	AX	154
Whitechapel	p; 5	DY	
William Brown St.	p. 5	DY	156
William Henry St.	p. 5	EY	
Windsor St.	p. 5	EZ	
York St.	p. 5	DZ	157

The names of main shopping streets are indicated in red at the beginning of the list of streets.

Derby Lodge, Roby Rd, L36 4HD, SW : 1 m. on A 5080 ✆ 480 4440, Fax 480 8132, – .
Meals 15.75 **st.** (dinner) and a la carte 15.40/29.95 ₫ 7.95 – **19 rm** ⊐ 55.00/110.00 **st.** – SB.

Travel Inn, Wilson Rd, Tarbock, L36 6AD, SE : 2 ¼ m. on A 5080 – ✆ 480 9614, Fax 480 9361 – rm .
Meals (grill rest.) a la carte approx. 16.00 **t.** – ⊐ 4.95 – **40 rm** 33.50 **t.**

at Knowsley E : 8 ½ m. by A 580 – BV – on B 5194 – ✉ Prescott – ✆ 0151.

BellTower, Ribblers Lane, L34 9HA, W : 1 ¼ m. by B 5194 ✆ 549 2222 – .

at Grassendale SE : 4 ½ m. on A 561 –BX – ✉ Liverpool – ✆ 0151.

Gulshan, 544-546 Aigburth Rd, L19 3QG, on A 561 ✆ 427 2273 –
Meals - Indian (dinner only) a la carte 10.50/18.95 **t.** ₫ 5.90.

ATS 15/37 Caryl St. ✆ 709 8032
ATS Wilson Road, Huyton ✆ 489 8386/7
ATS 190-194 St. Mary's Rd, Garston ✆ 427 3665
ATS 73-77 Durning Rd, Wavertree ✆ 263 7604
ATS Musker St., Crosby ✆ 931 3166
ATS Unit E, Liver Ind. Est., Long Lane, Aintree ✆ 524 1000

LIZARD Cornwall 403 E 34 **The West Country G.** – ✆ 01326.

Envir. : Lizard Peninsula★ - Mullion Cove★★★ (Church★) - Kynance Cove★★★ - Cadgwith★ - Coverack★ – Cury★ (Church★) - Gunwalloe Fishing Cove★ - St. Keverne (Church★) - Landewednack★ (Church★) – Mawgan-in-Meneage (Church★) - Ruan Minor (Church★) - St. Anthony-in-Meneage★.

♦London 326 – Penzance 24 – Truro 29.

Housel Bay , Housel Cove, TR12 7PG, ✆ 290417, Fax 290359, ≤ Housel Cove, – rest .
Meals (bar lunch Monday to Saturday)/dinner 21.00 **st.** and a la carte ₫ 5.50 – **23 rm** ⊐ 28.00/80.00 **st.** – SB.

Penmenner House , Penmenner Rd, TR12 7NR, ✆ 290370, ≤, – .
closed Christmas and New Year – **Meals** (by arrangement) 12.00 **st.** – **8 rm** ⊐ 24.00/46.00 **st.**

Parc Brawse House , Penmenner Rd, TR12 7NR, ✆ 290466, ≤, – rest .
March-November – **Meals** 9.00 **t.** – **6 rm** ⊐ 14.00/35.00 – SB.

LOCKINGTON Humbs – see Great Driffield.

LOFTUS Cleveland 402 R 20 – pop. 7 315 – ECD : Wednesday – ✉ Saltburn-by-the-Sea – ✆ 01287.

♦London 264 – ♦Leeds 73 – ♦Middlesbrough 17 – Scarborough 36.

Grinkle Park , Easington, TS13 4UB, SE : 3 ½ m. by A 174 ✆ 640515, Fax 641278, ≤, , park, – .
Meals 10.95/17.00 **t.** and dinner a la carte ₫ 5.00 – **20 rm** ⊐ 70.00/90.00 **t.** – SB.

LOLWORTH SERVICE AREA Cambs. – see Cambridge.

London

404 folds 42 to 44 – **London G.** – pop. 7 566 620 – ✆ 0171 or 0181: see heading of each area

✈ Heathrow, ✆ (0181) 759 4321, p. 8 AX – **Terminal** : Airbus (A1) from Victoria, Airbus (A2) from Paddington – Underground (Piccadilly line) frequent service daily.

✈ Gatwick, ✆ 01293 535353 and ✆ 0181 763 2020, p. 9 : by A 23 EZ and M 23 – **Terminal** : Coach service from Victoria Coach Station (Flightline 777, hourly service) – Railink (Gatwick Express) from Victoria (24 h service).

✈ London City Airport ✆ (0171) 474 5555, p. 7 : HV.

✈ Stansted, at Bishop's Stortford, ✆ 01279 680500, Fax 662066, NE : 34 m. p. 7 : by M 11 JT and A 120.

British Airways, Victoria Air Terminal : 115 Buckingham Palace Rd, SW1, ✆ (0171) 834 9411, Fax 828 7142, p. 32 BX.

Euston and Paddington ✆ 0345 090700.

ℹ British Travel Centre, 12 Regent St., Piccadilly Circus, SW1Y 4PQ ✆ (0171) 971 0026.
Selfridges, basement Services, Arcade, Selfridges Store, Oxford St. WI ✆ (0171) 730 3488.
Victoria Station Forecourt SWI ✆ (0171) 730 3488.

Major sights in London and the outskirts .... pp. 2 and 3
Maps and lists of streets .... pp. 4 to 33
Greater London .... pp. 4 to 13
Central London .... pp. 14 to 27
Detailed maps of :
Mayfair, Soho, St. James's, Marylebone .... pp. 28 and 29
South Kensington, Chelsea, Belgravia .... pp. 30 and 31
Victoria, Strand, Bayswater, Kensington .... pp. 32 and 33
Hotels and Restaurants
Alphabetical list of hotels and restaurants .... pp. 34 to 37
Alphabetical list of areas included .... p. 38
Establishments with stars and red Meals .... p. 39
Particularly pleasant hotels and restaurants .... p. 40
Restaurants classified according to type .... pp. 40 to 44
Hotels and Restaurants listed by boroughs .... pp. 46 to 74

Sights
Curiosités – Le curiosità
Sehenswürdigkeiten

HISTORIC BUILDINGS AND MONUMENTS

Palace of Westminster★★★ : House of Lords★★, Westminster Hall★★ (hammerbeam roof★★★), Robing Room★, Central Lobby★, House of Commons★, Big Ben★, Victoria Tower★ p. 26 LY – Tower of London★★★ (Crown Jewels★★★, White Tower or Keep★★★, St. John's Chapel★★, Beauchamp Tower★ Tower Hill Pageant★) p. 27 PVX.

Banqueting House★★ p. 26 LX – Buckingham Palace★★ (Changing of the Guard★★, Royal Mews★★) p. 32 BVX – Kensington Palace★★ p. 24 FX – Lincoln's Inn★★ p. 33 EV – London Bridge★ p. 27 PVX – Royal Hospital Chelsea★★ p. 31 FU – St. James's Palace★★ p. 29 EP – South Bank Arts Centre ★★ (Royal Festival Hall★, National Theatre★, County Hall★) p. 26 MX – The Temple★★ (Middle Temple Hall★) p. 22 MV – Tower Bridge★★ p. 27 PX.

Albert Memorial★ p. 30 CQ – Apsley House★ p. 28 BP – Burlington House★ p. 29 EM – Charterhouse★ p. 23 NOU – Commonwealth Institute★ p. 24 EY – Design Centre★ p. 29 FM – George Inn★, Southwark p. 27 PX – Gray's Inn★ p. 22 MU – Guildhall★ (Lord Mayor's Show★★) p. 23 OU – Imperial College of Science and Technology★ p. 30 CR – Dr Johnson's House★ p. 23 NUV **A** – Lancaster House★ p. 29 EP – Leighton House★ p. 24 EY – Linley Sambourne House★ p. 24 EY – Lloyds Building★★ p. 23 PV – Mansion House★ (plate and insignia★★) p. 23 PV **P** – The Monument★ (✻★) p. 23 PV **G** – Old Admiralty★ p. 26 KLX – Royal Exchange★ p. 23 PV **V** – Royal Opera Arcade★ (New Zealand House) p. 29 FGN – Royal Opera House★ (Covent Garden) p. 33 DX – Somerset House★ p. 33 EXY – Spencer House★★ p. 29 DP – Staple Inn★ p. 22 MU **Y** – Theatre Royal★ (Haymarket) p. 29 GM – Westminster Bridge★ p. 26 LY.

CHURCHES

The City Churches

St. Paul's Cathedral★★★ (Dome ≤★★★) p. 23 NOV.

St. Bartholomew the Great★★ (choir★) p. 23 OU **K** – St. Dunstan-in-the-East★★ p. 23 PV **F** – St. Mary-at-Hill★★ (woodwork★★, plan★) p. 23 PV **B** – Temple Church★★ p. 22 MV.

All Hallows-by-the-Tower (font cover★★ brasses★) p. 23 PV **Y** – Christ Church★ p. 23 OU **E** – St. Andrew Undershaft (monuments★) p. 23 PV **A** – St. Bride★ (steeple★★) p. 23 NV **J** – St. Clement Eastcheap (panelled interior★★) p. 23 PV **E** – St. Edmund the King and Martyr (tower and spire★) p. 23 PV **D** – St-Giles Cripplegate★ p. 23 OU **N** – St. Helen Bishopsgate★ (monuments★★) p. 23 PUV **R** – St. James Garlickhythe (tower and spire★, sword rests★) p. 23 OV **R** – St. Magnus the Martyr (tower★, sword rest★) p. 23 PV **K** – St. Margaret Lothbury★ (tower and spire★, woodwork★, screen★, font★) p. 23 PU **S** – St. Margaret Pattens (spire★, woodwork★) p. 23 PV **N** – St. Martin-within-Ludgate (tower and spire★, door cases★) p. 23 NOV **B** – St. Mary Abchurch★ (reredos★★, tower and spire★, dome★) p. 23 PV **X** – St. Mary-le-Bow (tower and steeple★★) p. 23 OV **G** – St. Michael Paternoster Royal (tower and spire★) p. 23 OV **D** – St. Nicholas Cole Abbey (tower and spire★) p. 23 OV **F** – St. Olave★ p. 23 PV **S** – St. Peter upon Cornhill (screen★) p. 23 PV **L** – St. Stephen Walbrook★ (tower and steeple★, dome★), p. 23 PV **Z** – St. Vedast (tower and spire★, ceiling★), p. 23 OU **E**.

Other Churches

Westminster Abbey★★★ (Henry VII Chapel★★★, Chapel of Edward the Confessor★★, Chapter House★★, Poets' Corner★) p. 26 LY.

Southwark Cathedral★★ p. 27 PX.

Queen's Chapel★ p. 29 EP – St. Clement Danes★ p. 33 EX – St. James's★ p. 29 EM – St. Margaret's★ p. 26 LY **A** – St. Martin-in-the-Fields★ p. 33 DY – St. Paul's★ (Covent Garden) p. 33 DX – Westminster Roman Catholic Cathedral★ p. 26 KY **B**.

PARKS

Regent's Park★★★ p. 21 HI (terraces★★), Zoo★★★.

Hyde Park – Kensington Gardens★★ (Orangery★) pp. 24 and 25 – St. James's Park★★ p. 26 KXY.

STREETS AND SQUARES

The City★★★ p. 23 NV.

Bedford Square★★ p. 22 KLU – Belgrave Square★★ p. 32 AVX – Burlington Arcade★★ p. 29 DM – The Mall★★ p. 29 FP – Piccadilly★ p. 29 EM – The Thames★★ pp. 25-27 – Trafalgar Square★★ p. 33 DY – Whitehall★★ (Horse Guards★) p. 26 LX.

Barbican★ p. 23 OU – Bond Street★ pp. 28-29 CK-DM – Canonbury Square★ p. 23 NS – Carlton House Terrace★ p. 29 GN – Cheyne Walk★ p. 25 GHZ – Covent Garden★ p. 33 DX – Fitzroy Square★ p. 22 KU – Jermyn Street★ p. 29 EN – Merrick Square★ p. 27 OY – Montpelier Square★ p. 31 EQ – The Piazza★(Covent Garden) p. 33 DX – Piccadilly Arcade★ p. 29 DEN – Portman Square★ p. 28 AJ – Queen Anne's Gate★ p. 26 KY – Regent Street★ p. 29 EM – Piccadilly Circus★ p. 29 FM – St. James's Square★ p. 29 FN – St. James's Street★ p. 29 EN – Shepherd Market★ p. 28 CN – Soho★ p. 29 – Trinity Church Square★ p. 27 OY – Victoria Embankment gardens★ p. 33 DEXY – Waterloo Place★ p. 29 FN.

MUSEUMS

British Museum★★★ p. 22 LU – National Gallery★★★ p. 29 GM – Science Museum★★★ p. 30 CR – Tate Gallery★★★ p. 26 LZ – Victoria and Albert Museum★★★ p. 31 DR.

Courtauld Institute Galleries★★ (Somerset House) p. 33 EXY – Museum of London★★ p. 23 OU **M** – National Portrait Gallery★★ p. 29 GM – Natural History Museum★★ p. 30 CS – Queen's Gallery★★ p. 32 BV – Wallace Collection★★ p. 28 AH.

Clock Museum★ (Guildhall) p. 22 OU – Imperial War Museum★ p. 27 NY – London Transport Museum★ p. 33 DX – Madame Tussaud's★ p. 21 IU **M** – Museum of Mankind★ p. 29 DM – National Army Museum★ p. 31 FU – Percival David Foundation of Chinese Art★ p. 22 KLT **M** – Sir John Soane's Museum★ p. 22 MU **M** – Wellington Museum★ p. 28 BP.

OUTER LONDON

Blackheath p. 11 HX terraces and houses★, Eltham Palace★ **A** – **Brentford** p. 8 BX Syon Park★★, gardens★ – **Bromley** p. 10 GY The Crystal Palace Park★ – **Chiswick** p. 9 CV Chiswick Mall★★, Chiswick House★ **D**, Hogarth's House★ **E** – **Dulwich** p. 10 Picture Gallery★ FX **X** – **Greenwich** pp. 10 and 11 : Cutty Sark★★ GV **F**, Footway Tunnel(≤ ★★) – National Maritime Museum★★ (Queen's House★★) GV **M**, Royal Naval College★★ (Painted Hall★, the Chapel★) GV **G**, The Park and Old Royal Observatory★ (Meridian Building : collection★★) HV **K**, Ranger's House★ GX **N** – **Hampstead** Kenwood House★★ (Adam Library★★, paintings★★) p. 5 EU **P**, Fenton House★, The Benton Fletcher Collection★ p. 20 ES – **Hampton Court** p. 8 BY (The Palace★★★, gardens★★★, Fountain Court★, The Great Vine★)– **Kew** p. 9 CX Royal Botanic Gardens★★★ : Palm House★★, Temperate House★, Kew Palace or Dutch House★★, Orangery★, Pagoda★, Japanese Gateway★ – **Hendon**★ p. 5, Royal Air Force Museum★★ CT **M** – **Hounslow** p. 8 BV Osterley Park★★ – **Lewisham** p. 10 GX Horniman Museum★ **M** – **Richmond** pp. 8 and 9 : Richmond Park★★, ✻★★★ CX, Richmond Hill✻★★ CX, Richmond Bridge★★ BX **R**, Richmond Green★★ BX **S** (Maids of Honour Row★★, Trumpeter's House★), Asgill House★ BX **B**, Ham House★★ BX **V** – **Shoreditch** p. 6 FU Geffrye Museum★ **M** – **Tower Hamlets** p. 6 GV Canary Wharf★ St. Katharine Dock★ **Y** – **Twickenham** p. 8 BX Marble Hill House★ **Z**, Strawberry Hill★ **A** .

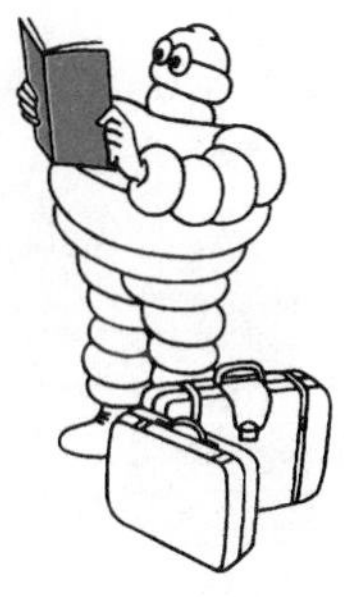

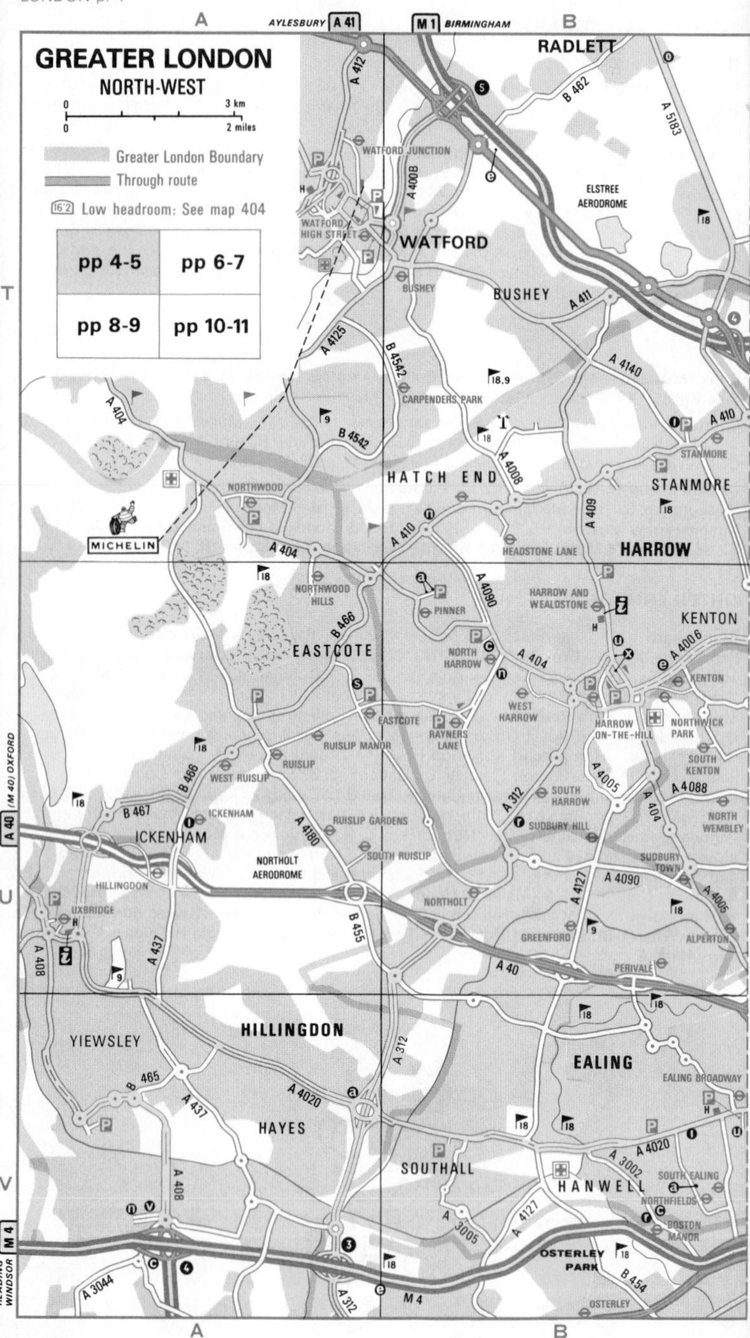
GREATER LONDON
NORTH-WEST
0 3 km
0 2 miles
Greater London Boundary
Through route
Low headroom: See map 404
pp 4-5
pp 6-7
pp 8-9
pp 10-11
AYLESBURY A 41
M 1 BIRMINGHAM
RADLETT
WATFORD JUNCTION
WATFORD HIGH STREET
WATFORD
ELSTREE AERODROME
BUSHEY
CARPENDERS PARK
HATCH END
STANMORE
HARROW
NORTHWOOD
NORTHWOOD HILLS
PINNER
HEADSTONE LANE
HARROW AND WEALDSTONE
KENTON
EASTCOTE
NORTH HARROW
WEST HARROW
RAYNERS LANE
HARROW ON-THE-HILL
NORTHWICK PARK
SOUTH KENTON
RUISLIP MANOR
RUISLIP
WEST RUISLIP
ICKENHAM
SOUTH HARROW
SUDBURY HILL
NORTH WEMBLEY
RUISLIP GARDENS
SOUTH RUISLIP
NORTHOLT AERODROME
SUDBURY TOWN
HILLINGDON
UXBRIDGE
NORTHOLT
GREENFORD
ALPERTON
PERIVALE
YIEWSLEY
HAYES
EALING
EALING BROADWAY
SOUTHALL
HANWELL
SOUTH EALING
NORTHFIELDS
BOSTON MANOR
OSTERLEY PARK
OSTERLEY
MICHELIN
A 40 (M 40) OXFORD
M 4 READING WINDSOR
A 412
A 400B
B 462
A 5183
A 411
A 4125
B 4542
A 4140
A 410
A 404
A 4008
A 409
A 4090
B 466
A 4006
A 312
A 4005
A 4088
B 467
A 4180
A 4127
A 4090
B 455
A 40
A 437
A 408
B 465
A 4020
A 3002
A 3005
B 454
A 3044
M 4
A
B
T
U
V

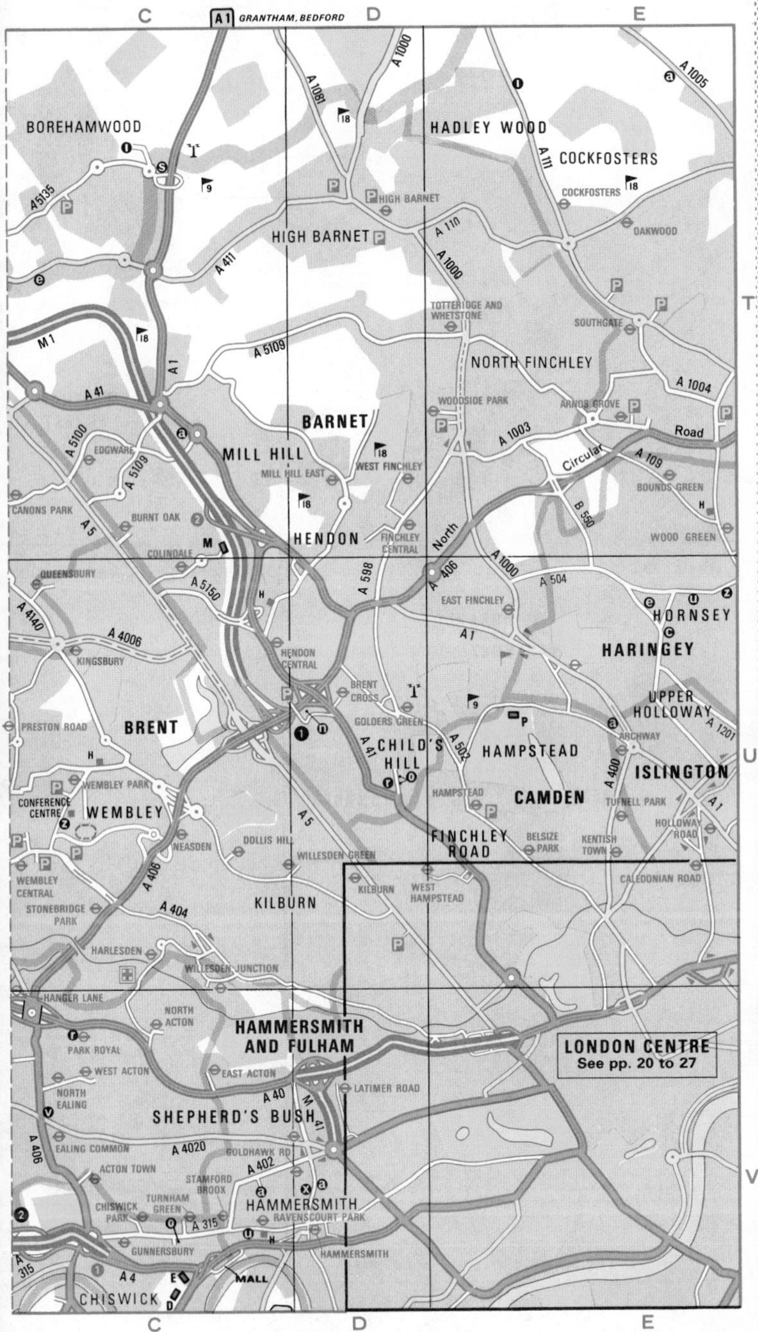

C
A1 GRANTHAM, BEDFORD
D
E
BOREHAMWOOD
HADLEY WOOD
COCKFOSTERS
HIGH BARNET
OAKWOOD
TOTTERIDGE AND WHETSTONE
SOUTHGATE
NORTH FINCHLEY
WOODSIDE PARK
ARNOS GROVE
BARNET
MILL HILL
EDGWARE
MILL HILL EAST
WEST FINCHLEY
BOUNDS GREEN
CANONS PARK
BURNT OAK
HENDON
FINCHLEY CENTRAL
WOOD GREEN
COLINDALE
QUEENSBURY
EAST FINCHLEY
HORNSEY
HARINGEY
KINGSBURY
HENDON CENTRAL
BRENT CROSS
UPPER HOLLOWAY
PRESTON ROAD
BRENT
GOLDERS GREEN
CHILD'S HILL
HAMPSTEAD
ARCHWAY
ISLINGTON
WEMBLEY PARK
CONFERENCE CENTRE
WEMBLEY
CAMDEN
TUFNELL PARK
NEASDEN
DOLLIS HILL
WILLESDEN GREEN
FINCHLEY ROAD
BELSIZE PARK
KENTISH TOWN
HOLLOWAY ROAD
WEMBLEY CENTRAL
KILBURN
WEST HAMPSTEAD
CALEDONIAN ROAD
STONEBRIDGE PARK
HARLESDEN
WILLESDEN JUNCTION
HANGER LANE
NORTH ACTON
HAMMERSMITH AND FULHAM
LONDON CENTRE See pp. 20 to 27
PARK ROYAL
WEST ACTON
EAST ACTON
LATIMER ROAD
NORTH EALING
SHEPHERD'S BUSH
EALING COMMON
GOLDHAWK RD
ACTON TOWN
STAMFORD BROOK
CHISWICK PARK
TURNHAM GREEN
HAMMERSMITH
RAVENSCOURT PARK
GUNNERSBURY
MALL
CHISWICK
North Circular Road
T
U
V

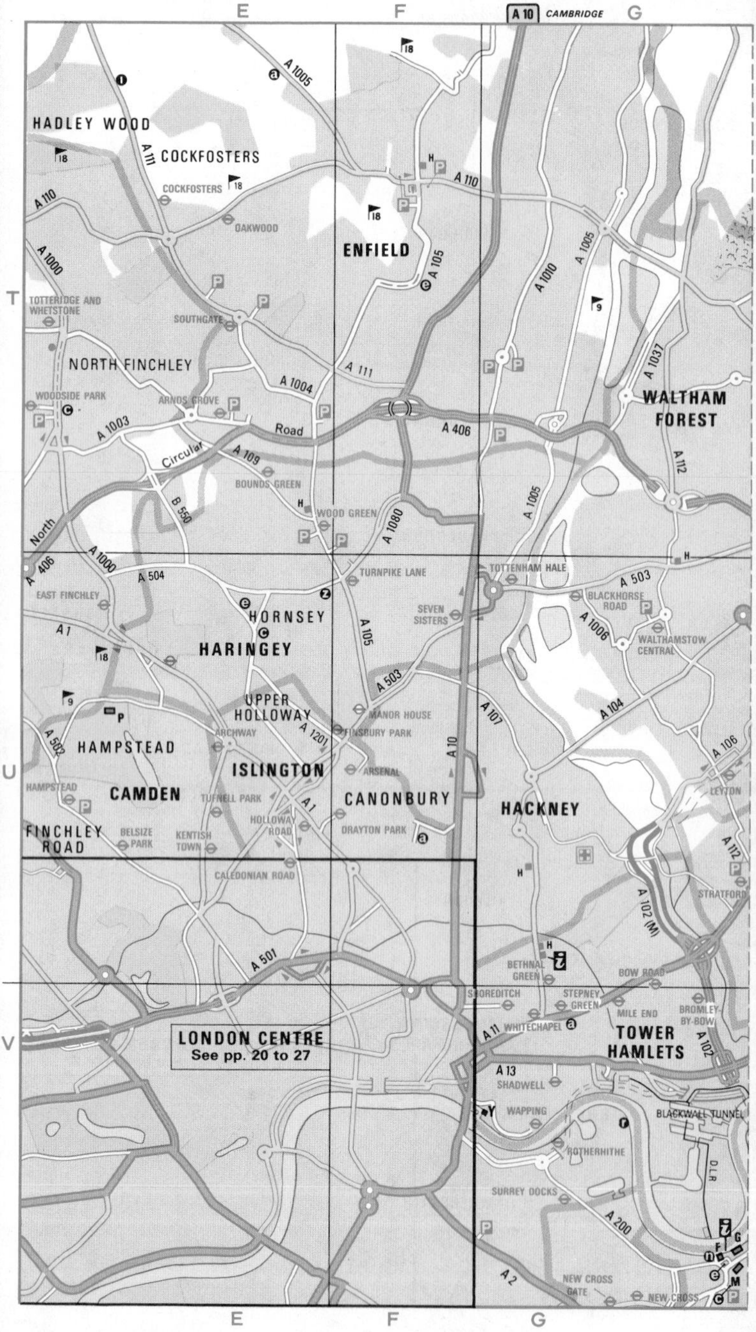

E F G
A 10 CAMBRIDGE

HADLEY WOOD
COCKFOSTERS
COCKFOSTERS
A 1005
A 111
A 110
OAKWOOD
ENFIELD
A 105
A 1000
TOTTERIDGE AND WHETSTONE
SOUTHGATE
NORTH FINCHLEY
A 111
A 1004
WOODSIDE PARK
ARNOS GROVE
A 1003
Road
A 406
Circular
A 109
BOUNDS GREEN
B 550
WOOD GREEN
A 1080
North
A 406
A 1010
A 1005
A 1037
WALTHAM FOREST
A 112
A 1005
A 1000
A 504
TURNPIKE LANE
TOTTENHAM HALE
A 503
BLACKHORSE ROAD
A 1006
WALTHAMSTOW CENTRAL
EAST FINCHLEY
HORNSEY
SEVEN SISTERS
A 1
HARINGEY
A 105
A 503
A 104
UPPER HOLLOWAY
MANOR HOUSE
A 107
A 502
HAMPSTEAD
ARCHWAY
A 1201
FINSBURY PARK
A 10
A 106
ISLINGTON
ARSENAL
HAMPSTEAD
CAMDEN
TUFNELL PARK
A 1
CANONBURY
HACKNEY
LEYTON
FINCHLEY ROAD
BELSIZE PARK
KENTISH TOWN
HOLLOWAY ROAD
DRAYTON PARK
A 112
CALEDONIAN ROAD
STRATFORD
A 102 (M)
A 501
BETHNAL GREEN
BOW ROAD
SHOREDITCH
STEPNEY GREEN
MILE END
BROMLEY-BY-BOW
A 11
WHITECHAPEL
TOWER HAMLETS
A 102

LONDON CENTRE
See pp. 20 to 27

A 13
SHADWELL
WAPPING
BLACKWALL TUNNEL
ROTHERHITHE
D.L.R.
SURREY DOCKS
A 200
A 2
NEW CROSS GATE
NEW CROSS

T U V
E F G

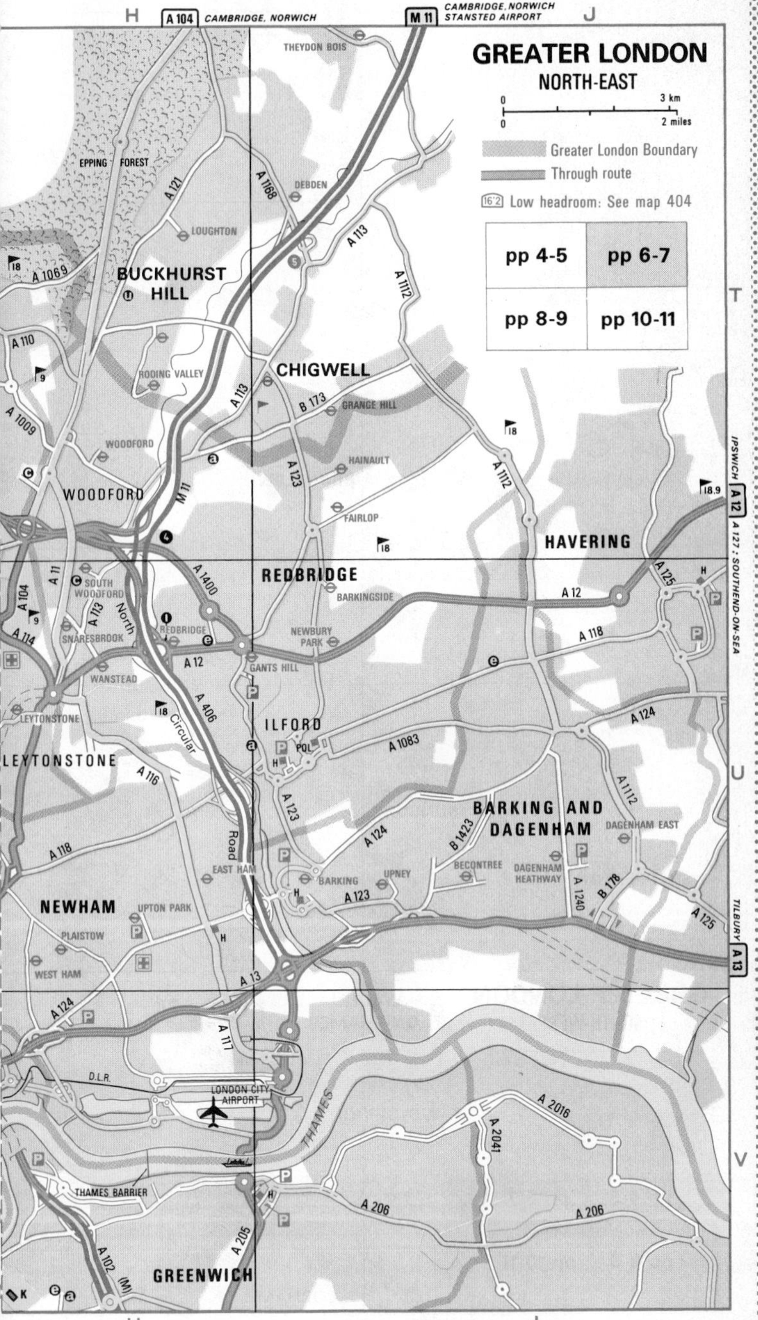
GREATER LONDON
NORTH-EAST
Greater London Boundary
Through route
Low headroom: See map 404
pp 4-5
pp 6-7
pp 8-9
pp 10-11
A 104 CAMBRIDGE, NORWICH
M 11 CAMBRIDGE, NORWICH STANSTED AIRPORT
IPSWICH A 12 A 127: SOUTHEND-ON-SEA
TILBURY A 13
THEYDON BOIS
EPPING FOREST
DEBDEN
LOUGHTON
BUCKHURST HILL
CHIGWELL
RODING VALLEY
GRANGE HILL
WOODFORD
HAINAULT
FAIRLOP
HAVERING
REDBRIDGE
SOUTH WOODFORD
BARKINGSIDE
SNARESBROOK
NEWBURY PARK
GANTS HILL
WANSTEAD
LEYTONSTONE
ILFORD
North Circular Road
BARKING AND DAGENHAM
DAGENHAM EAST
BECONTREE
DAGENHAM HEATHWAY
EAST HAM
BARKING
UPNEY
NEWHAM
UPTON PARK
PLAISTOW
WEST HAM
D.L.R.
LONDON CITY AIRPORT
THAMES
THAMES BARRIER
GREENWICH

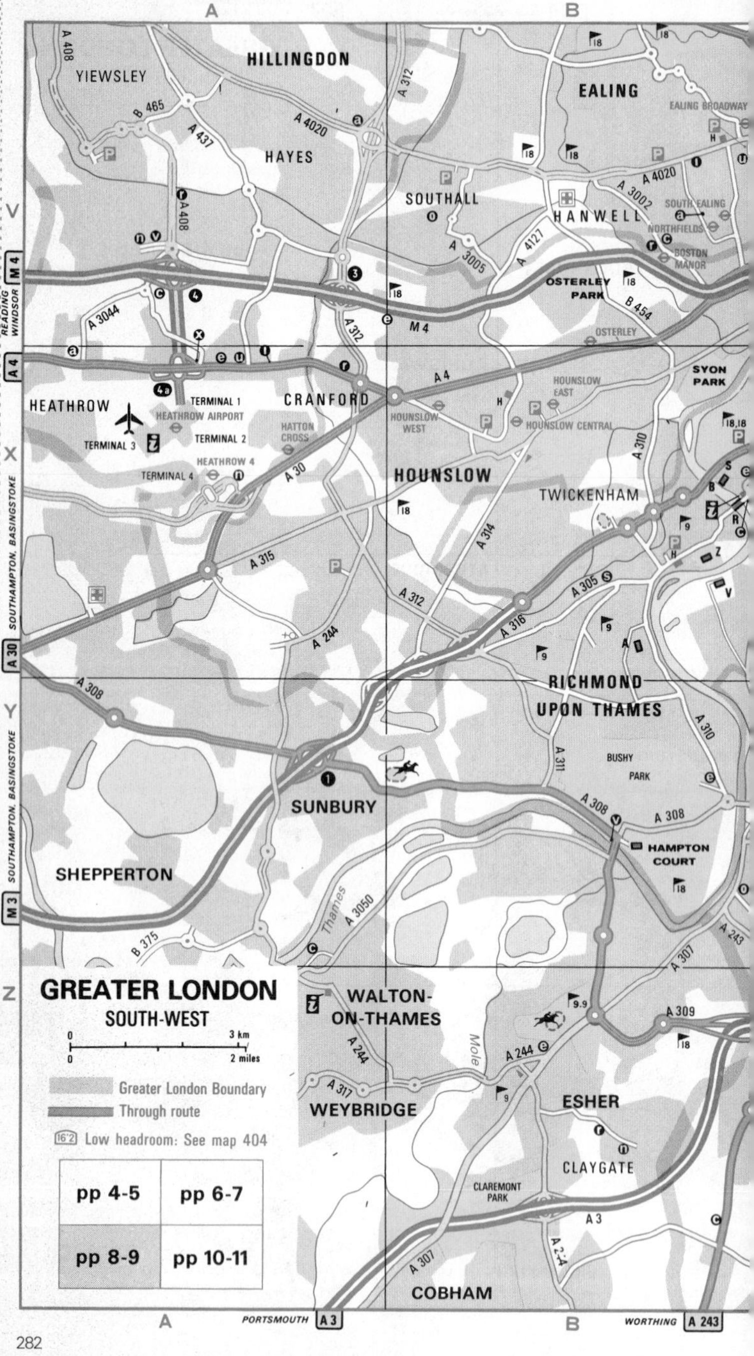

GREATER LONDON

SOUTH-WEST

0 3 km
0 2 miles

Greater London Boundary

Through route

16'2 Low headroom: See map 404

pp 4-5	pp 6-7
pp 8-9	pp 10-11

A B
V X Y Z

HILLINGDON
YIEWSLEY
HAYES
SOUTHALL
EALING
EALING BROADWAY
HANWELL
SOUTH EALING
NORTHFIELDS
BOSTON MANOR
OSTERLEY PARK
OSTERLEY
SYON PARK
HEATHROW
TERMINAL 1
TERMINAL 2
TERMINAL 3
TERMINAL 4
HEATHROW AIRPORT
HEATHROW 4
HATTON CROSS
CRANFORD
HOUNSLOW WEST
HOUNSLOW EAST
HOUNSLOW CENTRAL
HOUNSLOW
TWICKENHAM
RICHMOND UPON THAMES
BUSHY PARK
HAMPTON COURT
SUNBURY
SHEPPERTON
Thames
WALTON-ON-THAMES
Mole
WEYBRIDGE
ESHER
CLAYGATE
CLAREMONT PARK
COBHAM

A 408
B 465
A 437
A 4020
A 312
A 3044
A 4
M 4
A 3005
A 4127
A 3002
B 454
A 30
A 315
A 314
A 310
A 305
A 316
A 244
A 308
A 311
A 3050
B 375
A 317
A 307
A 309
A 243
A 3

READING WINDSOR M 4
A 4
SOUTHAMPTON, BASINGSTOKE A 30
SOUTHAMPTON, BASINGSTOKE M 3
PORTSMOUTH A 3
WORTHING A 243

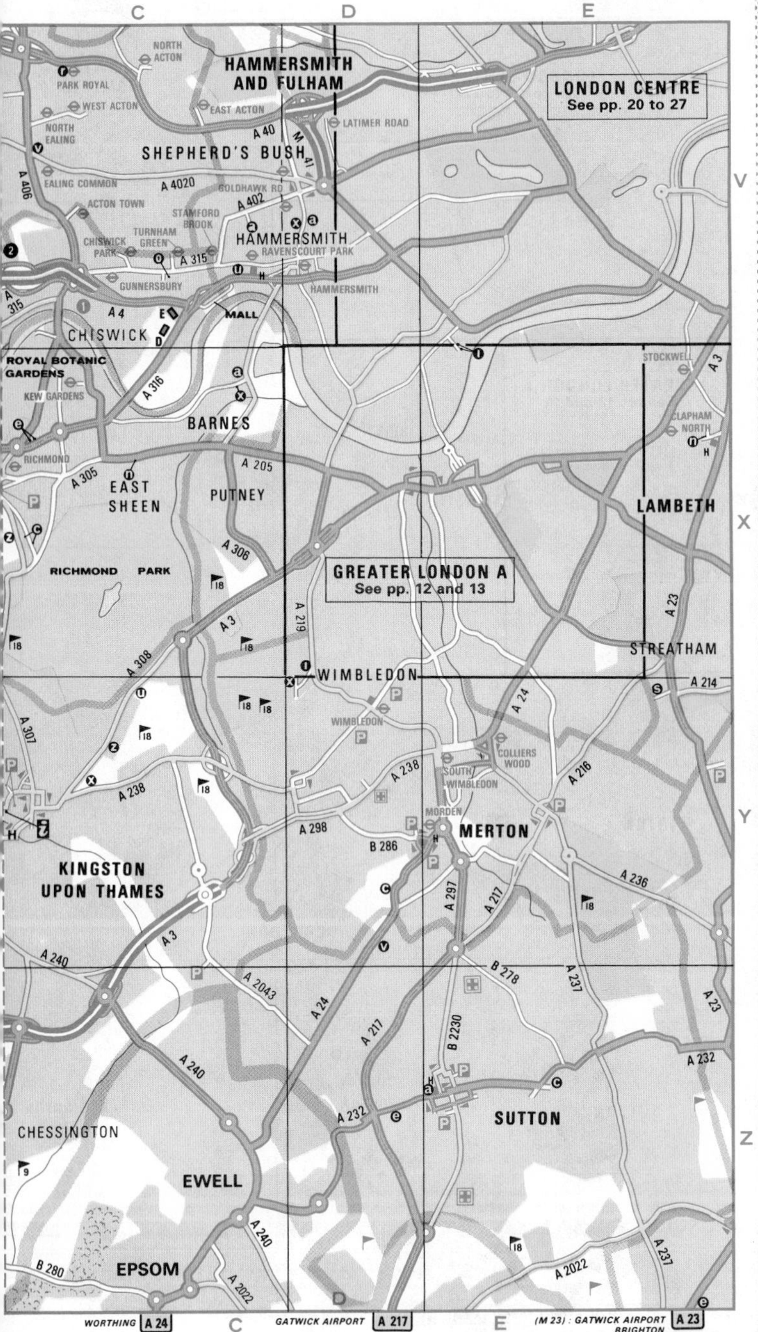

C
D
E
NORTH ACTON
PARK ROYAL
WEST ACTON
EAST ACTON
HAMMERSMITH AND FULHAM
LONDON CENTRE
See pp. 20 to 27
LATIMER ROAD
NORTH EALING
A 40
M 41
SHEPHERD'S BUSH
A 406
EALING COMMON
A 4020
GOLDHAWK RD
ACTON TOWN
A 402
STAMFORD BROOK
HAMMERSMITH
CHISWICK PARK
TURNHAM GREEN
A 315
RAVENSCOURT PARK
GUNNERSBURY
HAMMERSMITH
A 315
A 4
MALL
CHISWICK
ROYAL BOTANIC GARDENS
KEW GARDENS
A 316
STOCKWELL
A 3
V
BARNES
CLAPHAM NORTH
RICHMOND
A 305
EAST SHEEN
A 205
PUTNEY
LAMBETH
X
A 306
RICHMOND PARK
GREATER LONDON A
See pp. 12 and 13
A 219
A 3
A 23
A 308
STREATHAM
WIMBLEDON
A 214
A 307
A 24
WIMBLEDON
COLLIERS WOOD
A 238
SOUTH WIMBLEDON
A 216
A 238
MORDEN
Y
A 298
MERTON
B 286
KINGSTON UPON THAMES
A 236
A 297
A 217
A 3
A 240
B 278
A 237
A 2043
A 23
A 24
A 217
B 2230
A 240
A 232
A 232
SUTTON
CHESSINGTON
Z
EWELL
A 240
A 237
B 280
EPSOM
A 2022
A 2022
WORTHING A 24
C
GATWICK AIRPORT A 217
E
(M 23) : GATWICK AIRPORT BRIGHTON A 23

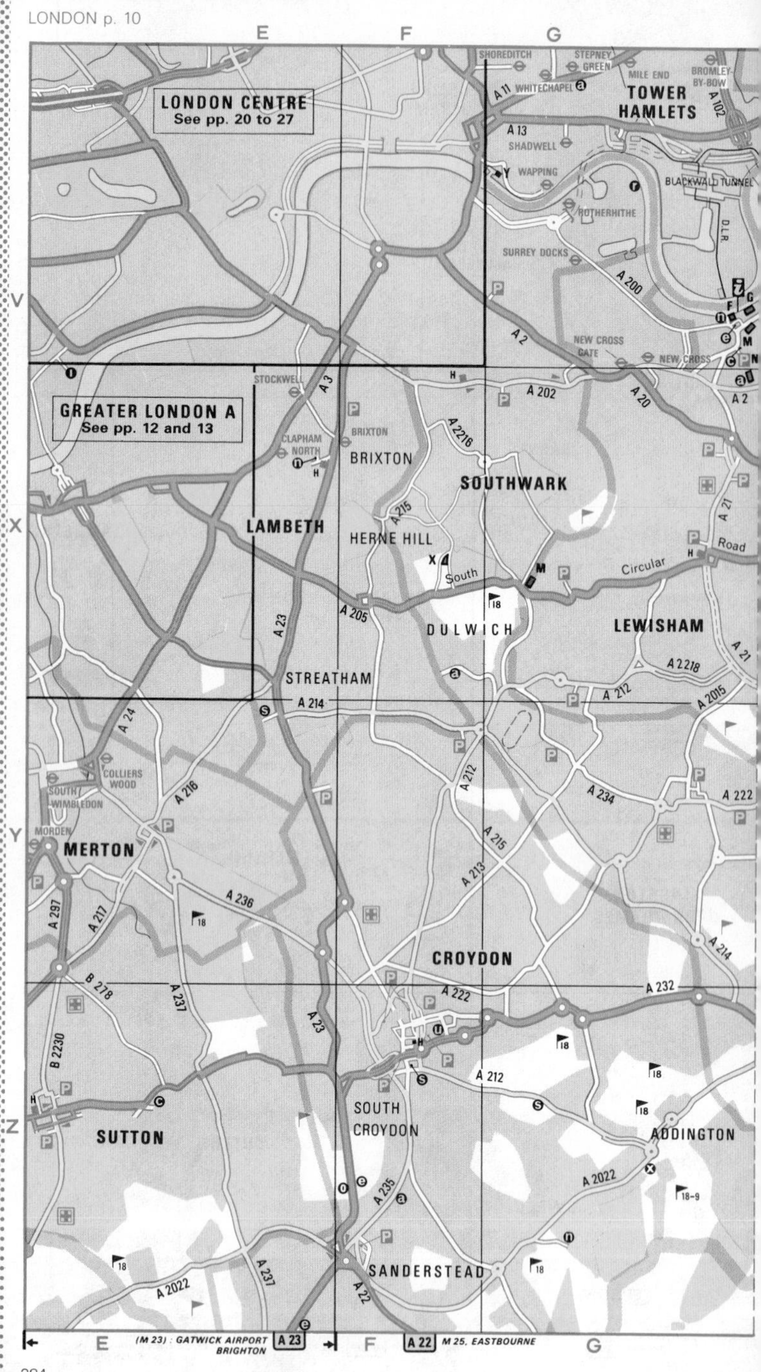
E
F
G
SHOREDITCH
STEPNEY GREEN
MILE END
BROMLEY-BY-BOW
A 11 WHITECHAPEL
TOWER HAMLETS
A 102
LONDON CENTRE
See pp. 20 to 27
A 13
SHADWELL
WAPPING
BLACKWALL TUNNEL
ROTHERHITHE
D.L.R.
SURREY DOCKS
A 200
V
A 2
NEW CROSS GATE
NEW CROSS
STOCKWELL
A 3
A 202
A 20
A 2
GREATER LONDON A
See pp. 12 and 13
CLAPHAM NORTH
BRIXTON
BRIXTON
A 2216
SOUTHWARK
X
LAMBETH
A 215
HERNE HILL
A 21
Road
South
Circular
A 205
A 23
DULWICH
LEWISHAM
A 21
STREATHAM
A 2218
A 212
A 214
A 2015
A 24
COLLIERS WOOD
SOUTH WIMBLEDON
A 216
A 212
A 234
A 222
MORDEN
Y
MERTON
A 215
A 213
A 236
A 297
A 217
A 214
CROYDON
B 278
A 237
A 222
A 232
A 23
B 2230
A 212
Z
SUTTON
SOUTH CROYDON
ADDINGTON
A 2022
A 235
SANDERSTEAD
A 22
A 2022
A 237
E
(M 23) : GATWICK AIRPORT BRIGHTON
A 23
F
A 22
M 25, EASTBOURNE
G

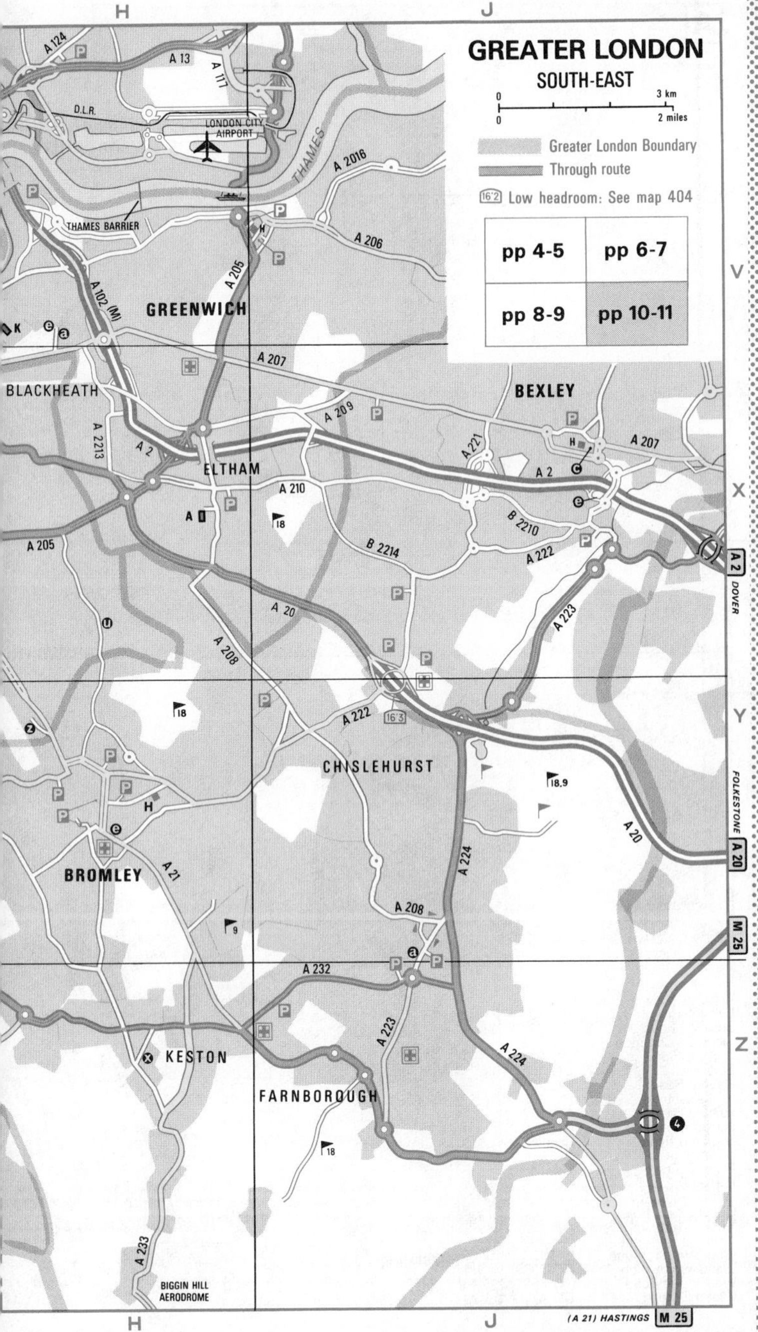

GREATER LONDON
SOUTH-EAST
0
3 km
0
2 miles
Greater London Boundary
Through route
16'2 Low headroom: See map 404
pp 4-5
pp 6-7
pp 8-9
pp 10-11
H
J
V
X
Y
Z
LONDON CITY AIRPORT
THAMES
THAMES BARRIER
D.L.R.
GREENWICH
BLACKHEATH
ELTHAM
BEXLEY
CHISLEHURST
BROMLEY
KESTON
FARNBOROUGH
BIGGIN HILL AERODROME
A 2 DOVER
FOLKESTONE A 20
M 25
(A 21) HASTINGS M 25

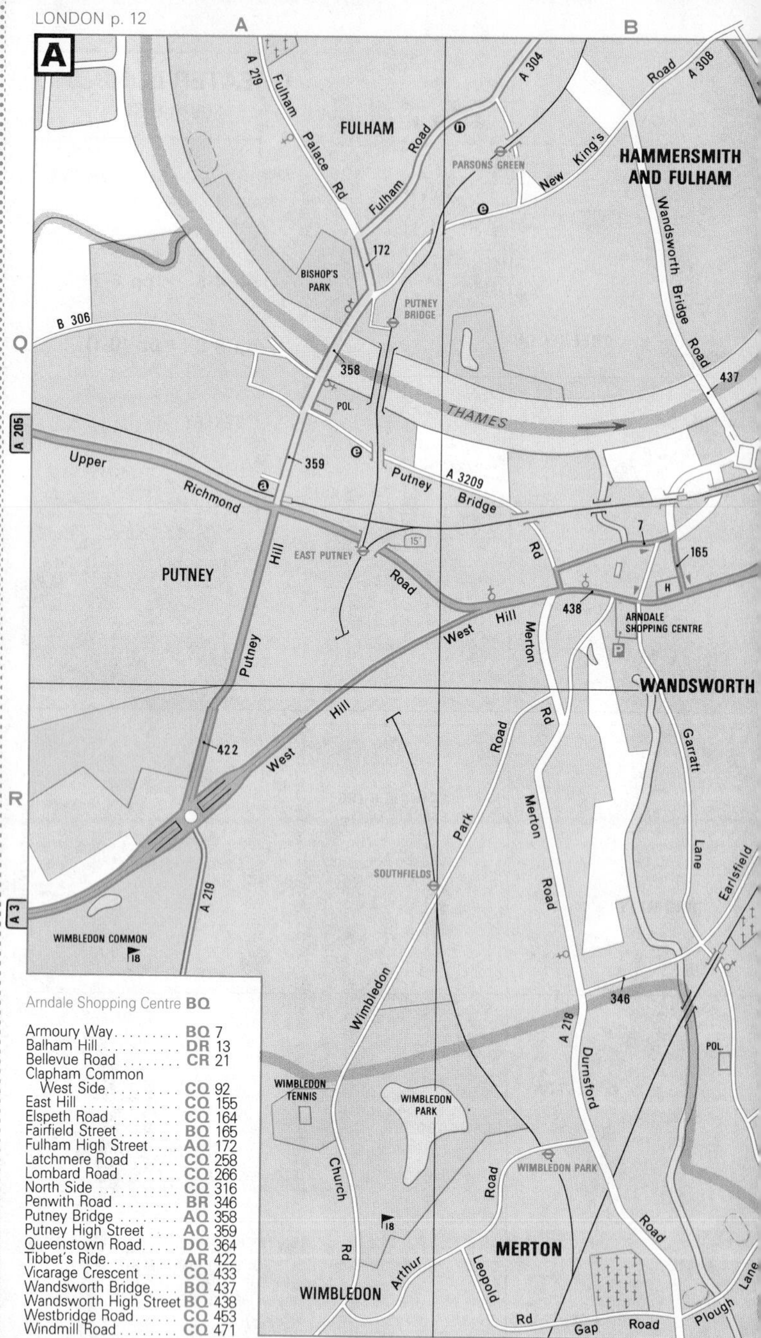

Arndale Shopping Centre **BQ**

Armoury Way .... BQ 7
Balham Hill .... DR 13
Bellevue Road .... CR 21
Clapham Common West Side .... CQ 92
East Hill .... CQ 155
Elspeth Road .... CQ 164
Fairfield Street .... BQ 165
Fulham High Street .... AQ 172
Latchmere Road .... CQ 258
Lombard Road .... CQ 266
North Side .... CQ 316
Penwith Road .... BR 346
Putney Bridge .... AQ 358
Putney High Street .... AQ 359
Queenstown Road ..... DQ 364
Tibbet's Ride .... AR 422
Vicarage Crescent ..... CQ 433
Wandsworth Bridge .... BQ 437
Wandsworth High Street BQ 438
Westbridge Road ...... CQ 453
Windmill Road .... CQ 471

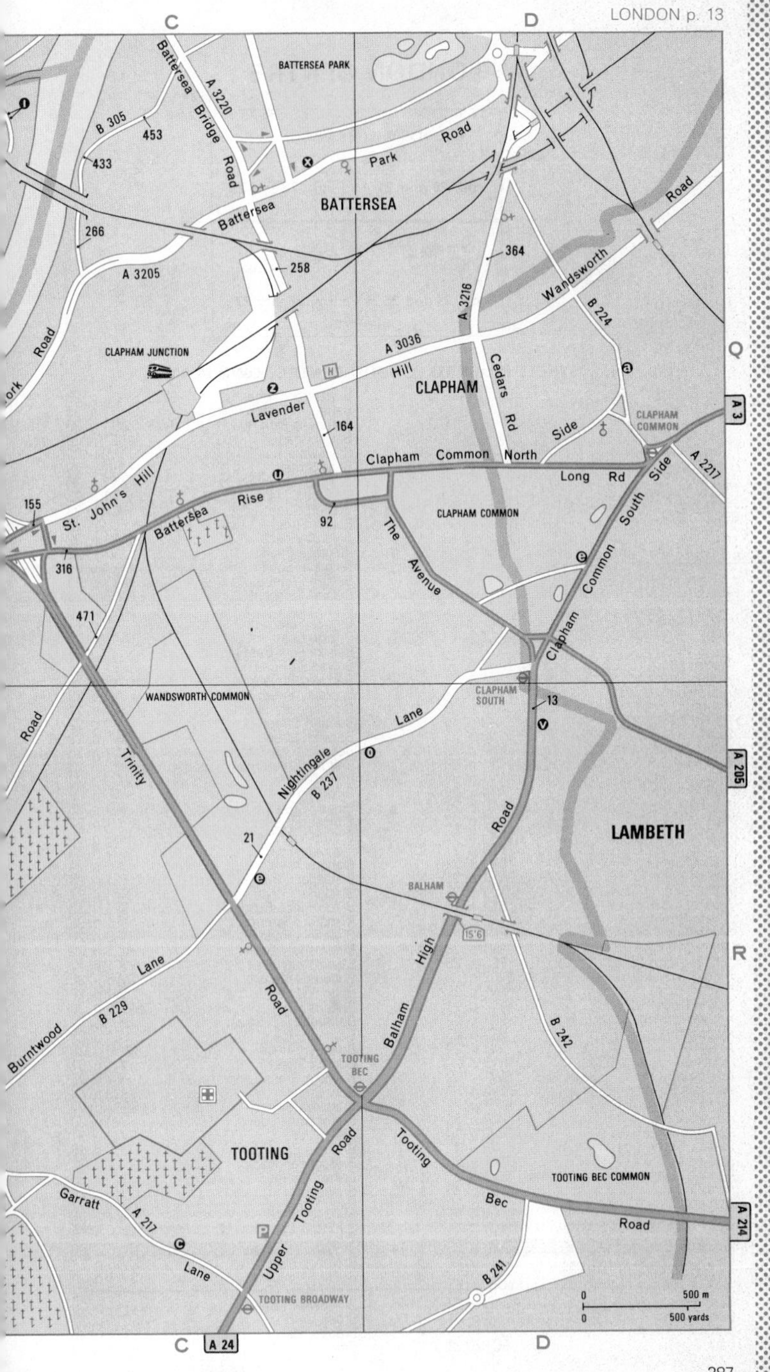
BATTERSEA PARK
BATTERSEA
CLAPHAM JUNCTION
CLAPHAM
CLAPHAM COMMON
WANDSWORTH COMMON
LAMBETH
TOOTING
TOOTING BEC COMMON
Battersea Bridge Road
Battersea Park Road
Wandsworth Road
Lavender Hill
Clapham Common North Side
Clapham Common South Side
St. John's Hill
Battersea Rise
The Avenue
Long Rd
Cedars Rd
Nightingale Lane
Trinity Road
Balham High Road
Burntwood Lane
Garratt Lane
Upper Tooting Road
Tooting Bec Road
A 3220
A 3205
A 3036
A 3216
A 2217
A 217
A 3
A 205
A 214
A 24
B 305
B 224
B 237
B 229
B 242
B 241
CLAPHAM COMMON
CLAPHAM SOUTH
BALHAM
TOOTING BEC
TOOTING BROADWAY
0 500 m
0 500 yards

LONDON CENTRE

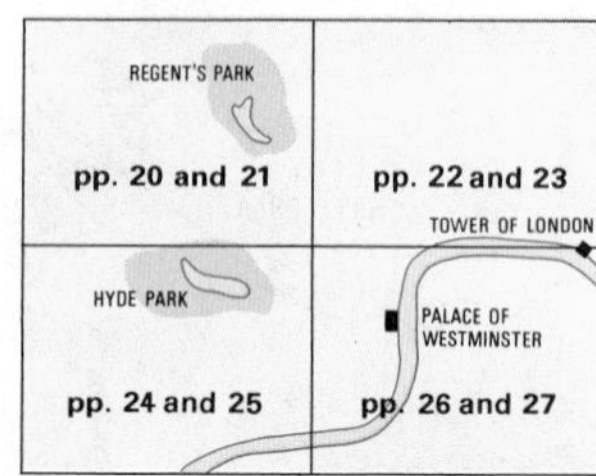

STREET INDEX TO LONDON CENTRE TOWN PLANS

Beauchamp Place . . . SW3 p. 31 **ER**
Brompton Road . . . SW1, SW3 p. 31 **DS**
Burlington Arcade . . . W1 p. 29 **DM**
Camden Passage . . . N1 p. 23 **NS** 70
Carnaby Street . . . W1 p. 29 **EK**
Jermyn Street . . . SW1 p. 29 **EN**
Kensington High Street . . . W8, W14 p. 24 **EY**
King's Road . . . SW3, SW10, SW6 p. 31 **DU**
Knightsbridge . . . SW1, SW7 p. 31 **EQ**
Middlesex Street . . . E1 p. 23 **PU**
New Bond Street . . . W1 p. 28 **CK**
Old Bond Street . . . W1 p. 29 **DM**
Oxford Street . . . W1 p. 28 **BK**
Piccadilly . . . W1 p. 29 **EM**
Portobello Road . . . W11, W10 p. 20 **EV**
Regent Street . . . W1 p. 29 **EM**
Sloane Street . . . SW1 p. 31 **FR**

Abbey Road . . . NW8 p. 20 **FS**
Abbey Street . . . SE1 p. 27 **PY**
Abbotsbury Road . . . W14 p. 24 **EY**
Abercorn Place . . . NW8 p. 20 **FT**
Abingdon Road . . . W8 p. 24 **EY** 2
Acacia Road . . . NW8 p. 21 **GS**
Adam Street . . . WC2 p. 33 **DY**
Adam's Row . . . W1 p. 28 **BM**
Addison Crescent . . . W14 p. 24 **EY** 3
Addison Road . . . W14 p. 24 **EY**
Adelaide Road . . . NW3 p. 21 **GS**
Agar Grove . . . NW1 p. 22 **KS**
Akenside Road . . . NW3 p. 20 **ES**
Albany Road . . . SE5 p. 27 **PZ**
Albany Street . . . NW1 p. 21 **JT**
Albert Bridge . . . SW3, SW11 p. 25 **HZ**
Albert Bridge Road . . . SW11 p. 25 **HZ**
Albert Embankment . . . SE1 p. 26 **LZ**
Albion Street . . . W2 p. 33 **EZ**
Aldersgate Street . . . EC1 p. 23 **OU**
Aldford Street . . . W1 p. 28 **BM**
Aldgate High Street . . . EC3 p. 23 **PV**
Aldwych . . . WC2 p. 33 **EX**
Allitsen Road . . . NW8 p. 21 **GS**
Allsop Place . . . NW1 p. 21 **HU** 4
Amwell Street . . . EC1 p. 22 **MT**
Appold Street . . . EC2 p. 23 **PU** 5
Argyll Street . . . W1 p. 29 **DJ**
Arkwright Road . . . NW3 p. 20 **ES**
Arlington Street . . . SW1 p. 29 **DN** 6
Artesian Road . . . W2 p. 32 **AZ**
Artillery Row . . . SW1 p. 32 **CX** 8
Arundel Street . . . WC2 p. 33 **EX**
Ashburn Place . . . SW7 p. 30 **BS**
Ashley Place . . . SW1 p. 32 **BX**
Atterbury Street . . . SW1 p. 26 **LZ** 9
Avenue Road . . . NW8, NW3 p. 21 **GS**
Avery Row . . . W1 p. 28 **CL** 12
Aybrook Street . . . W1 p. 28 **AH**
Baker Street . . . W1, NW1 p. 28 **AH**
Bark Place . . . W2 p. 32 **BZ**
Barkston Gardens . . . SW5 p. 30 **AT** 14
Barnsbury Road . . . N1 p. 22 **MS**
Barnsbury Street . . . N1 p. 23 **NS**
Baron's Court Road . . . W14 p. 24 **EZ**
Bartholomew Road . . . NW5 p. 22 **KS** 16
Basil Street . . . SW3 p. 31 **ER**
Bateman Street . . . W1 p. 29 **FK** 18
Bath Street . . . EC1 p. 23 **OT**

Battersea Bridge . . . SW3, SW11 p. 25 **GZ**
Battersea Bridge Road . . . SW11 p. 25 **GZ**
Battersea Park Road . . . SW8, SW11 p. 26 **JZ** 19
Baylis Road . . . SE1 p. 26 **MY**
Bayswater Road . . . W2 p. 32 **BZ**
Beak Street . . . W1 p. 29 **EL**
Beaufort Street . . . SW3 p. 30 **CU**
Bedfort Square . . . WC1 p. 22 **KU**
Bedfort Street . . . WC2 p. 33 **DX**
Beech Street . . . EC2 p. 23 **OU**
Belgrave Place . . . SW1 p. 32 **AX**
Belgrave Road . . . SW1 p. 32 **BY**
Belgrave Square . . . SW1 p. 32 **AV**
Belsize Avenue . . . NW3 p. 20 **ES**
Belsize Crescent . . . NW3 p. 20 **ES** 22
Belsize Lane . . . NW3 p. 20 **ES**
Belsize Park . . . NW3 p. 21 **GS**
Belsize Road . . . NW3 p. 20 **FS**
Belsize Park Gardens . . . NW3 p. 21 **GS**
Belvedere Road . . . SE1 p. 26 **MX** 23
Berkeley Square . . . W1 p. 28 **CM**
Berkeley Street . . . W1 p. 29 **DN**
Bermondsey Street . . . SE1 p. 27 **PY**
Bernard Street . . . WC1 p. 22 **LT** 25
Berwick Street . . . W1 p. 29 **FK** 26
Bessborough Street . . . SW1 p. 26 **KZ** 30
Bethnal Green Road . . . E1, E2 p. 23 **PT** 32
Bevis Marks . . . EC3 p. 23 **PU** 34
Bina Gardens . . . SW5 p. 30 **BT**
Binney Street . . . W1 p. 28 **BL** 35
Birdcage Walk . . . SW1 p. 32 **CV**
Bishop's Bridge Road . . . W2 p. 20 **FU**
Bishopsgate . . . EC2 p. 23 **PU** 36
Bishops Road . . . N6 p. 24 **EZ**
Blackfriars Bridge . . . EC4, SE1 p. 23 **NV** 38
Blackfriars Road . . . SE1 p. 27 **NX**
Black Prince Road . . . SE11, SE1 p. 26 **MZ**
Blandford Street . . . W1 p. 28 **AH**
Blomfield Road . . . W9 p. 20 **FU**
Bloomsbury Street . . . WC1 p. 22 **LU** 39
Bloomsbury Way . . . WC1 p. 22 **LU**
Bolton Gardens . . . SW5 p. 30 **AT**
Bolton Street . . . W1 p. 28 **CN**
Boltons (The) . . . SW10 p. 30 **BU**
Borough High Street . . . SE1 p. 27 **OY**
Borough Road . . . SE1 p. 27 **OY**
Boundary Road . . . NW8 p. 20 **FS**
Bourne Street . . . W1 p. 31 **FT**
Bowling Green Lane . . . EC1 p. 23 **NT** 43
Bow Street . . . WC2 p. 33 **DX**
Braganza Street . . . SE17 p. 27 **NZ**
Bramham Gardens . . . SW5 p. 30 **AT**
Bray Place . . . SW3 p. 31 **ET** 45
Bream's Buildings . . . EC4 p. 33 **EV** 47
Bressenden Place . . . SW1 p. 32 **BX** 48
Brewer Street . . . W1 p. 29 **EM**
Brewery Road . . . N7 p. 22 **LS**
Brick Street . . . W1 p. 28 **BP**
Bridgefoot . . . SE1 p. 26 **LZ** 49
Brixton Road . . . E16 p. 26 **MZ**
Broadhurst Gardens . . . NW6 p. 20 **FS**
Broadley Street . . . NW8 p. 21 **GU**
Broad Sanctuary . . . SW1 p. 26 **LY** 52
Broad Walk (The) . . . W8 p. 32 **BZ**
Broadwick Street . . . W1 p. 29 **EK**
Brook Drive . . . SE11 p. 27 **NY**
Brook's Mews . . . W1 p. 28 **CL**
Brook Street . . . W1 p. 28 **BL**

Street	District	Page	Grid	No.
Brushfield Street	E1	p. 23	PU	
Bruton Street	W1	p. 28	CM	
Bryanston Square	W1	p. 21	HU	
Bryanston Street	W1	p. 28	AK	
Buckingham Gate	SW1	p. 32	CV	56
Buckingham Palace Road	SW1	p. 32	AY	
Bunhill Row	EC1	p. 23	PU	
Bury Street	SW1	p. 29	EN	
Bute Street	SW7	p. 30	CS	59
Byward Street	EC3	p. 23	PV	62
Cadogan Gardens	SW3	p. 31	FS	
Cadogan Place	SW1	p. 31	FR	
Cadogan Square	SW1	p. 31	FS	
Cadogan Street	SW3	p. 31	ET	
Caledonian Road	N1, N7	p. 22	MS	
Cale Street	SW3	p. 31	DT	
Calshot Street	N1	p. 22	MT	
Calthorpe Street	WC1	p. 22	MT	65
Camberwell New Road	SE5	p. 27	NZ	
Camberwell Road	SE5	p. 27	OZ	
Cambridge Circus	WC2	p. 29	GK	
Cambridge Square	W2	p. 33	EZ	67
Camden High Street	NW1	p. 22	JS	
Camden Road	E11	p. 22	KS	
Camden Street	NW1	p. 22	KS	
Camomile Street	EC3	p. 23	PU	71
Campden Hill Road	W8	p. 24	EX	
Cannon Street	EC4	p. 23	OV	
Canonbury Road	N1	p. 23	NS	
Canonbury Square	N1	p. 23	NS	
Carey Street	WC2	p. 33	EV	
Carlisle Place	SW1	p. 32	BX	
Carlos Place	W1	p. 28	BM	
Carlton Gardens	SW1	p. 29	FP	74
Carlton Hill	NW8	p. 20	FS	
Carlton House Terrace	SW1	p. 29	FN	
Carlton Vale	NW6	p. 20	ET	
Carriage Drive East	SW11	p. 25	IZ	
Carriage Drive North	SW11	p. 25	IZ	75
Carriage Road (the)	SW7, SW11	p. 31	EQ	
Castle Lane	SW1	p. 32	CX	
Cavendish Square	W1	p. 28	CJ	
Central Street	EC1	p. 23	OT	
Chalk Farm Road	NW1	p. 21	IS	
Chancery Lane	WC2	p. 33	EV	
Chandos Place	WC2	p. 33	DY	
Chandos Street	W1	p. 28	CH	
Chapel Market	N1	p. 23	NS	78
Chapel Street	SW1	p. 32	AV	
Chapter Road	SE17	p. 27	OZ	
Charlbert Street	NW8	p. 21	HT	79
Charles II Street	SW1	p. 29	FN	
Charles Street	W1	p. 28	CN	
Charing Cross	SW1	p. 33	DY	
Charing Cross Road	WC2	p. 29	GJ	
Charterhouse Square	EC1	p. 23	OU	81
Charterhouse Street	EC1	p. 23	NU	83
Cheapside	EC2	p. 23	OV	
Chelsea Bridge	SW1, SW8	p. 25	IZ	
Chelsea Bridge Road	SW1	p. 25	IZ	
Chelsea Embankment	SW3	p. 25	HZ	
Chelsea Manor Street	SW3	p. 31	EU	
Chelsea Square	SW3	p. 31	DU	
Cheltenham Terrace	SW3	p. 31	FT	
Chepstow Crescent	W11	p. 32	AZ	84
Chepstow Place	W2	p. 32	AZ	
Chepstow Road	W2	p. 32	AZ	
Chesham Place	SW2	p. 31	FR	
Chesham Street	SW1	p. 31	FS	
Chester Road	NW1	p. 21	IT	
Chester Row	SW1	p. 32	AY	
Chester Square	SW1	p. 32	AX	88
Chester Street	SW1	p. 32	AV	
Cheval Place	SW7	p. 31	ER	
Cheyne Walk	SW3, SW10	p. 25	GZ	
Chilworth Street	W2	p. 32	CZ	90
Chippenham Road	W9	p. 20	EU	
Chiswell Street	EC1	p. 23	OU	
Church Row	NW3	p. 20	ES	
Church Street	NW8, NW2	p. 21	GU	
Circus Road	NW8	p. 21	GT	
City Road	EC1	p. 23	NT	
Clapham Road	SW9	p. 26	MZ	
Clarendon Place	W2	p. 33	EZ	93
Clarendon Road	W11	p. 24	EX	
Claverton Street	SW1	p. 26	KZ	
Clayton Street	SE11	p. 26	MZ	
Clerkenwell Road	EC1	p. 23	NU	
Cleveland Gardens	W2	p. 32	CZ	94
Cleveland Square	W2	p. 32	CZ	
Cleveland Street	W1	p. 22	KU	
Cleveland Terrace	W2	p. 32	CZ	
Clifford Street	W1	p. 29	DM	
Cliveden Place	SW1	p. 31	FS	
Cockspur Street	SW1	p. 29	GN	
Collingham Gardens	SW5	p. 30	AT	99
Collingham Road	SW5	p. 30	AT	101
Commercial Street	E1	p. 23	PU	
Conduit Street	W1	p. 29	DL	
Connaught Square	W2	p. 33	EZ	103
Connaught Street	W2	p. 33	EZ	
Constantine Road	NW3	p. 20	ES	106
Constitution Hill	SW1	p. 32	AV	
Copenhagen Street	N1	p. 22	LS	
Cork Street	W1	p. 29	DM	
Cornwall Crescent	W11	p. 20	EV	107
Cornwall Gardens	SW7	p. 30	AR	
Cornwall Road	SE1	p. 26	MX	108
Corporation Row	EC1	p. 23	NT	110
Courtfield Gardens	SW5	p. 30	AT	
Courtfield Road	SW7	p. 30	BS	
Coventry Street	W1	p. 29	FM	
Cowcross Street	EC1	p. 23	NU	113
Cranbourn Street	WC2	p. 33	DX	115
Cranley Gardens	SW7	p. 30	CT	
Craven Hill	W2	p. 32	CZ	
Craven Road	W2	p. 33	DZ	
Craven Street	WC2	p. 33	DY	
Craven Terrace	W2	p. 33	DZ	
Crawford Place	W1	p. 21	HU	116
Crawford Street	W1	p. 21	HU	
Cromwell Crescent	SW5	p. 24	EZ	119
Cromwell Place	SW7	p. 30	CS	120
Cromwell Road	SW7, SW5	p. 30	CS	
Crowndale Road	NW1	p. 22	KS	
Crucifix Lane	SE1	p. 27	PX	125
Culross Street	W1	p. 28	AM	
Curtain Road	EC2	p. 23	PT	126
Curzon Street	W1	p. 28	BN	
Cut (The)	SE1	p. 27	NX	
Dante Road	SE11	p. 27	NZ	129
D'Arblay Street	W1	p. 29	EK	
Davies Street	W1	p. 28	BK	
Dawes Road	SW6	p. 24	EZ	
Dawson Place	W2	p. 32	AZ	
Deanery Street	W1	p. 28	BN	132
Dean Street	W1	p. 29	FJ	
De Beauvoir Road	N1	p. 23	PS	
Delancey Street	NW1	p. 21	JS	
Delaware Road	W9	p. 20	FT	
Denbigh Street	SW1	p. 26	KZ	
Denman Street	W1	p. 29	FM	133
Denmark Street	WC2	p. 29	GJ	134
De Vere Gardens	W8	p. 30	BQ	
Devonshire Street	W1	p. 21	IU	
Devonshire Terrace	W2	p. 32	CZ	136
Dorset Road	SW8	p. 26	LZ	
Dorset Street	W1	p. 28	AH	
Dovehouse Street	SW3	p. 31	DU	
Dover Street	W1	p. 29	DM	
Downham Road	N1	p. 23	PS	
Downing Street	SW1	p. 26	LX	138
Downshire Hill	NW3	p. 20	ES	139
Draycott Avenue	SW3	p. 31	ET	
Draycott Place	SW3	p. 31	ET	
Drayton Gardens	SW10	p. 30	BT	
Druid Street	SE1	p. 27	PY	
Drury Lane	WC2	p. 33	DV	
Dufferin Street	EC1	p. 23	OT	141
Duke of Wellington Place	SW1	p. 32	AV	142
Duke of York Street	SW1	p. 29	EN	143
Duke's Place	EC3	p. 23	PV	145
Duke Street	W1	p. 28	BK	
Duke Street ST. JAMES	SW1	p. 29	EN	146
Duncannon Street	WC2	p. 33	DY	147
Dunraven Street	W1	p. 28	AL	149
Dunton Road	SE1	p. 27	PZ	
Durham Street	SE11	p. 26	MZ	150
Eagle Wharf Road	N1	p. 23	OS	
Eardley Crescent	SW5	p. 24	EZ	151
Earlham Street	WC2	p. 33	DV	153
Earl's Court Road	W8, SW5	p. 24	EY	
Eastbourne Terrace	W2	p. 33	DZ	
Eastcastle Street	W1	p. 29	EJ	
Eastcheap	EC3	p. 23	PV	154
East Heath Road	NW3	p. 20	ES	
East Road	N1	p. 23	PT	
East Street	SE17	p. 27	PZ	
Eaton Place	SW1	p. 32	AX	
Eaton Square	SW1	p. 32	AX	
Ebury Bridge	SW1	p. 25	IZ	156
Ebury Street	SW1	p. 32	AY	
Ebury Bridge Road	SW1	p. 25	IZ	
Eccleston Bridge	SW1	p. 32	BY	157
Eccleston Square	SW1	p. 32	BY	
Eccleston Street	SW1	p. 32	AY	

Street	District	Page	Grid	No.
Edgware Road	W2	p. 21	GU	
Edith Grove	SW10	p. 24	FZ	
Edith Road	W14	p. 24	EZ	
Edwardes Square	W8	p. 24	EY	158
Egerton Gardens	SW3	p. 31	DS	160
Egerton Terrace	SW3	p. 31	DR	161
Egerton Gardens Mews	SW3	p. 31	ER	162
Elephant and Castle	SE11	p. 27	OY	
Elephant Road	SE17	p. 27	OZ	163
Elgin Avenue	W9	p. 20	FT	
Elizabeth Street	SW1	p. 32	AY	
Elm Park Gardens	SW10	p. 30	CU	
Elm Park Road	SW3	p. 30	CU	
Elsworthy Road	NW3	p. 21	GS	
Elvaston Place	SW7	p. 30	BR	
Elystan Place	SW3	p. 31	ET	
Elystan Street	SW3	p. 31	DT	
Endell Street	WC2	p. 33	DV	
England's Lane	NW3	p. 21	HS	
Englefield Road	N1	p. 23	PS	
Ennismore Gardens	SW7	p. 31	DQ	
Essex Road	N1	p. 23	OS	
Essex Street	WC2	p. 33	EX	
Estcourt Road	SW6	p. 24	EZ	
Eton Avenue	NW3	p. 21	GS	
Euston Road	NW1	p. 22	LT	
Evelyn Gardens	SW7	p. 30	CU	
Eversholt Street	NW1	p. 22	KT	
Exeter Street	WC2	p. 33	DX	
Exhibition Road	SW7	p. 30	CQ	
Fairfax Road	NW6	p. 20	FS	
Fairhazel Gardens	NW6	p. 20	FS	
Falmouth Road	SE1	p. 27	OY	
Farm Street MAYFAIR	W1	p. 28	BM	
Fann Street	W1	p. 23	OU	166
Farringdon Road	EC1	p. 23	NU	
Farringdon Street	EC4	p. 23	NU	168
Fenchurch Street	EC3	p. 23	PV	
Fentiman Road	SW8	p. 26	LZ	
Fernhead Road	W9	p. 20	ET	
Fetter Lane	EC4	p. 23	NU	169
Fifth Avenue	W10	p. 20	ET	
Filmer Road	SW6	p. 24	EZ	
Finborough Road	SW10	p. 30	AU	
Finchley Road	NW8, NW3 NW2, NW11	p. 21	GS	
Fitzalan Street	SE11	p. 26	MZ	
Fitzjohn's Avenue	NW3	p. 21	GS	
Fitzroy Square	W1	p. 22	KU	
Fleet Road	NW3	p. 20	ES	
Fleet Street	EC4	p. 22	MV	
Flint Street	SE17	p. 27	PZ	
Flood Street	SW3	p. 31	EU	
Floral Street	WC2	p. 33	DX	
Foulis Terrace	SW7	p. 30	CT	170
Foxley Road	SW9	p. 27	NZ	
Frampton Street	NW8	p. 21	GT	
Francis Street	SW1	p. 32	CY	
Franklin's Row	SW3	p. 31	FU	
Frith Street	W1	p. 29	FK	
Frognal	NW3	p. 20	ES	
Frognal Rise	NW3	p. 20	ES	171
Fulham Road	SW3, SW10, SW6	p. 24	EZ	
Garden Row	SE1	p. 27	NY	173
Garrick Street	WC2	p. 33	DX	
Garway Road	W2	p. 32	BZ	
Gayton Road	NW3	p. 20	ES	
George Street	W1	p. 28	AJ	
Gerrard Street	W1	p. 29	GL	174
Gilbert Street	W1	p. 28	BL	175
Gillingham Street	SW1	p. 32	BY	
Gilston Road	SW10	p. 30	BU	
Giltspur Street	EC1	p. 23	OU	178
Glasshouse Street	W1	p. 29	EM	179
Glendower Place	SW7	p. 30	CS	180
Gliddon Road	W14	p. 24	EZ	182
Gloucester Avenue	NW1	p. 21	IS	
Gloucester Place	W1, NW1	p. 21	HU	
Gloucester Road	SW7	p. 30	BR	
Gloucester Square	W2	p. 33	EZ	
Gloucester Street	SW1	p. 27	JZ	
Gloucester Terrace	W2	p. 32	CZ	
Golborne Road	W10	p. 20	EU	
Golden Square	W1	p. 29	EL	
Goodge Street	W1	p. 22	KU	184
Goswell Road	EC1	p. 23	OT	
Gower Street	WC1	p. 22	KU	
Gracechurch Street	EC3	p. 23	PV	187
Grafton Street	W1	p. 29	DM	
Grange Road	SE1	p. 27	PY	
Granville Place	W1	p. 28	AK	188
Gray's Inn Road	WC1	p. 22	LT	
Gt. Castle Street	W1	p. 29	DJ	189
Gt. Cumberland Place	W1	p. 33	EZ	191
Gt. Dover Street	SE1	p. 27	PY	
Gt. Eastern Street	EC2	p. 23	PT	192
Gt. George Street	SW1	p. 26	LY	193
Gt. Marlborough Street	W1	p. 29	EK	
Gt. Peter Street	SW1	p. 26	LY	
Gt. Queen Street	WC2	p. 33	DV	
Gt. Russell Street	WC1	p. 22	LU	
Gt. Smith Street	SW1	p. 26	LY	196
Gt. Suffolk Street	SE1	p. 27	OX	
Gt. Tower Street	EC3	p. 23	PV	197
Gt. Western Road	W9, W11	p. 20	EU	
Gt. Windmill Street	W1	p. 29	FM	
Greek Street	W1	p. 29	GK	198
Greencroft Gardens	NW6	p. 20	FS	
Green Street	W1	p. 28	AL	
Grenville Place	SW7	p. 30	BS	
Gresham Street	EC2	p. 23	OU	
Greville Place	NW6	p. 20	FS	
Greycoat Place	SW1	p. 26	KY	200
Greyhound Road	W6, W14	p. 24	EZ	
Grosvenor Crescent	SW1	p. 32	AV	
Grosvenor Gardens	SW1	p. 32	BX	
Grosvenor Place	SW1	p. 32	AV	
Grosvenor Road	SW1	p. 26	JZ	
Grosvenor Square	W1	p. 28	BL	
Grosvenor Street	W1	p. 28	BL	
Grove End Road	NW8	p. 21	GT	
Guildhouse Street	SW1	p. 32	BY	201
Guilford Street	WC1	p. 22	LU	
Gunter Grove	SW10	p. 24	FZ	202
Gunterstone Road	W14	p. 24	EZ	203
Hackney Road	E2	p. 23	PT	
Half Moon Street	W1	p. 28	CN	
Halford Road	SW6	p. 24	EZ	
Halkin Street	SW1	p. 32	AV	
Halliford Street	N1	p. 23	OS	
Hall Road	NW8	p. 20	FT	
Hamilton Place	W1	p. 28	BP	205
Hamilton Terrace	NW8	p. 20	FT	
Hammersmith Road	W14, W6	p. 24	EZ	207
Hampstead Grove	NW3	p. 20	ES	208
Hampstead High Street	NW3	p. 20	ES	209
Hampstead Road	NW1	p. 22	KT	
Hanover Square	W1	p. 28	CK	210
Hanover Street	W1	p. 29	DK	
Hans Crescent	SW1	p. 31	ER	
Hans Place	SW1	p. 31	ER	
Hans Road	SW3	p. 31	ER	
Harcourt Terrace	SW10	p. 30	AU	
Harley Street WESTMINSTER	W1	p. 28	CH	
Harleyford Road	SE11	p. 26	LZ	
Harleyford Street	SE11	p. 26	MZ	211
Harper Road	SE1	p. 27	OY	
Harriet Street	SW1	p. 31	FQ	214
Harrington Gardens	SW7	p. 30	BT	
Harrington Road	SW7	p. 30	CS	215
Harrow Road	W2, W9 W10, NW10	p. 20	FU	
Harwood Road	SW6	p. 24	FZ	
Hasker Street	SW3	p. 31	ES	
Haverstock Hill	NW3	p. 21	HS	
Haymarket	SW1	p. 29	FM	
Hay's Mews	W1	p. 28	BN	
Heath Street	NW3	p. 20	ES	
Hemingford Road	N1	p. 22	MS	
Henrietta Place	W1	p. 28	BJ	
Henrietta Street	WC2	p. 33	DX	217
Herbrand Street	WC1	p. 22	LT	218
Hercules Road	SE1	p. 26	MY	219
Hereford Road	W2	p. 32	AZ	
Hertford Street	W1	p. 28	BP	220
Heygate Street	SE17	p. 27	OZ	
High Holborn	WC1	p. 22	LU	
Hill Street	W1	p. 28	BN	
Hobart Place	SW1	p. 32	AX	
Holbein Place	SW1	p. 31	FT	
Holbein Mews	SW1	p. 31	FT	223
Holborn	EC1	p. 22	MU	
Holborn Viaduct	EC1	p. 23	NU	
Holland Park	W11	p. 24	EX	
Holland Park Avenue	W11	p. 24	EX	
Holland Park Gardens	W11	p. 24	EX	224
Holland Road	W14	p. 24	EY	
Holland Street	W8	p. 24	EY	
Holland Walk	W8	p. 24	EY	225
Holland Villas Road	W14	p. 24	EY	
Holles Street	W1	p. 28	CJ	
Hollybush Hill	E11	p. 20	ES	227
Hollywood Road	SW10	p. 30	BU	
Horseferry Road	SW1	p. 26	KY	
Horseguards Avenue	SW1	p. 26	LX	228

Street	District	Page	Grid	No.
Hornton Street	W8	p. 24	FY	229
Houndsditch	EC3	p. 23	PU	
Howick Place	SW1	p. 32	CX	
Howland Street	W1	p. 22	KU	232
Hoxton Street	N1	p. 23	PT	
Hudson's Place	SW1	p. 32	BY	
Hugh Street	SW1	p. 32	BY	
Hunter Street	WC1	p. 22	LT	233
Hyde Park Gardens	W2	p. 33	DZ	
Hyde Park Square	W2	p. 33	EZ	234
Hyde Park Street	W2	p. 33	EZ	
Hyde Road	N1	p. 23	PS	235
Ifield Road	SW10	p. 30	AU	
Inverness Terrace	W2	p. 32	BZ	
Ixworth Place	NW6	p. 31	DT	
James Street	W1	p. 28	BJ	
James Street SOHO	WC2	p. 29	EL	
John Adam Street	WC2	p. 33	DY	
John Islip Street	SW1	p. 26	LZ	
John Ruskin Street	SE5	p. 27	OZ	
Jubilee Place	SW3	p. 31	ET	
Judd Street	WC1	p. 22	LT	
Keat's Grove	NW3	p. 20	ES	236
Kemble Street	WC2	p. 33	EV	
Kendal Street	W2	p. 33	EZ	
Kennington Lane	SE11	p. 26	MZ	
Kennington Oval	SE11	p. 26	MZ	
Kennington Park Road	SE11	p. 27	NZ	
Kennington Road	SE1, SE11	p. 26	MZ	
Kensal Road	W10	p. 20	ET	
Kensington Church Street	W8	p. 32	AZ	238
Kensington Court	W8	p. 30	AQ	241
Kensington Court Place	W8	p. 30	AR	242
Kensington Gardens Square	W2	p. 32	BZ	243
Kensington Gore	SW7	p. 30	CQ	
Kensington Palace Gardens	W8	p. 24	FX	
Kensington Park Road	W11	p. 20	EV	
Kensington Place	W8	p. 32	AZ	
Kensington Road	W8, SW7	p. 30	BQ	
Kensington Square	W8	p. 30	AQ	
Kentish Town Road	NW1, NW5	p. 22	JS	
Kenway Road	SW5	p. 24	FZ	245
Kilburn Lane	W10, W9	p. 20	ET	
Kilburn Park Road	NW6	p. 20	ET	
King Edward Street	EC1	p. 23	OU	247
Kingly Street	W1	p. 29	DK	
King's Cross Road	WC1	p. 22	LT	
Kingsland Road	E2, E8	p. 23	PT	
King Street ST. JAMES'S	SW1	p. 29	EN	
King Street STRAND	WC2	p. 33	DX	
Kingsway	WC2	p. 33	EV	
King William Street	EC4	p. 23	PV	250
Knaresborough Place	SW5	p. 30	AS	
Ladbroke Grove	W10, W11	p. 20	EU	
Lambeth Bridge	SW1, SE1	p. 26	LY	
Lambeth Palace Road	SE1	p. 26	MY	
Lambeth Road	SE1	p. 26	MY	
Lambeth Walk	SE11	p. 26	MZ	
Lancaster Gate	W2	p. 32	CDZ	256
Lancaster Grove	NW3	p. 21	GS	
Lancaster Place	SW19	p. 33	EX	
Lancaster Terrace	W2	p. 33	DZ	257
Lansdowne Walk	W11	p. 24	EX	
Lauderdale Road	W9	p. 20	FT	
Launceston Place	W8	p. 30	BR	259
Lawn Road	NW3	p. 20	ES	
Leadenhall Street	EC3	p. 23	PV	260
Lees Place	W1	p. 28	AL	
Leicester Square	WC2	p. 29	GM	261
Leinster Gardens	W2	p. 32	CZ	
Leinster Square	W2	p. 32	AZ	
Leinster Terrace	W2	p. 32	CZ	
Lennox Gardens	NW10	p. 31	ES	
Lennox Gardens Mews	SW3	p. 31	ES	263
Lever Street	EC1	p. 23	OT	
Lexham Gardens	W8	p. 30	AS	
Lexington Street	W1	p. 29	EL	
Lillie Road	SW6	p. 24	EZ	
Lincoln's Inn Fields	WC2	p. 33	EV	
Lisle Street	WC2	p. 29	GL	
Lisson Grove	NW1, NW8	p. 21	GT	
Little Boltons (The)	SW10	p. 30	BU	
Little Britain	EC1	p. 23	OU	264
Liverpool Road	N1, N7	p. 22	MS	
Liverpool Street	EC2	p. 23	PU	
Lloyd Baker Street	WC1	p. 22	MT	265
Lombard Street	EC3	p. 23	PV	268
London Bridge	SE1, EC4	p. 27	PX	
London Road	SE1	p. 27	NY	
London Street	W2	p. 33	DZ	
London Wall	EC2	p. 23	OU	
Long Acre	WC2	p. 33	DX	
Long Lane CITY	EC1	p. 23	OU	270
Long Lane SOUTHWARK	SE1	p. 27	PY	
Lothbury	EC2	p. 23	PU	273
Lots Road	SW10	p. 24	FZ	
Loudoun Road	NW8	p. 20	FS	
Lower Belgrave Street	SW1	p. 32	AX	
Lower Grosvenor Place	SW1	p. 32	BX	274
Lower Marsh	SE1	p. 26	MY	277
Lower Sloane Street	SW1	p. 31	FT	
Lower Terrace	NW3	p. 20	ES	
Lower Thames Street	EC3	p. 23	PV	278
Lowndes Square	SW1	p. 31	FQ	
Lowndes Street	SW1	p. 31	FR	
Luke Street	EC2	p. 23	PT	
Lupus Street	SW1	p. 26	JZ	
Lyall Street	SW1	p. 31	FR	
Lyndhurst Road	NW3	p. 20	ES	
Macklin Street	WC2	p. 33	DV	
Maddox Street	W1	p. 29	DK	
Maida Avenue	W2	p. 20	FU	
Maida Vale	W9	p. 20	FT	
Maiden Lane	WC2	p. 33	DY	
Mall (The)	SW1	p. 29	FP	
Malvern Road	NW6	p. 20	ET	
Manchester Square	W1	p. 28	AJ	281
Manchester Street	W1	p. 28	AH	
Manor Place	SE17	p. 27	OZ	
Manresa Road	SW3	p. 31	DU	
Mansell Street	E1	p. 23	PV	282
Marble Arch	W1	p. 33	EZ	
Margaret Street	W1	p. 29	DJ	
Market Place	W1	p. 29	DJ	286
Market Road	N7	p. 22	LS	
Markham Street	SW3	p. 31	ET	
Marlborough Place	NW8	p. 20	FT	
Marloes Road	W8	p. 24	FY	
Marshall Street	W1	p. 29	EK	
Marsham Street	SW1	p. 26	LY	
Marylebone High Street	W1	p. 21	IU	
Marylebone Lane	W1	p. 28	BJ	287
Marylebone Road	NW1	p. 21	HU	
Melbury Road	W14	p. 24	EY	
Merrick Square	SE1	p. 27	OY	
Merton Rise	NW3	p. 21	HS	
Midland Road	NW1	p. 22	LT	
Miles Street	SW8	p. 26	LZ	290
Millbank	SW1	p. 26	LY	
Milner Street	SW3	p. 31	ES	
Minories	EC3	p. 23	PV	
Monmouth Street	WC2	p. 33	DX	
Montagu Square	W1	p. 28	AH	
Montpelier Square	SW7	p. 31	EQ	
Montpelier Street	SW7	p. 31	ER	
Montpelier Walk	SW7	p. 31	DR	
Moore Street	SW3	p. 31	ES	
Moorgate	EC2	p. 23	PU	
Moreland Street	EC1	p. 23	OT	293
Mortimer Street	W1	p. 22	KU	
Moscow Road	W2	p. 32	BZ	
Mossop Street	SW3	p. 31	ES	
Mount Row	W1	p. 28	BM	
Mount Street	W1	p. 28	BM	
Munster Road	SW6	p. 24	EZ	
Musard Road	W6	p. 24	EZ	
Museum Street	WC1	p. 33	DV	294
Myddelton Street	EC1	p. 23	NT	296
Nassington Road	NW3	p. 20	ES	297
Neal Street	WC2	p. 33	DV	
Neate Street	SE5	p. 27	PZ	
Netherhall Gardens	NW3	p. 20	ES	
Nevern Place	SW5	p. 24	EZ	298
Nevern Square	SW5	p. 24	EZ	299
Neville Terrace	SW7	p. 30	CT	300
New Bridge Street	EC4	p. 23	NV	301
Newburn Street	SE11	p. 26	MZ	
New Cavendish Street	W1	p. 28	BH	
New Change	EC4	p. 23	OV	304
New Church Road	SE5	p. 27	PZ	
Newcomen Street	SE1	p. 27	PX	
New End Square	NW3	p. 20	ES	305
Newgate Street	EC1	p. 23	OU	
Newington Butts	SE1, SE11	p. 27	OZ	306
Newington Causeway	SE1	p. 27	OY	307
New Kent Road	SE1	p. 27	OY	
Newman Street	W1	p. 22	KU	
New North Road	N1	p. 23	OS	
New Oxford Street	WC1	p. 33	DV	308
New Row	WC2	p. 33	DX	
New Square	WC2	p. 33	EV	
Newton Road	W2	p. 32	BZ	
Newton Street	WC2	p. 33	DV	309
Nine Elms Lane	SW8	p. 26	KZ	
Noel Street	W1	p. 29	EJ	

Street	District	Page	Grid	No.
Norfolk Crescent	W2	p. 33	EZ	310
Norfolk Square	W2	p. 33	DZ	313
North Audley Street	W1	p. 28	AK	314
North Carriage Drive	W2	p. 33	EZ	
North End Road	W14, SW6	p. 24	EZ	
North Row	W1	p. 28	AL	
Northumberland Avenue	WC2	p. 26	LX	317
Notting Hill Gate	W11	p. 32	AZ	
Nutley Terrace	NW3	p. 20	ES	
Nuttall Street	N1	p. 23	PS	
Oakley Street	SW3	p. 31	DU	
Offord Road	N1	p. 22	MS	
Old Bailey	EC4	p. 23	NV	318
Old Broad Street	EC2	p. 23	PU	319
Old Brompton Road	SW7, SW5	p. 30	BT	
Old Burlington Street	W1	p. 29	DM	322
Old Church Street	SW3	p. 30	CU	
Old Compton Street	W1	p. 29	GK	323
Old Kent Road	SE1, SE15	p. 27	PZ	
Old Marylebone Road	NW1	p. 21	HU	324
Old Park Lane	W1	p. 28	BP	
Old Street	EC1	p. 23	OT	
Olympia Way	W14	p. 24	EY	326
Onslow Gardens	SW7	p. 30	CT	
Onslow Square	SW7	p. 30	CT	
Orange Street	WC2	p. 29	GM	
Orchard Street	W1	p. 28	AK	
Ordnance Hill	NW8	p. 21	GS	
Orme Court	W2	p. 32	BZ	328
Ormonde Gate	SW3	p. 31	FU	329
Ornan Road	NW3	p. 20	ES	331
Ossulton Street	NW1	p. 22	LT	
Outer Circle	NW1	p. 21	HT	
Oxford Circus	W1	p. 29	DJ	
Oxford Square	W2	p. 33	EZ	332
Paddington Street	W1	p. 21	IU	333
Page Street	SW1	p. 26	LZ	
Page's Walk	SE1	p. 27	PY	
Palace Court	W2	p. 32	BZ	
Palace Gardens Terrace	W8	p. 32	AZ	335
Palace Gate	W8	p. 30	BQ	
Palace Street	SW1	p. 32	BX	
Pall Mall	SW1	p. 29	FN	
Palmer Street	SW1	p. 32	CV	
Pancras Road	NW1	p. 22	KS	
Panton Street	SW1	p. 29	FM	336
Parade (The)	SW11	p. 25	HZ	
Park Crescent	W1	p. 21	IU	337
Parker Street	WC2	p. 33	DV	
Parkgate Road	SW11	p. 25	HZ	
Park Lane	W1	p. 28	AM	
Park Road	NW1, NW8	p. 21	HT	
Park Street	W1	p. 28	AL	
Park Village East	NW1	p. 21	JS	
Park Walk	SW10	p. 30	CU	
Parkway	NW1	p. 21	JS	
Parliament Hill	NW3	p. 20	ES	
Parliament Street	SW1	p. 26	LY	340
Parry Street	SW8	p. 26	LZ	341
Paul Street	EC2	p. 23	PT	
Pelham Street	SW7	p. 31	DS	
Pembridge Gardens	W2	p. 32	AZ	
Pembridge Road	W11	p. 32	AZ	
Pembridge Square	W2	p. 32	AZ	
Pembridge Villas	W11	p. 32	AZ	
Pembrocke Gardens	W8	p. 24	EY	342
Pembrocke Road	W8	p. 24	EZ	
Penn Street	N1	p. 23	PS	343
Penton Place	WC1	p. 27	OS	
Penton Rise	WC1	p. 22	MT	344
Penton Street	N1	p. 22	MT	345
Pentonville Road	N1	p. 22	LT	
Penywern Road	SW5	p. 24	FZ	347
Percival Street	EC1	p. 23	NT	
Petty France	SW1	p. 32	CV	
Philbeach Gardens	SW5	p. 24	EZ	348
Piccadilly Circus	W1	p. 29	FM	
Pilgrimage Street	SE1	p. 27	PY	349
Pimlico Road	SW1	p. 25	IZ	
Pitfield Street	N1	p. 23	PT	
Poland Street	W1	p. 29	EJ	
Pond Street	NW3	p. 20	ES	
Pont Street	SW1	p. 31	ER	
Poole Street	N1	p. 23	PS	350
Porchester Gardens	W2	p. 32	BZ	
Porchester Road	W2	p. 20	FU	351
Porchester Terrace	W2	p. 32	CZ	
Portland Place	W1	p. 21	JU	
Portland Street	SE17	p. 27	PZ	
Portman Square	W1	p. 28	AJ	
Potman Street	W1	p. 28	AK	
Portugal Street	WC2	p. 33	EV	
Poultry	EC2	p. 23	OV	352
Praed Street	W2	p. 21	GV	
Pratt Street	NW1	p. 22	KS	
Primrose Hill Road	NW3	p. 21	HS	
Prince Albert Road	NW1, NW8	p. 21	HS	
Prince Consort Road	SW7	p. 30	CR	
Prince's Gardens	SW7	p. 30	CR	356
Prince's Street	W1	p. 29	DK	
Princes Street	EC2	p. 23	PV	357
Queen Anne's Gate	SW1	p. 26	KY	
Queen Anne Street	W1	p. 28	BH	
Queensberry Place	SW7	p. 30	CS	360
Queensborough Terrace	W2	p. 32	CZ	
Queen's Circus	SW8	p. 25	IZ	361
Queen's Gardens	W2	p. 32	CZ	362
Queen's Gate	SW7	p. 30	BQ	
Queen's Gate Gardens	SW7	p. 30	BR	
Queen's Gate Place	SW7	p. 30	BR	363
Queen's Gate Terrace	SW7	p. 30	BR	
Queen's Grove	NW8	p. 21	GS	
Queen Street	EC4	p. 23	OV	365
Queen's Walk	SW1	p. 29	DN	
Queensway	W2	p. 32	BZ	
Queen Victoria Street	EC4	p. 23	OV	
Radnor Place	W2	p. 33	DZ	
Radnor Walk	SW3	p. 31	EU	
Randolph Avenue	W9	p. 20	FT	
Randoplh Street	NW1	p. 22	KS	366
Rawlings Street	SW3	p. 31	ES	
Redcliffe Gardens	SW10	p. 30	AU	
Redcliffe Square	SW10	p. 30	AU	
Redesdale Street	SW3	p. 31	EU	367
Red Lion Street	WC1	p. 22	MU	
Reeves Mews	W1	p. 28	AM	
Regency Street	SW1	p. 26	KZ	
Regent's Park Road	NW1	p. 21	HS	
Richmond Avenue	N1	p. 22	MS	
Robert Street	NW1	p. 22	JT	
Rochester Row	SW1	p. 32	CY	
Rodney Road	N1	p. 27	OZ	
Roland Gardens	SW7	p. 30	BT	
Roman Way	N7	p. 22	MS	
Romilly Street	W1	p. 29	GL	368
Rosebery Avenue	EC1	p. 22	MT	
Rosslyn Hill	NW3	p. 20	ES	
Rossmore Road	NW1	p. 21	HT	369
Royal College Street	NW1	p. 22	KS	
Royal Crescent	W11	p. 24	EX	371
Royal Hospital Road	SW3	p. 31	FU	
Rupert Street	W1	p. 29	FL	
Russell Square	WC1	p. 22	LU	
Russell Street	WC2	p. 33	DX	
Rutland Gate	SW7	p. 31	DQ	
Rylston Road	SW6	p. 24	EZ	
Sackville Street	W1	p. 29	EM	
St. Albans Grove	W8	p. 28	AR	
St. Andrews Street	EC4	p. 23	NU	372
St. Bride Street	EC4	p. 23	NV	376
St. George's Drive	SW1	p. 26	KZ	
St. George's Road	SE1	p. 27	NY	
St. George's Square	SW1	p. 26	KZ	
St. George Street	W1	p. 29	DL	
St. Giles Circus	W1, WC1, WC2	p. 29	GJ	
St. Giles High Street	WC2	p. 33	DV	377
St. James's Place	SW1	p. 29	EN	
St. James's Square	SW1	p. 29	FN	
St. James's Street	SW1	p. 29	EN	
St. James Street	E17	p. 33	DX	
St. John Street	EC1	p. 23	NT	
St. John's Wood High Street	NW8	p. 21	GT	378
St. John's Wood Park	NW8	p. 21	GS	379
St. John's Wood Road	NW8	p. 21	GT	
St. Leonard's Terrace	SW3	p. 31	FU	
St. Martin's Lane	WC2	p. 33	DY	
St. Martin's-le-Grand	EC1	p. 23	OU	380
St. Pancras Way	NW1	p. 22	KS	
St. Paul's Road	N1	p. 23	OS	
St. Petersburgh Place	W2	p. 32	BZ	
St. Peter's Street	N1	p. 23	OS	
St. Thomas Street	SE1	p. 27	PX	
Sardinia Street	WC2	p. 33	EV	381
Savile Row	W1	p. 29	DM	
Savoy Place	WC2	p. 33	DY	
Savoy Street	WC2	p. 33	EX	
Scarsdale Villas	W8	p. 24	EY	
Seagrave Road	SW6	p. 24	EZ	
Serle Street	WC2	p. 33	EV	
Serpentine Road	W2	p. 28	AP	
Seymour Street	W1, W2	p. 28	AK	
Shaftesbury Avenue	W1, WC2	p. 29	FL	
Sheffield Terrace	W8	p. 24	EX	
Shelton Street	WC2	p. 33	DX	
Shepherdess Walk	N1	p. 23	OT	
Shepherd Market	W1	p. 28	CN	

Shepherd Street W1 p. 28 BP
Shirland Road W9 p. 20 ET
Shoreditch High Street E1 p. 23 PT 384
Shorts Gardens WC2 p. 33 DV
Sidmouth Street WC1 p. 22 LT 385
Sinclair Road W14 p. 24 EY
Sloane Avenue SW3 p. 31 ET
Sloane Square SW1 p. 31 FT
Smith Street SW3 p. 31 EU
Snows Fields SE1 p. 27 PX 386
Soho Square W1 p. 29 FJ
Southampton Row WC1 p. 22 LU 387
Southampton Street WC2 p. 33 DX 388
South Audley Street W1 p. 28 BM
South Eaton Place SW1 p. 32 AY 389
South End Road NW3 p. 20 ES
South Hill NW3 p. 20 ES 390
South Lambeth Road SW8 p. 26 LZ
South Molton Street W1 p. 28 BK
South Parade SW3 p. 30 CU
South Place EC2 p. 23 PU 391
South Street W1 p. 28 BN
South Terrace SW7 p. 31 DS
Southwark Bridge SE1, EC4 p. 27 OV 395
Southwark Bridge Road SE1 p. 27 OY
Southwark Street SE1 p. 27 OX
Southwick Street W2 p. 33 EZ
Spa road SE16 p. 27 PY
Spencer Street EC1 p. 23 NT 398
Spital Square E1 p. 23 PU 399
Spring Street W2 p. 33 DZ
Stamford Street SE1 p. 26 MX
Stanhope Gardens SW7 p. 30 BS
Stanhope Place W2 p. 33 EZ 400
Stanhope Terrace W2 p. 33 DZ
Star Road W14 p. 24 EZ
Storeys Gate SW1 p. 26 LY 402
Strand WC2 p. 33 DY
Stratton Street W1 p. 29 DN
Sumner Place SW7 p. 30 CT
Sumner Street SE1 p. 27 OX
Sun Street EC2 p. 23 PU
Surrey Street WC2 p. 33 EX
Sussex Gardens W2 p. 33 DZ
Sussex Place W2 p. 33 DZ
Sussex Square W2 p. 33 DZ 404
Sutherland Avenue W9 p. 20 FU
Sutherland Street SW1 p. 25 JZ
Swinton Street WC1 p. 22 LT
Sydney Place SW7 p. 31 DT 405
Sydney Street SW3 p. 31 DT
Symons Street SW3 p. 31 FT 407
Tabard Street SE1 p. 27 OY 408
Tachbrook Street SW1 p. 26 KZ
Talgarth Road W14, W6 p. 24 EZ
Tavistock Place WC1 p. 22 LT
Tavistock Square WC1 p. 22 LT 409
Tavistock Street WC2 p. 33 DX
Tedworth Square SW3 p. 31 EU
Temple Place WC2 p. 33 EX
Templeton Place SW5 p. 24 EZ 410
Terminus Place SW1 p. 32 BX 412
Thayer Street W1 p. 28 BJ 413
Theobald's Road WC1 p. 22 LU
Thirleby Road SW1 p. 32 CX 416
Thornhill Road N1 p. 22 MS
Threadneedle Street EC2 p. 23 PV 417
Throgmorton Street EC2 p. 23 PU 418
Thurloe Place SW7 p. 30 CS 420
Thurloe Square SW7 p. 31 DS
Thurlow Street SE17 p. 27 PZ
Tilney Street W1 p. 28 BN 421
Tite Street SW3 p. 31 EU
Tooley Street SE1 p. 27 BX
Tothill Street SW1 p. 26 KY
Tottenham Court Road W1 p. 22 KU
Tower Bridge E1 p. 27 PX
Tower Bridge Road SE1 p. 27 PY
Tower Hill EC3 p. 23 PV 425
Trafalgar Avenue SE15 p. 27 PZ
Trafalgar Square WC2, SW1 p. 33 DY
Trebovir Road SW5 p. 24 FZ 426
Tregunter Road SW10 p. 30 BU
Trevor Place SW7 p. 31 EQ
Trevor Square SW7 p. 31 ER
Trinity Church Square SE1 p. 27 OY
Trinity Street SE1 p. 27 OY
Tyers Street SE11 p. 26 MZ
Union Street SE1 p. 27 NX
Upper Belgrave Street SW1 p. 32 AX
Upper Berkeley Street W1 p. 33 EZ
Upper Brook Street W1 p. 28 AM
Upper Grosvenor Street W1 p. 28 AM
Upper Ground SE1 p. 27 NX 428
Upper St. Martin's Lane WC2 p. 33 DX 430
Upper Street N1 p. 23 NS
Upper Thames Street EC4 p. 23 OV 431
Upper Woburn Place WC1 p. 22 LT 432
Vale (The) SW3 p. 30 CU
Vanston Place SW6 p.24 EZ
Vassal Road SW9 p. 27 NZ
Vauxhall Bridge SW1, SE1 p. 26 LZ
Vauxhall Bridge Road SW1 p. 32 BY
Vauxhall Street SE11 p. 26 MZ
Vauxhall Walk SE11 p. 26 LZ
Vere Street W1 p. 28 BJ
Victoria Embankment SW1
WC2, EC4 p. 33 DY
Victoria Grove W8 p. 30 BR
Victoria Road
KENSINGTON W8 p. 30 BQ
Victoria Street SW1 p. 32 BX
Vigo Street W1 p. 29 EM
Villiers Street WC2 p. 33 DY
Vincent Square SW1 p. 26 KZ
Vincent Street SW1 p. 26 LZ 436
Virginia Road E2 p. 23 PT
Walterton Road W9 p. 20 ET
Walton Street SW3 p. 31 ES
Walworth Road SE17 p. 27 OZ
Wandsworth Road SW8 p. 26 LZ
Wardour Street W1 p. 29 FJ
Warrington Crescent W9 p. 20 FT
Warwick Avenue W2, W9 p. 20 FU 441
Warwick Road SW5, W14 p. 24 EZ
Warwick Street W1 p. 29 EM 444
Warwick Way SW1 p. 25 JZ
Waterloo Bridge WC2, SE1 p. 33 EY
Waterloo Place SW1 p. 29 FN
Waterloo Road SE1 p. 27 NY
Waverton Street W1 p. 28 BN
Webber Street SE1 p. 27 NY
Weighhouse Street W1 p. 28 BK
Welbeck Street W1 p. 28 BH
Wellington Road NW8 p. 21 GT
Wellington Street WC2 p. 33 DX
Wells Street W1 p. 29 EJ
Wells Way SE5 p. 27 PZ
Well Walk NW3 p. 20 ES
Westbourne Crescent W2 p. 33 DZ 448
Westbourne Grove W2, W11 p. 32 AZ
Westbourne Park Road W2, W11 p. 20 EU
Westbourne Park Villas W2 p. 20 FU 449
Westbourne Street W2 p. 33 DZ 450
Westbourne Terrace W2 p. 33 DZ
Westbourne Road N7 p. 22 MS
Westbourne Terrace Road W2 p. 20 FU 452
West Cromwell Road SW5, W14 p. 24 EZ
West Halkin Street SW1 p. 31 FR
Westminster Bridge SW1, SE1 p. 26 LY
Westminster Bridge Road SE1 p. 26 MY
Weston Street SE1 p. 27 PY
West Smithfield EC1 p. 23 NU 454
Westway N18 p. 20 EU
Wetherby Gardens SW5 p. 30 BT
Wharfdale Road N1 p. 22 LS 455
Wharf Road N1 p. 23 OT
Whiston Road E2 p. 23 PS
Whitcomb Street WC2 p. 29 GM
Whitechapel High Street E1 p. 23 PU 456
Whitecross Street EC1, EC2 p. 23 OT
Whitehall SW1 p. 26 LX
Whitehall Court SW1 p. 26 LX 460
Whitehall Place SW1 p. 26 LX 462
Whitehead's Grove SW3 p. 31 ET 463
Whitmore Road N1 p. 23 PS 464
Wigmore Street W1 p. 28 BJ
Wild Street WC2 p. 33 DV
William IV Street WC2 p. 33 DY 467
William Street SW1 p. 31 FQ 468
Willoughby Road NW3 p. 20 ES 470
Willow Road NW3 p. 20 ES
Willow Walk SE1 p. 27 PY
Wilson Street EC2 p. 23 PU
Wilton Place SW1 p. 31 FQ
Wilton Road SW1 p. 32 BY
Wilton Street SW1 p. 32 AX
Wimpole Street W1 p. 28 BH
Woburn Place WC1 p. 22 LT
Woods Mews W1 p. 28 AL
Wormwood Street EC2 p. 23 PU 472
Worship Street EC2 p. 23 PU
Wyndham Road SE5 p. 27 OZ
York Road SE1 p. 27 MY
York Way N1, N7 p. 22 LS
Young Street W8 p. 30 AQ

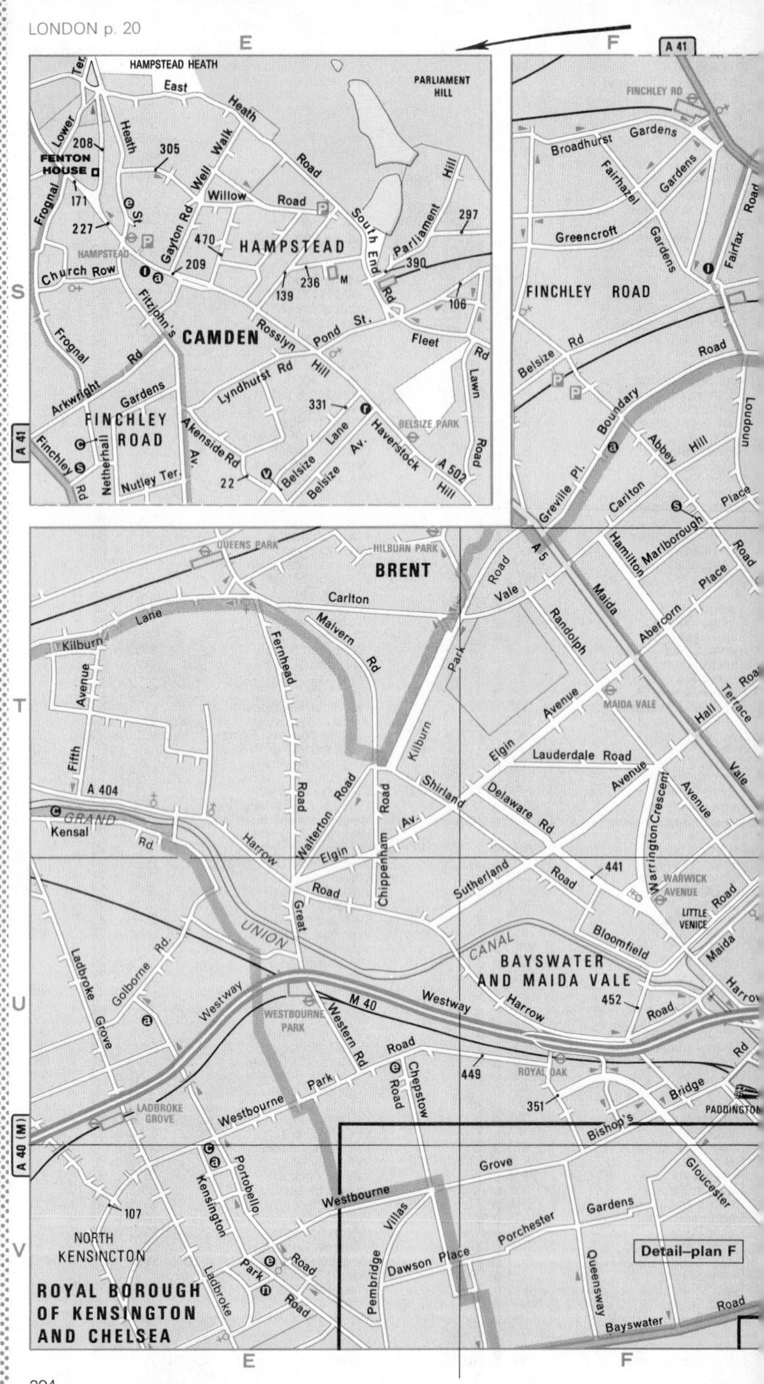
E
F
A 41
HAMPSTEAD HEATH
East
Heath
Road
PARLIAMENT HILL
Lower
Ter.
208
305
FENTON HOUSE
Heath
St.
Well
Walk
Willow
Road
South End
Rd
Parliament
Hill
297
Frognal
171
227
Gayton Rd
470
HAMPSTEAD
390
HAMPSTEAD
Church Row
209
139
236
M
106
Fitzjohn's
Rosslyn
Pond
St.
Fleet
CAMDEN
Frognal
Rd
Lyndhurst Rd
Hill
Lawn
Arkwright
Gardens
331
BELSIZE PARK
FINCHLEY ROAD
Akenside Rd
Haverstock
A 502
Av.
Finchley
Rd
Netherhall
Nutley Ter.
22
Belsize
Lane
Av.
Belsize
Hill
Road
FINCHLEY RD
Broadhurst
Gardens
Fairhazel
Gardens
Greencroft
Gardens
Fairfax
Road
FINCHLEY ROAD
Belsize
Rd
Road
Boundary
Loudoun
Abbey
Hill
Greville Pl.
Carlton
Place
A 5
Hamilton
Marlborough
Road
QUEENS PARK
HILBURN PARK
BRENT
Carlton
Road
Vale
Maida
Place
Abercorn
Kilburn
Lane
Malvern
Rd
Fernhead
Road
Randolph
Park
Kilburn
Avenue
Fifth
MAIDA VALE
Elgin
Avenue
Terrace
Hall
Vale
Lauderdale Road
A 404
GRAND
Kensal
Rd.
Harrow
Walterton
Road
Chippenham
Road
Shirland
Delaware Rd
Avenue
Warrington Crescent
Avenue
Elgin
Av.
Road
Sutherland
Road
441
WARWICK AVENUE
LITTLE VENICE
Road
UNION
Great
CANAL
Bloomfield
Maida
BAYSWATER AND MAIDA VALE
Harrow
Ladbroke
Grove
Golborne
Rd.
Westway
WESTBOURNE PARK
Western Rd
M 40
Westway
Harrow
452
Road
Rd
Road
449
ROYAL OAK
Westbourne
Park
Road
Chepstow
351
Bridge
PADDINGTON
Bishop's
A 40 (M)
LADBROKE GROVE
Portobello
Kensington
Grove
Gloucester
107
Westbourne
Villas
Gardens
Porchester
NORTH KENSINGTON
Dawson Place
Pembridge
Queensway
Park
Road
Road
Ladbroke
ROYAL BOROUGH OF KENSINGTON AND CHELSEA
Bayswater
Road
Detail-plan F
S
T
U
V

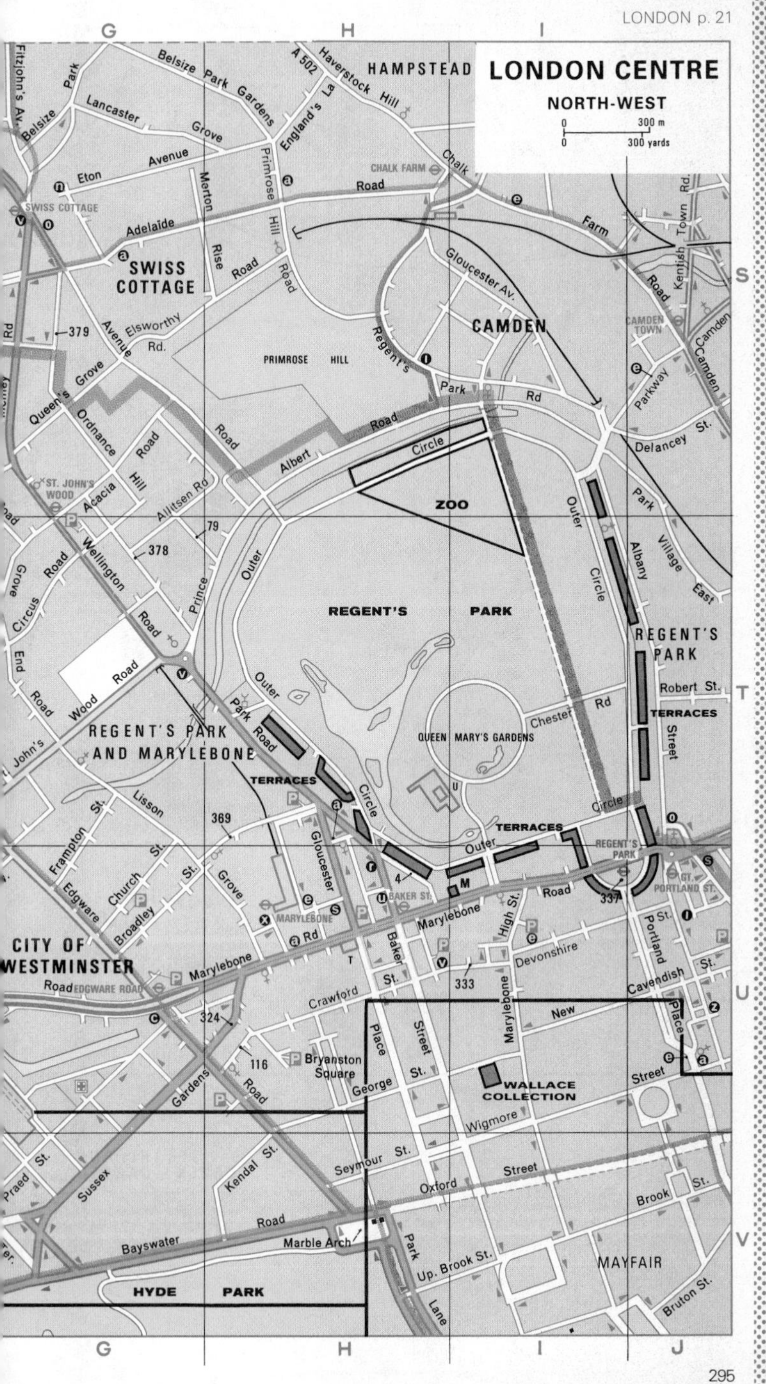
LONDON CENTRE
NORTH-WEST
0 300 m
0 300 yards
HAMPSTEAD
SWISS COTTAGE
CAMDEN
PRIMROSE HILL
ZOO
REGENT'S PARK
QUEEN MARY'S GARDENS
REGENT'S PARK AND MARYLEBONE
TERRACES
CITY OF WESTMINSTER
WALLACE COLLECTION
HYDE PARK
MAYFAIR
CHALK FARM
CAMDEN TOWN
ST. JOHN'S WOOD
BAKER ST.
MARYLEBONE
REGENT'S PARK
GT. PORTLAND ST.
EDGWARE ROAD
Marble Arch
Belsize Park Gardens
Haverstock Hill
England's La
Lancaster Grove
Avenue
Eton
Adelaide
Road
Merton Rise
Primrose Hill Road
Gloucester Av.
Regent's Park Rd
Chalk Farm Road
Kentish Town Rd.
Parkway
Delancey St.
Albert Road
Outer Circle
Albany Street
Park Village East
Robert St.
Chester Rd
Elsworthy Rd.
Avenue Road
Queen's Grove
Ordnance Hill
Acacia Road
Allitsen Rd
Wellington Road
Prince Albert Road
Grove End Road
Circus Road
St. John's Wood Road
Park Road
Lisson Grove
Frampton St.
Church St.
Edgware Road
Broadley St.
Gloucester Place
Baker Street
Marylebone Road
Marylebone High St.
Devonshire St.
Portland Place
Cavendish Place
New Cavendish Street
Crawford St.
Bryanston Square
George St.
Wigmore Street
Seymour St.
Oxford Street
Brook St.
Kendal St.
Sussex Gardens
Praed St.
Bayswater Road
Park Lane
Up. Brook St.
Bruton St.
Fitzjohn's Av.
379
378
79
369
333
337
324
116
4
G
H
I
J
S
T
U
V

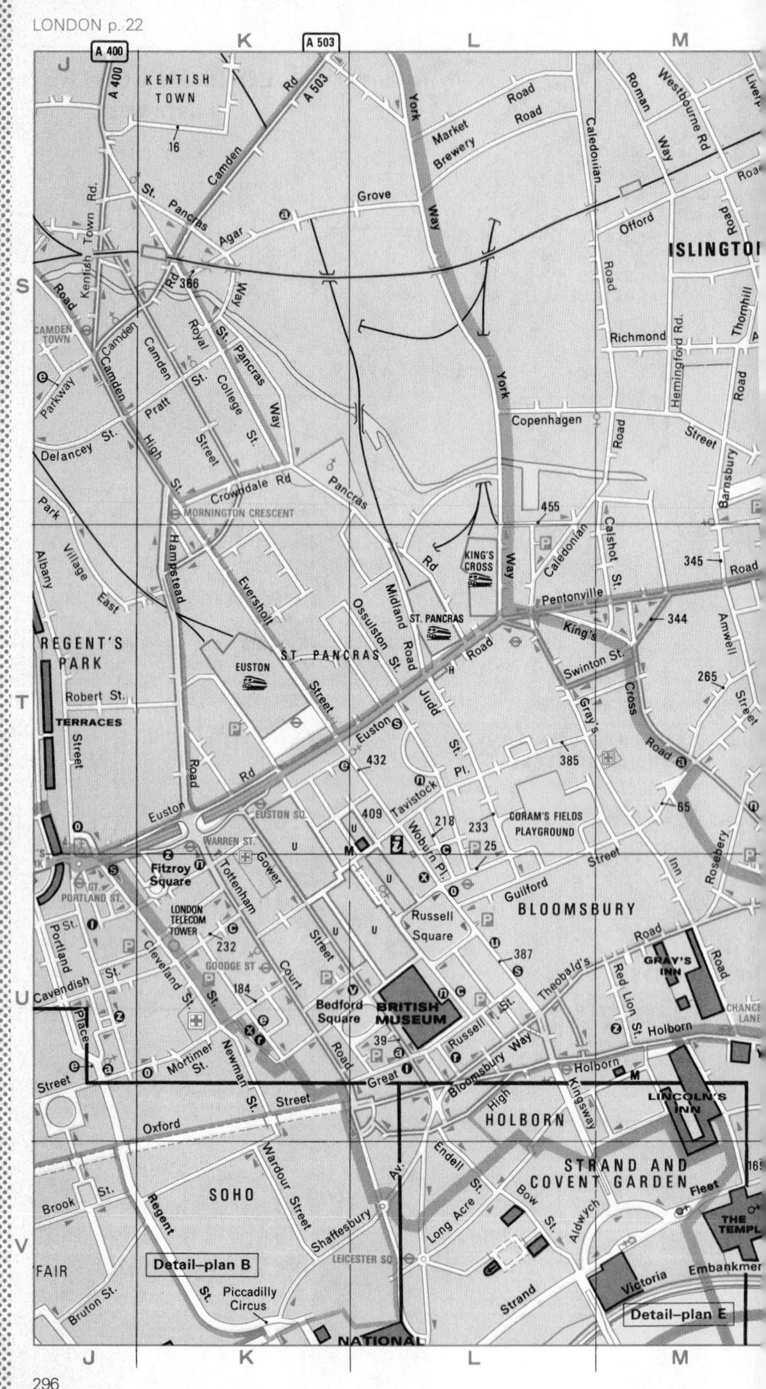
A 400
K
A 503
L
M
J
KENTISH TOWN
CAMDEN TOWN
MORNINGTON CRESCENT
ISLINGTON
REGENT'S PARK
TERRACES
ST. PANCRAS
EUSTON
KING'S CROSS
EUSTON SQ.
WARREN ST.
Fitzroy Square
GT. PORTLAND ST.
LONDON TELECOM TOWER
GOODGE ST
CORAM'S FIELDS PLAYGROUND
BLOOMSBURY
Russell Square
Bedford Square
BRITISH MUSEUM
GRAY'S INN
LINCOLN'S INN
HOLBORN
SOHO
STRAND AND COVENT GARDEN
LEICESTER SQ
Piccadilly Circus
THE TEMPLE
NATIONAL
Detail-plan B
Detail-plan E
S
T
U
V

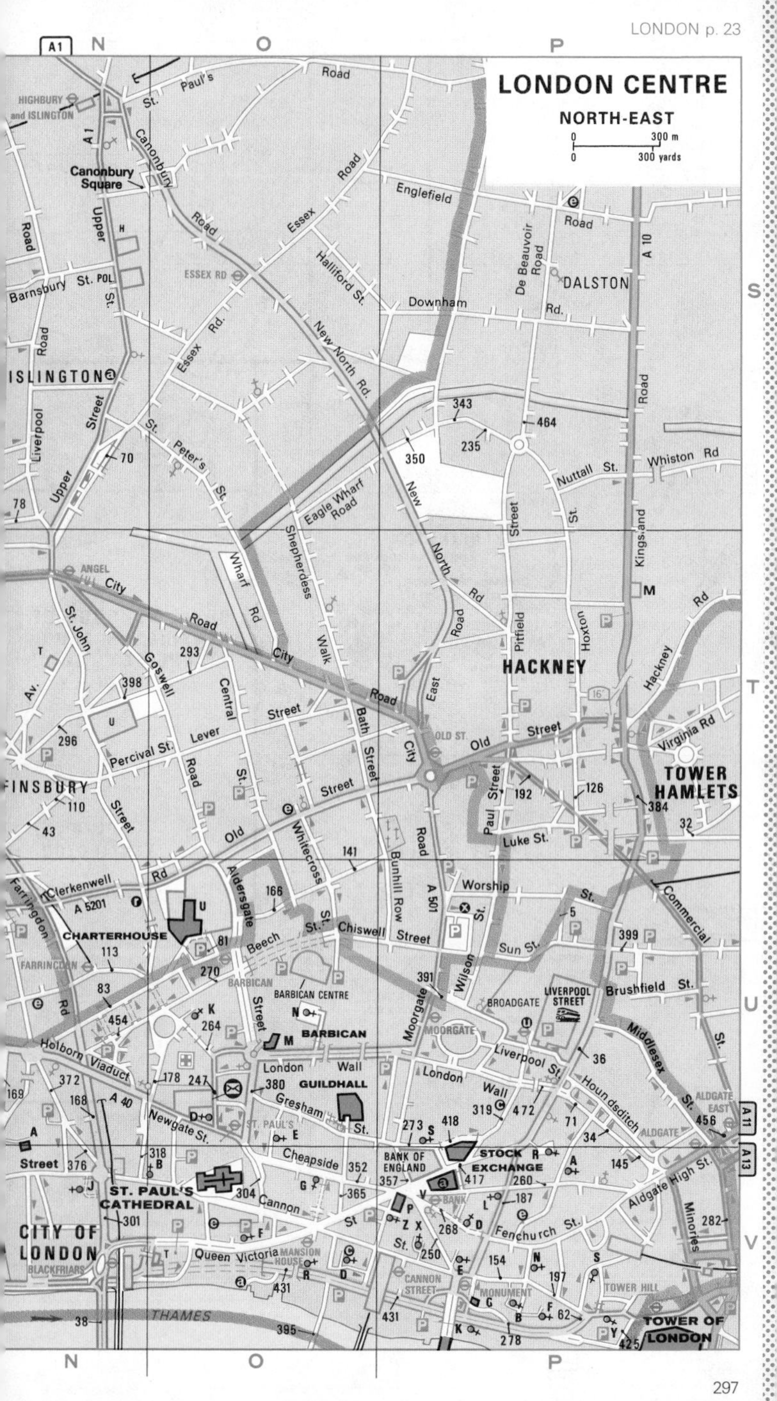
LONDON CENTRE
NORTH-EAST
0 300 m
0 300 yards
ISLINGTON
DALSTON
HACKNEY
TOWER HAMLETS
FINSBURY
CHARTERHOUSE
BARBICAN CENTRE
BARBICAN
GUILDHALL
STOCK EXCHANGE
BANK OF ENGLAND
ST. PAUL'S CATHEDRAL
CITY OF LONDON
LIVERPOOL STREET
TOWER OF LONDON
THAMES

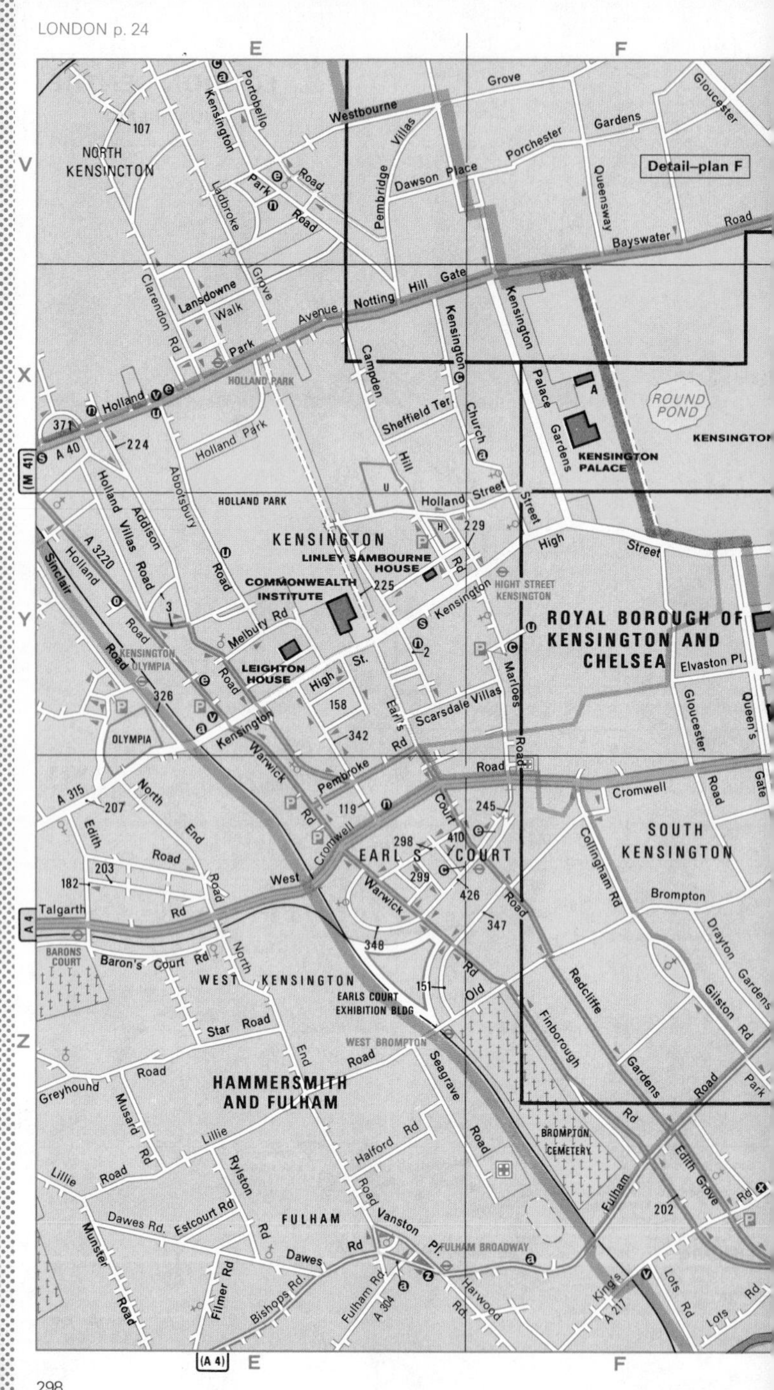
E
F
V
X
Y
Z
NORTH KENSINGTON
Detail-plan F
HOLLAND PARK
KENSINGTON
LINLEY SAMBOURNE HOUSE
COMMONWEALTH INSTITUTE
LEIGHTON HOUSE
KENSINGTON PALACE
ROUND POND
ROYAL BOROUGH OF KENSINGTON AND CHELSEA
KENSINGTON OLYMPIA
OLYMPIA
HIGHT STREET KENSINGTON
EARL'S COURT
SOUTH KENSINGTON
WEST KENSINGTON
EARLS COURT EXHIBITION BLDG
WEST BROMPTON
HAMMERSMITH AND FULHAM
BARONS COURT
BROMPTON CEMETERY
FULHAM
FULHAM BROADWAY
Westbourne
Grove
Porchester
Gardens
Queensway
Bayswater Road
Notting Hill Gate
Holland Park Avenue
Kensington High Street
Cromwell Road
West Cromwell Rd
Talgarth Rd
Lillie Road
Fulham Rd.
Dawes Rd.
Warwick Road
Earl's Court Road
Redcliffe Gardens
Finborough Rd
Edith Grove
King's Rd
(M 41)
A 40
A 3220
A 315
A 4
(A 4)
A 304
A 217

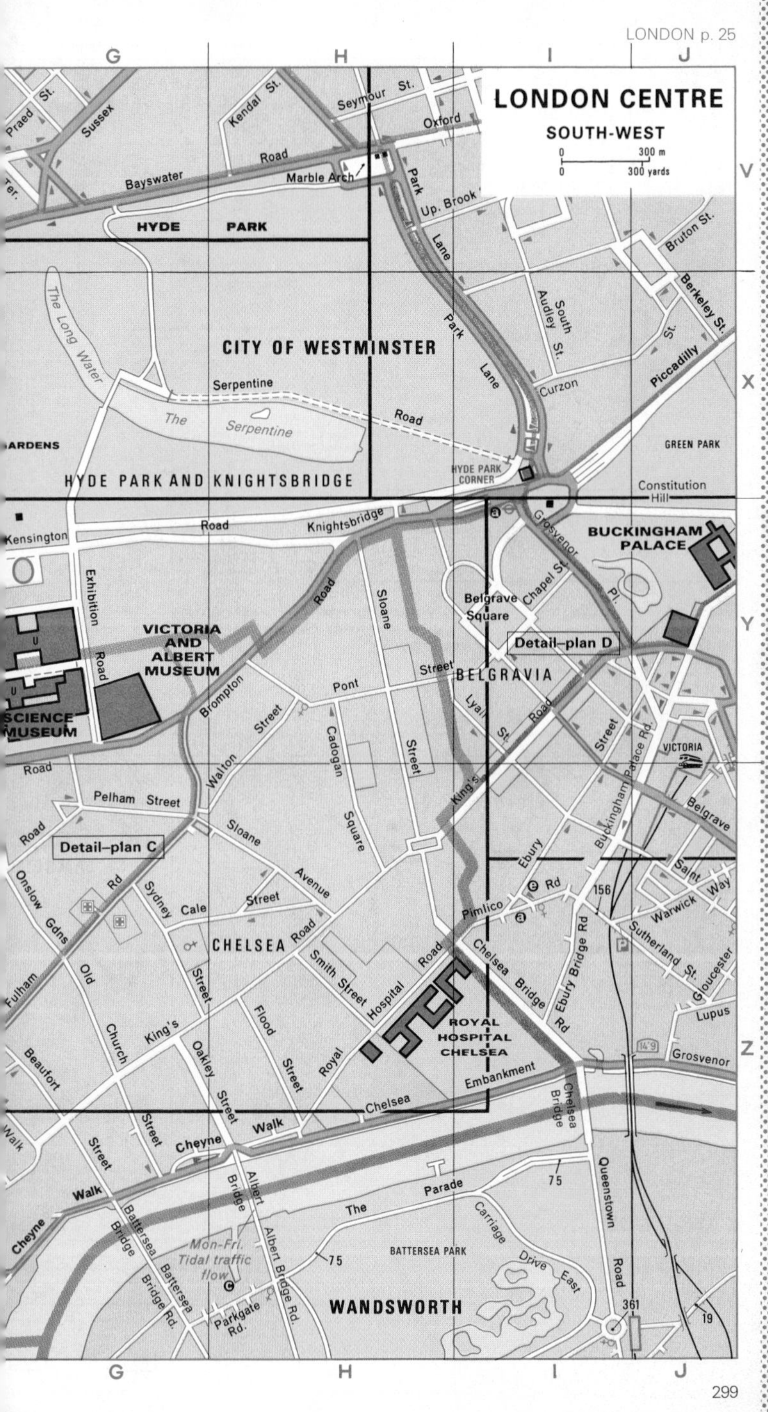
LONDON CENTRE
SOUTH-WEST
0 300 m
0 300 yards
G
H
I
J
V
X
Y
Z
HYDE PARK
CITY OF WESTMINSTER
HYDE PARK AND KNIGHTSBRIDGE
The Serpentine
The Long Water
Serpentine Road
Bayswater Road
Marble Arch
Oxford
Seymour St.
Kendal St.
Sussex
Praed St.
Park Lane
Up. Brook
South Audley St.
Curzon
Piccadilly
Berkeley St.
Bruton St.
GREEN PARK
HYDE PARK CORNER
Constitution Hill
BUCKINGHAM PALACE
Grosvenor Pl.
Chapel St.
Belgrave Square
Detail-plan D
BELGRAVIA
Knightsbridge
Kensington Road
Exhibition Road
VICTORIA AND ALBERT MUSEUM
SCIENCE MUSEUM
Brompton Road
Walton Street
Pont Street
Sloane Street
Cadogan Square
Lyall St.
Ebury Street
Buckingham Palace Rd.
VICTORIA
Belgrave Road
Pelham Street
Sloane Avenue
Detail-plan C
Onslow Gdns
Fulham Rd
Sydney Street
Cale Street
CHELSEA
King's Road
Old Church Street
Smith Street
Royal Hospital Road
Pimlico Rd
Ebury Bridge Rd
Chelsea Bridge Rd
ROYAL HOSPITAL CHELSEA
Flood Street
Oakley Street
Beaufort Street
Chelsea Embankment
Cheyne Walk
Chelsea Bridge
Saint George's Way
Warwick Way
Sutherland St.
Gloucester
Lupus
Grosvenor
Albert Bridge
Albert Bridge Rd.
Battersea Bridge
Battersea Bridge Rd.
Parkgate Rd.
Mon-Fri. Tidal traffic flow
The Parade
Carriage Drive East
BATTERSEA PARK
Queenstown Road
WANDSWORTH
156
75
361
19

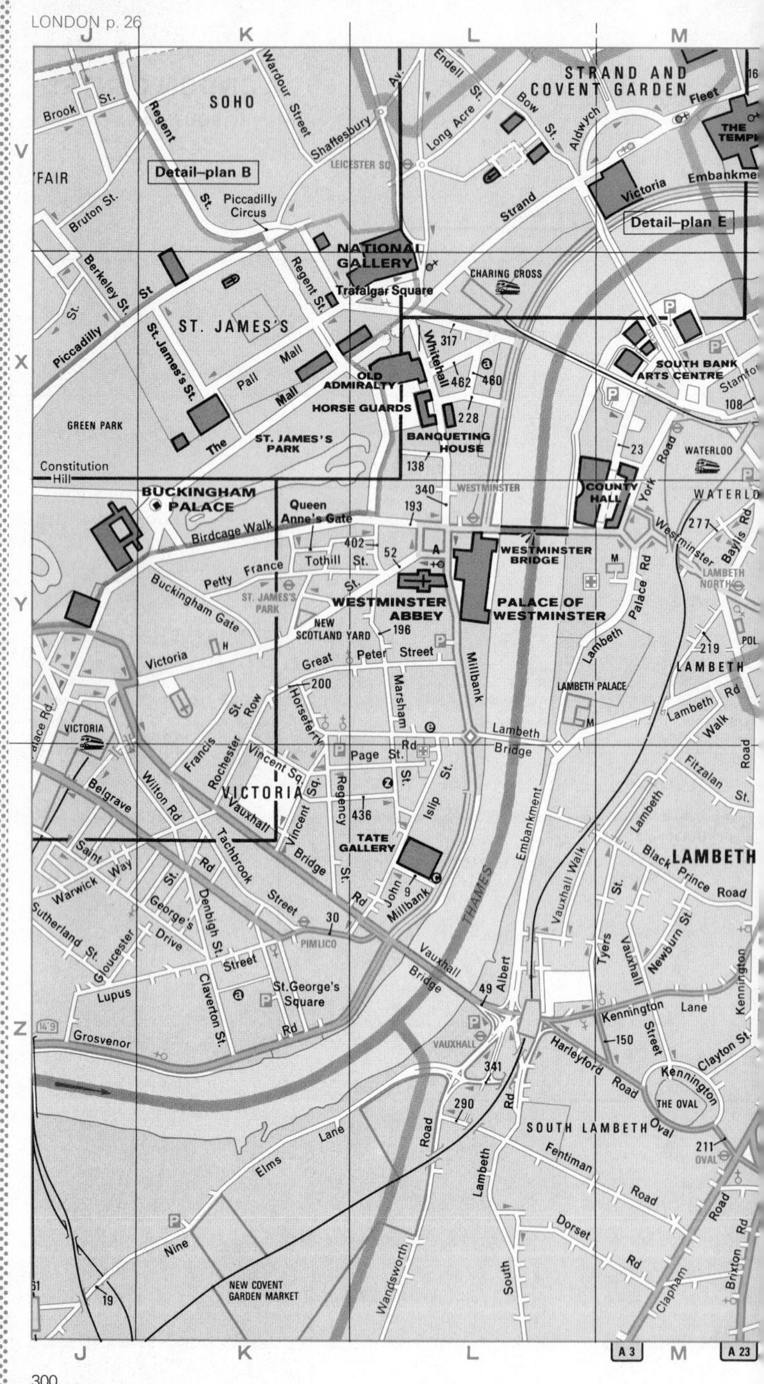
SOHO
STRAND AND COVENT GARDEN
Detail–plan B
Detail–plan E
Piccadilly Circus
LEICESTER SQ.
NATIONAL GALLERY
Trafalgar Square
CHARING CROSS
ST. JAMES'S
OLD ADMIRALTY
HORSE GUARDS
BANQUETING HOUSE
SOUTH BANK ARTS CENTRE
GREEN PARK
ST. JAMES'S PARK
Constitution Hill
BUCKINGHAM PALACE
WESTMINSTER
COUNTY HALL
WATERLOO
Queen Anne's Gate
Birdcage Walk
WESTMINSTER BRIDGE
WESTMINSTER ABBEY
PALACE OF WESTMINSTER
NEW SCOTLAND YARD
LAMBETH NORTH
LAMBETH PALACE
LAMBETH
VICTORIA
TATE GALLERY
PIMLICO
St.George's Square
VAUXHALL
THAMES
THE OVAL
SOUTH LAMBETH
OVAL
NEW COVENT GARDEN MARKET
A 3
A 23

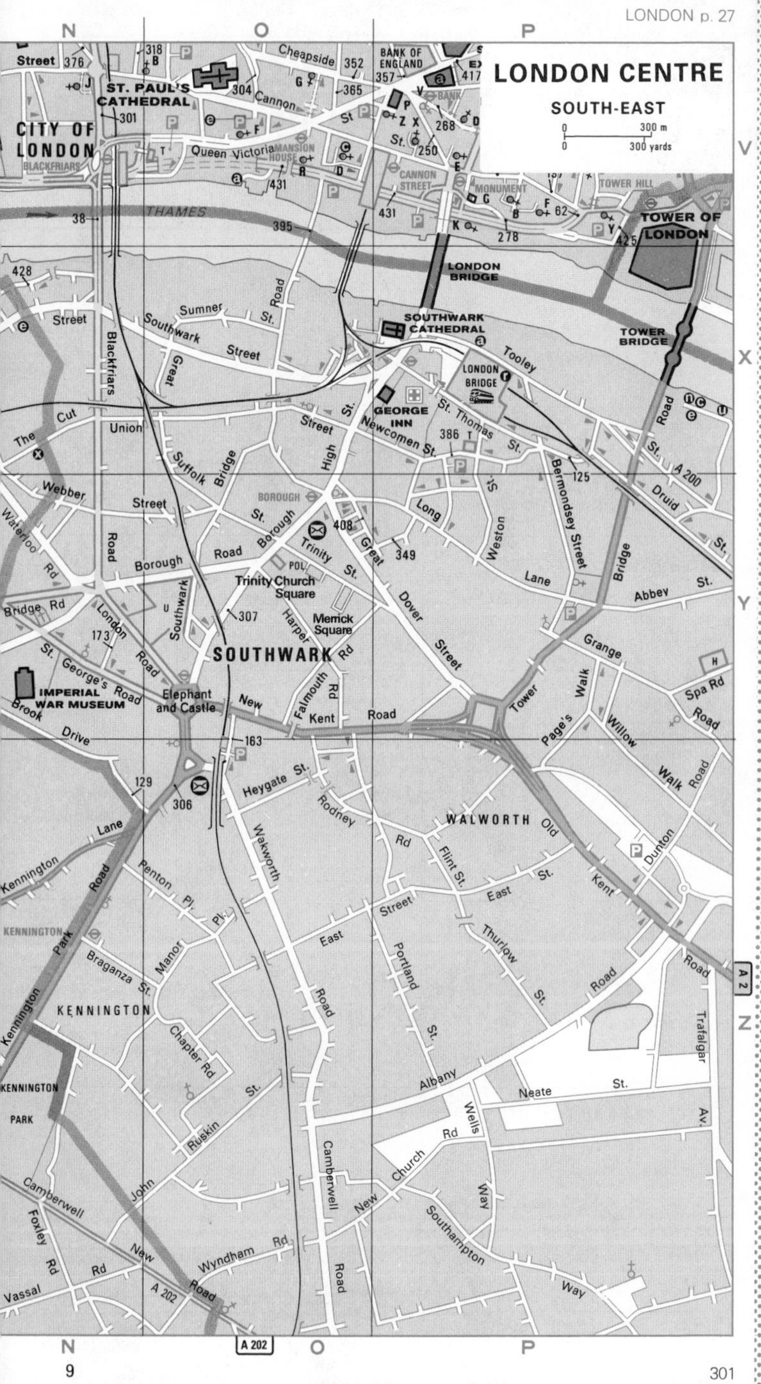
LONDON CENTRE
SOUTH-EAST
0 300 m
0 300 yards
CITY OF LONDON
ST. PAUL'S CATHEDRAL
BANK OF ENGLAND
Cheapside
Cannon St
Queen Victoria
MANSION HOUSE
BLACKFRIARS
CANNON STREET
MONUMENT
TOWER HILL
THAMES
TOWER OF LONDON
LONDON BRIDGE
SOUTHWARK CATHEDRAL
TOWER BRIDGE
Sumner St.
Southwark Street
Great
Blackfriars Road
Tooley
GEORGE INN
St. Thomas St.
Newcomen St.
The Cut
Union Street
Suffolk
Bridge
High St.
BOROUGH
Long
Weston St.
Bermondsey Street
Webber Street
Borough Road
Borough
Trinity St.
Great Dover Street
Trinity Church Square
Merrick Square
Harper Rd
SOUTHWARK
Abbey St.
Druid St.
Waterloo Rd
Bridge Rd
London Road
St. George's Road
IMPERIAL WAR MUSEUM
Elephant and Castle
New Kent Road
Falmouth Rd
Tower Bridge Road
Grange
Page's Walk
Willow Walk
Spa Rd
Brook Drive
Heygate St.
Rodney Rd
WALWORTH
Old Kent Road
Dunton
Flint St.
East St.
East Street
Kennington Lane
Kennington Park Road
KENNINGTON
Penton Pl.
Manor Pl.
Braganza St.
Wakworth Road
Portland St.
Thurlow St.
Trafalgar Av.
Chapter Rd
Albany Road
Neate St.
Wells Rd
KENNINGTON PARK
Ruskin
John
Camberwell Road
Church
New
Way
Southampton Way
Camberwell New Road
Foxley Rd
Vassal Rd
Wyndham Rd
A 202
A 2
A 200
N
O
P
V
X
Y
Z

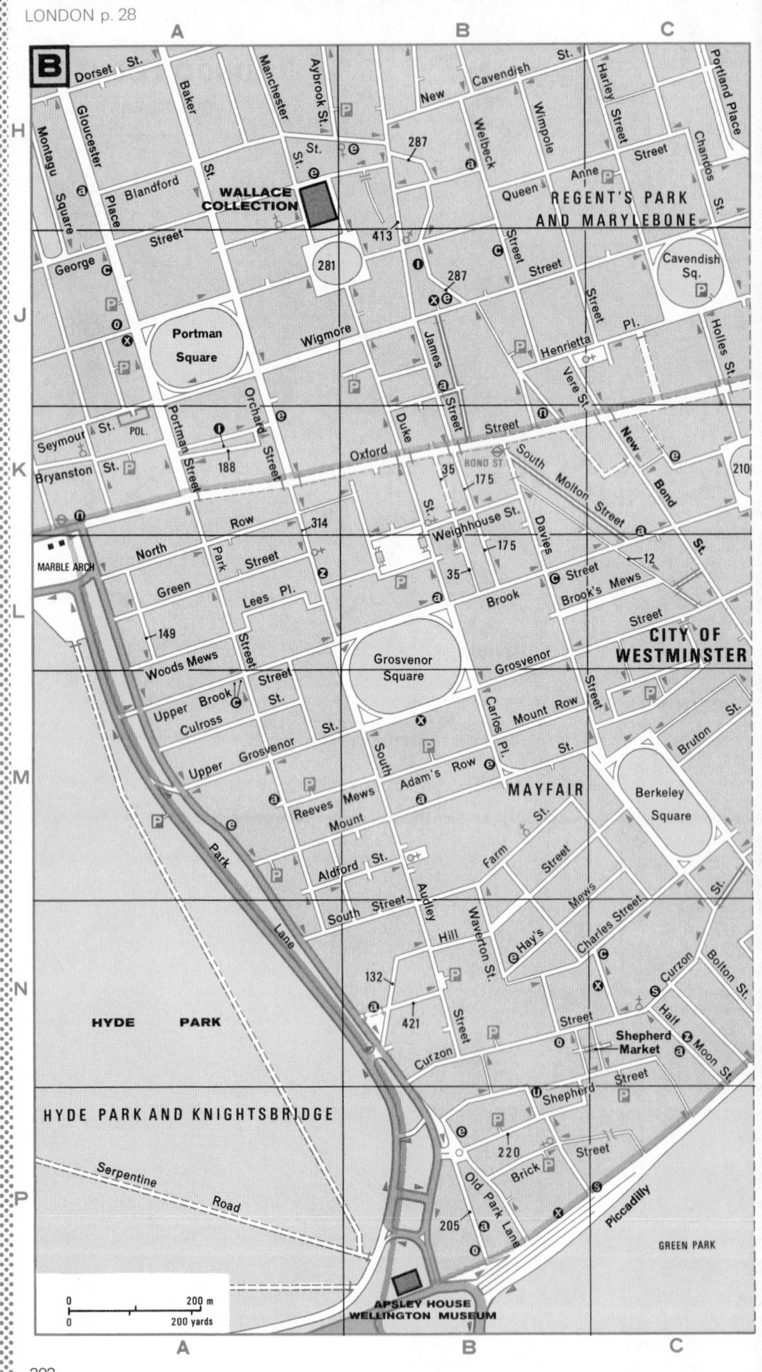

WALLACE COLLECTION
REGENT'S PARK AND MARYLEBONE
Portman Square
Cavendish Sq.
MARBLE ARCH
Grosvenor Square
CITY OF WESTMINSTER
MAYFAIR
Berkeley Square
HYDE PARK
HYDE PARK AND KNIGHTSBRIDGE
Serpentine Road
Park Lane
Oxford Street
Piccadilly
Shepherd Market
GREEN PARK
APSLEY HOUSE WELLINGTON MUSEUM
0 200 m
0 200 yards

Street	Grid	No.
Arlington Street	DN	6
Avery Row	CL	12
Bateman Street	FK	18
Berwick Street	FK	26
Binney Street	BL	35
Carlton Gardens	FP	74
Deanery Street	BN	132
Denman Street	FM	133
Denmark Street	GJ	134
Duke of York Street	EN	143
Duke Street ST. JAMES	EN	146
Dunraven Street	AL	149
Gerrard Street	GL	174
Gilbert Street	BL	175
Glasshouse Street	EM	179
Granville Place	AK	188
Great Castle Street	DJ	189
Greek Street	GK	198
Hamilton Place	BP	205
Hanover Square	CK	210
Hertford Street	BP	220
Leicester Square	GM	261
Manchester Square	AJ	281
Market Place	DJ	286
Marylebone Lane	BJ	287
North Audley Street	AK	314
Old Burlington Street	DM	322
Old Compton Street	GK	323
Panton Street	FM	336
Romilly Street	GL	368
Thayer Street	BJ	413
Tilney Street	BN	421
Warwick Street	EM	444

Oxford Street is closed to private traffic, Mondays to Saturdays : from 7 am to 7 pm between Portman Street and St. Giles Circus

Barkston Gardens .... AT 14	Cromwell Place .... CS 120	Foulis Terrace .... CT 170
Bray Place .... ET 45	Egerton Gardens .... DS 160	Glendower Place .... CS 180
Bute Street .... CS 59	Egerton Terrace .... DR 161	Harriet Street .... FQ 214
Collingham Gardens ..... AT 99	Egerton Gardens Mews .... ER 162	Harrington Road .... CS 215
Collingham Road .... AT 101		Holbein Mews .... FT 223

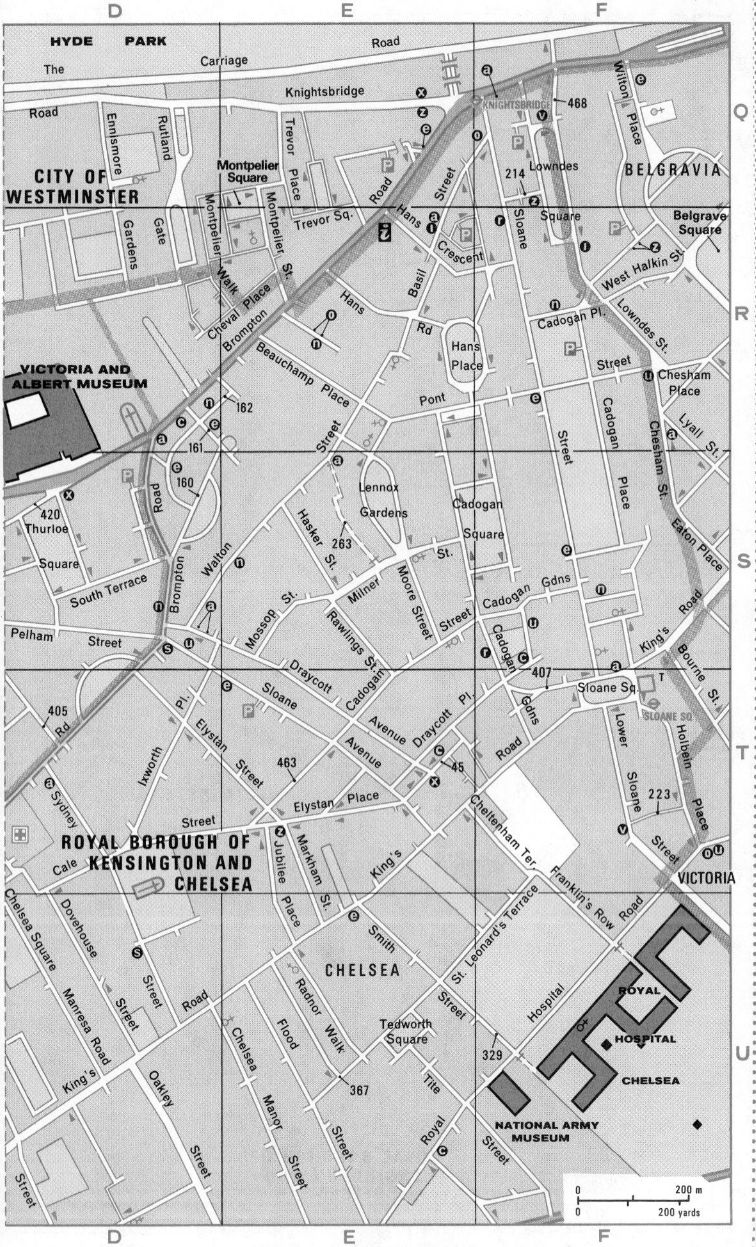

Kensington Court . . . . **AQ** 241	Ormonde Gate. . . . . **FU** 329	Sydney Place. . . . . **DT** 405
Kensington Court Place . . **AR** 242	Prince's Gardens. . . . . **CR** 356	Symons Street . . . . **FT** 407
Launceston Place . . . . **BR** 259	Queensberry Place . . . . . . **CS** 360	Thurloe Place. . . . . **CS** 420
Lennox Gardens Mews. . . **ES** 263	Queen's Gate Place . . . . . **BR** 363	Whitehead's Grove . . . . . . **ET** 463
Neville Terrace. . . . . **CT** 300	Redesdale Street. . . . . **EU** 367	William Street . . . . **FQ** 468

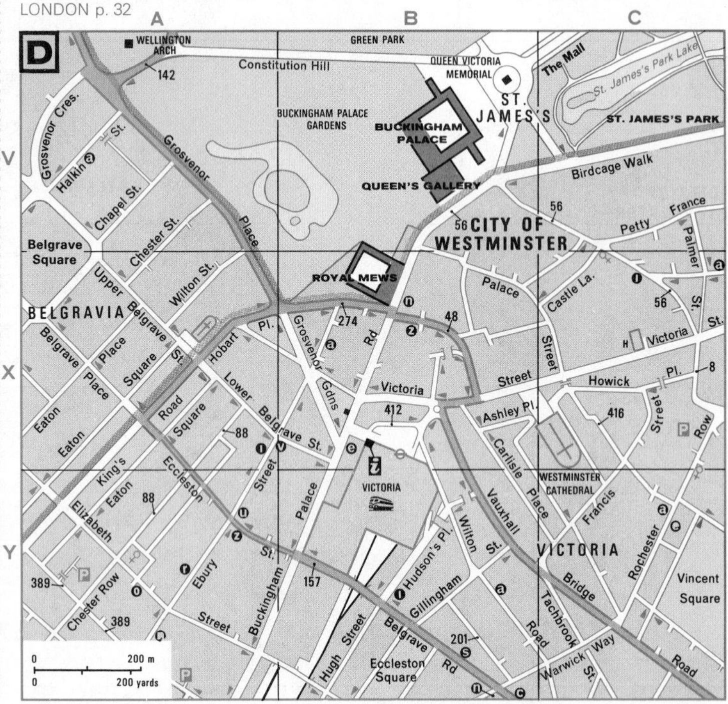

A B C

D

WELLINGTON ARCH
GREEN PARK
Constitution Hill
142
QUEEN VICTORIA MEMORIAL
The Mall
St. James's Park Lake
ST. JAMES'S
ST. JAMES'S PARK
BUCKINGHAM PALACE GARDENS
BUCKINGHAM PALACE
QUEEN'S GALLERY
Birdcage Walk
Grosvenor Cres.
Halkin St.
Chapel St.
Grosvenor Place
Belgrave Square
Chester St.
Upper Belgrave St.
Wilton St.
BELGRAVIA
56 CITY OF WESTMINSTER
56
Petty France
Palmer St.
Palace Street
Castle La.
56
ROYAL MEWS
274
48
Grosvenor Gdns
Hobart Pl.
Belgrave Place
Eaton Place
Eaton Square
Lower Belgrave St.
Victoria Street
Victoria St.
Howick Pl.
8
Rd
412
Ashley Pl.
416
Rochester Row
Eaton
Road
Square
88
Carlisle Place
WESTMINSTER CATHEDRAL
VICTORIA
Vauxhall Bridge Road
Francis Street
King's Road
Eccleston St.
Eaton
88
Elizabeth
Ebury Street
Buckingham Palace Road
Wilton St.
Hudson's Pl.
Gillingham
VICTORIA
Vincent Square
389
Chester Row
389
157
Street
Hugh Street
Belgrave Rd
Tachbrook St.
201
Warwick Way
Eccleston Square
Road
0 200 m
0 200 yards

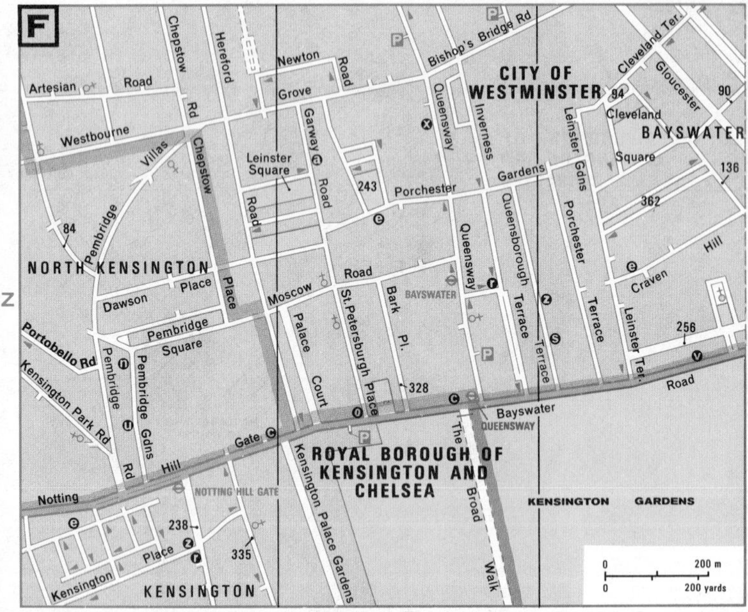

F

Chepstow Rd
Hereford
Newton Road
Bishop's Bridge Rd
Cleveland Ter.
Artesian Road
Grove
CITY OF WESTMINSTER
94
Gloucester Ter.
90
Westbourne
Queensway
Inverness
Leinster Gdns
Cleveland Square
BAYSWATER
Villas
Chepstow Place
Garway Road
Leinster Square
Road
243
Porchester Gardens
Gardens
136
362
84
Pembridge
Queensway
Queensborough Terrace
Porchester Terrace
Craven Hill
NORTH KENSINGTON
Moscow Road
St.Petersburg Place
Bark Pl.
BAYSWATER
Dawson Place
Pembridge Square
Palace Court
Leinster Ter.
256
Portobello Rd
Pembridge Rd
Pembridge Gdns
328
Terrace
Road
Kensington Park Rd
Bayswater
QUEENSWAY
Notting Hill Gate
ROYAL BOROUGH OF KENSINGTON AND CHELSEA
Kensington Palace Gardens
The Broad Walk
NOTTING HILL GATE
KENSINGTON GARDENS
238
Place
335
Kensington
KENSINGTON
0 200 m
0 200 yards

A B C

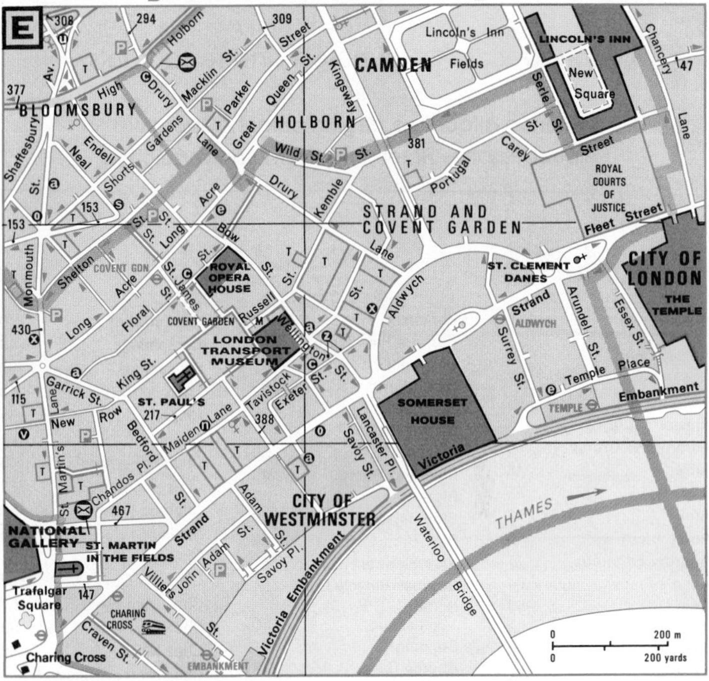

D E

E

BLOOMSBURY
CAMDEN
HOLBORN
Lincoln's Inn Fields
LINCOLN'S INN
New Square
ROYAL COURTS OF JUSTICE
STRAND AND COVENT GARDEN
ST. CLEMENT DANES
CITY OF LONDON
THE TEMPLE
ROYAL OPERA HOUSE
LONDON TRANSPORT MUSEUM
ST. PAUL'S
SOMERSET HOUSE
CITY OF WESTMINSTER
NATIONAL GALLERY
ST. MARTIN IN THE FIELDS
Trafalgar Square
CHARING CROSS
Charing Cross
EMBANKMENT
THAMES
Waterloo Bridge
Victoria Embankment
Strand
Aldwych
Fleet Street
0 200 m
0 200 yards

V X Y

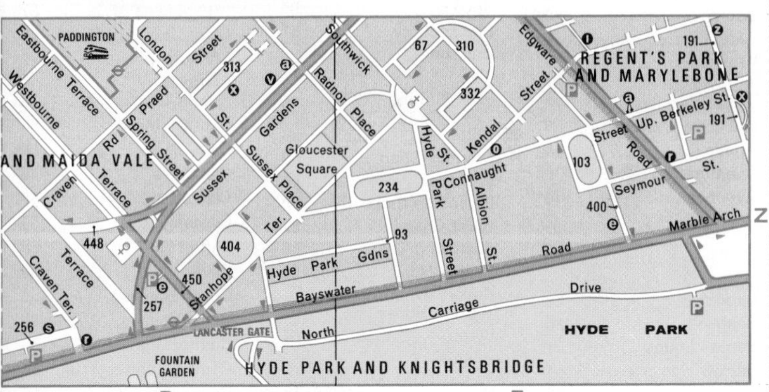

D E

Artillery Row	CVX	8
Bream's Buildings	EV	47
Bressenden Place	BX	48
Buckingham Gate	CV	56
Cambridge Square	EZ	67
Chepstow Crescent	AZ	84
Chester Square	AX	88
Chilworth Street	CZ	90
Clarendon Place	EZ	93
Cleveland Gardens	CZ	94
Connaught Square	EZ	103
Cranbourn Street	DX	115
Devonshire Terrace	CZ	136
Duke of Wellington Place	AV	142
Duncannon Street	DY	147
Earlham Street	DV	153
Eccleston Bridge	BY	157
Great Cumberland Place	EZ	191
Guildhouse Street	BY	201
Henrietta Street	DX	217
Hyde Park Square	EZ	234
Kensington Church Street	AZ	238
Kensington Gardens Square	BZ	243
Lancaster Gate	CDZ	256
Lancaster Terrace	DZ	257
Lower Grosvenor Place	BX	274
Museum Street	DV	294
New Oxford Street	DV	308
Newton Street	DV	309
Norfolk Crescent	EZ	310
Norfolk Square	DZ	313
Orme Court	BZ	328
Oxford Square	EZ	332
Palace Gardens Terrace	AZ	335
Queen's Gardens	CZ	362
St. Giles High Street	DV	377
Sardinia Street	EV	381
Southampton Street	DX	388
South Eaton Place	AY	389
Stanhope Place	EZ	400
Sussex Square	DZ	404
Terminus Place	BX	412
Thirleby Road	CX	416
Upper St. Martin's Lane	DX	430
Westbourne Crescent	DZ	448
Westbourne Street	DZ	450
William IV Street	DY	467

Alphabetical list of hotels and restaurants
Liste alphabétique des hôtels et restaurants
Elenco alfabetico degli alberghi e ristoranti
Alphabetisches Hotel- und Restaurantverzeichnis

	page pagina Seite
A	
Abbey Court	58
Academy	47
Accento (L')	65
Alastair Little	71
Albero and Grana	56
Alfred	48
Altro (L')	58
Amico (L')	73
Amsterdam	56
Andrew Edmunds	71
Anna's Place	54
Arcadia	58
Argyll	56
Aspects	65
Associés (Les)	52
Asuka	70
Aster House	59
Athenaeum	66
Auberge de Provence	73
Aubergine	55
Auntie's	48
Aventure (L')	70
Ayudhya	60
B	
Baboon	69
Bangkok	60
Bardon Lodge	51
Barrow House	61
Basil Street	55
Bayee Village	61
Beaufort	55
Beit Eddine	56
Belgo	49
Belvedere in Holland Park	57
Bengal Clipper	62
Benihana	48
Benihana	56
Bentley's	68
Berkeley	65
Berkshire	68
Berners Park Plaza	68
Bertorelli's	72
Bibendum	55
Bingham	62
Bistrot Bruno	71
Blakes	59
Bleeding Heart	48
Blooms	47
Bloomsbury Park	47
Blue Print Café	63
Blue Elephant	51
Bombay Bicycle Club	64
Bombay Brasserie	60
Bonnington	47
Bougie (La)	48
Boyd's	58
Brackenbury	51
Brasserie at the Café Royal	71
Brasserie du marché aux puces	58
Brittania	66
Bromley Court	46
Brown's	66
Bryanston Court	69
Burnt Chair	62
Busabong Too	56
Bustan (Al)	65
Butlers Wharf Chop House	63
Byron	64
C	
Cadogan	54
Café dell'Ugo	63
Café des Arts	48
Café du Jardin (Le)	72
Café Lazeez	60
Caldesi	69
Canal Brasserie	58
Cannizaro House	61
Cantina Del Ponte	63
Capital	54
Caprice (Le)	70
Carapace	48
Carnarvon	50
Castelletto (Il)	48
Chada	63
Chandni	47
Charles Bernard	48
Chase Lodge	62
Chateau (The)	67
Chelsea	55
Chesterfield	67
Chez Lindsay	62
Chez Max	57
Chez Max	60
Chez Moi	58
Chez Nico at Ninety Park Lane	67
China Jazz	49
Christopher's	72
Churchill Inter-Continental	68
Chutney Mary	56
Cibo	58
Claridge's	66
Clarke's	57
Claverley	55
Clifton Ford	68
Clive	48
Coach House	52
Collin House	73
Comfort Inn	56
Comfort Inn	64
Connaught	66
Conrad London	54
Copthorne Tara	57
Corney and Barrow	49
Coulsdon Manor	49
Cranley	59
Cranley Gardens	60
Criterion	71
Crowthers	62
Croydon Park	50
Cumberland	52

D

Dan's 56
Daphne's 56
Del Buongustaio . . . 64
Delhi Brasserie 60
Dell'Ugo 71
Delmere 64
Diplomat 65
Dolphin Square 73
Dorchester 66
Dordogne (La) 53
Dorset Square 69
Downstairs at One Ninety 60
Dragon City 61
Draycott 54
Drury Lane Moat House 49
Dukes 70
Durley House 54
Durrants 69

E

Egerton House 55
Eleven Cadogan Gardens 55
English Garden 56
Escargot (L') 71
Escargot Doré (L') . . 57
Estaminet (L') 72
Euston Plaza 48
Excelsior Heathrow 53

F

Fenja 55
Fenice (La) 57
Fifth Floor (at Harvey Nichols) 55
Finezza (La) 56
Five Sumner Place . . 59
Flemings 67
Fleurie 51
Florians 52
Fontana (La) 74
Formula Veneta 57
Forte Crest 53
Forte Crest Bloomsbury 47
Forte Crest Regent's Park 69
Forte Crest St. James's 70
Forte Posthouse 46
Forte Posthouse 48
Forte Posthouse 50
Forte Posthouse 53
Forte Travelodge . . . 61
Forte Travelodge . . . 61
47 Park Street 66
Forum 59
Four Regions 62
Four Seasons 66
Four Seasons 67
Franklin (The) 54
Friends 52
Fulham Road 56
Fung Shing 71

G

Gavroche (Le) 67
Gay Hussar 71
Gaylord 69
Giannino's 47
Gloucester 59
Good Earth 46
Good Earth 56
Gopal's 71
Gore 59
Goring 73
Grafton 47
Grafton (The) 61
Granada Lodge 54
Granita 54
Gran Paradiso 74
Gravier's 60
Greenhouse 68
Green's 70
Green Park 67
Gresham 65
Grill Room at the Café Royal . . . 71
Grosvenor Thistle . . 73
Grosvenor House . . . 66

H

Halcyon 57
Halkin 65
Hamilton 51
Hamilton House 73
Hampshire 71
Harewood 69
Harlingford 47
Harrington Hall 59
Hart House 69
Harvey's 64
Hazlitt's 71
Heathrow Park 53
Henley House 56
Hilaire 60
Hilton National 50
Hilton National London Olympia . 57
Hilton National Wembley 46
Ho-Ho 61
Holiday Inn 59
Holiday Inn 63
Holiday Inn 67
Holiday Inn Crowne Plaza 53
Holiday Inn Garden Court 46
Holiday Inn Garden Court 69
Holiday Inn Kings Cross 47
Holland Court 57
Hospitality Inn Piccadilly 70
Hotel (L') 55
Hotel 167 60
Howard 72
Hudson's 69
Hunan 73
Hyatt Carlton Tower 54
Hyde Park 65
Hyde Park Towers . . 64

I

Ikeda 68
Imari 49
Imperial City 49
Incontro (L') 73
Inn of Happiness . . . 73
Inter-Continental . . . 66
Issimo ! 49
Ivy 72

J

Jaflong 52
Jardin des Gourmets (Au) 71
Jarvis International Heathrow 54
Jashan 52
Jasmin 63
Joe Allen 72
John Howard 59
Jurys Kensington . . . 59

K

Kanishka 48
Kenilworth 47
Ken Lo's Memories of China 73

Kensington Close... 57
Kensington Palace Thistle 57
Kensington Park.... 57
Kensington Place... 58
Kensington Plaza... 59
Khan's of Kensington.... 60
Kingston Lodge 60
Knightsbridge...... 55
Knightsbridge Green 65

L

Laguna Tandoori ... 50
Laksmi............ 63
Lanesborough 65
Langan's Bistro 70
Langan's Brasserie . 68
Langham Court 69
Langham Hilton 68
Langorf 48
Launceston Place... 58
Laurent 46
Leith's 58
Lena's 63
Lexington 71
Lincoln House 69
Lindsay House 71
Loggia (La)........ 70
London Embassy ... 64
London Heathrow Hilton........... 53
London Hilton on Park Lane 66
London Kensington Hilton........... 57
London Regents Park Hilton........... 68
London Metropole.. 64
London Mews Hilton 67
Lowndes 65
Luigi's 63

M

Mabledon Court.... 47
Magno's Brasserie.. 72
Malabar........... 58
Mandarin.......... 58
Mao Tai........... 51
Marble Arch Marriott 68
Mario............. 50
Marlborough....... 47
Maroush III 69
Marriott........... 66
Matsuri 71
Maxim 50
May Fair Inter-Continental . 66
McClements 62
Memories of India.. 60
Meridien Piccadilly (Le) 66
Mesurier (Le) 54
Mezzaluna......... 46
Midi (Le).......... 51
Mijanou........... 73
Milestone (The) 57
Mimmo d'Ischia.... 74
Ming 71
Mitre 62
Miyama 49
Monkey's 56
Mon Plaisir 48
Montague Park..... 47
Montcalm 68
Mornington........ 64
Motcombs......... 65
Mountbatten....... 47
MPW's, The Canteen 55
Mr Tang's Mandarin 52
Mr Wing 57
Mulligans 68
Muscadet (Le) 70

N

Nakamura 70
Neal Street 48
New Happiness Garden 50
Nico Central 69
Nightingales 62
Norfolk Plaza 65
Noughts 'n' Crosses 50
Novotel 53
Now and Zen 72
Number Sixteen.... 59

O

Oak Lodge 50
Oak Room......... 67
Odette's 49
Oh Boy 64
O'Keefe's 68
Olde Village Bakery. 52
Olivo 74
192............... 58
Orchard........... 48
Oriental........... 67
Orso.............. 72
Overton's 70

P

Palms............. 52
Paolo's............ 50
Park Inn........... 58
Park International... 59
Park Lane 66
Parkwood 65
Partners Brasserie .. 63
Pastoria........... 70
Pearl of Knightsbridge . 65
Peking Diner....... 47
Pelham 59
Pembridge Court ... 58
Percy's............ 52
Periquito 56
Peter's............ 49
Petersham......... 62
Phoenicia 58
Phoenix 64
Pied à Terre 48
Pitagora........... 62
Plaza on Hyde Park . 64
Poissonnerie de l'Avenue 56
Pomme d'Amour (La) 57
Pont de la Tour (Le) 62
Poons............. 65
Poons............. 71
Poons of Russell Square.......... 48
Portobello 58
Poule au Pot (La)... 74
Primula (La) 57
Prince Regent...... 61
Princess Garden.... 67

Q - R

Quaglino's......... 70
Quai (Le).......... 49
Quality Chop House 54
Queen's Park 64
Quincy's 46
Radisson Edwardian 53
Ransome's Dock ... 63
Rathbone 69
Red 56
Red Fort 71
Regency 59
Regent London..... 68
Regents Park 69
Regents Park Marriott......... 49
Rembrandt 59
Reserve (La)....... 51

Restaurant, Marco Pierre White (The) 65
Richmond Gate 62
Ritz 70
Riva 62
Rive Gauche (La) 61
Roberto's 53
Rochester 73
Rouxl Britannia 54
Royal Chase 50
Royal China 64
Royal Court 55
Royal Horseguards Thistle 72
Royal Lancaster 64
Royal Trafalgar Thistle 70
Royal Westminster Thistle 73
RSJ 61
Rubens 73
Rules 72
Rushmore 56
Russell 47
Russell Court 57

S

Saigon 71
St. George's 68
St. James Court 72
St. Quentin 56
Sambuca 53
Sampan's 69
Santini 73
San Vincenzo (Al) 65
SAS Portman 68
Saveurs (Les) 67
Savoy 72
Savoy Court 69
Scala (La) 46
Scandic Crown 63
Scandic Crown 73
Scotts 67
Selfridge 68
Selsdon Park 50
Shanghai 58
Shaw's 60
Sheekey's 72
Shepherds 73
Sheraton Belgravia 65
Sheraton Heathrow 53
Sheraton Park Tower 54
Sheraton Skyline 53
Shogun 68
Sydney House 55
Simply Nico 73
Simpson's-in-the-Strand 72
Sloane 55
Snows on the Green 51
Soho Soho 71
Sonny's 62
Soufflé (Le) 67
Soulard 51
Spice Merchant 65
Spread Eagle 51
Square (The) 70
Sri Siam 71
Stafford 70
Stakis London Coburg 64
Stakis London St. Ermins 72
Stephen Bull 69
Stephen Bull's Bistro 54
Suntory 70
Surinders 58
Swallow 46
Swallow International 59
Swan 52
Swiss Cottage 48
Sydney House 55

T

Tabaq 64
Tandoori Nights 51
Tante Claire (La) 55
Taste of China 52
Taste of India 51
Tate Gallery 74
Tatsuso 49
Thai Castle 52
Thai Pepper 49
Thatched House 63
Thierry's 56
Tophams Ebury Court 73
Toto's 56
Trattoria Sorrentina 52
Travel Inn 50
Travel Inn 52
Travel Inn 53
Travel Inn 60
Travel Inn 61
Treasure of China 51
Truffe Noire (La) 63
Tui 60
Turner's 55
25 Dorset Square 69
Twenty Trinity Gardens 60
22 Jermyn Street 70

V - W

Vanbrugh 51
Vanderbilt 59
Veranda (La) 63
Villa Medici 74
Waldorf 72
Walsh's 69
Waltons 55
Washington 67
Waterfront Brasserie 53
Wellmeadow Lodge 50
Westbury 66
West Lodge Park 51
White House 49
Whites 64
Whittington's 49
Wilbraham 55
Willow 49
Wilsons 51
Winchester 73
Windmill on the Common 61
Windsor Castle Toby 50
Wódka 58
Woodford Moat House 61

X - Y - Z

Xian 47
Zen Central 67
Zen W3 48
Zoe 70

Don't confuse:

Comfort of hotels : 🏨🏨🏨🏨🏨 ... 🏠, 🏡, ⌂
Comfort of restaurants : XXXXX X
Quality of the cuisine : ✿✿✿, ✿✿, ✿, Meals

Alphabetical list of areas included
Liste alphabétique des quartiers cités
Elenco alfabetico dei quartieri citati
Liste der erwähnten Bezirke

	page pagina Seite
Addington	49
Barnes	62
Battersea	63
Bayswater and Maida Vale	64
Belgravia	65
Bermondsey	62
Bexley	46
Bexleyheath	46
Blackheath	51
Bloomsbury	47
Brent Cross	46
Brixton	60
Bromley	46
Camden Town	48
Canonbury	54
Carshalton	63
Central Harrow	52
Chadwell Heath	46
Chelsea	54
Chessington	60
Child's Hill	46
Chiswick	53
City of London	49
Clapham	63
Clapham Common	61
Coulsdon	49
Cranford	54
Crouch End	52
Croydon	50
Dalston	51
Dulwich	63
Ealing	50
Earl's Court	56
Eastcote	53
East Sheen	62
Enfield	50
Euston	48
Finsbury	54
Fulham	51
Greenwich	51
Hadley Wood	51
Hammersmith	51
Hampstead	48
Hampton Court	62
Hampton Wick	62
Hanwell	50
Hatch End	52
Hayes	53
Heathrow Airport	53
Heston Service Area	54
Holborn	49
Hornchurch	52
Hornsey	52
Hyde Park and Knightsbridge	65
Ickenham	53
Ilford	61
Islington	54
Kensington	57
Kenton	52
Keston	47
Kingston	60
Mayfair	66
Mill Hill	46
Morden	61
North Harrow	52
North Kensington	58
Orpington	47
Pinner	52
Putney	64
Regent's Park	49
Regent's Park and Marylebone	68
Richmond	62
Romford	52
Rotherhithe	63
St. James's	70
Sanderstead	50
Shepherd's Bush	51
Soho	71
South Harrow	52
South Kensington	59
Southwark	63
South Woodford	61
Stanmore	52
Stepney	63
Strand and Covent Garden	72
Streatham	61
Surbiton	60
Sutton	63
Swiss Cottage	49
Tooting	64
Twickenham	62
Victoria	72
Wandsworth	64
Waterloo	61
Wembley	46
Wimbledon	61
Woodford	61
Yiewsley	53

Starred establishments in London

Les établissements à étoiles de Londres

Gli esercizi con stelle a Londra

Die Stern-Restaurants Londons

✿✿✿

		Area	Page
XXXXX	**Chez Nico at Ninety Park Lane** (at Grosvenor House H.)	Mayfair	67
XXXX	**La Tante Claire**	Chelsea	55
XXXX	**The Restaurant, Marco Pierre White** (at Hyde Park H.)	Hyde Park & Knightsbridge	65

✿✿

		Area	Page
XXXX	**Le Gavroche**	Mayfair	67

✿

		Area	Page
(hotel)	**Connaught**	Mayfair	66
(hotel)	**Capital**	Chelsea	54
(hotel)	**Halkin**	Belgravia	65
XXXXX	**Oak Room** (at Le Meridien Piccadilly H.)	Mayfair	67
XXXX	**Four Seasons** (at Four Seasons H.)	Mayfair	67
XXXX	**Grill Room** at the Café Royal	Soho	71
XXXX	**Oriental** (at Dorchester H.)	Mayfair	67
XXXX	**Les Saveurs**	Mayfair	67
XXX	**Aubergine**	Chelsea	55
XXX	**MPW's, The Canteen**	Chelsea	55
XXX	**Leith's**	North Kensington	58
XXX	**Pied à Terre**	Bloomsbury	48
XXX	**The Square**	St. James's	70
XX	**Fulham Road**	Chelsea	56

Further establishments which merit your attention

Autres tables qui méritent votre attention

Altre tavole particolarmente interessanti

Weitere empfehlenswerte Häuser

Meals

		Area	Page
XXX	**Al Bustan**	Belgravia	65
XXX	**Bibendum**	Chelsea	55
XXX	**Chutney Mary**	Chelsea	55
XXX	**Fifth Floor** (at Harvey Nichols)	Chelsea	55
XXX	**Ivy**	Strand and Covent Garden	72
XXX	**Le Pont de la Tour**	Southwark	62
XX	**Al San Vincenzo**	Bayswater and Maida Vale	65
XX	**Le Caprice**	St. James's	70
XX	**Clarke's**	Kensington	57
XX	**Greenhouse**	Mayfair	68
XX	**Hilaire**	South Kensington	60
XX	**Nico Central**	Regent's Park and Marylebone	69
XX	**Percy's**	North Harrow	52
XX	**Simply Nico**	Victoria	73
X	**Alastair Little**	Soho	71
X	**Bistrot Bruno**	Soho	71
X	**Kensington Place**	Kensington	58
X	**Malabar**	Kensington	58

Particularly pleasant hotels and restaurants

Hôtels et restaurants agréables

Alberghi e ristoranti ameni

Angenehme Hotels und Restaurants

Mayfair

Claridge's . . . 69
Dorchester . . . 69
Oak Room (at Le Meridien Piccadilly H) . . . 70

Strand & Covent Garden

Savoy . . . 75

Mayfair

Connaught . . . 69
47 Park Street . . . 69
Oriental (at Dorchester H) . . . 70

Soho

Grill Room at the Café Royal . . . 74

Chelsea

Durley House . . . 58

Kensington

The Milestone . . . 60

South Kensington

Blakes . . . 62
Pelham . . . 62

Belgravia

Halkin . . . 68

Southwark

Le Pont de la Tour . . . 66

St James's

22 Jermyn Street . . . 73
Quaglino's . . . 74

Victoria

Goring . . . 76

Chelsea

Sydney House . . . 58

Restaurants classified according to type

Restaurants classés suivant leur genre

Ristoranti classificati secondo il loro genere

Restaurants nach Art und Einrichtung geordnet

Bistro

Bangkok (Royal Borough of Kensington & Chelsea - *South Kensington*) . . . 60

Bougie (La) (Camden - *Camden Town*) . . . 48

Langan's Bistro (City of Westminster - *Regent's Park & Marylebone*) . . . 70

Stephen Bull's Bistro (Islington - *Finsbury*) . . . 54

Seafood

Overton's (City of Westminster - *St. James's*) . . . 70

Scotts (City of Westminster - *Mayfair*) . . . 67

Bentleys (City of Westminster - *Mayfair*) . . . 68

Downstairs at One Ninety (Royal Borough of Kensington & Chelsea - *South Kensington*) . . . 60

Gravier's (Kingston-upon-Thames - *Kingston*) . . . 60

Park Inn (Royal Borough of Kensington & Chelsea - *North Kensington*) . . . 58

Poissonnerie de l'Avenue (Royal Borough of Kensington & Chelsea - *Chelsea*) . . . 56

Sheekey's (City of Westminster - *Strand & Covent Garden*) . . . 72

Walsh's (City of Westminster - *Regent's Park & Marylebone*) . . . 69

Chinese

- XXXX ✿ **Oriental** (City of Westminster - *Mayfair*) 67
- XXX **Inn of Happiness** (City of Westminster - *Victoria*) 73
- XXX **Now and Zen** (City of Westminster - *Strand and Covent Garden*) 72
- XXX **Pearl of Knightsbridge** (City of Westminster - *Hyde Park and Knightsbridge*) 65
- XXX **Princess Garden** (City of Westminster - *Mayfair*) 67
- XXX **Zen Central** (City of Westminster - *Mayfair*) 67
- XX **Bayee Village** (Merton - *Wimbledon*) 61
- XX **China Jazz** (Camden - *Regent's Park*) 49
- XX **Dragon City** (Redbridge - *Ilford*) 61
- XX **Four Regions** (Richmond-Upon-Thames - *Richmond*) 62
- XX **Good Earth** (Barnet - *Mill Hill*) 46
- XX **Good Earth** (Royal Borough of Kensington & Chelsea - *Chelsea*) 56
- XX **Ho-Ho** (Redbridge - *South Woodford*) 61
- XX **Hunan** (City of Westminster - *Victoria*) 73
- XX **Imperial City** (City of London) 49
- XX **Ken Lo's Memories of China** (City of Westminster - *Victoria*) 73
- XX **Mao Tai** (Hammersmith & Fulham - *Fulham*) 51
- XX **Maxim** (Ealing - *Ealing*) 50
- XX **Ming** (City of Westminster - *Soho*) 71
- XX **Mr Tang's Mandarin** (Harrow - *Stanmore*) 52
- XX **Mr Wing** (Royal Borough of Kensington & Chelsea - *Earl's Court*) 57
- XX **Park Inn** (Royal Borough of Kensington & Chelsea - *North Kensington*) 58
- XX **Peking Diner** (Bromley - *Bromley*) 47
- XX **Poons** (City of Westminster - *Bayswater and Maida Vale*) 65
- XX **Poons of Russel Square** (Camden - *Bloomsbury*) 48
- XX **Red** (Royal Borough of Kensington & Chelsea - *Chelsea*) 56
- XX **Royal China** (Wandsworth - *Putney*) 64
- XX **Sampan's** (City of Westminster - *Regent's Park & Marylebone*) 69
- XX **Shanghai** (Royal Borough of Kensington & Chelsea - *Kensington*) 58
- XX **Swan** (Harrow - *Hatch End*) 52
- XX **Taste of China** (Harrow - *Central Harrow*) 52
- XX **Treasure of China** (Greenwich - *Greenwich*) 51
- XX **Willow** (Croydon - *Addington*) 49
- XX **Xian** (Bromley - *Orpington*) 47
- XX **Zen W3** (Camden - *Hampstead*) 48
- X **Fung Shing** (City of Westminster - *Soho*) 71
- X **Jasmin** (Wandsworth - *Clapham*) 63
- X **Mandarin** (Royal Borough of Kensington & Chelsea - *Kensington*) 58
- X **New Happiness Garden** (Ealing - *Hanwell*) 50
- X **Poons** (City of Westminster - *Soho*) 71

English

- XXX **Shepherds** (City of Westminster - *Victoria*) 73
- XXX **Simpson's-in-the-Strand** (City of Westminster - *Strand & Covent Garden*) 72
- XX **English Garden** (Royal Borough of Kensington & Chelsea - *Chelsea*) 56
- XX **Green's** (City of Westminter - *St. James's*) 70
- XX **Hudson's** (City of Westminter - *Regent's park & Marylebone*) 69
- XX **Rules** (City of Westminter - *Strand & Covent Garden*) 72
- X **Tate Gallery** (City of Westminter - *Victoria*) 74
- X **Alfred** (Camden - *Bloomsbury*) 48
- X **Auntie's** (Camden - *Bloomsbury*) 48

French

- XXXXX ✿✿✿ **Chez Nico at Ninety Park Lane** (City of Westminster - *Mayfair*) 67
- XXXXX ✿ **Oak Room** (City of Westminster - *Mayfair*) 67
- XXXX ✿✿ **Gavroche (Le)** (City of Westminster - *Mayfair*) 67
- XXXX ✿ **Four Seasons** (City of Westminster - *Mayfair*) 67
- XXXX ✿ **Saveurs (Les)** (City of Westminster - *Mayfair*) 67
- XXXX ✿✿✿ **Tante Claire (La)** (Royal Borough of Kensington & Chelsea - *Chelsea*) 55
- XXX **Auberge de Provence** (City of Westminster - *Victoria*) 73
- XXX **Jardin des Gourmets (Au)** (City of Westminster - *Soho*) 71

French

XX **Associés (Les)** (Haringey - *Crouch End*) 52

XX **Chez Moi** (Royal Borough of Kensington & Chelsea - *North Kensington*) 58

XX **Dordogne (La)** (Hounslow - *Chiswick*) 53

XX **Escargot Doré (L')** (Kensington - *Kensington*) 57

XX **Grafton (The)** (Lambeth - *Clapham Common*) 61

XX **Gravier's** (Kingston-upon-Thames - *Kingston*) 60

XX **Mon Plaisir** (Camden - *Bloomsbury*) 48

XX **Poissonnerie de l'Avenue** (Royal Borough of Kensington & Chelsea - *Chelsea*) 56

XX **Pomme d'Amour (La)** (Royal Borough of Kensington & Chelsea - *Kensington*) 57

XX **Rive Gauche (La)** (Lambeth - *Waterloo*) 61

XX **St. Quentin** (Royal Borough of Kensington & Chelsea - *Chelsea*). 56

XX **Truffe Noire (La)** (Southwark - *Southwark*) 63

X **Aventure (L')** (City of Westminster - *Regent Park & Marylebone*) 70

X **Magno's Brasserie** (City of Westminster - *Strand & Covent Garden*) 72

X **Muscadet (Le)** (City of Westminster - *Regent's Park & Marylebone*) 70

X **Poule au Pot (La)** (City of Westminster - *Victoria*) 74

X **Soulard** (Hackney - *Dalston*) 51

Hungarian

XX **Gay Hussar** (City of Westminster - *Soho*) 71

Indian & Pakistani

XXX **Bengal Clipper** (Southwark - *Bermondsey*) 62

XXX **Bombay Brasserie** (Royal Borough of Kensington & Chelsea - *South Kensington*) 60

XXX **Chandni** (Bromley - *Bromley*)..... 47

XXX **Chutney Mary (Anglo-Indian)** (Royal Borough of Kensington & Chelsea - *Chelsea*) 56

XX **Cafe Lazeez** (Royal Borough of Kensington & Chelsea - *South Kensington*) 60

XX **Delhi Brasserie** (Royal Borough of Kensington & Chelsea - *South Kensington*) 60

XX **Gaylord** (City of Westminster - *Regent's Park & Marylebone*) 69

XX **Gopal's** (City of Westminster - *Soho*) 71

XX **Kanishka** (Camden - *Bloomsbury*). 48

XX **Khan's of Kensington** (Royal Borough of Kensington & Chelsea - *South Kensington*) 60

XX **Laguna Tandoori** (Ealing - *Ealing*).. 50

XX **Laksmi** (Tower Hamlets - *Stepney*) 63

XX **Memories of India** (Royal Borough of Kensington & Chelsea - *South Kensington*) 60

XX **Red Fort** (City of Westminster - *Soho*) 71

XX **Spice Merchant** (City of Westminster - *Bayswater & Maida Vale*) 65

XX **Tabaq** (Wandsworth - *Wandsworth*) 64

XX **Tandoori Nights** (Hammersmith & Fulham - *Hammersmith*) 51

X **Bombay Bicycle Club** (Wandsworth - *Wandsworth*) 64

X **Jaflong** (Harrow - *South Harrow*) . 52

X **Jashan** (Haringey - *Hornsey*) 52

X **Malabar** (Royal Borough of Kensington & Chelsea - *Kensington*) 58

X **Taste of India** (Greenwich - *Greenwich*) 51

Irish

XX **Mulligans** (City of Westminster - *Mayfair*) 68

Italian

- ✿ **Halkin** (City of Westminster - *Belgravia*) 65
- XXX **L'Incontro** (City of Westminster - *Victoria*) 73
- XXX **Santini** (City of Westminster - *Victoria*) 73
- XX **Amico (L')** (City of Westminster - *Victoria*) 73
- XX **Caldesi** (City of Westminster - *Regent's Park & Marylebone*) 69
- XX **Daphne's** (Royal Borough of Kensington & Chelsea - *Chelsea*) 56
- XX **Del Buongustaio** (Wandsworth - *Putney*) 64
- XX **Fenice (La)** (Royal Borough of Kensington & Chelsea - *Kensington*) 57
- XX **Finezza (La)** (Royal Borough of Kensington & Chelsea - *Chelsea*) 56
- XX **Formula Veneta** (Royal Borough of Kensington & Chelsea - *Earl's Court*) 57
- XX **Giannino's** (Bromley - *Keston*) 47
- XX **Gran Paradiso** (City of Westminster - *Victoria*) 74
- XX **Loggia (La)** (City of Westminster - *Regent's Park & Marylebone*) 70
- XX **Luigi's** (Southwark - *Dulwich*) 63
- XX **Mezzaluna** (Barnet - *Child's Hill*) 46
- XX **Orchard** (Camden - *Hampstead*) 48
- XX **Orso** (City of Westminster - *Strand & Covent Garden*) 72
- XX **Primula (La)** (Royal Borough of Kensington & Chelsea - *Earl's Court*) 57
- XX **San Vincenzo (Al)** (City of Westminster - *Bayswater & Maida Vale*) 65
- XX **Scala (La)** (Barking and Dagenham - *Chadwell Heath*) 46
- XX **Toto's** (Royal Borough of Kensington & Chelsea - *Chelsea*) 56
- XX **Trattoria Sorrentina** (Harrow - *Central Harrow*) 52
- XX **Veranda (La)** (Sutton - *Carshalton*) 63
- X **Accento (L')** (City of Westminster - *Bayswater and Maida Vale*) 65
- X **Altro (L')** (Royal Borough of Kensington & Chelsea - *North Kensington*) 58
- X **Bertorelli's** (City of Westminster - *Strand & Covent Garden*) 72
- X **Cantina Del Ponte** (Southwark - *Bermondsey*) 63
- X **Castelletto (Il)** (Camden - *Bloomsbury*) 48
- X **Cibo** (Royal Borough of Kensington & Chelsea - *Kensington*) 58
- X **Florians** (Haringey - *Crouch End*) 52
- X **Fontana (La)** (City of Westminster - *Victoria*) 74
- X **Issimo !** (City of London) 49
- X **Mario** (Croydon - *Croydon*) 50
- X **Mimmo d'Ischia** (City of Westminster - *Victoria*) 74
- X **Olivo** (City of Westminster - *Victoria*) 74
- X **Paolo's** (Ealing - *Ealing*) 50
- X **Pitagora** (Richmond-Upon-Thames - *Richmond*) 62
- X **Riva** (Richmond-Upon-Thames - *Barnes*) 62
- X **Roberto's** (Hillingdon - *Ickenham*) 53
- X **Sambuca** (Hillingdon - *Eastcote*) 53
- X **Villa Medici** (City of Westminster - *Victoria*) 74

Japanese

- XXX **Benihana** (Camden - *Hampstead*) 48
- XXX **Benihana** (Royal Borough of Kensington & Chelsea - *Chelsea*) 56
- XXX **Suntory** (City of Westminster - *St. James's*) 70
- XXX **Tatsuso** (City of London) 49
- XX **Asuka** (City of Westminster - *Regent's Park & Marylebone*) 70
- XX **Matsuri** (City of Westminster - *St. James's*) 71
- XX **Miyama** (City of London) 49
- XX **Shogun** (City of Westminster - *Mayfair*) 68
- X **Ikeda** (City of Westminster - *Mayfair*) 68
- X **Imari** (Camden - *Holborn*) 49
- X **Nakamura** (City of Westminster - *Regent's Park & Marylebone*) 70

Lebanese

XXX **Bustan (Al)** (City of Westminster - *Belgravia*) 65

XX **Maroush III** (City of Westminster - *Regent's Park & Marylebone*) 69

XX **Phoenicia** (Royal Borough of Kensington & Chelsea - *Kensington*) . 58

X **Beit Eddine** (Royal Borough of Kensington & Chelsea - *Chelsea*). 56

Polish

X **Wódka** (Royal Borough of Kensington & Chelsea - *Kensington*) 58

Spanish

XXX **Albero and Grana** (Royal Borough of Kensington & Chelsea - *Chelsea*) 56

Swedish

X **Anna's Place** (Islington - *Canonbury*) 54

Thai

XX **Blue Elephant** (Hammersmith & Fulham - *Fulham*) 51

XX **Busabong Too** (Royal Borough of Kensington & Chelsea - *Chelsea*) 56

XX **Chada** (Wandsworth - *Battersea*) . 63

XX **Lena's** (Wandsworth - *Battersea*) . 63

XX **Tui** (Royal Borough of Kensington & Chelsea - *South Kensington*) 60

X **Ayudhya** (Kingston-upon-Thames - *Kingston*) 60

X **Bangkok** (Royal Borough of Kensington & Chelsea - *South Kensington*) 60

X **Oh Boy** (Wandsworth - *Tooting*) . . 64

X **Sri Siam** (City of Westminster - *Soho*) 71

X **Thai Castle** (Harrow - *North Harrow*) 52

X **Thai Pepper** (Camden - *Swiss Cottage*) 49

Vietnamese

X **Saigon** (City of Westminster - *Soho*) 71

Boroughs and areas

Greater London is divided, for administrative purposes, into 32 boroughs plus the City : these sub-divide naturally into minor areas, usually grouped around former villages or quarters, which often maintain a distinctive character.

BARKING and DAGENHAM p. 7.

Chadwell Heath – ✉ Essex – ☎ 0181.

XX La Scala, 19a High Rd, RM6 6PU, ℘ 983 8818 – P JU **e**
Meals - Italian.

BARNET pp. 4 and 5.

Brent Cross – ✉ NW2 – ☎ 0181.

Holiday Inn Garden Court, Tilling Rd, NW2 3DS, ℘ 455 4777, Fax 455 4660 – |♦| ⇆ rm ▤ TV ☎ ♿ P – 🧑 50. AE ① VISA JCB. ✱ DU **n**
Meals (bar lunch)/dinner 11.95 **st.** and a la carte 4.95 – ☕ 8.25 – **153 rm** 69.00 **st.**

Child's Hill – ✉ NW2 – ☎ 0171.

XX **Mezzaluna,** 424 Finchley Rd, NW2 2HY, ℘ 794 3603 – AE VISA DU **o**
closed Saturday lunch and Monday – **Meals** - Italian a la carte 16.50/26.50 **t.** 5.50.

X **Quincy's,** 675 Finchley Rd, NW2 2JP, ℘ 794 8499 – ▤. AE VISA DU **r**
closed Sunday, Monday and 1 week Christmas – **Meals** (booking essential) (dinner only) 25.00 **t.** 4.50.

X **Laurent,** 428 Finchley Rd, NW2 2HY, ℘ 794 3603 – AE VISA DU **o**
closed Sunday, first 3 weeks August and Bank Holidays – **Meals** - Couscous a la carte 13.00 **t.**

Mill Hill – ✉ NW7 – ☎ 0181.

18 100 Barnet Way, Mill Hill ℘ 959 2282 CT.

XX **Good Earth,** 143 The Broadway, NW7 4RN, ℘ 959 7011, Fax 959 7464 – ▤. AE ① VISA CT **a**
closed 24 to 27 December – **Meals** - Chinese 17.50/25.50 **t.** and a la carte 4.00.

BEXLEY pp. 10 and 11.

Bexley – ✉ Kent – ☎ 01322.

Forte Posthouse, Black Prince Interchange, Southwold Rd, DA5 1ND, on A 2 ℘ 526900, Fax 526113 – |♦| ⇆ rm ▤ rest TV ☎ ♿ P – 🧑 70. AE ① VISA JX **e**
Meals a la carte approx. 15.00 **t.** 5.50 – **100 rm** 59.50/69.50 **st.**, 2 suites.

Bexleyheath – ✉ Kent – ☎ 0181.

Swallow, 1 Broadway, DA6 7JZ, ℘ 298 1000, Fax 298 1234, Fa, ▭ – |♦| ⇆ rm ▤ TV ☎ ♿ P – 🧑 200. AE ① VISA JX **c**
Galleria : **Meals** (dinner only and Sunday lunch) 25.00 **st.** – *Copper* : **Meals** 12.50/19.00 **st.** – **142 rm** ☕ 88.00/120.00 **st.** – SB.

BRENT pp. 4 and 5.

Wembley – ✉ Middx – ☎ 0181.

Hilton National Wembley, Empire Way, HA9 8DS, ℘ 902 8839, Fax 900 2201, Fa, ≘s, ▭ – |♦| ⇆ rm ▤ rest TV ☎ P – 🧑 300. AE ① VISA JCB CU **z**
Celebrities : **Meals** (carving rest.) 15.95/19.95 **st.** – *Terracotta* : **Meals** - Italian (dinner only) 15.95/19.95 **st.** – ☕ 10.25 – **306 rm** 119.00/146.00 **st.** – SB.

BROMLEY pp. 10 and 11.

18, 9 Cray Valley, Sandy Lane, St. Paul's Cray ℘ (01689) 831927, JY.

Bromley – ✉ Kent – ☎ 0181.

9 Magpie Hall Lane ℘ 462 7014 HY.

Bromley Court, Bromley Hill, BR1 4JD, ℘ 464 5011, Fax 460 0899, 🌳 – |♦| ⇆ rm TV ☎ P – 🧑 150. AE ① VISA HY **z**
Meals *(closed Saturday lunch)* 9.95/14.95 **st.** and a la carte 4.65 – **118 rm** ☕ 79.00/89.00 **st.**

XXX **Chandni,** 123-125 Mason's Hill, BR2 9HT, ☎ 290 4447, Fax 313 1477 – ▤. AE VISA HY **e**
closed 25 and 26 December – **Meals** - Indian 5.95/17.50 **t.** and a la carte 3.25.

XX **Peking Diner,** 71 Burnt Ash Lane, BR1 5AA, ☎ 464 7911 – ▤. AE VISA HX **u**
closed Sunday and 25-26 December – **Meals** - Chinese (Peking) 10.00/25.00 and a la carte 3.75.

Keston – ✉ Kent – 01689.

XX **Giannino's,** 6 Commonside, BR2 6BP, ☎ 856410 – AE VISA HZ **x**
closed Sunday, Monday, first 2 weeks August and 24 December-10 January – **Meals** - Italian 15.75 **t.** and a la carte 4.75.

Orpington – ✉ Kent – 01689.

18 High Elms, High Elms Rd, Downe, Orpington ☎ 858175 – 9, 18 Hewitts Golf Centre, Court Rd ☎ 896266.

XX **Xian,** 324 High St., BR6 0NG, ☎ 871881 – ▤. AE VISA JY **a**
closed Sunday lunch and second week August – **Meals** - Chinese (Peking, Szechuan) 7.50/12.60 **t.** and a la carte 5.20.

CAMDEN Except where otherwise stated see pp. 20-23.

Bloomsbury – ✉ NW1/W1/WC1 – 0171.

34-37 Woburn Pl., WC1H 0JR ☎ 580 4599.

Holiday Inn Kings Cross, 1 Kings Cross Rd, WC1X 9HX, ☎ 833 3900, Fax 917 6163, <, squash – rm ▤ TV ☎ – 240 MT **a**
397 rm, 8 suites.

Russell (Forte), Russell Sq., WC1B 5BE, ☎ 837 6470, Telex 24615, Fax 837 2857 – rm ▤ rest TV ☎ – 450 LU **o**
325 rm, 3 suites.

Marlborough (Radisson Edwardian), 9-14 Bloomsbury St., WC1B 3QD, ☎ 636 5601, Fax 636 0532 – rm ▤ rest TV ☎ – 200. AE VISA JCB. LU **i**
Meals 16.95 **st.** and a la carte – 10.95 – **167 rm** 85.00/197.00, 2 suites – SB.

Mountbatten (Radisson Edwardian), 20 Monmouth St., WC2H 9HD, ☎ 836 4300, Fax 240 3540 – rm ▤ rest TV ☎ – 75. AE VISA JCB.
Meals *(closed lunch Saturday and Sunday)* 18.00/35.00 **st.** and a la carte – 12.00 – **121 rm** 153.00/181.00 **st.**, 6 suites – SB. p.33 DV **o**

Grafton (Radisson Edwardian), 130 Tottenham Court Rd, W1P 9HP, ☎ 388 4131, Telex 297234, Fax 387 7394 – ▤ TV ☎ – 100. AE VISA JCB. KU **n**
Meals *(closed Saturday lunch)* 18.50 **st.** and a la carte – 10.00 – **320 rm** 111.00/140.00 **st.**, 4 suites – SB.

Kenilworth (Radisson Edwardian), 97 Great Russell St., WC1B 3LB, ☎ 637 3477, Fax 631 3133 – rm ▤ rest TV ☎ – 100. AE VISA JCB. LU **a**
Meals (carving rest.) 16.95 – 10.00 – **187 rm** 79.00/134.00 **st.**

Forte Crest Bloomsbury, Coram St., WC1N 1HT, ☎ 837 1200, Telex 22113, Fax 837 5374 – rm ▤ rest TV ☎ – 700 LT **c**
282 rm, 2 suites.

Montague Park, 12-20 Montague St., WC1B 5BJ, ☎ 637 1001, Telex 23307, Fax 637 2506 – ▤ rest TV ☎ – 80. AE VISA JCB. LU **c**
Meals (bar lunch)/dinner 12.50 **t.** and a la carte 5.75 – **109 rm** 95.00/170.00 **st.**

Blooms, 7 Montague St., WC1B 5BP, ☎ 323 1717, Fax 636 6498 – TV ☎. AE VISA JCB. LU **n**
Meals (room service only) 5.00/23.00 **st.** and dinner a la carte – **26 rm** 100.00/250.00 **st.** – SB.

Bonnington, 92 Southampton Row, WC1B 4BH, ☎ 242 2828, Telex 261591, Fax 831 9170 – rm ▤ rest TV ☎ – 250. AE VISA LU **s**
Meals *(closed lunch Saturday, Sunday and Bank Holidays)* 9.50/16.75 **st.** and a la carte 10.00 – **215 rm** 79.00/100.00 **st.**

Bloomsbury Park (Mt. Charlotte Thistle), 126 Southampton Row, WC1B 5AD, ☎ 430 0434, Telex 25757, Fax 242 0665 – rm TV ☎ – 30 LU **u**
95 rm.

Academy, 17-21 Gower St., WC1E 6HG, ☎ 631 4115, Fax 636 3442, – ▤ rest TV ☎. AE VISA JCB. KLU **v**
Meals *(closed lunch Saturday and Sunday)* 10.00/16.95 **st.** and a la carte 6.95 – 8.95 – **33 rm** 74.00/145.00 **s.** – SB.

Harlingford without rest., 61-63 Cartwright Gdns, WC1H 9EL, ☎ 387 1551, Fax 387 4616, – TV ☎ LT **n**
44 rm.

Mabledon Court without rest., 10-11 Mabledon Pl., WC1H 9BA, ☎ 388 3866, Fax 387 5686 – TV ☎. LT **s**
33 rm.

XXX ⚘ **Pied à Terre** (Neat), 34 Charlotte St., W1P 1HJ, ✆ 636 1178, Fax 916 1178 – ▤. AE ⓓ VISA JCB KU **e**
closed Saturday lunch, Sunday, last 2 weeks August, 2 weeks December-January and Bank Holidays – **Meals** 19.50/39.50 **st.** 7.00
Spec. Snails with morilles and asparagus, garlic purée, Roasted pigeon with a neck confit, fondant celeriac and liver sauce, Fillet of sea bass with a sardine purée and a bouillabaisse sauce.

XX **Neal Street,** 26 Neal St., WC2H 9PS, ✆ 836 8368, Fax 497 1361 – ▤. AE ⓓ VISA
closed Sunday, Christmas-New Year and Bank Holidays – **Meals** a la carte 29.90/45.45 **t.** 8.00. p. 33 DV **s**

XX **Mon Plaisir,** 21 Monmouth St., WC2H 9DD, ✆ 836 7243, Fax 379 0121 – AE ⓓ VISA JCB p. 33 DV **a**
closed Saturday lunch, Sunday and Bank Holidays – **Meals** - French 13.95 **st.** and a la carte 5.80.

XX **Poons of Russell Square,** 50 Woburn Pl., WC1H 0JE, ✆ 580 1188 – ▤. AE ⓓ VISA JCB LU **x**
closed 24 to 28 December – **Meals** - Chinese 10.00/25.00 **t.** and a la carte.

XX **Bleeding Heart,** Bleeding Heart Yard, EC1N 8SJ, off Greville St., Hatton Garden ✆ 242 2056, Fax 831 1402. AE ⓓ VISA JCB NU **e**
closed Saturday, Sunday and 2 weeks Christmas – **Meals** 13.95 t. and a la carte 17.20/22.65 **t.** 3.95.

XX **Kanishka,** 161 Whitfield St., W1P 5RY, ✆ 388 0860 – ▤. AE ⓓ VISA KTU **z**
closed lunch Saturday and Bank Holidays, Sunday and 25 to 26 December – **Meals** - Indian 6.95/25.00 **t.** and a la carte.

X **Auntie's,** 126 Cleveland St., W1P 5DN, ✆ 387 1548, Fax 387 3226 – AE ⓓ VISA
closed dinner Saturday and Sunday, 25 to 26 December and 1 January – **Meals** - English a la carte 13.30/20.50 **st.** 4.00. JU **s**

X **Il Castelletto,** 17 Bury Pl., WC1A 2IB, ✆ 405 2232 – ▤. AE ⓓ VISA LU **r**
closed Saturday lunch, Sunday and Bank Holidays – **Meals** - Italian 14.00 **t.** (lunch) and a la carte 16.50/21.60 **t.** 4.75.

X **Alfred,** 245 Shaftesbury Av., WC2H 8EH, ✆ 240 2566, Fax 497 0672 – ▤. AE VISA
closed Sunday dinner and 24 to 31 December – **Meals** - English a la carte 18.45/25.45 **t.** 6.00. DV **u**

Camden Town – ✉ NW1 – ☎ 0171.

X **La Bougie,** 7 Murray St., NW1 9RE, ✆ 485 6400 KS **a**
Meals - Bistro a la carte 13.25/16.00 4.00.

Euston – ✉ WC1 – ☎ 0171.

Euston Plaza, 17/18 Upper Woburn Pl., WC1H 0HT, ✆ 383 4105, Fax 383 4106, – rm ▤ TV ☎ ♿ – 110. AE ⓓ VISA JCB. KLT **e**
Meals 12.00/26.00 **st.** and dinner a la carte – 9.50 – **149 rm** 112.00/129.00 **st.**, 1 suite.

Hampstead – ✉ NW3 – ☎ 0171.

Winnington Rd, Hampstead ✆ 455 0203.

Swiss Cottage, 4 Adamson Rd, NW3 3HP, ✆ 722 2281, Fax 483 4588, « Antique furniture collection » – TV ☎ – 60. AE ⓓ VISA. GS **n**
Meals (bar lunch)/dinner 22.50 **t.** and a la carte 5.95 – **74 rm** 75.00/95.00 **t.**, 6 suites – SB.

Forte Posthouse, 215 Haverstock Hill, NW3 4RB, ✆ 794 8121, Fax 435 5586 – rm TV ☎ – 30. AE ⓓ VISA JCB ES **r**
Meals a la carte approx. 15.00 **t.** 5.50 – **140 rm** 59.50/69.50 **st.**

Clive (Hilton), Primrose Hill Rd, NW3 3NA, ✆ 586 2233, Fax 586 1659 – TV ☎ – 200. AE ⓓ VISA. HS **a**
Meals 15.00 **t.** and a la carte – **93 rm** 60.00/70.00 **t.**, 3 suites – SB.

Charles Bernard, 5-7 Frognal, NW3 6AL, ✆ 794 0101, Fax 794 0100 – TV ☎. AE ⓓ VISA. ES **s**
Meals (bar lunch)/dinner 15.00 **st.** and a la carte – **57 rm** 55.00/65.00 **st.**

Langdorf without rest., 20 Frognal, NW3 6AG, ✆ 794 4483, Fax 435 9055 – TV ☎. AE ⓓ VISA. ES **c**
5.50 – **31 rm** 61.00/115.00 **st.**

XXX **Benihana,** 100 Avenue Rd, NW3 3HF, ✆ 586 9508, Fax 586 6740 – ▤. AE ⓓ VISA JCB
closed Monday lunch and 25 December – **Meals** - Japanese (Teppan-Yaki) 8.45/13.95 **t.** and a la carte. GS **o**

XX **Carapace,** 118 Heath St., NW3 1DR, ✆ 435 8000, Fax 935 9582 – AE ⓓ VISA
Meals (dinner only and Sunday lunch)/dinner 13.80 **t.** and a la carte 4.60. ES **e**

XX **Zen W3,** 83-84 Hampstead High St., NW3 1RE, ✆ 794 7863, Fax 794 6956 – AE ⓓ VISA
Meals - Chinese a la carte 15.20/21.40 **t.** ES **a**

XX **Orchard,** 12a Belsize Terr., NW3 4AX, ✆ 794 4288 – ▤. AE VISA ES **v**
closed Bank Holidays – **Meals** - Italian 14.50 **t.** (lunch) and a la carte 20.50/24.00 **t.** 5.50.

X **Café des Arts,** 82 Hampstead High St., NW3 1RE, ✆ 435 3608 – AE ⓓ VISA
closed 25 and 26 December – **Meals** a la carte 14.00/21.20 **t.** 5.50. ES **i**

Holborn – ✉ WC2 – ☎ 0171.

Drury Lane Moat House (Q.M.H.), 10 Drury Lane, High Holborn, WC2B 5RE, ☎ 836 6666, Telex 8811395, Fax 831 1548 – rm – 100. AE VISA. p. 33 DV c
Meals *(closed lunch Saturday and Sunday)* 12.00/19.00 **t.** and a la carte 7.00 – 10.25 – **151 rm** 120.00/180.00 **st.**, 2 suites – SB.

Imari, 71 Red Lion St., WC1R 4NA, ☎ 405 0486, Fax 405 0473 – . AE VISA JCB MU z
closed Saturday lunch, Sunday and Bank Holidays – **Meals** - Japanese 9.00/25.00 **st.** and a la carte.

Regent's Park – ✉ NW1 – ☎ 0171.

White House, Albany St., NW1 3UP, ☎ 387 1200, Telex 24111, Fax 388 0091, – rm rest – 120. AE VISA JCB. JT o
Meals *(closed Saturday lunch, Sunday and Bank Holidays)* (bar lunch Saturday and Sunday) 18.75/22.75 **t.** and a la carte 8.00 – 10.75 – **561 rm** 105.00/150.00 **st.**, 15 suites.

Odette's, 130 Regent's Park Rd, NW1 8XL, ☎ 586 5486 – AE VISA HS i
closed Saturday lunch, Sunday dinner, 1 week Christmas and Bank Holidays – **Meals** 10.00 **t.** (lunch) and a la carte 19.00/25.50 **t.** 5.50.

China Jazz, 29-31 Parkway, NW1 7PN, ☎ 482 3940 – AE VISA JS e
closed Saturday lunch and 25 to 26 December – **Meals** - Chinese 10.00/24.00 **t.** and a la carte.

Belgo, 72 Chalk Farm Rd, NW1 8AN, ☎ 267 0718, Fax 267 7508 – AE VISA IS e
Meals 10.00/35.00 **t.** and a la carte.

Swiss Cottage – ✉ NW3 – ☎ 0171.

Regents Park Marriott, 128 King Henry's Rd, NW3 3ST, ☎ 722 7711, Telex 267396, Fax 586 5822, – rm – 400. AE VISA GS a
Meals 14.95/18.50 **st.** and a la carte 7.25 – 11.85 – **298 rm** 145.00/158.00 **s.**, 5 suites.

Peter's, 65 Fairfax Rd, NW6 4EE, ☎ 624 5804 – AE VISA FS i
closed Saturday lunch – **Meals** 11.95 **t.** and a la carte 4.00.

Thai Pepper, 115 Finchley Rd, NW3 6HY, ☎ 722 0026 – . AE VISA GS v
closed lunch Saturday and Sunday and Bank Holidays – **Meals** - Thai 17.00/20.00 **t.** and a la carte 3.90.

CITY OF LONDON – ☎ 0171 Except where otherwise stated see p. 23.

Tatsuso, 32 Broadgate Circle, EC2M 2QS, ☎ 638 5863, Fax 638 5864 – . AE VISA JCB PU u
closed Saturday, Sunday, and Bank Holidays – **Meals** - Japanese (booking essential) 19.00/70.00 **st.** and a la carte.

Le Quai, Riverside Walkway, 1 Broken Wharf, EC4V 3QQ, off High Timber St. ☎ 236 6480, Fax 236 6479 – . AE VISA JCB OV a
closed Saturday, Sunday and Bank Holidays – **Meals** (dinner booking essential) 32.50 and lunch a la carte.

Corney and Barrow, 109 Old Broad St., EC2N 1AP, ☎ 638 9308 – . AE VISA JCB PU c
closed Saturday, Sunday and Bank Holidays – **Meals** (lunch only) 20.95 **t.** and a la carte 4.50.

Miyama, 17 Godliman St., EC4V 5BD, ☎ 489 1937 – . AE VISA JCB OV e
closed Saturday dinner, Sunday and Bank Holidays – **Meals** - Japanese 15.00/20.00 **t.** and a la carte 5.00.

Imperial City, Royal Exchange, Cornhill, EC3V 3LL, ☎ 626 3437, Fax 338 0125 – . AE VISA PV a
closed Saturday, Sunday and Bank Holidays – **Meals** 13.80/24.80 **t.** and a la carte.

Whittington's, 21 College Hill, EC4R 2RP, ☎ 248 5855 – . AE VISA JCB OV c
closed Saturday, Sunday and Bank Holidays – **Meals** (lunch only) a la carte 22.70/26.70 **t.** 4.75.

Issimo! (Forte), 8-11 Lime St., EC3 7AA, ☎ 623 3616 – . AE VISA JCB PV e
closed Saturday, Sunday and Bank Holidays – **Meals** - Italian (lunch only)(booking essential) a la carte 18.65/22.95 **t.** 4.95.

CROYDON pp. 10 and 11.

Addington – ✉ Surrey – ☎ 0181 – 18, 18, 9 Addington Court, Featherbed Lane ☎ 657 0281/2/3, GZ – 18 The Addington, Shirley Church Rd ☎ 777 1055 GZ.

Willow, 88 Selsdon Park Rd, CR2 8JT, ☎ 657 4656 – . AE VISA GZ x
closed 25 to 27 December – **Meals** - Chinese (Peking, Szechuan) 13.50/16.50 **t.** and a la carte 4.50.

Coulsdon – ✉ Surrey – ☎ 0181 – 18 Coulsdon Court, Coulsdon Rd ☎ 660 6083.

Coulsdon Manor, Coulsdon Court Rd, via Stoats Nest Rd, CR5 2LL, ☎ 668 0414, Fax 668 3118, squash – rest – 180. AE VISA EZ e
Meals *(closed Saturday lunch) 14.95/17.50* **t.** and a la carte 5.95 – **35 rm** 76.00/86.00 **st.** – SB.

Croydon – ✉ Surrey – ☎ 0181.

Katherine St., CR9 1ET ✆ 760 5630.

Hilton National, Waddon Way, CR9 4HH, ✆ 680 3000, Fax 681 6171, Fs, ≘s, ☒ – |♦| ▤ TV ☎ ♿ P – 🏛 400. AE ⓘ VISA JCB. ✗ FZ **e**
Latitudes : **Meals** 12.95/18.00 **t.** 6.50 – *Ike's American Diner :* **Meals** a la carte 19.40/23.65 **t.** – ☐ 9.95 – **168 rm** 87.00 **t.** – SB.

Croydon Park, 7 Altyre Rd, CR9 5AA, ✆ 680 9200, Fax 760 0426, Fs, ≘s, ☒, squash – |♦| ⇔ rm ▤ TV ☎ P – 🏛 300. AE ⓘ VISA JCB FZ **u**
Oscars : **Meals** 13.95/14.95 **t.** 4.95 – **203 rm** ☐ 87.00/97.00 **st.**, 2 suite – SB.

Forte Posthouse, Purley Way, CR9 4LT, ✆ 688 5185, Fax 681 6438, ⚘ – ⇔ rm TV ☎ P – 🏛 170. AE ⓘ VISA FZ **o**
Meals a la carte approx. 15.00 **t.** 5.50 – **83 rm** 59.50/69.50 **st.**

Windsor Castle Toby, 415 Brighton Rd, South Croydon, CR2 6EJ, ✆ 680 4559, Fax 680 5121, ⚘ – ⇔ rm TV ☎ P. AE ⓘ VISA. ✗ FZ **a**
Meals (grill rest.) 7.95 **st.** and a la carte 4.75 – **29 rm** ☐ 60.00/70.00 **st.** – SB.

Travel Inn, Coombe Rd, CR0 5RB, on A 212 ✆ 686 2030, Fax 686 6435, ⚘ – ⇔ rm TV ♿ P. AE ⓘ VISA. ✗ GZ **s**
Meals (Beefeater grill) a la carte approx. 16.00 **t.** – ☐ 4.95 – **39 rm** 33.50 **t.**

Mario, 299 High St., CR0 1QL, ✆ 686 5624 – AE VISA FZ **s**
closed Saturday lunch, Monday dinner, Sunday, last 2 weeks August and Bank Holidays – **Meals** - Italian 12.50 **t.** and a la carte.

Sanderstead – ✉ Surrey – ☎ 0181.

18 Selsdon Park Hotel, Addington Rd, Sanderstead ✆ 657 8811 GZ.

Selsdon Park, Addington Rd, CR2 8YA, ✆ 657 8811, Fax 651 6171, ≤, Fs, ≘s, ☒ heated, ☒, 18, ⚘, park, ✗, squash – |♦| ⇔ rm TV ☎ P – 🏛 150. AE ⓘ VISA JCB
Meals (dancing Saturday) 15.50/25.00 **t.** and a la carte – ☐ 9.50 – **163 rm** 85.00/140.00 **t.**, 7 suites – SB. GZ **n**

EALING pp. 4 and 5.

Ealing – ✉ W5 – ☎ 0181.

18 West Middlesex, Greenford Rd ✆ 574 3450 BV – 9 Horsenden Hill, Woodland Rise ✆ 902 4555 BU.

Carnarvon, Ealing Common, W5 3HN, ✆ 992 5399, Fax 992 7082 – |♦| ⇔ rm TV ☎ P – 🏛 220. AE ⓘ VISA JCB. ✗ CV **v**
Meals a la carte 13.65/20.65 **st.** 5.50 – ☐ 9.95 – **145 rm** 85.00/105.00 **st.**

Maxim, 153-155 Northfield Av., W13 9QT, ✆ 567 1719 – ▤ BV **a**
Meals - Chinese (Peking).

Laguna Tandoori, 1-4 Culmington Par., Uxbridge Rd, W13 9BD, ✆ 579 9992 – ▤ BV **i**
closed 25 December – **Meals** - Indian 15.00 **t.** and a la carte 3.70.

Noughts 'n' Crosses, 77 The Grove, W5 5LL, ✆ 840 7568, Fax 840 1905 – AE VISA
closed Sunday dinner, Monday, August and 26 December-5 January – **Meals** (dinner only and Sunday lunch)/dinner 19.90 **t.** 4.45. BV **u**

Paolo's, 7 Hanger Green, W5 3EL, ✆ 997 8560 – AE ⓘ VISA CV **r**
closed Saturday lunch, Sunday and Bank Holidays – **Meals** - Italian 21.00/25.00 **t.** and a la carte 4.00.

Hanwell – ✉ W7 – ☎ 0181.

18 Brent Valley, Church Rd, ✆ 567 1287 BV.

Wellmeadow Lodge, 24 Wellmeadow Rd, W7 2AL, ✆ 567 7294, Fax 566 3468, ⚘ – ⇔ TV ☎. AE VISA. ✗ BV **r**
Meals (by arrangement) 15.00 – **6 rm** ☐ 45.00/72.00.

New Happiness Garden, 22 Boston Par., Boston Rd, W7 2DG, ✆ 567 9314 – AE ⓘ VISA BV **c**
closed Sunday, 25-26 December and 1 January – **Meals** - Chinese 12.00/23.00 **t.** and a la carte 4.25.

ENFIELD pp. 6 and 7.

18 Lee Valley, Picketts Lock Lane, Edmonton ✆ 803 3611 GT.

Enfield – ✉ Middx – ☎ 0181.

18 Whitewebbs, Beggars Hollow, Clay Hill ✆ 363 4454, N : 1 m. FT.

Royal Chace, The Ridgeway, EN2 8AR, ✆ 366 6500, Fax 367 7191, ☒ heated, ⚘ – TV ☎ P – 🏛 270. AE ⓘ VISA. ✗ ET **a**
closed 24 to 29 December – **Meals** *(closed Saturday lunch, Sunday dinner and Bank Holidays)* (bar lunch Monday to Saturday)/dinner 16.95 **st.** and a la carte 5.45 – **92 rm** ☐ 71.50/130.00 **st.**

Oak Lodge, 80 Village Rd, Bush Hill Park, EN1 2EU, ✆ 360 7082, ⚘ – TV ☎ ♿. AE ⓘ VISA JCB FT **e**
Meals (by arrangement) 17.50 **t.** 6.00 **5 rm** ☐ 55.00/80.00 **st.** – SB.

Hadley Wood – ✉ Herts – ☎ 0181.

West Lodge Park ⛱, off Cockfosters Rd, ✉ Barnet, EN4 0PY, ☎ 440 8311, Fax 449 3698, ≤, park – 🛗 ⇆ rest TV ☎ ♿ 🅟 – 80. AE VISA. ET **i**
Meals 18.95/22.50 **st.** – 8.75 – **45 rm** 64.50/170.00 **st.** – SB.

GREENWICH pp. 10 and 11.

Blackheath – ✉ SE3 – ☎ 0181.

Bardon Lodge, 15 Stratheden Rd, SE3 7TH, ☎ 853 4051, Fax 858 7387, – TV ☎ 🅟 – 40. AE VISA HV **a**
***Lamplight* : Meals** *(closed Sunday dinner)* (bar lunch Monday to Saturday)/dinner 13.95 **t.** and a la carte 5.25 – 4.95 – **30 rm** 53.50/85.00 **t.**

Vanbrugh, 21 St. John's Park, SE3 7TD, ☎ 853 5505 (Reservations : 853 4051), Fax 858 7387, – 🛗 TV ☎ 🅟. AE VISA.
Meals (see ***Bardon Lodge*** above) – 4.95 – **30 rm** 53.50/74.00 **t.**

Greenwich – ✉ SE10 – ☎ 0181.

🅘 46 Greenwich Church St., SE10 9BL ☎ 858 6376.

Hamilton, 14 West Grove, SE10 8QT, ☎ 694 9899, Fax 694 2370 – TV ☎ GX **a**
11 rm.

Treasure of China, 10-11 Nelson Rd, SE10 9JB, ☎ 858 9884, Fax 293 5327 – . AE VISA GV **e**
closed 25-26 December – **Meals** - Chinese (Peking, Szechuan) a la carte 14.60/19.50 **t.** 3.50.

Spread Eagle, 1-2 Stockwell St., SE10 9JN, ☎ 853 2333 – AE VISA GV **c**
closed Sunday dinner, 25 to 30 December and Bank Holiday Mondays – **Meals** 13.50 **t.** (lunch) and dinner a la carte 19.00/26.00 **t.**

Taste of India, 57 Greenwich Church St., SE10 9BL, ☎ 858 2668 – AE VISA GV **n**
Meals - Indian 12.00/15.00 **t.** and a la carte 3.50.

HACKNEY – p.23.

Dalston – ✉ N 1 – ☎ 0171.

Soulard, 113 Mortimer Rd, N1 4JY, ☎ 254 1314 – AE VISA PS **e**
closed Sunday, Monday, 2 weeks August and 1 week Christmas – **Meals** - French (dinner only) 15.00 **t.** and a la carte 9.50.

HAMMERSMITH and FULHAM Except where otherwise stated see pp. 24-25.

Fulham – ✉ SW6 – ☎ 0171.

La Reserve, 422-428 Fulham Rd, SW6 1DU, ☎ 385 8561, Fax 385 7662, « Contemporary decor » – 🛗 ⇆ rm TV ☎. AE VISA. FZ **a**
Meals *(closed Sunday dinner)* a la carte 13.50/21.00 **t.** 5.50 – **37 rm** 75.00/90.00 **t.** – SB.

Blue Elephant, 4-6 Fulham Broadway, SW6 1AA, ☎ 385 6595, Fax 386 7665 – . AE VISA EZ **z**
closed Saturday lunch and 24 to 27 December – **Meals** - Thai (booking essential) 25.00/28.00 **t.** and a la carte 5.95.

Mao Tai, 58 New Kings Rd., Parsons Green, SW6 4LS, ☎ 731 2520 – . AE VISA p. 12 BQ **e**
closed 25 to 27 December – **Meals** - Chinese (Szechuan) 7.00/15.00 **t.** and a la carte 5.00.

Fleurie, 755 Fulham Rd, SW6 5UU, ☎ 371 0695. AE VISA BQ **n**
closed Saturday lunch and Bank Holidays – **Meals** 12.50/15.00 **t.** and a la carte.

Le Midi, 488 Fulham Rd, SW6 5NH, ☎ 386 0657 – AE VISA EZ **a**
Meals 7.95/10.95 **t.** and a la carte 3.90.

Hammersmith – ✉ W6/W12/W14 – ☎ 0181.

Tandoori Nights, 319-321 King St., W6 9NH, ☎ 741 4328 – . AE VISA JCB p. 9 CV **u**
closed 25 and 26 December – **Meals** - Indian 9.95/18.00 **t.** and a la carte 5.95.

Snows on the Green, 166 Shepherd's Bush Rd, Brook Green, W6 7PB, ☎ (0171) 603 2142, Fax 602 7553 – VISA p. 9 CV **x**
closed Saturday lunch, Sunday dinner, New Year and Bank Holidays – **Meals** 12.50 **t.** (lunch) and a la carte 16.95/23.70 **t.**

Brackenbury, 129-131 Brackenbury Rd, W6 0BQ, ☎ 748 0107, Fax 741 0905 – AE VISA p. 9 CV **a**
closed lunch Monday and Saturday, Sunday dinner and 10 days Christmas-New Year – **Meals** a la carte 12.25/18.25 **t.** 4.25.

Shepherd's Bush – ✉ W12/W14 – ☎ 0171.

Wilsons, 236 Blythe Rd, W14 0HJ, ☎ 603 7267 – AE VISA p. 9 DV **a**
Meals 7.50/12.00 **t.** and a la carte.

HARINGEY pp. 6 and 7.

Crouch End – ✉ N 8 – ☎ 0181.

XX **Les Associés,** 172 Park Rd, N8 8JY, ☎ 348 8944 – VISA EU e
closed lunch Tuesday and Saturday, Sunday, Monday and August – **Meals** - French 15.95/35.00 **st.** and a la carte.

X **Florians,** 4 Topsfield Par., Middle Lane, N8 8RP, ☎ 348 8348 – VISA EU c
closed 25-26 December and Bank Holidays – **Meals** - Italian a la carte 18.50/21.75 **t.** 5.90.

Hornsey – ✉ N8 – ☎ 0181.

X **Jashan,** 19a Turnpike Lane, N8 0EP, ☎ 340 9880, Fax 347 8770 – AE VISA EU z
closed 25-26 December and Mondays except Bank Holidays – **Meals** - Indian (dinner only) 12.50 **t.** and a la carte.

HARROW pp. 4 and 5.

Central Harrow – ✉ Middx – ☎ 0181.

Civic Centre, Station Rd, HA1 2XF ☎ 424 1103/424 1100 BU.

Cumberland, 1 St. John's Rd, HA1 2EF, ☎ 863 4111, Fax 861 5668, – rm – 50. AE VISA. BU x
Meals 9.95/15.50 **st.** and a la carte 4.95 – **80 rm** 62.00/67.00 **st.**

XX **Trattoria Sorrentina,** 6 Manor Par., Sheepcote Rd, HA1 2JA, ☎ 427 9411 – . VISA BU x
closed Saturday lunch and Sunday – **Meals** - Italian 10.00/25.00 **t.** and a la carte 4.50.

XX Taste of China, 174 Station Rd, HA1 2RH, ☎ 863 2080 – BU u
Meals - Chinese.

Hatch End – ✉ Middx – ☎ 0181.

XX **Swan,** 322-326 Uxbridge Rd, HA5 4HR, ☎ 428 8821, Fax 420 1505 – . AE VISA JCB BT n
closed 25 and 26 December – **Meals** - Chinese (Peking) 12.00/19.50 **st.** and a la carte.

Kenton – ✉ Middx. – ☎ 0181.

Travel Inn, Kenton Rd, HA3 8AT, ☎ 907 1671, Fax 909 1604 – rm . AE VISA. BU e
Meals (Beefeater grill) a la carte approx. 16.00 **t.** – 4.95 – **44 rm** 33.50 **st.**

North Harrow – ✉ Middx. – ☎ 0181.

XX **Percy's,** 66-68 Station Rd, HA2 7SJ, ☎ 427 2021, Fax 427 8134 – . AE VISA BU n
closed Sunday and Monday – **Meals** (booking essential) a la carte 19.00/26.00 **t.** 4.90.

X **Thai Castle,** 28 The Broadwalk, Pinner Rd, HA2 6ED, ☎ 427 4732 – VISA BU c
closed lunch Saturday and Sunday and 25-26 December – **Meals** - Thai 9.00/39.00 **t.** and a la carte 3.35.

Pinner – ✉ Middx. – ☎ 0181.

X **Friends,** 11 High St., HA5 5PJ, ☎ 866 0286 – . AE VISA BU a
closed Sunday dinner and Bank Holidays – **Meals** 13.50/17.50 **t.** and a la carte 4.50.

X **Olde Village Bakery,** 33 High St., HA5 5PS, ☎ 868 4704 – AE VISA BU a
Meals 10.00 **t.** and a la carte 4.50.

South Harrow – ✉ Middx. – ☎ 0181.

X **Jaflong,** 299 Northolt Rd, HA2 8JA, ☎ 864 7345 – BU r
Meals - Indian 9.50/14.90 **t.** and a la carte.

Stanmore – ✉ Middx – ☎ 0181.

XX **Mr Tang's Mandarin** 28 The Broadway, HA7 4DW, ☎ 954 0339 – . AE VISA JCB BT i
Meals - Chinese (Peking) 15.00/17.00 **t.** and a la carte 4.00.

HAVERING pp. 6 and 7.

Hornchurch by A 12 – JT – on A 127 – ✉ Essex – ☎ 01708.

Palms, Southend Arterial Rd (A 127), RM11 3UJ, ☎ 346789, Fax 341719 – rm – 270. AE VISA JCB
Meals *(closed Saturday lunch)* 17.00 **st.** and a la carte 5.75 – 7.95 – **137 rm** 56.00 **t.**

Romford by A 118 – JU – ✉ Essex – ☎ 01708.

18, 9 Havering, Risebridge Chase, Lower Bedfords Rd ☎ 41429 JT.

Coach House without rest., 48 Main Rd, RM1 3DB, on A 118 ☎ 751901, Fax 730290, – rest . AE VISA.
32 rm 29.50/49.50 **st.**

HILLINGDON pp. 4 and 8.

Haste Hill, The Drive (01927) 422877 AU – Harefield Pl., The Drive (01895) 231169, by B 467 AU.

Eastcote – Middx – 0181 – Ruislip, Ickenham Rd (01895) 638835 AU.

Central Library, 14 High St., Uxbridge, UB8 1HD 01895 250706.

Sambuca, 113 Field End Rd, HA5 1QG, 866 7500 – AE VISA AU **s**
closed Sunday dinner, Monday and Bank Holidays – **Meals** - Italian (dinner only and Sunday lunch)/dinner a la carte 12.90/20.00 **t.** 3.80.

Hayes – Middx. – 0181.

Travel Inn, 362 Uxbridge Rd, UB4 0HF, 573 7479, Fax 569 1204 – rm . AE VISA. AV **a**
Meals (Beefeater grill) a la carte approx. 16.00 **t.** – 4.95 – **40 rm** 33.50 **t.**

Heathrow Airport – Middx – 0181.

Heathrow Terminals 1,2,3, Underground Station Concourse, TW6 2JA (0171) 730 3488/824 8000 AX.

Radisson Edwardian, 140 Bath Rd, Hayes, UB3 5AW, 759 6311, Fax 759 4559, , , – rm – 500. AE VISA JCB. AX **e**
***Henleys* : Meals** 18.00/28.00 **st.** and a la carte 6.25 – ***Brasserie* : Meals** a la carte approx. 20.50 **st.** – 12.00 – **442 rm** 153.00/224.00 **st.**, 17 suites – SB.

Holiday Inn Crowne Plaza Heathrow London, Stockley Rd, West Drayton, UB7 9NA, (01895) 445555, Fax 445122, , , , – rm – 200. AE VISA JCB. AV **v**
***Marlowe* : Meals** *(closed Sunday)* (dinner only) – ***Cafe Galleria* : Meals** – 10.95 – **373 rm** 120.00 **st.**, 2 suites.

Sheraton Skyline, Bath Rd, Hayes, UB3 5BP, 759 2535, Telex 934254, Fax 750 9150, « Exotic indoor garden », , – rm – 500 AX **u**
349 rm, 5 suites.

London Heathrow Hilton, Terminal 4, TW6 3AF, 759 7755, Telex 925094, Fax 759 7579, , , – rm – 240. AE VISA JCB. AX **n**
***Brasserie* : Meals** a la carte 16.75/26.50 **st.** 9.00 – ***Zen Oriental* : Meals** a la carte approx. 19.30 – 11.95 – **397 rm** 145.00/155.00 **st.**, 4 suites – SB.

Excelsior Heathrow (Forte), Bath Rd, West Drayton, UB7 0DU, 759 6611, Telex 24525, Fax 759 3421, , , – rm – 700 AX **x**
823 rm, 16 suites.

Forte Crest, Sipson Rd, West Drayton, UB7 0JU, 759 2323, Telex 934280, Fax 897 8659 – rm – 200 AV **c**
570 rm, 2 suites.

Sheraton Heathrow, Colnbrook by-pass, West Drayton, UB7 0HJ, 759 2424, Telex 934331, Fax 759 2091 – rm – 70. AE VISA JCB. AVX **a**
Meals 15.00/20.00 **t.** and a la carte 6.00 – 12.00 – **424 rm** 150.00/170.00, 1 suite – SB.

Novotel, Cherry Lane, West Drayton, UB7 9HB, (01895) 431431, Fax 431221, , – rm rest – 200. AE VISA JCB AV **n**
Meals 12.50/20.00 **st.** and a la carte 4.95 – **175 rm** 69.50 **st.**, 3 suites.

Forte Posthouse, Bath Rd, Hayes, UB3 5AJ, 759 2552, Fax 564 9265 – rm rest . AE VISA JCB AX **i**
Meals a la carte approx. 15.00 **t.** 5.50 – **186 rm** 59.50/69.50 **st.**

Heathrow Park (Mt. Charlotte Thistle), Bath Rd, Longford, West Drayton, UB7 0EQ, 759 2400, Telex 934093, Fax 759 5278 – rm – 700. AE VISA JCB
Meals (carving lunch) 12.00/14.75 **st.** and a la carte 5.50 – 8.25 – **306 rm** 75.00/160.00 **st.** – SB. off A 4 AX

Ickenham – Middx. – 01895.

Roberto's, 15 Long Lane, UB10 8TB, 632519 – . AE VISA JCB AU **i**
closed Sunday – **Meals** - Italian 12.95/16.00 **t.** and a la carte 6.95.

Yiewsley – Middx. – 0181.

Waterfront Brasserie, The Arena, Stockley Park, UB11 1AA, 899 1733, Fax 899 1711 – . AE VISA AV **r**
closed dinner Monday to Wednesday and Sunday – **Meals** (dancing Friday) 16.70 **t.** and a la carte.

HOUNSLOW pp. 8 and 9.

Wyke Green, Syon Lane, Isleworth (0181) 560 8777 BV – Airlinks, Southall Lane 561 1418 ABV – Hounslow Heath, Staines Rd 570 5271 BX.

24 The Treaty Centre, Hounslow High St., TW3 1ES 572 8279.

Chiswick – W4 – 0181.

La Dordogne, 5 Devonshire Rd, W4 2EU, 747 1836, Fax 994 9144 – AE VISA
closed lunch Saturday and Sunday and Bank Holidays – **Meals** - French a la carte 17.90/26.70 **t.** 4.60. CV **o**

Cranford - ✉ Middx. - ☎ 0181.

Jarvis International Heathrow, Bath Rd, TW5 9QE, ☎ 897 2121, Fax 897 7014, – ⎮ rm TV ☎ P – 120. AE VISA JCB. AX **r**
Meals *(closed Saturday lunch)* 9.95/15.95 **st.** and a la carte 6.95 – 6.95 – **60 rm** 69.00/79.00 **st.** – SB.

Heston Service Area - ✉ Middx. - ☎ 0181.

Granada Lodge without rest., TW5 9NA, on M 4 (between junctions 2 and 3 westbound carriageway) ☎ 574 5875, Fax 574 1891, Reservations (Freephone) 0800 555300 – TV ☎ & P. AE VISA ABV **e**
4.00 – **71 rm** 39.95 **st.**

ISLINGTON Except where otherwise stated see pp. 20-23.

Canonbury - ✉ N1 - ☎ 0171.

Anna's Place, 90 Mildmay Park, N1 4PR, ☎ 249 9379 p. 6 FU **a**
closed Sunday and Monday – **Meals** - Swedish (booking essential) a la carte 19.00/23.00 **t.**

Finsbury - ✉ WC1/EC1/EC2 - ☎ 0171.

Stephen Bull's Bistro, 71 St. John St., EC1M 4AN, ☎ 490 1750, Fax 490 3128 – . AE VISA NU **r**
closed Saturday lunch, Sunday, 1 week Christmas and Bank Holidays – **Meals** a la carte 15.25/22.00 **t.** 5.00.

Le Mesurier, 113 Old St., EC1V 9JR, ☎ 251 8117, Fax 608 3504 – AE VISA JCB OT **e**
closed Saturday, Sunday, 3 weeks August, 2 weeks Christmas-New Year and Bank Holidays – **Meals** (lunch only) (booking essential) a la carte 17.00/23.00 **t.** 4.50.

Rouxl Britannia, Triton Court, 14 Finsbury Sq., EC2A 1BR, ☎ 256 6997 – VISA PU **x**
***Le Restaurant* : Meals** *(closed Saturday, Sunday and Bank Holidays)* (lunch only) 21.75 **t.** 5.75 – ***Le Café* : Meals** *(closed Saturday, Sunday and* Bank Holidays) (lunch only) a la carte 11.30/16.45 **t.** 5.50.

Quality Chop House, 94 Farringdon Rd, EC1R 3EA, ☎ 837 5093 MT **n**
closed Saturday lunch and Christmas-New Year – **Meals** a la carte 13.75/19.50 **t.**

Islington - ✉ N1 - ☎ 0171.

Granita, 127 Upper St., N1 1PQ, ☎ 226 3222 – . VISA NS **a**
closed Tuesday lunch, Monday, 5 days Easter, 2 weeks August and 10 days Christmas – **Meals** 13.50 **t.** (lunch) and dinner a la carte 18.65/21.65 **t.**

KENSINGTON and CHELSEA (Royal Borough of).

Chelsea - ✉ SW1/SW3/SW10 - ☎ 0171 - Except where otherwise stated see pp. 30 and 31.

Hyatt Carlton Tower, 2 Cadogan Pl., SW1X 9PY, ☎ 235 1234, Telex 21944, Fax 245 6570, ≤, , , , – ⎮ rm TV ☎ – 260. AE VISA JCB. FR **n**
***Chelsea Room* : Meals** 22.50/29.50 **st.** – ***Rib Room* : Meals** *(closed 1 to 3 January)* 22.50/29.50 **st.** – 14.50 – **194 rm** 250.00 **s.**, 30 suites.

Sheraton Park Tower, 101 Knightsbridge, SW1X 7RN, ☎ 235 8050, Telex 917222, Fax 235 8231, ≤ – ⎮ rm TV ☎ & P – 60. AE VISA JCB. FQ **v**
Meals a la carte 18.80/34.30 **t.** 8.00 – 14.75 – **267 rm** 205.00/235.00 **s.**, 22 suites.

Conrad London, Chelsea Harbour, SW10 0XG, ☎ 823 3000, Fax 351 6525, ≤, , , – ⎮ rm TV ☎ & – 180. AE VISA JCB p. 13 CQ **i**
Meals 13.00/25.00 **t.** and a la carte – 17.00, **159 suites** 195.00/215.00 – SB.

Durley House, 115 Sloane St., SW1X 9PJ, ☎ 235 5537, Fax 259 6977, « Tastefully furnished Georgian town house », , – ⎮ TV ☎. AE VISA. FS **e**
Meals (room service only) a la carte 17.50/21.50 **t.** – 12.50 –, **11 suites** 195.00/300.00 **t.**.

✿ **Capital,** 22-24 Basil St., SW3 1AT, ☎ 589 5171, Fax 225 0011 – ⎮ TV ☎ – 25. AE VISA. ER **a**
Meals 25.00/40.00 **st.** and a la carte 34.50/44.50 **st.** – 12.50 – **48 rm** 184.50/340.75 **st.**
Spec. Langoustine risotto with pearls of caviar, tarragon and chives, Grilled beef fillet with sage, red onions and horseradish, sauce Sauternes, Assiette vanille.

Draycott, 24-26 Cadogan Gdns, SW3 2RP, ☎ 730 6466, Fax 730 0236, , , , – ⎮ rm TV ☎. AE VISA JCB. FS **c**
Meals (room service only) – 12.95 – **25 rm** 100.00/250.00 **t.**

Cadogan, 75 Sloane St., SW1X 9SG, ☎ 235 7141, Fax 245 0994, , – ⎮ rm rest TV ☎ – 30. AE VISA. FR **e**
Meals *(closed Saturday lunch)* 16.90/21.90 **t.** and dinner a la carte 6.25 – 12.50 – **60 rm** 135.00/175.00 **st.**, 5 suites – SB.

Franklin, 28 Egerton Gdns., SW3 2DB, ☎ 584 5533, Fax 584 5449, – ⎮ TV ☎. AE VISA. DS **e**
Meals (room service only) – 12.50 – **36 rm** 110.00/210.00 **s.**, 1 suite.

Basil Street, 8 Basil St., SW3 1AH, ☎ 581 3311, Fax 581 3693 – 55. FQ **o**
Meals (carving lunch Saturday) 14.95/19.75 **t.** 5.00 – 10.90 – **91 rm** 115.00/170.00 **st.**, 1 suite – SB.

Chelsea, 17-25 Sloane St., SW1X 9NU, ☎ 235 4377, Telex 919111, Fax 235 3705 – rm – 100. FR **r**
Meals 15.00 **st.** and a la carte 7.00 – 11.95 – **219 rm** 150.00/165.00 **st.**, 7 suites.

Sydney House, 9-11 Sydney St., SW3 6PU, ☎ 376 7711, Fax 376 4233, « Tastefully furnished Victorian town house » – DT **a**
Meals (room service only) – 11.00 – **21 rm** 110.00/175.00.

Egerton House, 17-19 Egerton Terr., SW3 2BX, ☎ 589 2412, Fax 584 6540, – DR **e**
Meals (room service only) 7.00 – 12.50 – **27 rm** 100.00/180.00, 1 suite.

Sloane, 29 Draycott Pl., SW3 2SH, ☎ 581 5757, Fax 584 1348, « Victorian town house, antiques » – ET **c**
Meals (room service only) – 9.00 – **12 rm** 120.00/190.00 **s.**

Fenja without rest., 69 Cadogan Gdns, SW3 2RB, ☎ 589 7333, Fax 581 4958, – FS **r**
11.75 – **12 rm** 130.00/195.00 **t.**

Beaufort without rest., 33 Beaufort Gdns, SW3 1PP, ☎ 584 5252, Telex 929200, Fax 589 2834, « English floral watercolour collection » – ER **n**
closed 23 to 27 December – **28 rm** 110.00/240.00 **s.**

Eleven Cadogan Gardens, 11 Cadogan Gdns, SW3 2RJ, ☎ 730 3426, Fax 730 5217 – FS **u**
Meals (room service only) 17.00/22.00 **t.** 5.50 – 10.00 – **55 rm** 98.00/188.00 **st.**, 5 suites.

Claverley without rest., 13-14 Beaufort Gdns, SW3 1PS, ☎ 589 8541, Fax 584 3410 – ER **o**
33 rm 65.00/175.00 **t.**

L'Hotel, 28 Basil St., SW3 1AT, ☎ 589 6286, Telex 919042, Fax 225 0011 – ER **i**
Le Metro : **Meals** (closed Sunday and Bank Holidays) a la carte 14.95/19.20 **t.** 6.50 – **12 rm** 125.00/145.00 **st.**

Royal Court, Sloane Sq., SW1W 8EG, ☎ 730 9191, Telex 296818, Fax 824 8381 – rm rest – 40. FST **a**
Meals 11.00/21.50 **st.** and a la carte 6.45 – 9.50 – **102 rm** 105.00/160.00 **st.** – SB.

Knightsbridge without rest., 12 Beaufort Gdns., SW3 1PT, ☎ 589 9271, Fax 823 9692 – ER **o**
22 rm.

Wilbraham, 1-5 Wilbraham Pl., Sloane St., SW1X 9AE, ☎ 730 8296, Fax 730 6815 – FS **n**
Meals *(closed Saturday lunch, Sunday and Bank Holidays)* (restricted menu) a la carte 8.70/17.45 **t.** 3.50 – 5.50 – **53 rm** 39.00/86.00.

XXXX ✿✿✿ **La Tante Claire** (Koffmann), 68-69 Royal Hospital Rd, SW3 4HP, ☎ 352 6045, Fax 352 3257 – EU **c**
closed Saturday, Sunday, 3 weeks Summer and 1 week Christmas – **Meals** - French (booking essential) 25.00/45.00 **st.** and a la carte 53.00 **st.**
Spec. Pied de cochon aux morilles, Coquilles St. Jacques, sauce encre, Chevreuil au chocolat amer et vinaigre de framboises.

XXX **Waltons,** 121 Walton St., SW3 2HP, ☎ 584 0204 – DS **a**
Meals 14.75/21.00 **t.** and a la carte 4.50.

XXX **Bibendum,** Michelin House, 81 Fulham Rd, SW3 6RD, ☎ 581 5817, Fax 823 7925 – DS **s**
closed 24 to 29 December – **Meals** 27.00 **t.** (lunch) and dinner a la carte 37.00/50.75 **t.** 5.75 **t.**

XXX ✿ **MPW's, The Canteen,** Harbour Yard, Chelsea Harbour, SW10 0XL, ☎ 351 7330, Fax 351 6189 – p. 13 CQ **i**
Meals a la carte 21.95/24.00 **t.**
Spec. Roast sea scallops 'gros sel', sauce vierge, Fillet of cod Viennoise with a grain mustard sabayon, Crème vanille with poached fruits.

XXX **Fifth Floor** (at Harvey Nichols), Knightsbridge, SW1X 7RJ, ☎ 235 5250, Fax 235 5020 – FQ **a**
closed Sunday and 25 to 26 December – **Meals** 21.50 **t.** and dinner a la carte 20.25/35.50 **t.** 4.75.

XXX ✿ **Aubergine** (Ramsay) 11 Park Walk, SW10 0AJ, ☎ 352 3449 –
closed Saturday lunch, Sunday, first 2 weeks August, 24 December-2 January and Bank Holidays – **Meals** (booking essential) 18.00/36.00 **t.** and a la carte CU **r**
Spec. Cappuccino of haricots blancs with truffle oil, Fillet of sea bass roasted with braised salsify, jus vanille, Bitter tarte au chocolat.

XXX **Turner's,** 87-89 Walton St., SW3 2HP, ☎ 584 6711, Fax 584 4441 –
closed Saturday lunch, 25 to 30 December and Bank Holidays – **Meals** 13.50/26.50 **st.** and a la carte 9.50. ES **n**

XXX **Chutney Mary,** 535 King's Rd, SW10 0SZ, ℘ 351 3113, Fax 351 7694 – ▤. AE VISA JCB p. 24 FZ **v**
Meals - Anglo-Indian 12.95 **t.** and a la carte 23.00/28.00 **t.** 4.50.

XXX **Albero & Grana,** Chelsea Cloisters, Sloane Av., SW3 3DX, ℘ 225 1048, Fax 581 3259 – ▤. AE VISA ET **e**
Meals - Spanish (dinner only) a la carte 26.00/37.00 **st.** 5.00.

XXX **Benihana,** 77 Kings Rd, SW3 4NX, ℘ 376 7799, Fax 376 7377 – ▤. AE VISA JCB EU **e**
Meals - Japanese (Teppan-Yaki) 8.75/60.00 **t.** and a la carte.

XX ✿ **Fulham Road,** 257-259 Fulham Rd, SW3 6HY, ℘ 351 7823, Fax 490 3128. AE VISA
closed Bank Holidays – **Meals** 19.50 **t.** (lunch) and a la carte 22.00/32.50 **t.** 6.00 CU **a**
Spec. Ravioli of suckling pig with wild mushroom consommé, Rare roast rump of lamb with aubergine and pepper stew, rosemary cream, Pecan pie with maple ice cream.

XX **Argyll,** 316 King's Rd, SW3 5UH, ℘ 352 0025, Fax 352 1652 – ▤. AE VISA
closed Monday lunch, Sunday and Bank Holidays – **Meals** 15.00 **t.** (lunch) and dinner a la carte 17.00/23.75 **t.** 7.00. CU **e**

XX **English Garden,** 10 Lincoln St., SW3 2TS, ℘ 584 7272 – ▤. AE VISA JCB ET **x**
closed 25 and 26 December – **Meals** - English 14.75 **t.** (lunch) and a la carte 22.75/31.50 **t.**

XX **St. Quentin,** 243 Brompton Rd, SW3 2EP, ℘ 589 8005, Fax 584 6064 – ▤. AE VISA JCB DR **a**
Meals - French 10.00 **t.** and a la carte 5.60.

XX **Poissonnerie de l'Avenue,** 82 Sloane Av., SW3 3DZ, ℘ 589 2457, Fax 581 3360 – ▤. AE VISA JCB DS **u**
closed Sunday, 10 days at Christmas and Bank Holidays – **Meals** - French Seafood 16.50 **t.** (lunch) and a la carte 19.00/29.50 **t.** 5.50.

XX **Daphne's,** 112 Draycott Ave., SW3 3AE, ℘ 589 4257, Fax 581 2232 – ▤. AE VISA
Meals - Italian a la carte 17.50/31.50 **t.** 6.50. DS **a**

XX **La Finezza,** 62-64 Lower Sloane St., SW1N 8BP, ℘ 730 8639 – ▤. AE VISA FT **v**
closed Sunday and Bank Holidays – **Meals** - Italian a la carte approx. 32.50 **t.** 7.50.

XX **Busabong Too,** 1a Langton St., SW10 0JL, ℘ 352 7517 – ▤. AE VISA
closed Christmas – **Meals** - Thai (dinner only) 24.95 **t.** and a la carte. p. 24 FZ **x**

XX **Toto's,** Walton House, Walton St., SW3 2JH, ℘ 589 0075 – AE VISA JCB ES **a**
closed 25 and 26 December – **Meals** - Italian 14.00 **st.** (lunch) and a la carte 35.00 approx. **st.**

XX **Good Earth,** 233 Brompton Rd, SW3 2EP, ℘ 584 3658, Fax 823 8769 – ▤. AE VISA JCB DR **c**
closed 24 to 27 December – **Meals** - Chinese 7.95/25.00 **t.** and a la carte 8.00.

XX **Dan's,** 119 Sydney St., SW3 6NR, ℘ 352 2718, Fax 352 3265 – AE VISA DU **s**
closed Saturday lunch, Sunday dinner, 24 December-2 January and Bank Holidays – **Meals** 16.50 **t.** and a la carte 5.00.

XX **Red,** 8 Egerton Garden Mews, SW3 2EH, ℘ 584 7007, Fax 584 0972. AE VISA
Meals - Chinese 6.00/30.00 **t.** and a la carte 4.50. DR **n**

X **Thierry's,** 342 King's Rd, SW3 5UR, ℘ 352 3365, Fax 352 3365 – ▤. AE VISA CU **c**
closed Christmas – **Meals** 9.90/13.50 **t.** and a la carte 5.50.

X **Monkey's,** 1 Cale St., Chelsea Green, SW3 3QT, ℘ 352 4711 – ▤. VISA ET **z**
closed Saturday, Sunday, 2 weeks Easter, 3 weeks August and Bank Holidays – **Meals** 17.50/22.50 **t.** and a la carte 5.50.

X **Beit Eddine,** 8 Harriet St., SW1 9JW, ℘ 235 3969. AE VISA FQ **z**
Meals - Lebanese a la carte 20.75/29.75 **t.** 5.50.

Earl's Court – ✉ SW5/SW10 – 0171 – Except where otherwise stated see pp. 30 and 31.

Comfort Inn without rest., 22-32 West Cromwell Rd, SW5 9QJ, ℘ 373 3300, Fax 835 2040 – ▤ – 100. AE VISA JCB p. 24 EZ **n**
8.50 – **125 rm** 68.00/86.00 **st.**

Periquito, 34-44 Barkston Gdns., SW5 0EW, ℘ 373 7851, Fax 370 6570 – rm – 70. AE VISA JCB. AT **e**
Meals 9.50/15.00 **t.** and a la carte – 7.00 – **75 rm** 64.00 **st.**

Henley House without rest., 30 Barkston Gdns., SE5 0EN, ℘ 370 4111, Fax 370 0026, – rest. AE VISA JCB. AT **e**
Meals (by arrangement) (dinner only) (unlicensed) – 3.40 – **20 rm** 55.00/79.00 **st.**

Rushmore without rest., 11 Trebovir Rd, SW5 9LS, ℘ 370 3839, Fax 370 0274 – . AE VISA JCB p. 24 EZ **c**
6.50 – **22 rm** 59.00/90.00 **st.**

Amsterdam without rest., 7 Trebovir Rd, SW5 9LS, ℘ 370 2814, Fax 244 7608 – . AE VISA JCB. p. 24 EZ **c**
2.75 – **20 rm** 49.00/62.00 **t.**

XX **Formula Veneta,** 14 Hollywood Rd, SW10 9HY, ☏ 352 7612 – ▤. AE ⓓ VISA BU **a**
closed Sunday dinner and Bank Holidays – **Meals** - Italian a la carte 13.50/19.00 ⚱ 4.00.

XX **Mr Wing,** 242-244 Old Brompton Rd, SW5 0DE, ☏ 370 4450, Fax 370 2624 – AE ⓓ VISA AU **a**
Meals - Chinese a la carte 20.50/30.00 **t.**

XX **La Primula,** 12 Kenway Rd, SW5 0RR, ☏ 370 5958 – ▤. AE VISA JCB p. 24 FZ **e**
closed lunch Saturday and Sunday, Easter and Christmas – **Meals** - Italian 8.50/14.50 **t.**

X **Chez Max,** 168 Ifield Rd, SW10 9AF, ☏ 835 0874 – VISA AU **c**
closed lunch Saturday and Monday, Sunday and Bank Holidays – **Meals** 15.50/23.50 **t.** ⚱ 9.00.

Kensington – ✉ SW7/W8/W11/W14 – ☏ 0171 – Except where otherwise stated see pp. 24-27.

The Milestone, 1-2 Kensington Court, W8 5DL, ☏ 917 1000, Fax 917 1010, – rm ▤ TV ☎. AE ⓓ VISA. p. 30 AQ **u**
***Chenestons :* Meals** 13.00**st.** (lunch)and a la carte 18.00/34.50 **st.** ⚱ 5.50 – ☕ 15.00 – **50 rm** 180.00/210.00 **st.**, 6 suites.

Halcyon, 81 Holland Park, W11 3RZ, ☏ 727 7288, Telex 266721, Fax 229 8516 – ▤ TV ☎. AE ⓓ VISA JCB. EX **u**
***The Room :* Meals** *(closed Saturday lunch)* 18.00 **t.** (lunch) and dinner a la carte 22.95/33.00 **t.** – ☕ 12.00 – **40 rm** 165.00/250.00 **st.**, 3 suites – SB.

Copthorne Tara, Scarsdale Pl., W8 5SR, ☏ 937 7211, Telex 918834, Fax 937 7100 – rm ▤ TV ☎ ♿ Ⓟ – 500. AE ⓓ VISA JCB. FY **u**
***Brasserie :* Meals** 17.00 **st.** and a la carte ⚱ 6.60 – ***Jerome K. Jerome :* Meals** *(closed Sunday)* (dinner only) 24.00 **st.** and a la carte ⚱ 9.80 – ☕ 11.30 – **817 rm** 110.00/145.00 **st.**, 8 suites.

Kensington Park (Mt. Charlotte Thistle), 16-32 De Vere Gdns, W8 5AG, ☏ 937 8080, Telex 929643, Fax 937 7616 – rm ▤ rest TV ☎ ♿ – 120. AE ⓓ VISA. p. 30 BQ **e**
***Moniques Brasserie :* Meals** 13.95/14.75**st.** and a la carte ⚱ 6.75 – ***Cairngorm Grill :* Meals** a la carte 17.30/27.70 **st.** ⚱ 6.75 – ☕ 10.75 – **325 rm** 120.00/175.00 **st.**, 7 suites – SB.

London Kensington Hilton, 179-199 Holland Park Av., W11 4UL, ☏ 603 3355, Telex 919763, Fax 602 9397 – rm ▤ TV ☎ ♿ Ⓟ – 300. AE ⓓ VISA JCB EX **s**
***Market :* Meals** *(closed Saturday lunch)* – ***Hiroko :* Meals** - Japanese – ☕ 12.50 – **596 rm** 99.00/155.00 **st.**, 7 suites.

Hilton National London Olympia, 380 Kensington High St., W14 8NL, ☏ 603 3333, Telex 22229, Fax 603 4846 – rm ▤ rest TV ☎ – 400. AE ⓓ VISA JCB. EY **a**
Meals (bar lunch Saturday)/dinner a la carte 17.00/26.50 **t.** ⚱ 7.00 – ☕ 12.50 – **394 rm** 115.00/160.00 **t.**, 11 suites – SB.

Kensington Palace Thistle (Mt. Charlotte Thistle), 8 De Vere Gdns, W8 5AF, ☏ 937 8121, Telex 262422, Fax 937 2816 – rm ▤ rest TV ☎ – 180. AE ⓓ VISA JCB. p. 30 BQ **a**
Meals 13.95/15.95 **st.** and a la carte ⚱ 6.25 – ☕ 10.75 – **297 rm** 95.00/135.00 **st.**, 1 suite – SB.

Kensington Close (Forte), Wrights Lane, W8 5SP, ☏ 937 8170, Fax 937 8289, squash – rm ▤ rest TV ☎ Ⓟ – 180 FY **c**
530 rm.

Holland Court without rest., 31 Holland Rd, W14 8HJ, ☏ 371 1133, Fax 602 9114, – TV ☎. AE ⓓ VISA. EY **c**
22 rm ☕ 65.00/100.00 **st.**

Russell Court without rest., 9 Russell Rd, W14 8JA, ☏ 603 1222, Fax 371 2286 – TV ☎. AE ⓓ VISA. EY **v**
– **18 rm** ☕ 39.50/49.50 **st.**

XX **Clarke's,** 124 Kensington Church St., W8 4BH, ☏ 221 9225, Fax 229 4564 – ▤. VISA EX **c**
closed Saturday, Sunday, 4 days Easter, 2 weeks August, 10 days Christmas and Bank Holidays – **Meals** 26.00/37.00 **st.** ⚱ 8.00.

XX **La Pomme d'Amour,** 128 Holland Park Av., W11 4UE, ☏ 229 8532 – ▤. AE ⓓ VISA EX **e**
closed Saturday lunch, Sunday and Bank Holidays – **Meals** - French 13.25/20.50 **t.** and a la carte ⚱ 4.50.

XX **L'Escargot Doré,** 2-4 Thackeray St., W8 5ET, ☏ 937 8508, Fax 937 8508 – ▤. AE ⓓ VISA p. 30 AQR **e**
closed Saturday lunch, Sunday, last 2 weeks August and Bank Holidays – **Meals** - French 15.50 **t.** and a la carte.

XX **Belvedere in Holland Park,** Holland House, off Abbotsbury Rd, W8 6LU, ☏ 602 1238, « 19C orangery in park » – ▤. AE ⓓ VISA EY **u**
closed Sunday dinner, 25 December and lunch 1 January – **Meals** a la carte 16.00/25.00 **t.**

XX **La Fenice,** 148 Holland Park Av., W11 4UE, ☏ 221 6090, Fax 221 4096 – ▤. AE ⓓ VISA
closed Saturday lunch, Monday and Bank Holidays – **Meals** - Italian 8.50/12.50 **t.** and a la carte ⚱ 4.75. EX **v**

XX **Launceston Place,** 1a Launceston Pl., W8 5RL, ℘ 937 6912, Fax 938 2412 – ▤. EN AE VISA p. 30 BR **a**
closed Saturday lunch, Sunday dinner and Bank Holidays – **Meals** 16.50 **t.** and a la carte ₰ 4.50.

XX **Arcadia,** Kensington Court, 35 Kensington High St., W8 5BA, ℘ 937 4294, Fax 937 4393 – ▤. EN AE VISA p. 30 AQ **s**
closed Saturday and Sunday lunch, 3 days Christmas and 28 August – **Meals** 16.00 **t.** (lunch) and a la carte 20.20/23.75 **t.**

XX **Boyd's,** 135 Kensington Church St., W8 7LP, ℘ 727 5452, Fax 221 0615 – ▤. EN AE ⓓ VISA p. 32 AZ **r**
closed Sunday, 2 weeks Christmas and Bank Holidays – **Meals** 14.00 **t.** (lunch) and a la carte 19.95/33.75 **t.**

XX **Phoenicia,** 11-13 Abingdon Rd, W8 6AH, ℘ 937 0120, Fax 937 7668 – ▤. EN AE ⓓ VISA EY **n**
closed 24 and 25 December – **Meals** - Lebanese 15.30/22.80 **st.** and a la carte ₰ 4.75.

XX **Shanghai,** 38c-d Kensington Church St., W8 4BX, ℘ 938 2501 – ▤. EN AE ⓓ VISA FX **a**
closed Saturday lunch, and Sunday – **Meals** - Chinese 12.50/24.50 **t.** and a la carte ₰ 4.20.

X **Kensington Place,** 201 Kensington Church St., W8 7LX, ℘ 727 3184, Fax 229 2025 – ▤. EN VISA p. 32 AZ **z**
closed 4 days Christmas – **Meals** 13.50 **t.** (lunch) and a la carte 15.50/29.50 **t.**

X **Cibo,** 3 Russell Gdns, W14 8EZ, ℘ 371 6271 – EN AE ⓓ VISA EY **o**
closed Saturday lunch – **Meals** - Italian a la carte 22.00/25.25 **t.** ₰ 5.90.

X **Malabar,** 27 Uxbridge St., W8 7TQ, ℘ 727 8800 – EN VISA p. 32 AZ **e**
closed last week August and 4 days at Christmas – **Meals** - Indian (booking essential) (buffet lunch Sunday) a la carte 14.15/26.80 **st.** ₰ 4.60.

X **Wódka,** 12 St. Albans Grove, W8 5PN, ℘ 937 6513, Fax 937 8621 – EN AE ⓓ VISA
closed lunch Saturday and Sunday and Bank Holidays – **Meals** - Polish a la carte 16.70/22.30 **t.** ₰ 4.50. p. 30 AR **c**

X **Mandarin,** 197c Kensington High St., W8 6BA, ℘ 937 1551 – ▤. EN AE ⓓ VISA EY **s**
closed 24 to 26 December – **Meals** - Chinese a la carte 15.00/20.00 **st.** ₰ 4.75.

North Kensington – ✉ W2/W10/W11 – ☎ 0171 – Except where otherwise stated see pp. 20-23.

🏨 **Abbey Court** without rest., 20 Pembridge Gdns, W2 4DU, ℘ 221 7518, Telex 262167, Fax 792 0858, « Tastefully furnished Victorian town house » – TV ☎. EN AE ⓓ VISA. ✻ p. 32 AZ **u**
22 rm ☐ 80.00/160.00 **t.**

🏨 **Pembridge Court,** 34 Pembridge Gdns, W2 4DX, ℘ 229 9977, Fax 727 4982, « Collection of antique clothing » – |♦| ▤ rest TV ☎. EN AE ⓓ VISA. ✻ p. 32 AZ **n**
Meals *(closed Sunday and Bank Holidays)* (dinner only) 9.95 **st.** and a la carte ₰ 4.95 – **20 rm** ☐ 90.00/150.00 **st.**

🏨 **Portobello,** 22 Stanley Gdns, W11 2NG, ℘ 727 2777, Fax 792 9641, « Attractive town house in Victorian terrace » – |♦| TV ☎. EN AE ⓓ VISA EV **n**
closed 23 December-2 January – **Meals** 15.00 **st.** and a la carte ₰ 4.75 – **25 rm** ☐ 70.00/180.00 **st.**

XXX ✿ **Leith's,** 92 Kensington Park Rd, W11 2PN, ℘ 229 4481 – ▤. EN AE ⓓ VISA EV **e**
closed 27-28 August and 4 days at Christmas – **Meals** (dinner only) 32.00 **t.** and a la carte 28.50/39.75 **t.** ₰ 7.25
Spec. Hors d'oeuvre trolley, Roast fillet of sea bass with scallops and a tomato and caper vinaigrette, Pot roasted guinea fowl with leek mousseline and sherry vinegar dressing.

XX **Chez Moi,** 1 Addison Av., Holland Park, W11 4QS, ℘ 603 8267 – ▤. EN AE ⓓ VISA
closed Saturday lunch, Sunday and Bank Holidays – **Meals** - French 14.00 **t.** (lunch) and a la carte 17.50/26.25 **t.** ₰ 4.50. p. 24 EX **n**

XX **Park Inn,** 6 Wellington Terr., Bayswater Rd, W2 4LW, ℘ 229 3553, Fax 229 3553 – ▤. EN AE VISA AZ **c**
Meals - Chinese Seafood (Peking) 5.00/12.00 **t.** and a la carte ₰ 4.50.

X **L'Altro,** 210 Kensington Park Rd, W11 1NR, ℘ 792 1066 – ▤. EN AE ⓓ VISA EUV **c**
closed Sunday dinner, 4 days Christmas and Bank Holidays – **Meals** - Italian a la carte 19.40/31.75 **t.** ₰ 5.95.

X **192,** 192 Kensington Park Rd, W11 2JF, ℘ 229 0482 – EN AE ⓓ VISA EV **a**
closed 25 to 26 December and Bank Holidays – **Meals** 10.50 **t.** (lunch)and a la carte17.00/24.50 **t.**

X **Canal Brasserie,** Canalot Studios, 222 Kensal Rd, W10 5BN, ℘ (0181) 960 2732 – EN VISA ET **c**
closed lunch Saturday and Sunday and dinner Monday and Tuesday – **Meals** a la carte 13.40/16.50 **t.**

X **Brasserie du Marché aux Puces,** 349 Portobello Rd, W10 5SA, ℘ (0181) 968 5828
closed Sunday dinner and Bank Holidays – **Meals** a la carte 16.45/19.45 **t.** ₰ 5.50. EU **a**

X **Surinder's,** 109 Westbourne Park Rd, W2 5QL, ℘ 229 8968 – EN AE VISA EU **e**
closed Sunday and Monday – **Meals** (dinner only) 14.95 **st.**

South Kensington – ✉ SW5/SW7/W8 – ☎ 0171 – Except where otherwise stated see pp. 30 and 31.

Harrington Hall, 5-25 Harrington Gdns, SW7 4JW, ☎ 396 9696, Fax 396 9090, Ⅰ₆, ≘s – |‡| ⇔ rm ▤ TV ☎ – 🔺 250. AE VISA JCB. ✻ BT **n**
Wetherby's **: Meals** 18.50/38.20 **t.** – ☐ 10.00 – **200 rm** 99.00/145.00 **st.** – SB.

Gloucester, 4-18 Harrington Gdns, SW7 4LH, ☎ 373 6030, Telex 917505, Fax 373 0409 – |‡| ⇔ rm ▤ TV ☎ P – 🔺 400. AE VISA JCB BS **r**
Meals a la carte 15.15/23.70 **t.** 🍷 10.00 – ☐ 13.50 – **542 rm** 150.00/185.00 **t.**, 6 suites.

Pelham, 15 Cromwell Pl., SW7 2LA, ☎ 589 8288, Fax 584 8444, « Tastefully furnished Victorian town house » – |‡| ▤ TV ☎. AE VISA. ✻ CS **z**
Meals *closed Sunday lunch and Saturday* 16.00/22.00 **t.** – ☐ 11.50 – **34 rm** 120.00/170.00 **t.**, 3 suites – SB.

Blakes, 33 Roland Gdns, SW7 3PF, ☎ 370 6701, Telex 8813500, Fax 373 0442, « Antique oriental furnishings » – |‡| ▤ rest TV ☎ P. AE VISA. ✻ BU **n**
Meals 32.00 (lunch) and a la carte 44.50/64.75 **t.** 🍷 8.00 – ☐ 16.50 – **46 rm** 125.00/300.00 **st.**, 6 suites – SB.

Rembrandt, 11 Thurloe Pl., SW7 2RS, ☎ 589 8100, Telex 295828, Fax 225 3363, Ⅰ₆, ≘s, ▢ – |‡| ⇔ rm ▤ rest TV ☎ – 🔺 250. AE VISA JCB. ✻ DS **x**
Meals 12.50/15.95 **st.** and a la carte 🍷 5.00 – ☐ 9.25 – **195 rm** 105.00/125.00 **st.** – SB.

Swallow International, Cromwell Rd, SW5 0TH, ☎ 973 1000, Telex 27260, Fax 244 8194, Ⅰ₆, ≘s, ▢ – |‡| ⇔ rm ▤ rest TV ☎ P – 🔺 200. AE VISA AS **c**
Meals (carving lunch) 14.50/15.95 **st.** and a la carte – ☐ 10.25 – **414 rm** 105.00/135.00 **st.**, 1 suite – SB.

Holiday Inn, 100 Cromwell Rd, SW7 4ER, ☎ 373 2222, Telex 911311, Fax 373 0559, Ⅰ₆, ≘s, 🌳 – |‡| ⇔ rm ▤ TV ☎ ♿ – 🔺 150. AE VISA JCB. ✻ BS **u**
Meals 9.95 **st.** and a la carte 🍷 6.50 – ☐ 10.95 – **143 rm** 140.00/165.00 **st.**, 19 suites – SB.

Regency, 100 Queen's Gate, SW7 5AG, ☎ 370 4595, Telex 267594, Fax 370 5555, Ⅰ₆, ≘s – |‡| ⇔ rm ▤ rest TV ☎ – 🔺 100. AE VISA JCB. ✻ CT **e**
Meals *(closed lunch Saturday and Sunday)* 16.50/18.50 **st.** and a la carte 🍷 6.00 – ☐ 13.50 – **192 rm** 85.00/120.00 **s.**, 6 suites – SB.

Vanderbilt (Edwardian), 68-86 Cromwell Rd, SW7 5BT, ☎ 589 2424, Fax 225 2293 – |‡| ▤ rest TV ☎ – 🔺 120. AE VISA JCB. ✻ BS **v**
Meals 13.50/15.50 – **223 rm.**

Jury's Kensington, 109-113 Queen's Gate, SW7 5LR, ☎ 589 6300, Telex 262180, Fax 581 1492 – |‡| ▤ rest TV ☎ – 🔺 80. AE VISA. ✻ CT **i**
Meals (bar lunch Monday to Saturday)/dinner 15.00/11.95 **st.** and a la carte – ☐ 7.25 – **171 rm** 65.00/175.00 **st.** –.

Forum (Inter-Con), 97 Cromwell Rd, SW7 4DN, ☎ 370 5757, Fax 373 1448, ≤, Ⅰ₆ – |‡| ⇔ rm ▤ rest TV ☎ ♿ P – 🔺 400. AE VISA JCB BS **x**
Meals 10.50/22.50 **st.** and a la carte 🍷 6.50 – ☐ 11.50 – **906 rm** 135.00/155.00 **st.**, 4 suites.

Gore, 189 Queen's Gate, SW7 5EX, ☎ 584 6601, Fax 589 8127, « Attractive decor » – |‡| ⇔ rm TV ☎. AE VISA JCB BR **n**
closed 24 and 25 December – ***Bistrot 190*** **: Meals** (only members and residents may book) a la carte 14.50/21.50 🍷 5.00 – (see also ***Downstairs at One Ninety*** below) – ☐ 9.50 – **54 rm** 99.00/146.00 **st.**

Cranley without rest., 10-12 Bina Gardens, SW5 0LA, ☎ 373 0123, Fax 373 9497, « Tasteful decor, antiques » – |‡| ⇔ TV ☎ BT **c**
32 rm, 4 suites.

John Howard, 4 Queen's Gate, SW7 5EH, ☎ 581 3011, Telex 8813397, Fax 589 8403 – |‡| ▤ TV ☎ BQ **i**
43 rm, 9 suites.

Park International, 117-125 Cromwell Rd, SW7 4DS, ☎ 370 5711, Telex 296822, Fax 244 9211 – |‡| TV ☎ – 🔺 40 AS **e**
117 rm.

Kensington Plaza, 61 Gloucester Rd, SW7 4PE, ☎ 584 8100, Telex 8950993, Fax 823 9175 – |‡| ▤ rest TV ☎ – 🔺 100. AE VISA BS **e**
Mongolian Brasserie **: Meals** (dinner only) 14.95 **st.** 🍷 3.75 – ☐ 4.75 – **88 rm** 69.00/85.00 **st.**

Number Sixteen without rest., 14-17 Sumner Pl., SW7 3EG, ☎ 589 5232, Fax 584 8615, « Attractively furnished Victorian town houses », 🌳 – |‡| TV ☎. AE VISA. ✻ CT **c**
36 rm ☐ 99.00/170.00 **t.**

Five Sumner Place without rest., 5 Sumner Pl., SW7 3EE, ☎ 584 7586, Fax 823 9962 – |‡| TV ☎. AE VISA JCB. ✻ DR **a**
13 rm ☐ 62.00/95.00 **s.**

Aster House without rest., 3 Sumner Pl., SW7 3EE, ☎ 581 5888, Fax 584 4925, 🌳 – ⇔ TV ☎. AE. ✻ CT **u**
12 rm 61.00/99.00.

Cranley Gardens without rest., 8 Cranley Gdns, SW7 3DB, ✆ 373 3232, Telex 894489, Fax 373 7944 – 🛗 TV ☎. AE VISA BT e
85 rm 63.00/89.00 **st.**

Hotel 167 without rest., 167 Old Brompton Rd, SW5 0AN, ✆ 373 3221, Fax 373 3360 – TV ☎. AE VISA JCB. BT r
19 rm 59.00/82.50 **st.**

XXX **Bombay Brasserie,** Courtfield Close, 140 Gloucester Rd, SW7 4UH, ✆ 370 4040, « Raj-style decor, conservatory garden » – ▤. VISA BS a
closed 25 and 26 December – **Meals** - Indian (buffet lunch) 14.95 **t.** and dinner a la carte 20.95/27.95 **t.** 4.95.

XX **Hilaire,** 68 Old Brompton Rd, SW7 3LQ, ✆ 584 8993 – ▤. AE VISA CT n
closed Saturday lunch and Sunday – **Meals** (booking essential) 17.00/21.50 **t.** and dinner a la carte 23.00/32.00 **t.** 6.75.

XX **Shaw's,** 119 Old Brompton Rd, SW7 3RN, ✆ 373 7774 – ▤. AE VISA BT v
closed Saturday lunch, Sunday dinner, 2 weeks August and 2 weeks Christmas-New Year – **Meals** 13.00/28.50 **t.** 9.50.

XX **Downstairs at One Ninety,** 190 Queen's Gate, SW7 5EU, ✆ 581 5666, Fax 581 8172 – ▤. AE VISA JCB BR n
closed Sunday and Christmas – **Meals** - Seafood (booking essential) (dinner only) a la carte 18.15/26.40 **t.** 12.00.

XX **Khan's of Kensington,** 3 Harrington Rd, SW7 3ES, ✆ 581 2900, Fax 581 2900 – ▤. AE VISA CS e
Meals - Indian 7.50/14.50 **t.** and a la carte 4.95.

XX **Tui,** 19 Exhibition Rd, SW7 2HE, ✆ 584 8359, Fax 352 8343 – AE VISA CS u
closed 5 days at Christmas and Bank Holiday Mondays – **Meals** - Thai 10.00 **st.** (lunch) and a la carte 13.50/20.20 **t.** 4.10.

XX **Delhi Brasserie,** 134 Cromwell Rd, SW7 4HA, ✆ 370 7617 – ▤. AE VISA AS a
closed 25 and 26 December – **Meals** - Indian 7.50/14.95 **t.** and a la carte.

XX **Cafe Lazeez,** 93-95 Old Brompton Rd, SW7 3LD, ✆ 581 9993, Fax 581 8200 – ▤. AE VISA JCB CT a
- North Indian – ***Restaurant :* Meals** (dinner only) a la carte 11.65/22.75 **t.** 4.75.
X **Cafe Meals** a la carte 11.65/22.75 **t.**

XX **Memories of India,** 18 Gloucester Rd, SW7 4RB, ✆ 589 6450 – ▤. AE VISA JCB BR s
Meals - Indian 14.50/20.00 and a la carte.

X **Bangkok,** 9 Bute St., SW7 3EY, ✆ 584 8529 – ▤. VISA CS v
closed Sunday, one week Christmas to New Year and Bank Holidays – **Meals** - Thai Bistro a la carte 13.40/20.25 **t.**

KINGSTON UPON THAMES

pp. 8 and 9.

Home Park, Hampton Wick ✆ (0181) 977 6645, BY.

Chessington – ✉ Surrey – ☎ 01372.

Travel Inn, Leatherhead Rd, KT9 2NE, on A 243 ✆ 744060, Fax 720889 – rm TV P. AE VISA. BZ c
Meals (Beefeater grill) a la carte approx. 16.00 **t.** – 4.95 – **42 rm** 33.50 **t.**

Kingston – ✉ Surrey – ☎ 0181.

Garrison Lane ✆ 391 0948 CZ.

Kingston Lodge (Forte), Kingston Hill, KT2 7NP, ✆ 541 4481, Fax 547 1013 – ▤ rest TV ☎ P – 60. AE VISA CY u
Meals (bar lunch Monday to Saturday)/dinner 18.95 **st.** and a la carte 5.95 – 7.50 – **62 rm** 95.00/127.50 **st.** – SB.

XX **Gravier's,** 9 Station Rd, Norbiton, KT2 7AA, ✆ 549 5557 – AE VISA CY x
closed Saturday lunch, Sunday, 1 week Easter, 1 week August, 1 week Christmas and Bank Holidays – **Meals** - French Seafood 16.50 **t.** (lunch) and a la carte 20.35/28.35 **t.** 4.50.

X **Ayudhya,** 14 Kingston Hill, KT2 7NH, ✆ 549 5984 – AE VISA CY z
closed Monday lunch, Easter Sunday, 25 December and 1 January – **Meals** - Thai 15.50/18.50 **t.** and a la carte 3.60.

Surbiton – ✉ Surrey – ☎ 0181.

XX **Chez Max,** 85 Maple Rd, KT6 4AW, ✆ 399 2365 – AE VISA BY o
closed Saturday lunch, Sunday, Monday, 24 to 30 December and Good Friday – **Meals** (booking essential) 15.95/19.45 **t.** and dinner a la carte 18.50/23.10 **t.** 7.00.

LAMBETH

Except where otherwise stated see pp.10 and 11.

Brixton – ✉ SW9 – ☎ 0171.

X **Twenty Trinity Gardens,** 20 Trinity Gdns, SW9 8DP, ✆ 733 8838 – VISA EX n
closed 25 and 26 December – **Meals** (dinner only and Sunday lunch)/dinner 16.75 **t.** and a la carte 5.00.

Clapham Common – ✉ SW4 – ☎ 0171.

Windmill on the Common, Clapham Common South Side, SW4 9DE, ☎ 673 4578, Fax 675 1486, – rm rest . DQ **e**
Meals (bar lunch Monday to Saturday)/dinner 18.50 **st.** and a la carte – **29 rm** 75.00/85.00 **st.**

The Grafton, 45 Old Town, SW4 OJL, ☎ 627 1048 – . p. 13 DQ **a**
closed Saturday lunch, Sunday, last 3 weeks August, 1 week Christmas and Bank Holidays – **Meals** - French 12.50/32.00 **t.** and a la carte 4.50.

Streatham – ✉ SW16 – ☎ 0181.

Barrow House without rest., 45 Barrow Rd, SW16 5PE, ☎ 677 1925, Fax 677 1925, « Victoriana », – . EY **s**
5 rm 20.00/45.00 **st.**

Waterloo – ✉ SE1 – ☎ 0171.

RSJ, 13a Coin St., SE1 8YQ, ☎ 928 4554 – . p. 27 NX **e**
closed Saturday lunch, Sunday, 25-26 December and Bank Holidays – **Meals** 15.95 **t.** and a la carte 5.25.

La Rive Gauche, 61 The Cut, SE1 8LL, ☎ 928 8645 – . p. 27 NX **x**
closed Saturday lunch and Sunday – **Meals** - French 12.00/16.85 **st.** and a la carte 5.50.

LONDON HEATHROW AIRPORT – see Hillingdon, London p. 56.

MERTON pp. 8 and 9.

Morden – ✉ Morden – ☎ 0181.

Forte Travelodge, Epsom Rd, SM4 5PH, SW : on A 24 ☎ 640 8227, Reservations (Freephone) 0800 850950 – . DY **c**
Meals (Harvester grill) a la carte approx. 16.00 **t.** – 5.50 – **32 rm** 33.50 **t.**

Wimbledon – ✉ SW19 – ☎ 0181.

Cannizaro House (Mt. Charlotte Thistle) , West Side, Wimbledon Common, SW19 4UF, ☎ 879 1464, Fax 879 7338, ≤, « 18C country house overlooking Cannizaro Park », – rm – 45. . DXY **x**
Meals 16.95/25.75 **t.** and a la carte – 9.75 – **44 rm** 105.00/175.00 **t.**, 2 suites – SB.

Bayee Village, 24 High St., SW19 5DX, ☎ 947 3533, Fax 944 8392 – . DX **i**
Meals - Chinese (Peking, Szechuan) 8.00/23.00 **st.** and a la carte 5.00.

REDBRIDGE pp. 6 and 7.

Town Hall, High Rd, IG1 1DD ☎ (0181) 478 3020 ext 2126.

Ilford – ✉ Essex – ☎ 0181.

Wanstead Park Rd ☎ 554 5174, HU – Fairlop Waters, Forest Rd, Barkingside ☎ 500 9911 JT.

Travel Inn, Redbridge Lane East, IG4 5BG, ☎ 550 6451 – rm . HU **i**
Meals (Beefeater grill) a la carte approx. 16.00 **t.** – 4.95 – **40 rm** 33.50 **t.**

Forte Travelodge, Beehive Lane, RG4 5DR, ☎ 550 4248, Reservations (Freephone) 0800 850950 – . HU **e**
Meals (Harvester grill) a la carte approx. 16.00 **t.** – **32 rm** 33.50 **t.**

Dragon City, 97 Cranbrook Rd, IG1 4PG, ☎ 553 0312 – HJU **a**
Meals - Chinese (Canton, Peking).

South Woodford – ✉ Essex – ☎ 0181.

Ho-Ho, 20 High Rd, E18 2QL, ☎ 989 1041 – . HU **c**
closed Saturday lunch – **Meals** - Chinese (Peking, Szechuan) 16.50/27.50 **st.** and a la carte.

Woodford – ✉ Essex – ☎ 0181.

Hainault Forest, Chigwell Row ☎ 500 2097, JT – Chingford, 158 Station Rd ☎ 529 2107, HT.

Prince Regent, Manor Rd, Woodford Bridge, IG8 8AE, ☎ 505 9966, Fax 506 0807, – rest – 350. HT **a**
Meals 12.75/14.75 **st.** and a la carte – **51 rm** 72.50/130.00 **t.** – SB.

Woodford Moat House (Q.M.H.), 30 Oak Hill, Woodford Green, IG8 9NY, ☎ 505 4511, Fax 506 0941, – – 150. . HT **c**
closed 3 days Christmas – **Meals** 15.00/17.50 **st.** and a la carte – 9.50 – **99 rm** 58.00/70.00 **st.** – SB.

RICHMOND-UPON-THAMES pp. 8 and 9.

Barnes – ✉ SW13 – ☏ 0181.

XX **Sonny's,** 94 Church Rd, SW13 0DQ, ✆ 748 0393, Fax 748 2698 – ▤. AE VISA CX x
closed Sunday dinner and lunch Bank Holidays – **Meals** 12.75 **t.** and a la carte 3.50.

X **Riva,** 169 Church Rd, SW13 9HR, ✆ 748 0434 – AE VISA CX a
closed Saturday lunch, Easter, last 2 weeks August, Christmas and Bank Holidays – **Meals** - Italian a la carte 14.50/25.00 **t.** 6.00.

East Sheen – ✉ SW14 – ☏ 0181.

XX **Crowther's,** 481 Upper Richmond Rd West, SW14 7PU, ✆ 876 6372 – ▤. VISA CX n
closed Saturday lunch, Sunday, Monday, 2 weeks August and 1 week Christmas – **Meals** (booking essential) 12.75/21.00 **t.** 4.75.

Hampton Court – ✉ Surrey – ☏ 0181.

Mitre, Hampton Court Rd, KT8 9BN, ✆ 979 9988, Fax 979 9777, ← – rm TV ☎ P – 25. AE VISA. BY v
Meals 14.50/18.50 **t.** and a la carte 8.00 – 8.50 – **35 rm** 89.00/115.00 **t.**, 1 suite – SB.

Hampton Wick – ✉ Surrey – ☏ 0181.

Chase Lodge, 10 Park Rd, KT1 4AS, ✆ 943 1862, Fax 943 9363 – TV ☎ P. AE VISA BY e
Meals (lunch by arrangement Monday to Saturday)/dinner a la carte approx. 17.00 **t.** 3.50 – **9 rm** 48.00/80.00 **t.** – SB.

Richmond – ✉ Surrey – ☏ 0181.

18, 18 Richmond Park, Roehampton Gate ✆ 876 3205/1795 CX – 18 Sudbrook Park ✆ 940 1463 CX.

Old Town Hall, Whittaker Av., TW9 1TP ✆ 940 9125.

Petersham ⑤, Nightingale Lane, Richmond Hill, TW10 6UZ, ✆ 940 7471, Telex 928556, Fax 940 9998, ←, – TV ☎ P – 50. AE VISA. CX c
Meals - (see ***Nightingales*** below) – **54 rm** 100.00/155.00 **st.**

Richmond Gate, 158 Richmond Hill, TW10 6RP, ✆ 940 0061, Fax 332 0354, – rm TV ☎ P – 50. AE VISA. CX c
Meals *(closed Saturday lunch)* 14.50/18.50 **t.** and a la carte – 7.00 – **64 rm** 89.00/155.00 **t.** – SB.

Bingham, 61-63 Petersham Rd, TW10 6UT, ✆ 940 0902, Fax 948 8737, – TV ☎ – 30. AE VISA. CX z
Meals *(closed Sunday and Bank Holidays)* (dinner only) 11.75 **t.** and a la carte 4.25 – **35 rm** 67.50/95.00 **t.**

XXX **Nightingales** (at Petersham H.), Nightingale Lane, Richmond Hill, TW10 6UZ, ✆ 940 7471, Telex 928556, Fax 940 9998, ←, – P. AE VISA CX c
Meals 18.50/28.50 **t.** and a la carte 8.50.

XX **Four Regions,** 102-104 Kew Rd, TW9 2PQ, ✆ 940 9044, Fax 332 6130 – ▤. AE VISA CX e
Meals - Chinese 10.00/30.00 **t.** and a la carte.

X **Burnt Chair,** 5 Duke St., TW9 1HP, ✆ 940 9488 – VISA BX e
closed Sunday, 2 weeks August, 24 to 29 December and Bank Holidays – **Meals** (dinner only) 15.00 **t.** and a la carte.

X **Chez Lindsay,** 11 Hill Rise, TW9 1JS, ✆ 948 7473 – VISA BX c
closed Saturday lunch, Sunday, 25 to 28 December and Bank Holiday Monday lunch – **Meals** - French Bistro a la carte 18.50/24.75 **t.** 5.75.

X Pitagora, 106 Kew Rd, TW9 5PQ, ✆ 948 2443 CX e
Meals - Italian.

Twickenham – ✉ Middx. – ☏ 0181.

9 Twickenham Park, Staines Rd ✆ 783 1698, BX.

44 York St., TW1 3BZ ✆ 891 1411.

XX **McClements,** 12 The Green, TW2 5AA, ✆ 755 0176, Fax 890 1372 – . VISA BX s
closed Sunday and Monday – **Meals** 15.00/25.00 **t.** and a la carte 6.00.

SOUTHWARK Except where otherwise stated see pp. 10 and 11.

Bermondsey – ✉ SE1 – ☏ 0171.

XXX **Le Pont de la Tour,** 36d Shad Thames, Butlers Wharf, SE1 2YE, ✆ 403 8403, Fax 403 0267, ←, « Riverside setting » – ▤. AE VISA p. 27 PX c
closed Saturday lunch and 4 days Christmas – **Meals** 25.00 **t.** (lunch) and dinner a la carte 26.50/37.75 **t.** 6.50.

XXX **Bengal Clipper,** Cardamom Building, Shad Thames, Butlers Wharf, SE1 2YE, ✆ 357 9001, Fax 357 9002 – ▤. AE VISA PX e
Meals - Indian a la carte 11.65/17.20 4.95.

Blue Print Café, Design Museum, Shad Thames, Butlers Wharf, SE1 2YD, ✆ 378 7031, Fax 378 6540, ≤, « Riverside setting », – AE VISA — p. 27 PX u
closed Sunday dinner and 4 days at Christmas – **Meals** a la carte 16.00/24.75 **t.**

Cantina Del Ponte, 36c Shad Thames, Butlers Wharf, SE1 2YE, ✆ 403 5403, Fax 403 0267, ≤, « Riverside setting » – AE VISA — p. 27 PX c
closed Sunday dinner and 4 days at Christmas – **Meals** - Italian-Mediterranean a la carte 16.15/24.25 **t.** 8.95.

Butlers Wharf Chop House, 36e Shad Thames, Butlers Wharf, SE1 2YE, ✆ 403 3403, Fax 403 3414, « Riverside setting, ≤ Tower Bridge » – AE VISA — PX n
closed Sunday dinner – **Meals** 19.50 **t.** (lunch) and dinner a la carte 22.00/27.50 **t.** 5.50.

Dulwich – ✉ SE19 – ☎ 0181.

Luigi's, 129 Gipsy Hill, SE19 1QS, ✆ 670 1843 – ▤. AE VISA — FX a
closed Saturday lunch, Sunday and Bank Holidays – **Meals** - Italian a la carte approx. 16.00 **t.**

Rotherhithe – ✉ SE16 – ☎ 0171.

Scandic Crown, 265 Rotherhithe St., Nelson Dock, SE16 1EJ, ✆ 231 1001, Fax 231 0599, ≤, Ls, ≘s, ▣, ✂ – |‡| ⇝ rm ▤ rest TV ☎ ♿ P – 🎪 350. AE VISA JCB. ✂ — GV r
Meals 18.95 **st.** and dinner a la carte 9.50 – ☐ 9.50 – **384 rm** 85.00/105.00 **st.**, 2 suites – SB.

Southwark – ✉ SE1 – ☎ 0171.

La Truffe Noire, 29 Tooley St., SE1 2QF, ✆ 378 0621, Fax 403 0689 – ▤. AE VISA JCB — p. 27 PX a
closed Saturday lunch, Sunday, 24 December-2 January and Bank Holidays – **Meals** - French 10.00 **st.** and a la carte 6.00.

Café dell'Ugo, 56-58 Tooley St., SE1 2SZ, ✆ 407 6001 – ▤. AE VISA — PX r
Meals 10.00 **t.** (dinner) and a la carte 14.85/24.35 **t.**

Le Guide change, changez de **guide Michelin** *tous les ans.*

SUTTON pp. 8 and 9.

Carshalton – ✉ Surrey – ☎ 0181.

La Veranda 18-19 Beynon Rd, SM5 3RL, ✆ 647 4370 – ▤. AE VISA — EZ a
Meals *(closed Sunday and Bank Holidays)* a la carte 18.60/26.90 **t.** 7.80.

Sutton – ✉ Surrey – ☎ 0181.

18, 9 Oak Sports Centre, Woodmansterne Rd, Carshalton ✆ 643 8363.

Holiday Inn, Gibson Rd, SM1 2RF, ✆ 770 1311, Fax 770 1539, Ls, ≘s, ▣ – |‡| ⇝ rm ▤ rest TV ☎ ♿ P – 🎪 220. AE VISA JCB — EZ a
Meals *(closed Saturday lunch)* 12.95/22.50 **st.** and a la carte 4.95 – ☐ 9.50 – **115 rm** 99.50/115.00 **st.**, 1 suite – SB.

Thatched House, 135-141 Cheam Rd, SM1 2BN, ✆ 642 3131, Fax 770 0684, – TV ☎ P – 🎪 50. VISA. ✂ — DZ e
Meals *(closed Sunday)* (dinner only) 15.50 **t.** 3.95 – **28 rm** ☐ 39.50/59.50 **st.** – SB.

Partners Brasserie, 23 Stonecot Hill, SM3 9HB, ✆ 644 7743 – ▤. AE VISA — DY v
closed Saturday lunch, Sunday, Monday and 1 week Christmas – **Meals** 9.95 **t.** and a la carte 4.00.

TOWER HAMLETS – pp. 6 and 7.

Bethnal Green Library, Cambridge Heath Rd, E2 0HL ✆ (0171) 980 4831.

Stepney – ✉ E1 – ☎ 0171.

Laksmi, 116 Mile End Rd, E1 4UN, ✆ 265 9403 – ▤ — GV a
Meals - Indian.

WANDSWORTH Except where otherwise stated see pp. 12 and 13.

Battersea – ✉ SW8/SW11 – ☎ 0171.

Ransome's Dock, 35-37 Parkgate Rd, SW11 4NP, ✆ 223 1611, Fax 924 2614 – AE VISA — p. 25 HZ c
closed Sunday dinner and Christmas – **Meals** 11.50 **t.** (lunch) and a la carte 17.50/23.75 **t.** 4.50.

Chada, 208-210 Battersea Park Rd, SW11 4ND, ✆ 622 2209 – ▤. AE VISA — CQ x
closed Saturday lunch and Bank Holidays – **Meals** - Thai a la carte 16.05/25.65 **st.**

Lena's, 196 Lavender Hill, SW11 1JA, ✆ 228 3735 – ▤ — CQ z
Meals - Thai.

Clapham – ✉ SW11 – ☎ 0171.

Jasmin, 50/52 Battersea Rise, SW11 1EG, ✆ 228 0336 – AE VISA — CQ u
Meals - Chinese (Canton, Peking) 5.50/12.80 **t.** and a la carte.

Putney – ✉ SW15 – ☎ 0181.

XX **Royal China,** 3 Chelverton Rd, SW15 1RN, ☎ 788 0907, Fax 785 2305 – ▤. AE VISA AQ **a**
Meals - Chinese a la carte 20.00/26.00 **t.**

XX **Del Buongustaio,** 283 Putney Bridge Rd, SW15 2PT, ☎ 780 9361, Fax 789 9659 – ▤. AE VISA AQ **e**
closed Saturday lunch, 29 August Christmas-New Year and Bank Holidays – **Meals** - Italian 19.50 **st.** and a la carte 5.80.

Tooting – ✉ SW17 – ☎ 0181.

X **Oh Boy,** 843 Garratt Lane, SW17 0PG, ☎ 947 9760 – ▤. AE VISA CR **c**
Meals - Thai (dinner only) a la carte 9.50/11.45 **st.** 3.60.

Wandsworth – ✉ SW12/SW17/SW18 – ☎ 0181.

XX **Harvey's,** 2 Bellevue Rd, SW17 7EG, ☎ 672 0114 – ▤. AE VISA CR **e**
closed lunch Saturday and Monday, Sunday, Christmas-New Year and Easter – **Meals** 13.50/21.50 **t.** 6.00.

XX **Tabaq,** 47 Balham Hill, SW12 9DR, ☎ 673 7820 – ▤. AE VISA DR **v**
Meals - Indian (dinner only) a la carte 11.20/23.75 **t.** 4.25.

X **Bombay Bicycle Club,** 95 Nightingale Lane, SW12 8NX, ☎ 673 6217 – AE VISA
closed Christmas – **Meals** - Indian (dinner only) a la carte approx. 17.75 **t.** DR **o**

WESTMINSTER (City of).

Bayswater and Maida Vale – ✉ W2/W9 – ☎ 0171 – Except where otherwise stated see pp. 32 and 33.

Royal Lancaster, Lancaster Terr., W2 2TY, ☎ 262 6737, Fax 724 3191, ← – rm ▤ – 1 400. AE VISA JCB. DZ **e**
Meals 22.50/27.50 **t.** and a la carte 8.00 – ☕ 14.50 – **398 rm** 147.00/176.00 **st.**, 20 suites – SB.

London Metropole, Edgware Rd, W2 1JU, ☎ 402 4141, Telex 23711, Fax 724 8866, ←, – rm ▤ – 1 200. AE VISA JCB. p. 21 GU **c**
Meals - (see *Aspects* below) – ☕ 14.40 – **716 rm** 135.00/200.00 **t.**, 26 suites.

Whites (Mt. Charlotte Thistle), Bayswater Rd, 90-92 Lancaster Gate, W2 3NR, ☎ 262 2711, Telex 24771, Fax 262 2147 – rm ▤. AE VISA JCB. CZ **v**
Meals *(closed Saturday lunch)* 17.50/21.50 **t.** and a la carte 7.15 – ☕ 10.25 – **52 rm** 145.00/225.00 **t.**, 2 suites – SB.

Plaza on Hyde Park (Hilton), 1-7 Lancaster Gate, W2 3NA, ☎ 262 5022, Telex 8954372, Fax 724 8666 – rm. AE VISA JCB. DZ **r**
Meals 9.90/15.00 **st.** and a la carte – ☕ 9.80 – **402 rm** 81.00/150.00 **st.** – SB.

Stakis London Coburg, 129 Bayswater Rd, W2 4RJ, ☎ 221 2217, Fax 229 0557 – rm – 80. AE VISA JCB BZ **c**
Meals - (see *Spice Merchant* below) – ☕ 7.50 – **131 rm** 75.00/85.00 **t.**, 1 suite – SB.

London Embassy (Jarvis), 150 Bayswater Rd, W2 4RT, ☎ 229 1212, Telex 27727, Fax 229 2623 – rm ▤ rest – 60. AE VISA. BZ **o**
Meals (carving rest.) 15.95 **t.** and a la carte 6.75 – ☕ 9.50 – **192 rm** 100.00/140.00 **st.**, 1 suite.

Hyde Park Towers, 41-51 Inverness Terr., W2 3JN, ☎ 221 8484, Fax 792 3201 – ▤ rest – 40. AE VISA JCB. BZ **r**
Meals (buffet lunch) 13.50 **st.** and a la carte 4.50 – ☕ 7.50 – **115 rm** 86.00/96.00 **st.**

Queen's Park, 48 Queensborough Terr., W2 3SS, ☎ 229 8080, Telex 21723, Fax 792 1330 – ▤ rest – 60. AE VISA JCB. CZ **s**
Meals *(closed Friday and Saturday)* (dinner only) a la carte 10.75/17.50 **t.** 5.70 – ☕ 7.50 – **86 rm** 86.00/106.00 **st.**

Mornington without rest., 12 Lancaster Gate, W2 3LG, ☎ 262 7361, Fax 706 1028 – AE VISA DZ **s**
68 rm ☕ 79.00/109.00 **st.**

Phoenix without rest., 1 Kensington Garden Sq., W2 4BH, ☎ 229 2494, Telex 298854, Fax 727 1419 – AE VISA JCB. BZ **e**
125 rm ☕ 69.00/140.00 **st.**

Byron without rest., 36-38 Queensborough Terr., W2 3SH, ☎ 243 0987, Telex 263431, Fax 792 1957 – ▤ AE VISA. CZ **z**
41 rm ☕ 75.50/89.00 **t.**, 1 suite.

Comfort Inn, 18-19 Craven Hill Gdns, W2 3EE, ☎ 262 6644, Fax 262 0673 – AE VISA. CZ **e**
Meals 15.00/25.00 **st.** and a la carte 4.00 – **60 rm** ☕ 57.00/86.00 **st.**

Delmere, 130 Sussex Gdns, W2 1UB, ☎ 706 3344, Fax 262 1863 – AE VISA JCB DZ **v**
Meals *(closed Sunday)* 16.00 **st.** and a la carte 6.50 – ☕ 6.00 – **38 rm** 58.40/72.80 **st.**

Gresham without rest., 116 Sussex Gdns, W2 1UA, ☎ 402 2920, Fax 402 3137 – |‡| TV ☎. AE ① VISA. ※ DZ a
38 rm ☐ 50.00/75.00 **st.**

Norfolk Plaza without rest., 29-33 Norfolk Sq., W2 1RX, ☎ 723 0792, Telex 266977, Fax 224 8770 – |‡| TV ☎. AE ① VISA JCB. ※ DZ x
81 rm ☐ 69.00/98.00 **st.**, 6 suites.

Parkwood without rest., 4 Stanhope Pl., W2 2HB, ☎ 402 2241, Fax 402 1574 – TV ☎. VISA. ※ EZ e
18 rm ☐ 39.75/67.50 **st.**

XXX **Aspects** (at London Metropole H.), Edgware Rd, W2 1JU, ☎ 402 4141, Telex 23711, Fax 724 8866, ≤ London – ▤. AE ① VISA JCB p. 64 GU c
Meals 18.50/29.50 **st.** and a la carte ₰ 8.50.

XX **Spice Merchant** (at Stakis London Coburg H.), 130 Bayswater Rd, W2 4RJ, ☎ 221 2442, Fax 229 0557 – ▤. AE ① VISA BZ c
Meals - Indian a la carte 11.45/16.15 **st.** ₰ 5.00.

XX **Poons,** Whiteleys, Queensway, W2 4YN, ☎ 792 2884 – ▤. AE ① VISA BZ x
closed 3 days at Christmas – **Meals** - Chinese a la carte 9.50/14.70 **t.** ₰ 5.50.

XX **Al San Vincenzo,** 30 Connaught St., W2 2AE, ☎ 262 9623 – VISA EZ o
closed Saturday lunch, Sunday and 2 weeks Christmas – **Meals** - Italian a la carte 21.95/30.50 **t.** ₰ 7.50.

X **L'Accento,** 16 Garway Rd, W2 4NH, ☎ 243 2201, Fax 243 2201 – VISA BZ a
closed Bank Holidays – **Meals** - Italian 10.50 **st.** and a la carte.

Belgravia – ✉ SW1 – ☎ 0171 – Except where otherwise stated see pp. 30 and 31.

Berkeley, Wilton Pl., SW1X 7RL, ☎ 235 6000, Telex 919252, Fax 235 4330, Fø, ≘s, ☐ – |‡| ▤ TV ☎ ⇔ – 🏠 220. AE ① VISA JCB. ※ FQ e
***Restaurant :* Meals** *(closed Saturday)* 19.50/21.00 **st.** – ***The Perroquet :* Meals** *(closed Sunday)* 16.00/21.00 **st.** and dinner a la carte ₰ 5.75 – ☐ 16.00 – **133 rm** 180.00/260.00 **s.**, 27 suites.

Lanesborough, 1 Lanesborough Pl., SW1X 7TA, ☎ 259 5599, Telex 911866, Fax 259 5606 – |‡| ⇔ rm ▤ TV ☎ ♿ P – 🏠 90. AE ① VISA JCB. ※ p. 25 IY a
***The Conservatory :* Meals** 22.50/28.50 **st.** ₰ 8.00 – ☐ 16.00 – **86 rm** 175.00/310.00 **s.**, 9 suites.

❀ **Halkin,** 5 Halkin St., SW1X 7DJ, ☎ 333 1000, Fax 333 1100, « Contemporary interior design » – |‡| ⇔ rm ▤ TV ☎ P – 🏠 25. AE ① VISA JCB. ※ p. 32 AV a
Meals - Italian *(closed lunch Saturday and Sunday)* 23.00 **st.** and a la carte 30.00/42.00 **st.** ₰ 9.50 – ☐ 13.50 – **36 rm** 190.00/240.00 **s.**, 5 suites
Spec. Duck ravioli with savoy cabbage and foie gras, Ragout of langoustines, rabbit and potato, Tiramisu.

Sheraton Belgravia, 20 Chesham Pl., SW1X 8HQ, ☎ 235 6040, Telex 919020, Fax 259 6243 – |‡| ⇔ rm ▤ TV ☎ P – 🏠 40. AE ① VISA JCB. ※ FR u
closed Christmas-New Year – **Meals** *(closed lunch Saturday and Sunday)* 10.00 **t.** (dinner) and a la carte 19.00/25.00 **t.** – ☐ 10.50 – **82 rm** 195.00/265.00 **s.**, 7 suites.

Lowndes (Hyatt), 21 Lowndes St., SW1X 9ES, ☎ 823 1234, Telex 919065, Fax 235 1154, Fø, ≘s – |‡| ⇔ rm ▤ TV ☎ – 🏠 25. AE ① VISA JCB. ※ FR i
***Brasserie 21 :* Meals** 11.95 **t.** ₰ 7.00 – ☐ 12.00 – **77 rm** 160.00/185.00 **s.**, 1 suite.

Diplomat without rest., 2 Chesham St., SW1X 8DT, ☎ 235 1544, Fax 259 6153 – TV ☎. AE ① VISA. ※ FR a
27 rm ☐ 65.00/130.00 **t.**

XXX **Al Bustan,** 27 Motcomb St., SW1X 8JU, ☎ 235 8277 – ▤. AE ① VISA FR z
Meals - Lebanese a la carte 24.00/35.00 **t.**

XX **Motcombs,** 26 Motcomb St., SW1X 8JU, ☎ 235 6382, Fax 245 6351 – ▤. AE ① VISA FR z
closed Saturday lunch, Sunday dinner and Bank Holidays – **Meals** 14.75/28.95 **t.** and a la carte ₰ 5.50.

Hyde Park and Knightsbridge – ✉ SW1/SW7 – ☎ 0171 – pp. 30 and 31.

Hyde Park (Forte), 66 Knightsbridge, SW1Y 7LA, ☎ 235 2000, Fax 235 4552, ≤, Fø – |‡| ⇔ rm ▤ TV ☎ ♿ – 🏠 250. AE ① VISA JCB. ※ FQ x
Park Room :* Meals** - Italian 25.00/29.50 **st.** ₰ 10.00 – (see also ***The Restaurant , Marco Pierre White below) – ☐ 15.00 – **166 rm** 199.00/275.00 **s.**, 19 suites – SB.

Knightsbridge Green without rest., 159 Knightsbridge, SW1X 7PD, ☎ 584 6274, Fax 225 1635 – |‡| TV ☎. AE VISA. ※ EQ z
closed 4 days at Christmas – ☐ 8.50 – **10 rm** 75.00/100.00 **st.**, **14 suites** 115.00 **st.**.

XXXX ❀❀❀ **The Restaurant, Marco Pierre White,** (at Hyde Park H.), 66 Knightsbridge, SW1Y 7LA, ☎ 259 5380, Fax 235 4552 – ▤. AE VISA FQ x
closed Saturday lunch, Sunday, last week December, first week January and Bank Holidays – **Meals** (booking essential) 25.00/65.00 **t.**
Spec. Millefeuille of crab and tomatoes with a tomato vinaigrette, Tronçonettes of turbot with grilled sea scallops and a Sauternes sauce, Caramelised apple tart with vanilla ice cream and caramel sauce.

XXX **Pearl of Knightsbridge,** 22 Brompton Rd, SW1X 7QN, ☎ 225 3888, Fax 225 0252 – ▤. AE VISA
closed 25 and 26 December – **Meals** - Chinese 20.00/30.00 **t.** and a la carte ₰ 7.00. EQ e

Mayfair – ✉ W1 – 0171 – pp. 28 and 29.

Dorchester, Park Lane, W1A 2HJ, ✆ 629 8888, Telex 887704, Fax 409 0114, – rm – 500. VISA JCB. BN **a**
Grill : **Meals** 23.50/28.00 **st.** and a la carte 29.30/40.30 **st.** 11.00 – ***Terrace :*** **Meals** *(dinner Friday and Saturday only)* – (see also ***Oriental*** below) – 14.50 – **194 rm** 195.00/255.00 **s.**, 53 suites – SB.

Claridge's, Brook St., W1A 2JQ, ✆ 629 8860, Telex 21872, Fax 499 2210 – – 60. VISA JCB. BL **c**
Restaurant : **Meals** *(closed Saturday lunch)* 26.00/36.00 **st.** and a la carte 5.75 – ***Causerie :*** **Meals** *(closed Saturday dinner and Sunday)* 16.00/30.00 **st.** 5.75 – 17.00 – **137 rm** 180.00/290.00 **s.**, 53 suites – SB.

Four Seasons, Hamilton Pl., Park Lane, W1A 1AZ, ✆ 499 0888, Telex 22771, Fax 493 1895, – rm – 500. VISA JCB. BP **a**
Lanes : **Meals** 22.75/25.00 **st.** and dinner a la carte 22.00/38.00 **st.** 7.00 – (see also ***Four Seasons*** below) – 14.75 – **201 rm** 210.00/265.00 **s.**, 26 suites.

Le Meridien Piccadilly, 21 Piccadilly, W1V 0BH, ✆ 734 8000, Telex 25795, Fax 437 3574, , squash – rm – 260. VISA JCB. EM **a**
Terrace Garden : **Meals** 18.50/21.00 **t.** and a la carte 7.50 – (see also ***Oak Room*** below) – 12.50 – **247 rm** 200.00/275.00, 18 suites.

Grosvenor House (Forte), Park Lane, W1A 3AA, ✆ 499 6363, Telex 24871, Fax 493 3341, – rm – 1 500. VISA JCB. AM **a**
Pavilion : **Meals** 13.50/21.50 **t.** and a la carte 8.00 – ***Pasta Vino :*** **Meals** *(closed Saturday lunch and Sunday)* a la carte 21.50/33.00 **t.** 8.00 – (see also ***Chez Nico at Ninety Park Lane*** below) – 14.50 – **383 rm** 180.00/225.00 **s.**, 71 suites – SB.

✿ **Connaught,** Carlos Pl., W1Y 6AL, ✆ 499 7070, Fax 495 3262 – rest VISA. BM **e**
The Restaurant and ***Grill Room :*** **Meals** (booking essential) 25.00/35.00 **t.** and a la carte 24.60/63.10 **t.** – **66 rm**, 24 suites
Spec. Galette Connaught aux 'diamants noirs', salade Aphrodite, Homard et langoustines grillés aux herbes, Crème brûlée d'un soir.

47 Park Street, 47 Park St., W1Y 4EB, ✆ 491 7282, Telex 22116, Fax 491 7281 – VISA JCB. AM **c**
Meals (room service)(see also ***Le Gavroche*** below) – 17.00 –, **52 suites** 235.00/380.00 **s.**

London Hilton on Park Lane, 22 Park Lane, W1Y 4BE, ✆ 493 8000, Telex 24873, Fax 493 4957, « London from rooftop restaurant », – rm – 1 250. VISA JCB. BP **e**
Windows : **Meals** *(closed Sunday dinner)* 30.95/44.00 **t.** and a la carte – ***Trader Vics :*** **Meals** *(closed Saturday lunch)* a la carte 23.00/30.50 **t.** 8.00 – 14.95 – **395 rm** 195.00/300.00 **s.**, 52 suites.

Brown's (Forte), 29-34 Albemarle St., W1A 4SW, ✆ 493 6020, Fax 493 9381 – rm – 70 DM **e**
112 rm, 6 suites.

Park Lane, Piccadilly, W1Y 8BX, ✆ 499 6321, Telex 21533, Fax 499 1965, – rm – 300. VISA JCB. BP **x**
Bracewells : **Meals** *(closed Saturday lunch and Sunday)* 19.50/35.00 **st.** and a la carte – ***Brasserie on the Park :*** **Meals** 10.95 **st.** and a la carte 7.50 – 12.95 – **278 rm** 165.00/185.00 **s.**, 30 suites.

Britannia (Inter-Con), Grosvenor Sq., W1A 3AN, ✆ 629 9400, Telex 23941, Fax 629 7736 – rm – 100. VISA JCB. BM **x**
Adam Room : **Meals** *(closed Saturday and Sunday)* 23.00/26.00 **st.** and a la carte 6.50 – (see also ***Shogun*** below) – 14.95 – **305 rm** 145.00/220.00, 12 suites.

Inter-Continental, 1 Hamilton Pl., Hyde Park Corner, W1V 0QY, ✆ 409 3131, Telex 25853, Fax 409 7461, – rm – 1 000. VISA JCB. BP **o**
Meals 21.00/24.50 **t.** and a la carte 7.00 – (see also ***Le Soufflé*** below) – 16.00 – **433 rm** 195.00/270.00 **s.**, 34 suites.

May Fair Inter-Continental, Stratton St., W1A 2AN, ✆ 629 7777, Telex 262526, Fax 629 1459, – rm – 300. VISA JCB. DN **z**
Meals (see ***The Chateau*** below) – 14.50 – **262 rm** 190.00/250.00, 25 suites.

Athenaeum, 116 Piccadilly, W1V 0BJ, ✆ 499 3464, Fax 493 1860, – rm – 55. VISA JCB. CP **s**
Bulloch's : **Meals** *(closed lunch Saturday and Sunday)* a la carte 24.50/31.50 **t.** – 14.50 – **111 rm** 165.00/230.00, 33 suites.

Marriott, Duke St., Grosvenor Sq., W1A 4AW, ✆ 493 1232, Telex 268101, Fax 491 3201, – rm – 600. VISA JCB. BL **a**
Diplomat : **Meals** 18.00/23.00 **st.** and a la carte 7.25 – 12.25 – **212 rm** 180.00/220.00 **s.**, 11 suites – SB.

Westbury (Forte), Conduit St., W1A 4UH, ✆ 629 7755, Telex 24378, Fax 495 1163 – rm – 120. VISA JCB DM **a**
Meals *(closed lunch Saturday and Sunday)* 21.50/25.00 **st.** and a la carte 10.75 – 13.00 **231 rm** 145.00/215.00 **st.**, 13 suites – SB.

Washington, 5-7 Curzon St., W1Y 8DT, ✆ 499 7000, Telex 24540, Fax 495 6172 – – 80. AE VISA JCB. CN **s**
Meals *(closed lunch Saturday and Sunday)* 19.95 **st.** and a la carte 🍷 6.95 – 9.95 – **169 rm** 148.00/258.00 **st.**, 4 suites.

Holiday Inn, 3 Berkeley St., W1X 6NE, ✆ 493 8282, Telex 24561, Fax 629 2827 – rm – 70. AE VISA JCB. DN **r**
Meals *(closed Saturday lunch)* 15.75 **t.** and a la carte 🍷 12.00 – 10.95 – **183 rm** 140.00/190.00 **st.**, 2 suites – SB.

Chesterfield, 35 Charles St., W1X 8LX, ✆ 491 2622, Telex 269394, Fax 491 4793 – rm rest – 110. AE VISA JCB. CN **c**
Meals *(closed Saturday lunch)* 7.50/18.50 **t.** and a la carte 🍷 7.50 – 10.95 – **106 rm** 120.00/170.00 **st.**, 4 suites.

Green Park, Half Moon St., W1Y 8BP, ✆ 629 7522, Telex 28856, Fax 491 8971 – rm rest – 70. AE VISA JCB. CN **a**
Meals *(closed lunch Saturday and Sunday)* 9.75/12.00 **st.** and a la carte 🍷 5.00 – 9.75 – **161 rm** 104.00/174.00 **st.**

Flemings, 7-12 Half Moon St., W1Y 7RA, ✆ 499 2964, Fax 499 1817 – rest – 45. AE VISA JCB. CN **z**
Meals 14.00/20.00 **st.** and a la carte 🍷 7.50 – 10.25 – **121 rm** 115.00/150.00 **st.**, 11 suites.

London Mews Hilton, 2 Stanhope Row, W1Y 7HE, ✆ 493 7222, Fax 629 9423 – rm – 50. AE VISA JCB BP **u**
Meals (light meals only) a la carte 14.45/24.20 **st.** 🍷 8.50 – 10.95 – **71 rm** 141.00/175.00 **st.**, 1 suite.

XXXXX ✿ **Oak Room** (at Le Meridien Piccadilly H.), 21 Piccadilly, W1V 0BH, ✆ 734 8000, Telex 25795, Fax 437 3574 – . AE VISA JCB EM **a**
closed Saturday lunch, Sunday and 1 to 21 August – **Meals** - French 24.50/46.00 **t.** and a la carte 38.50/46.50 **t.** 🍷 7.75
Spec. Salade de lapereau et grenouilles aux champignons des bois, Suprême de bar cuit à la vapeur au beurre de truffes, Pigeon fermier et artichauts poivrades, chutney aux pommes acides.

XXXXX ✿✿✿ **Chez Nico at Ninety Park Lane** (Ladenis) (at Grosvenor House H.), Park Lane, W1A 3AA, ✆ 409 1290, Fax 355 4877 – . AE VISA AM **e**
closed lunch Saturday and Bank Holiday Mondays, Sunday, 4 days at Easter and 10 days at Christmas – **Meals** - French (booking essential) 25.00/54.00 **st.**
Spec. Salad of crisp guinea fowl with french beans, truffle oil and truffles, Grilled scallops with sesame seeds and fresh vermicelli, Milk-fed veal cutlet with rosemary and sweet garlic.

XXXX ✿✿ **Le Gavroche** (Roux), 43 Upper Brook St., W1Y 1PF, ✆ 408 0881, Fax 409 0939 – . AE VISA AM **c**
closed Saturday, Sunday, 24 December-3 January and Bank Holidays – **Meals** - French (booking essential) 36.00/75.00 **st.** and a la carte 47.50/87.60 **st.** 🍷 10.00
Spec. Soufflé suissesse, L'Assiette du boucher, Omelette Rothschild.

XXXX ✿ **Oriental** (at Dorchester H.), Park Lane, W1A 2HJ, ✆ 629 8888, Telex 887704, Fax 409 0114 – . AE VISA BN **a**
closed Saturday lunch, Sunday and August – **Meals** - Chinese (Canton) 20.00/28.00 **st.** and a la carte 28.00/60.50 **st.** 🍷 11.00
Spec. Deep fried mixed seafood with mango wrapped in rice paper, Braised shark's fin soup with mixed seafood, Roasted Peking duck.

XXXX ✿ **Four Seasons** (at Four Seasons H.), Hamilton Pl., Park Lane, W1A 1AZ, ✆ 499 0888, Telex 22771, Fax 493 1895 – . AE VISA JCB BP **a**
Meals - French 25.00/45.00 **st.** and a la carte 34.50/48.75 **st.** 🍷 7.00
Spec. Pan fried fillet of red mullet with an orange powder coat and baby carrots, Saddle of rabbit wrapped in lettuce with Spring broad beans, Hot bitter chocolate cake with white chocolate ice cream.

XXXX ✿ **Les Saveurs,** 37a Curzon St., W1Y 8EY, ✆ 491 8919, Fax 491 3658 – . AE VISA
closed Saturday, Sunday, 2 weeks August, 2 weeks Christmas-New Year and Bank Holidays – **Meals** - French 21.00/39.00 **t.** 🍷 8.00 BN **o**
Spec. Foie gras Aubergine, Roast guinea fowl with tapenade, Café irlandais glacé.

XXXX **Le Soufflé** (at Inter-Continental H.), 1 Hamilton Pl., Hyde Park Corner, W1V 0QY, ✆ 409 3131, Telex 25853, Fax 409 7461 – . AE VISA JCB BP **o**
closed Saturday lunch, Sunday dinner, Monday, August and 2 weeks Christmas-New Year – **Meals** 27.50/45.00 **t.** and a la carte 34.50/44.50 **t.** 🍷 9.00.

XXX **Princess Garden,** 8-10 North Audley St., W1Y 1WF, ✆ 493 3223, Fax 491 2655 – . AE VISA JCB AL **z**
closed 1 week Christmas – **Meals** - Chinese (Peking, Szechuan) 33.00 **t.** (lunch) and a la carte 22.00/39.00 **t.** 🍷 8.00.

XXX **Zen Central,** 20 Queen St., W1X 7PJ, ✆ 629 8089 – . AE VISA CN **x**
Meals - Chinese 28.00/50.00 **t.** and a la carte 19.50/35.50 **t.**

XXX **The Chateau** (at May Fair Inter-Continental H.), Stratton St., W1A 2AN, ✆ 915 2842, Fax 629 1459 – . AE VISA JCB DN **z**
Meals 22.00/29.50 **t.** and a la carte 🍷 4.50.

XXX **Scotts,** 20 Mount St., W1Y 6HE, ✆ 629 5248, Fax 499 8246 – . AE VISA JCB BM **a**
closed Saturday lunch, Sunday and 24 to 26 December – **Meals** - Seafood a la carte 29.25/50.00 **t.**

XX **Greenhouse,** 27a Hay's Mews, W1X 7RJ, ℘ 499 3331, Fax 225 0011 – ▤. AE VISA *closed Saturday lunch, 1 to 7 January and Bank Holidays* – **Meals** a la carte 22.75/33.75 **t.** 7.50. BN **e**

XX **Bentley's,** 11-15 Swallow St., W1R 7HD, ℘ 734 4756, Fax 287 2972 – ▤. AE VISA JCB EM **i**
closed Sunday and Bank Holidays – **Meals** - Seafood 19.50 **t.** and a la carte.

XX **Langan's Brasserie,** Stratton St., W1X 5FD, ℘ 491 8822 – ▤. AE VISA DN **e**
closed Saturday lunch, Sunday and Bank Holidays – **Meals** (booking essential) a la carte 19.05/30.45 **t.**

XX **Mulligans,** 13-14 Cork St., W1X 1PF, ℘ 409 1370, Fax 409 2732 – ▤. AE VISA DM **c**
closed Saturday lunch, Sunday, 25 December-1 January and Bank Holidays – **Meals** - Irish a la carte 16.75/30.00 **t.** 4.25.

XX **Shogun** (at Britannia H.) Adams Row, W1Y 5DE, ℘ 493 1255 – ▤. AE VISA JCB
closed Monday – **Meals** - Japanese (dinner only) 30.00 **t.** and a la carte. BM **x**

X **Ikeda,** 30 Brook St., W1Y 1AG, ℘ 629 2730, Fax 628 6982 – ▤. AE VISA JCB CKL **a**
closed Saturday lunch and Sunday – **Meals** - Japanese 15.00/38.00 **t.** and a la carte.

X **O'Keefe's,** 19 Dering St., W1R 9AA, ℘ 495 0878, Fax 629 7082 CK **e**
closed Saturday dinner and Sunday – **Meals** a la carte approx. 14.00 **t.** 6.50.

Regent's Park and Marylebone – ✉ NW1/NW6/NW8/W1 – ☎ 0171 – Except where otherwise stated see pp. 28 and 29.

Basement Services Arcade, Selfridges Store, Oxford St., W1 ℘ 730 3488/824 8000.

Regent London, 222 Marylebone Rd, NW1 6JQ, ℘ 631 8000, Telex 8813733, Fax 631 8080, « Victorian Gothic architecture, atrium and winter garden », – rm ▤ – 350. AE VISA JCB. p. 21 HU **a**
***The Dining Room :* Meals** 21.50/29.00 **st.** and a la carte 7.50 – 13.25 – **307 rm** 160.00/255.00 **s.**, 2 suites.

Churchill Inter-Continental, 30 Portman Sq., W1A 4ZX, ℘ 486 5800, Telex 264831, Fax 486 1255, – rm ▤ – 200. AE VISA JCB. AJ **x**
Meals *(closed Saturday lunch)* a la carte 17.00/31.00 **t.** – 14.50 – **406 rm** 190.00/250.00, 37 suites.

Langham Hilton, 1 Portland Pl., W1N 3AA, ℘ 636 1000, Fax 323 2340, – rm ▤ – 320. AE VISA JCB. p. 21 JU **e**
***Memories of the Empire :* Meals** 21.25/29.75 **st.** and a la carte – 14.75 – **364 rm** 180.00/275.00 **s.**, 20 suites – SB.

Selfridge (Mt. Charlotte Thistle), Orchard St., W1H 0JS, ℘ 408 2080, Fax 629 8849 – rm ▤ – 220. AE VISA JCB. AK **e**
***Fletchers :* Meals** *(closed Sunday)* 16.95/24.50 **st.** and a la carte 6.50 – ***Orchard :* Meals** 16.95/19.50 **st.** 6.50 – 10.25 – **293 rm** 145.00/160.00 **st.**, 2 suites.

SAS Portman, 22 Portman Sq., W1H 9FL, ℘ 486 5844, Telex 261526, Fax 935 0537, – rm ▤ – 350. AE VISA JCB. AJ **o**
Meals 15.00/31.00 **st.** 6.00 – 12.50 – **259 rm** 130.00/170.00 **s.**, 13 suites.

Berkshire (Radisson Edwardian), 350 Oxford St., W1N 0BY, ℘ 629 7474, Telex 22270, Fax 629 8156 – rm ▤ – 40. AE VISA JCB. BK **n**
Meals *(closed Saturday, Sunday and Bank Holiday lunch)* 23.40 **st.** and a la carte 7.00 – 13.50 – **145 rm** 158.00/245.00 **st.**, 2 suites.

London Regent's Park Hilton, 18 Lodge Rd, NW8 7JT, ℘ 722 7722, Telex 23101, Fax 483 2408 – ▤ – 150. AE VISA JCB. p. 21 GT **v**
***Minsky's :* Meals** 14.95/19.95 **t.** and a la carte 7.45 – ***Kashinoki :* Meals** - Japanese *(closed Monday, 25 to 26 December and 1 to 3 January)* 9.00/30.00 **t.** 8.00 – 11.30 – **374 rm** 115.00/130.00 **st.**, 3 suites.

Clifton Ford, 47 Welbeck St., W1M 8DN, ℘ 486 6600, Telex 22569, Fax 486 7492 – ▤ – 150 BH **a**
198 rm, 2 suites.

Montcalm, Great Cumberland Pl., W1A 2LF, ℘ 402 4288, Telex 28710, Fax 724 9180, – rm ▤ – 80. AE VISA JCB. p. 33 EZ **x**
Meals *(closed Saturday lunch and Sunday)* 20.00/25.00 **t.** and a la carte 8.00 – 14.00 – **105 rm** 160.00/200.00, 11 suites.

Marble Arch Marriott, 134 George St., W1H 6DN, ℘ 723 1277, Fax 402 0666, – rm ▤ – 150. AE VISA JCB. p. 33 EZ **i**
Meals 17.95/24.95 **st.** and a la carte 7.00 – 11.85 – **237 rm** 135.00/145.00 **s.**, 2 suites – SB.

Berners Park Plaza, 10 Berners St., W1A 3BE, ℘ 636 1629, Telex 25759, Fax 580 3972 – rm ▤ rest – 150. AE VISA JCB. EJ **r**
Meals 15.95 **st.** and a la carte – 10.75 – **227 rm** 120.00/140.00 **st.**, 3 suites.

St. George's (Forte), Langham Pl., W1N 8QS, ℘ 580 0111, Fax 436 7997, ← – rm ▤ – 35 p. 21 JU **a**
83 rm, 3 suites.

Forte Crest Regents Park, Carburton St., W1P 8EE, ☎ 388 2300, Telex 22453, Fax 387 2806 – lift ⇔ rm ▤ rest TV ☎ – 🏛 600 p. 21 JU **i**
315 rm, 2 suites.

Rathbone, Rathbone St., W1P 1AJ, ☎ 636 2001, Telex 28728, Fax 636 3882 – lift ⇔ rm ▤ TV ☎. AE VISA JCB. ✻ p. 22 KU **x**
Meals *(closed lunch Saturday and Sunday)* 15.00 **t.** 4.50 – ☕ 8.50 – **72 rm** 120.00/145.00 **st.** – SB.

Dorset Square, 39-40 Dorset Sq., NW1 6QN, ☎ 723 7874, Fax 724 3328, « Attractively furnished Regency town houses », – lift ▤ TV ☎. AE VISA. ✻ p. 21 HU **s**
Meals *(closed Sunday lunch and Saturday)* a la carte 17.00/23.75 **t.** – ☕ 9.50 – **37 rm** 95.00/165.00 **t.**

25 Dorset Square without rest., 25 Dorset Sq., NW1 6QN, ☎ 262 7505, Fax 723 0194, « Regency town houses » – lift TV ☎. AE VISA. ✻ HU **e**
☕ 8.50 – **12 suites** 170.00/250.00 **st.**.

Durrants, 26-32 George St., W1H 6BJ, ☎ 935 8131, Fax 487 3510, « Converted Georgian houses with Regency façade » – lift TV ☎ – 🏛 60. AE VISA. ✻ AH **e**
Meals 19.00 **t.** and a la carte 6.75 – ☕ 8.25 – **93 rm** 85.00/105.00 **st.**, 3 suites.

Savoy Court, Granville Pl., W1H 0EH, ☎ 408 0130, Fax 493 2070 – lift ▤ rest TV ☎. AE VISA JCB. ✻ AK **i**
Meals (buffet lunch)/dinner 13.50 – ☕ 9.00 – **94 rm** 81.00/118.00.

Langham Court, 31-35 Langham St., W1N 5RE, ☎ 436 6622, Fax 436 2303 – lift TV ☎ – 🏛 80. AE VISA JCB. ✻ p. 21 JU **z**
Meals *(closed lunch Saturday, Sunday and Bank Holidays)* 16.95/17.95 **t.** and a la carte 4.95 – ☕ 9.50 – **60 rm** 115.00/139.00 **st.**

Holiday Inn Garden Court, 57-59 Welbeck St., W1M 8HS, ☎ 935 4442, Telex 894630, Fax 487 3782 – lift ⇔ rm ▤ rest TV ☎ – 🏛 180. AE VISA JCB. ✻ BJ **c**
Meals *(closed lunch Saturday and Sunday)* 12.95/13.95 6.00 – ☕ 9.00 – **138 rm** 100.00/130.00 **st.**

Harewood, Harewood Row, NW1 6SE, ☎ 262 2707, Fax 262 2975 – lift ▤ rest TV ☎. AE VISA JCB p. 21 HU **x**
Meals (dinner only) 16.50 **st.** 4.95 – ☕ 8.50 – **92 rm** 65.00/89.00 **st.** – SB.

Hart House without rest., 51 Gloucester Pl., W1H 3PE, ☎ 935 2288, Fax 935 8516 – TV ☎. AE VISA. ✻ AH **a**
16 rm ☕ 45.00/75.00 **st.**

Regents Park, 156 Gloucester Pl., NW1 6DT, ☎ 258 1911, Fax 258 0288 – ▤ rest TV ☎
***Singapore Garden :* Meals** - South East Asian – **29 rm.** HT **a**

Bryanston Court without rest., 56-60 Great Cumberland Pl., W1H 7FD, ☎ 262 3141, Fax 262 7248 – lift TV ☎. AE VISA JCB. ✻ p. 33 EZ **z**
54 rm ☕ 70.00/90.00 **st.**

Lincoln House without rest., 33 Gloucester Pl., W1H 3PD, ☎ 486 7630, Fax 486 0166 – TV ☎. AE VISA. ✻ AJ **c**
22 rm ☕ 39.00/65.00 **st.**

XX **Walsh's,** 5 Charlotte St., W1P 1HD, ☎ 637 0222, Fax 637 0224 – ▤. AE VISA JCB p. 22 KU **r**
closed Saturday lunch, Sunday and Bank Holidays – **Meals** - Seafood a la carte 23.00/35.00 **st.**

XX **Hudson's,** 221b Baker St., NW1, ☎ 935 3130 – AE VISA HU **r**
closed 25 December – **Meals** - English 12.50/15.00 **t.** and a la carte 4.50.

XX **Nico Central,** 35 Great Portland St., W1N 5DD, ☎ 436 8846 – ▤. AE VISA DJ **c**
closed Saturday lunch, Sunday, 4 days Easter, 10 days Christmas and Bank Holiday Mondays – **Meals** 21.00/25.00 **st.** 9.00.

XX **Caldesi,** 15-17 Marylebone Lane, W1M 5FE, ☎ 935 9226 – ▤. AE VISA JCB BJ **e**
closed Saturday lunch, Sunday and Bank Holidays – **Meals** - Italian 10.95 **t.** and a la carte 3.75.

XX **Gaylord,** 79-81 Mortimer St., W1N 7TB, ☎ 580 3615 – ▤. AE VISA JCB
Meals - Indian 11.95/13.95 **t.** and a la carte. p. 22 KU **o**

XX **Maroush III,** 62 Seymour St., W1H 5AF, ☎ 724 5024 – ▤. AE VISA EZ **r**
closed Christmas Day – **Meals** - Lebanese 12.00/50.00 **t.** and a la carte 7.00.

XX **Stephen Bull,** 5-7 Blandford St., W1H 3AA, ☎ 486 9696 – ⇔ ▤. AE VISA BH **e**
closed Saturday lunch, Sunday, 1 week Christmas and Bank Holidays – **Meals** a la carte 20.00/27.50 **t.** 5.50.

XX **Baboon** 76 Wigmore St., W1H 9DQ, ☎ 224 2992, Fax 935 9588 – ▤. AE VISA JCB
closed Saturday lunch, Sunday and Bank Holidays – **Meals** 12.50 **t.** and a la carte. BJ **x**

XX **Sampan's** (at Cumberland H.), Marble Arch, W1A 4RF, ☎ 262 1234 – AE VISA JCB
closed Sunday, 1 week Christmas and Bank Holidays – **Meals** - Chinese (Canton) (dinner only) 15.50 and a la carte 6.50. AK **n**

XX **Asuka,** Berkeley Arcade, 209a Baker St., NW1 6AB, ☎ 486 5026 – AE VISA JCB *closed Saturday lunch, Sunday and Bank Holidays* – **Meals** - Japanese 12.50/23.90 **st.** and a la carte. p. 21 HU **u**

XX **La Loggia,** 68 Edgware Rd, W2 2EQ, ☎ 723 0554 – ▤. AE VISA JCB p. 33 EZ **a** *closed Saturday lunch, Sunday and Bank Holidays* – **Meals** - Italian 13.80/15.50 **st.** and a la carte 🌢 4.80.

X **Le Muscadet,** 25 Paddington St., W1M 3RF, ☎ 935 2883 – ▤. VISA HU **v** *closed Saturday lunch, Sunday, last 3 weeks August and 2 weeks Christmas-New Year* – **Meals** - French a la carte 21.60/26.00 **t.** 🌢 8.20.

X **L'Aventure,** 3 Blenheim Terr., NW8 0EH, ☎ 624 6232 – AE VISA p. 20 FS **s** *closed Saturday lunch, 4 days Easter, 1 week Christmas and Bank Holidays* – **Meals** - French 18.50/25.00 **t.** 🌢 7.25.

X **Nakamura,** 31 Marylebone Lane, W1M 5FH, ☎ 935 2931 – AE VISA JCB BJ **i** *closed Sunday lunch and Saturday* – **Meals** - Japanese 6.00/37.90 **t.** and a la carte.

X **Langan's Bistro,** 26 Devonshire St., W1N 1RJ, ☎ 935 4531 – ▤. AE VISA *closed Saturday lunch, Sunday and Bank Holidays* – **Meals** 16.95 **t.** p. 21 IU **e**

X **Zoe,** 3-5 Barrett St., St. Christopher's Pl., W1M 5HH, ☎ 224 1122, Fax 935 5444 – ▤. AE VISA BJ **a** *closed Sunday and Bank Holidays* – **Meals** 10.00 **t.** and a la carte.

St. James's – ✉ W1/SW1/WC2 – ☎ 0171 – pp. 28 and 29.

🏨 **Ritz,** Piccadilly, W1V 9DG, ☎ 493 8181, Telex 267200, Fax 493 2687, « Elegant restaurant in Louis XVI style » – ▤ TV ☎ – 🏛 50. AE VISA JCB. ✻ DN **a** **Meals** (dancing Friday and Saturday evenings) 26.00/43.50 **st.** and a la carte approx. 52.00 **st.** 🌢 12.50 – ☕ 14.50 – **116 rm** 161.00/251.00 **s.**, 14 suites – SB.

🏨 **Dukes** 🐦, 35 St. James's Pl., SW1A 1NY, ☎ 491 4840, Fax 493 1264 – ▤ rest TV ☎ – 🏛 55. AE VISA JCB. ✻ EP **x** **Meals** *(closed Saturday lunch)* (residents only) a la carte 17.00/35.75 **t.** 🌢 6.75 – ☕ 12.50 – **38 rm** 125.00/185.00, **26 suites** 210.00/400.00.

🏨 **22 Jermyn Street,** 22 Jermyn St., SW1Y 6HL, ☎ 734 2353, Fax 734 0750 – TV ☎. AE VISA JCB FM **e** **Meals** (restricted room service only) a la carte 22.00/26.50 **t.** 🌢 6.35 – ☕ 13.00 – **5 rm** 170.00 **s.**, **13 suites** 220.00/250.00 **s.**.

🏨 **Stafford** 🐦, 16-18 St. James's Pl., SW1A 1NJ, ☎ 493 0111, Telex 28602, Fax 493 7121 – ▤ rest TV ☎ – 🏛 35. AE VISA JCB. ✻ DN **u** **Meals** *(closed Saturday lunch)* 22.50/25.00 **st.** and a la carte 🌢 7.00 – ☕ 12.00 – **70 rm** 184.00/215.00 **st.**, 4 suites – SB.

🏨 Forte Crest St. James's, 81 Jermyn St., SW1Y 6JF, ☎ 930 2111, Fax 839 2125 – ⊬ rm ▤ rest TV ☎ 🚗 – 🏛 80 EN **i** **253 rm**, 3 suites.

🏨 **Royal Trafalgar Thistle** (Mt. Charlotte Thistle), Whitcomb St., WC2H 7HG, ☎ 930 4477, Telex 298564, Fax 925 2149 – ⊬ rm TV ☎. AE VISA JCB. ✻ GM **r** **Meals** 13.75 **st.** and a la carte 🌢 6.40 – ☕ 10.50 – **108 rm** 105.00/130.00 **st.** – SB.

🏨 **Hospitality Inn Piccadilly** (Mt. Charlotte Thistle) without rest., 39 Coventry St., W1V 8EL, ☎ 930 4033, Telex 8950058, Fax 925 2586 – ⊬ rm TV ☎. AE VISA JCB. ✻ ☕ 9.25 – **92 rm** 115.00/130.00 **t.** FGM **a**

🏨 **Pastoria,** 3-6 St. Martin's St., off Leicester Sq., WC2H 7HL, ☎ 930 8641, Telex 25538, Fax 925 0551 – ▤ rest TV ☎ – 🏛 60. AE VISA JCB. ✻ GM **v** **Meals** *(closed Saturday lunch and Sunday)* 15.00 **t.** and a la carte – ☕ 9.25 – **58 rm** 99.00/119.00 **st.**

XXX **Quaglino's,** 16 Bury St., SW1Y 6AL, ☎ 930 6767, Fax 839 2866 – ▤. AE VISA *closed lunch 1 January, dinner 24 December and 25-26 December* – **Meals** (booking essential) 12.95 **t.** (lunch) and a la carte 20.25/29.50 **t.** 🌢 6.95. EN **r**

XXX **Suntory,** 72-73 St. James's St., SW1A 1PH, ☎ 409 0201, Fax 499 0208 – ▤. AE VISA JCB EP **z** *closed Sunday and Bank Holidays* – **Meals** - Japanese 15.00/90.00 **st.** and a la carte 22.30/83.50 **st.** 🌢 7.00.

XXX **Overton's,** 5 St. James's St., SW1A 1EF, ☎ 839 3774, Fax 839 4330 – ▤. AE VISA JCB EP **a** *closed Saturday lunch, Sunday dinner, 10 days Christmas-New Year and Bank Holidays* – **Meals** - Seafood 19.50/27.50 **t.** 🌢 5.50.

XXX ✿ **The Square,** 32 King St., SW1Y 6RJ, ☎ 839 8787, Fax 321 2124 – ▤. AE VISA EN **v** *closed lunch Saturday and Sunday* – **Meals** 36.00 **t.** (dinner) and lunch a la carte 25.00/30.00 **t.**

Spec. Seared tuna with tartare of vegetables and soy wilted greens, Rump of lamb with aubergine, rosemary and olive oil, Port roasted figs with cinnamon fritters.

XX **Le Caprice,** Arlington House, Arlington St., SW1A 1RT, ☎ 629 2239, Fax 493 9040 – ▤. AE VISA DN **c** *closed 24 December-2 January* – **Meals** a la carte 22.25/36.00 **t.**

XX **Green's,** 36 Duke St., SW1Y 6DF, ☎ 930 4566, Fax 930 1383 – ▤. AE VISA JCB EN **n** *closed Sunday dinner, 25-26 December and 1 January* – **Meals** - English rest. a la carte 24.50/30.50 **t.**

XX **Matsuri,** 15 Bury St., SW1Y 6AL, ✆ 839 1101, Fax 930 7010 – ▤. AE VISA JCB EN **r**
closed Sunday and Bank Holidays – **Meals** - Japanese (Teppan-Yaki, Sushi) 12.00/49.50 **t.** and a la carte.

X **Criterion,** 224 Piccadilly, W1V 9LB, ✆ 925 0909, Fax 839 1494, « 19C Neo-Byzantine decor » – AE VISA FM **c**
closed Sunday dinner, 25-26 December and 1 January – **Meals** - Brasserie a la carte 14.00/21.45 **t.**

Soho – ✉ W1/WC2 – ☎ 0171 – pp. 28 and 29.

Hampshire (Radisson Edwardian), Leicester Sq., WC2H 7LH, ✆ 839 9399, Telex 914848, Fax 930 8122 – rm ▤ TV ☎ – 80. AE VISA JCB. GM **s**
Meals 19.50/27.50 **st.** and a la carte – 13.50 – **119 rm** 184.00/220.00 **st.**, 5 suites – SB.

Hazlitt's without rest., 6 Frith St., W1V 5TZ, ✆ 434 1771, Fax 439 1524 – TV ☎. AE VISA JCB. FK **u**
closed Christmas – **22 rm** 98.00/122.00 **s.**, 1 suite.

XXXX ✿ **Grill Room at the Café Royal** (Forte), 68 Regent St., W1R 6EL, ✆ 437 9090, Fax 439 7672, « Rococo decoration » – ▤. AE VISA JCB EM **e**
closed Saturday lunch, Sunday and Bank Holidays – **Meals** 22.50/39.00 **st.** and a la carte 35.00/55.00 **st.** 9.00
Spec. Escalopes of fresh foie gras with a ragout of celeriac and truffle sauce, Roasted fillet of sea bass with fennel, sundried tomatoes and saffron, Pyramid of walnut ganache with vanilla sauce.

XXX **Au Jardin des Gourmets,** 5 Greek St., W1V 5LA, ✆ 437 1816, Fax 437 0043 – ▤. AE VISA GJ **a**
closed lunch Saturday and Bank Holidays, Sunday and 25-26 December – ***Restaurant :*** **Meals** - French a la carte 23.50/32.45 **t.**

XX **Brasserie** – **Meals** *closed lunch Saturday and Sunday* 10.95/17.50 **st.** 5.75.

XXX **Lindsay House,** 21 Romilly St., W1V 5TG, ✆ 439 0450, Fax 581 2848 – ▤. AE VISA JCB GL **i**
closed 25 and 26 December – **Meals** 10.00 **t.** (lunch) and a la carte 22.75/27.50 **t.** 4.50.

XX **L'Escargot,** 48 Greek St., W1V 5LQ, ✆ 437 2679, Fax 437 0790 – ▤. AE VISA
closed Saturday lunch and Sunday – **Meals** a la carte approx. 23.50 **t.** 5.25. GK **e**

XX **Lexington,** 45 Lexington St., W1R 3LG, ✆ 434 3401, Fax 287 2997 – ▤. AE VISA EK **e**
closed Saturday lunch, Sunday, 1 week Christmas and Bank Holidays – **Meals** 16.00 **t.** (dinner) and a la carte 19.00/24.25 **t.**

XX **Red Fort,** 77 Dean St., W1V 5HA, ✆ 437 2115, Fax 434 0721 – ▤. AE VISA FJK **r**
Meals - Indian (buffet lunch) 12.50 **t.** and dinner a la carte 20.85/25.85 **t.**

XX **Brasserie at the Café Royal** (Forte), 68 Regent St., W1R 6EL, ✆ 437 9090, Fax 439 7672 – ▤. AE VISA JCB EM **e**
closed Sunday dinner – **Meals** 15.50/17.50 **st.** and a la carte 6.50.

XX **Soho Soho** (first floor), 11-13 Frith St., W1, ✆ 494 3491, Fax 437 3091 – ▤. AE VISA
closed Saturday lunch and Sunday – **Meals** a la carte approx. 35.00 **st.** FK **s**

XX **Ming,** 35-36 Greek St., W1V 5LN, ✆ 734 2721 – ▤. AE VISA JCB GK **c**
closed Sunday and Bank Holiday lunch – **Meals** - Chinese 10.00/19.50 **t.** and a la carte 6.00.

XX **Gopal's,** 12 Bateman St., W1V 5TD, ✆ 434 0840 – ▤. AE VISA FK **e**
closed 25 and 26 December – **Meals** - Indian 13.00/19.50 **t.** and a la carte.

XX **Gay Hussar,** 2 Greek St., W1V 6NB, ✆ 437 0973, Fax 437 9920 – ▤. AE VISA
closed Sunday and Bank Holidays – **Meals** - Hungarian 16.00 **t.** (lunch)and a la carte 17.85/26.10 **t.** 7.50. GJ **c**

X **dell 'Ugo,** 56 Frith St., W1V 5TA, ✆ 734 8300, Fax 734 8784 – AE VISA FK **z**
closed Sunday and Bank Holidays – **Meals** 10.00 **t.** and a la carte 16.40/20.70 **t.**

X **Sri Siam,** 14 Old Compton St., W1V 5PE, ✆ 434 3544 – ▤. AE VISA GK **r**
closed Sunday lunch – **Meals** - Thai 9.50/14.95 **t.** and a la carte 4.60.

X **Alastair Little,** 49 Frith St., W1V 5TE, ✆ 734 5183 – AE VISA FK **o**
closed Saturday lunch, Sunday, 25 to 26 December and Bank Holidays – **Meals** (booking essential) 25.00 **t.** (lunch) and a la carte 35.00/44.50 **t.** 6.00.

X **Bistrot Bruno,** 63 Frith St., W1V 5TA, ✆ 734 4545, Fax 287 1027 – ▤. AE VISA FK **z**
closed Saturday lunch, Sunday and Christmas to New Year – **Meals** a la carte 18.00/26.00 **t.** 4.75.

X **Poons,** 4 Leicester St., Leicester Sq., WC2 7BL, ✆ 437 1528 – ▤. AE VISA GM **e**
closed 24 to 28 December – **Meals** - Chinese 7.50/20.00 **t.** and a la carte.

X **Andrew Edmunds,** 44 Lexington St., W1R 3LH, ✆ 437 5708 – VISA EK **c**
Meals a la carte 11.15/17.85 **t.** 4.00.

X **Fung Shing,** 15 Lisle St., WC2H 7BE, ✆ 437 1539 – ▤. AE VISA GL **a**
Meals - Chinese (Canton) 12.50/40.00 **t.** and a la carte 4.25.

X **Saigon,** 45 Frith St., W1V 5TE, ✆ 437 7109 – ▤. AE VISA FGK **x**
closed Sunday and Bank Holidays – **Meals** - Vietnamese 15.80/19.50 **t.**

Strand and Covent Garden – ✉ WC2 – ☎ 0171 – Except where otherwise stated see p. 33.

Savoy, Strand, WC2R 0EU, ☎ 836 4343, Telex 24234, Fax 240 6040, Lö, ≘s, ⊡ – |‡| ⇷ rm ▤ TV ☎ ⇔ – 🔬 500. ⊡ AE ⓓ VISA JCB. ✻ DEY **a**
Grill **: Meals** *(closed Saturday lunch, Sunday, August and Bank Holidays)* 31.00 **st.** (dinner) and a la carte 26.65/43.40 **st.** ₫ 6.00 – ***River*** **: Meals** 26.50/39.50 **st.** and a la carte 26.50/58.50 **st.** ₫ 6.00 – ☕ 15.75 – **154 rm** 180.00/275.00 **s.**, 48 suites.

Howard, 12 Temple Pl., WC2R 2PR, ☎ 836 3555, Telex 268047, Fax 379 4547 – |‡| ⇷ rm ▤ TV ☎ ⇔ – 🔬 100. ⊡ AE ⓓ VISA. ✻ EX **e**
Meals 25.00 **st.** and a la carte ₫ 4.75 – ☕ 15.50 – **133 rm** 190.00/226.00 **st.**, 2 suites.

Waldorf (Forte), Aldwych, WC2B 4DD, ☎ 836 2400, Telex 24574, Fax 836 7244 – |‡| ⇷ rm ▤ rm TV ☎ – 🔬 450. ⊡ AE ⓓ VISA JCB. ✻ EX **x**
Meals (in bar Sunday lunch) 25.00/28.00 **t.** and a la carte ₫ 7.00 – ☕ 12.95 – **285 rm** 160.00/200.00 **st.**, 7 suites – SB.

XXX **Simpson's-in-the-Strand,** 100 Strand, WC2R 0EW, ☎ 836 9112, Fax 836 1381 – ▤. ⊡ AE ⓓ VISA JCB EX **o**
closed 25 to 26 December – **Meals** - English (booking essential) 10.00 **t.** and a la carte 15.00/30.25 **t.** ₫ 4.95.

XXX **Ivy,** 1 West St., WC2H 9NE, ☎ 836 4751, Fax 497 3644 – ▤. ⊡ AE ⓓ VISA p. 29 GK **z**
closed August Bank Holiday – **Meals** 14.00 **t.** (lunch) and a la carte 19.75/37.25 **t.**

XXX **Now and Zen,** 4a Upper St. Martin's Lane, WC2H 9EA, ☎ 497 0376, Fax 497 0378 – ▤. ⊡ AE ⓓ VISA DX **x**
closed 25 December – **Meals** - Chinese a la carte approx. 16.00.

XX **Christopher's,** 18 Wellington St., WC2E 7DD, ☎ 240 4222, Fax 240 3357 – ⊡ AE ⓓ VISA EX **z**
closed 24 December-2 January and Bank Holidays – **Meals** a la carte 19.50/35.50 ₫ 10.00.

XX **Orso,** 27 Wellington St., WC2E 7DA, ☎ 240 5269, Fax 497 2148 – ▤ EX **z**
closed 24 and 25 December – **Meals** - Italian (booking essential) a la carte 19.50/25.50 **t.** ₫ 5.00.

XX **Rules,** 35 Maiden Lane, WC2E 7LB, ☎ 836 5314, Fax 497 1081, « London's oldest restaurant with antique collection of drawings, paintings and cartoons ». ⊡ AE VISA DX **n**
closed 23 to 26 December – **Meals** - English 12.95/15.95 **t.** and a la carte 20.65/22.20 **t.** ₫ 4.60.

XX **L'Estaminet,** 14 Garrick St., off Floral St., WC2 9BJ, ☎ 379 1432 – ⊡ AE VISA DX **a**
closed Sunday – **Meals** - French a la carte 21.00/24.00 **t.**

XX **Sheekey's,** 28-32 St. Martin's Court, WC2N 4AL, ☎ 240 2565, Fax 240 0545 – ▤. ⊡ AE VISA DX **z**
Meals - Seafood 17.95/19.95 **t.** and a la carte.

XX **Bertorelli's,** 44a Floral St., WC2E 9DA, ☎ 836 3969, Fax 836 1868 – ▤. ⊡ AE ⓓ VISA JCB DX **c**
closed Sunday and 25-26 December – **Meals** - Italian a la carte 14.00/20.50 **t.**

X **Le Cafe du Jardin,** 28 Wellington St., WC2E 7BD, ☎ 836 8769, Fax 836 4123 – ▤. ⊡ AE ⓓ VISA EX **a**
Meals a la carte 16.70/25.95 **t.** ₫ 4.50.

X **Magno's Brasserie,** 65a Long Acre, WC2E 9JH, ☎ 836 6077, Fax 379 6184 – ▤. ⊡ AE ⓓ VISA JCB DV **e**
closed Saturday lunch, Sunday, Christmas and Bank Holidays – **Meals** - French 13.50/16.50 **t.** and a la carte ₫ 6.75.

X **Joe Allen,** 13 Exeter St., WC2E 7DT, ☎ 836 0651, Fax 497 2148 – ▤ EX **c**
closed 24 and 25 December – **Meals** a la carte 16.50/22.00 **t.**

Victoria – ✉ SW1 – ☎ 0171 – Except where otherwise stated see p. 32.

ℹ Victoria Station Forecourt, SW1V 1JU ☎ 730 3488/824 8000.

St. James Court, Buckingham Gate, SW1E 6AF, ☎ 834 6655, Fax 630 7587, Lö, ≘s – |‡| ⇷ rm ▤ TV ☎ – 🔬 180. ⊡ AE ⓓ VISA JCB. ✻ CX **i**
Mediterranée **: Meals** a la carte approx. 15.00 **t.** – (see also ***Auberge de Provence*** and ***Inn of Happiness*** below) – ☕ 13.20 – **375 rm** 140.00/175.00 **s.**, 18 suites – SB.

Royal Horseguards Thistle (Mt. Charlotte Thistle), 2 Whitehall Court, SW1A 2EJ, ☎ 839 3400, Telex 917096, Fax 925 2263 – |‡| ⇷ rm ▤ rest TV ☎ – 🔬 60. ⊡ AE ⓓ. ✻ p. 26 LX **a**
Meals 19.50 **t.** and a la carte – **368 rm**, 8 suites.

Stakis London St. Ermin's, Caxton St., SW1H 0QW, ☎ 222 7888, Fax 222 6914 – |‡| ⇷ rm ▤ rest TV ☎ – 🔬 150. ⊡ AE ⓓ VISA JCB. ✻ CX **a**
Meals *(closed Saturday and Sunday lunch)* (carving rest.) 12.75/16.50 **t.** and a la carte – ☕ 9.75 – **283 rm** 115.00/129.00 **t.**, 7 suites – SB.

Goring, 15 Beeston Pl., Grosvenor Gdns, SW1W 0JW, 396 9000, Telex 919166, Fax 834 4393 – 50. AE VISA. BX **a**
Meals 17.50/32.00 **t.** 7.50 – 12.00 – **73 rm** 125.00/155.00 **s.**, 5 suites – SB.

Royal Westminster Thistle (Mt. Charlotte Thistle), 49 Buckingham Palace Rd, SW1W 0QT, 834 1821, Telex 916821, Fax 931 7542 – rm – 160. AE VISA. BX **z**
Meals *(closed Sunday and Bank Holidays)* (bar lunch)/dinner 19.50 **st.** and a la carte 5.20 – 10.25 – **134 rm** 122.00/145.00 **st.** – SB.

Grosvenor Thistle (Mt. Charlotte Thistle), 101 Buckingham Palace Rd, SW1W 0SJ, 834 9494, Telex 916006, Fax 630 1978 – rm – 200. AE VISA JCB. BX **e**
Meals (carving rest.) 16.35 **st.** and a la carte 6.00 – 8.95 – **360 rm** 98.00/130.00 **st.**, 6 suites.

Dolphin Square, Dolphin Sq., SW1V 3LX, 834 3800, Fax 798 8735, squash – rest – 50. AE VISA. KZ **a**
Meals 11.95/17.95 **st.** and dinner a la carte 5.50 – 9.95 – **14 rm** 101.00/121.00 **st.**, **137 suites** 126.00/147.00 **st.**.

Scandic Crown, 2 Bridge Pl., SW1V 1QA, 834 8123, Fax 828 1099, – rm – 180. AE VISA. BY **i**
Meals 12.95/17.95 **st.** and a la carte 5.00 – 10.50 – **205 rm** 115.00/145.00 **st.**, 5 suites – SB.

Rubens, 39-41 Buckingham Palace Rd, SW1W 0PS, 834 6600, Fax 828 5401 – rm rest – 75. AE VISA JCB. BX **n**
Meals *(closed Saturday and Sunday lunch)* (carving rest.) 14.95 **st.** and a la carte 6.00 – 8.95 – **188 rm** 97.00/123.00 **st.**, 1 suite.

Rochester, 69 Vincent Sq., SW1P 2PA, 828 6611, Fax 233 6724 – rest – 80. AE VISA JCB. CY **e**
Meals 16.95/17.95 **st.** and a la carte 5.00 – 9.50 – **70 rm** 105.00/145.00 **st.**

Tophams Ebury Court, 28 Ebury St., SW1W 0LU, 730 8147, Fax 823 5966 – – 30. AE VISA JCB AX **i**
Meals (in bar Saturday lunch and Sunday) a la carte 16.70/24.85 **t.** 5.95 – **42 rm** 70.00/120.00 **t.**

Winchester without rest., 17 Belgrave Rd, SW1V 1RB, 828 2972, Fax 828 5191 – . BY **s**
18 rm 58.00/65.00 **st.**

Hamilton House without rest., 60 Warwick Way, SW1V 1SA, 821 7113, Fax 630 0806 – . VISA. BY **n**
40 rm 40.00/65.00 **st.**

Collin House without rest., 104 Ebury St., SW1W 9QD, 730 8031, Fax 730 8031 – AY **r**
closed 2 weeks Christmas – **13 rm** 34.00/56.00 **st.**

XXX **Inn of Happiness** (at St. James Court H.), Buckingham Gate, SW1E 6AF, 821 1931, Fax 630 7587 – . AE VISA JCB CX **i**
closed Saturday lunch – **Meals** - Chinese (buffet lunch Sunday) 15.50/25.00 **t.** and a la carte 6.25.

XXX **Auberge de Provence** (at St. James Court H.), Buckingham Gate, SW1E 6AF, 821 1899, Fax 630 7587 – . AE VISA JCB CX **i**
closed Saturday lunch, Sunday, 1 week January, 2 weeks August and Bank Holidays – **Meals** - French 24.50/42.00 **t.** and a la carte.

XXX **L'Incontro,** 87 Pimlico Rd, SW1W 8PH, 730 6327, Fax 730 5062 – . AE VISA p. 31 FT **u**
closed lunch Saturday and Sunday, 25 to 26 December and Bank Holidays – **Meals** - Italian 16.50 **st.** (lunch) and a la carte 25.90/41.00 **st.** 7.50.

XXX **Santini,** 29 Ebury St., SW1W 0NZ, 730 4094, Fax 730 0544 – . AE VISA
closed lunch Saturday and Sunday, 25 to 26 December and Bank Holidays – **Meals** - Italian a la carte 23.40/42.50 **t.** 7.00. ABX **v**

XXX **Shepherds,** Marsham Court, Marsham St., SW1P 4LA, 834 9552, Fax 233 6047 – . AE VISA
closed Saturday, Sunday and Bank Holidays – **Meals** - English 19.95 **t.** p. 26 LZ **z**

XX **Simply Nico,** 48a Rochester Row, SW1P 1JU, 630 8061 – . AE VISA
closed Saturday lunch, Sunday, 4 days at Easter, 10 days Christmas-New Year and Bank Holidays – **Meals** (booking essential) 23.50 **st.** 9.00. CY **a**

XX **Mijanou,** 143 Ebury St., SW1W 9QN, 730 4099, Fax 823 6402 – . AE VISA
closed Saturday, Sunday, 1 week Easter, 3 weeks August, 2 weeks Christmas-New Year and Bank Holidays – **Meals** 16.50/38.50 **t.** and a la carte. AY **n**

XX **Ken Lo's Memories of China,** 67-69 Ebury St., SW1W 0NZ, 730 7734, Fax 730 2992 – . AE VISA JCB AY **u**
closed Sunday lunch and Bank Holidays – **Meals** - Chinese 15.00 **t.** and a la carte.

XX **L'Amico,** 44 Horseferry Rd, SW1P 2AF, 222 4680 – AE VISA p. 26 LY **e**
closed Saturday and Sunday – **Meals** - Italian (booking essential) 14.00/26.00 **t.** and a la carte 4.25.

XX **Hunan,** 51 Pimlico Rd, SW1W 8NE, 730 5712 – AE VISA p. 25 IZ **a**
closed Sunday lunch, 24 to 26 December and 1 January – **Meals** - Chinese (Hunan) 19.80 **t.** (dinner) and a la carte 13.10/50.80 **t.** 4.50.

XX **Tate Gallery,** Tate Gallery, Millbank, SW1P 4RG, ☎ 887 8877, Fax 887 8007, « Rex Whistler murals » – ▤ p. 26 LZ **c**
closed Sunday – **Meals** (booking essential) (lunch only) a la carte 16.55/25.85 **t.** 6.75.

XX **Gran Paradiso,** 52 Wilton Rd, SW1V 1DE, ☎ 828 5818, Fax 828 3608 – AE VISA JCB BY **a**
closed Saturday lunch, Sunday and last 2 weeks August – **Meals** - Italian a la carte 16.50/ 20.50 **t.** 3.50.

X **Olivo,** 21 Eccleston St., SW1W 9LX, ☎ 730 2505 – ▤. AE VISA AY **z**
closed lunch Saturday and Sunday, 1 week August and Bank Holidays – **Meals** - Italian 15.50 **t.** (lunch) and a la carte 18.05/22.30 **t.**

X **La Poule au Pot,** 231 Ebury St., SW1W 8UT, ☎ 730 7763 – ▤. AE VISA p. 25 IZ **e**
closed Bank Holidays – **Meals** - French 13.50 **t.** (lunch) and dinner a la carte 20.00/25.00 **t.**

X **Mimmo d'Ischia,** 61 Elizabeth St., SW1W 9PP, ☎ 730 5406, Fax 730 9439 – ▤. AE VISA AY **o**
closed Sunday and Bank Holidays – **Meals** - Italian a la carte approx. 30.00 **t.**

X **Villa Medici,** 35 Belgrave Rd, SW1 5AX, ☎ 834 4932 – AE VISA JCB BY **c**
closed Saturday lunch, Sunday and Bank Holidays – **Meals** - Italian 12.90 **t.** and a la carte 3.80.

X **La Fontana,** 101 Pimlico Rd, SW1W 8PH, ☎ 730 6630 – AE VISA p. 31 FT **o**
closed Bank Holidays – **Meals** - Italian a la carte 18.50/28.00 **t.** 6.00.

LONGBRIDGE Warks. – see Warwick.

LONG CRENDON Bucks. 403 404 R 28 – ✉ Aylesbury – ☎ 01844.

♦London 50 – Aylesbury 11 – ♦Oxford 15.

✗ **Angel Inn,** Bicester Rd, HP18 9EE, ✆ 208268, « Part 16C inn » – P. VISA
closed Sunday lunch April-September and Sunday dinner – **Meals** a la carte 13.50/20.50 **st.** 4.00.

LONG EATON Derbs. 402 403 404 Q 25 – see Nottingham (Notts.).

LONGFORD W. Mids. 403 404 P 26 – see Coventry.

LONG MARSTON N. Yorks. 402 Q 22 – see York.

LONG MARSTON Warks. – see Stratford-upon-Avon.

LONG MELFORD Suffolk 404 W 27 **Great Britain G.** – pop. 3 519 – ECD : Thursday – ☎ 01787.

See : Melford Hall★ *AC*.

♦ London 62 – ♦Cambridge 34 – Colchester 18 – ♦Ipswich 24.

Bull (Forte), Hall St., CO10 9JG, ✆ 378494, Fax 880307, « Part 15C coaching inn » – TV ☎ P – 60. AE VISA JCB
Meals (bar lunch Monday to Saturday)/dinner 17.95 **t.** and a la carte 6.95 – 8.50 – **25 rm** 65.00/110.00 **t.** – SB.

Black Lion, The Green, CO10 9DN, ✆ 312356, Fax 374557 – TV ☎ P. AE VISA
closed Christmas and first two weeks January – ***Countrymen :*** **Meals** *(closed Sunday dinner and Monday)* 10.00/20.00 **t.** – **8 rm** 50.00/105.00 **st.**, 1 suite – SB.

✗✗✗ **Chimneys,** Hall St., CO10 9JR, ✆ 379806, Fax 312294, « Part 16C cottage », – AE VISA
closed Sunday dinner – **Meals** 14.50/27.50 **st.** and a la carte 4.50.

✗ **Scutchers Bistro,** Westgate St., CO10 9DP, on A 1092 ✆ 310200, Fax 310157, – AE VISA
closed Sunday, first 2 weeks March and Bank Holiday Mondays – **Meals** a la carte 14.40/17.70 **t.**

LONGNOR Shrops. – see Shrewsbury.

LONGNOR Staffs. 402 403 404 O 24 – pop. 1 580 – ✉ Buxton – ☎ 01298.

♦London 161 – Derby 29 – ♦Manchester 31 – ♦Stoke-on-Trent 22.

Ye Olde Cheshire Cheese, High St., SK17 0NS, ✆ 83218 – TV P. VISA.
Meals *(closed Sunday dinner and Monday)* 13.00 **t.** and a la carte 4.60 – **3 rm** 20.00/30.00 **t.**

LONG PRESTON N. Yorks. 402 N 21 – ✉ Skipton – ☎ 01729.

♦London 232 – Bradford 28 – Kendal 36 – ♦Leeds 47.

Country House, BD23 4NJ, ✆ 840246, – TV P. VISA.
closed 10 December-1 February – **Meals** (residents only)(dinner only)(unlicensed) 12.50 **st.** **7 rm** 30.00/50.00 **st.**

LONGRIDGE Lancs. 402 M 22 – pop. 7 349 – ☎ 01772.

♦London 241 – Blackburn 12 – Burnley 18.

✗✗✗ ✿✿ **Paul Heathcote's** (Heathcote), 104-106 Higher Rd, PR3 3SY, NE : ½ m. by B 5269 following signs for Jeffrey Hill ✆ 784969, Fax 785713 – . AE VISA
closed lunch Tuesday to Thursday, Saturday lunch and Monday – **Meals** 22.50/32.50 **st.** and a la carte 29.00/38.00 **t.**
Spec. Clear tomato juice with chervil and Summer vegetables, Breast of Goosnargh duckling with cider potatoes and dumplings, Assiette Heathcote's.

LONGSTOCK Hants. 403 404 P 30 – see Stockbridge.

LONG SUTTON Lincs. 404 U 25 – pop. 4 938 – ☎ 01406.

♦London 100 – Lincoln 51 – ♦Leicester 67 – ♦Norwich 54.

Forte Travelodge without rest., Wisbech Rd, PE12 9AG, SE : 1 m. at junction of A 17 with A 1101 ✆ 362230, Reservations (Freephone) 0800 850950 – TV & P. AE VISA.
40 rm 33.50 **t.**

LOOE Cornwall 403 G 32 **The West Country G.** – pop. 5 265 – ECD : Thursday – ☎ 01503.

See : Town★ – Monkey Sanctuary★ *AC*.

18 Bin Down ✆ (0150) 34 239 – 18 Whitsand Bay Hotel, Portwrinkle, Torpoint ✆ 30276.

ℹ The Guildhall, Fore St., PL13 1AA ✆ 262072.

♦London 264 – ♦Plymouth 21 – Truro 39.

Klymiarven ⚘, Barbican Hill, East Looe, PL13 1BH, E : 2 m. by A 387 off B 3253 or access from town on foot ℘ 262333, ≤ Looe and harbour, ⛱ heated, ⛱ – TV ☎ Ⓟ. VISA
closed 23-30 December – **Meals** (bar lunch)/dinner 14.50 **t.** and a la carte 4.00 – **14 rm** 33.00/97.00 **t.** – SB.

Harescombe Lodge ⚘ without rest., Watergate, PL13 2NE, NW : 2 ¾ m. by A 387 turning right opposite Waylands Farm onto single track road ℘ 263158, – Ⓟ.
3 rm 38.00 **s.**

at Sandplace N : 2 ¼ m. on A 387 – ✉ Polperro – ☎ 01503 :

Polraen Country House, PL13 1PJ, ℘ 263956, – TV Ⓟ. VISA
Meals 12.00/25.00 **st.** and a la carte 5.75 – **5 rm** 27.50/48.00 **st.** – SB.

at Widegates NE : 3 ½ m. on B 3253 – ✉ Looe – ☎ 01503 :

Coombe Farm ⚘, PL13 1QN, on B 3253 ℘ 240223, ≤ countryside, ⛱ heated, park – TV ☎ Ⓟ.
March-October – **Meals** 12.00 **st.** 3.50 – **10 rm** 20.00/48.00 **st.** – SB.

at Talland Bay SW : 4 m. by A 387 – ✉ Looe – ☎ 01503 :

Talland Bay ⚘, PL13 2JB, ℘ 72667, Fax 72940, ≤, « Country house atmosphere », ⛱ heated, – rest TV ☎ Ⓟ. AE VISA.
closed January – **Meals** (bar lunch Monday to Saturday)/dinner 22.50 **t.** and a la carte 3.75 – **20 rm** (dinner included) 75.00/170.00 **t.**, 1 suite – SB.

Allhays Country House ⚘, PL13 2JB, ℘ 72434, Fax 72929, ≤, – TV ☎ Ⓟ. AE VISA JCB
closed Christmas and New Year – **Meals** (dinner only) 13.50 **st.** 4.40 – **7 rm** 36.00/72.00 **st.** – SB.

LOSTWITHIEL Cornwall 403 G 32 **The West Country G.** – pop. 2 452 – ECD : Wednesday – ☎ 01208.

Envir. : Lanhydrock★★, N : 4 m. by B 3268 – Restormel Castle★ *AC* (✻★) N : 1 m. – Bodmin (St. Petroc Church★) NW : 6 m. by B 3268.

18 Lower Polscoe ℘ 873550 – 18 Lanhydrock, Lostwithiel road, Bodmin ℘ 73600.

Lostwithiel Community Centre, Liddicoat Rd, PL22 0HE ℘ 872207.

London 273 – Plymouth 30 – Truro 23.

Restormel Lodge, 17 Castle Hill, PL22 0DD, on A 390 ℘ 872223, Fax 873568, ⛱ heated, – TV ☎ Ⓟ. AE
Meals (bar lunch)/dinner 16.00 and a la carte – **32 rm** 44.50/60.00 **t.** – SB.

LOUGHBOROUGH Leics. 402 403 404 Q 25 – pop. 44 895 – ECD : Wednesday – ☎ 01509.

18 Lingdale, Joe Moore's Lane, Woodhouse Eaves ℘ 890703.

John Storer House, Wards End, LE11 3HA ℘ 230131.

London 117 – Birmingham 41 – Leicester 11 – Nottingham 15.

Friendly, New Ashby Rd, LE11 0EX, E : 2 m. on A 512 ℘ 211800, Fax 211868, ⛱, – rm TV ☎ & Ⓟ – 250. AE VISA JCB
Meals 10.00/15.00 and a la carte – 6.75 – **94 rm** 57.00/94.00 **st.** – SB.

Cedars, Cedar Rd, LE11 2AB, SE : 1 m. by Leicester Rd ℘ 214459, Fax 233573, ⛱ heated, – TV ☎ Ⓟ
37 rm.

Garendon Park, 92 Leicester Rd, LE11 2AQ, S : ½ m. on A 6 ℘ 236557 – TV. AE VISA
Meals (by arrangement) 8.00 **st.** – **9 rm** 21.50/40.00 **st.** – SB.

at Quorn SE : 3 m. by A 6 – ✉ Loughborough – ☎ 01509 :

Quorn Country, 66 Leicester Rd, LE12 8BB, ℘ 415050, Fax 415557, – rm rm TV ☎ Ⓟ – 50. AE VISA
Meals *(closed Saturday lunch)* 12.45/18.45 **t.** and a la carte 4.95 – **16 rm**, 3 suites – SB.

Quorn Grange, 88 Wood Lane, LE12 8DB, ℘ 412167, Fax 415621, – TV ☎ & Ⓟ – 100. VISA
Meals 9.95/24.95 **t.** and a la carte 4.90 – 5.85 – **17 rm** 75.00/95.00 **t.** – SB.

ATS Bridge St. ℘ 218447/218472

When visiting Ireland,
use the Michelin Green Guide **"Ireland".**
- *Detailed descriptions of places of interest*
- *Touring programmes*
- *Maps and street plans*
- *The history of the country*
- *Photographs and drawings of monuments, beauty spots, houses...*

LOUTH Lincs. 402 404 U 23 – ☎ 01507.

♦London 156 – Boston 34 – Great Grimsby 17 – Lincoln 26.

Kenwick Park, LN11 8NR, SE : 2 ¼ m. by B 1520 on A 157 ℘ 608806, Fax 608027, park, squash – rest – 30.
Meals a la carte 17.00/32.00 **st.** 4.50 – **19 rm** 69.50/95.00 **st.** – SB.

Beaumont, Victoria Rd, LN11 0BX, ℘ 605005, Fax 607768 – – 100.
Meals 12.95 **st.** and a la carte 3.00 – **16 rm** 48.00/65.00 **st.** – SB.

Brackenborough Arms, Cordeaux Corner, Brackenborough, LN11 0SZ, N : 2 m. by A 16 ℘ 609169, Fax 609413 – – 30.
closed 25 and 26 December – **Meals** a la carte 11.60/21.90 **t.** 5.00 – **18 rm** 49.50/55.00 **t.** – SB.

ATS 179 Newmarket ℘ 601975

LOWER SLAUGHTER Glos. 403 404 O 28 – see Bourton-on-the-Water.

LOWER SWELL Glos. 403 404 O 28 – see Stow-on-the-Wold.

LOWESTOFT Suffolk 404 Z 26 **Great Britain G.** – pop. 59 430 – ECD : Thursday – ☎ 01502.

Envir. : The Broads★.

Rookery Park, Carlton Colville ℘ 560380.

East Point Pavillion, Royal Lane, NR33 0AP ℘ 523000 (summer only).

♦London 116 – ♦Ipswich 43 – ♦Norwich 30.

Hatfield, Esplanade, NR33 0QP, ℘ 565337, Fax 511885 – – 55.
Meals 8.95 **t.** and a la carte 4.75 – **33 rm** 45.00/98.00 **t.** – SB.

Rockville House, 6 Pakefield Rd, NR33 0HS, ℘ 581011 – rest .
Meals 10.00 **st.** 2.95 – **7 rm** 22.00/43.50 **st.** – SB.

at Oulton NW : 2 m. by B 1074 – ✉ Lowestoft – ☎ 01502 :

Parkhill, Parkhill, NR32 5DQ, N : ½ m. on A 1117 ℘ 730322, Fax 731695, – – 150.
Meals *(closed Sunday dinner)* a la carte 13.90/24.90 **st.** 5.00 – **16 rm** 45.00/75.00 **t.**, 2 suites – SB.

ATS 263 Whapload Rd ℘ 561581

LOW FELL Tyne and Wear – see Gateshead.

LOW LAITHE N. Yorks. – see Pateley Bridge.

LUCKINGTON Wilts. 403 404 N 29 – ✉ Chippenham – ☎ 01666.

♦London 116 – ♦Bristol 20 – Gloucester 32 – Swindon 27.

Manor Farm without rest., Alderton, SN14 6NL, SE : 1 ¼ m. by Alderton rd ℘ 840271, – .
3 rm 28.00/50.00.

LUDDENDEN FOOT W. Yorks. – see Halifax.

LUDLOW Shrops. 403 L 26 **Great Britain G.** – pop. 9 395 – ECD : Thursday – ☎ 01584.

See : Town★ – Castle★ *AC* – Feathers Hotel★ – St. Laurence's Parish Church★ (Misericords★).

Exc. : Stokesay Castle★ *AC*, NW : 6 ½ m. by A 49.

Castle St., SY8 1AS ℘ 875053.

♦London 162 – ♦Birmingham 39 – Hereford 24 – Shrewsbury 29.

Feathers, Bull Ring, SY8 1AA, ℘ 875261, Fax 876030, « Part Elizabethan house » – rest – 60.
Meals 14.00/21.50 **st.** and a la carte 4.75 – **40 rm** 72.00/140.00 **st.** – SB.

Overton Grange, Overton Rd, SY8 4AD, S : 1 ¾ m. on B 4361 ℘ 873500, Fax 873524, – – 160.
Meals 11.50/19.50 and a la carte 4.95 – **16 rm** 33.50/89.00 **t.** – SB.

Dinham Hall, Dinham, SY8 1EJ, ℘ 876464, Fax 876019, – .
Meals (light lunch)/dinner 18.50 **st.** and a la carte 4.75 – **12 rm** – SB.

Cliffe, Dinham, SY8 2JE, W : ½ m. via Dinham Bridge ℘ 872063, – .
Meals (bar lunch Monday to Saturday)/dinner 12.95 **st.** – **9 rm** 27.50/54.00 **st.** – SB.

- **No. 28,** 28 Lower Broad St., SY8 1PQ, ℘ 876996, Fax 876996 – ⇎ rest TV. AE VISA
  Meals 15.00 **st.** 4.50 – **4 rm** 35.00/50.00 **st.**
- **Dinham Weir,** Dinham Bridge, SY8 1EH, ℘ 874431, ←, – ⇎ rm TV ☎ P. AE VISA.
  Meals 12.50 **st.** and a la carte – **8 rm** 50.00/70.00 – SB.
- **Cecil,** Sheet Rd, SY8 1LR, ℘ 872442, – ⇎ TV P. VISA
  closed 18 December-1 January – **Meals** (by arrangement) 11.00 **st.** – **10 rm** 17.50/41.00 **st.** – SB.

ATS Weeping Cross Lane ℘ 872401

LUPTON Cumbria 402 L 21 – see Kirkby Lonsdale.

LUTON Beds. 404 S 28 **Great Britain G.** – pop. 171 671 – ECD : Wednesday – 01582.
See : Luton Hoo★ (Wernher Collection★★) *AC* X.
18 Stockwood Park, London Rd ℘ 413704, X – 18, 9 South Beds, Warden Hill Rd, ℘ 575201.
Luton International Airport : ℘ 405100, E : 1½m. X – **Terminal** : Luton Bus Station.
65-67 Bute St., LU1 2EY ℘ 401579 – Information Desk, London Luton Airport, LU2 9LY ℘ 405100.
♦London 35 – ♦Cambridge 36 – ♦Ipswich 93 – ♦Oxford 45 – Southend-on-Sea 63.

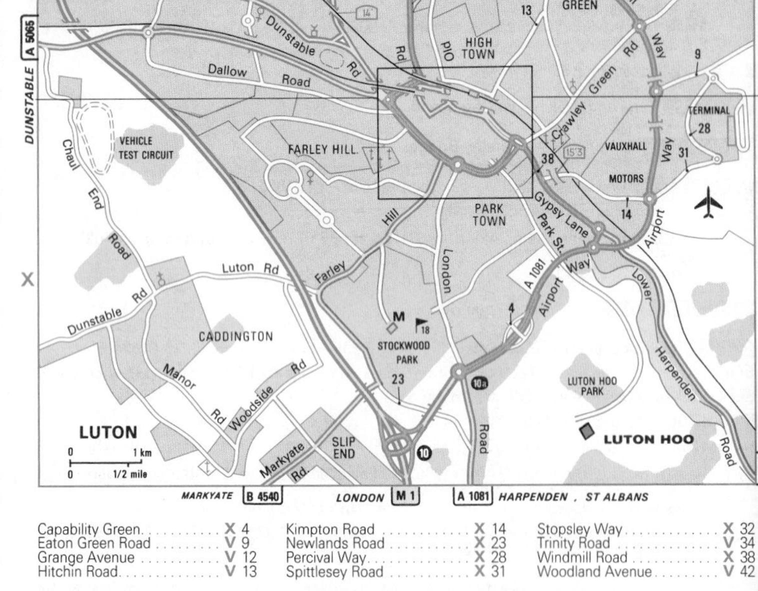

Capability Green	X 4	Kimpton Road	X 14	Stopsley Way	X 32
Eaton Green Road	V 9	Newlands Road	X 23	Trinity Road	V 34
Grange Avenue	V 12	Percival Way	X 28	Windmill Road	X 38
Hitchin Road	V 13	Spittlesey Road	X 31	Woodland Avenue	V 42

- **Strathmore Thistle** (Mt. Charlotte Thistle), Arndale Centre, LU1 2TR, ℘ 34199, Telex 825763, Fax 402528 – rest TV ☎ P – 200 – **147 rm**, 3 suites. Y n
- **Chiltern** (Forte), Waller Av., Dunstable Rd, LU4 9RU, NW : 2 m. on A 505 ℘ 575911, Fax 581859 – ⇎ rm rest TV ☎ P – 250. AE VISA V r
  Meals *(closed lunch Saturday and Bank Holidays)* 14.95 **st.** (dinner) and a la carte 13.65/21.15 **st.** – 8.95 – **91 rm** 74.00/86.00 **st.** – SB.

LUTON

Arndale Centre .... YZ
George St .... Z

Bute Street .... Y 3
Church Street .... Y 5
Dallow Road .... Y 7
Dunstable Road .... Y 8
King Street .... Z 16
Liverpool Road .... Y 17
Manchester Street .... Y 19
Market Hill .... Z 20
Mill Street .... Y 20
Old Bedford Road .... Y 24
Park Square .... Z 26
Park Street West .... Z 27
Silver Street .... Y 30
Upper George Street .... Z 36
Windmill Road .... Z 38

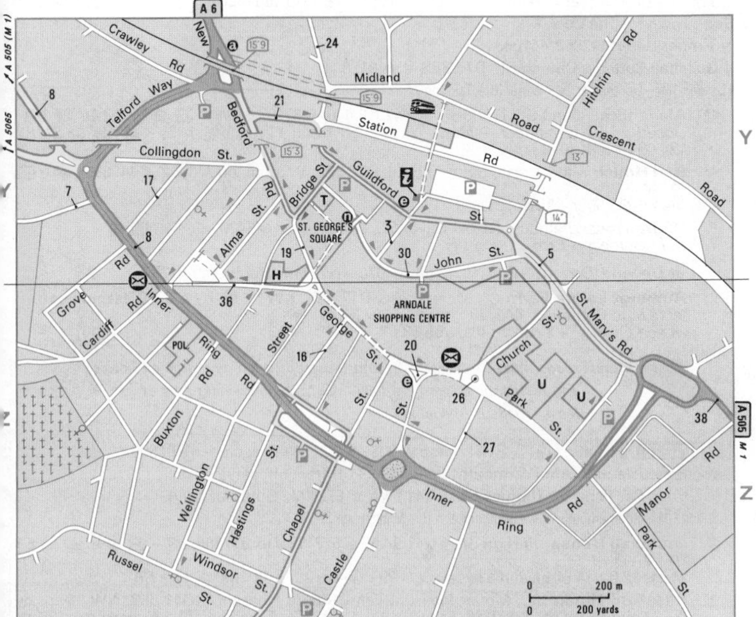

🏨 **Gateway**, 641 Dunstable Rd, LU4 8RQ, NW : 2 ¾ m. on A 505 ✆ 575955, Fax 490065 – lift – ⇔ rm TV ☎ P – 🏛 70 — V **u**
117 rm.

🏨 **Red Lion**, Castle St., LU1 3AA, ✆ 413881, Fax 23864 – ⇔ rm ▤ rest TV ☎ P – 🏛 50 — Z **e**
38 rm.

🏨 **Leaside**, 72 New Bedford Rd, LU3 1BT, ✆ 417643, Fax 34961 – TV ☎ P. AE VISA. — Y **a**
closed 25 and 26 December – **Meals** *(closed Saturday lunch, Sunday dinner and Bank Holidays)* 16.00 **t.** and a la carte 🍷 4.00 – **14 rm** ☕ 40.00/50.00 **st.**

ATS 67 Kingsway ✆ 597519

ATS High St., Oakley Rd, Leagrave ✆ 507020/592381

LUTTERWORTH Leics. 403 404 Q 26 – pop. 7 380 – ECD : Wednesday – ☎ 01455.

18 Ullesthorpe Court, Frolesworth Rd ✆ 209023.

◆London 93 – ◆Birmingham 34 – ◆Coventry 14 – ◆Leicester 16.

🏨 **Denbigh Arms**, 24 High St., LE17 4AD, ✆ 553537, Fax 556627 – TV ☎ P – 🏛 50. AE VISA
Meals 6.50/9.95 **st.** 🍷 5.50 – **31 rm** ☕ 55.00/65.00 **st.** – SB.

LYDFORD Devon 403 H 32 **The West Country G.** – pop. 1 734 – ✉ Okehampton – ☎ 0182 282.

See : Village★★ (Lydford Gorge★★).

◆London 234 – Exeter 33 – ◆Plymouth 24.

Castle Inn, EX20 4BH, ✆ 242, Fax 454, « 16C inn », – TV P. AE VISA
Meals *(closed 25 December)* (bar lunch)/dinner 14.95 **t.** and a la carte 🍷 4.50 – **8 rm** ☕ 27.50/55.00 **t.** – SB.

LYFORD Oxon – ✉ Wantage – ☎ 01235.
♦London 70 – ♦Oxford 11 – Reading 30 – Swindon 19.

- Lyford Manor without rest., OX12 0EG, ☎ 868204, Fax 868266, « Part 15C farm-house », – P.
  3 rm.

LYME REGIS Dorset 403 L 31 **The West Country G.** – pop. 3 566 – ECD : Thursday – ☎ 01297.
See : Town★ – The Cobb★.
Timber Hill ☎ 442963/442043.
Guildhall Cottage, Church St., DT7 3BS ☎ 442138.
♦London 160 – Dorchester 25 – Exeter 31 – Taunton 27.

- **Alexandra,** Pound St., DT7 3HZ, ☎ 442010, Fax 443229, ←, – TV ☎ P. AE VISA
  closed 24-30 December – **Meals** 12.50/17.50 **t.** and a la carte 4.45 – **26 rm** 57.00/124.00 **t.** – SB.
- **Red House** without rest., Sidmouth Rd, DT7 3ES, W : ¾ m. on A 3052 ☎ 442055, – TV P.
  March-October – **3 rm** 38.00/48.00 **s.**
- **White House** without rest., 47 Silver St., DT7 3HR, ☎ 443420, ← – TV P
  April-October – **7 rm** 40.00 **st.**

at Uplyme (Devon) NW : 1¼ m. on A 3070 – ✉ Lyme Regis – ☎ 01297 :

- **Amherst Lodge Farm** without rest., DT7 3XH, NW : 1 m. by A 3070, taking left turn in Yawl to Cathole ☎ 442773, – TV P.
  March-October – **3 rm** 30.00/56.50 **t.**

Town plans : *roads most used by traffic and those on which guide- listed hotels and restaurants stand are fully drawn; the beginning only of lesser roads is indicated.*

LYMINGTON Hants. 403 404 P 31 – pop. 7 838 – ECD : Wednesday – ☎ 01590.
to the Isle of Wight (Yarmouth) (Wightlink Ltd) frequent services daily (30 mn).
Waitrose Car Park, St. Thomas St., SO41 9NA ☎ 672422 (Summer only).
♦London 104 – Bournemouth 18 – ♦Southampton 19 – Winchester 32.

- **Stanwell House,** 15 High St., SO41 9AA, ☎ 677123, Fax 677756, – TV ☎ – 25. AE VISA
  Meals 12.50/14.50 **st.** and a la carte 4.95 – **35 rm** 55.00/100.00 **st.** – SB.
- **Passford House**, Mount Pleasant Lane, Mount Pleasant, SO41 8LS, NW : 2 m. by A 337 and Sway rd ☎ 682398, Fax 683494, ←, heated, park, – TV ☎ P – 100. AE VISA
  Meals 11.95/21.00 **st.** and a la carte – **54 rm** 75.00/135.00 **st.**, 1 suite – SB.
- **Albany House,** 3 Highfield, SO41 9GB, ☎ 671900, – rest TV P.
  closed 23-29 December – **Meals** (by arrangement) 13.50 **s.** – **3 rm** 35.00/56.00 **s.** – SB.
- **Efford Cottage,** Everton, SO41 0JD, W : 2 m. on A 337 ☎ 642315, Fax 642315, – TV P
  Meals (by arrangement) 10.00 **s.** – **3 rm** 18.00/40.00 **s.** – SB.
- XXX **Gordleton Mill** with rm, Silver St., Hordle, SO41 6DJ, NW : 3½ m. by A 337 and Sway Rd ☎ 682219, Fax 683073, « Part 17C mill, riverside setting », – rest TV ☎ P. AE VISA
  – ***Provence :*** **Meals**- French *(closed Sunday dinner and Monday in winter) booking essential* 17.50/23.50 **t.** and a la carte 30.30/39.00 **t.** 9.00 – **7 rm** 69.00/115.00 **t.** – SB.
- X **Limpets,** 9 Gosport St., SO41 9BG, ☎ 675595 – VISA
  closed November and 25-26 December – **Meals** *(closed Sunday and Monday except Bank Holidays)* 12.50/22.00 **t.** and a la carte 5.50.

ATS Marsh Lane ☎ 675938/9

LYMPSTONE Devon 403 J 32 – see Exmouth.

LYNDHURST Hants. 403 404 P 31 **Great Britain G.** – pop. 3 141 – ECD : Wednesday – ☎ 01703.
Envir. : New Forest★★ (Bolderwood Ornamental Drive★★, Rhinefield Ornamental Drive★★).
18, 9 Dibden, Main Rd ☎ 845596 – 18 New Forest, Southampton Rd ☎ 282752.
New Forest Museum & Visitor Centre, Main Car Park, SO43 7NY ☎ 282269.
♦London 95 – Bournemouth 20 – ♦Southampton 10 – Winchester 23.

- **Parkhill**, Beaulieu Rd, SO43 7FZ, SE : 1¼ m. on B 3056 ☎ 282944, Fax 283268, ←, « Tastefully furnished country house », heated, park – rest TV ☎ P – 45. AE VISA
  Meals 16.00/25.00 **t.** and a la carte – **17 rm** 43.00/135.00 **t.**, 3 suites – SB.
- **Crown,** 9 High St., SO43 7NF, ☎ 282922, Fax 282751, – TV ☎ P – 50. AE VISA JCB
  Meals (bar lunch)/dinner 16.00 **st.** and a la carte 7.50 – **39 rm** 59.00/89.00 **st.**, 1 suite – SB.

Beaulieu, Beaulieu Rd, SO42 7YQ, SE : 3½ m. on B 3056 ☎ 293344, Fax 292729, ▣, ⛉ – ⅍ rest ▣ ☎ ℗ – 🎪 30. ▣ ▣ ▣ VISA
Meals (dinner only) 15.00 **t.** 🍾 6.70 – **17 rm** ☐ 52.00/84.00 **t.**, 1 suite – SB.

Ormonde House, Southampton Rd, SO43 7BT, ☎ 282806, Fax 283775, ⛉ – ⅍ rest ▣ ☎ ♿ ℗. ▣ ▣ VISA
closed Christmas – **Meals** *(closed Sunday)* (dinner only)(by arrangement) 13.00 🍾 5.00 – **14 rm** ☐ 28.00/60.00 **st.** – SB.

Whitemoor House without rest., Southampton Rd, SO43 7BU, ☎ 282186 – ⅍ ▣ ℗. ▣ VISA. ⚘
8 rm ☐ 25.00/50.00 **st.**

LYNMOUTH Devon 403 I 30 – see Lynton.

LYNTON Devon 403 I 30 **The West Country G.** – pop. 1 870 (inc. Lynmouth) – ECD : Thursday – ✆ 01598.

See : Town★ (≤★★).

Envir. : Valley of the Rocks★, W : 1 m. – Watersmeet★, E : 1½ m. by A 39.

Exc. : Exmoor National Park★★ – Doone Valley★, SE : 7½ m. by A 39 (access from Oare on foot).

ℹ Town Hall, Lee Rd, EX35 6BT ☎ 52225.

♦London 206 – Exeter 59 – Taunton 44.

Lynton Cottage ⛫, North Walk Hill, EX35 6ED, ☎ 52342, Fax 52597, ≤ bay and Countisbury Hill, ⛉ – ▣ ☎ ℗. ▣ ▣ ▣ VISA
closed January – **Meals** 14.00/28.00 **t.** and a la carte 🍾 6.50 – **16 rm** ☐ 42.00/109.00 **t.** – SB.

Hewitt's at the Hoe ⛫, North Walk, EX35 6HJ, ☎ 752293, Fax 752489, ≤ bay and Countisbury Hill, « Victorian house in wooded cliffside setting », park – ⅍ ▣ ☎ ℗. ▣ VISA. ⚘
Meals 14.50/21.50 **st.** and dinner a la carte 🍾 6.25 – **10rm** ☐ 45.00/90.00 **st.** – SB.

Seawood ⛫, North Walk, EX35 6HJ, ☎ 52272, ≤ bay and headland – ⅍ rest ▣ ℗
mid March-October – **Meals** (dinner only) 16.00 **t.** – **12 rm** ☐ (dinner included) 40.00/80.00 **t.** – SB.

Chough's Nest ⛫, North Walk, EX35 6HJ, ☎ 53315, ≤ bay and Countisbury Hill – ⅍ ▣ ℗. ⚘
April-October – **Meals** (bar lunch)/dinner 12.00 **st.** – **12 rm** ☐ 25.00/50.00 **st.**

Crown, Sinai Hill, EX35 6AG, ☎ 752253, Fax 53311 – ▣ ☎ ℗
14 rm.

Victoria Lodge, Lee Rd, EX35 6BS, ☎ 53203, ⛉ – ⅍ ▣ ℗. ⚘
closed mid November - mid February – **Meals** (dinner only) 14.00 **st.** 🍾 4.00 – **10 rm** ☐ 30.00/60.00 **st.**

Rockvale ⛫, Lee Rd, EX35 6HW, off Lee Rd ☎ 52279, ≤ – ⅍ ▣ ☎ ℗. ▣ VISA. ⚘
March-October – **Meals** (by arrangement) 12.00 **st.** – **8 rm** ☐ 18.00/48.00 **st.** – SB.

Longmead House, Longmead, EX35 6DQ, ☎ 752523, ⛉ – ⅍ ℗
April-October – **Meals** 12.00 **st.** 🍾 4.00 – **8 rm** ☐ 16.00/40.00 **st.** – SB.

at Lynmouth – ✉ Lynmouth – ✆ 01598 :

Tors ⛫, EX35 6NA, ☎ 53236, Fax 52544, ≤ Lynmouth and bay, ⛱ heated, ⛉ – ▣ ▣ ☎ ℗. ▣ ▣ ▣ VISA JCB
closed 4 January-28 February – **Meals** 26.50 **st.** (dinner) and a la carte – **35 rm** ☐ 37.00/94.00 **st.** – SB.

Rising Sun, The Harbour, EX35 6EQ, ☎ 53223, Fax 53480, ≤, « Part 14C inn », ⛉ – ⅍ ▣ ☎. ▣ ▣ ▣ VISA. ⚘
Meals 14.50/21.50 **t.** and dinner a la carte 🍾 6.25 – **15 rm** ☐ 45.00/99.00 **t.**, 1 suite – SB.

Beacon ⛫ without rest., Countisbury Hill, EX35 6ND, E : ½ m. on A 39 ☎ 53268, ≤ Sea, ⛉ – ▣ ℗. ⚘
Easter-September – **7 rm** 23.00/45.00.

Countisbury Lodge ⛫, Tors Park, EX35 6NB, off Countisbury Hill ☎ 52388, ≤ – ⅍ rest ℗. ▣ VISA
closed December to February except Christmas – **Meals** 12.50 **st.** 🍾 3.75 – **6 rm** ☐ (dinner included) 57.50/77.00 **st.** – SB.

Heatherville ⛫, Tors Park, EX35 6NB, by Tors Rd ☎ 52327 – ⅍ rest ▣ ℗
March-October – **Meals** 12.00 **s.** – **8 rm** ☐ 22.00/44.00 **s.**

at Hillsford Bridges S : 4½ m. by A 39 – ✉ Lynton – ✆ 01598 :

Combe Park ⛫, EX35 6LE, ☎ 52356, ⛉ – ℗
April-October – (residents only) (dinner only) 18.00 **t.** 🍾 7.15 – **9 rm** ☐ 50.00/65.00 **t.** – SB.

at Woody Bay W : 3¼ m. on Coast road – ✉ Parracombe – ✆ 01598 :

Woody Bay ⛫, EX31 4QX, ☎ 763264, ≤ Woody Bay – ⅍ rest ℗
14 rm.

at Martinhoe W : 4 ¼ m. via Coast road – ✉ Barnstaple – ☎ 0159 83 :

Old Rectory ⛰, EX31 4QT, ☎ 368, Fax 567, ⛱ – ✖ rest TV P. ✖
End of March-October – **Meals** (dinner only) 23.00 **st.** 4.50 – **8 rm** ☐ (dinner included) 56.00/110.00 **st.**

LYONSHALL Heref. and Worcs. 403 L 27 – see Kington.

LYTHAM Lancs. 402 L 22 – see Lytham St. Anne's.

LYTHAM ST. ANNE'S Lancs. 402 L 22 – pop. 39 599 – ECD : Wednesday – ☎ 01253.

⛳ Fairhaven, Lytham Hall Park, Ansdell ☎ 736741 – ⛳ St. Annes Old Links, Highbury Rd ☎ 723597.

ℹ 290 Clifton Drive South, SY8 1LH ☎ 725610.

♦London 237 – ♦Blackpool 7 – ♦Liverpool 44 – Preston 13.

Dalmeny, 19-33 South Promenade, FY8 1LX, ☎ 712236, Fax 724447, ≘s, ▣, squash – lift ✖ rest TV ☎ P – 🏛 250. AE VISA. ✖
closed 24 to 26 December – ***C'est la vie :*** **Meals** 10.00/11.50 **st.** and a la carte – ***Carvery :*** **Meals** (dinner only and Sunday lunch) 11.50 **st** – ☐ 6.00 – **104 rm** 40.00/85.00 **st.**

Bedford, 307-311 Clifton Drive South, FY8 1HN, ☎ 724636, Fax 729244, Fб, ≘s – lift ✖ rest TV ☎ P – 🏛 100. AE ⓓ VISA JCB
closed 29 December – **Meals** 7.50/13.50 **st.** and a la carte 3.80 – **36 rm** ☐ 35.00/59.00 **st.** – SB.

at Lytham SE : 3 m. by A 584 – ✉ Lytham – ☎ 01253 :

Clifton Arms, West Beach, FY8 5QJ, ☎ 739898, Fax 730657, ≤, ≘s – lift TV ☎ P – 🏛 150. AE ⓓ VISA. ✖
Meals 14.50 **t.** and a la carte 5.95 **40 rm** – ☐ 75.50/94.00 **t.**, 3 suites – SB.

Les prix Pour toutes précisions sur les prix indiqués dans ce guide, reportez-vous à l'introduction.

MACCLESFIELD Ches. 402 403 404 N 24 – pop. 49 024 – ECD : Wednesday – ☎ 01625.

⛳ The Tytherington ☎ 434562 – ⛳ Shrigley Hall, Shrigley Park, Pott Shrigley ☎ 575755.

ℹ Town Hall, Council Offices, SK10 1DX ☎ 504114.

♦London 186 – Chester 38 – ♦Manchester 18 – ♦Stoke-on-Trent 21.

Sutton Hall ⛰, Bullocks Lane, Sutton, SK11 0HE, SE : 2 m. by A 523 ☎ (01260) 253211, Fax 252538, ⛱, park – TV ☎ P. AE VISA
Meals 10.95/19.95 **t.** 5.50 – **10 rm** ☐ 68.95/85.00 **st.**

Chadwick House, 55 Beech Lane, SK10 2DS, N : ¼ m. on A 538 ☎ 615558, Fax 615558, ≘s – ✖ TV P. AE ⓓ VISA. ✖
Meals *(closed Saturday, Sunday and Bank Holidays)* (residents only) (dinner only) 7.95 **st.** 3.00 – **13 rm** ☐ 35.00/55.00 **st.**

at Bollington N : 3 ½ m. by A 523 on B 5090 – ✉ Macclesfield – ☎ 01625 :

XX **Mauro's,** 88 Palmerston St., SK10 5PW, ☎ 573898 – AE VISA
closed Sunday – **Meals** - Italian (lunch first Sunday each month) 12.50/27.25 **t.**

at Adlington N : 5 m. on A 523 – ✉ Macclesfield – ☎ 01625 :

Shrigley Hall ⛰, Shrigley Park, Pott Shrigley, SK10 5SB, E : 2 m. on Pott Shrigley rd ☎ 575757, Fax 573323, « Early 19C country house in park », Fб, ≘s, ▣, ⛳, ✖, squash – lift ✖ rm TV ☎ P – 🏛 250. AE ⓓ VISA
Oakridge : **Meals** *(closed Saturday lunch)* (dancing Saturday evening) 16.50/19.50 **st.** and a la carte 4.50 – **156 rm** ☐ 60.00/150.00 **st.** – SB.

Forte Travelodge without rest., London Rd South, SK12 4NA, on A 523 ☎ 875292, Reservations (Freephone) 0800 850950 – TV ♿ P. AE VISA
32 rm 33.50 **st.**

ATS 115 Hurdsfield Rd ☎ 425481/425233/424237

MACKWORTH Derbs. 402 403 404 P 25 – see Derby.

MAGHAM DOWN E. Sussex – see Hailsham.

MAIDENBOWER W. Sussex – see Crawley.

MAIDENCOMBE Devon 403 J 32 – see Torquay.

MAIDENHEAD Berks. 404 R 29 – pop. 59 809 – ECD : Thursday – ☎ 01628.

⛳ Bird Hills, Drift Rd, Hawthorn Hill ☎ 771030 – ⛳ Shoppenhangers Rd ☎ 24693 X.

ℹ The Library, St. Ives Rd, SL6 1QU ☎ 781110.

♦London 33 – ♦Oxford 32 – Reading 13.

MAIDENHEAD

High Street . . . . Y
Nicholson's Walk
Shopping Centre . . . . . YZ

Bad Godesberg Way . . . . . Y 2
Belmont Park Avenue . . . . V 3
Blackamoor Lane . . . . V 5
Boyn Hill Avenue . . . . Z 6
Braywick Road . . . . Z 7
Bridge Street . . . . Y 9
College Road . . . . V 13
Cookham Road . . . . Y 14
Crescent (The) . . . . Y 15
Ferry Road . . . . X 17
Frascati Way . . . . YZ 18
Furze Platt Road . . . . V 20
Grenfell Place . . . . Z 21
Gringer Hill . . . . V 22
Harrow Lane . . . . V 24
High Street
BRAY-ON-THAMES . . . X 25
King's Grove . . . . Z 27
Linden Avenue . . . . V 28
Lower Cookham Road . . . V 29
Manor Lane . . . . X 31
Market Street . . . . Y 32
Norreys Drive . . . . X 35
Oldfield Road . . . . V 36
Ray Street . . . . V 38
Ray Mill Rd West . . . . V 39
St. Ives Road . . . . Y 41
St. Mark's Road . . . . V 42
Stafferton Way . . . . Z 43
Upper Bray Road . . . . X 43

For business or tourist interest : MICHELIN Red Guide Main Cities EUROPE.

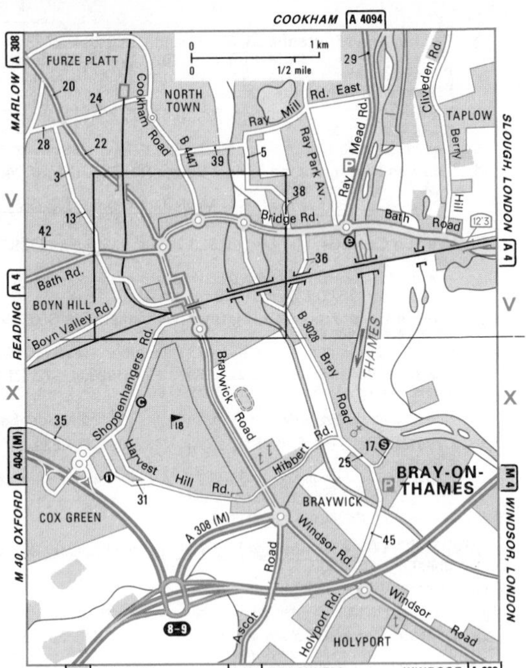

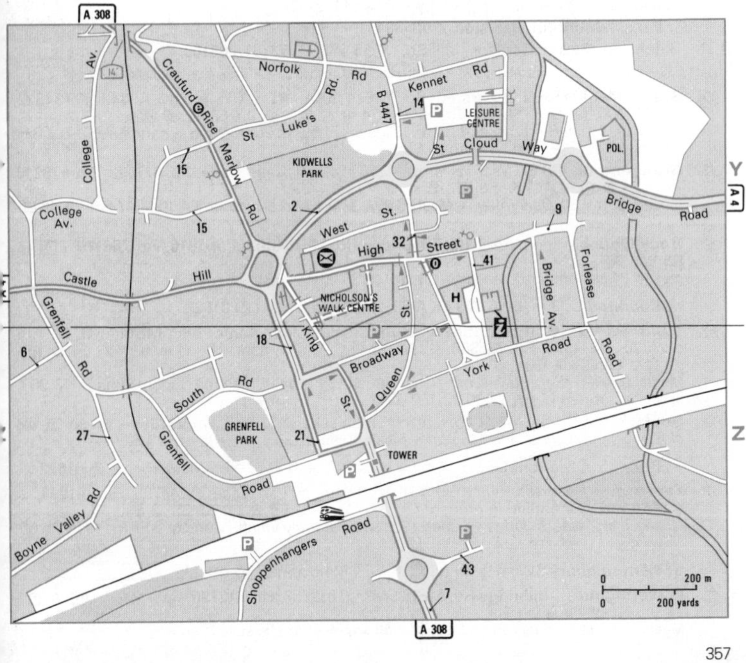

A 308
College Av.
Craufurd Rise
Norfolk Rd
Kennet Rd
B 4447
LEISURE CENTRE
St Luke's Rd.
St Cloud Way
POL.
KIDWELLS PARK
Marlow Rd
West St.
High Street
Bridge Road
A 4
Castle Hill
NICHOLSON'S WALK CENTRE
King St.
Bridge Av.
Forlease Road
Grenfell Rd
Broadway
York Road
South Rd
Queen St.
GRENFELL PARK
TOWER
Grenfell Road
Boyne Valley Rd
Shoppenhangers Road
Y
Z
200 m
200 yards
A 308

Holiday Inn Maidenhead, Manor Lane, SL6 2RA, ✆ 23444, Fax 770035, squash – rm rest – 400. X n
Promenade : **Meals** *(closed Saturday lunch)* 15.95/18.50 **st.** and a la carte 6.75 – 10.95 – **187 rm** 99.00/225.00 **st.**, 2 suites.

Fredrick's, Shoppenhangers Rd, SL6 2PZ, ✆ 35934, Fax 771054, – – 50. X c
closed 24 to 30 December – **Meals** (see below) – **36 rm** 135.00/180.00 **t.**, 1 suite.

Thames Riviera, at the bridge, Bridge Rd, SL6 8DW, ✆ 74057, Fax 776586, – – 50. V e
closed 26 to 30 December – **Meals** (light lunch Saturday and Bank Holidays) 17.50 **t.** and a la carte 4.75 – **51 rm** 78.00/118.00 **t.** – SB.

Walton Cottage, Marlow Rd, SL6 7LT, ✆ 24394, Fax 773851 – – 30. Y e
closed 24 December-4 January – **Meals** *(closed Friday to Sunday and Bank Holidays)* (dinner only) 16.00 **t.** 5.50 – **66 rm** 70.00/105.00 **t.**

XXX **Fredrick's** (at Fredrick's H.), Shoppenhangers Rd, SL6 2PZ, ✆ 24737, Fax 771054, – X c
closed Saturday lunch and 24 to 30 December – **Meals** 21.50/29.50 **t.** and a la carte 8.00.

XX **Jasmine Peking,** 29 High St., SL6 1JG, ✆ 20334 – Y o
Meals - Chinese a la carte 13.00/25.00 **st.**

at Littlewick Green W : 3 ¼ m. by A 4 – V – ✉ Maidenhead – ☎ 01628 :

Crystals, Bath Rd, SL6 3RQ, on A 4 ✆ 822085, Fax 829211 – – 30.
Meals *(closed Sunday dinner)* 5.00/15.00 **t.** and dinner a la carte 3.95 – **19 rm** 69.00 **t.** – SB.

ATS Denmark St., Cordwallis Est. ✆ 20161

MAIDEN NEWTON Dorset 403 404 M 31 **The West Country G.** – pop. 937 – ECD : Thursday – ✉ Dorchester – ☎ 01300.

Envir. : Cerne Abbas★, NE : 5 ½ m.

♦London 143 – Bournemouth 35 – ♦Bristol 55 – Taunton 34 – Weymouth 16.

XX **Le Petit Canard,** Dorchester Rd, DT2 0BE, ✆ 320536 –
closed Sunday, Monday and one week late June – **Meals** (booking essential) (dinner only) 22.50 **t.** 5.50.

MAIDSTONE Kent 404 V 30 **Great Britain G.** – pop. 86 067 – ECD : Wednesday – ☎ 01622.

Envir. : Leeds Castle★ *AC*, SE : 4 ½ m. by A 20 and B 2163.

Tudor Park, Ashford Rd, Bearsted ✆ 734334.

The Gatehouse, Palace Gardens, Mill St., ME15 6YE ✆ 673581/602169.

♦London 36 – ♦Brighton 64 – ♦Cambridge 84 – Colchester 72 – Croydon 36 – ♦Dover 45 – Southend-on-Sea 49.

Stakis Maidstone, Bearsted Rd, ME14 5AA, NE : 1 ½ m. by A 249 ✆ 734322, Fax 734600, – rm rest – 90.
Meals (bar lunch Saturday and Bank Holidays) 11.50/16.95 **st.** and a la carte 7.50 – 8.50 **136 rm** 91.00/119.00 **st.**, 3 suites – SB.

Grangemoor, 4-8 St. Michael's Rd, ME16 8BS, off Tonbridge Rd ✆ 677623, Fax 678246, – – 100.
closed 26 to 30 December – **Meals** 8.00/12.00 **t.** and a la carte 4.10 – **47 rm** 45.00/52.00 **t.**

Rock House without rest., 102 Tonbridge Rd, ME16 8SL, ✆ 751616, Fax 756119 –
closed 24 December-1 January – **11 rm** 35.00/44.00 **st.**

at Bearsted E : 3 m. by A 249 on A 20 – ✉ Maidstone – ☎ 01622 :

Tudor Park H. Golf & Country Club (Country Club), Ashford Rd, ME14 4NQ, E : 1 m. on A 20 ✆ 734334, Fax 735360, park, squash – – 300.
Meals *(closed Saturday lunch)* (bar lunch Saturday) (carving lunch)/dinner 18.00 **t.** and a la carte – **117 rm** 90.00/126.00 **st.** – SB.

XX **Soufflé,** The Green, ME14 4DN, off Yeoman Lane ✆ 737065, Fax 737065 –
closed Sunday dinner and Monday – **Meals** 16.95/20.25 **t.** and a la carte 5.50.

at Boughton Monchelsea S : 4 ½ m. by A 229 on B 2163 – ✉ Maidstone – ☎ 01622 :

Tanyard, Wierton Hill, ME17 4JT, S : 1 ½ m. by Park Lane ✆ 744705, Fax 741998, « 14C tannery standing in orchards », – rest
closed first 2 weeks January – **Meals** *(closed Saturday lunch, Monday and Tuesday)* 15.50/25.00 **t.** 3.80 – **6 rm** 50.00/115.00 **t.**

at Wateringbury SW : 4 ½ m. on A 26 – ✉ Maidstone – ☎ 01622 :

Wateringbury, Tonbridge Rd, ME18 5NS, ✆ 812632, Fax 812720, – rm – 75.
Meals 12.95 **st.** (dinner) and a la carte – **40 rm** 55.00/60.00 **st.**

at Larkfield W : 3 ¼ m. on A 20 – ✉ Maidstone – ☎ 01732 :

Larkfield Priory (Forte), 812 London Rd, ME20 6HJ, ℘ 846858, Fax 846786 – ⇆ TV ☎ P – 80. VISA JCB
Meals (bar lunch Monday to Saturday)/dinner a la carte 23.45/30.00 **st.** 6.10 – 8.50 – **52 rm** 59.50 **st.** – SB.

ATS 165 Upper Stone St. ℘ 758738/758664

MALDON Essex 404 W 28 – pop. 52 843 – ECD : Wednesday – ☎ 01621.

18 Forrester Park, Beckingham Rd ℘ 891406 – 9, 9 Bunsay Downs, Little Baddow Rd, Woodham Walter ℘ (01245) 412648/412369.

Coach Lane, CM9 7UH ℘ 856503.

London 42 – Chelmsford 9 – Colchester 17.

Blue Boar (Forte), Silver St., CM9 7QE, ℘ 852681, Fax 856202 – ⇆ TV ☎ P – 30. AE VISA
Meals 11.25/19.95 **t.** and a la carte 6.00 – 8.50 – **28 rm** 65.00/90.00 **st.** – SB.

ATS 143-147 High St. ℘ 856541

MALMESBURY Wilts. 403 404 N 29 **The West Country G.** – pop. 5 853 – ECD : Thursday – ☎ 01666.

See : Town★ – Market Cross★★ – Abbey★.

Town Hall, Market Lane, SN16 9BZ ℘ 823748.

London 108 – Bristol 28 – Gloucester 24 – Swindon 19.

Whatley Manor, Easton Grey, SN16 0RB, W : 2 ½ m. on B 4040 ℘ 822888, Fax 826120, ≤, « Part 18C manor house », heated, park, – TV ☎ P – 40. AE VISA
Meals 15.00/29.00 **t.** 6.00 – **29 rm** 85.00/136.00 **t.** – SB.

Old Bell, Abbey Row, SN16 0BW, ℘ 822344, Fax 825145, « Part 13C former abbots hostel », – TV ☎ P – 25. AE VISA.
Meals 9.75/18.50 **st.** and a la carte – **32 rm** 60.00/95.00 **st.** – SB.

Knoll House, Swindon Rd, SN16 9LU, ℘ 823114, Fax 823897, – TV ☎ P. AE VISA
Meals 24.50 **t.** (dinner) and a la carte 12.50/22.50 **t.** 4.50 – **22 rm** 55.50/75.00 **t.** – SB.

at Crudwell N : 4 m. on A 429 – ✉ Malmesbury – ☎ 01666 :

Crudwell Court, SN16 9EP, ℘ 577194, Fax 577853, « 17C former vicarage, gardens », heated – ⇆ rest TV ☎ P. AE VISA
Meals 14.50/24.50 **t.** 6.95 – **15 rm** 50.00/114.00 **t.** – SB.

Mayfield House, SN16 9EW, ℘ 577409, Fax 577977, – TV ☎ P – 30. AE VISA
Meals (bar lunch Monday to Saturday)/dinner 15.95 **t.** 3.65 – **20 rm** 40.00/58.00 **t.** – SB.

MALPAS Ches. 402 403 L 24 – pop. 3 684 – ☎ 01948.

London 177 – Birmingham 60 – Chester 15 – Shrewsbury 26 – Stoke-on-Trent 30.

XX **Market House,** Church St., SY14 8NU, ℘ 860400, – VISA
closed Sunday dinner, Monday to Wednesday and first week January – **Meals** (booking essential) (dinner only and Sunday lunch)/dinner 12.25 **st.** and a la carte 5.75.

at Tilston NW : 3 m. on Tilston Rd – ✉ Malpas – ☎ 01829 :

Tilston Lodge without rest., SY14 7DR, ℘ 250223, « Rare breed farm animals », – ⇆ TV P.
3 rm 30.00/54.00 **st.**

MALTON N. Yorks. 402 R 21 **Great Britain G.** – pop. 4 294 – ECD : Thursday – ☎ 01653.

Envir. : Castle Howard★★ (Park★★★) *AC*, W : 6 m.

18 (2x) Malton & Norton, Welham Park, Norton ℘ 692959.

58 Market Place, YO17 0OW ℘ 600048 (summer only).

London 229 – Kingston-upon-Hull 36 – Scarborough 24 – York 17.

Green Man, 15 Market St., YO17 0LY, ℘ 600370, Fax 696006 – TV ☎ P – 80
Meals (grill rest.) – **23 rm**, 1 suite.

Greenacres Country, Amotherby, YO17 0TG, W : 2 ½ m. on B 1257 ℘ 693623, Fax 693623, – ⇆ TV P. VISA.
closed mid November-1 March – **Meals** *(closed Sunday)* (residents only) (dinner only) 12.00 3.50 – **9 rm** 26.50/53.00 **st.** – SB.

Oakdene, 29 Middlecave Rd, YO17 0NE, ℘ 693363, – ⇆ rest TV P.
Meals (by arrangement) 14.00 **st.** – **6 rm** 35.00/60.00 **st.** – SB.

at Wharram-Le-Street SE : 6 m. on B 1248 – ✉ Malton – ☎ 01944 :

Red House, YO17 9TL, ✆ 768455, ⟂, ✕ – ⊭ TV P
closed 1 week Christmas – **Meals** (by arrangement) 12.00 **s.** 3.00 – **3 rm** ☐ 23.00/46.00 – SB.

ATS 27 Commercial St., Norton ✆ 692567/693525

MALVERN Heref. and Worcs. 403 404 N 27 – see Great Malvern.

MALVERN WELLS Heref. and Worcs. 403 404 N 27 – see Great Malvern.

MANCHESTER Gtr. Manchester 402 403 404 N 23 **Great Britain G.** – pop. 404 861 – ☎ 0161.

See : City★ - Castefield Heritage Park★ CZ – Town Hall★ CZ – City Art Gallery★ CZ **M2** – Cathedral★ (Stalls and Canopies★) CY.

Heaton Park, Prestwick ✆ 798 0295, ABV – Houldsworth, Longford Rd West, Higher Levenshulme ✆ 224 5055 – Chorlton-cum-Hardy, Barlow Hall, Barlow Hall Rd ✆ 881 3139 – William Wroe, Pennybridge Lane, Flixton ✆ 748 8680.

Manchester International Airport : ✆ 489 3000, S : 10 m. by A 5103 – AX – and M 56 – **Terminal :** Coach service from Victoria Station.

Town Hall, Lloyd St., M60 2LA ✆ 234 3157/8 – Manchester Airport, International Arrivals Hall, M90 3NY ✆ 436 3344/489 6412.

♦London 202 – ♦Birmingham 86 – ♦Glasgow 221 – ♦Leeds 43 – ♦Liverpool 35 – ♦Nottingham 72.

Plans on following pages

Victoria and Albert, Water St., M60 9EA, ✆ 832 1188, Fax 834 2484, « Converted 19C warehouse, television themed interior », Fa, ≘s – |♦| ⊭ rm ▤ rest TV ☎ ♿ P – 🎓 250. AE VISA. ✻ AX **u**
Cafe Maigret : **Meals** a la carte 10.45/20.00 **st.** - (see also ***Sherlock Holmes*** below) – ☐ 10.50 – **128 rm** 125.00 **st.**, 4 suites.

Holiday Inn Crowne Plaza Midland, 16 Peter St., M60 2DS, ✆ 236 3333, Fax 228 2241, Fa, ≘s, ☐, squash – |♦| ⊭ rm ▤ TV ☎ ♿ P – 🎓 600. AE VISA JCB. ✻ CZ **x**
French rest. : **Meals** *(closed Sunday)* (dinner only) 32.50/45.00 **st.** 15.00 – ***Trafford Room :*** **Meals** *(closed Saturday lunch)* (carving rest.) 17.95 **st.** 9.00 – ***Wyvern*** *(closed Sunday)* 10.00/40.00 **st.** and a la carte 9.00 – **296 rm** 118.00/136.00 **st.**, 7 suites – SB.

Ramada, Blackfriars St., Deansgate, M3 2EQ, ✆ 835 2555, Telex 669699, Fax 835 3077 – |♦| ⊭ rm ▤ rest TV ☎ ♿ P – 🎓 400. AE VISA JCB CY **v**
Meals 12.50/18.50 **st.** and a la carte 5.75 – ☐ 9.90 – **200 rm** 88.00/120.00 **st.**, 5 suites.

Copthorne Manchester, Clippers Quay, Salford Quays, M5 3DL, ✆ 873 7321, Telex 669090, Fax 873 7318, Fa, ≘s, ☐ – |♦| ⊭ rm ▤ rest TV ☎ ♿ P – 🎓 150. AE VISA. ✻ AX **n**
Meals 15.95 **t.** and a la carte – ☐ 10.25 – **166 rm** 102.00/123.00 **st.**

Portland Thistle (Mt. Charlotte Thistle), 3-5 Portland St., Piccadilly Gdns, M1 6DP, ✆ 228 3400, Fax 228 6347, ≘s – |♦| ⊭ rm ▤ rest TV ☎ – 🎓 270. AE VISA JCB CZ **a**
Meals 14.95/17.95 **st.** and a la carte 5.50 – ☐ 9.85 – **204 rm** 91.00/122.00 **st.**, 1 suite – SB.

Castlefield, Liverpool Rd, M3 4JR, ✆ 832 7073, Fax 839 0326, Fa, ≘s, ☐ – |♦| ▤ rest TV ☎ ♿ P – 🎓 65. AE VISA AX **v**
closed 24 to 26 December and 30 December-1 January – **Meals** 5.95/20.00 **st.** and a la carte 4.20 – **48 rm** ☐ 65.00/70.00 **st.**

Chester Court, 728-730 Chester Rd, Stretford, M32 0RS, SW : 2 ½ m. on A 56 ✆ 877 5375, Fax 877 5431 – |♦| TV ☎ P. AE VISA. ✻ AX **a**
Meals *(closed Saturday and Sunday)* (bar lunch)/dinner 10.75 **st.** and a la carte 2.95 – **23 rm** ☐ 55.00 **st.** – SB.

XXX **Sherlock Holmes** (at Victoria and Albert H.), Water St., M60 9EA, ✆ 832 1188, Fax 832 2484 – P. AE VISA AX **u**
Meals *(closed Saturday lunch and Sunday dinner)* 14.95/28.50 **st.** and a la carte 9.85.

XX **Brasserie St Pierre,** 57-63 Princess St., M2 4EQ, ✆ 228 0231, Fax 228 0231 – AE VISA CZ **s**
closed Saturday lunch Monday dinner, Sunday and Bank Holidays – **Meals** 15.95/29.95 **t.** and a la carte 6.45.

XX **Quan Ju De,** 44 Princess St., M1 6DE, ✆ 236 5236 – ▤. AE VISA CZ **i**
Meals - Chinese (Peking) 9.50/24.50 **st.** and a la carte.

XX **Royal Orchid,** 36 Charlotte St., M1 4FD, ✆ 236 5183, Fax 236 8830. AE VISA CZ **o**
closed Monday and Saturday lunch and Sunday – **Meals** - Thai 8.50/16.00 **t.** and a la carte.

XX **Isola Bella,** Dolefield, Crown Sq., M3 3EN, ✆ 831 7099, Fax 839 1561 – ▤. AE VISA CZ **e**
closed Sunday and Bank Holidays – **Meals** - Italian a la carte 11.50/20.50 **st.** 4.80.

XX **Giulio's Terrazza,** 14 Nicholas St., M1 4FE, ✆ 236 4033, Fax 228 6501 – ▤. AE VISA JCB CZ **r**
closed Sunday and Bank Holidays – **Meals** - Italian 8.50/14.90 **t.** and a la carte 5.80.

XX **Gaylord,** Amethyst House, Marriott's Court, Spring Gdns, M2 1EA, ✆ 832 6037 – ▤. AE VISA CZ **c**
closed 25 December and 1 January – **Meals** - Indian 11.95/14.95 **t.** and a la carte 5.45.

X **Yang Sing,** 34 Princess St., M1 4JY, ✆ 236 2200, Fax 236 5934 – ▤. AE VISA CZ **n**
closed Christmas Day – **Meals** - Chinese (Canton) (booking essential) 13.50 **t.**

X **Market,** 104 High St., M4 1HQ, ✆ 834 3743 – AE VISA CY **o**
closed Sunday to Tuesday, 1 week Easter, August and 1 week Christmas – **Meals** - Bistro (dinner only) a la carte 14.65/21.95 **t.** 4.75.

X **Koreana,** Kings House, 40a King St. West, M3 2WY, ✆ 832 4330, Fax 832 2293 – AE VISA CZ **z**
closed lunch Saturday and Bank Holidays, Sunday, 25-26 December and 1 January – **Meals** - Korean 19.50 **t.** 6.50.

at Northenden S : 5¼ m. by A 5103 - AX – ✉ Manchester – ☎ 0161 :

Forte Posthouse, Palatine Rd, M22 4FH, ✆ 998 7090, Fax 946 0139 – rm TV ☎ P – 150. AE VISA JCB
Meals a la carte approx. 15.00 **t.** 5.50 – **190 rm** 56.00/69.50 **st.**

at Didsbury S : 5½ m. by A 5103 - AX - on A 5145 – ✉ Manchester – ☎ 0161 :

X **Est, Est, Est !,** 756 Wilmslow Rd, M20 0DW, ✆ 445 8209 – ▤. AE VISA
closed Saturday lunch and 25-26 December – **Meals** - Italian 9.95 **t.** and a la carte.

at Manchester Airport S : 9 m. by A 5103 – AX – off M 56 – ✉ Manchester – ☎ 0161 :

Manchester Airport Hilton, Outwood Lane, Ringway, M90 4WP, ✆ 436 4404, Fax 436 1521, – rm ▤ TV ☎ P – 300. AE VISA JCB.
Meals 19.75 7.50 – 11.50 – **222 rm** 109.00/180.00 **st.**

Forte Crest, Ringway Rd, Wythenshawe, M22 5NS, ✆ 437 5811, Telex 668721, Fax 436 2340, , , – rm ▤ TV ☎ P – 200
290 rm, 2 suites.

Etrop Grange, Thorley Lane, M90 4EG, ✆ 499 0500, Fax 499 0790 – rm TV ☎ P – 80. AE VISA
Meals (light lunch Saturday) 14.95/32.50 **t.** 5.50 – 8.95 – **39 rm** 94.50 **t.**, 2 suites.

Travel Inn, Finney Lane, Heald Green, SK8 2QH, E : 2 m. by B 5166 ✆ 499 1944, Fax 437 4910 – rm TV P – 70. AE VISA. BX
Meals (Beefeater grill) a la carte approx. 16.00 **t.** – 4.95 – **41 rm** 33.50 **t.**

XXX **Moss Nook,** Ringway Rd, Moss Nook, M22 5NA, ✆ 437 4778, Fax 498 8089 – P. AE VISA
closed Saturday lunch, Sunday, Monday and 24 December-9 January – **Meals** 16.50/29.00 **t.** and a la carte 6.50.

at Chorlton-Cum-Hardy SW : 5 m. by A 5103 on A 6010 – ✉ Manchester – ☎ 0161 :

Cornelius, 175 Manchester Rd, M16 0ED, ✆ 862 9565, Fax 862 9028 – TV ☎ P – 40. AE VISA AX **e**
Meals - Italian *(closed Saturday lunch)* a la carte approx. 9.45 3.75 – **20 rm** 50.00/65.00 **t.**

Sabre D'or, 392 Wilbraham Rd, M21 1UH, ✆ 881 5055, Fax 881 1546 – TV P AX **c**
Meals 6.00/10.00 **st.** – **18 rm** 25.00/50.00 **st.**

XX **Peking Palace,** 285 Barlow Moor Rd, M21 2GH, S : 1 m. on A 5145 ✆ 881 2954 – ▤. AE VISA AX
closed Monday except Bank Holidays – **Meals** - Chinese (Peking) (dinner only) 15.50 **t.** and a la carte.

at Worsley W : 7¼ m. by M 602 – AV – and M 62 (eastbound) on A 572 – ✉ Manchester – ☎ 0161 :

Novotel Manchester West, Worsley Brow, M28 2YA, at junction 13 of M 62 ✆ 799 3535, Telex 669586, Fax 703 8207, heated – rm ▤ rest TV ☎ P – 220. AE VISA JCB
Meals 11.50/13.00 **st.** and dinner a la carte 4.95 – 7.50 – **119 rm** 49.50 – SB.

XX **Tung Fong,** 2 Worsley Rd, M28 2NL, on A 572 ✆ 794 5331, Fax 727 9598 – ▤. AE VISA
Meals - Chinese (Peking) 20.50/27.50 **st.** and a la carte 5.00.

at Swinton NW : 4 m. by A 580 – AV - and A 572 on B 5231 – ✉ Manchester – ☎ 0161 :

New Ellesmere (Premier), East Lancs Rd, M27 3AA, SW : ½ m. on A 580 ✆ 728 2791, Fax 794 8222 – TV ☎ P. AE VISA.
Meals (grill rest.) 7.00/13.55 **t.** 3.75 – 3.45 – **27 rm** 39.50 **t.** – SB.

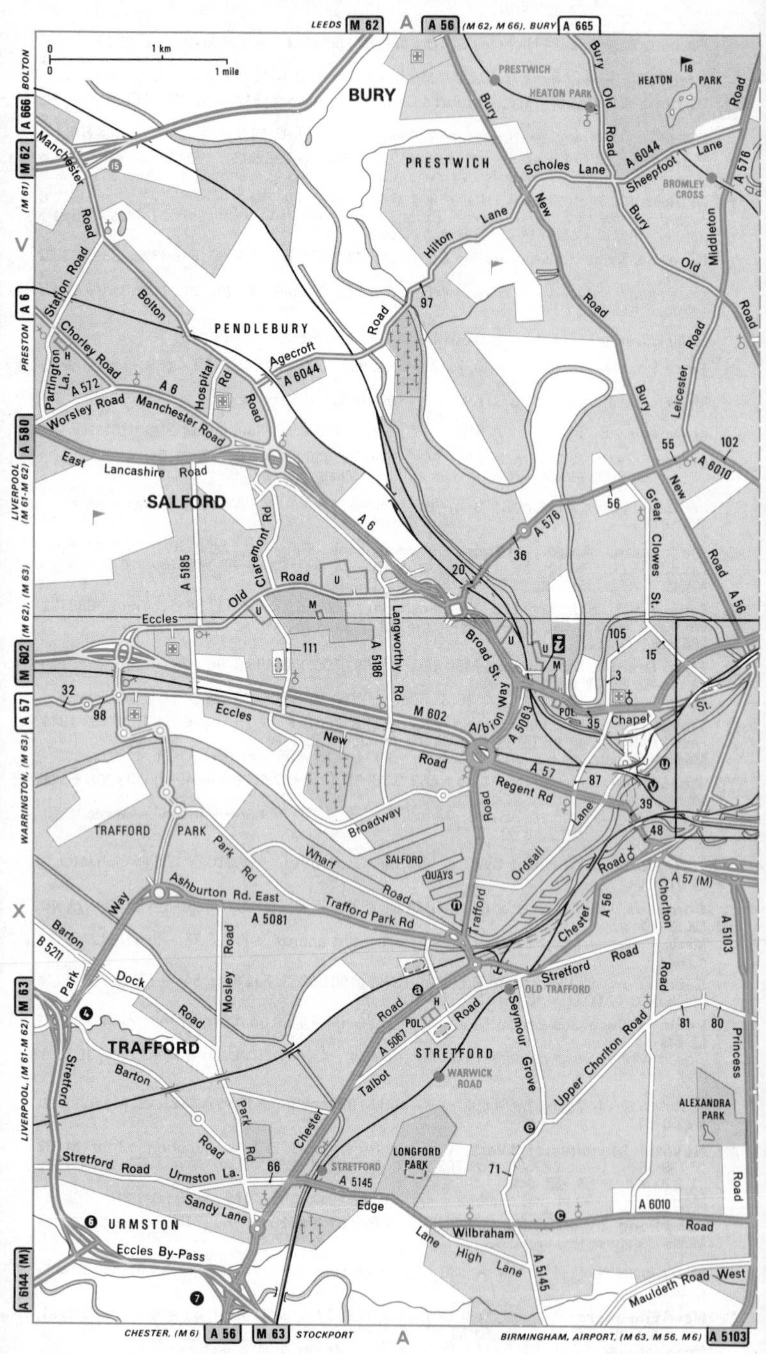
LEEDS M 62
A 56 (M 62, M 66), BURY A 665
BOLTON A 666
M 62 (M 61)
PRESTON A 6
LIVERPOOL (M 61-M 62) A 580
M 602 (M 62), (M 63)
WARRINGTON, (M 63) A 57
LIVERPOOL (M 61-M 62) M 63
A 6144 (M)
CHESTER, (M 6) A 56
M 63 STOCKPORT
BIRMINGHAM, AIRPORT, (M 63, M 56, M 6) A 5103
BURY
PRESTWICH
HEATON PARK
PENDLEBURY
SALFORD
TRAFFORD
TRAFFORD PARK
SALFORD QUAYS
STRETFORD
OLD TRAFFORD
WARWICK ROAD
LONGFORD PARK
ALEXANDRA PARK
URMSTON
BROMLEY CROSS
Bury New Road
Bury Old Road
Scholes Lane
Sheepfoot Lane
Hilton Lane
Agecroft Road
Bolton Road
Station Road
Manchester Road
Chorley Road
Partington La.
Worsley Road
Hospital Rd
East Lancashire Road
Old Road
Claremont Rd
Langworthy Rd
Eccles New Road
Broad St.
Albion Way
Great Clowes St.
Chapel St.
Regent Rd
Ordsall Lane
Broadway
Wharf Road
Trafford Road
Park Rd
Ashburton Rd. East
Trafford Park Rd
Barton Dock Road
Mosley Road
Chester Road
Stretford Road
Chorlton Road
Upper Chorlton Road
Seymour Grove
Talbot Road
Princess Road
Stretford Road
Urmston La.
Sandy Lane
Edge Lane
Wilbraham Road
High Lane
Eccles By-Pass
Mauldeth Road West
Middleton Road
Leicester Road

MANCHESTER

BUILT UP AREA

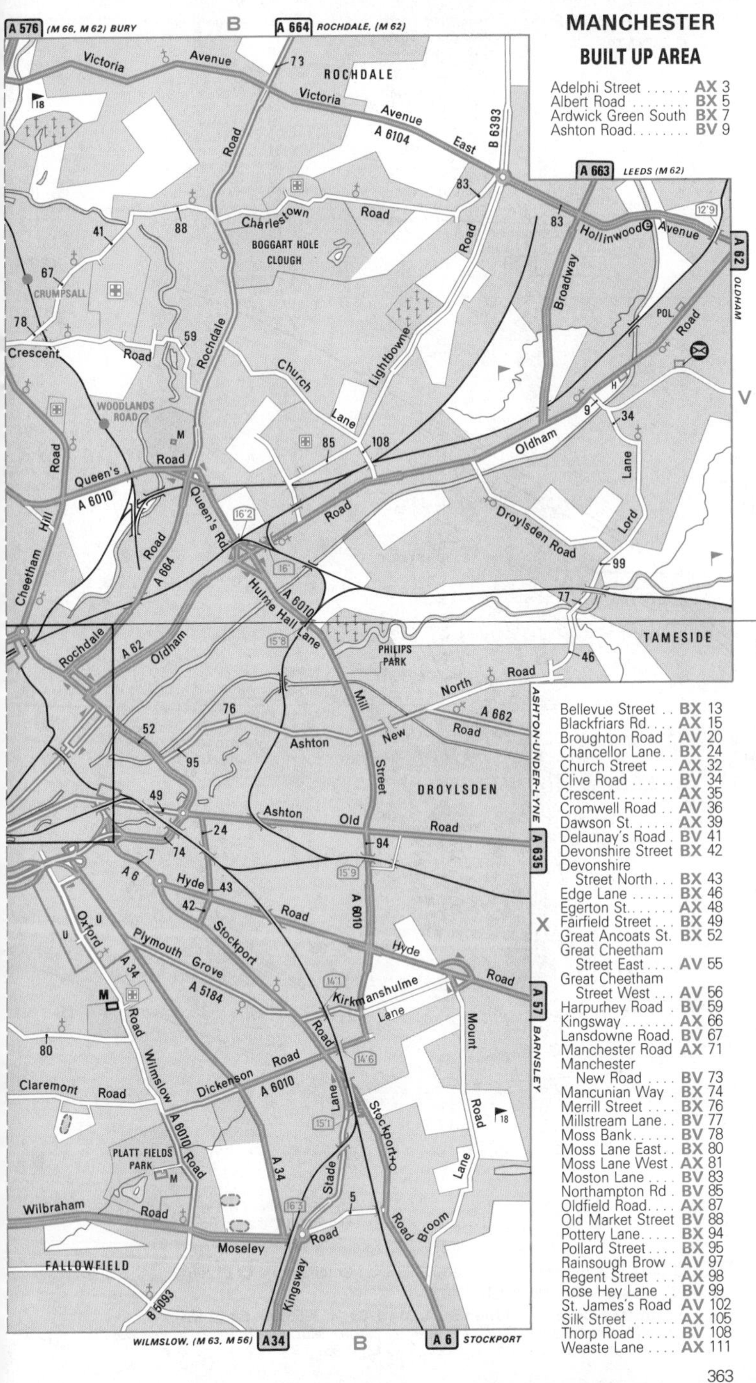

Adelphi Street . . . . . . AX 3
Albert Road . . . . BX 5
Ardwick Green South BX 7
Ashton Road. . . . . BV 9

Bellevue Street . . BX 13
Blackfriars Rd. . . . AX 15
Broughton Road . AV 20
Chancellor Lane . . BX 24
Church Street . . . AX 32
Clive Road . . . . . . BV 34
Crescent. . . . . AX 35
Cromwell Road . . AV 36
Dawson St. . . . . . AX 39
Delaunay's Road . BV 41
Devonshire Street BX 42
Devonshire Street North . . . BX 43
Edge Lane . . . . . . BX 46
Egerton St. . . . . . . AX 48
Fairfield Street . . . BX 49
Great Ancoats St. BX 52
Great Cheetham Street East . . . . AV 55
Great Cheetham Street West . . . AV 56
Harpurhey Road . BV 59
Kingsway . . . . AX 66
Lansdowne Road. BV 67
Manchester Road AX 71
Manchester New Road . . . . BV 73
Mancunian Way . BX 74
Merrill Street . . . . BX 76
Millstream Lane . . BV 77
Moss Bank . . . . . . BV 78
Moss Lane East . . BX 80
Moss Lane West . AX 81
Moston Lane . . . . BV 83
Northampton Rd . BV 85
Oldfield Road. . . . AX 87
Old Market Street BV 88
Pottery Lane. . . . . BX 94
Pollard Street . . . . BX 95
Rainsough Brow . AV 97
Regent Street . . . AX 98
Rose Hey Lane . . BV 99
St. James's Road AV 102
Silk Street . . . . . . AX 105
Thorp Road . . . . . BV 108
Weaste Lane . . . . AX 111

MANCHESTER
CENTRE

Street	Grid	No.
Arndale Shopping Centre	CY	
Deansgate	CYZ	
Lower Mosley Street	CZ	
Market Place	CY	
Market Street	CY	75
Mosley Street	CZ	
Princess Street	CZ	
Addington Street	CY	2
Albert Square	CZ	6
Aytoun Street	CZ	10
Blackfriars Road	CY	15
Blackfriars Street	CY	17
Brazennose Street	CZ	18
Cannon Street	CY	21
Cateaton Street	CY	22
Charlotte Street	CZ	25
Cheetham Hill Road	CY	27
Chepstow Street	CZ	28
Chorlton Street	CZ	29
Church Street	CY	31
Dale Street	CZ	38
Ducie Street	CZ	45
Fairfield Street	CZ	49
Fennel Street	CY	50
Great Bridgewater Street	CZ	53
Great Ducie Street	CY	57
High Street	CY	62
John Dalton Street	CZ	63
King Street	CZ	64
Liverpool Road	CZ	68
Lloyd Street	CZ	69
Lower Byrom St.	CZ	70
Nicholas Street	CZ	84
Parker Street	CZ	91
Peter Street	CZ	92
St. Ann's Street	CY	101
St. Peter's Square	CZ	104
Spring Gardens	CZ	106
Viaduct Street	CY	109
Whitworth Street West	CZ	112
Withy Grove	CY	113
York Street	CZ	115

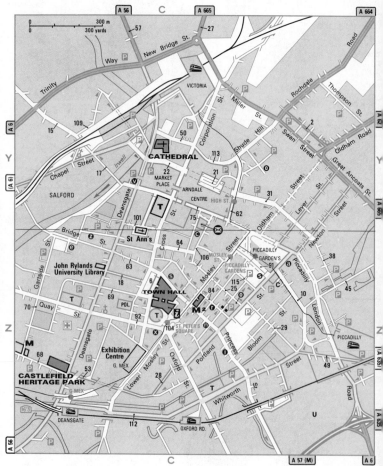

ATS Chester St. ☎ 236 5505
ATS 98 Wilmslow Rd, Rusholme ☎ 224 6296
ATS Warren Rd, Trafford Park ☎ 872 7631
ATS 122 Higher Rd, Urmston ☎ 748 6990/5923
ATS 20/28 Waterloo Rd ☎ 832 7752

MANNINGTREE Essex 404 X 28 – pop. 709 – ✉ Colchester – ☎ 01206.
◆London 67 – Colchester 10 – ◆Ipswich 12.

✕ **Stour Bay Café,** 39-43 High St., CO11 1AH, ☎ 396687 – MC AE VISA
closed lunch Tuesday-Thursday, Sunday dinner, Monday, 18 to 30 September and 24 to 31 December – **Meals** a la carte 13.85/21.15 **t.** 🍷 4.95.

MARAZION Cornwall 403 D 33 **The West Country G.** – pop. 1 417 – ECD : Wednesday – ✉ Penzance – ☎ 01736.

Envir. : St. Michael's Mount★★ (≤★★) – Ludgvan★ (Church★) N : 2 m. by A 30 – Chysauster★, N : 2 m. by A 30 – Gulval★ (Church★) W : 2½ m.

Praa Sands, Germoe Cross Rd ☎ (01736) 763445.

♦London 318 – Penzance 3 – Truro 26.

- **Mount Haven,** Turnpike Rd, TR17 0DQ, ☎ 710249, Fax 711658, ≤ St. Michael's Mount and Mount's Bay – ⇔ rest TV ☎ P. AE VISA
  closed 1 week Christmas – **Meals** (closed lunch October to March) 7.75/17.50 **st.** and a la carte 3.95 – **17 rm** 34.00/70.00 **st.** – SB.
- **Old Eastcliffe** without rest., Eastcliff Lane, TR17 0AZ, ☎ 710298, ≤, – ⇔ P.
  April-mid October – **6 rm** 25.00/48.00 **s.**

at St. Hilary E : 2½ m. by Turnpike Rd, on B 3280 – ✉ Penzance – ☎ 01736 :

- **Enny's**, Trewhelln Lane, TR20 9BZ, ☎ 740262, heated, – TV.
  closed 24 to 26 December – **Meals** (by arrangement) 15.00 **t.** – **6 rm** 30.00/50.00 **st.** – SB.

at Perranuthnoe SE : 1¾ m. by A 394 – ✉ Penzance – ☎ 01736 :

- **Ednovean House**, TR20 9LZ, ☎ 711071, ≤ St. Michael's Mount and Mount's Bay, – ⇔ rest P. AE VISA
  Meals 13.50 **st.** 4.50 – **9 rm** 20.00/44.00 **st.**

MARCH Cambs. 402 404 U 26 – pop. 16 832 – ☎ 01345.

Frogs Abbey, Grange Rd ☎ 52364.

♦London 93 – ♦Cambridge 34 – ♦Norwich 63.

- **Olde Griffin,** High St., PE15 9JS, ☎ 52517, Fax 50086 – TV ☎ P – 100. AE VISA.
  Meals 9.95 **st.** (lunch) and a la carte 14.75/20.55 **st.** 3.95 – **20 rm** 35.00/47.50 **st.** – SB.

Le Guide change, changez de **guide Michelin** *tous les ans.*

MARDEN Heref. and Worcs. – see Hereford.

MARKET BOSWORTH Leics. 402 403 404 P 26 – pop. 2 019 – ✉ Nuneaton – ☎ 01455.

♦London 109 – ♦Birmingham 30 – ♦Coventry 23 – ♦Leicester 22.

- **Softleys,** Market Pl., CV13 0JS, ☎ 290464 – ⇔ TV ☎. AE VISA.
  Meals *(closed Sunday)* (in bar) 12.50/14.50 **t.** and a la carte 5.25 – **3 rm** 40.00/50.00 **t.**

MARKET DEEPING Lincs. 404 T 25 – ✉ Peterborough (Cambs.) – ☎ 01778.

♦London 94 – ♦Leicester 39 – Lincoln 43 – ♦Nottingham 54.

- XX **Caudle House** with rm, 43 High St., PE6 8ED, ☎ 347595, Fax 348529, – TV ☎. VISA.
  closed first 2 weeks August – **Meals** *(closed Sunday dinner and Monday)* (dinner only and Sunday lunch) (booking essential) 15.50/29.50 **st.** 4.90 – **2 rm** 32.00/45.00 **st.** – SB.

MARKET HARBOROUGH Leics. 404 R 26 – pop. 16 563 – ECD : Wednesday – ☎ 01858.

Oxendon Rd ☎ 463684.

Pen Lloyd Library, Adam and Eve St., LE16 7LT ☎ 462649/462699.

♦London 88 – ♦Birmingham 47 – ♦Leicester 15 – Northampton 17.

- **Three Swans,** 21 High St., LE16 7NJ, ☎ 466644, Fax 433101 – ⇔ rm TV ☎ & P – 100. AE VISA JCB.
  Meals *(closed Sunday dinner)* (bar lunch Monday to Saturday) 12.95/17.95 **t.** 6.45 – **36 rm** 62.00/87.00 **t.** – SB.

at Glooston NE : 7½ m. by A 6 and B 6047 off Hallaton Rd – ✉ Market Harborough – ☎ 01858 :

- X **Old Barn Inn** with rm, LE16 7ST, ☎ 545215 – ⇔ rm TV P. VISA.
  Meals *(closed Monday lunch and Sunday dinner)* 10.95/12.50 **st.** and a la carte 4.10 – **3 rm** 37.50/49.50 **st.** – SB.

at Marston Trussell (Northants.) W : 3½ m. by A 427 – ✉ Market Harborough – ☎ 01858 :

- **Sun Inn,** LE16 9TY, ☎ 465531, Fax 433155 – TV ☎ P – 60. AE VISA
  closed 25 December – **Meals** 14.95/16.95 **t.** and a la carte 4.50 – **17 rm** 39.50/55.00 **t.**

ATS 47-49 Kettering Rd ☎ 464535

MARKET LAVINGTON Wilts. 403 404 O 29 – see Devizes.

MARKET RASEN Lincs. 402 404 T 23 – ☎ 01673.

♦London 156 – Boston 41 – Great Grimsby 19 – Lincoln 16.

Bleasby House, Legsby, LN8 3QN, SE : 4¼ m. by B 1202 ☎ 842383, « Working farm », – TV P.
Meals (by arrangement) 12.00 **st.** – **3 rm** 18.00/36.00 **st.**

MARKET WEIGHTON Humbs. 402 R-S 22 – ✉ York – ☎ 01430.

♦London 206 – ♦Kingston-upon-Hull 19 – York 20.

Londesborough Arms, 44 High St., YO4 3AH, ☎ 872214, Fax 872214 – TV ☎ P – 150. AE VISA.
Meals a la carte 11.10/20.50 **st.** 5.95 – **16 rm** 42.50/70.00 **st.** – SB.

MARKFIELD Leics. 402 403 404 Q 25 – pop. 4 657 – ☎ 01530.

♦London 113 – ♦Birmingham 45 – ♦Leicester 6 – ♦Nottingham 24.

Field Head, Markfield Lane, LE67 9PS, on B 5327 ☎ 245454, Fax 243740 – rm TV ☎ P – 50. AE VISA.
Meals a la carte 9.80/19.15 – **28 rm** 52.50/58.00 **t.** – SB.

Granada Lodge without rest., Little Shaw Lane, LE6 0PP, NW : 1 m. on A 50, Fax 244580, Reservations (Freephone) 0800 555300 – TV ☎ P. AE VISA.
4.00 – **39 rm** 39.95 **st.**

MARKHAM MOOR Notts. – ✉ Retford – ☎ 01777.

♦London 143 – Lincoln 18 – ♦Nottingham 28 – ♦Sheffield 27.

Forte Travelodge without rest., DN22 0QU, A 1 northbound ☎ 838091, Reservations (Freephone) 0800 850950 – TV P. AE VISA.
40 rm 33.50 **t.**

MARKINGTON N. Yorks. 402 P 21 – see Harrogate.

MARKS TEY Essex 404 W 28 – see Colchester.

MARLBOROUGH Wilts. 403 404 O 29 **The West Country G.** – pop. 6 788 – ECD : Wednesday – ☎ 01672.

See : Town★.

Envir. : Savernake Forest★★ (Grand Avenue★★★) SE : 2 m. by A 4 – Whitehorse (≤★) NW : 5 m. – West Kennett Long Barrow★, Silbury Hill★, W : 6 m. by A 4.

Exc. : Ridgeway Path★★ – Avebury★★ (The Stones★, Church★) W : 7 m. by A 4 – Littlecote★★ (arms and armour★, Roman mosaic floor★) *AC*, E : 10 m. by A 4 – Crofton Beam Engines★ *AC*, SE : 9 m. by A 346 – Wilton Windmill★ *AC*, SE : 10 m. by A 346 and A 338.

18 The Common ☎ 512147.

Car Park, George Lane, SN8 1EE ☎ 513989.

♦London 84 – ♦Bristol 47 – ♦Southampton 40 – Swindon 12.

Ivy House, High St., SN8 1HJ, ☎ 515333, Fax 515338 – rm TV ☎ P – 50. AE VISA
***Garden :* Meals** 10.95/16.50 **t.** and a la carte 5.50 – **26 rm** 45.00/85.00 **t.** – SB.

Castle and Ball (Forte), High St., SN8 1LZ, ☎ 515201, Fax 515895 – TV ☎ P – 45. AE VISA
Meals 12.25/17.95 **t.** and a la carte 6.70 – 8.50 – **36 rm** 70.00/100.00 **st.** – SB.

Moran's, 2-3 London Rd, SN8 1PQ, ☎ 512405, Fax 512405 – AE VISA
closed Monday, Sunday and 25-29 December – **Meals** (booking essential) (dinner only) a la carte 17.90/24.20 **t.** 4.50.

at Ogbourne St. George NE : 3¾ m. by A 345 – ✉ Marlborough – ☎ 01672 :

Parklands, SN8 1SL, ☎ 841555 – rm TV ☎ P. VISA
closed Christmas – **Meals** *(closed Sunday)* (lunch by arrangement)/dinner 17.50 **st.** and a la carte 4.50 – **10 rm** 45.00/60.00 **st.** – SB.

Laurel Cottage without rest, Southend, SN8 1SG, S : ½ m. on A 345 ☎ 841288, « 16C thatched cottage », – TV P.
early March-October – **4 rm** 26.00/40.00.

at Burbage SE : 5¾ m. by A 346 – ✉ Marlborough – ☎ 01672 :

Old Vicarage without rest., Eastcourt, SN8 3AG, by Taskers Lane ☎ 810495, Fax 810663, – TV P. VISA.
closed Christmas and New Year – **3 rm** 35.00/60.00 **s.**

ATS 120/121 London Rd ☎ 512274

Pour voyager rapidement, utilisez les cartes Michelin "Grandes Routes" :
970 Europe, 980 Grèce, 984 Allemagne, 985 Scandinavie-Finlande,
986 Grande-Bretagne-Irlande, 987 Allemagne-Autriche-Benelux, 988 Italie,
989 France, 990 Espagne-Portugal, 991 Yougoslavie.

MARLOW Bucks. 404 R 29 – pop. 17 310 – ECD : Wednesday – ☎ 01628.

ℹ C/o Court Garden, Leisure Complex, Pound Lane, SL7 2AE ℘ 483597 (summer only).

♦London 35 – Aylesbury 22 – ♦Oxford 29 – Reading 14.

Danesfield House ⚘, Medmenham, SL7 2EY, SW : 2 ½ m. on A 4155 ℘ 891010, Fax 890408, « Italian Renaissance style mansion, ≤ terraced gardens and River Thames », heated, park, ⚘ – |‡| ▤ rest TV ☎ P – 🏛 80. AE VISA. ⚘
Meals 19.50/32.50 **s.** and a la carte – **87 rm** ⊐ 125.00/145.00 **st.**, 2 suites – SB.

Compleat Angler (Forte), Marlow Bridge, Bisham Rd, SL7 1RG, ℘ 484444, Fax 486388, ≤ River Thames, « Riverside setting and grounds », ⚘, ⚘ – |‡| ⚘ rm TV ☎ ♿ P – 🏛 120. AE VISA JCB
Meals 22.95/32.50 **t.** and a la carte 🍷 7.50 – ⊐ 11.95 – **60 rm** 125.00/190.00 **st.**, 2 suites – SB.

Country House without rest., Bisham Rd, SL7 1RP, ℘ 890606, Fax 890983, ⚘ – TV ☎ P. AE VISA. ⚘
9 rm ⊐ 64.00/78.00 **st.**

Holly Tree House without rest., Burford Close, Marlow Bottom, SL7 3NF, N : 2 m. by A 4155 and Wycombe Rd, off Marlow Bottom ℘ 891110, Fax 481278, heated, ⚘ – TV ☎ P. AE VISA
5 rm ⊐ 54.50/72.50 **st.**

Villa D'este, 2 Chapel St., SL7 1DD, ℘ 472012 – AE VISA
closed Saturday lunch – **Meals** - Italian 12.00 **t.** (lunch) and a la carte 🍷 3.50.

MARPLE Gtr. Manchester 402 403 404 N 23 – pop. 18 708 – ECD : Wednesday – ☎ 0161.

♦London 190 – Chesterfield 35 – ♦Manchester 11.

Springfield, 99 Station Rd, SK6 6PA, ℘ 449 0721, ⚘ – ⚘ rm TV ☎ P. AE VISA. ⚘
Meals *(closed Friday to Sunday)* (dinner only) 14.50 **st.** and a la carte 🍷 6.50 – **6 rm** ⊐ 40.00/50.00.

MARSDEN W. Yorks. 402 404 O 23 – ✉ Huddersfield – ☎ 01484.

♦London 195 – ♦Leeds 22 – ♦Manchester 18 – ♦Sheffield 30.

Hey Green ⚘, Waters Rd, HD7 6NG, NW : 1 ¼ m. by Station Rd and Reddisher Rd ℘ 844235, Fax 847605, ⚘ – TV ☎ P. AE VISA. ⚘
Meals 19.00 **t.** and a la carte 🍷 4.95 – **9 rm** ⊐ 55.00/70.00 **t.**, 1 suite – SB.

MARSTON MORETAINE Beds. 404 S 27 – see Bedford.

MARSTON TRUSSELL Northants. 404 R 26 – see Market Harborough.

MARTINHOE Devon – see Lynton.

MARTOCK Somerset 403 L 31 **The West Country G.** – pop. 4 982 – ☎ 01935.

See : Village★ - All Saints★★.

Envir. : Montacute House★★ *AC*, SE : 4 m. – Muchelney★★ (Parish Church★★) NW : 4½ m. by B 3165.

♦London 148 – Taunton 19 – Yeovil 6.

Hollies, Bower Hinton, TA12 6LG, S : 1 m. on B 3165 ℘ 822232, Fax 822249, ⚘ – TV ☎ P – 🏛 100. AE VISA
Meals (in bar) a la carte 14.00/20.00 🍷 3.75 – **30 rm** ⊐ 47.50/70.00 **t.**

MARWELL ZOOLOGIAL PARK Hants. – see Winchester.

MARY TAVY Devon 403 H 32 – see Tavistock.

MASHAM N. Yorks. 402 P 21 – pop. 1 171 – ECD : Thursday – ✉ Ripon – ☎ 01765.

♦London 231 – ♦Leeds 38 – ♦Middlesbrough 37 – York 32.

King's Head, Market Pl., HG4 4EF, ℘ 689295 – TV ☎ – 🏛 35. AE VISA. ⚘
Meals (bar lunch Monday to Saturday)/dinner a la carte 7.00/13.30 **t.** – **10 rm** ⊐ 39.00/58.00 **t.**

Bank Villa, HG4 4DB, on A 6108 ℘ 689605, ⚘ – ⚘
March-October – **Meals** 15.00 **st.** 🍷 3.50 – **7 rm** ⊐ 26.00/36.00 **st.**

Floodlite, 7 Silver St., HG4 4DX, ℘ 689000 – AE VISA
closed Tuesday to Thursday lunch, Monday and 2 weeks January-February – **Meals** 10.50 **st.** (lunch) and a la carte 13.20/26.70 **t.** 🍷 4.25.

at Jervaulx Abbey NW : 5½ m. on A 6108 – ✉ Ripon – ☎ 01677 :

Jervaulx Hall ⚘, HG4 4PH, ℘ 460235, Fax 460263, ≤, « Victorian manor house, country house atmosphere », ⚘, park – ⚘ rest ☎ P
March-November – **Meals** (dinner only) 22.50 **t.** 🍷 5.40 – **10 rm** ⊐ (dinner included) 75.00/130.00 **t.** – SB.

MATLOCK Derbs. 402 403 404 P 24 **Great Britain G.** – pop. 10 465 – ECD : Thursday – ☎ 01629.

Exc. : Hardwick Hall** *AC*, E : 12½m. by A 615 and B 6014.

ℹ The Pavilion, DE4 3NR ✆ 55082.

◆London 153 – Derby 17 – ◆Manchester 46 – ◆Nottingham 24 – ◆Sheffield 24.

- **Riber Hall** ⛰, Riber, DE4 5JU, SE : 3 m. by A 615 ✆ 582795, Fax 580475, « Part Elizabethan manor house », 🌳, 🎾 – ⛔ rest 📺 ☎ Ⓟ. AE ⓓ VISA. ✻
  Meals 14.50 **t.** (lunch) and dinner a la carte 22.00/27.00 **t.** – ☕ 7.50 – **11 rm** 79.50/143.00 **t.** – SB.
- New Bath (Forte), New Bath Rd, Matlock Bath, DE4 3PX, S : 1 ½ m. on A 6 ✆ 583275, Fax 580268, ≘s, ⛱ heated, 🏊, 🌳, 🎾 – ⛔ 📺 ☎ Ⓟ – 🏫 130. AE ⓓ VISA
  Meals *(bar lunch Saturday and Bank Holiday Mondays)* 11.25/18.95 **st.** and a la carte 🍷 6.95 – ☕ 8.95 – **55 rm.**
- **Temple,** Matlock Bath, DE4 3PG, S : 1 ¾ m. by A 6 ✆ 583911, Fax 580851, ←, 🌳 – ⛔ rest 📺 ☎ Ⓟ. AE ⓓ VISA. ✻
  Meals 11.50/18.00 **st.** and a la carte 🍷 4.80 – **14 rm** ☕ 39.00/64.00 **st.** – SB.
- **Hodgkinson's,** 150 South Par., Matlock Bath, DE4 3NR, S : 1 ¼ m. on A 6 ✆ 582170, « Victoriana » – 📺 ☎ Ⓟ. AE VISA
  closed Christmas – **Meals** *(closed Sunday)* (dinner only) 24.00 **t.** 🍷 5.00 – **7 rm** ☕ 30.00/80.00 **t.** – SB.

at Tansley E : 1 ¾ m. on A 615 – ✉ Matlock – ☎ 01629 :

- **Lane End House,** Green Lane, DE4 5FJ, off Church St. ✆ 583981, 🌳 – ⛔ 📺 Ⓟ
  Meals (by arrangement)(communal dining) 14.50 – **3 rm** ☕ 30.00/50.00 **s.** – SB.

at Dethick SE : 4 m. by A 615 – ✉ Matlock – ☎ 01629 :

- **Manor Farm** ⛰, DE4 5GG, ✆ 534246, ←, 🌳, park – ⛔ 📺 Ⓟ. ✻
  closed Christmas – **Meals** (by arrangement) 11.50 **st.** – **3 rm** ☕ 28.00/36.00 **st.**

MAWDESLEY Lancs. 402 L 23 – ✉ Ormskirk – ☎ 01704.

◆London 217 – ◆Liverpool 28 – ◆Manchester 28 – Preston 15.

- **Mawdesley,** Hall Lane, L40 2QZ, N : ½ m. ✆ 822552, Fax 822096, ≘s, 🏊 📺 ☎ ♿ Ⓟ – 🏫 50. AE ⓓ VISA. ✻
  Meals (grill rest.) a la carte 11.50/19.00 **st.** 🍷 3.95 – **25 rm** ☕ 39.50/80.00 **st.**

MAWNAN SMITH Cornwall 403 E 33 – see Falmouth.

MAYFIELD E. Sussex 404 U 30 – pop. 3 515 – ECD : Wednesday – ☎ 01435.

◆London 46 – ◆Brighton 25 – Eastbourne 22 – Lewes 17 – Royal Tunbridge Wells 9.

- **Rose and Crown,** Fletching St., TN20 6TE, ✆ 872200, Fax 872200 – 📺 Ⓟ. VISA. ✻
  Meals 19.50 **t.** and a la carte **t.** 🍷 5.65 – ☕ 6.95 – **4 rm** 38.00/48.00 **t.**
- Middle House, High St., TN20 6AB, ✆ 872146, Fax 873423, 🌳 – 📺 ☎ Ⓟ
  7 rm.

at Five Ashes SW : 2 ¾ m. on A 267 – ✉ Mayfield – ☎ 01825 :

- **Coles Hall,** TN20 6JH, S : ¾ m. on A 267 ✆ 830274, ←, 🌳, park – 📺 Ⓟ
  Meals (by arrangement) 8.50 **st.** – **3 rm** ☕ 15.00/32.00 **st.**

MEADOW HEAD S. Yorks. – see Sheffield.

MEALSGATE Cumbria 402 K 19 – ✉ Carlisle – ☎ 0169 73.

- **Old Rectory** ⛰, Boltongate, CA5 1DA, SE : 1 ½ m. by B 5299 on Ireby rd ✆ 71647, 🌳 – ⛔ Ⓟ. VISA. ✻
  March-November – **Meals** (by arrangement) (communal dining) 19.95 **t.** – **3 rm** ☕ 45.00/70.00.

MEDWAY SERVICE AREA Kent – ✉ Gillingham – ☎ 01634.

ℹ Pavilion Farthing Corner, M 2 Motorway, Gillingham, ME8 8PG ✆ 360323.

◆London 39 – Canterbury 22 – Maidstone 11.

- Pavilion Lodge without rest., ME8 8PW, on M 2 ✆ 377337, Fax 360848 – ⛔ 📺 ♿ Ⓟ
  58 rm.

MELBOURN Cambs. 404 U 27 – pop. 4 006 – ✉ Royston (Herts.) – ☎ 01763.

◆London 44 – ◆Cambridge 10.

- **Melbourn Bury** ⛰, Royston Rd, SG8 6DE, SW : ¾ m. ✆ 261151, Fax 262375, ←, « Tastefully furnished country house of Tudor origin », 🌳, park – 📺 Ⓟ. AE VISA. ✻
  closed Easter and Christmas-New Year – **Meals** *(closed Sunday dinner)* (booking essential) (residents only) (communal dining) (dinner only) 15.00 **st.** 🍷 4.20 – **3 rm** ☕ 47.00/80.00 **st.**
- **Chiswick House** without rest., 3 Chiswick End, SG8 6LZ, NW : 1 m. by Meldreth rd, off Whitecroft Rd ✆ 260242, 🌳 – ⛔ Ⓟ
  6 rm ☕ 32.00/40.00 **st.**

XX **Pink Geranium,** 25 Station Rd, SG8 6DX, ☎ 260215, Fax 262110, – P. VISA
closed Sunday dinner and Monday – **Meals** 14.95/29.95 **t.** and a la carte 5.95.

XX **Sheen Mill** with rm, Station Rd, SG8 6DX, ☎ 261393, Fax 261376, ←, – TV ☎ P. AE VISA.
closed Bank Holidays – **Meals** *(closed Sunday dinner)* 14.95/21.50 **t.** and a la carte 4.50 – **8 rm** 48.00/80.00 **t.** – SB.

MELKSHAM Wilts. 403 404 N 29 **The West Country G.** – pop. 13 074 – ECD : Wednesday – 01225.

Envir. : Corsham Court** *AC*, NW : 4½ m. by A 365 and B 3353 – Lacock* (Lacock Abbey* *AC*, High Street*, St. Cyriac*, Fox Talbot Museum of Photography* *AC*) N : 3½ m. by A 350.

The Roundhouse, Church St., SN12 6LS ☎ 707424.

London 113 – Bristol 25 – Salisbury 35 – Swindon 28.

Beechfield House, Beanacre, SN12 7PU, N : 1 m. on A 350 ☎ 703700, Fax 790118, ←, « Country house and gardens », heated, – rest TV ☎ P – 50. AE VISA
Meals 9.95/19.50 **t.** 4.95 – **24 rm** 55.00/95.00 **t.** – SB.

Shurnhold House without rest., Shurnhold, SN12 8DG, NW : 1 m. on A 365 ☎ 790555, « Jacobean manor house, gardens » – TV ☎ P. VISA.
3.50 – **4 rm** 45.00/115.00 **st.**

Sandridge Park, Sandridge, SN12 7QU, E : 2 m. on A 3102 ☎ 706897, Fax 702838, ←, « Victorian mansion », park – rm TV P. VISA.
closed Christmas – **Meals** *(booking essential)* (residents only) (communal dining) (dinner only) 22.00 **s.** 2.50 – **4 rm** 35.00/70.00 **s.**

X **Toxique** with rm, 187 Woodrow Rd, SN12 7AY, NE : 1¼ m. by A 3102 and Forest rd ☎ 702129, – rest P. AE VISA.
Meals *(closed Sunday dinner, Monday and Tuesday)* (booking essential) (dinner only and Sunday lunch)/dinner 26.50 **st.** 5.10 – **4 rm** 50.00/80.00 **st.**

at Shaw NW : 1½ m. on A 365 – Melksham – 01225 :

Shaw Country, Bath Rd, SN12 8EF, on A 365 ☎ 702836, Fax 790275, – rest TV ☎ P. AE VISA
Meals (residents only Sunday dinner) 12.00 **t.** and a la carte – **13 rm** 40.00/78.00 **st.** – SB.

MELLOR Lancs. – see Blackburn.

MELTHAM W. Yorks. 402 404 O 23 – pop. 7 852 – Huddersfield – 01484.

18 Thick Hollins Hall ☎ 850227.

London 192 – Leeds 21 – Manchester 23 – Sheffield 26.

Durker Roods, Bishops Way, HD7 3AG, ☎ 851413, Fax 851843, – TV ☎ P – 80. AE VISA
Meals *(closed Saturday lunch and Sunday dinner)* 11.00/13.50 **t.** and a la carte 4.50 – **31 rm** 40.00/51.00 **t.** – SB.

MELTON MOWBRAY Leics. 402 404 R 25 – pop. 23 379 – ECD : Thursday – 01664.

18 Waltham Rd, Thorpe Arnold ☎ 62118.

Melton Carnegie Museum, Thorpe End, LE13 1RB ☎ 69946.

London 113 – Leicester 15 – Northampton 45 – Nottingham 18.

Stapleford Park, LE14 2EF, E : 5 m. by B 676 on Stapleford rd ☎ (01572) 787522, Fax 787651, ←, « Part 16C and 19C mansion in park », – rest TV ☎ P – 200. AE VISA
Meals 15.00/42.50 **t.** and a la carte – **38 rm** 135.00/200.00 **t.**, 1 suite – SB.

Quorn Lodge, 46 Asfordby Rd, LE13 0HR, ☎ 66660, Fax 480660 – TV ☎ P. AE VISA.
Meals (bar lunch Monday to Saturday)/dinner 11.50 **t.** 3.25 – **11 rm** 42.50/57.50 **t.**

Harboro (Forte), Burton St., LE13 1AF, ☎ 60121, Fax 64296 – rm TV P
26 rm.

at Old Dalby NW : 8½ m. by A 6006 on Old Dalby rd – Melton Mowbray – 01664 :

Home Farm without rest., 9 Church Lane, LE14 3LB, ☎ 822622, – P. VISA.
5 rm 21.00/35.00 **s.**

ATS Leicester Rd ☎ 62072

MEMBURY Devon – see Axminster.

MENDLESHAM GREEN Suffolk 404 W 27 – see Stowmarket.

MERE Wilts. 403 404 N 30 The West Country G. – pop. 2 201 – ECD : Wednesday – ☎ 01747.
Envir. : Stourhead★★★ AC, NW : 4 m. by B 3095 and B 3092.
Exc. : Longleat House★★★ AC, N : 9½ m. by A 303 and B 3092.
The Square, BA12 6JJ ☎ 861211.
London 113 – Exeter 65 – Salisbury 26 – Taunton 40.

Chetcombe House, Chetcombe Rd, BA12 6AZ, ☎ 860219, – rest. AE VISA
Meals (lunch by arrangement)/dinner 15.00 **s.** 3.00 – **5 rm** 29.00/50.00 **s.** – SB.

Chantry, Church St., BA12 6DS, ☎ 860264, Fax 860264, « 15C chantry priests house », heated, – rm.
closed Christmas and New Year – **Meals** (booking essential) 18.00 **st.** – **3 rm** 27.00/54.00 **st.**

MERIDEN W. Mids. 403 404 P 26 – see Coventry.

MEVAGISSEY Cornwall 403 F 33 The West Country G. – pop. 3 655 – ECD : Thursday – ☎ 01726.
See : Town★★.
London 287 – Newquay 21 – Plymouth 44 – Truro 20.

Mevagissey House, Vicarage Hill, PL26 6SZ, ☎ 842427, ≤, – rest. VISA
March-October – **Meals** 14.00 4.25 – **6 rm** 18.00/48.00.

MEYSEY HAMPTON Glos. – ✉ Cirencester – ☎ 01285.
London 101 – Bristol 44 – Gloucester 26 – Oxford 29.

Masons Arms, 28 High St., GL7 5JT, ☎ 850164 – . VISA
Meals *(closed Sunday dinner)* 12.95 **st.** (dinner) and a la carte 8.95/10.85 **st.** 4.50 – **9 rm** 28.00/45.00 **st.**

MICKLETON Glos. 403 404 O 27 – see Chipping Campden.

MICKLE TRAFFORD Ches. – see Chester.

MIDDLECOMBE Somerset – see Minehead.

MIDDLEHAM N. Yorks. 402 O 21 – pop. 754 – ECD : Thursday – ☎ 01969.
London 233 – Kendal 45 – Leeds 47 – York 45.

Miller's House, Market Pl., DL8 4NR, ☎ 622630, Fax 623570, – rest. VISA.
closed January – **Meals** (dinner only) 21.50 **t.** 2.75 – **7 rm** 33.50/84.00 **st.** – SB.

Waterford House, 19 Kirkgate, DL8 4PG, ☎ 622090, Fax 624020, « Part 17C house, antiques », – rest. VISA
Meals (lunch by arrangement)/dinner 19.50 **st.** and a la carte – **5 rm** 40.00/60.00 **st.**

at Carlton SW : 4½ m. on Coverdale Rd – ✉ Leyburn – ☎ 01969 :

Foresters Arms with rm, DL8 2BB, ☎ 40272 – . VISA
Meals *(closed Saturday lunch, Sunday dinner and Monday)* a la carte 19.95 **t.** 8.95 – **3 rm** 30.00/55.00 **t.** – SB.

at West Scrafton SW : 6 m. by Coverdale Rd – ✉ Leyburn – ☎ 01969 :

Coverdale Country, Swineside, DL8 4RX, ☎ 40601, ≤, – rest
8 rm.

MIDDLESBROUGH Cleveland 402 Q 20 – pop. 140 849 – ECD : Wednesday – ☎ 01642.
Middlesbrough Municipal, Ladgate Lane ☎ 315533 – Brass Castle Lane ☎ 316430.
Teesside Airport : ☎ (01325) 332811, SW : 13 m. by A 66 - AZ - and A 19 on A 67.
51 Corporation Rd, TS1 1LT ☎ 243425.
London 246 – Kingston-upon-Hull 89 – Leeds 66 – Newcastle upon Tyne 41.

Plan opposite

Baltimore, 250 Marton Rd, TS4 2EZ, ☎ 224111, Fax 226156 – – 25. AE VISA. BZ **e**
Meals 13.75 **st.** and a la carte 4.50 – **30 rm** 72.50/84.50 **st.**, 1 suite – SB.

Marton Way Toby, Marton Rd, TS4 3BS, ☎ 817651, Fax 829409 – rm – 85. AE VISA BZ **a**
Meals 16.95 **t.** and a la carte – **53 rm** 36.50/46.50 **t.** – SB.

Grey House, 79 Cambridge Rd, TS5 5NL, ☎ 817485, – . VISA AZ **n**
Meals (by arrangement) 8.50 **s.** – **9 rm** 30.00/49.00 **s.**

ATS Murdock Rd (off Sotherby Rd), Cargo Fleet ☎ 249245/6

MIDDLESBROUGH

Street	Square	No.
Cleveland Centre	ABY	
Corporation Road	BY	8
Dundas Street	ABY	12
Grange Road	ABY	
Hill Street Centre	AY	
Linthorpe Road	AY	
Newport Road	AY	
Albert Road	BY	2
Ayresome Green Lane	AZ	3
Bridge Street West	AY	4
Bright Street	BY	5
Clairville Road	BZ	6
Cleveland Street	BY	7
Devonshire Road	AZ	10
Eastbourne Road	AZ	14
Ferry Road	BY	15
Finsbury Street	AZ	16
Gresham Road	AZ	18
Hartington Road	AY	19
Longford Street	AZ	22
Ormesby Road	BZ	24
Princes Road	AZ	26
St. Barnabas Road	AZ	27
Saltersgill Avenue	BZ	28
Sussex Street	AY	30
Tees Bridge Approach Road	AZ	34
West Terrace	BZ	35
Westbourne Grove	BZ	36
Wilson Street	AY	38
Woodlands Road	BZ	39
Zetland Street	ABY	41

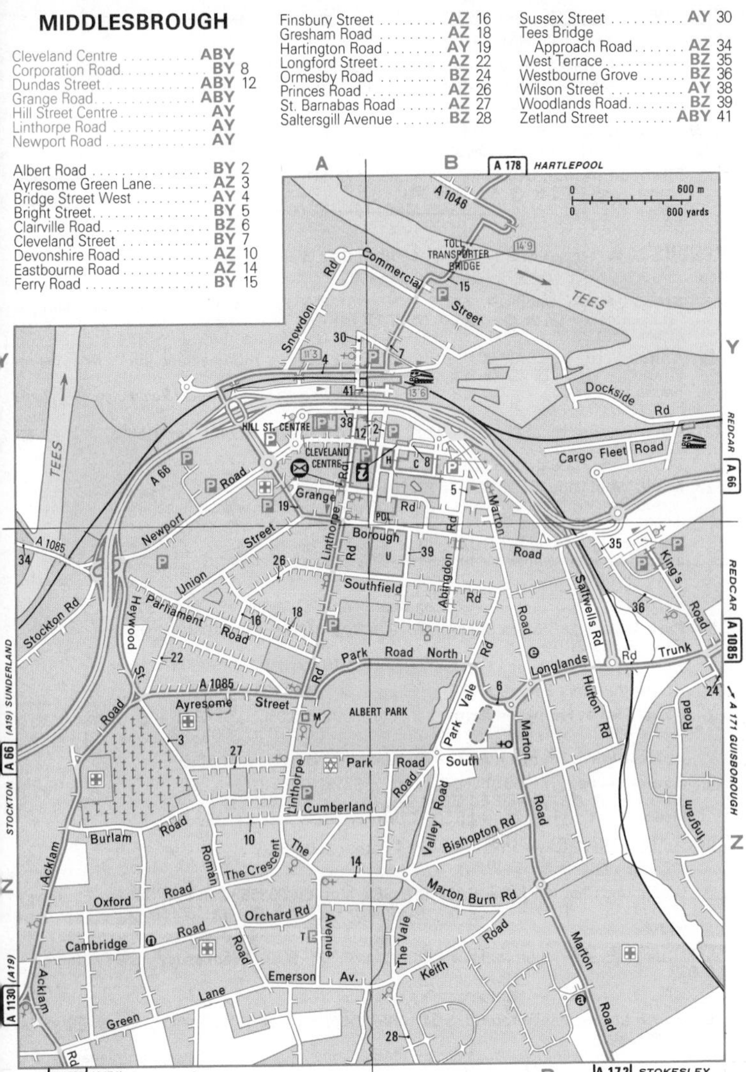

Great Britain and *Ireland* is now covered by an *Atlas* at a scale of 1 inch to 4.75 miles.

Three easy to use versions: Paperback, Spiralbound and Hardback.

MIDDLETON N.Yorks. - see Pickering.

MIDDLETON-IN-TEESDALE Durham 401 402 N 20 – pop. 1 477 – ☎ 01833.

Middleton Crafts, Courtyard of Teesdale Hotel, DL12 0QG ☎ 40400.

♦London 232 – ♦Carlisle 56 – ♦Leeds 78 – ♦Middlesbrough 35 – ♦Newcastle upon Tyne 49.

Teesdale, Market Sq., DL12 0QG, ☎ 640264, Fax 640651 – TV ☎ P. VISA
Meals (bar lunch Monday to Saturday)/dinner 17.95 **t.** and a la carte 4.50 – **12 rm** 38.50/95.00 **t.** – SB.

MIDDLETON STONEY Oxon. 403 404 Q 28 – pop. 304 – ECD : Saturday – ☎ 01869.

♦London 66 – Northampton 30 – ♦Oxford 12.

Jersey Arms, OX6 8SE, ✆ 343234, Fax 343565, – TV ☎ P. VISA.
Meals *(closed Sunday dinner)* a la carte 18.50/26.85 **t.** 4.95 – **13 rm** 59.50/72.00 **st.**, 3 suites.

MIDDLE WALLOP Hants. 403 404 P 30 – ✉ Stockbridge – ☎ 01264.

♦London 80 – Salisbury 11 – ♦Southampton 21.

Fifehead Manor, SO20 8EG, on A 343 ✆ 781565, Fax 781400, « Converted 16C manor house », – TV ☎ P. VISA
closed 23 December to 3 January – **Meals** 18.50/28.00 t. 5.00 – **16 rm** 50.00/110.00 **t.** – SB.

MIDHURST W. Sussex 404 R 31 – pop. 4 916 – ECD : Wednesday – ☎ 01730.

♦London 57 – ♦Brighton 38 – Chichester 12 – ♦Southampton 41.

Spread Eagle, South St., GU29 9NH, ✆ 816911, Fax 815668, « 15C hostelry, antique furnishings » – TV ☎ P – 50. VISA
Meals 16.50/32.00 **t.** 5.00 – 3.75 – **40 rm** 62.00/145.00 **t.**, 1 suite – SB.

Angel, North St., GU29 9DN, ✆ 812421, Fax 815928, « 16C coaching inn », – rm TV ☎ P – 60. VISA.
Brasserie :* Meals** 11.50/16.50**t.** and a la carte 4.75 (see also ***Cowdray Room below) – **17 rm** 55.00/130.00 **t.** – SB.

XXX **Cowdray Room** (at Angel H.), North St., GU29 9DN, ✆ 812421, Fax 815928, – P. VISA
Meals 15.95/21.00 **t.** and a la carte 4.75.

X **Mida,** Wool Lane, GU29 9BY, ✆ 813284
closed Sunday, Monday, 1 week May and 1 week October – **Meals** (lunch by arrangement)/dinner a la carte 19.00/33.00 **t.**

X **Maxine's,** Red Lion St., GU29 9PB, ✆ 816271 – . VISA
closed Sunday dinner, Monday, Tuesday and first week January – **Meals** 12.95 **st.** and a la carte.

at Bepton SW : 2½ m. by A 286 on Bepton rd – ✉ Midhurst – ☎ 01730 :

Park House, South Bepton, GU29 0JB, ✆ 812880, Fax 815643, heated, , – TV ☎ P. VISA
Meals (by arrangement) 10.50/17.50 **t.** 5.45 – **10 rm** 52.00/90.00 **t.**, 1 suite.

at Stedham W : 2 m. by A 272 – ✉ Midhurst – ☎ 01730 :

X **Nava Thai at Hamilton Arms,** School Lane, GU29 0NZ, ✆ 812555 – P. VISA
closed Monday except Bank Holidays – **Meals** - Thai 15.00/20.00 **t.** and a la carte 4.50.

at Trotton W : 3¼ m. on A 272 – ✉ Petersfield (Hants.) – ☎ 01730 :

Southdowns, GU31 5JN, S : 1 m. ✆ 821521, Fax 821790, , , , – rm rest TV ☎ P – 100. VISA.
Meals 19.50 **t.** and a la carte 5.50 – **22 rm** 59.00/99.00 **t.** – SB.

MIDSOMER NORTON Avon 403 M 30 – ✉ Bath – ☎ 01761.

♦London 129 – Bath 10 – ♦Bristol 15 – Wells 8.

Centurion, Charlton Lane, BA3 4BD, SE : 1 m. by B3355, Charlton Rd and Fosseway ✆ 417711, Fax 418357, ≤, , 9, , squash – TV ☎ P – 180.
44 rm.

MILFORD-ON-SEA Hants. 403 404 P 31 – pop. 3 953 – ECD : Wednesday – ✉ Lymington – ☎ 01590.

♦London 109 – Bournemouth 15 – ♦Southampton 24 – Winchester 37.

South Lawn, Lymington Rd, SO41 0RF, ✆ 643911, Fax 644820, – rest TV ☎ P. VISA.
closed mid December-mid January – **Meals** (dinner only and Sunday lunch)/dinner 20.00 **t.** 6.25 – **24 rm** 47.50/84.00 **t.** – SB.

Westover Hall, Park Lane, SO41 0PT, ✆ 643044, Fax 644490, ≤ – TV ☎ P. VISA
Meals 12.50/17.00 **st.** 6.90 – **13 rm** 40.00/100.00 **st.** – SB.

XX **Rocher's,** 69-71 High St., SO41 0QG, ✆ 642340 – VISA
closed Monday, Tuesday and 2 weeks June – Meals - French (dinner only and Sunday lunch) 22.90 **t.**

MILTON DAMEREL Devon 403 H 31 – pop. 451 – ☎ 01409.

♦London 249 – Barnstaple 21.

Woodford Bridge, EX22 7LL, N : 1 m. on A 388 ✆ 261481, Fax 261585, , , , , , squash – TV ☎ P
10 rm.

MILTON KEYNES Bucks. 404 R 27 – pop. 93 305 – ☎ 01908.

Abbey Hill, Monks Way, Two Mile Ash ☎ 563845 – Windmill Hill, Tattenhoe Lane, Bletchley ☎ 378623 – Wavendon Golf Centre, Lower End Rd, Wavendon ☎ 281811.

411 Secklow Gate East, NK9 3PB ☎ 232525/231742.

London 56 – Birmingham 72 – Bedford 16 – Northampton 18 – Oxford 37.

Forte Crest, 500 Saxon Gate West, Milton Keynes Central, MK9 2HQ, ☎ 667722, Fax 674714, – rm – 150
149 rm, 2 suites.

Hilton National Milton Keynes, Timbold Drive, Kents Hill, MK7 6HL, SE : 4 m. by A 4146 and A 421 off Brickhill St. (V10) ☎ 694433, Fax 695533, « Contemporary interior », – rm rest – 300
148 rm, 1 suite.

Shenley Church Inn (Toby), Burchard Cres., Shenley Church End, MK5 6HQ, SW : 2 m. by A 509 and Portway (H5) off Watling St. (V4) ☎ 505467, Fax 502308 – rm – 100. AE VISA.
Meals (grill rest.) 7.95 and a la carte – **50 rm** 65.00/75.00 **st.**

Peartree Bridge Inn (Toby), Milton Keynes Marina, Waterside, Peartree Bridge, MK6 3PE, SE : 1 3/4 m. by A 509 off A 4146 ☎ 691515, Fax 690274, « Marina setting beside the Grand Union Canal » – rm
39 rm.

Friendly, Monks Way, Two Mile Ash, MK8 8LY, NW : 2 m. by A 509 and A 5 at junction with A 422 ☎ 561666, Fax 568303, – rm – 120. AE VISA JCB.
Meals (carving rest.) (bar lunch Saturday)/dinner 13.50 **st.** 5.50 – 6.75 – **88 rm** 70.50/94.00 **st.** – SB.

Caldecotte Arms (Premier), Bletcham Way (H10), Caldecotte, MK7 8HP, SE : 5 1/2 m. by A 509 and A 5, taking 2nd junction left signposted Milton Keynes (South and East) ☎ 366188, Fax 366603, « Windmill feature, lakeside setting » – . AE VISA.
Meals (Millers Kitchen) – 3.45 – **40 rm** 39.50 **t.**

Broughton, Broughton Village, MK10 9AA, E : 4 m. by A 509 off A 5130 ☎ 667726, Fax 604844, –
30 rm.

Wayfarer, Willen Lake, MK15 9HQ, E : 2 m. by A 509 off Brickhill St. (V 10) ☎ 675222, Fax 674679, « Lakeside setting » – – 50
41 rm.

Travel Inn, Secklow Gate West, Central Milton Keynes, MK9 3BZ, ☎ 663388, Fax 607481 – rm – 50. AE VISA.
Meals (Beefeater grill) a la carte approx. 16.00 **t.** – 4.95 – **38 rm** 33.50 **t.**

Jaipur, Elder House, 502 Eldergate, Station Sq., MK9 1LR, ☎ 669796, Fax 694464 – .
AE VISA
Meals - Indian (buffet lunch Sunday) 20.00/30.00 **t.** and a la carte 7.95.

at Hanslope NW : 9 m. by A 5 and A 508 on Hanslope rd – ✉ Milton Keynes – ☎ 01908 :

Hatton Court, Bullington End, MK19 7BQ, SE : 1 1/2 m. on Wolverton rd ☎ 510044, Fax 510945, – rm – 50. AE VISA
Meals (bar lunch Saturday) 11.95/14.95 **t.** – 7.50 – **20 rm** 65.00/95.00 **t.** – SB.

ATS 38 Victoria Rd, Bletchley ☎ 640420

MILTON-UNDER-WYCHWOOD Oxon – pop. 1 631 – ☎ 01993.

London 83 – Birmingham 52 – Gloucester 35 – Oxford 27.

Hillborough, The Green, OX7 6JH, ☎ 830501, Fax 832005 – . AE VISA
Meals 14.50/21.00 **st.** and a la carte 5.40 – **10 rm** 40.00/58.00 **t.** – SB.

MINCHINHAMPTON Glos. 403 404 N 28 – ☎ 01453.

London 115 – Bristol 26 – Gloucester 11 – Oxford 51.

Hunters Lodge without rest., Dr Brown's Rd, GL6 9BT, ☎ 883588, Fax 731449, « Cotswold stone house on Minchinhampton common », – .
closed 3 days at Christmas – **3 rm** 25.00/40.00.

Markey's Tea & Supper Room, The Old Ram, Market Sq., GL6 9BW, ☎ 882287 – .
VISA
closed Monday and dinner Tuesday and Sunday, two weeks June-July and one week New Year – **Meals** 8.75 **t.** (lunch) and dinner a la carte **t.** 3.75.

MINEHEAD Somerset 403 J 30 **The West Country G.** – pop. 6 543 – ECD : Wednesday – ☏ 01643.

See : Town★ - Higher Town (Church Steps★, St. Michael's★) – West Somerset Railway★ *AC*.

Envir. : Dunster★★ - Castle★★ *AC* (upper rooms ≤★) Water Mill★ *AC*, St. George's Church★, Dovecote★, SE : 2½ m. by A 39 – Selworthy★ (Church★, ≤★★) W : 4½ m. by A 39.

Exc. : Exmoor National Park★★ – Cleeve Abbey★★ *AC*, SE : 6½ m. by A 39.

The Warren, Warren Rd ☎ 702057.

17 Friday St., TA24 5UB ☎ 702624.

London 187 – Bristol 64 – Exeter 43 – Taunton 25.

Northfield, Northfield Rd, TA24 5PU, ☎ 705155, Fax 707715, ≤ bay, « Gardens », Lö, – TV ☎ P – 60. AE VISA
Meals 16.95 **t.** (dinner) and lunch a la carte – **24 rm** 43.00/94.00 – SB.

Benares, Northfield Rd, TA24 5PT, ☎ 704911, Fax 706373, ≤, « Gardens » – rest TV ☎ P. AE VISA
26 March-October – **Meals** (bar lunch)/dinner 16.50 **t.** – **19 rm** 43.50/81.00 **t.** – SB.

Beacon Country House, Beacon Rd, TA24 5SD, ☎ 703476, ≤, , , park – TV ☎ P. VISA
Meals a la carte 21.70/23.75 **st.** 7.00 – **8 rm** 50.00/80.00 **t.** – SB.

Channel House, Church Path, TA24 5QG, off Northfield Rd ☎ 703229, ≤, – TV ☎ P. VISA
closed December-February except Christmas – **Meals** (dinner only) 16.00 **st.** and a la carte 4.80 – **8 rm** 73.50/109.00 **st.** – SB.

Wyndcott, Martlet Rd, TA24 5QE, ☎ 704522, ≤, – TV ☎ P. VISA
Meals (lunch by arrangement)/dinner 14.95 **st.** 3.95 – **11 rm** 27.95/55.95 **st.** – SB.

Beaconwood, Church Rd, North Hill, TA24 5SB, ☎ 702032, ≤ sea and Minehead, heated, , – rest TV ☎ P. VISA
March-October – **Meals** (bar lunch)/dinner 13.95 **st.** 3.00 – **14 rm** 34.00/52.00.

Remuera, Northfield Rd, TA24 5QH, ☎ 702611, – rest TV P. VISA
March-October – **Meals** (dinner only) 17.00 5.00 – **7 rm** 29.00/46.00.

York House Inn, 48 The Avenue, TA24 5AN, ☎ 705151, Fax 707899 – TV ☎ P. AE VISA.
Meals 10.00 **st.** – **15 rm** 23.00/50.00 **st.** – SB.

at Middlecombe W : 1½ m. by A 39 – ✉ Minehead – ☏ 01643 :

Periton Park, TA24 8SW, ☎ 706885, Fax 706885, ≤, – rest TV ☎ P. AE VISA
Meals (dinner only) 20.00 **st.** – **8 rm** 65.00/90.00 **st.**

ATS Bampton St. ☎ 704808/9

MINSTER Kent 404 Y 29 – see Ramsgate.

MINSTER LOVELL Oxon. 403 404 P 28 – pop. 1 613 – ✉ Witney – ☏ 01993.

London 72 – Gloucester 36 – Oxford 16.

Old Swan, Main St., Old Minster, OX8 5RN, ☎ 774441, Fax 702002, « 14C inn », , , park, – TV ☎ P. AE VISA
Meals a la carte 17.20/22.95 **st.** – **16 rm** 60.00/75.00 **st.**

XX **Lovells at Windrush Farm** with rm., Windrush Farm, Old Minster Lovell, OX8 5RN, ☎ 779802, Fax 779802, – rest P. AE VISA JCB
closed January – **Meals** *(closed lunch Saturday and Sunday and Monday)* (booking essential) 13.50/27.50 **t.** 9.00 – **2 rm** (dinner included) 90.00/145.00 **t.**

MISTERTON Somerset 403 L 31 – see Crewkerne.

MOBBERLEY Ches. 402 403 404 N 24 – see Knutsford.

MONK FRYSTON N. Yorks. 402 Q 22 – pop. 737 – ✉ Lumby – ☏ 01977.

London 190 – Kingston-upon-Hull 42 – Leeds 13 – York 20.

Monk Fryston Hall, LS25 5DU, ☎ 682369, Fax 683544, « Italian garden », park – rest TV ☎ P – 50. AE VISA
Meals 14.50/24.00 **t.** and a la carte 5.80 – **28 rm** 64.00/99.00 **st.** – SB.

MONKTON COMBE Avon – see Bath.

MONKTON FARLEIGH Wilts. 403 404 N 29 – see Bradford-on-Avon.

MONTACUTE Somerset 403 L 31 – see Yeovil.

MORCHARD BISHOP Devon 403 I 31 – pop. 978 – ✉ Crediton – ☏ 01363.

London 217 – Barnstaple 28 – Exeter 17 – Taunton 40.

Wigham, EX17 6RJ, NE : 1 m. by Eastington rd turning right at post box after ½ m. ☎ 877350, ≤, « 16C longhouse, working farm », heated – TV P.
5 rm.

MORCOTT SERVICE AREA Leics. – see Uppingham.

MORECAMBE Lancs. 402 L 21 – pop. 41 432 – ECD : Wednesday – 01524.
Bare 418050 – Heysham, Trumacar Park, Middleton Rd 851011.
Station Buildings, Central Promenade, LA4 4DB 582808.
London 248 – Blackpool 29 – Carlisle 66 – Lancaster 4.

Strathmore, Marine Rd, East Promenade, LA4 5AP, 421234, Fax 414242, ≤ – TV – 180. AE VISA.
Meals 9.95/19.95 **st.** and a la carte 5.00 – **51 rm** 59.00/88.00 **st.** – SB.

Prospect, 363 Marine Rd, East Promenade, LA4 5AQ, 417819, ≤ – TV. AE VISA
Easter to November – **Meals** (by arrangement) 6.00 **st.** – **14rm** 17.00/34.00 **st.** – SB.

ATS Westgate 68075/62011

MORETON Mersey. – 0151.
London 225 – Birkenhead 4 – Liverpool 5.

Lee Ho, 308 Hoylake Rd, L46 6DE, W : 1/4 m. on A 553 677 6440 – . AE VISA
closed Sunday, 31 July-20 August and Bank Holidays – **Meals** - Chinese (dinner only) 24.00 **t.** and a la carte.

MORETONHAMPSTEAD Devon 403 I 32 **The West Country G.** – pop. 1 380 – ECD : Thursday – Newton Abbot – 01647.
Envir. : Dartmoor National Park★★ (Brent Tor ≤★★, Haytor Rocks ≤★).
Manor House Hotel 40355.
London 213 – Exeter 13 – Plymouth 28.

Wray Barton Manor without rest., TQ13 8SE, SE : 1 1/2 m. on A 382 40467, Fax 40628, – TV
April-October – **5 rm** 17.00/46.00 **st.**

Moorcote without rest., TQ13 8LS, NW : 1/4 m. on A 382 40966, – TV .
April-October – **6 rm** 26.00/36.00 **st.**

Reverend Woodforde, 11a Cross St., TQ13 8NL, 40691
closed January-Easter – **Meals** *(closed Sunday)* (dinner only) a la carte 17.00/22.50 **t.** 4.50.

MORETON-IN-MARSH Glos. 403 404 O 28 **Great Britain G.** – pop. 2 802 – ECD : Wednesday – 01608.
Envir. : Chastleton House★★, SE : 5 m. by A 44.
London 86 – Birmingham 40 – Gloucester 31 – Oxford 29.

Manor House, High St., GL56 0LJ, 650501, Fax 651481, « 16C manor house, gardens », , – rest TV – 75. AE VISA.
Meals 8.50/18.50 **t.** and a la carte – **38 rm** 55.00/95.00 **t.**, 1 suite.

Redesdale Arms, High St., GL56 0AW, 650308, Fax 651843 – TV – 70. AE VISA.
Meals (bar lunch Monday to Saturday)/dinner 16.95 **t.** and a la carte – 3.45 – **15 rm** 29.50 **st.**, 2 suites.

Treetops, London Rd, GL56 0HE, 651036, – TV . VISA
Meals (by arrangement) 10.00 – **6 rm** 30.00/40.00.

Townend Cottage and Coach House, High St., GL56 0AD, 650846, – rm TV.
closed February and 24 to 26 December – **Meals** (by arrangement) 15.00 3.50 – **4 rm** 36.00/39.50.

Marsh Goose, High St., GL56 0AX, 652111 – . AE VISA
closed Sunday dinner and Monday – **Meals** 13.50/31.00 **t.** and lunch a la carte 4.25.

Annies, 3 Oxford St., GL56 0LA, 651981 – AE VISA
closed Sunday dinner and 18 January-10 February – **Meals** (dinner only and Sunday lunch)/dinner 20.00 **st.** and a la carte 4.75.

MORPETH Northd. 401 402 O 18 – pop. 14 394 – ECD : Thursday – 01670.
The Common 519980 – The Chantry, Bridge St., NE61 1PJ 511323.
London 301 – Edinburgh 93 – Newcastle upon Tyne 15.

Linden Hall , Longhorsley, NE65 8XF, NW : 7 1/2 m. by A 192 on A 697 516611, Fax 788544, ≤, « Country house in extensive grounds », , , , , park, – rest TV – 300. AE VISA
Meals 16.50/35.00 **st.** and a la carte – **49 rm** 97.50/125.00 **st.**, 1 suite – SB.

ATS Coopies Lane Ind. Est. 514627

MORSTON Norfolk – see Blakeney.

MORTEHOE Devon 403 H 30 – see Woolacombe.

For the quickest route use the Michelin Main Road Maps:
970 Europe, 980 Greece, 984 Germany, 985 Scandinavia-Finland,
986 Great Britain and Ireland, 987 Germany-Austria-Benelux, 988 Italy,
989 France, 990 Spain-Portugal and 991 Yugoslavia.

MORWENSTOW Cornwall 403 G 31 The West Country G. – pop. 696 – ✉ Bude – ☎ 01288.
See : Morwenstow (Church★, cliffs★★).
Envir. : E : Tamar River★★.
♦London 259 – Exeter 58 – ♦Plymouth 51 – Truro 60.

Old Vicarage , EX23 9SR, ☎ 331369, ≤, – ⇔ P. ✻
closed December and January – **Meals** 15.00 – **3 rm** 19.00/38.00.

MOTCOMBE Dorset 403 404 N 30 – see Shaftesbury.

MOULSFORD Oxon. 403 404 Q 29 The West Country G. – pop. 491 – ☎ 01491.
Exc. : Ridgeway Path★★.
♦London 58 – ♦Oxford 17 – Reading 13 – Swindon 37.

XXX **Beetle and Wedge** with rm, Ferry Lane, OX10 9JF, ☎ 651381, Fax 651376, ≤, « Thames-side setting », – ⇔ TV ☎ P. AE VISA JCB. ✻
closed Christmas Day – **Meals** – **The Dining Room** *(closed Sunday dinner and Monday)* (booking essential) 17.50 **t.** (lunch) and a la carte 30.45/44.50 **t.** 5.50 – **10 rm** 85.00/140.00 **t.** – SB.

X **Boathouse : Meals** (booking essential) a la carte 19.75/29.50 **t.** 5.50.

MOULTON Northants. 404 R 27 – see Northampton.

MOULTON N. Yorks. 402 P 20 – pop. 151 – ✉ Richmond – ☎ 01325.
♦London 243 – ♦Leeds 53 – ♦Middlesbrough 25 – ♦Newcastle upon Tyne 43.

XX **Black Bull Inn,** DL10 6QJ, ☎ 377289, Fax 377422, « Brighton Belle Pullman coach » – P. AE VISA
closed Sunday dinner and 24 to 26 December – **Meals** 13.75 **t.** (lunch) and a la carte 17.00/26.25 **t.**

MOUSEHOLE Cornwall 403 D 33 The West Country G. – ECD : Wednesday except summer – ✉ Penzance – ☎ 01736.
See : Village★.
Envir. : Penwith★★ – Lamorna (The Merry Maidens and The Pipers Standing Stone★) SW : 3 m. by B 3315.
Exc. : Land's End★ (cliff scenery★★★) W : 9 m. by B 3315.
♦London 321 – Penzance 3 – Truro 29.

Lobster Pot, TR19 6QX, ☎ 731251, Fax 731140, ≤ – ⇔ rest TV ☎. VISA. ✻
closed 3 January to 2 February – **Meals** (bar lunch Monday to Saturday)/dinner 15.25 **t.** and a la carte 6.25 – **25 rm** 27.00/99.00 **t.** – SB.

Carn Du , Raginnis Hill, TR19 6SS, ☎ 731233, ≤ Mounts Bay, – ⇔ rest TV P. AE VISA. ✻
Meals (bar lunch)/dinner 14.95 st. 4.25 – **7 rm** 25.00/60.00 **st.**

MUCH BIRCH Heref. and Worcs. – see Hereford.

MUCH WENLOCK Shrops. 402 403 M26 Great Britain G. – pop. 3 232 – ☎ 01952.
See : Priory★ *AC*.
Envir. : Ironbridge Gorge Museum★★ *AC* (The Iron Bridge★★ – Coalport China Museum★★ - Blists Hill Open Air Museum★★ – Museum of the River and Visitor Centre★) NE : 4½ m. by A 4169 and B 4380.
ℹ The Museum, High St., TF13 6HR ☎ 727679 (summer only).
♦London 154 – ♦Birmingham 34 – Shrewsbury 12 – Worcester 37.

Bourton Manor , Bourton, TF13 6QE, SW : 2 ¾ m. on B 4378 ☎ (01746) 36531, Fax 36683, ≤, – TV ☎ P – 40. AE VISA JCB
Meals (bar lunch)/dinner a la carte 15.00/18.00 **st.** 4.75 – **8 rm** 44.00/110.00 **st.** – SB.

Wheatland Fox, High St., TF13 6AD, ☎ 727292 – TV ☎ P. AE VISA
Meals *(closed dinner Sunday and Monday to non residents)* a la carte 10.00/15.25 **st.** 4.85 – **5 rm** 37.50/60.00 **st.** – SB.

Brockton Grange without rest., Brockton, TF13 6JR, SW : 5 ½ m. by B 4378 on Easthope rd ☎ (01746) 36443, Fax 36443, , , park – ⇔ TV P. ✻
March-October – **3 rm** 35.00/48.00 **st.**

Old Barn without rest., 45 Sheinton St., TF13 6HR, ☎ 728191, – ⇔ TV P. ✻
closed December – **4 rm** 28.00/38.00.

MUDEFORD Dorset 403 404 O 31 – see Christchurch.

MULLION Cornwall 403 E 33 **The West Country G.** – pop. 2 646 – ECD : Wednesday – ✉ Helston – ☎ 01326.

See : Mullion Cove★★★ (Church★) – Lizard Peninsula★.

Envir. : Kynance Cove★★★, S : 5 m.

Exc. : Helston (Flora Day Furry Dance★★) (May) N : 7½ m. by A 3083 – Culdrose (Flambards Village Theme Park★) *AC*, N : 6 m. by A 3083 – Wendron (Poldark Mine★) N : 9½ m. by A 3083 and B 3297.

18 Cury, Helston ☎ 240276.

◆London 323 – Falmouth 21 – Penzance 21 – Truro 26.

- **Polurrian**, TR12 7EN, SW : ½ m. ☎ 240421, Fax 240083, ← Mounts Bay, Fб, ≘s, ⛱ heated, ⛱, 🌳, ⚔, squash – TV ☎ P. AE VISA
  closed January and February – **Meals** (bar lunch Monday to Saturday) 21.00 **st.** and a la carte 🍷 5.20 – **38 rm** ⊏ (dinner included) 76.00/172.00 **st.**, 1 suite – SB.

MUNGRISDALE Cumbria 401 402 L 19 20 – pop. 330 – ✉ Penrith – ☎ 0176 87.

◆London 301 – ◆Carlisle 33 – Keswick 8.5 – Penrith 13.

- **Mill** 🐦, CA11 0XR, ☎ 79659, 🌳 – ⊁ rest TV P
  March-October – **Meals** (dinner only) 21.00 **t.** 🍷 3.95 – **9 rm** ⊏ 28.00/65.00 **t.** – SB.
- **Mosedale House** 🐦, Mosedale, CA11 0XQ, N : 1 m. by Mosedale rd ☎ 79371 – ⊁ TV ♿ P
  Meals 11.50 – **6 rm** ⊏ 19.50/52.00 **st.**

NAILSWORTH Glos. 403 404 N 28 – pop. 5 114 – ☎ 01453.

◆London 120 – ◆Bristol 30 – Swindon 41.

- **Egypt Mill**, GL6 0EA, ☎ 833449, Fax 836098, 🌳 – TV ☎ P – 🏛 100. AE VISA. ⚔
  Meals 8.80/14.00 **st.** and a la carte 🍷 4.50 – **14 rm** ⊏ 37.50/65.00 **st.** – SB.
- **Aaron Farm**, Nympsfield Rd, GL6 0ET, W : ¾ m. by Spring Hill ☎ 833598, Fax 836737 – ⊁ rm TV P
  Meals 8.00/20.00 **s.** – **3 rm** ⊏ 20.00/34.00 **st.**
- **Apple Orchard House**, Orchard Close, Springhill, GL6 0LX, ☎ 832503, Fax 836213, 🌳 – TV P. AE VISA
  Meals 11.00 – **3 rm** ⊏ 20.00/40.00 **st.**
- **William's Bistro**, 3 Fountain St., GL6 0BL, ☎ 835507, Fax 835950 – VISA
  closed Sunday, Monday, Christmas to New Year and Bank Holiday Tuesdays – **Meals** - Seafood (dinner only) a la carte 17.00/24.00 **st.** 🍷 3.50.
- **Waterman's Stone Cottage**, Old Market, GL6 0BX, ☎ 832808 – AE VISA
  closed Sunday and Monday – **Meals** (dinner only) a la carte 17.00/24.00 **t.** 🍷 4.50.

NANTWICH Ches. 402 403 404 M 24 – pop. 11 695 – ECD : Wednesday – ☎ 01270.

🅸 Church House, Church Street, CW5 5RG ☎ 610983/610880.

◆London 176 – Chester 20 – ◆Liverpool 45 – ◆Stoke-on-Trent 17.

- **Rookery Hall** 🐦, Worleston, CW5 6DQ, N : 2 ½ m. by A 51 on B 5074 ☎ 610016, Fax 626027, ←, « Part 18C country house », 🐟, 🌳, park, ⚔ – 🛗 ⊁ TV ☎ ♿ P – 🏛 100. AE VISA. ⚔
  Meals (booking essential) 16.50/25.00 **st.** and a la carte – **42 rm** ⊏ 95.00/190.00 **st.**, 3 suites – SB.
- Peacock (Premier), 221 Crewe Rd, CW5 6NE, E : 1 m. on A 534 ☎ 624069, Fax 610113 – ⊁ TV ☎ ♿ P
  Meals (grill rest.) – **37 rm.**
- **Oakland House** without rest., 252 Newcastle Rd, Blakelow, Shavington, CW5 7ET, E : 2½ m. by A 51 on A 500 ☎ 67134, 🌳 – ⊁ TV P. ⚔
  5 rm ⊏ 20.00/32.00 **s.**
- **Churche's Mansion**, Hospital St., CW5 0RY, E : ¼ m. ☎ 625933, Fax 74256, « Timbered Elizabethan house », 🌳 – P. VISA
  closed Sunday dinner, Monday and 1 week January – **Meals** 15.50/24.00 **t.**

at Burland W : 2½ m. on A 534 – ✉ Nantwich – ☎ 01270 74 :

- **Burland Farm** without rest., Wrexham Rd, CW5 8ND, W : ¾ m. on A 534 ☎ 210, Fax 412, « Working farm », 🌳 – TV P
  closed December and January – **3 rm** ⊏ 25.00/40.00.

NATIONAL EXHIBITION CENTRE W. Mids. 403 404 O 26 – see Birmingham.

NAWTON N. Yorks. – see Helmsley.

NAYLAND Essex 404 W 28 – see Colchester.

NEAR SAWREY Cumbria 402 L 20 – see Hawkshead.

NEEDHAM MARKET Suffolk 404 X 27 – pop. 4 377 – ECD : Tuesday – ☎ 01449.

♦London 77 – ♦Cambridge 47 – ♦Ipswich 8.5 – ♦Norwich 38.

Forte Travelodge without rest., Norwich Rd., IP6 8LP, Beacon Hill Service Area, at junction of A 14 with A 140 ✆ 721640, Reservations (Freephone) 0800 850950 – TV ♿ P. VISA.
40 rm 33.50 **t.**

Pipps Ford, Norwich Rd roundabout, IP6 8LJ, SE : 1 ¾ m. by B 1078 at junction of A 14 with A 140 ✆ 760208, Fax 760561, « Elizabethan farmhouse », – P.
closed mid December-mid January – **Meals** (by arrangement) 18.50 **t.** – **6 rm** 17.00/65.00 **st.** – SB.

NETHERTON Mersey. – see Liverpool.

NETHER WESTCOTE Oxon. – see Stow-on-the-Wold.

NETTLEBED Oxon. 404 R 29 – ✉ Henley-on-Thames – ☎ 01491.

♦London 44 – ♦Oxford 19 – Reading 9.

White Hart, High St., RG9 5DD, ✆ 641245, Fax 641423, « Part 15C inn », – TV ☎ P – 40. VISA.
Meals a la carte 9.95/18.95 st. – **6 rm** 49.50/79.50 **st.** – SB.

NETTLETON SHRUB Wilts. 403 404 N 29 – see Castle Combe.

NEW ALRESFORD Hants. 403 404 Q 30 – pop. 5 041 – ✉ Alresford – ☎ 01962.

♦London 63 – ♦Portsmouth 40 – Reading 33 – ♦Southampton 20.

Hunters with rm, 32 Broad St., SO24 9AQ, ✆ 732468, Fax 732468, « Former coaching inn », – TV – 60. VISA.
closed 24 to 30 December – **Meals** *(closed Sunday dinner)* 9.95/13.95 **t.** and dinner a la carte 4.50 – **3 rm** 37.50/47.50 **st.**

NEWARK-ON-TRENT Notts. 402 404 R 24 **Great Britain G.** – pop. 24 749 – ECD : Thursday – ☎ 01636.

See : St. Mary Magdalene★.

Kelwick Coddington ✆ 626241.

The Gilstrap Centre, Castlegate, NG24 1BG ✆ 78962.

♦London 127 – Lincoln 16 – ♦Nottingham 20 – ♦Sheffield 42.

Grange, 73 London Rd, NG24 1RZ, S : ½ m. on Grantham (A1) rd ✆ 703399, Fax 702328, – TV ☎ P. VISA.
closed Christmas and New Year – **Meals** (lunch by arrangement)/dinner 12.95 **t.** and a la carte – **15 rm** 45.00/65.00 **t.** – SB.

at North Muskham N : 4 ½ m. by A 46 and A 1 – ✉ Newark-on-Trent – ☎ 01636.

Forte Travelodge without rest., NG23 6HT, N : ½ m. on A1 (southbound carriageway) ✆ 703635, Reservations (Freephone) 0800 850950 – TV ♿ P. VISA.
30 rm 33.50 **t.**

ATS 70 William St. ✆ 77531

NEWBURY Berks. 403 404 Q 29 **The West Country G.** – pop. 31 488 – ECD : Wednesday – ☎ 01635.

Exc. : Littlecote★★ (arms and armour★, Roman mosaic floor★) *AC*, W : 10 m. by A 4.

Newbury and Crookham, Bury's Bank Road ✆ 40035 – Donnington Valley, Old Oxford Rd ✆ 32488.

The Wharf, RG14 5AS ✆ 30267.

♦London 67 – ♦Bristol 66 – ♦Oxford 28 – Reading 17 – ♦Southampton 38.

Donnington Valley H. & Golf Course, Old Oxford Rd, Donnington, RG16 9AG, N : 1 ¾ m. by A 4 on B 4494 ✆ 551199, Fax 551123, park – rm rest TV ☎ ♿ P – 140. VISA
Gallery : **Meals** 12.50/14.50 **st.** and a la carte 6.50 – 8.50 – **58 rm** 87.50/127.50 **st.** – SB.

Foley Lodge, Stockcross, RG16 8JU, NW : 2 m. by A 4 on B 4000 ✆ 528770, Fax 528398, – rm TV ☎ P – 220. VISA.
Meals a la carte 15.50/21.70 **t.** – **69 rm** 95.00/140.00 **t.**, 1 suite – SB.

Jarvis Elcot Park, RG16 8NJ, W : 5 m. by A 4 ✆ (01488) 658100, Fax 658288, park, – rm rest TV ☎ ♿ P – 110. VISA
Meals 9.95/15.00 **t.** and dinner a la carte 4.50 – **75 rm** 93.25/126.50 **t.** – SB.

Hilton National, Pinchington Lane, RG14 7HL, S : 2 m. by A 34 ✆ 529000, Fax 529337, – rm rest TV ☎ ♿ P – 190. VISA
Meals (bar lunch Saturday) 13.50/16.50 **st.** and a la carte 6.25 – 10.25 – **109 rm** 85.00/150.00 **st.** – SB.

Stakis Newbury, Oxford Rd, RG16 8XY, N : 3 ¼ m. on A 34 ✆ 247010, Fax 247077, – rm rest TV ☎ ♿ P – 30. VISA
Meals *(closed lunch Saturday and Bank Holidays)* 9.75/15.95 **st.** and dinner a la carte 6.50 – 8.50 – **110 rm** 81.00/91.00 **t.**, 2 suites – SB.

Chequers (Forte), 7-8 Oxford St., RG13 1JB, ℘ 38000, Fax 37170, – 80.
Meals (bar lunch Monday to Saturday)/dinner 16.95 **t.** and a la carte 6.70 – 8.50 – **56 rm** 65.00/85.00 **st.** – SB.

Blue Boar Inn, North Heath, RG16 8UE, N : 4¾ m. on B 4494 ℘ 248236, Fax 248506 –
Meals (in bar Sunday) a la carte 12.00/22.45 **t.** – **15 rm** 42.00/47.00 **t.** – SB.

Starwood without rest., 1 Rectory Close, off Pound St., RG14 6DF, SW : ¼ m. by Enborne rd ℘ 49125 –
4 rm 19.00/38.00 **st.**

at Woolton Hill SW : 4½ m. by A 34 off A 343 – ✉ Newbury – 01635 :

Hollington House, RG15 9XR, SW : ½ m. on East End rd ℘ 255100, Fax 255075, ≤, « Edwardian country house, gardens », heated, park, – rm – 45.
Meals 16.75/28.50 **t.** and dinner a la carte 12.50 – **19 rm** 85.00/275.00 **t.**, 1 suite.

at Hamstead Marshall SW : 5½ m. by A 4 – ✉ Newbury – 01488 :

White Hart Inn, Kintbury Rd, RG15 0HW, ℘ 58201, –
Meals - Italian (closed Sunday and 25 to 26 December) a la carte 12.75/28.50 **st.** – **6 rm** 40.00/60.00 **t.**

at Speen W : 1¾ m. on A 4 – ✉ Newbury – 01635 :

Hare & Hounds, Bath Rd, RG13 1QY, ℘ 521152, Fax 47708 –
Meals 5.95/16.00 **st.** and dinner a la carte 4.95 – **29 rm** 52.00/60.00 **st.**, 1 suite – SB.

ATS 30 Queens Rd ℘ 42250

NEWBY BRIDGE Cumbria 402 L 21 **Great Britain G.** – ECD : Saturday – ✉ Ulverston – 0153 95.

Envir. : Lake Windermere★★.

♦London 270 – Kendal 16 – Lancaster 27.

Lakeside H. on Lake Windermere, Lakeside, LA12 8AT, NE : 1 m. on Hawkshead rd ℘ 31207, Telex 65149, Fax 31699, ≤, « Lakeside setting », – 100.
closed first two weeks January – **Meals** (bar lunch Monday to Saturday)/dinner 22.50 **st.** 5.00 – **67 rm** 60.00/120.00 **st.**, 2 suites – SB.

Whitewater, The Lakeland Village, LA12 8PX, SW : 1½ m. by A 590 ℘ 31133, Fax 31881, squash – 70.
Meals (bar lunch Monday to Saturday)/dinner a la carte 14.40/23.40 **st.** – **35 rm** 60.00/97.00 **st.** – SB.

Swan, LA12 8NB, ℘ 31681, Fax 31917, ≤, – rest – 65.
Meals (bar lunch Monday to Saturday)/dinner 21.00 **t.** and a la carte 4.95 – **35 rm** 59.00/120.00 **t.**, 1 suite – SB.

at Cartmell Fell NE : 3¼ m. by A 590 off A 592 – ✉ Grange-over-Sands – 0153 95 :

Lightwood Farmhouse, LA11 6NP, ℘ 31454, ≤, –
February-November – **Meals** (by arrangement) 13.00 4.00 – **8 rm** 25.00/43.00 **st.**

at Bowland Bridge NE : 4¼ m. by A 590 off A 592 – ✉ Grange-over-Sands – 0153 95 :

Hare and Hounds, LA11 6NN, ℘ 68333, –
Meals (residents only) (bar lunch)/dinner 11.00 **t.** 5.00 – **16 rm** 35.00/68.00 **t.** – SB.

NEWBY WISKE N. Yorks. – see Northallerton.

NEWCASTLE AIRPORT Tyne and Wear 401 402 O 19 – see Newcastle upon Tyne.

NEWCASTLE-UNDER-LYME Staffs. 402 403 404 N 24 **Great Britain G.** – pop. 119 091 – ECD : Thursday – 01782.

Exc. : Wedgwood Visitor's Centre★ *AC*, SE : 6½ m. by A 34 Z.

18 Newcastle Municipal, Keele Rd ℘ 627596.

Ironmarket, ST5 1AT ℘ 711964.

♦London 161 – ♦Birmingham 46 – ♦Liverpool 56 – ♦Manchester 43.

Plan of Built up Area : see Stoke-on-Trent

Forte Posthouse, Clayton Rd, Clayton, ST5 4DL, S : 2 m. on A 519 ℘ 717171, Fax 717138, – rm – 70.
Meals a la carte approx. 15.00 **t.** 5.50 – **119 rm** 56.00/69.50 **st.**

Clayton Lodge (Jarvis), Clayton Rd, Clayton, ST5 4AF, S : 1¼ m. on A 519 ℘ 613093, Fax 711896 – rm – 280.
***Hobsons* : Meals** (lunch by arrangement Monday to Saturday)/dinner 16.00 **st.** 6.50 – 8.50 – **49 rm** 70.00/90.00 **st.** – SB. on Stoke-on-Trent town plan V **e**

ATS Lower St. ℘ 622431

NEWCASTLE-UNDER-LYME
CENTRE

High Street . . . . YZ

Albert Street . . . . Y
Barracks Road . . . . YZ
Blackfriars Road . . . . Z 9
Brook Lane . . . . Z
Brunswick Street . . . . Y
Church Street . . . . Y 20
Friarswood Road . . . . Z
George Street . . . . Y
Hassell Street . . . . Y
Higherland . . . . Z 37
Iron Market . . . . Y 38
King Street . . . . Y
Lancaster Road . . . . Z
Liverpool Road . . . . Y 41
Lower Street . . . . YZ
Merrial Street . . . . Y 47
North Street . . . . Y 51
Parkstone Avenue . . . . Z
Pool Dam . . . . Z
Queen Street . . . . Y
Ryecroft . . . . Y
Vessey Terrace . . . . Z 73
Victoria Road . . . . Z

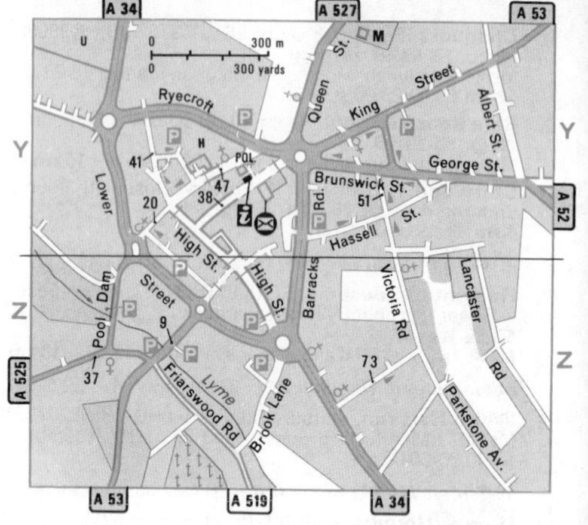

NEWCASTLE UPON TYNE Tyne and Wear 401 402 O 19 **Great Britain G.** – **pop. 259 541** – ☎ 0191.

See : City★★ – Grey Street★ CZ – Quayside★ CZ : Composition★, All Saints Church★ (interior★) – Castle Keep★ *AC* CZ – Laing Art Gallery and Museum★ *AC* CY **M1** – Museum of Antiquities★ CY **M2.**

Envir. : Hadrian's Wall★★, W : by A 69 AV.

Exc. : Beamish : North of England Open-Air Museum★★ *AC*, SW : 7 m. by A 692 and A 6076 AX – Seaton Delaval Hall★ *AC*, NE : 11 m. by A 189 - BV - and A 190.

High Gosforth Park ☏ 236 4480/4867 – Broadway East, Gosforth ☏ 285 6710, BV – City of Newcastle, Three Mile Bridge, Gosforth ☏ 285 1775, – Wallsend, Bigges Main ☏ 262 1973, NE : by A 1058, BV – Whickham, Hollinside Park ☏ 488 7309.

Newcastle Airport : ☏ 286 0966, NW : 5 m. by A 696, AV – **Terminal** : Bus Assembly : Central Station Forecourt.

to Norway (Bergen, Haugesund and Stavanger) (Color Line) 2-3 weekly – to Denmark (Esbjerg) (Scandinavian Seaways) (summer only) (18 h) – to Sweden (Gothenburg) (Scandinavian Seaways) weekly (22 h) – to Germany (Hamburg) (Scandinavian Seaways) 1 daily (23 h 30 mn).

Central Library, Princess Sq., NE99 1DX ☏ 261 0691 – Nevylla Street, NE1 5DL ☏ 230 0030 – Newcastle Airport, Woolsington, NE13 8BX ☏ 271 1929.

♦London 276 – ♦Edinburgh 105 – ♦Leeds 95.

Plans on following pages

Copthorne Newcastle, The Close, Quayside, NE1 3RT, ☏ 222 0333, Telex 53340, Fax 230 1111, ≤, Ⅎ₆, ⇌, ▢ – |‡| ⇹ rm ▤ rest ▣ ☎ ♿ ℗ – 🎭 200. AE ⓓ VISA JCB. ✂ CZ **z**
Meals 12.95/16.50 **t.** and a la carte ▯ 5.75 – ▭ 9.95 – **156 rm** 105.00/240.00 **t.** – SB.

Vermont, Castle Garth, NE1 1RQ, ☏ 233 1010, Fax 233 1234, ≤, Ⅎ₆ – |‡| ⇹ rm ▤ rest ▣ ☎ ♿ ℗ – 🎭 200. AE ⓓ VISA. ✂ CZ **s**
Brasserie* : Meals** 13.50/15.50 **t.** ▯ 6.50 - (see also ***Blue Room below) – ▭ 8.50 – **95 rm** 105.00/115.00 **t.**, 6 suites – SB.

Forte Crest, New Bridge St., NE1 8BS, ☏ 232 6191, Fax 261 8529 – |‡| ⇹ rm ▤ rest ▣ ☎ ♿ ℗ – 🎭 400 CY **n**
165 rm, 1 suite.

County Thistle (Mt. Charlotte Thistle), Neville St., NE99 1AH, ☏ 232 2471, Fax 232 1285 – |‡| ⇹ rm ▣ ☎ ℗ – 🎭 130. AE ⓓ VISA CZ **a**
Meals *(closed Saturday lunch)* 10.50/16.50 **st.** and dinner a la carte ▯ 5.50 – ▭ 9.25 – **115 rm** 74.00/85.00 **st.** – SB.

Surtees, 12-16 Dean St., NE1 1PG, ☏ 261 7771, Fax 230 1322 – |‡| ▣ ☎. AE ⓓ VISA. ✂ CZ **u**
Meals - Café-restaurant (bar lunch Monday to Friday)/dinner 15.00 **s.** and a la carte – **27 rm** ▭ 57.50/67.50 **st.**

Novotel, Ponteland Rd, Kenton, NE3 3HZ, at junction of A1 (M) with A 696 ☏ 214 0303, Fax 214 0633, Ⅎ₆, ⇌, ▢ – |‡| ⇹ rm ▤ rest ▣ ☎ ♿ ℗ – 🎭 220. AE ⓓ VISA
Meals a la carte 12.25/22.35 **st.** ▯ 4.95 – ▭ 7.50 – **126 rm** 52.50 **st.** AV **a**

Bank Top Toby, Ponteland Rd., Kenton, NE3 3TY, at junction of A1 (M) with A 696 ☏ 214 0877, Fax 214 0095 – ⇹ rm ▤ rest ▣ ☎ ♿ ℗ – 🎭 50 AV **a**
30 rm.

Swallow, 1 Newgate Arcade, Newgate St., NE1 5SX, ☎ 232 5025, Fax 232 8428 – rm – 100. AE VISA CZ **o**
Meals 10.50/15.50 **st.** and a la carte 5.00 – **93 rm** 80.00/93.00 **st.** – SB.

Imperial Swallow, Jesmond Rd, NE2 1PR, ☎ 281 5511, Fax 281 8472, – rm – 120. AE VISA CY **c**
Meals (light lunch Saturday) 6.95/14.95 **st.** and a la carte – **121 rm** 78.00/90.00 **st.** – SB.

Waterside, 48-52 Sandhill, Quayside, NE1 3JF, ☎ 230 0111, Fax 230 1615 – . AE VISA. CZ **r**
Meals - Café-restaurant *(closed lunch Sunday and Bank Holidays)* 5.95/15.50 **t.** and a la carte 3.70 – **20 rm** 45.00/74.00 **st.** – SB.

New Kent, 127 Osborne Rd, Jesmond, NE2 2TB, ☎ 281 1083, Fax 281 3369 – . AE VISA. BV **c**
Meals (bar lunch)/dinner 9.90 **st.** and a la carte 5.20 – **32 rm** 59.00/79.00 **st.** – SB.

Forte Travelodge without rest., Whitemare Pool, NE10 8YB, at junction of A 194 with A 184 ☎ 438 3333, Reservations (Freephone) 0800 850950 – . AE VISA. BX
41 rm 33.50 **t.**

Avenue, 2 Manor House Rd, NE2 2LU, at junction with Osborne Av. ☎ 281 1396 – . BV **x**
closed 23 to 29 December – **Meals** (by arrangement) 7.50 **st.** – **10 rm** 20.00/40.00 **st.**

Westland, 27 Osborne Av., Jesmond, NE2 1JR, ☎ 281 0412, Fax 281 5005 – BV **z**
15 rm.

✪ **21 Queen Street** (Laybourne), 21 Queen St., Quayside, NE1 3UG, ☎ 222 0755, Fax 221 0761 – AE VISA CZ **c**
closed Saturday lunch, Sunday, last 2 weeks August and Bank Holidays – **Meals** 17.00 **t.** (lunch) and a la carte 25.00/43.00 **t.** 6.00
Spec. Carpaccio of Tweed salmon with pepper relish, Roast turbot with a confit of onions, wild mushrooms and meat juices, Caramel soufflé with a salad of oranges and orange sorbet.

Blue Room (at Vermont H.) Castle Garth, NE1 1RQ, ☎ 233 1010, Fax 233 1234 – . AE VISA CZ **s**
Meals *(closed Sunday and Monday)* (dinner only) 25.00 **t.** and a la carte 6.50.

Fisherman's Lodge, Jesmond Dene, Jesmond, NE7 7BQ, ☎ 281 3281, Fax 281 6410 – . AE VISA BV **e**
closed Saturday lunch, Sunday, 25 to 28 December, 1 to 3 January and Bank Holidays – **Meals** 17.00/28.00 **t.** and a la carte 5.00.

Vujon, 29 Queen St., Quayside, NE1 3UG, ☎ 221 0601, Fax 221 0602 – . AE VISA JCB CZ **i**
closed Sunday lunch and 25 December – **Meals** - Indian a la carte 18.00/29.80 **t.** 4.50.

The Blackgate, The Side, NE1 3JE, ☎ 261 7356 – AE VISA CZ **x**
closed Saturday lunch, Sunday, Monday dinner, 25 to 26 December and Bank Holidays – **Meals** 13.25 **t.** and a la carte 5.95.

Leela's, 20 Dean St., NE1 1PG, ☎ 230 1261 – . AE VISA CZ **e**
closed Sunday and Bank Holidays – **Meals** - South Indian 9.95/16.95 **t.** and a la carte 5.95.

Courtney's, 5-7 The Side, NE1 3JE, ☎ 232 5537 – . AE VISA CZ **v**
closed Saturday lunch, Sunday, 2 weeks May, 1 week Christmas and Bank Holidays – **Meals** 14.50 **t.** (lunch) and a la carte 16.25/24.70 **t.**

Barn Again Bistro 21a Leazes Park Rd, NE1 4PF, ☎ 230 3338 – VISA CY **a**
closed Saturday lunch, Sunday, Monday and Bank Holidays – **Meals** a la carte 11.00/18.60 **t.** 3.60.

at Gosforth N : 4 ¾ m. by B 1318 – AV – ✉ Tyneside – ☎ 0191 :

Swallow Gosforth Park, High Gosforth Park, NE3 5HN, on B 1318 ☎ 236 4111, Fax 236 8192, ←, , park, , squash – rm rest – 600. AE VISA.
Brandling : **Meals** 14.50/19.50 **t.** 7.50 – ***Conservatory :*** **Meals** 11.95/20.50 **t.** 7.50 – **173 rm** 100.00/120.00 **st.**, 5 suites – SB.

at Seaton Burn N : 8 m. by B 1318 – AV – ✉ Newcastle upon Tyne – ☎ 0191 :

Holiday Inn, Great North Rd, NE13 6BP, N : ¾ m. at junction with A 1 ☎ 236 5432, Fax 236 5432, – rm – 400. AE VISA JCB.
Meals (carving lunch) 12.50/17.50 **st.** and a la carte – 9.75 – **149 rm** 98.50/108.50 **st.**, 1 suite – SB.

at Boldon E : 7 ¾ m. by A 184 – BX – ☎ 0191 :

Friendly, Witney Way, Boldon Business Park, NE35 9PE, ☎ 519 1999, Fax 519 0655, – rm rest – 200. AE VISA.
Meals *(closed Saturday lunch)* 8.25/13.50 **st.** and a la carte 5.50 – 6.75 – **82 rm** 57.75/82.00 **st.** – SB.

Forsters, 2 St. Bedes, Station Rd, East Boldon, NE36 OLE, ☎ 519 0929 – AE VISA
closed Sunday, Monday and Bank Holidays – **Meals** (dinner only) 15.00 **t.** and a la carte 3.95.

NEWCASTLE UPON TYNE

Adelaide Terrace . . . . AX 2
Atkinson Road . . . . AX 3
Bath Street . . . . BX 4
Bensham Road . . . . AX 6
Benton Bank . . . . BV 8
Buddle Street . . . . BV 13
Byker Bridge . . . . BV 15
Church Avenue . . . . AV 16
Church Road . . . . AV 18
Clayton Road . . . . BV 21
Coldwell Lane . . . . BX 22
Coldwell Street . . . . BX 24
Condercum Road . . . . AX 26
Fossway . . . . BV 31
Haddrick's Mill Road . . . . . BV 36
High Street West . . . . BV 37
Jesmond Dene Road . . . . . . BV 39
Killingworth Road . . . . BV 42
Lobley Hill Road . . . . AX 45
Matthew Bank . . . . BV 49
Neptune Road . . . . BV 51
Red Hall Drive . . . . BV 61
Redheugh Bridge . . . . AX 62
Saltwell Road . . . . BX 69
Shipdon Road . . . . AX 71
Springfield Road . . . . AV 72
Station Road . . . . BX 73
Stephenson Road . . . . BV 74
Sunderland Road . . . . BX 76
Sutton Street . . . . BV 77
Swalwell Bank . . . . ABX 79
Waverdale Avenue . . . . BV 83
West Farm Avenue . . . . BV 87
Whickham Bank . . . . AX 88
Windy Nook Road . . . . BX 89

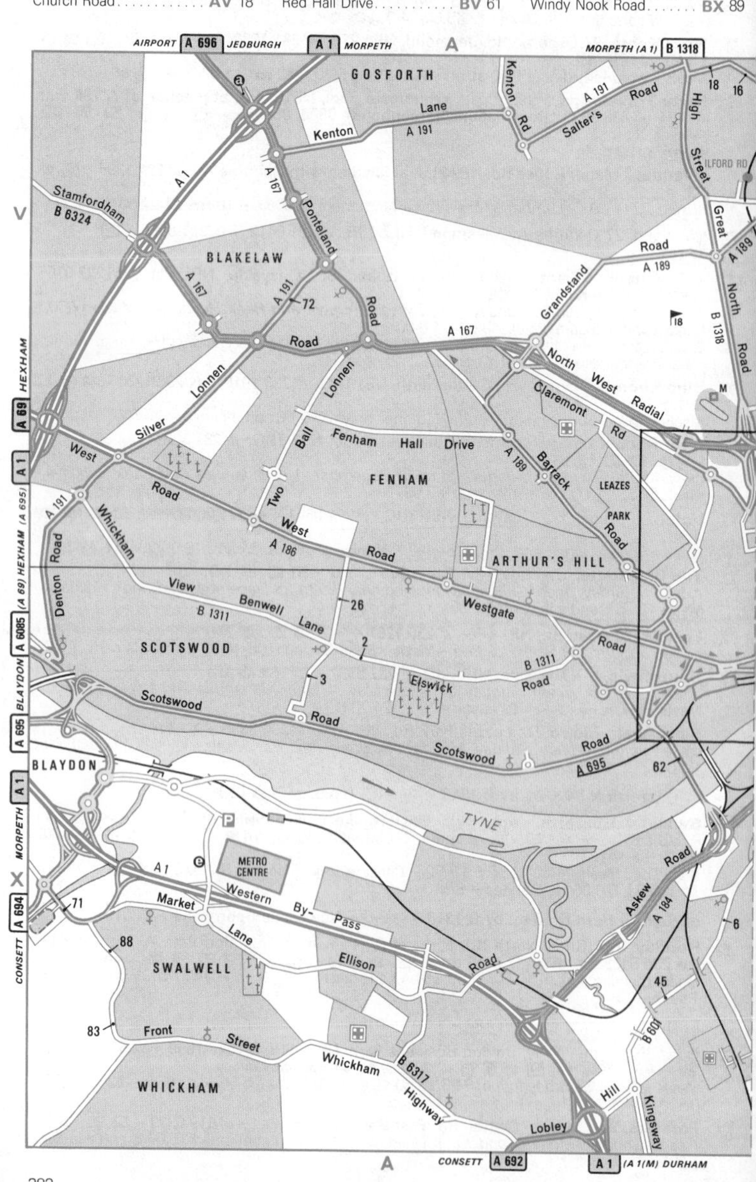

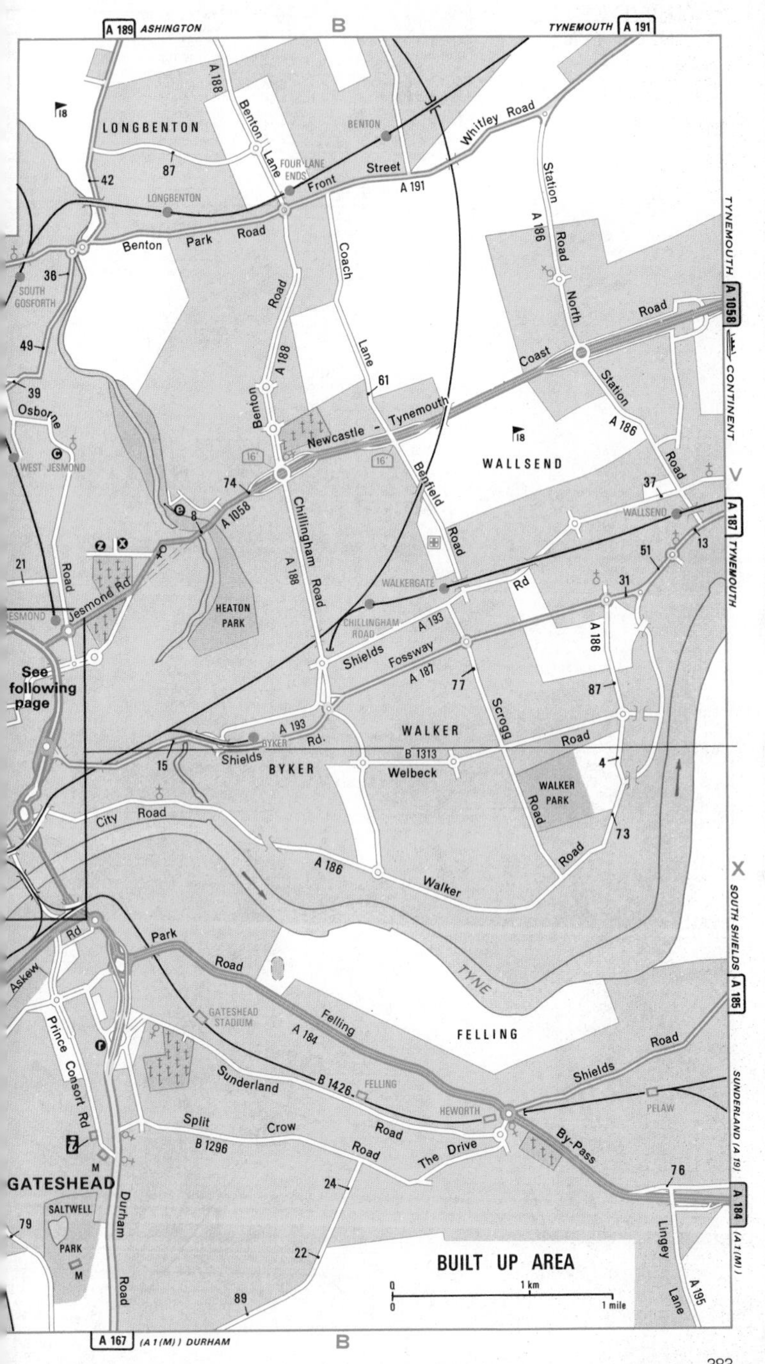
A 189 ASHINGTON
B
TYNEMOUTH A 191
LONGBENTON
BENTON
FOUR LANE ENDS
Benton Lane
A 188
Whitley Road
Front Street
A 191
Station Road
A 186
North
Benton Park Road
LONGBENTON
SOUTH GOSFORTH
Coach Lane
Coast Road
A 1058
CONTINENT
TYNEMOUTH
Station Road
A 186
Benton Road
A 188
Newcastle - Tynemouth
WALLSEND
Osborne
WEST JESMOND
A 1058
Chillingham Road
A 188
Benfield Road
V
WALLSEND
A 187 TYNEMOUTH
Jesmond Rd
HEATON PARK
WALKERGATE
Rd
CHILLINGHAM ROAD
A 193
Shields
Fossway
A 187
A 186
See following page
JESMOND
A 193
BYKER
Rd.
Shields
WALKER
Scrogg Road
BYKER
B 1313
Welbeck
Road
WALKER PARK
City Road
A 186
Walker Road
X
SOUTH SHIELDS A 185
TYNE
Park Road
Askew Rd
GATESHEAD STADIUM
Felling
A 184
FELLING
Prince Consort Rd
Sunderland Road
B 1426
FELLING
HEWORTH
Shields Road
PELAW
SUNDERLAND (A 19)
Split Crow Road
B 1296
The Drive
By-Pass
GATESHEAD
SALTWELL PARK
Durham Road
A 184 (A 1(M))
Lingey Lane
A 195
BUILT UP AREA
1 km
1 mile
A 167 (A 1(M)) DURHAM
B

NEWCASTLE UPON TYNE

Blackett Street . . . . CY
Eldon Square Shopping Centre . . . . . CYZ
Grey Street . . . . CZ
Newgate Street . . . . CZ
Pilgrim Street. . . . . CZ 57

Bridge Street. . . . . CZ 10
Broad Chare . . . . CZ 12
Collingwood Street. . . . . CZ 25
Forth Street . . . . CZ 30
George Street . . . . CZ 32
Great North Road . . . . CY 33
Jesmond Road . . . . CY 40
John Dobson Street . . . . CY 41
Leazes Park Road . . . . CY 43
Low Friar Street. . . . . CZ 46
Market Street . . . . CZ 47

Mosley Street . . . . CZ 50
Neville Street. . . . . CZ 52
New Bridge St. West . . . . CY 53
Northumberland Street . . . . . . CY 56
Railway Street . . . . CZ 60
Rutherford Street . . . . CZ 63
St. Mary's Place . . . . CY 65
St. Nicholas Street . . . . CZ 66
Scotswood Road. . . . . CZ 70
Thornton Street. . . . . CZ 80
Wellington Street . . . . CY 84

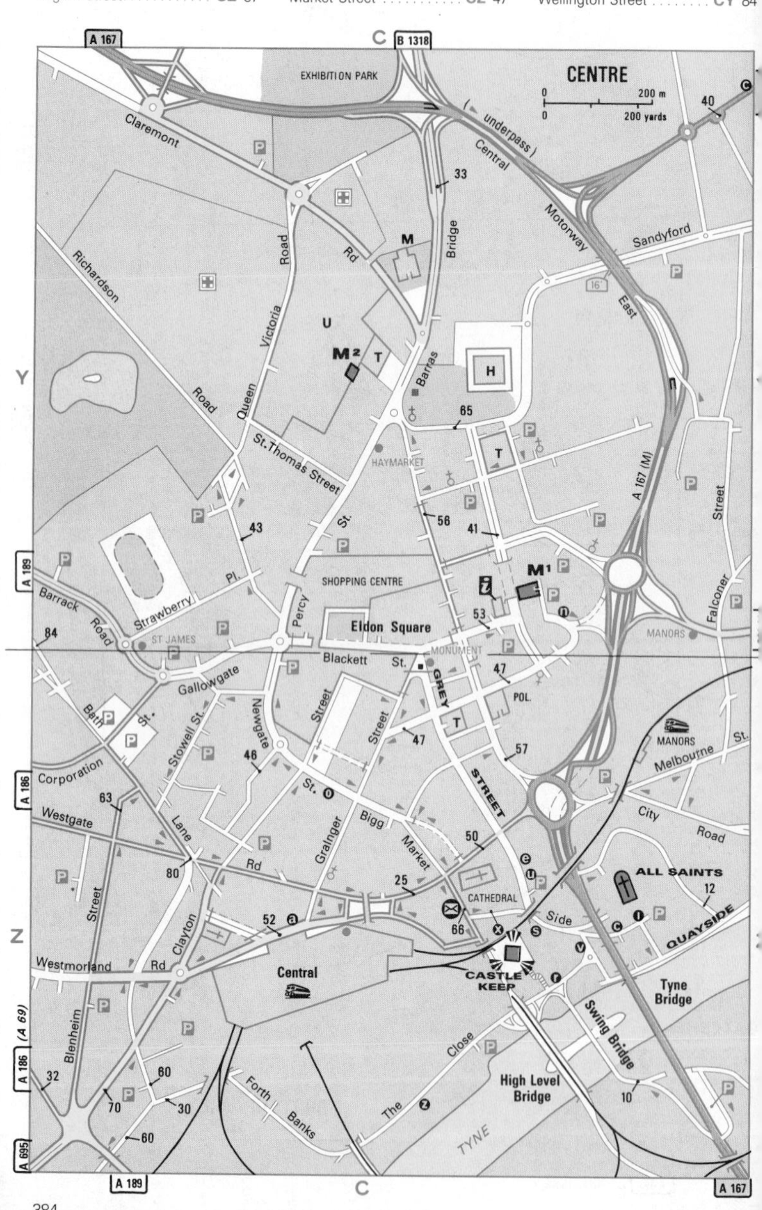

at Whickham SW : 5½ m. by A 184, A 1 and A 692 on B 6317 - AX – ✉ Newcastle upon Tyne – ☎ 0191 :

Gibside Arms, Front St., NE16 4JG, ☎ 488 9292, Fax 488 8000 – rest – **45 rm.**

at Newcastle Airport NW : 6 ¾ m. by A 167 off A 696 AV – ✉ Newcastle upon Tyne – ☎ 01661 :

Airport Moat House, Woolsington, NE13 8DJ, ☎ 824911, Telex 537121, Fax 860157 – rm rest – 400. AE VISA
Meals *(closed Saturday lunch)* 10.95/15.00 **st.** and a la carte 7.50 – 7.50 – **98 rm** 75.00/95.00 **t.**, 2 suites – SB.

at Ponteland NW : 8 ¼ m. by A 167 on A 696 – ✉ Newcastle upon Tyne – ☎ 01661 :

XX **Horton Grange** with rm, Seaton Burn, NE13 6BU, NE : 3½ m. by Morpeth rd ☎ 860686, Fax 860308, – rest . VISA.
closed 25 and 26 December – **Meals** *(closed Sunday to non-residents)* (booking essential) (dinner only) 32.00 **t.** 4.90 – **9 rm** 59.00/80.00 **t.** – SB.

ATS 80/90 Blenheim St. ☎ 232 3921/232 5031
ATS Newton Park Garage, Newton Rd, Heaton ☎ 281 2243
ATS White St, Walker ☎ 262 0811

NEWENT Glos. 403 404 M 28 – ☎ 01989.
♦London 109 – Gloucester 10 – Hereford 22 – Newport 44.

Orchard House, Aston Ingham Rd, Kilcot, GL18 1NP, SW : 2 ¼ m. by B 4221 on B 4222 ☎ 720417, – . VISA.
Meals 15.50 **st.** 4.00 – **3 rm** 30.00/59.00 **st.**

NEWHAVEN E. Sussex 404 U 31 – pop. 10 210 – ECD : Wednesday – ☎ 01273.
to France (Dieppe) (Stena Sealink Line) 4 daily (4 h).
♦London 63 – ♦Brighton 9 – Eastbourne 14 – Lewes 7.

Hotels and restaurants see : Lewes NW : 7 m. by A 26.

NEWINGTON Kent 404 V/W 29 – ☎ 01795.
♦London 40 – Canterbury 20 – Maidstone 13.

Newington Manor, Callaways Lane, ME9 7LU, ☎ 842053, Fax 844273, – . AE VISA.
closed 26 to 31 December – **Meals** *(closed Saturday lunch, Sunday dinner and Bank Holiday Mondays)* 13.60 **st.** and a la carte 5.95 – 4.00 – **12 rm** 57.00/88.00 **st.** – SB.

NEWLYN Cornwall 403 D 33 – see Penzance.

NEWMARKET Suffolk 404 V 27 – pop. 15 861 – ECD : Wednesday – ☎ 01638.
18 Links, Cambridge Rd ☎ 662708.
63 The Rookery, CB8 8HT ☎ 667200.
♦London 64 – ♦Cambridge 13 – ♦Ipswich 40 – ♦Norwich 48.

Bedford Lodge, Bury Rd, CB8 7BX, NE : ½ m. on B 1506 ☎ 663175, Fax 667391, – – 200
49 rm, 7 suites.

Newmarket Moat House (Q.M.H.), Moulton Rd, CB8 8DY, ☎ 667171, Fax 666533 – – 80
47 rm.

White Hart, High St., CB8 8JP, ☎ 663051, Fax 667284 – – 150. AE VISA.
Meals 8.75/16.75 **st.** and a la carte – **23 rm** 45.95/49.95 **st.**

at Six Mile Bottom (Cambs.) SW : 6 m. on A 1304 – ✉ Newmarket – ☎ 01638 :

Swynford Paddocks, CB8 0UE, ☎ 570234, Fax 570283, <, « Country house », , park, – rest – 30. AE VISA.
closed 4 days Christmas-New Year – **Meals** (bar lunch Saturday) 22.50 **st.** (dinner) and a la carte 18.50/26.00 **st.** 4.50 – **15 rm** 70.00/107.00 **st.** – SB.

ATS 2 Exeter Rd ☎ 662521

NEWMILLERDAM W. Yorks. – see Wakefield.

NEW MILTON Hants. 403 404 P 31 – ECD : Wednesday – ☎ 01425.

Barton-on-Sea, Milford Rd ✆ 615308.

♦London 106 – Bournemouth 12 – ♦Southampton 21 – Winchester 34.

Chewton Glen, Christchurch Rd, BH25 6QS, W : 2 m. by A 337 and Ringwood Rd on Chewton Farm Rd ✆ 275341, Fax 272310, ≤, « Gardens », heated, park, – rest – 100. AE VISA
Meals 25.00/50.00 **st.** and dinner a la carte 36.00/48.00 **st.** 6.50 – 16.50 – **45 rm** 180.00/280.00 **st.**, 13 suites – SB
Spec. Ravioli of langoustine with squash and a coriander sauce, Fillet of English lamb wrapped in crispy shredded potatoes, tarragon jus, A selection of caramel desserts.

NEWPORT Essex 404 U 28 – pop. 2 178 – ✉ Saffron Walden – ☎ 01799.

♦London 38 – ♦Cambridge 21 – Colchester 41.

XX **Village House,** High St., CB11 3PF, ✆ 41560 – Ⓟ. VISA
closed Sunday, Monday and January – **Meals** (dinner only) a la carte 19.00/24.00 **t.** 5.25.

NEWPORT Shrops. 402 403 404 M 25 **Great Britain G.** – pop. 9 664 – ECD : Thursday – ☎ 01952.

Exc. : Weston Park★★, SE : 6½ m. by A 41 and A 5.

♦London 150 – ♦Birmingham 33 – Shrewsbury 18 – ♦Stoke-on-Trent 21.

Royal Victoria, St. Mary's St., TF10 7AB, ✆ 820331, Fax 820209 – Ⓟ – 100. AE VISA
Meals *(closed Sunday dinner)* (light lunch)/dinner 10.50 **st.** and a la carte 4.95 – **24 rm** 35.00/55.00 **t.** – SB.

Die Preise Einzelheiten über die in diesem Führer angegebenen Preise finden Sie in der Einleitung.

NEWPORT I.O.W. 403 404 Q 31 – see Wight (Isle of).

NEWPORT PAGNELL Bucks. 404 R 27 – pop. 14 374 – ECD : Thursday – ☎ 01908.

♦London 57 – Bedford 13 – Luton 21 – Northampton 15.

Coach House (Country Club), London Rd, Moulsoe, MK16 0JA, SE : 1½ m. by B 526 on A 509 ✆ 613688, Fax 617335, – rm Ⓟ – 180. AE VISA
Meals (bar lunch Saturday) 11.60/21.40 **t.** and a la carte 5.25 – 7.50 – **49 rm** 72.00 **t.** – SB.

Swan Revived, High St., MK16 8AR, ✆ 610565, Fax 210995 – Ⓟ – 70. AE VISA
Meals 12.95 **t.** and a la carte 3.95 – **42 rm** 58.00/70.00 **st.** – SB.

NEWQUAY Cornwall 403 E 32 **The West Country G.** – pop. 17 390 – ECD : Wednesday – ☎ 01637.

Envir. : Penhale Point and Kelsey Head★ (≤★★) SW : by A 3075 Y – Trerice★ *AC*, SE : 3½ m. by A 392 - Y - and A 3058.

Exc. : St. Agnes - St. Agnes Beacon (✻★★) SW : 12½ m. by A 3075 - Y - and B 3285.

Tower Rd ✆ 872091 Z – Treloy ✆ 878554.

Newquay Airport : ✆ 860551 Y.

Municipal Offices, Marcus Hill, TR7 1BD ✆ 871345.

♦London 291 – Exeter 83 – Penzance 34 – ♦Plymouth 48 – Truro 14.

Plan opposite

Bristol, Narrowcliff, TR7 2PQ, ✆ 875181, Fax 879347, ≤, – Ⓟ – 200. AE VISA Z r
Meals 9.95/16.00 **t.** and a la carte – **73 rm** 50.00/90.00 **t.**, 1 suite – SB.

Trebarwith, Trebarwith Cres., TR7 1BZ, ✆ 872288, Fax 875431, ≤ bay and coast, – rest Ⓟ. AE VISA Z a
April-October – **Meals** (bar lunch)/dinner 13.50 **st.** 6.00 – **41 rm** 27.00/55.00 **st.** – SB.

Kilbirnie, Narrowcliff, TR7 2RS, ✆ 875155, Fax 850769, heated, – Ⓟ. VISA Z e
Meals (bar lunch)/dinner 10.50 4.25 – 5.50 – **68 rm** (dinner included) 40.00/80.00 **t.** – SB.

Windsor, Mount Wise, TR7 2AY, ✆ 875188, heated, squash – rest Ⓟ. AE VISA Z n
closed January – **Meals** (bar lunch)/dinner 15.00 **st.** and a la carte 3.50 – **45 rm** 38.00/70.00 **st.** – SB.

Esplanade, Esplanade Rd, Pentire, TR7 1PS, ✆ 873333, Fax 851413, ≤, – Ⓟ. AE VISA Y a
closed January – **Meals** (dinner only and Sunday lunch)/dinner 7.00 **st.** 3.75 – **76 rm** (dinner included) 34.00/68.00 **st.**

New Garth, Narrowcliff, TR7 2PG, ✆ 873250, Fax 850564, ≤ – Ⓟ Z c
51 rm.

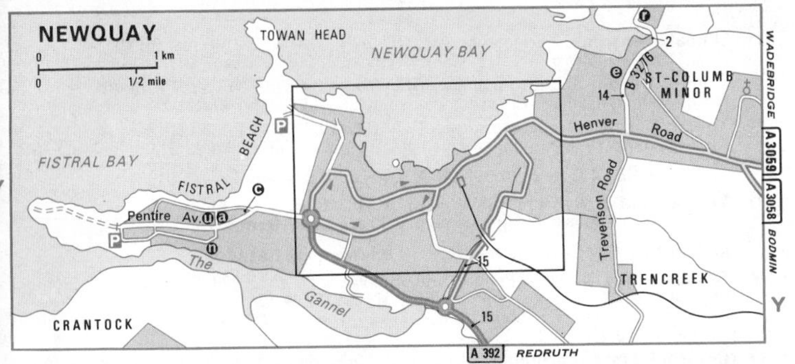

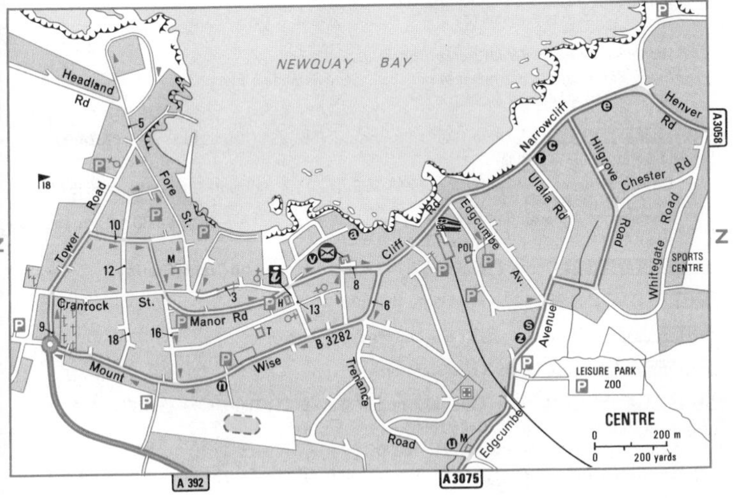

Bank Street . . . . Z 3
East Street . . . . Z 8
Fore Street . . . . Z

Alexandra Road . . . . Y 2

Beacon Road . . . . Z 5
Berry Road . . . . Z 6
Higher Tower Road . . . . Z 9
Hope Terrace . . . . Z 10
Jubilee Street . . . . Z 12

Marcus Hill . . . . Z 13
Porth Way . . . . Y 14
Trevemper Road . . . . Y 15
St. Georges Road . . . . Z 16
St. John's Road . . . . Z 18

Water's Edge, Esplanade Rd, Pentire, TR7 1QA, ☎ 872048, < Fistral Bay, – TV ☎ P. VISA. Y **u**
May-September – **Meals** (residents only) (dinner only) 4.50 – **20 rm** (dinner included) 38.00/72.00 **t.** – SB.

Corisande Manor, Riverside Av., Pentire, TR7 1PL, ☎ 872042, < Gannel Estuary, – TV P. VISA Y **n**
6 May-14 October – **Meals** (bar lunch)/dinner 12.50 4.95 – **19 rm** 29.50/70.00 **st.** – SB.

Philema, Esplanade Rd, Pentire, TR7 1PY, ☎ 872571, Fax 873188, <, – TV ☎ P – **31 rm.** Y **c**

Whipsiderry, Trevelgue Rd, Porth, TR7 3LY, NE : 2 m. by A 392 off B 3276 ☎ 874777, <, heated, – rest TV P. VISA Y
closed October to 23 December – **Meals** (bar lunch)/dinner 16.75 **t.** 4.95 – **23 rm** 29.00/80.00 **st.** – SB.

Porth Veor Manor, Porth Way, TR7 3LW, ☎ 873274, Fax 851690, – TV P. AE VISA Y **e**
Meals 8.95/12.85 **t.** and dinner a la carte 3.75 – **16 rm** 40.00/80.00 **t.** – SB.

Trenance Lodge, 83 Trenance Rd, TR7 2HW, ☎ 876702, Fax 872034, heated, – TV P. VISA. Z **u**
Meals (dinner only) 16.00 **t.** and a la carte 4.00 – **5 rm** 25.00/50.00 – SB.

Windward, Alexandra Rd, Porth Bay, TR7 3NB, ☎ 873185 – rest TV P. AE VISA. Y **r**
Meals (residents only)(dinner only) 9.00 **st.** 3.95 – **14 rm** 22.00/42.00 **st.**

Wheal Treasure, 72 Edgcumbe Av., TR7 2NN, ☎ 874136 – rest. Z z
April-October – **Meals** 7.00 **st.** 3.00 – **12 rm** 22.00/44.00 **st.** – SB.

Copper Beech, 70 Edgcumbe Av., TR7 2NN, ☎ 873376 – rest. Z s
closed January-Easter – **15 rm** (dinner included) 27.00/54.00 **st.**

Towan Beach, 7 Trebarwith Cres., TR7 1DX, ☎ 872093 – VISA. Z v
April-September – **Meals** (by arrangement) 8.50 **st.** 3.50 – **6 rm** 21.00/46.00 **st.** – SB.

at Trerice SE : 4 3/4 m. by A 392 off A 3058– Y – ✉ Newquay – 01872 :

Trewerry Mill, TR8 5HS, W : 1/2 m. ☎ 510345, – .
April-October – **Meals** (by arrangement) 7.00 **s.** 2.90 – **6 rm** 16.50/33.00 **t.**

at Crantock SW : 4 m. by A 3075 – Y – ✉ Newquay – 01637 :

Crantock Bay, West Pentire, TR8 5SE, W : 3/4 m. ☎ 830229, Fax 831111, ← Crantock Bay, , , , , – rest . VISA
April-early November – **Meals** (buffet lunch)/dinner 14.95 **t.** 4.00 – **34 rm** (dinner included) 43.00/106.00 **t.** – SB.

Crantock Plains Farmhouse, Cubert, TR8 5PH, SE : 1 1/2 m. bearing right at the fork in the road ☎ 830253, – .
closed Christmas – **Meals** (by arrangement) 8.50 **st.** – **7 rm** 15.00/41.00.

*Wenn Sie an ein Hotel im Ausland schreiben,
fügen Sie Ihrem Brief einen internationalen Antwortschein bei
(im Postamt erhältlich).*

NEWTON POPPLEFORD Devon 403 K 31 – pop. 1 765 – ✉ Ottery St. Mary – 01395.
♦London 208 – Exeter 10 – Sidmouth 4.

Coach House, Southerton, EX11 1SE, N : 1 m. by Venn Ottery Rd ☎ 568577, – . VISA.
Meals (booking essential) (bar lunch)/dinner 11.00 **st.** and a la carte 4.80 – **6 rm** 30.00/70.00 **st.** – SB.

NEWTON SOLNEY Derbs. 402 403 404 P 25 – see Burton-upon-Trent (Staffs.).

NITON I.O.W. 403 404 Q 32 – see Wight (Isle of).

NORMAN CROSS Cambs. 404 T 26 – see Peterborough.

NORMANTON PARK Leics. – see Stamford.

NORTHALLERTON N. Yorks. 402 P 20 – pop. 9 628 – ECD : Thursday – 01609.
Applegarth Car Park, DL7 8LZ ☎ 776864.
♦London 238 – ♦Leeds 48 – ♦Middlesbrough 24 – York 33.

Golden Lion (Forte), 114 High St., DL7 8PP, ☎ 777411, Fax 773250 – – 150. VISA JCB
Meals (bar lunch Monday to Saturday)/dinner 16.95 **t.** and a la carte 6.70 – 8.50 – **21 rm** 55.00/65.00 **t.** – SB.

Windsor, 56 South Par., DL7 8SL, ☎ 774100 – . VISA
Meals (by arrangement) 8.50 **st.** – **6 rm** 20.00/37.00 **st.**

XX **Pietro and Nino Romanby Court,** High St., DL7 8PG, ☎ 774918 – VISA
closed Sunday, Monday, 18 to 31 January and Bank Holidays except Good Friday – **Meals** - Italian a la carte 8.45/22.85 **t.** 4.95.

at Staddlebridge NE : 7 1/2 m. by A 684 on A 19 at junction with A 172 – ✉ Northallerton – 01609 :

XX **McCoys at the Tontine** with rm, DL6 3JB, on southbound carriageway ☎ 882671, Fax 882660, « 1930's decor » – . VISA
closed Sunday and Monday – **Meals** (dinner only) a la carte 22.70/35.05 **t.** – **6 rm** 79.00/99.00 **t.**

X **Bistro : Meals** a la carte 15.00/25.00 **t.**

at Newby Wiske S : 2 1/2 m. by A 167 – ✉ Northallerton – 01609 :

Solberge Hall, DL7 9ER, NW : 1 1/4 m. on Warlaby rd ☎ 779191, Fax 780472, ←, , park – – 100. VISA
Meals 6.50/19.50 **st.** and dinner a la carte 5.95 – **24 rm** 55.00/85.00 **st.**, 1 suite – SB.

NORTHAMPTON Northants. 404 R 27 **Great Britain G.** – pop. 180 567 – 01604.
Exc. : All Saints, Brixworth★, N : 7 m. on A 508 Y.
18, 9 Delapre, Eagle Drive, Nene Valley Way ☎ 764036/763957, Z – 18 Collingtree Park, Windingbrook Lane ☎ 700000.
Visitor Centre, Mr Grant's House, 10 St. Giles Square, NN1 1DA ☎ 604180.
♦London 69 – ♦Cambridge 53 – ♦Coventry 34 – ♦Leicester 42 – Luton 35 – ♦Oxford 41.

NORTHAMPTON

Abington Street X
Drapery . . . . X 18
Gold Street X
Grosvenor Centre X
Weston
Favell Centre . . . . Y

Abington Square . . . . . . X 2
Ashley Way . . . . Y 3
Bewick Road . . . . Y 4
Billing Road . . . . X 7
Bridge Street . . . . X 8
Campbell Street . . . . . . X 9
Charnwood
Avenue . . . . Y 10
Church Lane . . . . X 13
College Street . . . . X 14
Derngate . . . . X 15
Earl Street . . . . X 19
Greyfriars . . . . X 23
Guildhall Road . . . . X 24
Horse
Shoe Street . . . . X 28
Kettering Road . . . . X 30
Kingsthorpe Grove . . . . Y 34
Lower Mounts . . . . X 35
Mare Fair . . . . X 37
Oaklands Drive . . . . Y 38
Overstone Road . . . . X 39
Park Avenue North . . . . Y 40
Park Avenue South . . . . Z 43
Rushmere Road . . . . Z 44
St. Andrew's Road . . . . Y 45
St. Edmund's Road . . . . X 48
St. James's Road . . . . Z 49
St. John's Street . . . . X 50
St. Leonard's Road . . . . Z 52
St. Michael's Road . . . . X 53
Sheep Street . . . . X 54
Silver Street . . . . X 55
Spencer Bridge Road . . . . X, Z 57
Towcester Road . . . . Z 58
Upper Mounts . . . . X 59
Waveney Way . . . . Y 60
West Bridge . . . . X 62
Windrush Way . . . . Y 63

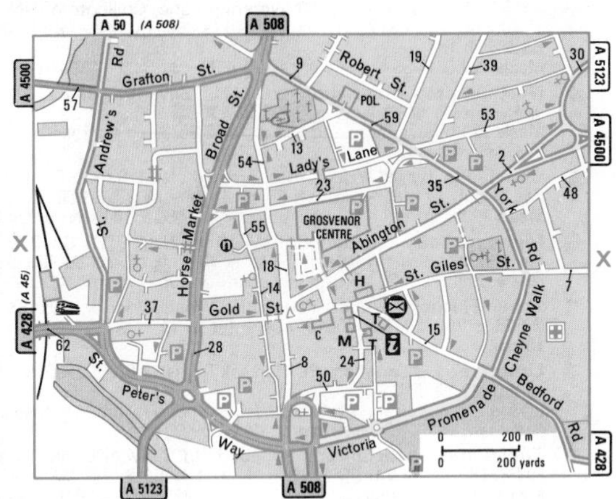

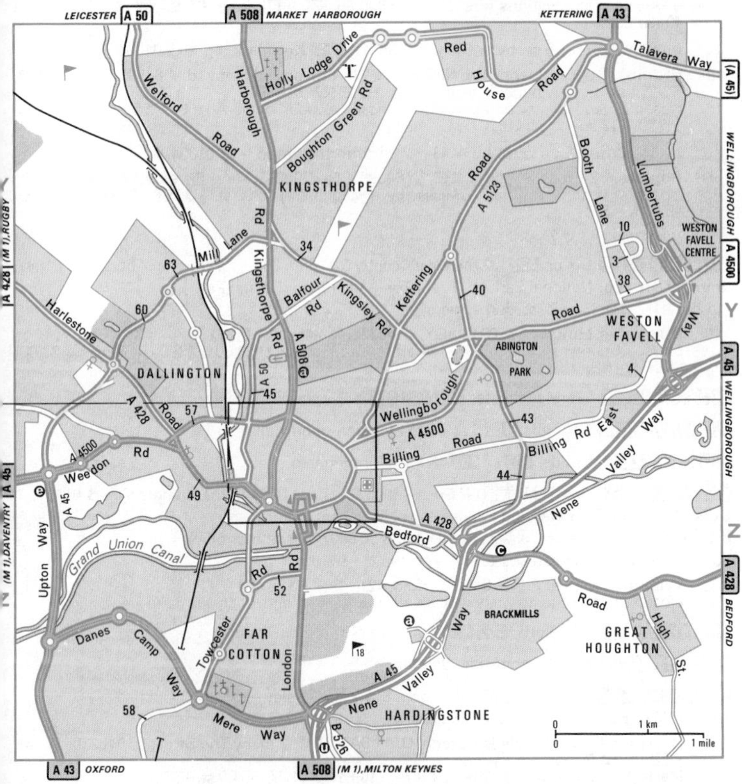

LEICESTER A 50
A 508 MARKET HARBOROUGH
KETTERING A 43
(A 45)
WELLINGBOROUGH
A 4500
A 45 WELLINGBOROUGH
A 428 BEDFORD
A 428 (M 1), RUGBY
A 45 (M 1), DAVENTRY
A 43 OXFORD
A 508 (M 1), MILTON KEYNES
Y
Z
Holly Lodge Drive
Harborough Rd
Boughton Green Rd
Red House Road
Talavera Way
Welford Road
KINGSTHORPE
Kettering Road
A 5123
Booth Lane
Lumbertubs Way
WESTON FAVELL CENTRE
Mill Lane
Kingsthorpe Rd
Balfour Rd
Kingsley Rd
Harlestone Rd
DALLINGTON
WESTON FAVELL
ABINGTON PARK
Wellingborough Road
A 4500
Billing Road
Billing Rd East
Valley Way
A 428
Spencer Bridge Road
A 4500
Weedon Rd
A 45
Upton Way
Grand Union Canal
Bedford Road
Nene Valley Way
BRACKMILLS
GREAT HOUGHTON
High St.
Danes Camp Way
Towcester Rd
FAR COTTON
London Rd
HARDINGSTONE
Mere Way
B 526
1 km
1 mile

Swallow, Eagle Drive, NN4 7HW, SE : 2 m. by A 428 off A 45 ℘ 768700, Fax 769011, Ⅎ₅, ≘s, ▢ – ⇔ rm ▤ rest ▣ ☎ ♿ ℗ – 🏛 150. ▣ AE ◑ VISA Z a
closed 27 and 28 December – **Meals** 13.50/18.25 **st.** and a la carte ₤ 6.00 – **120 rm** ☐ 92.00/130.00 **st.** – SB.

Stakis Northampton, 100 Watering Lane, Collingtree, NN4 0XW, S : 3 m. on A 508 ℘ 700666, Telex 312523, Fax 702850, Ⅎ₅, ≘s, ▢, ⛱ – ⇔ rm ▤ rest ▣ ☎ ♿ ℗ – 🏛 300. ▣ AE ◑ VISA Z
Meals 12.50/17.95 **t.** and a la carte ₤ 4.90 – ☐ 9.25 – **136 rm** 94.00/104.00 **st.**, 3 suites – SB.

Northampton Moat House (Q.M.H.), Silver St., NN1 2TA, ℘ 22441, Fax 230614, ≘s – |‡| ⇔ rm ▣ ☎ ℗ – 🏛 600. ▣ AE ◑ VISA X n
Meals 12.75 **st.** (lunch) and a la carte 15.95/32.95 **st.** ₤ 4.50 – ☐ 7.50 – **136 rm** 74.00/93.00 **st.**, 4 suites – SB.

Courtyard by Marriott, Bedford Rd, NN4 0YF, SE : 1 ½ m. on A 428 ℘ 22777, Fax 35454, Ⅎ₅ – |‡| ⇔ rm ▤ ▣ ☎ ♿ ℗ – 🏛 30. ▣ AE ◑ VISA JCB Z c
Meals 12.95 **st.** and a la carte ₤ 5.45 – ☐ 7.50 – **104 rm** 66.00/86.00 **st.** – SB.

Midway Toby, London Rd, Wootton, NN4 0TG, S : 2 ½ m. on A 508 ℘ 769676, Fax 769523 – ⇔ rm ▤ rest ▣ ☎ ♿ ℗ – 🏛 60. ▣ AE ◑ VISA Z
Meals (grill rest.) 20.00 **t.** and a la carte ₤ 4.95 – **29 rm** ☐ 59.95/69.95 **t.** – SB.

Queen Eleanor, Newport Pagnell Rd West, Wootton, NN4 0JJ, S : 1 ¾ m. by A 508 on B 526 ℘ 700220, Fax 706191, ⛱ – ▣ ☎ ℗ – 🏛 60 Z u
19 rm.

Lime Trees, 8 Langham Pl., Barrack Rd, NN2 6AA, ℘ 32188, Fax 233012 – ▤ rest ▣ ☎ ℗. ▣ AE ◑ VISA. ⛔ Y a
closed 24 to 26 December and 31 December-1 January – **Meals** (bar lunch)/dinner 15.00 **t.** and a la carte ₤ 4.95 – **21 rm** ☐ 44.00/59.00 **st.**

Travel Inn, Harpole Turn, Weedon Rd, NN7 4DD, W : 3 ¾ m. on A 45 ℘ 832340, Fax 831807 – ⇔ rm ▣ ♿ ℗ – 🏛 60. ▣ AE ◑ VISA. ⛔ Z
Meals (Beefeater grill) a la carte approx. 16.00 **t.** – ☐ 4.95 – **51 rm** 33.50 **t.**

Forte Travelodge without rest., Upton Way (Ring Rd), NN5 6EG, SW : 1 ¾ m. by A 45 ℘ 758395, Reservations (Freephone) 0800 850950 – ▣ ♿ ℗. ▣ AE VISA. ⛔ Z e
40 rm 33.50 **t.**

at Spratton N : 7 m. by A 508 off A 50 – Y – ✉ Northampton – ☎ 01604 :

Broomhill ⛰, Holdenby Rd, NN6 8LD, SW : 1 m. on Holdenby rd ℘ 845959, Fax 845834, ≤, ⛱ heated, ⛱, park, 🎾 – ▣ ☎ ℗. ▣ AE ◑ VISA. ⛔
closed 25 and 26 December – **Meals** *(closed Sunday dinner)* 10.50/17.50 **t.** and a la carte ₤ 5.30 – **13 rm** ☐ 55.00/70.00 **t.** – SB.

at Moulton NE : 4 ½ m. by A 43 – Y – ✉ Northampton – ☎ 01604 :

Poplars, 33 Cross St., NN3 1RZ, ℘ 643983, Fax 790233, ⛱ – ▣ ℗. ▣ AE VISA
closed 1 week Christmas – **Meals** (by arrangement) 15.00 **st.** ₤ 3.75 – **21 rm** ☐ 35.00/45.00 **t.** – SB.

ATS Kingsthorpe Rd ℘ 713303

NORTH BOVEY Devon 403 I 32 **The West Country G.** – pop. 368 – ✉ Newton Abbot – ☎ 01647.
Envir. : Dartmoor National Park★★ (Brent Tor ≤★★, Haytor Rocks ≤★).
♦London 214 – Exeter 13 – ♦Plymouth 31 – Torquay 21.

Blackaller House ⛰, TQ13 8QY, ℘ 40322, ≤, ⛱ – ⇔ ▣ ℗
closed January and February – **Meals** (by arrangement) 20.00 **t.** ₤ 2.00 – **5 rm** ☐ 27.00/60.00 **t.** – SB.

NORTHENDEN Gtr. Manchester 402 403 404 N 23 – see Manchester.

NORTH FERRIBY Humbs. 402 S 22 – see Kingston-upon-Hull.

NORTHFIELD W. Mids. 403 ㉒ 404 ⑳ – see Birmingham.

NORTHLEACH Glos. 403 404 O 28 **Great Britain G.** – pop. 1 654 (inc. Eastington) – ☎ 01451.
See : Church of SS. Peter and Paul★ – Wool Merchants' Brasses★.
ℹ Cotswold Countryside Collection, GL54 3JH ℘ 860715 (summer only).
♦London 84 – ♦Birmingham 63 – Gloucester 21 – ♦Oxford 28 – Swindon 24.

Wickens, Market Pl., GL54 3EJ, ℘ 860421 – ⇔. ▣ AE VISA
closed Sunday and Monday – **Meals** 19.50 **s.** (dinner) and lunch a la carte ₤ 4.75.

NORTH MUSKHAM Notts. 402 404 R 24 – see Newark-on-Trent.

NORTH NEWINGTON Oxon – see Banbury.

NORTH NIBLEY Glos. 403 404 M 29 – pop. 814 – ✉ Dursley – ☎ 01453.
♦London 115 – ♦Bristol 21 – Gloucester 20 – Swindon 32.

Burrows Court ⛰, Nibley Green, GL11 6AZ, NW : 1 m. by The Street ℘ 546230, ⛱, ⛱ – ▣ ℗. ▣ AE VISA. ⛔
Meals (bar lunch)/dinner 12.50 **s.** ₤ 3.75 – **10 rm** ☐ 28.50/45.00 **st.** – SB.

NORTH PERROT Somerset – see Crewkerne.

NORTH PETHERTON Somerset 403 K 30 – see Bridgwater.

NORTH SOMERCOTES Lincs. 402 404 U 23 – ✉ Louth – ☎ 01507.

♦London 165 – Boston 42 – Great Grimsby 16 – Lincoln 40.

Wickham House without rest., Church Lane, Conisholme, LN11 7LX, W : 1 ¾ m. by A 1031 ☎ 358465, – TV P.
closed Christmas and New Year – **3 rm** 26.00/36.00 **st.**

NORTH STIFFORD Essex 404 ㊹ – ✉ Grays – ☎ 01375.

♦London 22 – Chelmsford 24 – Southend-on-Sea 20.

Stifford Moat House (Q.M.H), High Rd, RM16 1UE, at junction of A 13 with A 1012 ☎ 390909, Fax 390426, – rm TV ☎ P – 120. AE VISA
Meals *(closed Saturday lunch)* 13.00/30.00 **st.** and a la carte 6.00 – 8.75 – **96 rm** 59.00/115.00 **t.** – SB.

NORTH STOKE Oxon. – see Wallingford.

NORTH WALSHAM Norfolk 403 404 Y 25 **Great Britain G.** – pop. 9 534 – ECD : Wednesday – ☎ 01692.

Exc. : Blicking Hall★★ *AC*, W : 8½ m. by B 1145, A 140 and B 1354.

♦London 125 – ♦Norwich 16.

Beechwood, 20 Cromer Rd, NR28 0HD, ☎ 403231, Fax 407284, – rest TV ☎ P. AE VISA
Meals 6.00/14.00 **t.** and dinner a la carte 3.25 – **9 rm** 29.00/52.00 **t.** – SB.

Toll Barn without rest., NR28 0JB, S : 1 ½ m. on B 1150 ☎ 403063, Fax 406582, – TV P
closed Christmas – **6 rm** 42.00/46.00.

I prezzi Per ogni chiarimento sui prezzi qui riportati, consultate le spiegazioni alle pagine dell'introduzione.

NORTH WALTHAM Hants. 403 404 Q 30 – pop. 727 – ✉ Basingstoke – ☎ 01256.

♦London 59 – Reading 24 – Southampton 24 – Swindon 52.

Wheatsheaf, RG25 2BB, S : ¾ m. on A 30 ☎ 398282, Fax 398253 – rm TV ☎ P – 80. AE VISA
Meals *(closed Saturday lunch and Bank Holidays)* 9.50/15.00 **st.** and a la carte – **28 rm** 53.50/60.00 **st.** – SB.

NORTON Shrops. – see Telford.

NORTON ST PHILIP Somerset 403 404 N 30 – see Bath (Avon).

NORWICH Norfolk 404 Y 26 **Great Britain G.** – pop. 120 895 – ☎ 01603.

See : City★★ - Cathedral★★ Y – Castle (Museum and Art Gallery★ *AC*) Z – Market Place★ Z.

Envir. : Sainsbury Centre for Visual Arts★ *AC*, W : 3 m. by B 1108 - X.

Exc. : Blicking Hall★★ *AC*, N : 11 m. by A 140 – V - and B 1354 – NE : The Broads★.

Royal Norwich, Drayton High Road, Hellesdon ☎ 425712, V – Sprowston Park, Wroxham Rd ☎ 410657 – Costessy Park, Costessey ☎ 746333 – Bawburgh, Long Lane ☎ 746390.

Norwich Airport : ☎ 411923, N : 3½ m. by A 140 V.

The Guildhall, Gaol Hill, NR2 1NF ☎ 666071.

♦London 109 – ♦Kingston-upon-Hull 148 – ♦Leicester 117 – ♦Nottingham 120.

Plans on following pages

Sprowston Manor, Wroxham Rd, Sprowston, NR7 8RP, NE : 3 ¼ m. on A 1151 ☎ 410871, Fax 423911, – rest rest TV ☎ P – 120. AE VISA. V
Meals 18.00/19.50 **st.** and a la carte 5.95 – 8.50 – **95 rm** 79.00/85.00 **st.**, 1 suite – SB.

Nelson, Prince of Wales Rd, NR1 1DX, ☎ 760260, Fax 620008, – rm rest TV ☎ P – 90. VISA. Z **a**
Meals 9.75/14.50 **st.** and a la carte 4.25 – **132 rm** 73.50/99.50 **st.** – SB.

Maid's Head (Q.M.H.), Tombland, NR3 1LB, ☎ 761111, Fax 613688 – rm TV ☎ P – 100. AE VISA Y **u**
5.95/14.95 **t.** and a la carte – 8.50 – **80 rm** 79.00/98.00 **t.**, 1 suite – SB.

Stakis Norwich, Norwich Airport, NR6 6JA, N : 3 m. by A 140 ☎ 410544, Fax 789935, – rm rest TV ☎ P – 450. AE VISA JCB V
Meals (carving lunch) 12.50/16.00 **st.** and a la carte 4.50 – **108 rm** 65.00/80.00 **st.** – SB.

Friendly, 2 Barnard Rd, Bowthorpe, NR5 9JB, W : 3 ½ m. by A 1074 on A 47 – V – ☎ 741161, Fax 741500, – rm rest TV ☎ P – 180. AE VISA.
Meals *(closed Saturday lunch)* (carving lunch)/dinner 13.50 **st.** and a la carte 13.50/19.40 **st.** 5.50 – 6.75 – **80 rm** 57.75/82.00 – SB.

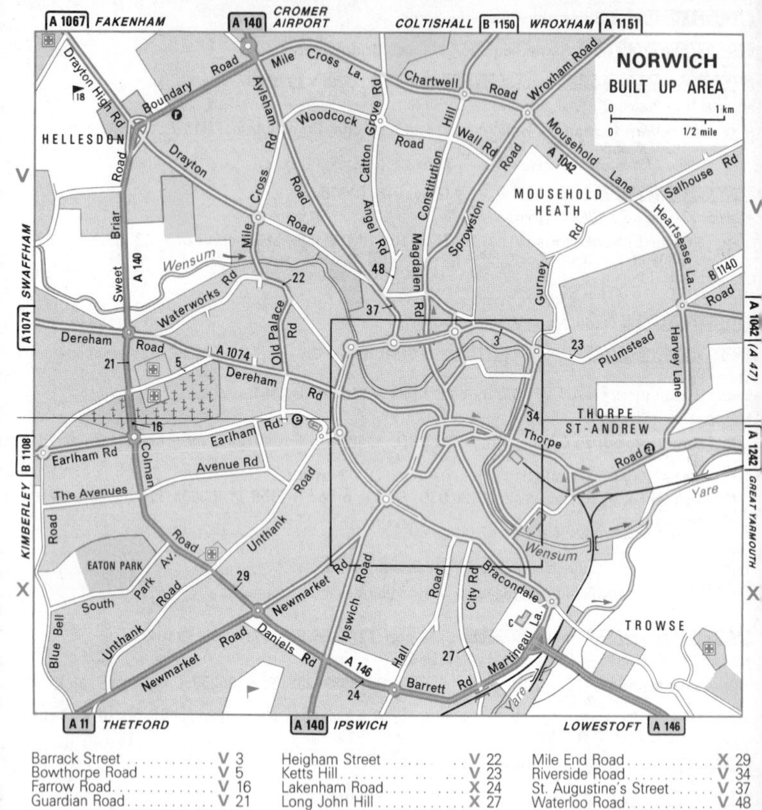

Barrack Street . . . . V 3
Bowthorpe Road . . . . V 5
Farrow Road. . . . . V 16
Guardian Road . . . . V 21
Heigham Street . . . . V 22
Ketts Hill . . . . V 23
Lakenham Road . . . . X 24
Long John Hill . . . . X 27
Mile End Road . . . . X 29
Riverside Road . . . . V 34
St. Augustine's Street . . . . . V 37
Waterloo Road . . . . V 48

Forte Posthouse, Ipswich Rd, NR4 6EP, S : 2¼ m. on A 140 ☏ 56431, Fax 506400, – rm – 65. AE VISA JCB X
Meals a la carte approx. 15.00 **t.** 5.50 – **116 rm** 56.00 **st.**

Norwich, 121 Boundary Rd, NR3 2BA, on A 47 ☏ 787260, Fax 400466, – rm rest – 300. AE VISA. V r
Meals *(closed lunch Saturday and Bank Holiday Mondays)* (carving lunch)/dinner 11.95/14.45 **st.** and a la carte 4.75 – **108 rm** 61.50/77.00 **t.** – SB.

Beeches, 4-6 Earlham Rd, NR2 3DB, ☏ 621167, Fax 620151, – AE VISA. VX e
closed 23 December-31 January – **Meals** (dinner only) 12.50 **t.** 4.00 – **27 rm** 43.00/55.00 **t.** – SB.

Annesley House, 6-8 Newmarket Rd, NR2 2LA, ☏ 624553, Fax 624553, – rest AE VISA. Z c
Meals (bar lunch)/dinner 13.50 **t.** and a la carte 3.95 – **23 rm** 52.50/62.50 **t.** – SB.

Cumberland, 212-216 Thorpe Rd, NR1 1TJ, ☏ 34550, Fax 33355 – AE VISA JCB. X a
closed 25 December-4 January – **Meals** *(closed Sunday lunch)* 9.95/16.50 **t.** and a la carte 3.95 – **25 rm** 36.50/75.00 **t.** – SB.

Old Rectory without rest., Watton Rd, Little Melton, NR9 3PB, W : 5½ m. on B 1108 ☏ 812121, Fax 812521, – X
closed Christmas – **3 rm** 32.00/58.00 **st.**

Adlard's (Adlard), 79 Upper St. Giles St., NR2 1AB, ☏ 633522 – AE VISA Z e
closed Sunday, Monday and 1 week Christmas – **Meals** 15.00/32.00 **t.**
Spec. Char grilled smoked salmon with a tartlet of quails egg, beurre blanc, Rack of English lamb with pesto crust and ratatouille tart, Tulip of Armagnac and prune ice cream with hot spiced compote of prunes.

Marco's, 17 Pottergate, NR2 1DS, ☏ 624044 – . AE VISA Y e
closed Sunday, Monday and 3 weeks September-October – **Meals** - Italian 14.00 **t.** (lunch) and a la carte 23.90/30.10 **t.** 4.85.

NORWICH

Castle Mall Shopping Centre . . . . Z
Elm Hill . . . . Y
Gentleman's Walk . . . . Z 17
London Street . . . . YZ 26
St. Andrew's Street . . . . Y 36
St. Stephen's Street . . . . Z

Bank Plain . . . . Y 2
Bethel Street . . . . Z 4
Castle Meadow . . . . Z 6
Cattle Market Street . . . . Z 7
Chapel Field North . . . . Z 9
Charing Cross . . . . Y 10
Colegate . . . . Y 14
Exchange Street . . . . YZ 15
Grapes Hill . . . . Y 19
Market Avenue . . . . Z 28

Rampant Horse Street . . . . . . Z 32
Red Lion Street . . . . Z 33
St. George's Street . . . . Y 38
Thorn Lane . . . . Z 42
Timber Hill . . . . Z 43
Tombland . . . . Y 45
Upper King Street . . . . Y 46
Wensum Street . . . . Y 49
Westlegate . . . . Z 50
Whitefriars . . . . Y 51

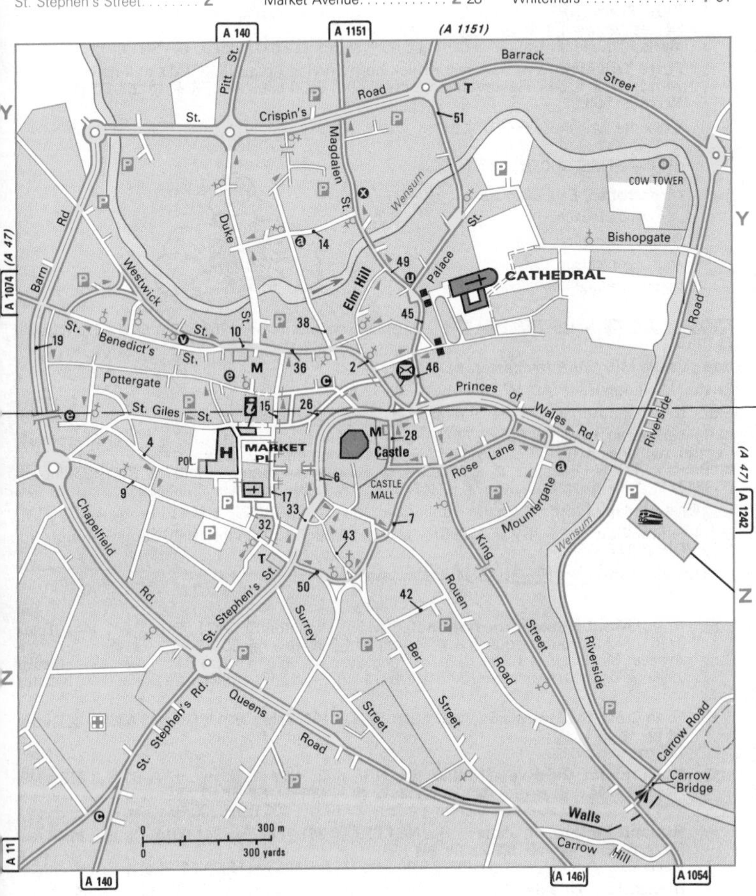

XX **By Appointment,** 27-29 St. Georges St., NR3 1AB, ☎ 630730 – ⇹. AE VISA — Y **a**
closed Sunday and Monday – **Meals** (dinner only) a la carte 19.40/25.10 **t.** 6.95.

XX **Brasted's,** 8-10 St. Andrew's Hill, NR2 1AD, ☎ 625949, Fax 766445 – AE VISA — Y **c**
closed Saturday lunch, Sunday, 24 December to 3 January and Bank Holidays – **Meals** 12.50 **t.** (lunch) and a la carte 21.50/27.00 **t.**

X **Bombay,** 9-11 Magdalen St., NR3 1LE, ☎ 666618 – AE VISA JCB — Y **x**
Meals - Indian a la carte approx. 9.85 **t.**

X **St. Benedicts Grill,** 9 St. Benedicts St., NR2 4PE, ☎ 765377 – AE VISA — Y **v**
closed Sunday, Monday and 25 to 31 December – **Meals** a la carte 14.05/18.60 **t.**

at Horsham St. Faith N : 4½ m. by A 140 – V – ✉ Norwich – ☎ 01603 :

Elm Farm Chalet, Norwich Rd, NR10 3HH, ☎ 898366, Fax 897129, – ⇹ TV ☎ P. AE VISA.
Meals (by arrangement) 12.00 **t.** 2.80 – **18 rm** 29.50/56.00 **t.** – SB.

at Thorpe St. Andrew E : 2 ½ m. on A 1242 – X – ✉ Norwich – ☎ 01603 :

Oaklands, 89 Yarmouth Rd, NR7 0HH, on A 1242 ✆ 34471, Fax 700318, – rest TV ☎ P – 120
38 rm.

at Hethersett SW : 6 m. by A 11 – X – ✉ Norwich – ☎ 01603 :

Park Farm, NR9 3DL, on B 1172 ✆ 810264, Fax 812104, , , , , park, – rest rest TV ☎ P – 120. AE VISA.
Meals 10.50/14.50 **t.** and a la carte 6.00 – **38 rm** 60.00/120.00 **t.** – SB.

Forte Travelodge without rest., Thickthorn Service Area, NR13 9AU, at junction of A 11 with A 47 ✆ 57549, Reservations (Freephone) 0800 850950 – TV ♿ P. AE VISA
40 rm 33.50 **t.**

ATS Mason Rd, Mile Cross Lane ✆ 423471 ATS Aylsham Rd, Aylsham Way ✆ 426316

NOTTINGHAM Notts. 402 403 404 Q 25 **Great Britain G.** – pop. 263 522 – ECD : Thursday – ☎ 0115.

See : Castle Museum★ (alabasters★) *AC*, CZ **M.**

Envir. : Wollaton Hall★ *AC*, W : 3 m. by A 609 AZ **M.**

Exc. : Newstead Abbey★ *AC*, N : 9 m. by A 611 - AY - and B 683.

18 Bulwell Forest, Hucknall Rd ✆ 9770576, AY – 18 Wollaton Park ✆ 9787574, AZ – 18 Mapperley, Central Av., Plains Rd ✆ 9265611, BY – 18 Nottingham City, Lawton Drive ✆ 9278021 – 18 Beeston Fields, Beeston ✆ 9257062 – 18 Ruddington Grange, Wilford Rd, Ruddington ✆ 9846141, BZ – 9, 9 Edwalton ✆ 9234775, BZ - 9 (x 3) Cotgrave ✆ 9334686.

East Midlands Airport, Castle Donington : ✆ (01332) 810621, SW : 15 m. by A 453 AZ.

1-4 Smithy Row, NG1 2BY ✆ 470661 – at West Bridgford : County Hall, Loughborough Rd, NG2 7QP ✆ 977 3558.

♦London 135 – ♦Birmingham 50 – ♦Leeds 74 – ♦Manchester 72.

Plans on following pages

Royal Moat House International (Q.M.H.), Wollaton St., NG1 5RH, ✆ 941 4444, Telex 37101, Fax 947 5667, squash – rm TV ☎ P – 500. AE VISA CY **e**
***Avenue* : Meals** *(closed Saturday lunch and Sunday)* 7.50/14.95 **t.** 6.95 – ***Marcellos* : Meals**-Italian *(closed Sunday lunch)* 5.45/12.75 **t.** 4.85 – 8.50 – **198 rm** 72.50/90.00 **t.**, 3 suites – SB.

Forte Crest, St. James's St., NG1 6BN, ✆ 947 0131, Telex 37211, Fax 948 4366 – rm TV ☎ P – 600 CY **a**
130 rm.

Nottingham Gateway, Nuthall Rd, NG8 6AZ, NW : 3 ¼ m. on A 610 ✆ 979 4949, Fax 979 4744 – rm rest TV ☎ ♿ P – 250. AE VISA. AY
Meals 4.50/25.00 **st.** and a la carte 4.75 – 6.50 – **106 rm** 52.00/85.00 **st.** – SB.

Rutland Square, St. James's St., NG1 6FJ, ✆ 941 1114, Fax 941 0014 – rm rest TV ☎ ♿ P – 150. AE VISA. CZ **c**
Meals 10.50/15.00 **t.** and la carte 9.00 – 7.75 – **103 rm** 55.00/62.00 **t.**, 1 suite – SB.

Strathdon Thistle (Mt. Charlotte Thistle), 44 Derby Rd, NG1 5FT, ✆ 941 8501, Fax 948 3725 – rm rest TV ☎ ♿ – 120. AE VISA CY **c**
Meals *(closed Saturday lunch)* 13.20/15.20 **st.** and a la carte 5.00 – 8.95 – **68 rm** 68.00/130.00 **st.** – SB.

Nottingham Moat House (Q.M.H.), Mansfield Rd, NG5 2BT, ✆ 960 2621, Fax 969 31506 – rm TV ☎ ♿ P – 180. AE VISA BY **u**
Meals 8.95/16.50 **t.** 6.00 – 7.85 – **169 rm** 58.80/78.75 **st.**, 3 suites – SB.

Holiday Inn Garden Court Castle Marina Park, off Castle Boulevard, NG7 1GX, ✆ 950 0600, Fax 950 0433 – rm rest TV ☎ ♿ P – 40. AE VISA JCB
Meals *(closed lunch Saturday and Sunday)* (bar lunch)/dinner 15.00 **st.** and a la carte – 7.50 – **100 rm** 64.50 **st.** – SB. AZ **e**

Priory Toby, Derby Rd, Wollaton Vale, NG8 2NR, W : 3 m. on A 52 ✆ 922 1691 – rm TV ☎ P. AE VISA. AZ **s**
Meals 7.95 **t.** and a la carte – **31 rm** 62.00/73.00 **t.**

Friendly George, George St., NG1 3BP, ✆ 947 5641, Fax 948 3292 – rm TV ☎ P – 150. AE VISA. DY **e**
Meals *(closed lunch Saturday and Sunday)* 13.50 **st.** (dinner) and a la carte 13.50/19.40 **st.** 5.50 – 6.75 – **70 rm** 54.75/70.00 **st.** – SB.

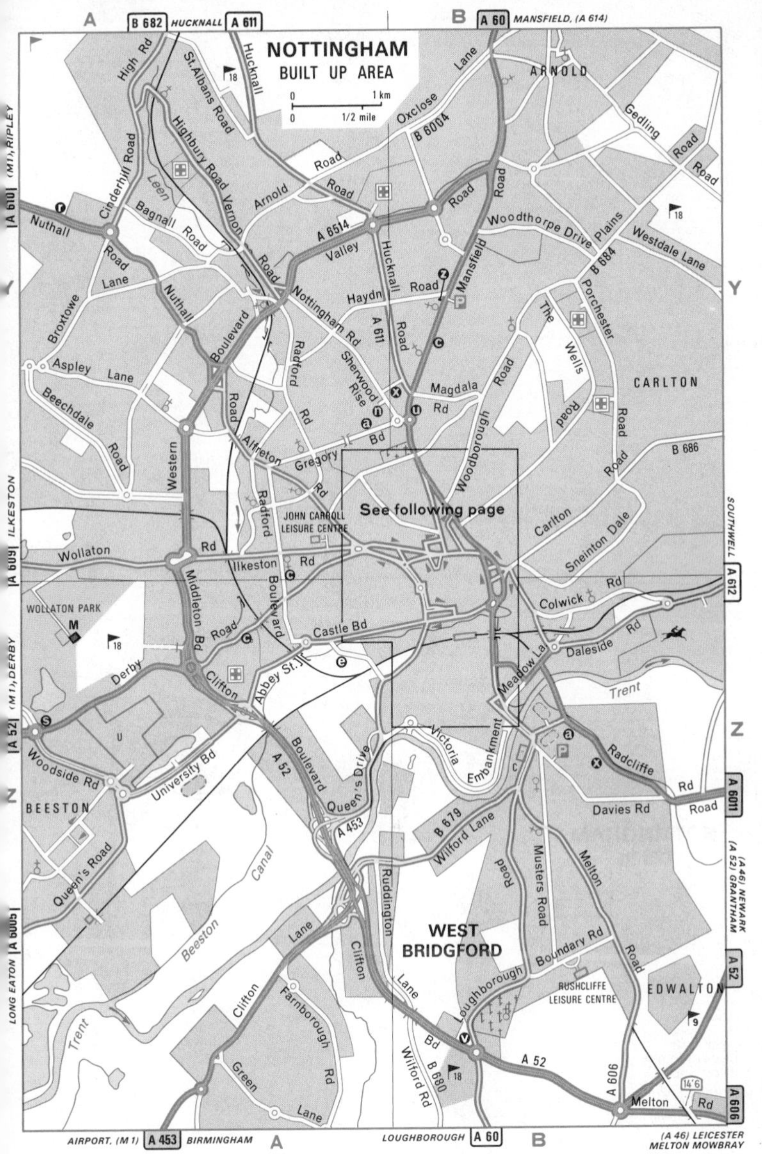

🏨 **Stage,** Gregory Boulevard, NG7 6LB, ✆ 960 3261, Fax 969 1040 – ⇔ rm 📺 ☎ 🅟 – 🧑‍🤝‍🧑 40. AE VISA — AY a

Meals (bar lunch Monday to Saturday)/dinner 10.95 **st.** and a la carte 🍷 5.50 – **52 rm** ☕ 35.00/49.50 **st.** – SB.

🏨 **Woodville,** 340 Mansfield Rd, NG5 2EF, ✆ 960 6436, Fax 985 6846 – rest 📺 ☎ 🅟 – 🧑‍🤝‍🧑 100. AE VISA. — BY c

Meals *(closed Sunday dinner and Bank Holiday Mondays)* (bar lunch Monday to Saturday)/dinner 9.95 **st.** and a la carte 🍷 4.00 – ☕ 3.95 – **45 rm** 39.50/52.50 **st.** – SB.

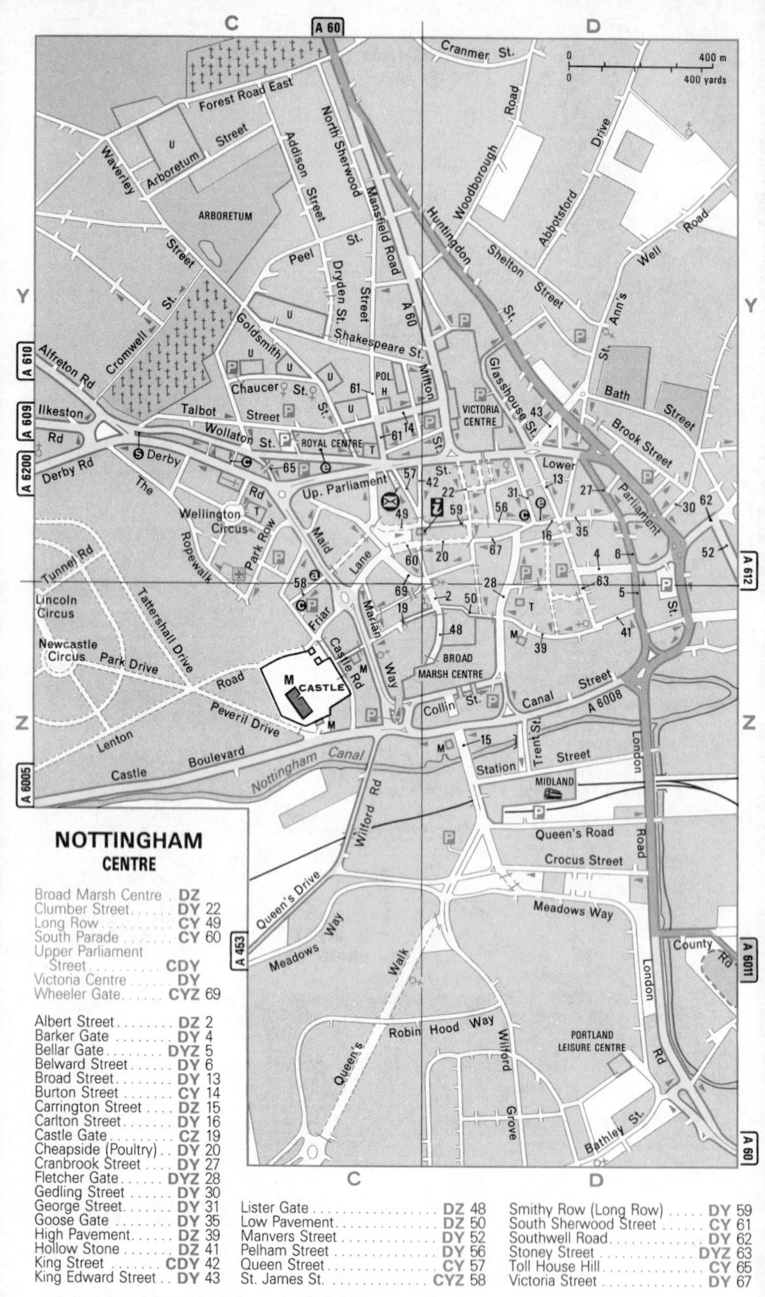

If you find you cannot take up a hotel booking you have made, please let the hotel know immediately.

Greenwood Lodge, Third Av., Sherwood Rise, NG7 6JH, ℘ 962 1206, Fax 962 1206, – . AY **n**
Meals (residents only) (communal dining) (dinner only) (unlicensed) a la carte 9.50/18.00 – **5 rm** 26.00/39.50.

Lucieville St. James, 349 Derby Rd, NG7 2DZ, ℘ 978 7389, Fax 979 0346, – . AZ **c**
Meals (residents only) 7.50/30.00 **st.** and a la carte 9.50 – 9.50 – **8 rm** 45.00/135.00 **st.** – SB.

Nuthall Lodge, 432 Nuthall Rd., NG8 5DQ, NW : 2 ¾ m. on A 610 ℘ 978 4080, Fax 979 0346 – . AY **r**
closed 31 December-2 January – **Meals** (residents only) 12.00/18.40 **st.** and a la carte 4.75 – 7.50 – **7 rm** 35.00/55.00 **st.** – SB.

Claremont without rest., 2 Hamilton Rd, Sherwood Rise, NG5 1AU, ℘ 960 8587, Fax 960 8587, – . BY **x**
closed Christmas – **14 rm** 29.40/41.15 **t.**

Sonny's, 3 Carlton St., NG1 1NL, ℘ 947 3041, Fax 950 7776 – DY **c**
closed 1 week Christmas and Bank Holidays – **Meals** 13.95 **t.** and a la carte 6.75.

Saagar, 473 Mansfield Rd, Sherwood, NG5 2DR, ℘ 962 2014 – . BY **z**
closed Christmas Day – **Meals** - Indian 7.00/9.00 **t.** and a la carte 4.90.

Ben Bowers, 128 Derby Rd (basement), NG1 5FB, ℘ 941 3388 – CY **s**
closed Monday and Saturday lunch, Sunday and 25 to 26 December – **Meals** 8.95/20.00 **t.** and a la carte 4.75.

Higoi, 57 Lenton Boulevard, NG7 2FQ, ℘ 942 3379 – AY **c**
closed Sunday and lunch Monday-Tuesday – **Meals** - Japanese 5.90/32.50 **st.** and a la carte.

at West Bridgford SE : 2 m. on A 52 – ✉ Nottingham – 0115 :

Swans, 84-90 Radcliffe Rd, NG2 5HH, ℘ 981 4042, Fax 945 5745 – – 50. . BZ **a**
Meals *(closed Saturday lunch and Sunday dinner)* 13.95 **t.** and a la carte 8.95 – **30 rm** 39.50/49.50 **t.**, 1 suite – SB.

Windsor Lodge, 116 Radcliffe Rd, NG2 5HG, ℘ 952 8528, Fax 952 0020 – – 30. . BZ **x**
Meals *(closed Friday to Sunday)* (residents only) (dinner only) 14.75 **st.** and a la carte – **48 rm** 33.00/52.00 **st.** – SB.

Nottingham Knight, Loughborough Rd, NG11 6LS, S : 2 m. on A 60 at junction with A 52 ℘ 921 1171, Fax 405034 – rm BZ **v**
Meals (grill rest.) – **42 rm.**

at Plumtree SE : 5 ¾ m. by A 60 - BZ - off A 606 – ✉ Nottingham – 0115 :

Perkins, Old Railway Station, Station Rd, NG12 5NA, ℘ 937 3695, Fax 937 6405 – .
closed Sunday, Monday and Bank Holidays – **Meals** - Bistro a la carte 14.50/19.15 **t.**

at Long Eaton (Derbs.) SW : 8 m. on A 6005 – AZ – ✉ Long Eaton – 0115 :

Novotel, Bostock Lane, NG10 4EP, NW : 1 ¾ m. by A 6005 on B 6002 ℘ 972 0106, Fax 946 5900, heated, – rm – 200.
Meals 8.00/15.00 **st.** and dinner a la carte – 7.50 – **105 rm** 42.50 **st.**

Sleep Inn, Bostock Lane, NG10 5NL, NW : 1 ¾ m. by A 6005 on B 6002 ℘ 946 0000, Fax 946 0726 – rm – 60. .
closed 24 December-3 January – **Meals** a la carte 9.50/16.50 **t.** 4.95 – 4.95 – **101 rm** 29.95/39.50 **t.**

at Sandiacre (Derbs.) SW : 7 ½ m. by A 52 – AZ – on B 5010 – ✉ Nottingham – 0115 :

Forte Posthouse, Bostocks Lane, NG10 5NJ, SW : ¾ m. at junction 25 of M 1 ℘ 939 7800, Fax 949 0469 – rm – 50.
Meals a la carte approx. 15.00 **t.** 5.50 – **91 rm** 56.00/69.50 **t.**

ATS 116 Highbury Rd, Bulwell ℘ 927 8824
ATS 66 Castle Boulevard ℘ 947 6678
ATS 126-132 Derby Rd, Stapleford ℘ 939 2986
ATS Oxford St., Long Eaton, Derbs. ℘ 973 2156

NUNEATON Warks. 403 404 P 26 – pop. 60 377 – ECD : Thursday – 01203.

Purley Chase, Pipers Lane, Ridge Lane ℘ 393118.

Nuneaton Library, Church St., CV11 4DR ℘ 384027.

♦London 107 – ♦Birmingham 25 – ♦Coventry 10 – ♦Leicester 18.

Longshoot Toby, Watling St., CV11 6JH, NE : 2 ½ m. on A 47 at junction with A 5 ℘ 329711, Fax 344570 – rm . .
closed 2 weeks Christmas-New Year – **Meals** (grill rest.) 7.95 **t.** and a la carte 4.75 – **47 rm** 45.00/55.00 **t.**

Travel Inn, Coventry Rd, CY10 7PJ, S : 2½ m. by A 444 on B 4113 ℘ 343584, Fax 327156, – rm TV & P. AE VISA.
closed 24 to 26 December – **Meals** (Beefeater grill) a la carte approx. 16.00 **t.** – 4.95 – **48 rm** 33.50 **t.**

Forte Travelodge, St. Nicholas Park Drive, CV11 6EN, NE : 1½ m. by A 47 (Hinkley Rd) ℘ 353885, Reservations (Freephone) 0800 850950 – TV & P. AE VISA.
Meals (Harvester grill) a la carte approx. 16.00 **t.** – 4.95 – **28 rm** 33.50 **t.**

Forte Travelodge without rest., CV10 7TF, S : 1½ m. on A 444 (southbound carriageway) ℘ 382541, Reservations (Freephone) 0800 850950 – TV & P. AE VISA.
40 rm 33.50 **t.**

at Sibson (Leics.) N : 7 m. on A 444 – ✉ Nuneaton – 01827 :

Millers', Main Rd, CV13 6LB, ℘ 880223, Fax 880223 – TV ☎ P. AE VISA
Meals *(closed Saturday lunch)* 10.95/14.95 st. 4.00 – 5.95 – **40 rm** 41.50/49.50 **st.** – SB.

at Bulkington SE : 4 m. by B 4114 on B 4112 – ✉ Nuneaton – 01203 :

Weston Hall, Weston Lane, CV12 9RU, NW : 1¼ m. by B 4112 ℘ 312989 – TV ☎ P – 70. AE VISA
Meals 14.95/16.45 **st.** and a la carte – **25 rm** 45.00/80.00 **st.** – SB.

ATS Weddington Rd ℘ 341130/341139

NUNNINGTON N. Yorks. 402 R 21 – see Helmsley.

OADBY Leics. 402 403 404 R 26 – see Leicester.

OAKHAM Leics. 402 404 R 25 – pop. 8 691 – ECD : Thursday – 01572.

Oakham Library, Catmose St., LE15 6HW ℘ 724329.

London 103 – Leicester 26 – Northampton 35 – Nottingham 28.

Whipper-Inn, Market Pl., LE15 6DT, ℘ 756971, Fax 757759 – TV ☎ – 50. AE VISA
Meals 9.95/12.95 **t.** and a la carte – **24 rm** 55.00/80.00 **st.** – SB.

Barnsdale Lodge, The Avenue, Rutland Water, LE15 8AH, E : 2 m. on A 606 ℘ 724678, Fax 724961 – rest TV ☎ P – 220. VISA JCB
Meals 9.00/20.00 **st.** and a la carte – **17 rm** 49.50/79.50 **st.** – SB.

Boultons, 4 Catmose St., LE15 6HW, ℘ 722844, Fax 724473 – TV ☎ & P – 60. AE VISA
Meals 14.00 **st.** and a la carte 5.50 – **25 rm** 45.00/55.00 **st.** – SB.

at Hambleton E : 3 m. by A 606 – ✉ Oakham – 01572 :

Hambleton Hall, LE15 8TH, ℘ 756991, Fax 724721, ≤ Rutland water, heated, , park, – TV ☎ P. AE VISA
Meals 29.50 **st.** and a la carte 6.50 – **15 rm** 120.00/265.00 **st.** – SB
Spec. Chilled consommé of tomatoes with a langoustine and basil cream, Crispy roast Gressingham duck with a cherry and almond sauce, Dome of nougatine filled with crème brûlée.

OAKLEY Hants. 403 404 Q 30 – see Basingstoke.

OBORNE Dorset 403 404 M 31 – see Sherborne.

OCKHAM Surrey 404 S 30 – pop. 407 – ✉ Ripley – 01483.

London 27 – Guildford 9.

Hautboy, Ockham Lane, GU23 6NP, ℘ 225355, Fax 211176, – rest TV ☎ P. AE VISA.
Meals 13.95/22.50 **t.** and a la carte 5.00 – 5.95 – **5 rm** 78.00/98.00 **t.**

ODIHAM Hants. 404 R 30 – pop. 4 886 – ECD : Wednesday – 01256.

London 51 – Reading 16 – Winchester 25.

George, 100 High St., RG25 1LP, ℘ 702081, Fax 704213, « 15C inn » – rm TV ☎ P. AE VISA
Meals *(closed dinner Sunday and Monday)* a la carte 18.75/25.25 **t.** 5.25 – **18 rm** 62.00/85.00 **t.**

OGBOURNE ST. GEORGE Wilts. 403 404 O 29 – see Marlborough.

OKEHAMPTON Devon 403 H 31 **The West Country G.** – pop. 4 641 – ECD : Wednesday – 01837.

Exc. : S : Dartmoor National Park★★ (Brent Tor ≤★★, Haytor Rocks ≤★) – Lydford★★ (Lydford Gorge★★) S : 8 m. by B 3260 and A 386.

Okehampton ℘ 52113.

Court Yard, 3 West St., EX20 1HQ ℘ 53020 (summer only).

London 226 – Exeter 25 – Plymouth 30.

Forte Travelodge without rest., Sourton Cross, EX20 4LY, SW : 4 m. by A 30 on A 386 ℘ 52124, Reservations (Freephone) 0800 850950 – TV & P. AE VISA.
32 rm 33.50 **t.**

at Sourton SW : 5 m. by A 30 on A 386 – ✉ Okehampton – ☎ 01837 86 :

Collaven Manor ⚘, EX20 4HH, SW : ¾ m. on A 386 ☎ 522, Fax 570, « 15C manor house, gardens » – ⚡ rest TV ☎ P. AE VISA
closed 3 January to 1 February – **Meals** *(closed Monday lunch)* 9.95/18.95 **t.** – **9 rm** 45.00/69.00 **t.** – SB.

ATS Crediton Rd ☎ 53277/52799

OLD Northants. – ☎ 01604.

◆London 77 – ◆Birmingham 58 – ◆Leicester 26 – Northampton 6.

Wold Farm ⚘, Harrington Rd, NN6 9RJ, ☎ 781258, park – ⚡ P
Meals (by arrangement) (communal dining) 12.00 **s.** – **6 rm** 22.00/44.00 **s.**

OLD BROWNSOVER Warks. – see Rugby.

OLD BURGHCLERE Berks. 404 Q 29 – pop. 286 – ✉ Newbury – ☎ 01635.

◆London 77 – ◆Bristol 76 – Newbury 10 – Reading 27 – ◆Southampton 28.

Dew Pond, RG15 9LH, ☎ 278408, ← – ⚡ P. VISA
closed Sunday, Monday, first 2 weeks January and 2 weeks August – **Meals** (dinner only) 16.50 **t.** and a la carte 6.00.

OLDBURY W. Mids. – see Birmingham.

OLD BYLAND N.Yorks. – see Helmsley.

OLD DALBY Leics. 402 404 R 25 – see Melton Mowbray.

OLDHAM Gtr. Manchester 402 404 N 23 – pop. 107 095 – ECD : Tuesday – ☎ 0161.

18 Crompton and Royton, High Barn, Royton ☎ 624 2154 – 18 Lees New Rd ☎ 624 4986.

Central Library, 84 Union St., OL1 1DN ☎ 678 4654.

◆London 212 – ◆Leeds 36 – ◆Manchester 7 – ◆Sheffield 38.

Plan : see Manchester

Smokies Park, Ashton Rd, Bardsley, OL8 3HX, S : 2 ¾ m. on A 627 ☎ 624 3405, Telex 667490, Fax 627 5262, – TV ☎ P – 150. AE VISA.
Meals (bar lunch Saturday) (dancing Friday and Saturday evenings) 13.50 **st.** and a la carte 5.00 – **47 rm** 52.00/75.00 – SB.

De Vere Bower, Hollinwood Av., Chadderton, OL9 8DE, SW : 3¼ m. by A 62 on A 6104 ☎ 682 7254, Fax 683 4605, – ⚡ rm TV ☎ P – 200. AE VISA BV **e**
Meals *(closed Saturday lunch)* 12.00 **st.** and a la carte 4.80 – **63 rm** 65.00/75.00 **st.** – SB.

Avant, Windsor Rd, Manchester St., OL8 4AS, ☎ 627 5500, Fax 627 5896 – ⚡ rm rest TV ☎ P – 250. AE VISA. BV
Meals *(closed Sunday lunch)* 8.50/14.75 **t.** and a la carte 6.75 – **101 rm** 62.50/70.50 **t.**, 2 suites – SB.

Periquito, Manchester St., OL8 1UZ, ☎ 624 0555, Fax 627 2031, – ⚡ rm TV ☎ P – 320. AE VISA JCB BV
Meals (bar lunch Monday to Saturday)/dinner 14.00 **st.** and a la carte 7.95 – 6.00 – **130 rm** 39.00 **st.**

ATS 169-171 Huddersfield Rd ☎ 633 1551 ATS 179-185 Hollins Rd ☎ 627 0180/665 1958

OLD SODBURY Avon 403 404 M 29 – ECD : Thursday – ✉ Bristol – ☎ 01454.

18, 9 Chipping Sodbury ☎ 312024.

◆London 110 – Bristol 14 – Gloucester 30 – Swindon 29.

Sodbury House without rest., BS17 6LU, ☎ 312847, Fax 273105, – TV ☎ P – 30. AE VISA.
closed 24 December-4 January – **13 rm** 40.00/70.00 **t.**

Dornden ⚘, Church Lane, BS17 6NB, ☎ 313325, Fax 312263, ←, – TV P
closed 3 weeks September-October and Christmas-New Year – **Meals** 8.50 **t.** – **9 rm** 34.00/49.00 **t.** – SB.

OMBERSLEY Heref. and Worcs 403 404 N 27 – ☎ 01905.

◆London 148 – ◆Birmingham 42 – Leominster 33.

Greenlands ⚘ without rest., Uphampton, WR9 0JP, NW : 1 ½ m. by A 449 taking second turning to Uphampton ☎ 620873, ←, « 16C cottage », – ⚡ TV P
3 rm 17.00/38.00 **st.**

ORMSKIRK Lancs. 402 L 23 – pop. 21 939 – ECD : Wednesday – ☎ 01695.

◆London 219 – ◆Liverpool 12 – Preston 18.

Beaufort, High Lane, Burscough, L40 7SN, NE : 1 ¾ m. by B 5319 on A 59 ☎ 892655, Fax 895135 – TV ☎ P – 40
21 rm.

OSWESTRY Shrops. 402 403 K 25 – pop. 33 508 – ECD : Thursday – ☎ 01691.

Aston Park ☎ 610221 – Llanymynech Pant ☎ 830542.

Mile End Services, SY11 4JA ☎ 662488 – The Heritage Centre, The Old School, Church Ter., SY11 2TE ☎ 662753 (summer only).

London 182 – Chester 28 – Shrewsbury 18.

Wynnstay, Church St., SY11 2SZ, ☎ 655261, Fax 670606, – 180.
Meals a la carte 14.50/23.20 **t.** 4.25 – 8.95 – **26 rm** 49.95/65.00 **t.**, 1 suite – SB.

Forte Travelodge without rest., Mile End Service Area, SY11 4JA, SE : 1 ¼ m. at junction of A 5 with A 483 ☎ 658178, Reservations (Freephone) 0800 850950 – .
40 rm 33.50 **t.**

Ashfield, Llwyn-y-Maen, Trefonen Rd, SY10 9DD, SW : 1½ m. ☎ 655200, – rest
10 rm.

Starlings Castle with rm, Bron y Garth, SY10 7NU, NW : 7 ¼ m. by B 4579, via Selattyn ☎ 718464, Fax 718464, – .
Meals (lunch by arrangement Monday to Saturday)/dinner a la carte 17.75/24.50 **t.** – 4.00 – **8 rm** 25.00/40.00 **t.**

Sebastian, 45 Willow St., SY11 1AQ, ☎ 655444, Fax 653452 –
closed Tuesday and Saturday lunch, Sunday and Monday – **Meals** 15.95/17.95 **st.** and dinner a la carte.

ATS Oswald Rd ☎ 653540/653256

OTLEY Suffolk 404 X 27 – pop. 1 381 – ✉ Ipswich – ☎ 01473.

London 83 – Ipswich 7.5 – Norwich 43.

Otley House , IP6 9NR, ☎ 890253, Fax 890009, , « Part 17C manor house », – .
March-October – **Meals** *(closed Sunday except at Bank Holidays)* (by arrangement) (communal dining) 16.50 **st.** 4.00 – **4 rm** 42.00/62.00 **st.**

OTLEY W. Yorks. 402 O 22 – pop. 13 596 – ☎ 01943.

West Busk Lane ☎ 461015.

Council Offices, 8 Boroughgate, LS21 3AH ☎ 477707.

London 216 – Harrogate 14 – Leeds 12 – York 28.

Chevin Lodge , Yorkgate, LS21 3NU, S : 2 m. by East Chevin Rd ☎ 467818, Fax 850335, « Pine log cabin village », , , , park, – – 120. .
Meals *(closed Saturday lunch)* 10.50/17.25 **st.** and a la carte – **51 rm** 82.00/102.00 **st.** – SB.

OULTON Suffolk – see Lowestoft.

OUNDLE Northants. 404 S 26 – pop. 3 996 – ECD : Wednesday – ✉ Peterborough – ☎ 01832.

Benefield Rd ☎ 273267.

14 West St., PE8 4EF ☎ 274333.

London 89 – Leicester 37 – Northampton 30.

Talbot (Forte), New St., PE8 4EA, ☎ 273621, Fax 274545, – – 50.
Meals (bar lunch Monday to Saturday)/dinner 22.95 **st.** and a la carte 6.95 – 8.50 – **38 rm** 55.00/65.00 **st.**, 1 suite – SB.

at Fotheringhay N : 3¾ m. by A 427 off A 605 – ✉ Peterborough (Cambs.) – ☎ 01832 :

Castle Farm, PE8 5HZ, ☎ 226200, « Riverside garden » – rm .
Meals (by arrangement) 9.00 **st.** – **6 rm** 30.00/48.00 **st.**

at Upper Benefield W : 5 m. on A 427 – ✉ Peterborough (Cambs.) – ☎ 01832 :

Wheatsheaf, PE8 5AN, ☎ 205254, Fax 205245, – .
Meals 14.00 **t.** and a la carte – **9 rm** 45.00/55.00 **st.** – SB.

OUTLANE W. Yorks. – see Huddersfield.

OVER PEOVER Ches. 402 403 404 M 24 – see Knutsford.

OWER Hants 403 404 P 31 – see Romsey.

THE CHANNEL TUNNEL Map Guide

260 *French edition*
with tourist sights in England

261 *English edition*
with tourist sights on the Continent

OXFORD Oxon. 403 404 Q 28 **Great Britain G.** – pop. 110 103 – ECD : Thursday – 01865.

See : City*** - Christ Church** (Hall** *AC*, Tom Quad*, Tom Tower*, Cathedral* *AC* - Choir Roof*) BZ – Merton College** *AC* BZ – Magdalen College** BZ – Ashmolean Museum** BY **M2** – Bodleian Library** (Ceiling**, Lierne Vaulting*) *AC* BZ **F** – St. John's College* BY – The Queen's College* BZ – Lincoln College* BZ – Trinity College (Chapel*) BY – New College (Chapel*) *AC*, BZ – Radcliffe Camera* BZ **A** – Sheldonian Theatre* *AC*, BZ **G** – University Museum* BY **M3** – Pitt Rivers Museum* BY **M4**.

Envir. : Iffley Church* AZ **A**.

Exc. : Woodstock : Blenheim Palace*** (The Grounds***) *AC*, NW : 8 m. by A 4144 and A 34 AY.

St. Aldates, OX1 1DY ✆ 726871.

London 59 – Birmingham 63 – Brighton 105 – Bristol 73 – Cardiff 107 – Coventry 54 – Southampton 64.

Plans on following pages

Randolph (Forte), Beaumont St., OX1 2LN, ✆ 247481, Fax 791678 – rm – 300. AE VISA JCB BY **n**
Meals 17.00/35.00 **t.** and a la carte 8.50 – 10.50 – **104 rm** 100.00/160.00 **t.**, 5 suites – SB.

Old Parsonage, 1 Banbury Rd, OX2 6NN, ✆ 310210, Fax 311262, « Part 17C house », – . AE VISA. BY **e**
closed 24 to 26 December – **Meals** (room service and meals in bar only) a la carte 17.55/27.90 **t.** 5.90 – **30 rm** 105.00/190.00.

Eastgate (Forte), High St., OX1 4BE, ✆ 248244, Fax 791681 – rest . AE VISA JCB BZ **c**
Meals (bar lunch Monday to Saturday)/dinner 17.95 **st.** and a la carte 4.65 – 8.50 – **43 rm** 85.00/105.00 **st.** – SB.

Oxford Moat House (Q.M.H.), Wolvercote Roundabout, OX2 8AL, ✆ 59933, Telex 837926, Fax 310259, , , , squash – rm rest – 150. AE VISA AY
closed 27 to 30 December – **Meals** (bar lunch Saturday) (carving lunch) 10.50/16.50 **st.** 5.75 – 9.50 – **155 rm** 92.00/170.00 **st.** – SB.

Linton Lodge (Hilton), Linton Rd, OX2 6UJ, ✆ 53461, Fax 310365, – – 120. AE JCB AY **n**
Meals *(closed Saturday lunch)* 8.90/17.25 **st.** 7.50 – 9.95 – **70 rm** 95.00/115.00 **st.** – SB.

Bath Place, 4-5 Bath Pl., OX1 3SU, ✆ 791812, Fax 791834, « 17C Flemish weavers cottages » – rest rest . AE VISA. BY **a**
Meals *(closed Tuesday lunch, Sunday dinner and Monday)* 16.50/21.50 **t.** and a la carte 5.00 – 7.50 – **8 rm** 70.00/100.00 **t.** 2 suites.

Pine Lodge without rest., 201 Cumnor Hill, OX2 9PJ, SW : 3 ¼ m. by A 420 off B 4044 ✆ 862217, Fax 864468 – AY **z**
6 rm.

Cotswold House without rest., 363 Banbury Rd, OX2 7PL, ✆ 310558, Fax 310558, – . AY **c**
7 rm 36.00/53.00 **st.**

Chestnuts without rest., 45 Davenant Rd, OX2 8BU, ✆ 53375, Fax 53375 – . AY **s**
closed 22 December-6 January – **4 rm** 32.00/48.00.

Marlborough House without rest., 321 Woodstock Rd, OX2 7NY, ✆ 311321, Fax 515329 – . VISA. AY **v**
closed 23 December-2 January – **12 rm** 53.00/63.00 **t.**

Mount Pleasant, 76 London Rd., Headington, OX3 9AJ, ✆ 62749, Fax 62749 – . AE VISA JCB. AY **a**
Meals 15.00 **st.** 4.50 – **8 rm** 45.00/75.00 – SB.

Dial House without rest., 25 London Rd, Headington, OX3 7RE, ✆ 69944, –
closed Christmas and New Year – **8 rm** 40.00/50.00 **st.** AY **o**

Tilbury Lodge without rest., 5 Tilbury Lane, Botley, OX2 9NB, W : 2 m. by A 420 off B 4044 ✆ 862138, Fax 863700, – . VISA. AZ **e**
9 rm 40.00/61.00 **st.**

Fifteen North Parade, 15 North Parade Av., OX2 6LX, ✆ 513773 – VISA AY **r**
closed Sunday dinner, Monday and last 2 weeks August – **Meals** 12.00/22.00 **t.** and a la carte 5.75.

Michel's Café Français, 146 London Rd, Headington, OX3 9ED, ✆ 62587 – AE VISA AY **u**
closed 1 January lunch, 25-26 December and Bank Holidays – **Meals** 7.45/14.95 **t.** and a la carte 5.95. BZ **a**

Gee's, 61 Banbury Rd, OX2 6PE, ✆ 53540, Fax 310308, « Conservatory » – . VISA AY **r**
closed 25 and 26 December – **Meals** a la carte 15.90/25.45 **t.** 6.95.

Michael's, 36 St. Michael's St., OX1 2EB, ✆ 724241

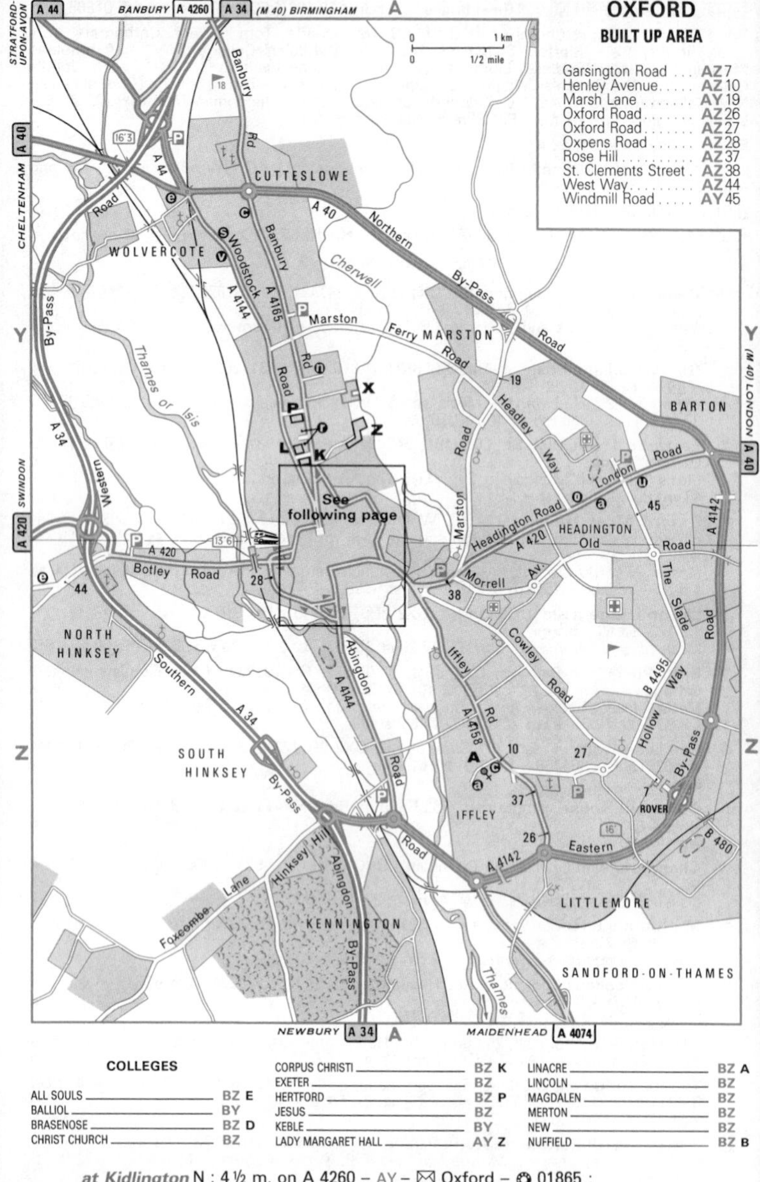

COLLEGES

ALL SOULS	BZ	E	CORPUS CHRISTI	BZ	K	LINACRE	BZ	A
BALLIOL	BY		EXETER	BZ		LINCOLN	BZ	
BRASENOSE	BZ	D	HERTFORD	BZ	P	MAGDALEN	BZ	
CHRIST CHURCH	BZ		JESUS	BZ		MERTON	BZ	
			KEBLE	BY		NEW	BZ	
			LADY MARGARET HALL	AY	Z	NUFFIELD	BZ	B

at Kidlington N : 4 ½ m. on A 4260 – AY – ✉ Oxford – ☎ 01865 :

Bowood House, 238 Oxford Rd, OX5 1EB, ✆ 842288, Fax 841858 – ⇔ rest TV ☎ ♿ P. AE VISA. ✗
closed 24 December-2 January – **Meals** *(closed Sunday)* (dinner only) a la carte 8.75/16.15 **st.** – **22 rm** ☐ 32.00/62.00 – SB.

at Wheatley E : 7 m. by A 40 – AY – ✉ Oxford – ☎ 01865 :

Forte Travelodge, London Rd, OX9 1JH, ✆ 875705, Reservations (Freephone) 0800 850950 – TV ♿ P. AE AE VISA. ✗
Meals (Harvester grill) a la carte approx. 16.00 **t.** – ☐ 5.50 – **24 rm** 33.50 **t.**

OXFORD

Broad Street . . . . BZ 3
Clarendon Shopping Centre BZ
Cornmarket Street. . . . . BZ 6
George Street . . . . BZ 9
High Street . . . . BZ
Queen Street. . . . . BZ 34
Westgate Shopping Centre BZ

Blue Boar Street . . . . BY 2
Castle Street . . . . BZ 5
Hythe Bridge Street . . . . . . BZ 12
Little Clarendon Street . . . . BY 13
Logic Lane. . . . . BZ 14
Magdalen Street. . . . . BYZ 16
Magpie Lane . . . . BZ 17
New Inn Hall Street . . . . . . BZ 20
Norfolk Street . . . . BZ 21
Old Greyfriars Street. . . . . . BZ 23

Oriel Square . . . . BZ 24
Park End Street . . . . BZ 30
Pembroke Street . . . . BZ 31
Queen's Lane . . . . BZ 33
Radcliffe Square . . . . BZ 35
St. Michael
Street . . . . BZ 40
Turl Street . . . . BZ 41
Walton Crescent . . . . BY 42
Worcester Street . . . . BZ 47

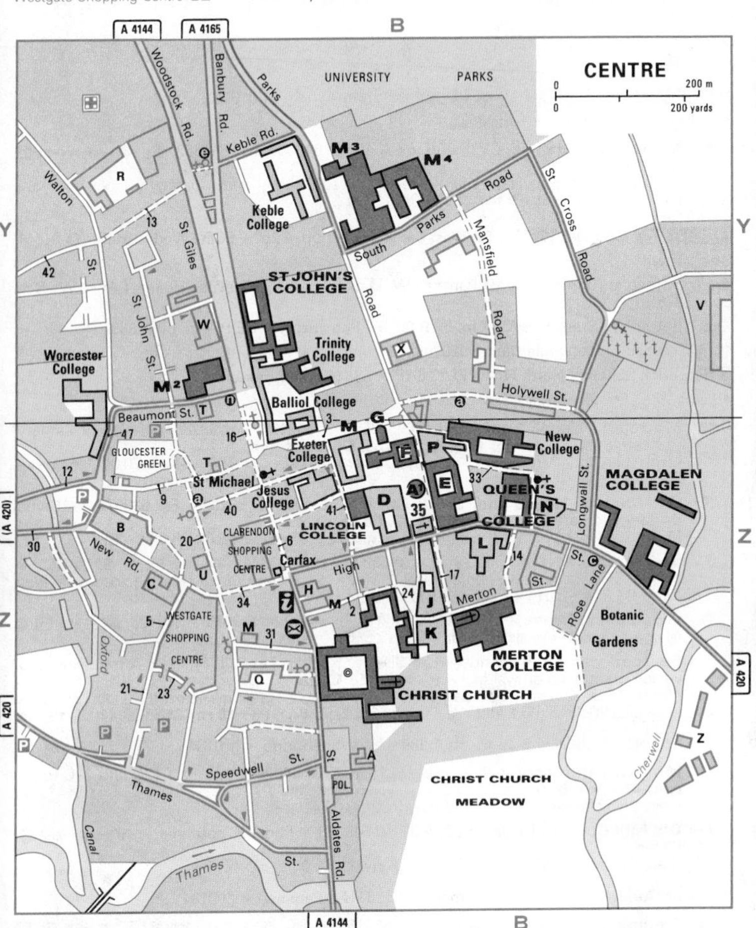

COLLEGES (CONTINUED)

ORIEL	BZ J	ST CROSS	BY W	SOMERVILLE	BY R
PEMBROKE	BZ Q	ST EDMUND'S	BZ N	TRINITY	BY
QUEEN'S	BZ	ST HILDA'S	BZ Z	UNIVERSITY	BZ L
ST ANNE'S	AY K	ST HUGH'S	AY P	WADHAM	BY X
ST ANTHONY'S	AY L	ST JOHN'S	BY	WOLFSON	AY X
ST CATHERINE'S	BY V	ST PETER'S	BZ U	WORCESTER	BY

at Iffley SE : 2 m. by A 4158 – ✉ Oxford – ☎ 01865 :

Hawkwell House, Church Way, OX4 4DZ, ☎ 749988, Fax 748525, – rest – 150. AE VISA AZ **c**
Meals (bar lunch Monday to Saturday)/dinner 15.00 **t.** and a la carte – **21 rm** 70.00/150.00 **t.** – SB.

The Tree, Church Way, OX4 4EY, ☎ 775974, Fax 747554, – . AE VISA. AZ **a**
Meals a la carte 8.25/11.70 **t.** 3.50 – **7 rm** 48.00/60.00 **st.** – SB.

at Great Milton SE : 12 m. by A 40 off A 329 – AY – ✉ Oxford – ☎ 01844 :

Le Manoir aux Quat' Saisons (Blanc) ⑤, Church Rd, OX44 7PD, ℘ 278881, Fax 278847, ←, « Part 15C and 16C manor house, gardens », heated, park, – rest rest ☎ – 35. VISA.
Meals 29.50/65.00 **st.** and a la carte 60.00/79.00 **st.** 14.00 – 14.50 – **16 rm** 165.00/325.00 **st.**, 3 suites – SB
Spec. Queue de homard et son ravioli, Carré d'agneau de lait "Highgrove" rôti et chou farci, Le paquet surprise du Manoir.

ATS Pony Rd, Horspath Trading Est., Cowley ℘ 777188
ATS 2 Stephen Rd, Headington ℘ 61732

OXHILL Warks. 403 404 P 27 – ✉ Stratford-upon-Avon – ☎ 01926.
♦London 85 – ♦Birmingham 32 – ♦Oxford 25.

Nolands Farmhouse, CV35 0RJ, on A 422 ℘ 640309, Fax 641662, – rest VISA.
closed Christmas to New Year – **Meals** *(closed Sunday and Monday)* (dinner only) a la carte 17.00/20.30 **st.** – **9 rm** 25.00/40.00 **st.**

PADSTOW Cornwall 403 F 32 **The West Country G.** – pop. 4 250 – ECD : Wednesday – ☎ 01841.
See : Town★.
Envir. : Trevone (Cornwall Coast Path★★) W : 3 m. by B 3276 – Trevose Head★ (←★★) W : 6 m. by B 3276.
Exc. : Bedruthan Steps★, SW : 7 m. by B 3276 – Pencarrow★, SE : 11 m. by A 389.
18, 9 Trevose, Constantine Bay ℘ 520208.
Red Brick Building, North Quay, PL28 8AF ℘ 533449 (summer only).
♦London 288 – Exeter 78 – ♦Plymouth 45 – Truro 23.

Metropole (Forte), Station Rd, PL28 8DB, ℘ 532486, Fax 532867, ← Camel Estuary, heated, – ☎ – 50. VISA JCB
Meals (bar lunch Monday to Saturday)/dinner 25.00 **st.** – 8.50 – **44 rm** 70.00/105.00 **st.** – SB.

Old Custom House Inn, South Quay, PL28 8ED, ℘ 532359, Fax 533372, ← Camel Estuary and harbour – rest ☎ VISA
Meals (bar lunch)/dinner a la carte 19.85/30.30 **t.** – **27 rm** 58.00/76.00 **t.** – SB.

St. Petroc's, 4 New St., PL28 8EA, ℘ 532700, Fax 533344 – rest ☎. VISA.
closed 23 December-1 February and 1 May – **St. Petrocs Bistro : Meals** *(closed Monday)* 13.95 **t.** 8.00 – **8 rm** 20.00/75.00 **t.** – SB.

Woodlands, Treator, PL28 8RU, W : 1¼ m. by A 389 on B 3276 ℘ 532426, –
March-October – **Meals** 10.00 **st.** – **9 rm** 35.00/50.00 **st.** – SB.

Seafood with rm, Riverside, PL28 8BY, ℘ 532485, Fax 533344, ←, « Attractively converted granary on quayside » – ☎. VISA
closed 17 December-1 February and 1 May – **Meals** - Seafood *(closed Sunday)* (booking essential) 20.25/27.85 **t.** and a la carte 32.25/49.25 **t.** 5.00 – **10 rm** 38.00/110.00 **t.** – SB.

at Little Petherick S : 3 m. on A 389 – ✉ Wadebridge – ☎ 01841 :

Molesworth Manor without rest., PL27 7QT, ℘ 540292, ←, « Part 17C and 19C rectory », – .
closed November – 1.75 – **10 rm** 19.00/50.00 **s.**

Old Mill Country House, PL27 7QT, ℘ 540388, « Part 16C corn mill », – rest .
March-October – **Meals** 11.45 3.00 – **6 rm** 40.00/54.00.

at Constantine Bay SW : 4 m. by B 3276 – ✉ Padstow – ☎ 01841 :

Treglos ⑤, PL28 8JH, ℘ 520727, Fax 521163, ←, , – rest ☎ . VISA.
17 March-4 November – **Meals** 11.00/19.50 **st.** and a la carte 5.90 – **41 rm** 50.50/92.00 **st.**, 3 suites – SB.

at Treyarnon Bay SW : 4¾ m. by B 3276 – ✉ Padstow – ☎ 01841 :

Waterbeach ⑤, PL28 8JW, ℘ 520292, Fax 521102, ←, , – ☎ . VISA.
April-October – **Meals** (bar lunch)/dinner 12.50 **t.** 3.25 – **17 rm** 30.00/84.00 **t.**, 4 suites.

PADWORTH Berks. – ✉ Reading – ☎ 01734.
♦London 58 – Basingstoke 12 – Reading 10.

Padworth Court (Country Club), Bath Rd, RG7 5HT, on A 4 ℘ 714411, Fax 714442, – rm ☎ – 180. VISA.
Meals *(closed Saturday lunch)* 9.95/14.50 **st.** and a la carte 5.75 – 7.50 – **50 rm** 65.70/95.00 **st.** – SB.

PAIGNTON Devon 403 J 32 **The West Country G.** – pop. 39 565 – ECD : Wednesday – ☎ 01803.
See : Torbay★ - Kirkham House★ *AC* Y **B**.
Envir. : Paignton Zoo★★ *AC*, SW : ½ m. by A 3022 AY (see Plan of Torbay).
ℹ The Esplanade, TQ4 6BN ☎ 558383.
♦London 226 – Exeter 26 – ♦Plymouth 29.

Plan of Built up Area : see Torbay

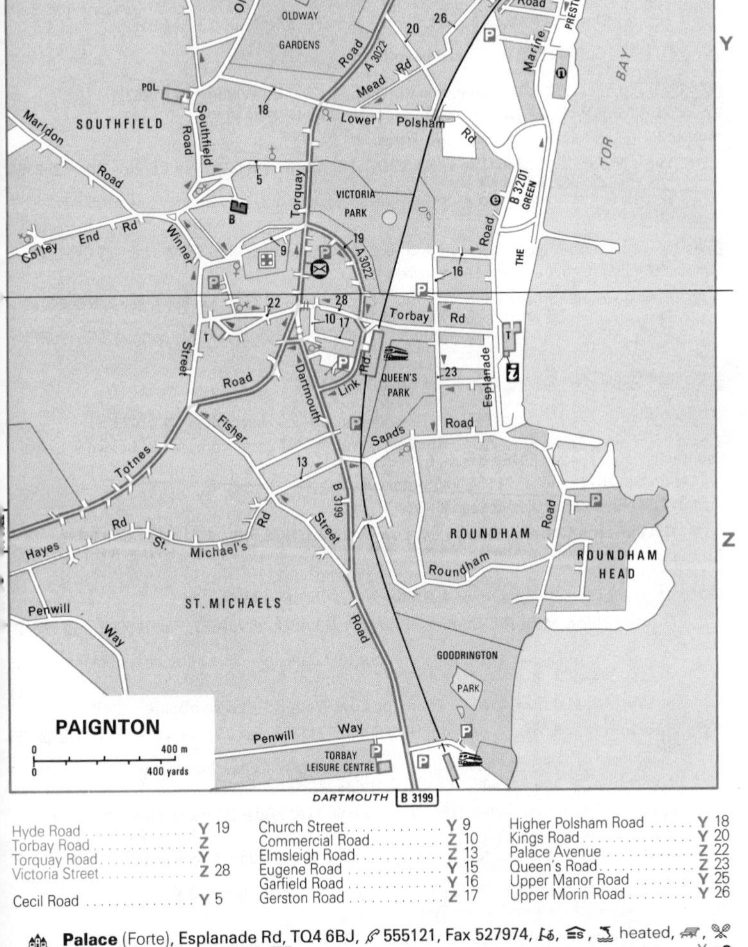

Hyde Road ... Y 19
Torbay Road ... Z
Torquay Road ... Y
Victoria Street ... Z 28

Cecil Road ... Y 5

Church Street ... Y 9
Commercial Road ... Z 10
Elmsleigh Road ... Z 13
Eugene Road ... Y 15
Garfield Road ... Y 16
Gerston Road ... Z 17

Higher Polsham Road ... Y 18
Kings Road ... Y 20
Palace Avenue ... Z 22
Queen's Road ... Z 23
Upper Manor Road ... Y 25
Upper Morin Road ... Y 26

🏨 **Palace** (Forte), Esplanade Rd, TQ4 6BJ, ☎ 555121, Fax 527974, ⛹, ≘s, ⛱ heated, 🌳, 🎾 – 🏢 ⇆ 📺 ☎ 🅿. AE 🅾 VISA — Y **e**
Meals 9.95/16.95 **st.** and dinner a la carte 🍷 9.00 – **52 rm** ☕ 39.00/118.00 **st.**

Redcliffe, 4 Marine Drive, TQ3 2NL, ✆ 526397, Fax 528030, ≤ Torbay, heated, – TV ☎ P – 40. AE VISA.
Meals (bar lunch Monday to Saturday)/dinner 14.75 **t.** and a la carte 4.75 – **59 rm** 46.00/92.00 **t.** – SB.

ATS Orient Rd ✆ 556888/558975

PAINSWICK Glos. 403 404 N 28 **Great Britain G.** – pop. 1 757 – ECD : Saturday – 01452.
See : Town★.
The Library, Stroud Rd, GL6 6DT ✆ 813552 (summer only).
◆London 107 – ◆Bristol 35 – Cheltenham 10 – Gloucester 7.

Painswick, Kemps Lane, GL6 6YB, SE : ½ m. by Bisley St., St. Marys St. and Tibbiwell ✆ 812160, Fax 814059, « Part 18C Palladian house », – TV ☎ P. AE VISA
Meals 14.50/28.00 **st.** and a la carte – **20 rm** 62.00/120.00 **st.** – SB.

Damsell's Lodge without rest., The Park, GL6 6SR, N : 1 m. by A 46 on Sheepscombe rd ✆ 813777, ≤, – TV P.
3 rm 22.00/40.00 **s.**

Country Elephant, New St., GL6 6XH, ✆ 813564 – VISA JCB
closed Monday lunch, Sunday dinner, 25 to 26 December, 1 to 24 January and Bank Holiday Mondays – **Meals** 15.50 **t.** (lunch) and a la carte 17.95/26.95 6.95.

PAKENHAM Suffolk 404 W 27 – see Ixworth.

PARBOLD Lancs. 402 L 23 **Great Britain G.** – pop. 4 129 – ✉ Wigan – 01257.
Envir. : Rufford Old Hall★ (Great Hall★) *AC*, NW : 4 m. by B 5246.
◆London 212 – ◆Liverpool 25 – ◆Manchester 24 – Preston 19.

High Moor, High Moor Lane, WN6 9QA, NE : 3 m. by B 5246 and Chorley Rd ✆ 252364, Fax 255120 – P. AE VISA
closed Sunday dinner and Monday – **Meals** (dinner only and Sunday lunch)/dinner 23.50/28.00 5.00.

PARKGATE Ches. 402 403 K 24 – pop. 3 789 – ECD : Wednesday – ✉ Wirral – 0151.
◆London 206 – Birkenhead 10 – Chester 11 – ◆Liverpool 12.

Parkgate, Boathouse Lane, L64 6RD, N : ½ m. on B 5135 ✆ 336 5001, Fax 336 8504, – rm rest TV ☎ P – 100. AE VISA
Meals (dancing Friday and Saturday night) 9.50/12.95 **t.** and a la carte 4.25 – **27 rm** 49.50/69.00 **t.** – SB.

PATCHWAY Avon 403 404 M 29 – see Bristol.

PATELEY BRIDGE N. Yorks. 402 O 21 **Great Britain G.** – ✉ Harrogate – 01423.
Exc. : Fountains Abbey★★★ *AC* – Studley Royal★★ *AC* (≤★ from Anne Boleyn's Seat) – Fountains Hall (Façade★), NE : 8½ m. by B 6265.
14 High St., HG3 5AW ✆ 711147 (summer only).
◆London 225 – ◆Leeds 28 – ◆Middlesbrough 46 – York 32.

Grassfields Country House, Low Wath Rd, HG3 5HL, ✆ 711412, – TV P
March-November – **Meals** (residents only) (dinner only) 12.00 **t.** 3.00 – **9 rm** 27.00/50.00 – SB.

at Low Laithe SE : 2¾ m. on B 6165 – ✉ Harrogate – 01423 :

Dusty Miller, Main Rd, Summer Bridge, HG3 4BU, ✆ 780837, Fax 780065 – P. AE VISA
closed 2 weeks August and 25 December to 1 January – **Meals** (by arrangement Sunday and Monday)(dinner only) 24.00 **st.** and a la carte 20.70/30.80 4.90.

at Wath-in-Nidderdale NW : 2¼ m. by Low Wath Rd – ✉ Harrogate – 01423 :

Sportsman's Arms with rm, HG3 5PP, ✆ 711306, Fax 712524, – rm TV P. VISA
closed 25 December – **Meals** (in bar Monday to Saturday lunch and Sunday dinner)/dinner 16.50 **st.** and a la carte 5.00 – **7 rm** 30.00/58.00 **st.**

at Ramsgill-in-Nidderdale NW : 5 m. by Low Wath Rd – ✉ Harrogate – 01423 :

Yorke Arms, HG3 5RL, ✆ 755243, Fax 755243 – rest TV ☎ P. VISA.
Meals (bar lunch Monday to Saturday)/dinner 19.50 **t.** 4.95 – **14 rm** 50.00/85.00 **t.** – SB.

PATRICK BROMPTON N. Yorks. 402 P 21 – pop. 145 – ✉ Bedale – 01677.
◆London 228 – ◆Leeds 48 – ◆Newcastle upon Tyne 33 – York 41.

Elmfield House, Arrathorne, DL8 1NE, NW : 2¼ m. by A 684 on Richmond rd ✆ 450558, Fax 450557, , park – rest TV ☎ P. VISA.
Meals 12.50 **st.** 4.50 – **9 rm** 29.00/44.00 **st.**

PAULERSPURY Northants. 403 404 R 27 – see Towcester.

PAYHEMBURY Devon – see Honiton.

PEASMARSH E. Sussex 404 W 31 – see Rye.

PEMBURY Kent 404 U 30 – see Royal Tunbridge Wells.

PENCRAIG Heref. and Worcs. – see Ross-on-Wye.

PENDOGGETT Cornwall 403 F 32 – ✉ Port Isaac – ☎ 01208.
♦London 264 – Newquay 22 – Truro 30.

- **Cornish Arms,** PL30 3HH, on B 3314 ✆ 880263, Fax 880335, « Retaining 16C features » – TV ☎ P. AE VISA
  Meals (bar lunch Monday to Saturday)/dinner 17.50 **t.** and a la carte 4.50 – **7 rm** 49.00/78.00 **t.** – SB.

PENKRIDGE Staffs. 402 403 404 N 25 – ✉ Stafford – ☎ 01785.
♦London 140 – ♦Birmingham 25 – Derby 41 – ♦Leicester 56 – Shrewsbury 27 – ♦Stoke-on-Trent 23.

- **Bridge House,** Stone Cross, ST19 5AS, on A 449 ✆ 714426 – rm TV P
  Meals *(closed Sunday dinner to non-residents)* 22.00 **t.** and a la carte 3.50 – **9 rm** 25.00/35.00 **t.**

PENRITH Cumbria 401 402 L 19 – pop. 13 330 – ECD : Wednesday – ☎ 01768.
18 Salked Rd ✆ 62217/65429 – Robinson's School, Middlegate, CA11 7PT ✆ 64466.
♦London 290 – ♦Carlisle 24 – Kendal 31 – Lancaster 48.

- **North Lakes,** Ullswater Rd, CA11 8QT, S : 1 m. at junction 40 of M 6 ✆ 68111, Fax 68291, squash – rm TV ☎ P – 200. AE VISA
  Meals *(closed Saturday lunch)* 11.95/18.00 6.95 – **85 rm** 89.00/128.00 **st.** – SB.
- **Forte Travelodge** without rest., Redhills, CA11 0DT, SW : 1 ½ m. by A 592 on A 66 ✆ 66958, Reservations (Freephone) 0800 850950 – TV P. AE VISA.
  32 rm 33.50 t.
- **Woodland House,** Wordsworth St., CA11 7QY, ✆ 864177, Fax 890152 – TV P.
  Meals (by arrangement) 9.50 **s.** 4.00 – **8 rm** 23.00/39.00 **s.**
- **Passepartout,** 51-52 Castlegate, CA11 7HY, ✆ 65852 – . VISA
  closed Sunday and first 2 weeks November – **Meals** (dinner only) a la carte 12.00/25.75 **t.** 4.00.

ATS Gilwilly Ind. Est. ✆ 65656/7

PENSHURST Kent 404 U 30 **Great Britain G.** – pop. 1 509 – ☎ 01892.
Envir. : Hever Castle★ *AC*, W : 6 m. by B 2176 and B 2027.
♦London 38 – Maidstone 19 – Royal Tunbridge Wells 6.

- **Swale Cottage** without rest., Old Swaylands Lane, TN11 8AH, SE : 1 m. by B 2176 off Poundsbridge Lane ✆ 870738, ≤, – TV P.
  3 rm 36.00/56.00.

PENZANCE Cornwall 403 D 33 **The West Country G.** – pop. 20 284 – ECD : Wednesday – ☎ 01736.
See : Town★ - Outlook★★★ – Western Promenade (≤★★★) YZ – National Lighthouse Centre★ *AC* Y – Chapel St.★ Y – Maritime Museum★ *AC* Y **M1**.
Envir. : Penwith★★ – Trengwainton Garden★★ (≤★★) *AC*, NW : 2 m. by St. Clare Street Y – Sancreed - Church★★ (Celtic Crosses★★) W : 3 ½ m. by A 30 Z – St. Michael's Mount★★ (≤★★) E : 4 m. by B 3311 - Y - and A 30 – Lanyon Quoit★, NW : 3 ½ m. by St. Clare Street – Newlyn★, SW : 1 ½ m. by B 3315 Z – St. Madron (St. Maddern★) NW : 1 ½ m. by St. Clare Street Y.
Exc. : Morvah (≤★★) NW : 6½m. by St. Clare Street Y – Zennor (Church★) NW : 6 m. by B 3311 Y – Prussia Cove★, E : 8 m. by B 3311 – Y - and A 394 – Land's End★ (cliff scenery★★★) SW : 10 m. by A 30 Z.
Access to the Isles of Scilly by helicopter ✆ 63871, Fax 64293.
to the Isles of Scilly (Hugh Town) (Isles of Scilly Steamship Co. Ltd) (summer only) (2 h 40 mn).
Station Rd, TR18 2NF ✆ 62207.
♦London 319 – Exeter 113 – ♦Plymouth 77 – Taunton 155.

Plan on next page

- **Abbey,** Abbey St., TR18 4AR, ✆ 66906, Fax 51163, « Attractively furnished 17C house », – TV P. AE VISA Y **u**
  closed 3 days at Christmas – **Meals** (booking essential) (dinner only) 22.50 **t.** 4.50 – **6 rm** 65.50/130.00 **t.**, 1 suite – SB.
- **Tarbert,** 11 Clarence St., TR18 2NU, ✆ 63758, Fax 331336 – TV ☎. AE VISA. Y **i**
  closed 23 December-26 January – **Meals** (dinner only) 14.00 **st.** and a la carte 4.50 – **12 rm** 27.50/55.00 **st.** – SB.
- **Sea and Horses,** 6 Alexandra Terr., TR18 4NX, ✆ 61961 – TV ☎ P. VISA. Z **s**
  mid February-mid November – **Meals** (bar lunch)/dinner 9.95 **st.** 3.50 – **11 rm** 25.00/50.00 **st.**

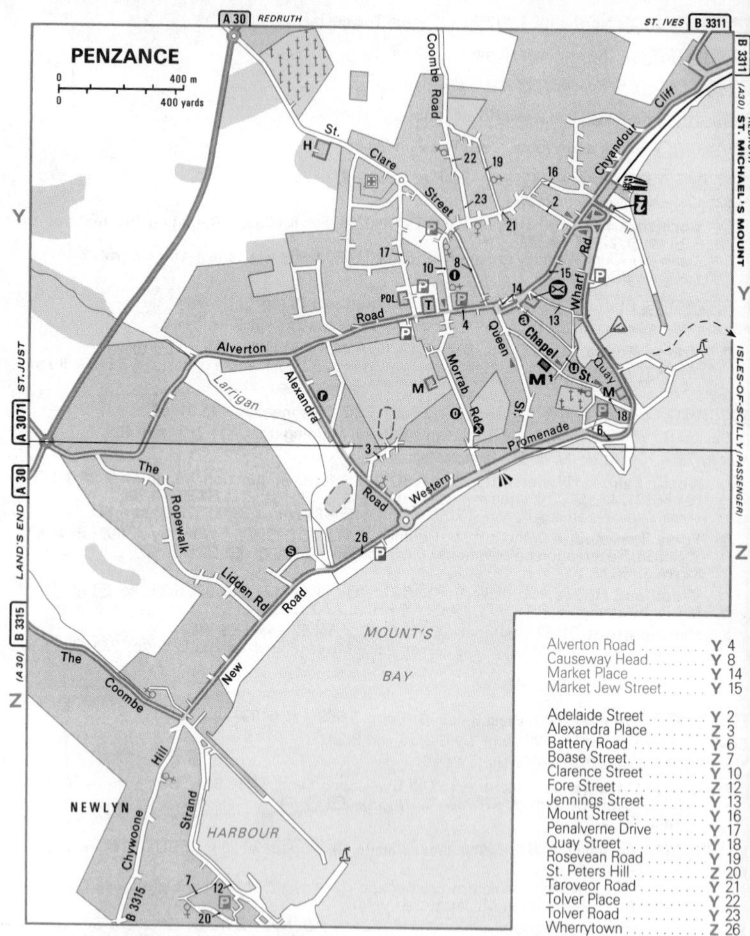

Estoril, 46 Morrab Rd, TR18 4EX, ✆ 62468 – rest TV ☎ P. VISA. — Y **o**
closed January – **Meals** 11.00 **st.** 3.50 – **10 rm** 26.00/50.00 **st.** – SB.

Woodstock without rest., 29 Morrab Rd, TR18 4EZ, ✆ 69049 – TV. AE VISA — Y **x**
4 rm 10.00/64.00.

Dunedin, Alexandra Rd, TR18 4LZ, ✆ 62652 – rest TV — Y **r**
closed Christmas and New Year – **Meals** 6.00 3.50 – **9 rm** 13.00/30.00.

Harris's, 46 New St., TR18 2LZ, ✆ 64408 – AE VISA — Y **a**
closed Monday lunch, Monday dinner October-May, Sunday, 2 weeks February and 2 weeks November – **Meals** (restricted lunch)/dinner a la carte 17.40/30.50 t. 4.90.

at Newlyn SW : 1 ½ m. on B 3315 – Z – ✉ Penzance – ☎ 01736 :

Higher Faugan, TR18 5NS, SW : ¾ m. on B 3315 ✆ 62076, Fax 51648, heated, park, – TV ☎ P. AE VISA
Booking essential November-February – **Meals** (bar lunch)/dinner 16.50 **st.** 3.90 – **12 rm** 45.00/98.00 **t.** – SB.

at Drift SW : 2 ½ m. on A 30 – Z – ✉ Penzance – ☎ 01736 :

Rose Farm without rest., Chyanhal, Buryas Bridge, TR19 6AN, SW : ¾ m. on Chyanhal rd ✆ 731808, « Working farm », – TV P.
closed Christmas – **3 rm** 23.00/38.00 **st.**

ATS Jelbert Way, Eastern Green Ind. Est ✆ 62768

ATS Units 25-26, Stable Hobba Ind. Est., Newlyn ✆ 69100

PERRANUTHNOE Cornwall 403 D 33 – see Marazion.

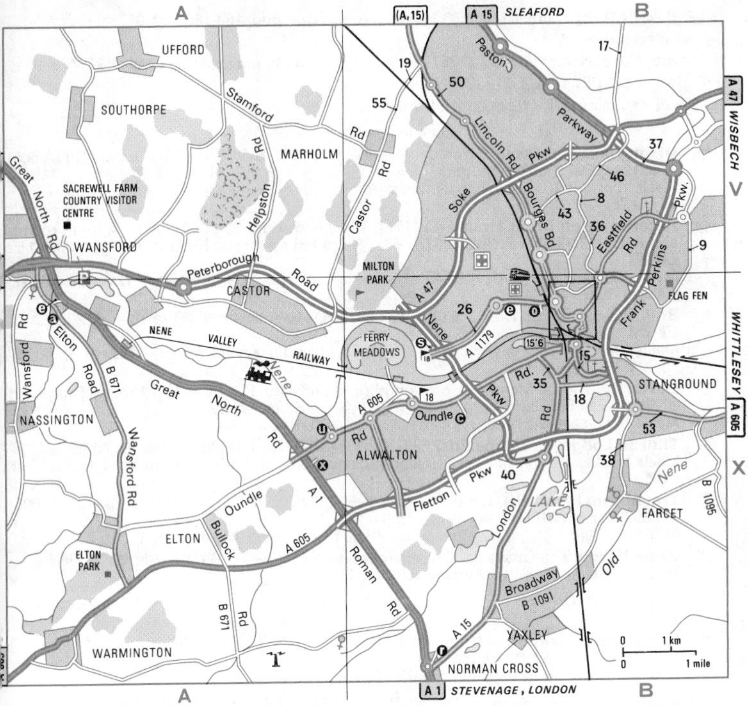

A
B
(A 15)
A 15 SLEAFORD
A 47 WISBECH
V
WHITTLESEY
A 605
X
A 1 STEVENAGE, LONDON
UFFORD
SOUTHORPE
Stamford
Rd
MARHOLM
Helpston
Rd
Castor
Rd
SACREWELL FARM
COUNTRY VISITOR
CENTRE
Great
North
Rd
WANSFORD
Peterborough
Road
CASTOR
MILTON
PARK
Paston
Parkway
Lincoln Rd
Pkw
Soke
Bourges Bd
Eastfield
Rd
Perkins
Pkw.
Frank
FLAG FEN
NENE
VALLEY
RAILWAY
FERRY
MEADOWS
A 47
Nene
A 1179
Rd.
STANGROUND
Wansford
Rd
Elton
Road
B 671
Great
North
Rd
NASSINGTON
A 605
Oundle
Rd
ALWALTON
Pkw
Fletton
Pkw
London
LAKE
Nene
B 1095
FARCET
Oundle
ELTON
Bullock
Rd
A 605
Roman
Rd
ELTON
PARK
Old
Broadway
B 1091
B 671
Rd
WARMINGTON
A 15
YAXLEY
NORMAN CROSS
0
1 km
0
1 mile
17
19
50
55
37
46
8
43
36
9
26
15'6
15
35
18
53
38
40

PETERBOROUGH

Bridge Street	Z	
Church Street	YZ	
Long Causeway	Y	25
Queensgate Shopping Centre	Y	
Rivergate Shopping Centre	Z	
Cattle Market Road	Y	2
City Road	Y	3
Cowgate	Y	5
Cross Street	Z	6
Dogsthorpe Road	BV	8
Edgerley Drain Road	BV	9
Embankment Road	Z	12
Exchange Street	Y	13
Fletton Avenue	BX	15
Geneva Street	Y	16
Guntons Road	BV	17
High Street	BX	18
Hurn Road	BV	19
Longthorpe Parkway	BX	26
Market Way	Y	28
Midgate	Y	29
New Road	Y	34
New Road	BX	35
Park Road	BV	36
Paston Parkway	BV	37
Peterborough Road	BX	38
Phorpres Way	BX	40
Rivergate	Z	42
St Paul's Road	BV	43
Thorpe Road	Y	45
Welland Road	BV	46
Wentworth Street	Z	48
Werrington Parkway	BV	50
Wheelyard	Y	52
Whittlesey Road	BX	53
Woodcroft Road	BV	55

A 15
Y
Z
A 1179
(A 1139)
A 15
Bright
St.
Lincoln Rd
Rd
Broadway
Northminster
Park
Bourges
Bd
Westgate
PASSPORT
OFFICE
QUEENSGATE
SHOPPING CENTRE
CATHEDRAL
Church
St.
Priestgate
St.
Rd
Peters
St
Bridge
Bourges
Boulevard
Bishops
Rd
RIVERGATE
SHOPPING CENTRE
POL.
Nene
0
100 m
0
100 yards
16
34
28
2
3
29
52
25
13
45
5
6
48
42
12

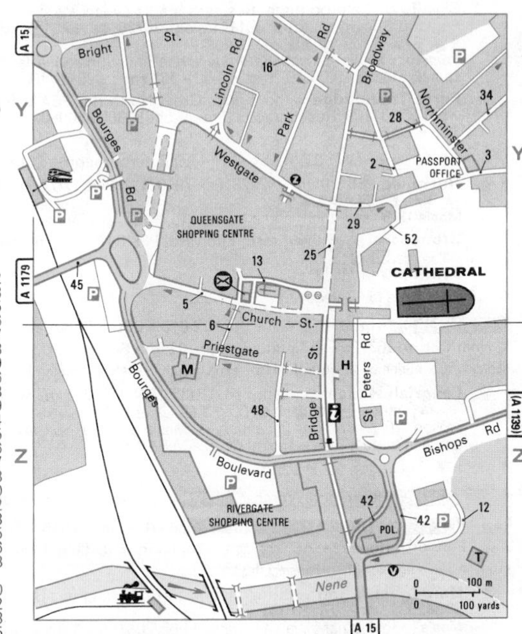

PETERBOROUGH Cambs. 402 404 T 26 **Great Britain G.** – pop. 153 166 – ☎ 01733.
See : Cathedral** *AC* Y.
Thorpe Wood, Nene Parkway ☎ 267701, BX – Orton Meadows, Ham Lane ☎ 237478, BX.
45 Bridge St., PE1 1HA ☎ 317336.
London 85 – Cambridge 35 – Leicester 41 – Lincoln 51.

Plan on preceding page

Orton Hall, The Village, Orton Longueville, PE2 7DN, SW : 2½ m. by Oundle Rd (A 605) ☎ 391111, Fax 233629, park – rm – 120. BX **c**
Meals (bar lunch Monday to Saturday)/dinner 19.95 **t.** and a la carte 5.50 – 7.95 – **50 rm** 75.00/136.00 **t.** – SB.

Peterborough Moat House (Q.M.H.), Thorpe Wood, PE3 6SG, SW : 2¼ m. at roundabout 33 ☎ 260000, Fax 262737, – rm rest – 400. BX **s**
Meals (bar lunch Saturday) 15.45 **st.** and a la carte 5.75 – 9.50 – **121 rm** 65.00 **st.**, 4 suites – SB.

Bull, Westgate, PE1 1RB, ☎ 61364, Fax 557304 – rm rest – 200. Y **z**
Meals (dancing Saturday evening) 12.50/13.95 **t.** and a la carte 4.95 – **103 rm** 68.50/79.00 **t.**, 1 suite – SB.

Butterfly, Thorpe Meadows, off Longthorpe Parkway, PE3 6GA, W : 1 m. by Thorpe Rd ☎ 64240, Fax 65538 – rm – 80. BX **e**
Meals 11.50 **st.** and a la carte 4.75 – 6.50 – **70 rm** 57.50/80.00 **t.** – SB.

Thorpe Lodge, 83 Thorpe Rd, PE3 6JQ, ☎ 348759, Fax 891598 –
Meals *(closed Sunday dinner)* (bar lunch)/dinner 15.00 **st.** 4.00 – **18 rm** 35.00/65.00 **st.** – SB. BX **o**

Travel Inn, Ham Lane, Orton Meadows, PE2 0UU, SW : 3½ m. by Oundle Rd (A 605) ☎ 235794, Fax 391055 – rm BX **a**
Meals (Beefeater grill) a la carte approx. 16.00 **t.** – 4.95 – **40 rm** 33.50 **t.**

Grain Barge, The Quayside, Embankment Rd, PE1 1EG, ☎ 311967 –
Meals - Chinese (Peking) a la carte 10.00/25.00 **t.** Z **v**

at Norman Cross S : 5¾ m. on A 15 at junction with A 1 – ✉ Peterborough – ☎ 01733 :

Forte Posthouse, Great North Rd, PE7 3TB, ☎ 240209, Fax 244455, – – 50. BX **r**
Meals a la carte approx. 15.00 **t.** 5.50 – **93 rm** 56.00 **t.**

at Alwalton SW : 5¾ m. on Oundle Rd (A 605) – ✉ Peterborough – ☎ 01733 :

Swallow, Peterborough Business Park, Lynch Wood, PE2 6GB, (opposite East of England Showground) ☎ 371111, Fax 236725, – rm rest – 275. AX **u**
Emperor : **Meals** *(closed Saturday lunch* and Sunday) a la carte 16.00/30.00 **st.** 4.50 – *Laurels* : **Meals** 13.00/15.75 **st.** 4.50 – **161 rm** 90.00/105.00 **st.**, 2 suites – SB.

Forte Travelodge without rest., Great North Rd, PE7 3UR, A 1 (southbound carriageway) ☎ 231109, Reservations (Freephone) 0800 850950 – AX **x**
32 rm 33.50 **t.**

at Wansford W : 8½ m. by A 47 – ✉ Peterborough – ☎ 01780 :

Haycock, PE8 6JA, ☎ 782223, Fax 783031, « Part 17C coaching inn », – – 150. AX **e**
Meals 18.50 **st.** (lunch) and a la carte 15.40/21.40 – **50 rm** 69.00/98.00 **st.**, 1 suite – SB.

Stoneacre without rest., Elton Rd, PE8 6JT, S : ½ m. on unmarked drive ☎ 783283, – rm AX **a**
5 rm 22.00/46.00 **st.**

ATS Wareley Rd (off George St.) ☎ 67112/3

PETERSFIELD Hants. 404 R 30 – pop. 12 618 – ECD : Thursday – ☎ 01730.
Heath Rd ☎ 263725 – County Library, 27 The Square, GU32 3HH ☎ 268829.
London 59 – Brighton 45 – Guildford 25 – Portsmouth 19 – Southampton 32 – Winchester 19.

Langrish House , Langrish, GU32 1RN, W : 3½ m. by A 272 ☎ 266941, Fax 260543, park – – 60.
closed 25 December-2 January – **Meals** *(closed Sunday and Bank Holidays)* 12.75 **t.** and a la carte 3.75 – **18 rm** 35.40/65.00 **t.** – SB.

ATS 15 & 31 Dragon St. ☎ 265151

PETERSTOW Heref. and Worcs. 403 404 M 28 – see Ross-on-Wye.

PETWORTH W. Sussex 404 S 31 **Great Britain G.** – pop. 3 866 – ECD : Wednesday – ☎ 01798.
See : Petworth House** *AC* – , Osiers Farm ☎ (01903) 44097.
London 54 – Brighton 31 – Portsmouth 33.

Horseguards Inn with rm, Upperton Rd, Tillington, GU28 9AF, W : 1½ m. by A 272 ☎ 342332, –
Meals (booking essential) a la carte 14.65/20.25 t. – **3 rm** 32.00/54.00 **t.**

at Sutton S : 5 m. by A 283 – ✉ Pulborough – ☎ 0179 87 :

White Horse Inn, RH20 1PS, ☎ 221, Fax 291, – TV ☎ P. VISA.
Meals 12.00 **t.** and a la carte – **5 rm** 48.00/58.00 **st.** – SB.

PEVENSEY E. Sussex 404 V 31 – ☎ 01323.
♦London 74 – ♦Brighton 25 – Folkestone 49.

Priory Court, BN24 5LG, ☎ 763150, – TV P. VISA
Meals 12.00 **st.** and a la carte – **10 rm** 25.00/38.00 **st.** – SB.

PICKERING N. Yorks. 402 R 21 – pop. 6 269 – ECD : Wednesday – ☎ 01751.
Eastgate Car Park, YO18 7DP ☎ 473791.
♦London 237 – ♦Middlesbrough 43 – Scarborough 19 – York 25.

Forest and Vale, Malton Rd, YO18 7DL, ☎ 472722, Fax 472972, – TV ☎ P – 40. AE VISA – **17 rm.**

White Swan, Market Pl., YO18 7AA, ☎ 472288, Fax 472288 – rm TV ☎ P. VISA
***St. Emilion :* Meals** (lunch by arrangement Monday to Saturday)/dinner 19.50 **t.** 4.00 – **12 rm** 55.00/76.00 **t.**, 1 suite – SB.

The Lodge, Middleton Rd, YO18 8NQ, W : ½ m. ☎ 472976, – TV ☎ P. AE VISA.
Meals (bar lunch Monday to Friday)/dinner 20.50 – **9 rm** 30.00/60.00 **st.** – SB.

at Middleton NW : 1½ m. on A 170 – ✉ Pickering – ☎ 01751 :

Cottage Leas, YO18 8PN, N : 1 m. ☎ 472129, – TV ☎ P. VISA
Meals (dinner only and Sunday lunch)/dinner 15.95 **t.** and a la carte 4.50 – **11 rm** (dinner included) 48.00/110.00 **t.** – SB.

Sunnyside, Carr Lane, YO18 8PD, ☎ 476104, Fax 476104, – rest TV P
March-October **Meals** (by arrangement) 12.00 – **3 rm** 24.00/38.00.

PICKHILL N. Yorks. 402 P 21 – pop. 412 – ✉ Thirsk – ☎ 01845.
♦London 229 – ♦Leeds 41 – ♦Middlesbrough 30 – York 34.

Nags Head, YO7 4JG, ☎ 567391, Fax 567212, « Part 18C inn », – rest TV ☎ P. VISA
Meals (lunch by arrangement Monday to Saturday) (in bar Sunday dinner)/dinner 17.50 **st.** and a la carte 4.25 – **15 rm.**

PILLING Lancs. 402 L 22 – pop. 2 204 – ✉ Preston – ☎ 01253.
♦London 243 – ♦Blackpool 11 – Burnley 43 – ♦Manchester 49.

Springfield House, Wheel Lane, PR3 6HL, ☎ 790301, Fax 790907, – TV ☎ P. VISA
Meals *(closed lunch Monday and Saturday)* 8.50/15.95 **st.** 4.35 – **7 rm** 35.00/55.00 **st.** – SB.

PIMPERNE Dorset 403 404 N 31 – see Blandford Forum.

PINHOE Devon 403 J 31 – see Exeter.

PITTON Wilts. – see Salisbury.

PLUCKLEY Kent 404 W 30 – pop. 883 – ☎ 01233.
♦London 53 – Folkestone 25 – Maidstone 18.

Elvey Farm, TN27 0SU, W : 2 m. by Smarden rd and Marley Farm rd, off Mundy Bois rd ☎ 840442, Fax 840726, ≤, « Converted oast house and barn », – TV P. VISA JCB
Meals (by arrangement) – **8 rm** 39.50/59.50 **t.**

PLUMTREE Notts. – see Nottingham.

PLYMOUTH Devon 403 H 32 **The West Country G.** – pop. 243 373 – ECD : Wednesday – ☎ 01752.

See : Town★★ - Smeaton's Tower (≤★★) *AC* BZ **A** – Plymouth Dome★ *AC* BZ – Royal Citadel (Ramparts ≤★★) *AC* BZ – Elizabethan House★ *AC* – City Museum and Art Gallery★ BZ **M.**

Envir. : Saltram House★★ *AC*, E : 3½ m. BY **A** – Anthony House★ *AC*, W : 5 m. by A 374 – Mount Edgcumbe (≤★) *AC*, SW : 2 m. by passenger ferry from Stonehouse AZ.

Exc. : NE : Dartmoor National Park★★ (Brent Tor ≤★★, Haytor Rocks ≤★) BY – Buckland Abbey★★ *AC*, N : 7½ m. by A 386 ABY – Yelverton Paperweight Centre★, N : 10 m. by A 386 ABY.

18 Staddon Heights, Plymstock ☎ 402475 – 9 Elfordleigh, Colebrook, Plympton ☎ 336428.

Plymouth City (Roborough) Airport : ☎ 772752, N : 3½ m. by A 386 ABY.

to France (Roscoff) (Brittany Ferries) 1-2 daily (6 h) – to Spain (Santander) (Brittany Ferries) (23 h).

Island House, 9 The Barbican, PL1 2LS ☎ 264849/264851.
♦London 242 – ♦Bristol 124 – ♦Southampton 161.

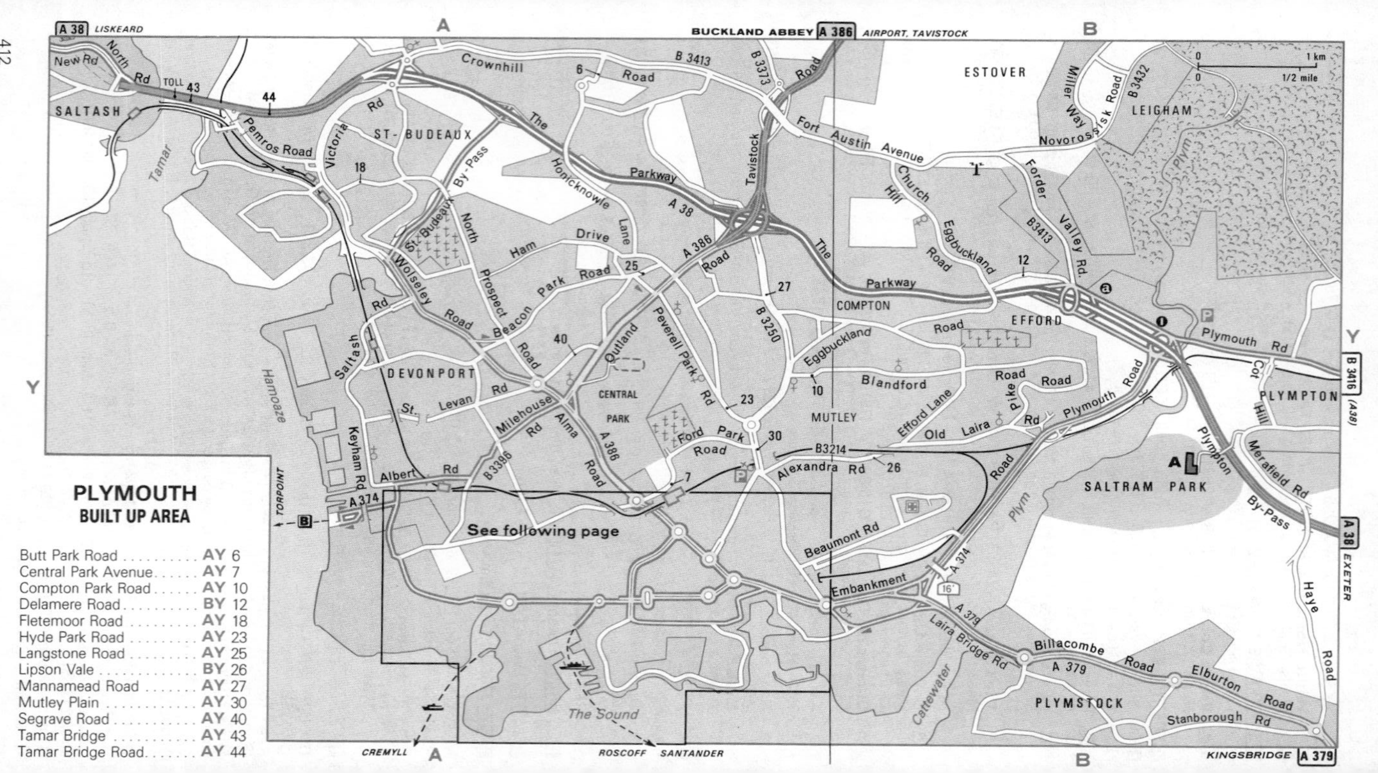

PLYMOUTH
BUILT UP AREA

Butt Park Road	AY	6
Central Park Avenue	AY	7
Compton Park Road	AY	10
Delamere Road	BY	12
Fletemoor Road	AY	18
Hyde Park Road	AY	23
Langstone Road	AY	25
Lipson Vale	BY	26
Mannamead Road	AY	27
Mutley Plain	AY	30
Segrave Road	AY	40
Tamar Bridge	AY	43
Tamar Bridge Road	AY	44

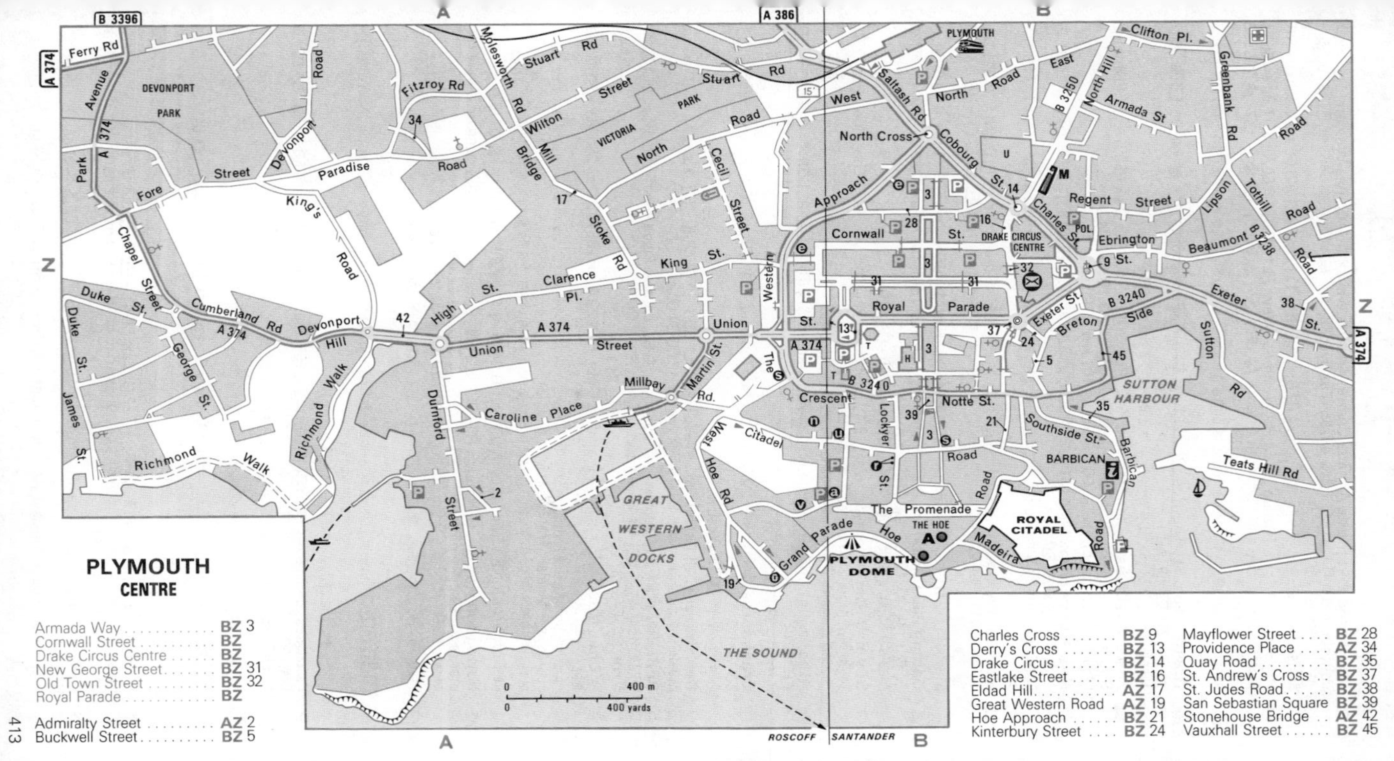
PLYMOUTH
CENTRE
Armada Way . . . . BZ 3
Cornwall Street . . . . BZ
Drake Circus Centre . . . . . . BZ
New George Street . . . . BZ 31
Old Town Street . . . . BZ 32
Royal Parade . . . . BZ
Admiralty Street . . . . AZ 2
Buckwell Street . . . . BZ 5
Charles Cross . . . . BZ 9
Derry's Cross . . . . BZ 13
Drake Circus . . . . BZ 14
Eastlake Street . . . . . . BZ 16
Eldad Hill . . . . AZ 17
Great Western Road . AZ 19
Hoe Approach . . . . . . BZ 21
Kinterbury Street . . . . BZ 24
Mayflower Street . . . . BZ 28
Providence Place . . . . AZ 34
Quay Road . . . . BZ 35
St. Andrew's Cross . . BZ 37
St. Judes Road . . . . . BZ 38
San Sebastian Square BZ 39
Stonehouse Bridge . . AZ 42
Vauxhall Street . . . . . BZ 45

Copthorne Plymouth, Armada Centre, Armada Way, PL1 1AR, (via Western Approach southbound) ℘ 224161, Telex 45756, Fax 670688, Fs, ≘s, ▢ – |‡| ⇔ rm TV ☎ ♿ P – 🕴 70. AE ① VISA BZ **e**
Meals 15.95 **st.** and dinner a la carte 6.50 – ☐ 8.95 – **131 rm** 78.00/88.00 **st.**, 4 suites – SB.

Plymouth Moat House (Q.M.H.), Armada Way, PL1 2HJ, ℘ 662866, Telex 45637, Fax 673816, ≤ city and Plymouth Sound, Fs, ≘s, ▢ – |‡| ⇔ rm TV ☎ ♿ P – 🕴 250. AE ① VISA BZ **s**
Meals 13.50/19.00 **t.** and dinner a la carte 7.25 – ☐ 9.00 – **210 rm** 77.00/95.00 **st.**, 1 suite – SB.

Grand, Elliott St., The Hoe, PL1 2PT, ℘ 661195, Fax 600653, ≤ – |‡| ⇔ rm TV ☎ P – 🕴 70. AE ① VISA BZ **a**
Meals 9.50/18.50 **st.** and dinner a la carte – **77 rm** ☐ 65.00/105.00 **t.** – SB.

Forte Posthouse, Cliff Rd, The Hoe, PL1 3DL, ℘ 662828, Fax 660974, ≤ Plymouth Sound, ▢ heated – |‡| ⇔ rm TV ☎ P – 🕴 80. AE ① VISA JCB AZ **v**
Meals a la carte approx. 15.00 **t.** 5.50 – **102 rm** 56.00 **st.**, 4 suites.

New Continental, Millbay Rd, PL1 3LD, ℘ 220782, Fax 227013, Fs, ≘s, ▢ – |‡| TV ☎ P – 🕴 350. AE VISA AZ **s**
Meals (bar lunch Saturday) 7.75/15.50 **st.** and a la carte 6.00 – **99 rm** ☐ 67.00/123.00 **st.** – SB.

Novotel Plymouth, 270 Plymouth Rd., Marsh Mills Roundabout, PL6 8NH, ℘ 221422, Telex 45711, Fax 221422(ext. 126), ▢ heated – |‡| ⇔ rm ▤ rest TV ☎ ♿ P – 🕴 200. AE ① VISA BY **i**
Meals 11.00 **st.** (dinner) and a la carte 12.45/20.85 **st.** 4.95 – ☐ 7.50 – **100 rm** 39.50 **st.**

Campanile, Longbridge Rd, Marsh Mills, PL6 8LD, ℘ 601087, Fax 223213 – ⇔ rm TV ☎ ♿ P – 🕴 30. AE ① VISA BY **a**
Meals 9.85 **st.** 4.65 – ☐ 4.25 – **51 rm** 35.75 **st.** – SB.

Bowling Green without rest., 9-10 Osborne Pl., Lockyer St., The Hoe, PL1 2PU, ℘ 667485, Fax 255150 – TV ☎. AE ① VISA BZ **r**
closed 1 week Christmas – **12 rm** ☐ 28.00/46.00 **st.**

Athenaeum Lodge without rest., 4 Athenaeum St., The Hoe, PL1 2RH, ℘ 665005 – TV P. ✻ BZ **u**
8 rm ☐ 22.00/36.00 **st.**

Cranbourne without rest., 282 Citadel Rd, The Hoe, PL1 2PZ, ℘ 263858, Fax 263858 – TV. AE VISA BZ **r**
14 rm ☐ 15.00/35.00 **st.**

Sea Breezes, 28 Grand Par., West Hoe, PL1 3DJ, ℘ 667205 – TV. VISA AZ **o**
Meals (by arrangement) 9.50 **s.** – **7 rm** ☐ 15.00/34.00 **st.** – SB.

Berkeley's of St. James without rest., 4 St. James Place East, The Hoe, PL1 3AS, ℘ 221654 – ⇔ TV. AE ① VISA. ✻ AZ **n**
5 rm ☐ 16.00/32.00.

✿ **Chez Nous** (Marchal), 13 Frankfort Gate, PL1 1QA, ℘ 266793, Fax 266793 – AE ① VISA AZ **e**
closed Sunday, Monday, first 3 weeks February, first 3 weeks September and Bank Holidays – **Meals** - French 30.50 **t.** 10.00
Spec. Croustade de ris d'agneau au Madère, Lieu jaune grillé au pistou, Trio de sorbets et ses fruits.

at Colebrook NE : 5 ¼ m. by A 374 off B 3416 - BY – ✉ Plymouth – ☎ 01752 :

Boringdon Hall ⑤, Boringdon Hill, PL7 4DP, N : ½ m. ℘ 344455, Fax 346578, « Part 16C manor », ≘s, ▢, park, ✻ – TV ☎ P – 🕴 120. AE ① VISA
Meals 16.95 **st.** and a la carte 5.00 – **41 rm** ☐ 60.00/95.00 **st.** – SB.

ATS Teats Hill Rd, Coxside ℘ 266217/227964 — ATS Miller Way, Novorossisk Rd, Estover ℘ 769123

POCKLINGTON Humbs. 402 R 22 – pop. 6 878 – ECD : Wednesday – ✉ York (N. Yorks.) – ☎ 01759.

♦London 213 – ♦Kingston-upon-Hull 25 – York 13.

Feathers, 56 Market Pl., YO4 2AH, ℘ 303155, Fax 304382 – ⇔ rest TV ☎ P. AE ① VISA. ✻
Meals 10.95 **t.** and a la carte 5.95 – **12 rm** ☐ 39.50/49.50 **t.**

PODIMORE Somerset – see Yeovil.

POLPERRO Cornwall 403 G 33 **The West Country G.** – pop. 1 192 – ✉ Looe – ☎ 01503.

See : Village★.

♦London 271 – ♦Plymouth 28.

Claremont, Fore St., PL13 2RG, ℘ 72241, Fax 72241 – TV ☎ P. AE VISA
Meals *(closed October-March)* (bar lunch)/dinner 18.00 **st.** and a la carte 4.85 – **10 rm** ☐ 17.00/58.00 **st.** – SB.

Lanhael House, Langreek Rd, PL13 2PW, ℘ 72428, Fax 72428, ▢ heated, ✻ – ⇔ rest TV P. ✻
April-September – **Meals** (by arrangement) 12.00 **st.** – **5 rm** ☐ 26.00/38.00 **st.**

X **Kitchen,** Fish Na Bridge, The Coombes, PL13 2RQ, ℰ 72780 – VISA
closed Monday to Thursday October-Easter and Sunday – **Meals** (dinner only) a la carte 16.40/20.00 **t.** 6.30.

PONTELAND Tyne and Wear 401 402 O 19 – see Newcastle upon Tyne.

POOLE Dorset 403 404 O 31 **The West Country G.** – pop. 133 050 – ECD : Wednesday – 01202.

See : Town★ – Museums★ *AC* (Waterfront **M1**, Scaplen's Court **M2**).

Envir. : Compton Acres★★, (English Garden ≤★★★) *AC*, SE : 3 m. by B 3369 BX on Bournemouth town plan – Brownsea Island★ (Baden-Powell Stone ✵★★) *AC*, by boat from Poole Quay or Sandbanks BX on Bournemouth town plan.

18 Parkstone, Links Rd ℰ 707138 – 18 Bulbury Woods, Lytchett Matravers ℰ (01929) 459574.

to France (Cherbourg) (Brittany Ferries Truckline) 1-2 daily (4 h 15 mn) – to France (St. Malo) (Brittany Ferries) (8 h).

The Quay, BH15 1HE ℰ 673322 – Dolphin Shopping Centre – Passenger Ferry Terminal (summer only).

♦London 116 – Bournemouth 4 – Dorchester 23 – Weymouth 28.

Plan of Built up Area : see Bournemouth

POOLE

Dolphin Shopping Centre

Street	No.	Street	No.	Street	No.
Church Street	3	Emerson Road	4	Market St.	14
		Falkland Sq.	6	New Orchard	16
		Fishermans Rd	7	New Street	17
		Furnell Rd	8	Serpentine Rd.	18
		Holes Bay Rd	10	Thames St.	19
		Labrador Drive	12	Towngate Bridge	21
		Longfleet Rd	13	Westons Lane	22

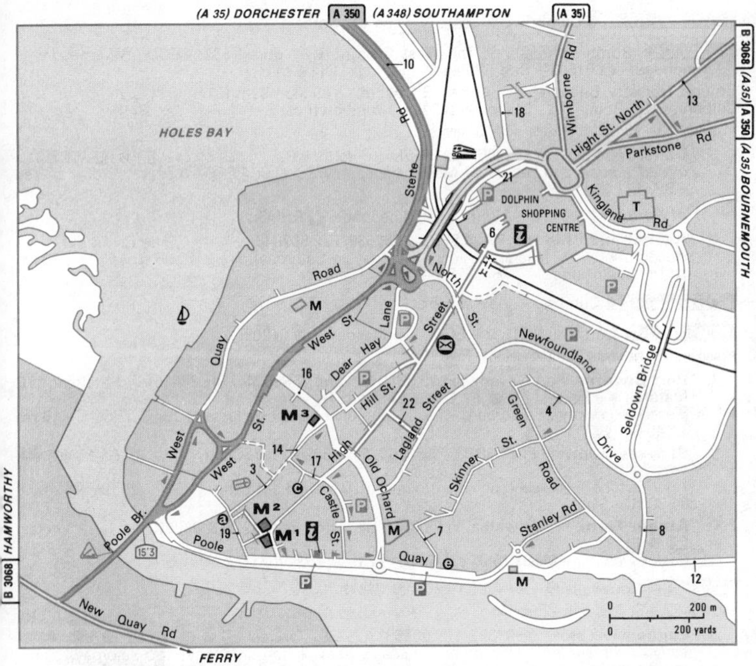

Haven, Banks Rd, Sandbanks, BH13 7QL, SE : 4 ¼ m. on B 3369 ℰ 707333, Fax 708796, ≤ Ferry, Old Harry Rocks and Poole Bay, heated, squash – 180. VISA on Bournemouth town plan BX **c**
Meals 14.50/22.00 **st.** and a la carte 4.75 – (see also **La Roche** below) – **92 rm** 65.00/150.00 **st.**, 2 suites – SB.

🏨 **Mansion House,** 7-11 Thames St., BH15 1JN, off Poole Quay ✆ 685666, Fax 665709, « 18C town house » – ▤ rest TV ☎ P – 🏛 25. AE VISA. ✻ **a**
Meals *(in bar Saturday lunch and Sunday dinner)* 16.50/24.95 **st.** 6.50 – **28 rm** 75.00/150.00 **st.** – SB.

🏨 **Salterns,** 38 Salterns Way, Lilliput, BH14 8JR, ✆ 707321, Fax 707488, ≤, squash – ⇹ rm ▤ rest TV ☎ P – 🏛 80. AE VISA. ✻ on Bournemouth town plan BX **e**
Meals 15.50/25.00 **t.** 4.50 – 8.50 – **20 rm** 66.00/86.00 **t.** – SB.

🏨 **Quay Thistle** ⛵, The Quay, BH15 1HD, ✆ 666800, Fax 684470 – |♦| ⇹ rm ▤ rest TV ☎ P – 🏛 30. AE VISA JCB **e**
Meals 16.95/18.95 **t.** and a la carte 5.00 – 10.00 – **68 rm** 79.00/89.00 **t.** – SB.

🏨 Arndale Court, Wimborne Rd, BH15 2BY, ✆ 683746, Fax 668838 – TV ☎ P – 🏛 40
32 rm. on Bournemouth town plan ABX **r**

🏨 **Sea Witch,** 47 Haven Rd, Canford Cliffs, BH13 7LH, ✆ 707697 – ⇹ rm TV ☎ P. VISA on Bournemouth town plan CX **u**
Meals (closed Sunday dinner and Monday) 9.95/14.95 **st.** and dinner a la carte **t.** 2.50 – **10 rm** 29.95/65.00 **st.** – SB.

🏨 **Inn in the Park,** Pinewood Rd, Branksome Park, BH13 6JS, ✆ 761318 – TV P. VISA. ✻ on Bournemouth town plan CX **a**
Meals *(closed dinner Sunday and Monday)* (bar lunch)/dinner 11.95 **t.** and a la carte – **5 rm** 30.00/45.00 **t.**

XX **La Roche** (at Haven H.), Banks Rd, Sandbanks, BH13 7QL, ✆ 707333, Fax 708796 – ⇹ P. AE VISA on Bournemouth town plan BX **c**
closed Sunday – **Meals** a la carte 27.40/29.50 **st** 4.75.

X **Isabel's,** 32 Station Rd, Lower Parkstone, BH14 8UD, ✆ 747885 – AE VISA
closed Sunday, 25 to 26 December and 2 to 3 January – **Meals** (dinner only) 17.00 **t.** and a la carte. on Bournemouth town plan BX **a**

X **John B's,** 20 Old High St., BH15 1BP, ✆ 672440 – AE VISA **c**
closed Sunday except Bank Holidays – **Meals** (dinner only) 19.50 **t.**

ATS 1 Fernside Rd ✆ 733301/733326

POOLEY BRIDGE Cumbria 401 402 L 20 – see Ullswater.

PORLOCK Somerset 403 J 30 **The West Country G.** – pop. 1 332 – ECD : Wednesday – ✉ Minehead – ☎ 01643 – **See** : Village★ - Porlock Hill (≤★★).
Envir. : Dunkery Beacon★★★ (≤★★★) S : 5½ m. – Luccombe★ (Church★) 3 m. by A 39 – Culbone★ (St. Beuno) W : 3½ m. by B 3225, 1½ m. on foot.
♦London 190 – ♦Bristol 67 – Exeter 46 – Taunton 28.

🏨 **Oaks,** TA24 8ES, ✆ 862265, Fax 862265, ≤ Porlock Bay, 🌳 – ⇹ rest TV ☎ P. VISA
closed January and February – **Meals** (dinner only) 20.00 **st.** 5.00 – **9 rm** 45.00/80.00 **st.** – SB.

at Porlock Weir NW : 1½ m. – ✉ Minehead – ☎ 01643 :

🏨 **Anchor and Ship Inn,** TA24 8PB, ✆ 862636, Fax 862843, ≤, 🌳 – TV ☎ P. VISA
closed January – **Meals** (bar lunch Monday to Saturday)/dinner 18.95 **st.** 5.75 – **20 rm** (dinner included) 77.75/135.50 – SB.

PORTINSCALE Cumbria – see Keswick.

PORT ISAAC Cornwall 403 F 32 – ECD : Wednesday – ☎ 01208.
♦London 266 – Newquay 24 – Tintagel 14 – Truro 32.

🏨 **Port Gaverne,** Port Gaverne, PL29 3SQ, S : ½ m. ✆ 880244, Fax 880151, « Retaining 17C features » – ⇹ rest TV ☎ P. AE VISA
closed 8 January-25 February – **Meals** (bar lunch)/dinner a la carte 18.50/22.50 **t.** – **16 rm** 49.00/98.00 **t.** – SB.

Slipway, Slipway, PL29 3RH, ✆ 880264, Fax 880264, « 16C inn » – ☎ P. AE VISA. ✻
April-October – **Meals** (bar lunch)/dinner 15.00 **t.** and a la carte 3.95 – **10 rm** 24.00/64.00 **st.** – SB.

Archer Farm ⛵, Trewetha, PL29 3RU, SE : ½ m. by B 3276 ✆ 880522, ≤, 🌳 – ⇹ rest TV ☎ P
Easter-October – **Meals** 15.00 **s.** 3.75 – **5 rm** 25.50/57.00 **s.**

PORTLOE Cornwall 403 F 33 – ✉ Truro – ☎ 01872.
♦London 296 – St. Austell 15 – Truro 15.

🏨 **Lugger,** TR2 5RD, ✆ 501322, Fax 501691, ≤, ⛱ – ⇹ rest TV ☎ P. AE VISA. ✻
early February-late November – **Meals** (bar lunch Monday to Saturday)/dinner 25.00 **t.** and a la carte 4.00 – **19 rm** (dinner included) 64.00/128.00 **t.** – SB.

PORTSCATHO Cornwall 403 F 33 **The West Country G.** – ECD : Wednesday and Saturday – ✉ Truro – ☎ 01872.
Envir. : St. Just-in-Roseland Church★★, W : 4 m. by A 3078 – St. Anthony-in-Roseland (≤★★) S : 3½ m.
♦London 298 – ♦Plymouth 55 – Truro 16.

Roseland House ⑤, Rosevine, TR2 5EW, N : 2 m. by A 3078 ☎ 580644, Fax 580801, ← Gerrans Bay, – rest. ☎ P. VISA.
Meals 9.50/16.50 **st.** 4.50 – **18 rm** (dinner included) 36.00/96.00 **st.** – SB.

Gerrans Bay, 12 Tregassick Rd, TR2 5ED, ☎ 580338, ←, – P. AE VISA
April-October and Christmas – **Meals** (bar lunch Monday to Saturday)/dinner 19.50 **st.** 4.50 – **14 rm** (dinner included) 38.00/96.00 **st.** – SB.

PORTSMOUTH and SOUTHSEA Hants. 403 404 Q 31 **Great Britain G.** – pop. 174 697 – ☎ 01705.

See : City★ – Naval Portsmouth BY : H.M.S. Victory★★★ *AC*, The Mary Rose★★, Royal Naval Museum★★ *AC* – Old Portsmouth★ BYZ : The Point (←★★) – St. Thomas Cathedral★ – Southsea (Castle★ *AC*) AZ – Royal Marines Museum, Eastney★ *AC*, AZ **M1**.

Envir. : Portchester Castle★ *AC*, NW : 5½m. by A 3 and A 27 AY.

Great Salterns, Porthsmouth Golf Centre, Burrfields Rd ☎ 664549/699519 AY – Crookhorn Lane, Widley ☎ 372210/372299 – Southwick Park, Pinsley Drive, Southwick ☎ 380131.

to France (Cherbourg) (P & O European Ferries Ltd) 2-3 daily (4 h 45 mn) day, (8 h 45 mn) night – to France (Le Havre) (P & O European Ferries Ltd) 3 daily (5 h 45 mn) day, (7 h) night – to France (Caen) (Brittany Ferries) 2-3 daily (6 h), (St. Malo) 1 daily (9 h) – to the Isle of Wight (Fishbourne) (Wightlink Ltd) frequent services daily (35 mn) – to Spain (Santander) (Brittany Ferries) (30 h) – to Spain (Bilbao) (P & O European Ferries Ltd) (30 h).

to the Isle of Wight (Ryde) (Wightlink Ltd) frequent services daily (15 mn) – from Southsea to the Isle of Wight (Ryde) (Hovertravel Ltd) frequent services daily (10 mn).

The Hard, PO1 3QJ ☎ 826722 – Clarence Esplanade, PO5 3ST ☎ 832464 (summer only) – Continental Ferryport, Rudmore Roundabout, PO2 8QN ☎ 838635 (summer only) 102 Commercial Rd, PO1 1EJ ☎ 838382.

London 78 – Brighton 48 – Salisbury 44 – Southampton 21.

Plans on following pages

Hilton National, Eastern Rd, Farlington, PO6 1UN, NE : 5 m. on A 2030 ☎ 219111, Fax 210762, – rm ☎ P – 230. AE VISA AY **c**
Meals (bar lunch Saturday) 14.95 **st.** and a la carte 5.50 – 9.25 – **118 rm** 60.00 **t.** – SB.

Innlodge, Burrfields Rd, PO3 5HH, ☎ 650510, Fax 693458, – rm rest ☎ P – 120. AE VISA. AY **u**
Meals a la carte 9.20/19.65 **t.** 5.25 – 6.50 – **73 rm** 41.50/120.00 **t.**

Forte Posthouse, Pembroke Rd, PO1 2TA, ☎ 827651, Fax 756715, – rm ☎ P – 220. AE VISA CZ **o**
Meals a la carte approx. 15.00 **t.** 5.50 – **163 rm** 56.00 **st.**

Hospitality Inn (Mt. Charlotte Thistle), South Par., Southsea, PO4 0RN, ☎ 731281, Telex 86719, Fax 817572, ← – rm ☎ – 200 AZ **r**
113 rm, 2 suites.

Green Farm Toby, Copnor Rd, Hilsea, PO3 5HS, ☎ 654645, Fax 654287 – rm rest ☎ P – 35. AE VISA. AY **e**
closed 21 December-2 January – **Meals** (grill rest.) a la carte 10.20/16.15 **t.** 4.95 – **30 rm** 57.50/67.50 **t.**

Sallyport, High St., Old Portsmouth, PO1 2LU, ☎ 821860 – ☎. AE VISA. BZ **a**
Meals (bar lunch Monday to Saturday)/dinner a la carte 7.95/16.00 **t.** – **10 rm** 32.00/59.00 **st.** – SB.

Seacrest, 11-12 South Par., Southsea, PO5 2JB, ☎ 733192, Fax 832523, ← – rest ☎ P. AE VISA AZ **e**
Meals (residents only) (dinner only) 14.95 **t.** 3.95 – **28 rm** 38.00/60.00 **t.** – SB.

Beaufort, 71 Festing Rd, Southsea, PO4 0NQ, ☎ 823707, Fax 870270 – ☎ P. AE VISA. AZ **n**
Meals (dinner only) 12.90 **st.** and a la carte 4.75 – **20 rm** 40.00/60.00 **st.** – SB.

Fortitude Cottage without rest., 51 Broad St., Old Portsmouth, PO1 2JD, ☎ 823748 – AE. BY **c**
closed 24 and 25 December – **3 rm** 28.00/44.00 **st.**

St. Margaret's, 3 Craneswater Gate, Southsea, PO4 0NZ, ☎ 820097, – rest. VISA. AZ **i**
closed 2 weeks Christmas – **Meals** (by arrangement) 9.00 **st.** – **14 rm** 26.00/44.00 **st.** – SB.

Glencoe without rest., 64 Whitwell Rd, Southsea, PO4 0QS, ☎ 737413 – VISA AZ **u**
7 rm 16.50/38.00 **st.**

Cranbourne House without rest., 6 Herbert Rd, Southsea, PO4 0QA, ☎ 824981 – . AZ **a**
closed December and January **3 rm** 22.00/38.00 **st.**

Ashwood without rest., 10 St. David's Rd, Southsea, PO5 1QN, ☎ 816228, Fax 753955 – . AZ **c**
closed 21 December-1 January – **7 rm** 16.00/34.00.

Bistro Montparnasse, 103 Palmerston Rd, Southsea, PO5 3PS, ☎ 816754, Fax 816754 – AE VISA CZ **a**
closed Sunday, Monday, 2 weeks January, 1 week August and Bank Holidays – **Meals** (dinner only) 12.50/15.00 **t.** and a la carte 15.60/24.80 **t.** 5.00.

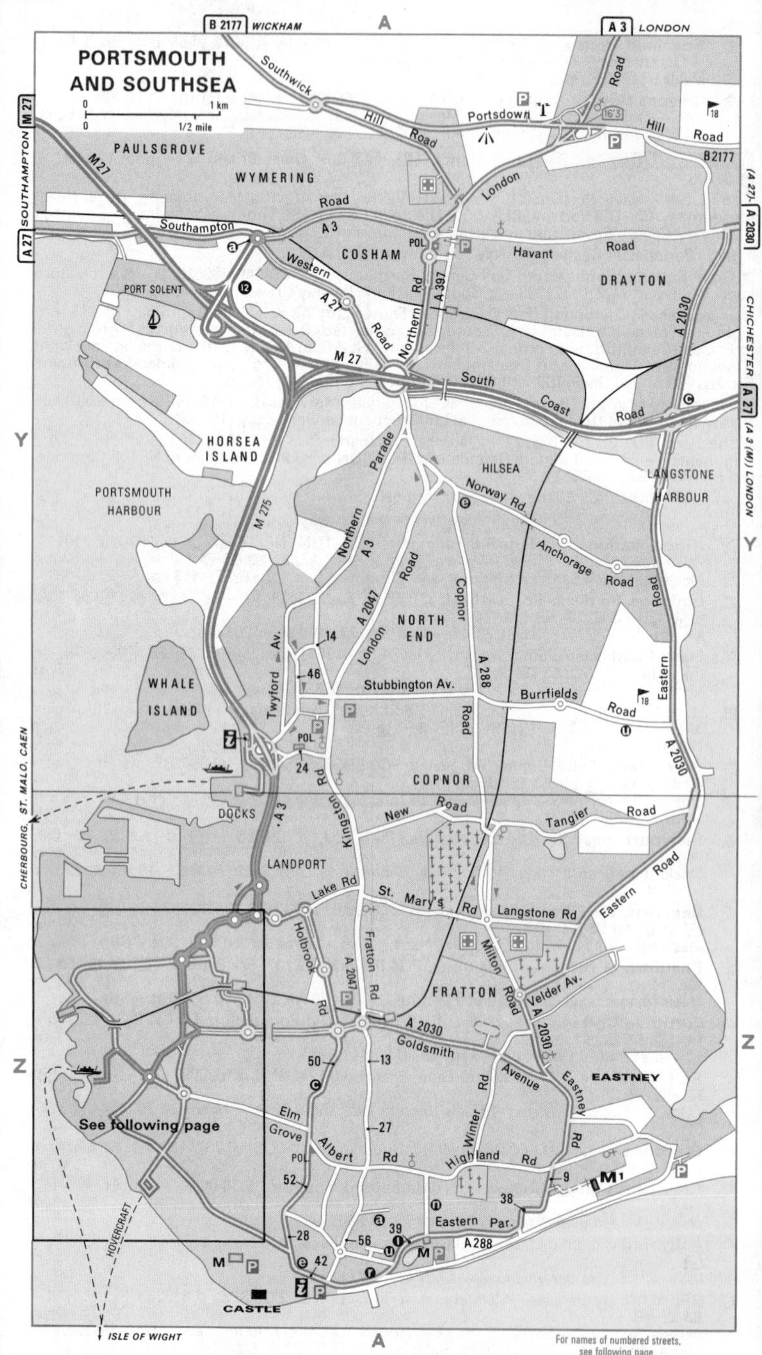

For names of numbered streets, see following page.

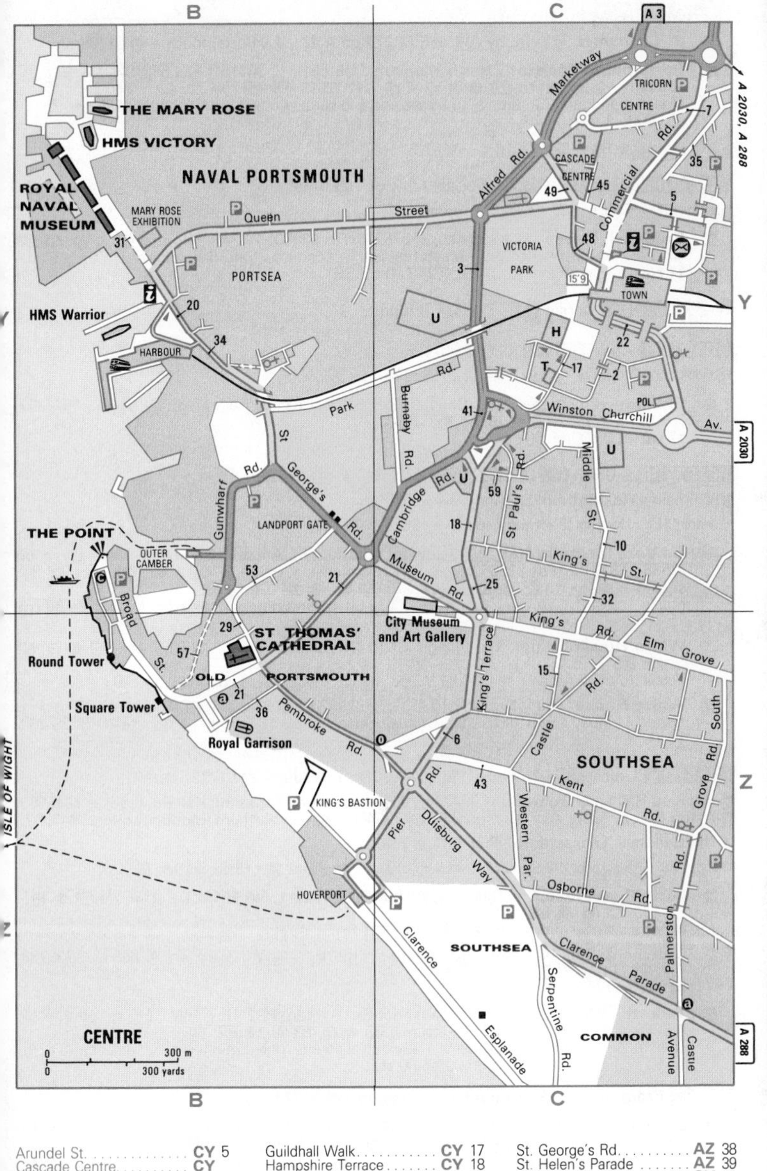

Arundel St. . . . . CY 5
Cascade Centre. . . . . CY
Charlotte St. . . . . CY 7
Commercial Rd . . . . CY
Palmerston Rd. . . . . CZ
Tricorn Centre . . . . CY

Alec Rose Lane. . . . . CY 2
Anglesea Rd . . . . CY 3
Bellevue Terrace . . . . CZ 6
Cromwell Rd . . . . AZ 9
Eldon St. . . . . CY 10
Fawcett Rd . . . . AZ 13
Gladys Avenue . . . . AY 14
Great Southsea St. . . . . . . CZ 15

Guildhall Walk. . . . . CY 17
Hampshire Terrace . . . . CY 18
Hard (The) . . . . BY 20
High St. . . . . BYZ 21
Isambard Brunel Rd . . . . . . CY 22
Kingston Crescent . . . . AY 24
Landport Terrace. . . . . CY 25
Lawrence Rd . . . . AZ 27
Lennox Rd South . . . . AZ 28
Lombard St. . . . . BYZ 29
Main Rd. . . . . BY 31
Norfolk St. . . . . CYZ 32
Ordnance Row . . . . BY 34
Paradise St. . . . . CY 35
Penny St. . . . . BZ 36

St. George's Rd. . . . . AZ 38
St. Helen's Parade . . . . AZ 39
St. Michael's Rd . . . . CY 41
South Parade. . . . . AZ 42
Southsea Terrace . . . . CZ 43
Spring St. . . . . CY 45
Stamshaw Rd . . . . AY 46
Stanhope Rd . . . . CY 48
Unicorn Rd . . . . CY 49
Victoria Rd North . . . . AZ 50
Victoria Rd South . . . . AZ 52
Warblington St. . . . . BY 53
Waverley Rd . . . . AZ 56
White Hart Rd. . . . . BYZ 57
Wiltshire St. . . . . CY 59

at Cosham N : 4½ m. by A 3 and M 275 on A 27 – ✉ Portsmouth – ☎ 01705 :

Portsmouth Marriott, North Harbour, PO6 4SH, ☎ 383151, Fax 388701, squash – rm – 280. AE VISA. AY a
Meals (bar lunch Saturday) 15.95 **st.** and a la carte 5.50 – 10.50 – **169 rm** 75.00/95.00 **st.**, 1 suite – SB.

ATS 3 Margate Rd ☎ 827544

POWBURN Northd 401 402 O 17 – ✉ Alnwick – ☎ 01665.

◆London 312 – ◆Edinburgh 73 – ◆Newcastle upon Tyne 36.

Breamish House, NE66 4LL, ☎ 578266, Fax 578500, ←, – rest. VISA
closed January-14 February – **Meals** (bar lunch Monday to Saturday)/dinner 21.50 **t.** 5.95 – **11 rm** (dinner included) 70.00/142.00 **t.** – SB.

POWERSTOCK Dorset 403 L 31 – see Bridport.

POYNTON Ches. 402 403 N 23 – ☎ 01625.

◆London 193 – Chester 44 – ◆Manchester 12 – ◆Stoke-on-Trent 28.

Spinney without rest., 59 Chester Rd, SK12 1JG, W : ¼ m. on A 5149 ☎ 871397, Fax 871397, – . VISA JCB
12 rm 35.00/68.00 **st.**

PRESTBURY Ches. 402 403 404 N 24 – pop. 3 623 – ☎ 01625.

Wilmslow Rd, Mottram St. Andrews ☎ 828135.

◆London 184 – ◆Liverpool 43 – ◆Manchester 17 – ◆Stoke-on-Trent 25.

De Vere Mottram Hall, Wilmslow Rd, Mottram St. Andrew, SK10 4QT, NW : 2¼ m. on A 538 ☎ 828135, Fax 828950, ←, « Part 18C mansion, gardens », park, squash – rm – 275. AE VISA.
Meals *(closed Saturday lunch)* 18.00/30.00 **st.** and dinner a la carte 7.00 – **130 rm** 105.00/140.00 **st.**, 3 suites – SB.

White House Manor, The Village, SK10 4HP, ☎ 829376, Fax 828627, – . AE VISA
Meals (room service or see ***White House*** below) – 8.50 – **8 rm** 65.00/110.00 **t.**

White House, The Village, SK10 4DG, ☎ 829376, Fax 828627 – . AE VISA
closed Monday lunch and Sunday dinner – **Meals** 11.95/18.50 **t.** and a la carte 20.75/28.40 **t.** 5.00.

PRESTON Lancs. 402 L 22 – pop. 126 082 – ECD : Thursday – ☎ 01772.

Fulwood Hall Lane, Fulwood ☎ 794234/700436 – Ingol, Tanterton Hall Rd, Ingol ☎ 734556 – Aston & Lea, Tudor Av., Blackpool Rd ☎ 726480 – Penwortham, Blundell Lane ☎ 743207.

The Guildhall, Lancaster Rd, PR1 1HT ☎ 253731.

◆London 226 – ◆Blackpool 18 – Burnley 22 – ◆Liverpool 30 – ◆Manchester 34 – ◆Stoke-on-Trent 65.

Forte Posthouse, The Ringway, PR1 3AU, ☎ 259411, Fax 201923 – rm – 100. AE VISA
Meals a la carte approx. 15.00 **t.** 5.50 – **121 rm** 56.00 **st.**

Claremont, 516 Blackpool Rd, Ashton, PR2 1HY, NW : 2 m. on A 5085 ☎ 729738, Fax 726274, –
14 rm.

Tulketh, 209 Tulketh Rd, off Blackpool Rd, Ashton, PR2 1ES, NW : 2¼ m. by A 6 off A 5085 ☎ 728096, Fax 723743 – rest. AE VISA.
closed 24 December-2 January – **Meals** (residents only) (dinner only) a la carte 6.75/14.50 **st.** 4.00 – **12 rm** 35.00/44.00 **st.**

at Broughton N : 3 m. on A 6 – ✉ Preston – ☎ 01772 :

Broughton Park (Country Club), 418 Garstang Rd, PR3 5JB, ☎ 864087, Fax 861728, squash – rm – 200. AE VISA.
***Courtyard* : Meals** *(closed lunch Saturday and Bank Holidays* except Christmas) 10.95/18.95 **t.** 5.75 – 9.00 – **98 rm** 75.00/100.00 **t.** – SB.

at Samlesbury E : 2½ m. by A 59 – ✉ Preston – ☎ 01772 :

Swallow Trafalgar, Preston New Rd, PR5 0UL, E : 1 m. at junction of A 59 with A 677 ☎ 877351, Fax 877424, squash – rm rest – 250. AE VISA
Meals (closed Saturday lunch) 9.50/15.50 **st.** and a la carte – **78 rm** 78.00/95.00 **st.** – SB.

Tickled Trout, Preston New Rd, PR5 0UJ, W : 1 m. on A 59 ☎ 877671, Fax 877463, ←, – rm – 100
72 rm.

at Bamber Bridge S : 5 m. by A 6 on B 6258 – ✉ Preston – ☎ 01772 :

Novotel, Reedfield Place, Walton Summit, PR5 6AB, SE : ¾ m. by A 6 at junction 29 of M 6 ✆ 313331, Telex 677164, Fax 627868, heated, – rm – 180. AE VISA
Meals 10.85 **st.** (dinner) and a la carte 10.15/18.65 **st.** 5.35 – 7.50 – **98 rm** 39.50 **st.**

Poachers, Lobstock Lane, PR5 6BJ, S : ½ m. on A 6 ✆ 234100, Fax 629525 – rm . AE VISA.
Meals (grill rest.) a la carte approx. 18.00 **t.** – 4.95 – **40 rm** 33.00 **st.**

at Lea W : 3 ½ m. on A 583 – ✉ Preston – ☎ 01772 :

Travel Inn, Blackpool Rd, PR4 0XL, on A 583 ✆ 720476, Fax 729971 – rm . AE VISA.
Meals (Beefeater grill) a la carte approx. 16.00 **t.** – 4.95 – **38 rm** 33.50 **t.**

ATS 296-298 Aqueduct St, Ashton ✆ 257688

PRESTWICH Gtr. Manchester – ✉ Manchester – ☎ 0161.

London 205 – Leeds 40 – Liverpool 30 – Manchester 5.

Village H & Leisure Club, George St., M25 8WS, S : 1 ¾ m. by A 56 ✆ 798 8905, Fax 773 5562, squash – – 100. AE VISA
Meals (grill rest.) (bar lunch Saturday) 8.00/12.00 **st.** and a la carte – **39 rm** 60.00/ 80.00 **st.** – SB.

PRIDDY Somerset 403 L 30 – see Wells.

PUCKERIDGE Herts. 404 U 28 – see Ware.

PUCKRUP Glos. – see Tewkesbury.

PUDDINGTON Ches. 402 403 K 24 – see Chester.

PUDSEY W. Yorks. 402 P 22 – see Leeds.

PULBOROUGH W. Sussex 404 S 31 – pop. 4 309 – ECD : Wednesday – ☎ 01798.

18, 9 West Chiltington, Broadford Bridge Rd ✆ 813574.

London 49 – Brighton 25 – Guildford 25 – Portsmouth 35.

Chequers, Church Pl., RH20 1AD, NE : ¼ m. on A 29 ✆ 872486, Fax 872715, – . AE VISA
Meals (bar lunch Monday to Saturday)/dinner 20.45 **s.** 4.95 – **11 rm** 47.50/82.00 **st.** – SB.

Stane Street Hollow, Codmore Hill, RH20 1BG, NE : 1 m. on A 29 ✆ 872819 –
closed Sunday dinner, Monday, Tuesday, two weeks early June and 2 weeks late October – **Meals** - Swiss (booking essential) 13.50 **t.** (lunch) and a la carte 16.50/24.50 **t.** 6.50.

at West Chiltington E : 2 ¾ m. by A 283 on West Chiltington rd – ✉ Pulborough – ☎ 01798 :

New House Farm without rest., Broadford Bridge Rd, RH20 2LA, ✆ 812215, – .
closed Christmas – **3 rm** 30.00/44.00 **st.**

PURTON Wilts. 403 404 O 29 – pop. 3 926 – ✉ Swindon – ☎ 01793.

London 94 – Bristol 41 – Gloucester 31 – Oxford 38 – Swindon 5.

Pear Tree at Purton, Church End, SN5 9ED, S : ½ m. by Church St. on Lydiard Millicent rd ✆ 772100, Fax 772369, « Conservatory restaurant », – – 60. AE VISA JCB
Meals *(closed Saturday lunch)* 17.50/27.50 **st.** 6.00 – **16 rm** 92.00/102.00 **st.**, 2 suites – SB.

QUORN Leics. – see Loughborough.

RADLETT Herts. 404 T 28 – pop. 7 749 – ECD : Wednesday – ☎ 01923.

18 Aldenham, Church Lane ✆ 853929.

London 21 – Luton 15.

Plan : see Greater London (North-West)

Tim's Table, 335 Watling St., WD7 7LB, ✆ 854388 – . AE VISA
Meals - Chinese (Peking, Szechuan) 10.50/16.50 **t.** and a la carte 4.00.

RAMSBOTTOM Gtr. Manchester 402 N 23 – pop. 13 743 – ☎ 01706.

London 223 – Blackpool 39 – Burnley 12 – Leeds 46 – Manchester 13 – Liverpool 39.

Old Mill, Springwood St., off Carr St., BL0 9DS, ✆ 822991, Fax 822291, – . AE VISA.
Meals 7.50/12.50 **t.** and a la carte 4.05 – **36 rm** 45.50/65.00 **t.** – SB.

Village, 18 Market Pl., BL0 9HT, ✆ 825070 – . AE VISA
closed Sunday dinner, Monday and Tuesday **Meals** 8.95/14.95 **t.** and lunch a la carte 4.50.

RAMSGATE Kent 404 Y 30 – pop. 36 678 – ECD : Thursday – 01843.

to France (Dunkerque) (Sally Ferries) 5 daily (2 h 30 mn) – to Belgium (Ostend) (Sally Ferries) 6 daily (4 h) – Argyle Centre, Queen St., CT11 9EE 591086.

London 77 – Dover 19 – Maidstone 45 – Margate 4.5.

Jarvis Marina Resort, Harbour Par., CT11 8LJ, 588276, Fax 586866, ≤, – rm rest – 120 – **59 rm.**

San Clu, Victoria Par., East Cliff, CT11 8DT, 592345, Fax 580157, ≤ – . AE VISA
Meals (bar lunch Monday to Saturday)/dinner 11.75 **st.** and a la carte 6.50 – **33 rm** 50.00/130.00 **st.** – SB.

at Minster W : 5½ m. by A 253 on B 2048 – Ramsgate – 01843 :

Morton's Fork, 42 Station Rd, CT12 4BZ, 823000, Fax 821224 – rest . AE VISA.
Meals *(closed Sunday dinner and Monday)* 12.95 **t.** and a la carte 5.50 – 6.50 – **3 rm** 33.00/42.00 **t.** –.

ATS 82-84 Bellevue Rd 595829

RAMSGILL-IN-NIDDERDALE N. Yorks. 402 O 21 – see Pateley Bridge.

RASKELF N. Yorks. – see Easingwold.

RAVENSTONEDALE Cumbria 402 M 20 – pop. 886 – ECD : Thursday – Kirkby Stephen – 0153 96.

London 280 – Carlisle 43 – Kendal 19 – Kirkby Stephen 5.

Black Swan, CA17 4NG, 23204, – rest . AE VISA JCB
Meals 11.50/23.00 **t.** and a la carte 4.50 – **15 rm** 46.00/66.00 **st.** – SB.

Fat Lamb, Crossbank, Fell End, CA17 4LL, SE : 2 m. on A 683 23242, ≤, –
Meals 12.50/17.00 **t.** and a la carte 3.25 – **12 rm** 32.00/56.00 **t.** – SB.

RAWTENSTALL Lancs. – Rossendale – 01706.

London 228 – Blackpool 34 – Burnley 10 – Leeds 41 – Manchester 18 – Liverpool 44.

XX **Rose,** Market St., Waterfoot, BB4 7AR, E : 1½ m. on A 681 215788. VISA
closed Tuesday lunch, Sunday dinner, Monday, 2 to 10 January and 22 July-1 August – **Meals** 9.25/21.50.

READING Berks. 403 404 Q 29 – pop. 128 877 – 01734 – Calcot Park, Calcot 427124 – Town Hall, Blagrave St., RG1 1QH 566226.

London 43 – Brighton 79 – Bristol 78 – Croydon 47 – Luton 62 – Oxford 28 – Portsmouth 67 – Southampton 46.

Plan opposite

Holiday Inn (Q.M.H.), Caversham Bridge, Richfield Av., RG1 8BD, 391818, Fax 391665, ≤, « Thames-side setting », – rm rest – 250. AE VISA JCB X **e**
Meals (bar lunch Saturday and Bank Holidays) 9.95/18.95 **t.** and a la carte 6.95 – 8.95 – **107 rm** 106.00 **st.**, 4 suites – SB.

Ramada, Oxford Rd, RG1 7RH, 586222, Telex 847785, Fax 597842, – rm – 220. AE VISA JCB. Z **i**
Meals (buffet lunch)/dinner 13.50/17.50 **st.** and a la carte 6.00 – 8.95 – **193 rm** 99.00 **st.**, 1 suite – SB.

Forte Posthouse, 500 Basingstoke Rd, RG2 0SL, S : 2 ½ m. on A 33 875485, Fax 311958, – rm – 100. AE VISA JCB X **a**
Meals a la carte approx. 15.00 **t.** 5.50 – **138 rm** 59.50/69.50 **st.**

Hillingdon Prince, 39 Christchurch Rd, RG2 7AN, 311391, Fax 756357 – rm – 25. AE VISA X **s**
Meals *(closed dinner Sunday and Bank Holidays and 25 to 31 December)* 12.95/17.50 **st.** and a la carte **st.** 4.50 – **40 rm** 50.00/75.00 **st.**

Upcross, Berkeley Av., RG1 6HY, 590796, Fax 576517, – – 40. AE VISA Y **c**
closed 26 December-3 January – **Meals** *(closed Saturday lunch)* 15.00 **st.** and a la carte 6.00 – **20 rm** 49.00/59.00 **st.** – SB.

Rainbow Corner, 132-138 Caversham Rd, RG1 8AY, 588140, Fax 586500 – . AE VISA X **u**
Meals *(closed Sunday)* (dinner only) 15.50 **t.** and a la carte 4.95 – 4.95 – **22 rm** 54.00/65.00 **t.** – SB.

Forte Travelodge, 387 Basingstoke Rd, RG2 0JE, S : 2 m. on A 33 750618, Reservations (Freephone) 0800 850950 – . AE VISA. X **c**
Meals (Harvester grill) a la carte approx. 16.00 **t.** – 5.50 – **36 rm** 33.50 **t.**

Dittisham without rest, 63 Tilehurst Rd, RG3 2JL, 569483, – . VISA
5 rm 19.00/40.00. X **v**

XX **Michel's Brasserie,** 62 Christchurch Rd, RG2 7AZ, 872823 – AE VISA JCB X **n**
closed 25 December and 1 January – **Meals** - French 7.45/14.95 and a la carte.

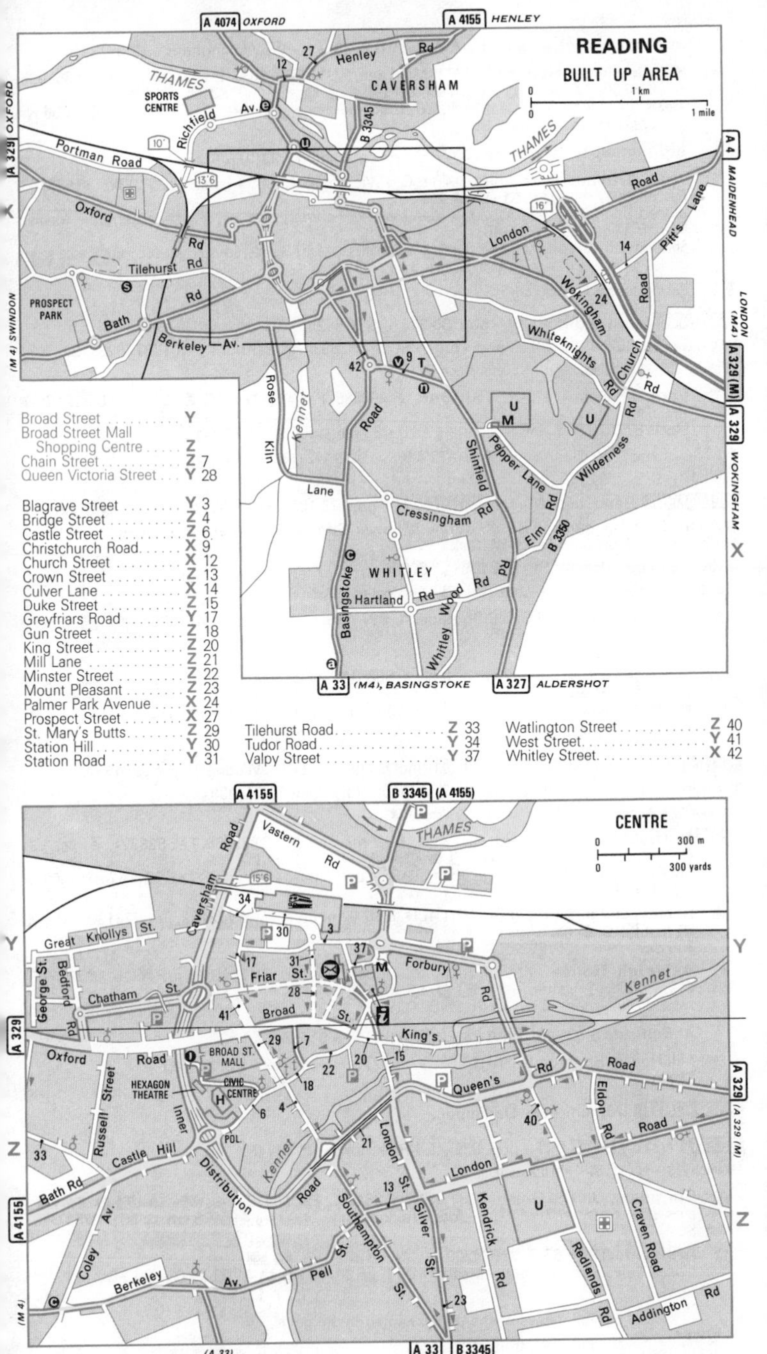

Broad Street . . . . Y
Broad Street Mall Shopping Centre . . . . . Z
Chain Street . . . . Z 7
Queen Victoria Street . . . Y 28

Blagrave Street . . . . Y 3
Bridge Street . . . . Z 4
Castle Street . . . . Z 6
Christchurch Road. . . . . . X 9
Church Street . . . . X 12
Crown Street . . . . Z 13
Culver Lane . . . . X 14
Duke Street . . . . Z 15
Greyfriars Road . . . . Y 17
Gun Street . . . . Z 18
King Street . . . . Z 20
Mill Lane . . . . Z 21
Minster Street . . . . Z 22
Mount Pleasant . . . . Z 23
Palmer Park Avenue . . . . X 24
Prospect Street . . . . X 27
St. Mary's Butts. . . . . Z 29
Station Hill . . . . Y 30
Station Road . . . . Y 31
Tilehurst Road. . . . . Z 33
Tudor Road. . . . . Y 34
Valpy Street . . . . Y 37
Watlington Street . . . . Z 40
West Street. . . . . Y 41
Whitley Street. . . . . X 42

at Sindlesham SE : 5 m. by A 329 on B 3030 – X – ✉ Wokingham – ☎ 01734 :

Reading Moat House (Q.M.H.), Mill Lane, RG11 5DF, NW : ½ m. by Mole Rd ✆ 351035, Fax 666530, – rm rest – 80. AE VISA
Meals (bar lunch Saturday) 14.50/28.50 **st.** and dinner a la carte 6.75 – 10.00 – **95 rm** 97.00/119.00 **st.**, 1 suite – SB.

at Shinfield S : 4¼ m. on A 327 – X – ✉ Reading – ☎ 01734 :

XXX ✿✿ **L'Ortolan** (Burton-Race) The Old Vicarage, Church Lane, RG2 9BY, ✆ 883783, Fax 885391, – AE VISA
closed Sunday dinner, Monday, last 2 weeks February and last 2 weeks August – **Meals** - French 31.50/63.00 **t.** 8.10
Spec. Homard à la vapeur, sauce vierge, salade de pommes de terre à la truffe, Coeur de filet de boeuf aux escargots et girolles, fumet de vin rouge, Assiette de fruits d'été.

ATS Basingstoke Rd ✆ 580651

REDCAR Cleveland 402 Q 20 – pop. 35 373 – ☎ 01642.

Wilton ✆ 465265 – Cleveland, Queen St. ✆ 483693 – Saltburn ✆ (01287) 622812.

London 255 – Middlesbrough 9 – Scarborough 43.

Park, 3-5 Granville Terr., TS10 3AR, ✆ 490888, Fax 486147 – – 50. AE VISA.
Meals 8.50/18.60 **t.** and a la carte 4.75 – **33 rm** 38.00/65.00 **t.**

ATS Limerick Rd, Dormanstown ✆ 477100/477163 ATS 162 Lord St. ✆ 484013

REDDITCH Heref. and Worcs. 403 404 O 27 – pop. 78 106 – ECD : Wednesday – ☎ 01527.

Abbey Park, Dagnell End Rd ✆ 63918 – Lower Grinsty, Green Lane, Callow Hill ✆ 543309 – Pitcheroak, Plymouth Rd ✆ 541054.

Civic Square, Alcester St., B98 8AH ✆ 60806.

London 111 – Birmingham 15 – Cheltenham 33 – Stratford-upon-Avon 15.

Southcrest, Pool Bank, Southcrest, B97 4JS, ✆ 541511, Fax 402600, – – 70
58 rm.

Old Rectory, Ipsley Lane, Ipsley, B98 0AP, ✆ 523000, Fax 517003, – rest AE VISA.
Meals (residents only) (communal dining) (dinner only) 15.95 **st.** – **10 rm** 54.00/82.00 **st.**

ATS Pipers Rd, Park Farm Ind. Est., Park Farm South ✆ 502002/502027

REDHILL Surrey 404 T 30 – pop. 48 241 (inc. Reigate) – ECD : Wednesday – ☎ 01737.

Redhill & Reigate, Clarence Lodge, Pendleton Rd ✆ 244626/244433.

London 22 – Brighton 31 – Guildford 20 – Maidstone 34.

Nutfield Priory, Nutfield, RH1 4EN, E : 2 m. on A 25 ✆ 822066, Fax 823321, , park, squash – – 80. AE VISA.
Meals *(closed Saturday lunch)* 16.00/19.95 **t.** and dinner a la carte – 5.75 – **51 rm** 105.00/125.00 **t.**, 1 suite –.

Hunters Lodge, Nutfield Rd, RH1 4ED, E : 1¾ m. on A 25 ✆ 773139, Fax 778190, – rest
25 rm.

Ashleigh House without rest., 39 Redstone Hill, RH1 4BG, on A 25 ✆ 764763, Fax 780308, heated, – VISA.
closed Christmas – **8 rm** 25.30/50.00 **st.**

at Salfords S : 2½ m. on A 23 – ✉ Redhill – ☎ 01737 :

Mill House, Brighton Rd, RH1 5BT, ✆ 767277, Fax 778099 –
21 rm.

REDWORTH Durham – see Darlington.

REETH N. Yorks. 402 O 20 – pop. 939 – ✉ Richmond – ☎ 01748.

London 253 – Leeds 53 – Middlesbrough 36.

Burgoyne, On The Green, DL11 6SN, ✆ 884292, Fax 884292, – VISA
closed 2 January-10 February – **Meals** (dinner only) 21.00 **t.** 4.65 – **8 rm** 50.00/75.00 **t.** – SB.

Arkleside, DL11 6SG, ✆ 884200, – VISA
closed November-January – **Meals** 17.00 **t.** 5.50 – **9 rm** 41.00/78.00 **st.** – SB.

Prices For full details of the prices quoted in the guide, consult the introduction.

REIGATE Surrey 404 T 30 – pop. 52 007 – ECD : Wednesday – 01737.
◆London 26 – ◆Brighton 33 – Guildford 20 – Maidstone 38.

Bridge House, Reigate Hill, RH2 9RP, N : 1 ¼ m. on A 217 ℘ 246801, Fax 223756 – – 50.
Meals (dancing Wednesday to Saturday evenings) 15.75/24.00 **st.** and a la carte – 7.50 – **37 rm** 50.00/75.00 **st.**

Cranleigh, 41 West St., RH2 9BL, ℘ 223417, Fax 223734, heated, , – .
closed 24 to 31 December **Meals** (by arrangement) (dinner only) 18.00 **t.** 4.50 – **9 rm** 39.00/65.00 **t.** – SB.

The Dining Room, 59a High St., RH2 9AE, ℘ 226650 – .
closed Saturday lunch, Sunday, 1 week Easter, 1 week Summer and 2 weeks Christmas – **Meals** 9.95/17.70 **t.** and a la carte.

La Barbe, 71 Bell St., RH2 7AN, ℘ 241966, Fax 241966 – .
closed Saturday lunch, Sunday and Bank Holidays – **Meals** - French 17.95/22.95 **st.** 5.00.

RENDCOMB Glos. 403 404 O 28 – see Cirencester.

RETFORD Notts. – see East Retford.

REYDON Suffolk – see Southwold.

RICHMOND N. Yorks. 402 O 20 **Great Britain G.** – pop. 7 862 – ECD : Wednesday – 01748.
See : Castle★ *AC* – Georgian Theatre Royal and Museum★.
Bend Hagg ℘ 825319 – Catterick Garrison, Leyburn Rd ℘ 833401.
Friary Gardens, Victoria Rd, DL10 4AJ ℘ 850252/825994.
◆London 243 – ◆Leeds 53 – ◆Middlesbrough 26 – ◆Newcastle upon Tyne 44.

King's Head, Market Pl., DL10 4HS, ℘ 850220, Fax 850635 – – 100.
Meals (bar lunch Monday to Saturday)/dinner 17.95 **st.** and a la carte 4.25 – **28 rm** 53.00/97.00 **st.** – SB.

West End, 45 Reeth Rd., DL10 4EX, W : ½ m. on A 6108 ℘ 824783, –
closed 2 weeks Christmas-New Year – **Meals** 12.00 **st.** 4.30 **5 rm** 18.50/37.00 **st.**

Whashton Springs Farm , DL11 7JS, NW : 3 ½ m. on Ravensworth rd ℘ 822884, « Working farm », , park – .
closed mid December-February – **Meals** (by arrangement) 12.00 **st.** 2.50 – **8 rm** 27.00/42.00 **st.**

at Kirby Hill NW : 4 ½ m. by Ravensworth rd – ✉ Richmond – 01748 :

Shoulder of Mutton Inn, DL11 7JH, ℘ 822772 – .
Meals *(closed Monday lunch)* (in bar) a la carte 6.25/13.25 **st.** 3.25 – **5 rm** 25.00/39.00 **st.**

ATS Reeth Rd ℘ 824182/3

RIDGEWAY Derbs. – see Sheffield (S. Yorks.).

RINGWOOD Hants. 403 404 O 31 – pop. 9 813 – ECD : Monday and Thursday – 01425.
Ringwood ℘ 402431 – Moors Valley, Horton Rd ℘ 479776.
The Furlong, BH24 1AZ ℘ 470896 (summer only).
◆London 102 – Bournemouth 11 – Salisbury 17 – ◆Southampton 20.

Moortown Lodge, 244 Christchurch Rd, BH24 3AS, ℘ 471404, Fax 476052 – rest .
closed Christmas-mid January – **Meals** *(closed Sunday to non-residents)* (dinner only) 14.95 **t.** 4.95 – **6 rm** 32.00/80.00 **t.** – SB.

at Avon S : 4 m. on B 3347 – ✉ Christchurch – 01425 :

Tyrrells Ford , BH23 7BH, ℘ 672646, Fax 672262, , park – – 25.
Meals 14.95/18.95 **t.** and dinner a la carte 4.95 – **16 rm** 50.00/90.00 **st.** – SB.

at St Leonards (Dorset) SW : 3 m. on A 31 – ✉ Ringwood – 01425 :

St. Leonards, 185 Ringwood Rd, BH24 2NP, ℘ 471220, Fax 480274, , – rm – 80
33 rm.

RIPLEY N. Yorks. 402 P 21 – pop. 193 – ✉ Harrogate – 01423.
◆London 213 – Bradford 21 – ◆Leeds 18 – ◆Newcastle upon Tyne 79.

Boar's Head, HG3 3AY, ℘ 771888, Fax 771509, « 18C coaching inn within estate village of Ripley Castle », , – – 80.
Meals 14.50 **t.** (lunch) and a la carte 22.75/30.40 **t.** 4.95 – **25 rm** 75.00/130.00 **t.** – SB.

at Burnt Yates W : 2 ¾ m. on B 6165 – ✉ Harrogate – ☎ 01423 :

Bay Horse Inn, HG3 3EJ, on B 6165 ☎ 770230, – rm. **Meals** (bar lunch Monday to Saturday)/dinner 14.95 **t.** and a la carte 5.50 – **14 rm** 40.00/55.00 **t.** – SB.

RIPLEY Surrey 404 S 30 – pop. 1 697 – ECD : Wednesday – ☎ 01483.

◆London 28 – Guildford 6.

XXX **Michels',** 13 High St., GU23 6AQ, ☎ 224777, – AE VISA
closed Saturday lunch, Sunday dinner, Monday and 1 January – **Meals** 19.00/21.00 **t.** and a la carte 4.25.

RIPON N. Yorks. 402 P 21 **Great Britain G.** – pop. 13 806 – ECD : Wednesday – ☎ 01765.

See : Town★ – Cathedral★ (Saxon Crypt★★) *AC*.

Envir. : Fountains Abbey★★★ *AC* : Studley Royal★★ *AC* (<★ from Anne Boleyn's Seat) – Fountains Hall (Façade★), SW : 2 ½ m. by B 6265 – Newby Hall (Tapestries★) *AC*, SE : 3 ½ m. by B 6265.

Ripon City, Palace Rd ☎ 603640.

Minster Rd, HG4 1LT ☎ 604625 (summer only).

◆London 222 – ◆Leeds 26 – ◆Middlesbrough 35 – York 23.

Ripon Spa, Park St., HG4 2BU, E : ¼ m. on B 6265 ☎ 602172, Fax 690770, – 150. AE VISA JCB
Meals 10.50/18.00 **t.** and a la carte – **40 rm** 56.20/98.00 **t.** – SB.

ATS Dallamires Lane ☎ 601579

ROADE Northants. – pop. 2 527 – ☎ 01604.

◆London 66 – ◆Coventry 36 – Northampton 5.5.

XX **Roadhouse,** 16 High St., NN7 2NW, ☎ 863372 – AE VISA
closed Sunday dinner, Monday and 2 weeks summer – **Meals** 15.75 **st.** and dinner a la carte 17.75/24.25 5.00.

ROBIN HOOD'S BAY N.Yorks. 402 S 20 – ✉ Whitby – ☎ 01947.

Plantation House without rest., Thorpe Lane, YO22 4RN, ☎ 880036, –
March-November – **3 rm** 26.00/32.00 **s.**

ROCHDALE Gtr. Manchester 402 N 23 – pop. 96 359 – ☎ 01706.

18 Edenfield Rd, Bagslate ☎ 46024 – 18 Marland, Springfield Park ☎ 49801 – 9 Lobden, Whitworth ☎ 343228 – 9,(x 3) Castle Hawk, Heywood Rd ☎ 40841.

The Clock Tower, Town Hall, OL16 1AB ☎ 356592.

◆London 224 – ◆Blackpool 40 – Burnley 11 – ◆Leeds 45 – ◆Manchester 12 – ◆Liverpool 40.

Norton Grange, Manchester Rd, Castleton, OL11 2XZ, SW : 3 m. by A 58 on A 644 ☎ 30788, Fax 49313, – rm – 100. AE VISA
Meals *(closed Saturday lunch and Sunday dinner)* 9.95/17.95 **t.** and a la carte 5.95 – **49 rm** 82.50/92.50 **t.**, 1 suite – SB.

Castleton, Manchester Rd, Castleton, OL11 2XX, ☎ 357888, park – AE VISA.
Meals *(closed lunch Saturday and Bank Holidays)* 8.50/12.50 **t.** and a la carte 4.30 – **13 rm** 50.00/70.00 **t.**

XX **After Eight,** 2 Edenfield Rd, OL11 5AA, W : 1 m. on A 680 ☎ 46432. AE VISA
closed Sunday, Monday, 1 to 14 May, 26 to 30 December and 1 January **Meals** (dinner only) a la carte 16.30/20.10 **t.** 4.30.

XX **French Connection,** Edenfield Rd, Cheesden, Norden, OL12 7TY, W : 5 m. on A 680 ☎ 50167, < – VISA
closed Monday and 31 July-15 August – **Meals** a la carte 18.25/29.10 **t.** 4.40.

ATS Royds St. ☎ 32411/49935 ATS Castleton Moor, Nixon St. (ASDA) ☎ 57068

ROCHESTER Kent 404 V 29 **Great Britain G.** – pop. 23 840 – ECD : Wednesday – ✉ Chatham – ☎ 01634.

See : Castle★ *AC* – Cathedral★ *AC*.

Eastgate Cottage, High St., ME1 1EW ☎ 843666.

◆London 30 – ◆Dover 45 – Maidstone 8 – Margate 46.

Bridgewood Manor, Maidstone Rd, ME5 9AX, SE : 3 m. by A 2 on A 229 ☎ 201333, Fax 201330, – rm rest – 150. AE VISA.
Meals 13.50/19.50 **st.** and a la carte 6.25 – **96 rm** 87.00/105.00 **st.**, 4 suites – SB.

Forte Posthouse, Maidstone Rd, ME5 9SF, SE : 2 ½ m. by A 2 on A 229 ☎ 687111, Fax 864876, – rm rest – 120. AE VISA
Meals a la carte approx. 15.00 **t.** 5.50 – **105 rm** 56.00/69.50 **t.**

ROCK Cornwall 403 F 32 **The West Country G.** – ECD : Wednesday – ✉ Wadebridge – ☎ 01208.
Exc. : Pencarrow★, SE : 8½m. by B 3314 and A 389.
◆London 288 – Newquay 22 – ◆Plymouth 45 – Truro 30.

St. Enodoc 🐕, PL27 6LA, ✆ 863394, Fax 863394, ≤, ♨, ≘s, 🏊 heated, 🌳, squash – 🚭 rest 📺 ☎ 🅟
13 rm.

ROCKBOURNE Hants. 403 404 O 31 – see Fordingbridge.

RODBOROUGH Glos. – see Stroud.

ROGATE W. Sussex 404 R 30 – pop. 1 785 – ✉ Petersfield (Hants.) – ☎ 01730.
⛳ Old Thorns, Longmoor Rd ✆ 724555.
◆London 63 – ◆Brighton 42 – Guildford 29 – ◆Portsmouth 23 – ◆Southampton 36.

Mizzards Farm 🐕 without rest., GU31 5HS, SW : 1 m. by Harting rd ✆ 821656, Fax 821655, ≤, « 17C farmhouse », 🏊 heated, 🌳, park – 🚭 📺 🅟. ✱
closed Christmas – **3 rm** 34.00/54.00 **st.**

ROLLESTON-ON-DOVE Staffs. 402 403 404 P 25 – see Burton-upon-Trent.

ROMALDKIRK Durham 402 N 20 – see Barnard Castle.

ROMSEY Hants. 403 404 P 31 **Great Britain G.** – pop. 14 818 – ECD : Wednesday – ☎ 01794.
See : Abbey★ (interior★★).
Envir. : Broadlands★ *AC*, S : 1 m..
⛳ Dunwood Manor, Shootash Hill ✆ 40549 – ⛳ Nursling ✆ (01703) 732218 – ⛳ Wellow, Ryedown Lane, East Wellow ✆ 322872.
ℹ Bus Station Car Park, Broadwater Rd, SO51 8BF ✆ 512987.
◆London 82 – Bournemouth 28 – Salisbury 16 – ◆Southampton 8 – Winchester 10.

White Horse (Forte), Market Pl., SO51 8ZJ, ✆ 512431, Fax 517485 – 🚭 📺 ☎ 🅟 – 🏛 30
33 rm.

Spursholt House 🐕, Salisbury Rd, SO51 6DJ, W : 1¼ m. by A 31 on A 27 ✆ 512229, Fax 523142, « Part 17C mansion, gardens » – 🚭 rm 🅟. ✱
Meals (by arrangement) 12.50 **st.** **3 rm** 20.25/45.00 **st.**

XXX **Old Manor House,** 21 Palmerston St., SO51 8GF, ✆ 517353, « Timbered 16C house » – 🅟. AE VISA
closed Sunday dinner, Monday and 24 to 31 December – **Meals** 17.50 **st.** (lunch) and a la carte 19.50/28.50 **t.** 🍷 5.50.

at Ower SW : 3¼ m. on A 31 – ✉ Romsey – ☎ 01703.

New Forest Heathlands, Romsey Rd, SO51 6ZJ, on A 31 ✆ 814333, Fax 812123, ≘s, 🌳 – 🚭 rest 📺 ☎ 🅟 – 🏛 200. AE VISA. ✱
Meals *(closed Saturday lunch)* 7.75/15.75 **t.** and a la carte – **52 rm** 63.00/92.00 **t.** – SB.

ROSEDALE ABBEY N. Yorks. 402 R 20 **Great Britain G.** – pop. 332 (Rosedale) – ✉ Pickering – ☎ 01751.
Envir. : ≤★ on road to Hutton-le-Hole.
◆London 247 – ◆Middlesbrough 27 – Scarborough 25 – York 36.

Blacksmith's Arms, Hartoft End, YO18 8EN, SE : 2½ m. on Pickering rd ✆ 417331, Fax 417167, ≤, 🌳 – 🚭 rest 📺 ☎ 🅟. AE VISA
Meals 12.95/22.50 🍷 4.50 – **14 rm** (dinner included) 75.00/130.00 – SB.

Milburn Arms, YO18 8RA, ✆ 417312, Fax 417312, 🌳 – 📺 ☎ 🅟. VISA
Meals (bar lunch Monday to Saturday)/dinner a la carte 17.85/23.85 **t.** 🍷 4.95 – **11 rm** 44.50/74.00 **t.**

White Horse Farm, YO18 8SE, NW : ¼ m. by Thorgill rd ✆ 417239, Fax 417781, 🌳 – 📺 ☎ 🅟. AE VISA
closed 24 and 25 December – **Meals** (bar lunch Monday to Saturday)/dinner 18.50 **t.** 🍷 5.45 – **15 rm** 35.00/70.00 **t.** – SB.

ROSSINGTON S. Yorks. 402 403 404 Q 23 – see Doncaster.

ROSS-ON-WYE Heref. and Worcs. 403 404 M 28 **Great Britain G.** – pop. 9 606 – ECD : Wednesday – ☎ 01989.
See : Market House★ – Yat Rock (≤★).
Envir. : SW : Wye Valley★ – Goodrich Castle★ *AC*, SW : 3½m. by A 40.
ℹ 20 Broad St., HR9 7EA ✆ 562768.
◆London 118 – Gloucester 15 – Hereford 15 – Newport 35.

Chase, Gloucester Rd, HR9 5LH, ✆ 763161, Fax 768330, 🌳 – 📺 ☎ 🅟 – 🏛 275. AE VISA. ✱
Meals (bar lunch Saturday and Bank Holidays) 12.50/25.00 **st.** and a la carte 🍷 4.50 – **39 rm** 60.00/75.00 **st.** – SB.

Royal (Forte), Palace Pound, HR9 5HZ, 565105, Fax 768058, ≤, – rest TV ☎ P – 80. AE VISA JCB
Meals (bar lunch Monday to Saturday)/dinner 15.95 **st.** and a la carte 7.50 – 8.50 – **40 rm** 59.00/108.00 **st.** – SB.

Edde Cross House without rest., Edde Cross St., HR9 7BZ, 565088, – TV.
Booking essential, closed December and January – **3 rm** 36.00/46.00 **st.**

Sunnymount, Ryefield Rd, HR9 5LU, off Gloucester Rd 563880 – rest P. AE VISA.
closed 25 and 26 December – **Meals** (by arrangement) 15.00 **st.** 3.75 – **6 rm** 26.00/48.00 **st.** – SB.

Pheasants, 52 Edde Cross St., HR9 7BZ, 565751 – AE VISA
closed Sunday, Monday and 24 December-2 January – **Meals** (dinner only) 13.50/19.50 **st.** and a la carte 5.50.

at Yatton NE : 5 ¾ m. by A 449 – ✉ Ross-on-Wye – 01531 :

Rocks Place, HR9 7RD, 660218, Fax 660460, ≤, – rm TV ☎ P. VISA.
Meals *(closed Sunday dinner)* (lunch by arrangement Monday to Saturday)/dinner 14.95 **t.** – **7 rm** 35.00/65.00 **t.** – SB.

at Kerne Bridge S : 3 ¾ m. on B 4234 – ✉ Ross-on-Wye – 01600 :

Lumleys, HR9 5QT, 890040, – ☎ P.
Meals (by arrangement) 12.50 – **3 rm** 22.50/38.00 **st.** – SB.

at Glewstone SW : 3 ¼ m. by A 40 – ✉ Ross-on-Wye – 01989 :

Glewstone Court, HR9 6AW, 770367, Fax 770282, ≤, « Part Georgian and Victorian country house », – TV ☎ P. VISA
closed 25 to 27 December – **Meals** 12.50/22.00 **t.** – **7 rm** 40.00/90.00 **st.** – SB.

at Pencraig SW : 3 ¾ m. on A 40 – ✉ Ross-on-Wye – 01989 :

Pencraig Court, HR9 6HR, 770306, ≤, – TV ☎ P. AE VISA.
closed February and March – **Meals** (bar lunch)/dinner 13.00 and a la carte 3.00 – **11 rm** 45.00/60.00 **t.** – SB.

at Peterstow W : 2 ½ m. on A 49 – ✉ Ross-on-Wye – 01989 :

Pengethley Manor, HR9 6LL, NW : 1 ½ m. on A 49 730211, Fax 730238, ≤, « Georgian country house », heated, , park – TV ☎ P – 50. AE VISA JCB
Meals 16.00/24.00 **t.** and dinner a la carte – **21 rm** 70.00/160.00 **st.**, 3 suites – SB.

Peterstow Country House, HR9 6LB, 562826, Fax 567264, ≤, « Converted Georgian rectory », , park – rest TV ☎ P – 40. AE VISA.
closed first 2 weeks January – **Meals** 12.50/28.50 **st.** 4.50 – **9 rm** 38.50/69.00 **st.** – SB.

ATS Ind. Est., Alton Rd 64638

ROSTHWAITE Cumbria 402 K 20 – see Keswick.

ROTHBURY Northd 401 402 O 18 **Great Britain G.** – pop. 1 805 – ECD : Wednesday – ✉ Morpeth – 01669.

See : Cragside House★ (interior★) *AC*.

National Park Information Centre, Church House, Church St., NE65 7UP 620887 (summer only).

London 311 – Edinburgh 84 – Newcastle upon Tyne 29.

Orchard, High St., NE65 7TL, 620684, – rest TV.
mid March-mid November – **Meals** 13.00 **t.** 4.00 – **6 rm** 22.00/44.00 **t.**

ROTHERHAM S. Yorks. 402 403 404 P 23 – pop. 122 374 – ECD : Thursday – 01709.

Thrybergh Park 850466 – Grange Park, Upper Wortley Rd 559497 – Phoenix, Brinsworth 382624.

Central Library, Walker Pl., S65 1JH 823611.

London 166 – Kingston-upon-Hull 61 – Leeds 36 – Sheffield 6.

Rotherham Moat House (Q.M.H.), 102-104 Moorgate Rd, S60 2BG, 364902, Fax 368960, – rm rest TV ☎ P – 120. AE VISA.
Meals (bar lunch Monday to Saturday)/dinner 14.50 **st.** and a la carte 5.50 – 8.95 – **77 rm** 64.00/72.00 **st.**, 3 suites – SB.

Swallow, West Bawtry Rd, S60 4NA, SE : 2¼ m. on A 630 830630, Fax 830549, – rm TV ☎ P – 300. AE VISA
Meals 12.95/16.50 **st.** and a la carte – **98 rm** 78.00/96.00 **st.**, 2 suites – SB.

Travel Inn, Bawtry Rd, S65 3JB, E : 2 m. by A 6021 on A 631 543216, Fax 531546 – rm TV P. AE VISA.
Meals (Beefeater grill) a la carte approx. 16.00 **t.** – 4.95 – **37 rm** 33.50 **t.**

Campanile, Lowton Way, Hellaby Ind. Est., S66 8RY, E : 5 m. by A 6021 and A 631 off Denby Way 700255, Fax 545169 – rm TV ☎ P. AE VISA
Meals 9.85 **t.** and a la carte – 4.25 – **50 rm** 35.75.

at Bramley E : 4 m. by A 6021 off A 631 – ✉ Rotherham – ☎ 01709 :

Elton, Main St., S66 0SF, ✆ 545681, Fax 549100 – ⇔ rm TV ☎ P. AE VISA JCB
closed 25 December – **Meals** 10.50/17.50 **st.** and a la carte 4.50 – **29 rm** 50.00/78.00 **st.** – SB.

ATS Eastwood Works, Fitzwilliam Rd ✆ 371556/372391

ROTHERWICK Hants – see Hook.

ROTHLEY Leics. 402 403 404 Q 25 – see Leicester.

ROTTINGDEAN E. Sussex 404 T 31 – pop. 8 949 – ECD : Wednesday – ✉ Brighton – ☎ 01273.

♦London 58 – ♦Brighton 4 – Lewes 9 – Newhaven 5.

Braemar without rest., Steyning Rd, BN2 7GA, ✆ 304263,
15 rm 15.00/30.00 **t.**

ROUGHAM GREEN Suffolk – see Bury St. Edmunds.

ROWDE Wilts. 403 404 N 29 – see Devizes

ROWNHAMS SERVICE AREA Hants. 403 404 P 31 – ✉ Southampton – ☎ 01703.

M 27 Services (southbound), SO1 8AW ✆ 730345.

Road Chef Lodge without rest., S01 8AW, M 27 between junctions 3 and 4 (southbound carriageway) ✆ 741144, Fax 740204 – ⇔ TV ☎ & P
39 rm.

ROWSLEY Derbs. 402 403 404 P 24 **Great Britain G.** – pop. 451 – ECD : Thursday – ✉ Matlock – ☎ 01629.

Envir. : Chatsworth★★★ (Park and Garden★★★) *AC*, N : by B 6012.

♦London 157 – Derby 23 – ♦Manchester 40 – ♦Nottingham 30.

Peacock (Jarvis), Bakewell Rd, DE4 2EB, ✆ 733518, Fax 732671, « 17C stone house, antiques », – TV ☎ P. AE VISA
Meals 13.35/24.50 7.50 – **14 rm** 55.00/107.50.

East Lodge, DE4 2EF, on A 6 ✆ 734474, Fax 733949, , park – TV ☎ & P. AE VISA.
Meals 10.50/21.00 **t.** and lunch a la carte 4.95 – **14 rm** 54.00/95.00 **t.** – SB.

ROWTON Ches. 402 403 L 24 – see Chester.

ROYAL LEAMINGTON SPA Warks. 403 404 P 27 – pop. 56552 – ECD : Monday and Thursday – ☎ 01926.

18 Leamington and County, Golf Lane, Whitnash ✆ 425961 on plan of Warwick.

Jephson Lodge, Jephson Gardens, The Parade, CV32 4AB ✆ 311470.

♦London 99 – ♦Birmingham 23 – ♦Coventry 9 – Warwick 3.

Plan on next page

Mallory Court , Harbury Lane, Bishop's Tachbrook, CV33 9QB, S : 2¼ m. by B 4087 (Tachbrook Rd) ✆ 330214, Fax 451714, ≤, « Country house in extensive gardens », , , squash – TV ☎ P. AE VISA. — plan of Warwick Z
closed 2 to 12 January – **Meals** (booking essential) 23.50/30.00 **st.** and a la carte 40.00/54.00 **st.** – 11.25 – **10 rm** 98.00/360.00 **st.** – SB.

Manor House (Forte), Avenue Rd, CV31 3NJ, ✆ 423251, Fax 425933 – ⇔ TV ☎ P – 100. AE VISA — V **i**
Meals (bar lunch Monday to Saturday)/dinner 16.95 **t.** and a la carte 6.75 – 8.50 – **53 rm** 60.00/75.00 **t.** – SB.

Inchfield, 64 Upper Holly Walk, CV32 4JL, ✆ 883777, Fax 330467, – ⇔ rm TV ☎ P – 40. AE VISA. — U **o**
Meals *(closed Saturday lunch and Sunday dinner)* 10.25/14.75 **t.** and a la carte 4.50 – 6.50 – **22 rm** 50.00/90.00 **st.** – SB.

Falstaff (Mt. Charlotte Thistle), 16-20 Warwick New Rd, CV32 5JQ, ✆ 312044, Fax 450574 – rest TV ☎ P – 50 — Z **s**
63 rm.

Regent, 77 Parade, CV32 4AX, ✆ 427231, Telex 311715, Fax 450728 – ⇔ rest TV ☎ P – 100 — V **a**
80 rm.

Courtyard by Marriott, Olympus Av., Tachbrook Park, CV34 6RJ, SW : 1½ m. by A 452 ✆ 425522, Fax 881322, – ⇔ rm rest TV ☎ & P – 50. AE VISA JCB
Meals *(closed lunch Saturday and Sunday)* 13.75 **t.** and a la carte 5.75 – 7.50 – **94 rm** 40.00/85.00 **st.** — plan of Warwick Z **v**

ROYAL LEAMINGTON SPA

Parade .... UV
Regent Street............... UV
Royal Priors Shopping Centre ... U
Warwick Street.............. U

Adelaïde Road V
Avenue Road .... V 2
Bath Street .... V 3
Beauchamp Avenue........... U
Beauchamp Hill .... U 4
Binswood Street.............. U 6
Brandon Parade .... U 10
Church Hill .... UV 16
Clarendon Avenue .... U
Clarendon Place .... U 18
Dale Street.................. UV
Hamilton Terrace .... V 21
High Street .... V 22
Holly Walk.................. U
Kenilworth Road.............. U
Leam Terrace V
Leicester Street .... U
Lillington Avenue .... U
Lillington Road .... U
Lower Avenue................ V 28
Newbold Terrace .... V 30
Northumberland Road .... U 33
Old Warwick Road V
Priory Terrace .... V 37
Radford Road V
Regent Grove................ UV 40
Rugby Road .... U
Russell Terrace V
Spencer Street .... V 44
Tachbrook Road .... V 47
Victoria Terrace.............. V 49
Willes Road .... UV

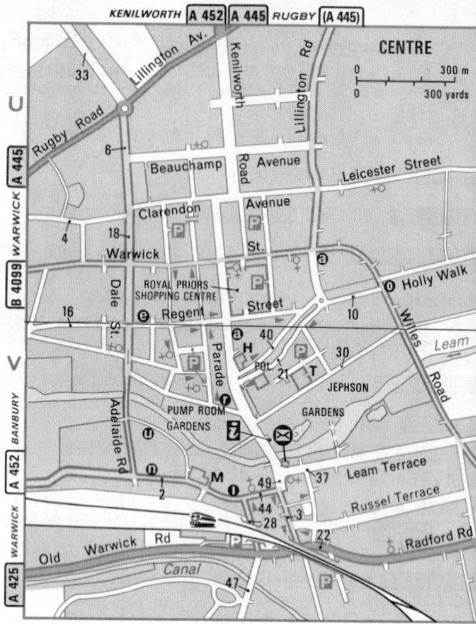

🏨 **Lansdowne,** 87 Clarendon St., CV32 4PF, ☎ 450505, Fax 421313 – TV ☎ P. VISA.
Meals (dinner only) 20.75 **t.** 4.65 – **15 rm** 49.95/59.90 **t.** – SB. U a

🏨 **Adams,** 22 Avenue Rd, CV31 3PQ, ☎ 450742, Fax 313110, « Regency town house », – rm TV ☎ P. AE VISA. V n
Meals (lunch by arrangement)/dinner 20.00 **st.** and a la carte 5.50 – **14 rm** 39.50/62.75 **t.** – SB.

🏨 **Eaton Court,** 1-7 St. Marks Rd, CV32 6DL, ☎ 885848, Fax 885848, – rm TV ☎ P – 100. AE VISA JCB plan of Warwick Z e
closed 24 December-2 January – **Meals** (lunch by arrangement)/dinner 13.95 **t.** and a la carte 4.00 – **36 rm** 45.00/75.00 **t.** – SB.

York House, 9 York Rd, CV31 3PR, ☎ 424671 – rm TV ☎. AE VISA. V u
closed 24 December-1 January – **Meals** (by arrangement) 12.50 **t.** – **8 rm** 21.00/46.00 **t.** – SB.

Flowerdale House without rest., 58 Warwick New Rd, CV32 6AA, ☎ 426002, – TV P. VISA. plan of Warwick Z c
6 rm 24.00/40.00 **s.**

Coverdale House without rest., 8 Portland St., CV32 5HE, ☎ 330400, Fax 833388 – TV ☎. VISA U e
7 rm 31.00/42.00 **st.**

XX **Les Plantagenets,** 15 Dormer Pl., CV32 5AA, ☎ 451792 – AE VISA V r
closed Sunday and Bank Holidays – **Meals** - French 12.50/18.50 **t.** and dinner a la carte.

ATS 52-54 Morton St. ☎ 339643/4

ROYAL TUNBRIDGE WELLS Kent 404 U 30 **Great Britain G.** – pop. 57 699 – ECD : Wednesday – ☎ 01892.

See : The Pantiles★ B **26** – Calverley Park★ B.

Langton Rd ☎ 523034 A.

The Old Fish Market, The Pantyles, TN2 5TN ☎ 515675.

London 36 – Brighton 33 – Folkestone 46 – Hastings 27 – Maidstone 18.

Plan opposite

Spa, Mount Ephraim, TN4 8XJ, ☎ 520331, Fax 510575, ←, park, – rm TV ☎ & P – 300. AE VISA A v
Meals (bar lunch Saturday) a la carte 23.00/34.00 **t.** 4.50 – 8.50 – **72 rm** 69.00/84.00 **st.**, 4 suites.

Russell, 80 London Rd, TN1 1DZ, ☎ 544833, Fax 515846 – rm TV ☎ P. AE VISA JCB. B a
Meals a la carte 13.15/25.25 **st.** 5.80 – **26 rm** 68.00/90.00 **t.** – SB.

Swan, The Pantiles, TN2 5TD, ☎ 541450, Fax 541465 – TV ☎ P – 55 A a
17 rm.

ROYAL TUNBRIDGE WELLS

Street	Map	No.
Calverley Road	B	
High Street	B	14
Mount Pleasant Road	B	25
Pantiles (The)	B	26
Royal Victoria Place Shopping Centre	B	
Benhall Mill Road	A	3
Bishop's Down	A	4
Calverley Park Gardens	B	7
Crescent Road	B	9
Fir Tree Road	A	10
Grosvenor Road	B	12
Hall's Hole Road	A	13
High Rocks Lane	A	16
Hungershall Park Road	A	17
Lansdowne Road	B	18
Lower Green Road	A	20
Major York's Road	A	22
Mount Ephraim	A	23
Mount Ephraim Road	B	24
Prospect Road	A	27
Rusthall Road	A	28
St. John's Road	B	29
Tea Garden Lane	A	30
Vale Road	B	33
Victoria Road	B	34
Warwick Park	B	35

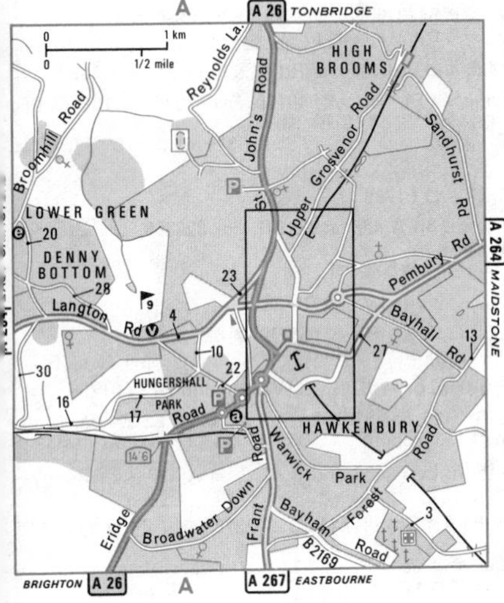

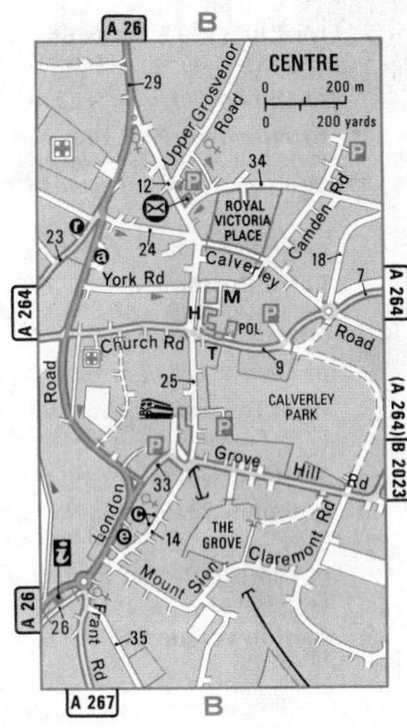

XX **Cheevers,** 56 High St., TN1 1XF, ℘ 545524, Fax 535956 – AE VISA — B c
closed Sunday and Monday – **Meals** 17.50/25.00 **t.** 4.35.

XX **Chi,** 26 London Rd, TN1 1DA, ℘ 513888 – AE VISA — B e
closed lunch Saturday and Sunday and 25-26 December – **Meals** - Chinese 10.00/22.50 **t.** and a la carte 4.00.

XX **Xian,** 54 High St., TN1 1XF, ℘ 522930 – AE VISA — B c
closed Sunday lunch and 25 to 27 December – **Meals** - Chinese 9.85/19.50 **t.** and a la carte 4.10.

at Pembury NW : 4 m. by A 264 off A 21 - A – ✉ Royal Tunbridge Wells – ☎ 01892 :

Jarvis Pembury, 8 Tonbridge Rd, TN2 4QL, ℘ 823567, Fax 823931, – rm TV ☎ & P – 200. AE VISA
Meals 11.95/18.00 **st.** and dinner a la carte 6.00 – 8.25 – **74 rm** 75.00/85.00 **t.**, 6 suites – SB.

at Frant S : 2 ½ m. on A 267 – A – ✉ Royal Tunbridge Wells – ☎ 01892 :

Old Parsonage without rest., Church Lane, TN3 9DX, ℘ 750773, Fax 750773, ≤, « Georgian rectory », – TV P.
3 rm 39.00/56.00 **st.**

at Rusthall W : 1 ¾ m. by A 264 – ✉ Royal Tunbridge Wells – ☎ 01892 :

Danehurst, 41 Lower Green Rd, TN4 8TW, ℘ 527739, Fax 514804, – TV P. VISA. — A e
closed last 2 weeks August – **Meals** 22.95 **s.** – **5 rm** 25.00/55.00 **s.** – SB.

RUAN-HIGH-LANES Cornwall 403 F 33 – see Veryan.

RUCKHALL Heref. and Worcs. – see Hereford.

> Bitte beachten Sie die Geschwindigkeitsbeschränkungen in Großbritannien
> – 60 mph (= 96 km/h) außerhalb geschlossener Ortschaften
> – 70 mph (= 112 km/h) auf Straßen mit getrennten Fahrbahnen und Autobahnen.

RUGBY Warks. 403 404 Q 26 – pop. 84 563 – ECD : Wednesday – ☎ 01788.

Whitefields Hotel, Coventry Rd, Thurlaston ☎ 521800.

The Library, St. Matthews St., CV21 3BZ ☎ 535348.

London 88 – Birmingham 33 – Leicester 21 – Northampton 20 – Warwick 17.

Grosvenor, Clifton Rd, CV21 3QQ, ☎ 535686, Fax 541297, – TV ☎ P. AE VISA JCB.
Meals *(closed Saturday lunch)* 18.60/22.60 **st.** and a la carte – **20 rm** 67.50/77.50 **st.**, 1 suite – SB.

Mr Chan's, 3-5 Castle St., CV21 2TP, ☎ 542326, Fax 542326 – AE VISA
closed Christmas – **Meals** - Chinese 19.50 **t.** and a la carte.

at Old Brownsover N : 2 m. by A 426 and Brownsover Rd – ✉ Rugby – ☎ 01788 :

Brownsover Hall, Brownsover Lane, CV21 1HU, ☎ 546100, Fax 579241, « 18C Gothic style hall », – rm TV ☎ P – 80. AE VISA
Meals *(closed lunch Saturday and Bank Holidays)* 9.95/17.95 **t.** – **31 rm** 79.50/115.00 **st.** – SB.

at Crick SE : 6 m. on A 428 – ✉ Crick – ☎ 01788 :

Forte Posthouse, NN6 7XR, W : ½ m. on A 428 ☎ 822101, Fax 823955, – rm TV ☎ P – 200. AE VISA JCB
Meals a la carte approx. 15.00 **t.** 5.50 – **88 rm** 56.00 **st.**

at Kilsby SE : 6¼ m. by A 428 on A 5 – ✉ Rugby – ☎ 01788 :

Hunt House, Main Rd, CV23 8XR, ☎ 823282, – P. AE VISA
closed Sunday and Monday – **Meals** (dinner only) 19.50 **t.** 4.95.

at West Haddon (Northants.) SE : 10 m. on A 428 – ✉ West Haddon – ☎ 01788 :

Pytchley, 23 High St., NN6 7AP, ☎ 510426, Fax 510209, – TV ☎ P. AE VISA.
closed 25 December – **Meals** (grill rest) 13.50 approx. 3.50 – **14 rm** 39.00/50.00 **st.**

at Stretton Under Fosse NW : 7 ½ m. by A 426 and B 4112 on A 427 – ✉ Rugby – ☎ 01788 :

Ashton Lodge, CV23 0PJ, N : 1 m. by A 427 on B 4112 ☎ 832278, – TV ☎ P. AE VISA
Meals *(closed Sunday, 26 December to 1 January and Bank Holidays)* (bar lunch)/dinner 9.50/16.95 **t.** and a la carte 3.50 – **11 rm** 37.00/57.00 **t.**

ATS 73 Bath St. ☎ 574705

RUGELEY Staffs. 402 403 404 O 25 – pop. 17 043 – ECD : Wednesday – ☎ 01889.

London 134 – Birmingham 31 – Derby 29 – Stoke-on-Trent 22.

Forte Travelodge without rest., Western Springs Rd, WS15 2AS, at junction of A 51 with A 460 ☎ 570096, Reservations (Freephone) 0800 850950 – TV P. AE VISA.
32 rm 33.50 **t.**

ATS Mill Lane ☎ 582500

RUNCORN Ches. 402 403 L 23 – pop. 63 995 – ECD : Wednesday – ☎ 01928.

Clifton Rd ☎ 572093.

57-61 Church St., WA7 1LG ☎ 576776.

London 202 – Liverpool 14 – Manchester 29.

Forte Posthouse, Wood Lane, Beechwood, WA7 3HA, SE : ½ m. off junction 12 of M 56 ☎ 714000, Fax 714611, – rm TV ☎ P – 500. AE VISA JCB
Meals a la carte approx. 15.00 **t.** 5.50 – **135 rm** 56.00 **t.**

Campanile Lowlands Rd, WA7 5TP, beside the railway station ☎ 581771, Fax 581730 – rm TV ☎ P – 30. AE VISA
Meals 9.85 **st.** and a la carte 4.65 – 4.25 – **53 rm** 35.75 **st.**

ATS Sandy Lane, Weston Point ☎ 567715/6

RUSHDEN Northants. 404 S 27 – pop. 23 592 – ☎ 01933.

London 74 – Cambridge 42 – Northampton 14 – Peterborough 25.

Forte Travelodge without rest., NN10 9EP, on A 45, (eastbound carriageway) ☎ 57008, Reservations (Freephone) 0800 850950 – TV P. AE VISA.
40 rm 33.50 **t.**

RUSHLAKE GREEN E. Sussex 404 U 31 – ✉ Heathfield – ☎ 01435.

London 54 – Brighton 26 – Eastbourne 13.

Stone House, TN21 9QJ, ☎ 830553, Fax 830726, « Part 14C, part Georgian country house, antiques », park – TV ☎ P
closed 24 December-4 January – **Meals** (residents only) (dinner only) 24.95 **st.** 4.85 – **8 rm** 71.25/165.00 **st.** – SB.

RUSTHALL Kent – see Royal Tunbridge Wells.

RYE E. Sussex 404 W 31 **Great Britain G.** – pop. 4 207 – ECD : Tuesday – 01797.
See : Old Town★★ : Mermaid Street★, St. Mary's Church (≤★).
The Heritage Centre, Strand Quay, TN31 7AY ☏ 226696 (summer only).
♦London 61 – ♦Brighton 49 – Folkestone 27 – Maidstone 33.

George (Forte), High St., TN31 7JP, ☏ 222114, Fax 224065 – ⇔ TV ☎ P – 60. AE VISA JCB
Meals (bar lunch Monday to Saturday)/dinner 15.95 **st.** 6.40 – 8.50 – **22 rm** 70.00/75.00 **st.** – SB.

Mermaid Inn, Mermaid St., TN31 7EU, ☏ 223065, Fax 225069, « 15C inn » – TV ☎ P. AE VISA.
Meals 13.95/19.00 **t.** and a la carte 4.50 – **28 rm** 58.00/116.00 **t.** – SB.

Jeake's House without rest., Mermaid St., TN31 7ET, ☏ 222828, Fax 222623 – TV ☎. AE VISA
12 rm 22.50/80.00 **st.**

Green Hedges without rest., Rye Hill, TN31 7NH, N : ½ m. off A 268 on unmarked rd ☏ 222185, heated, – ⇔ TV. VISA.
closed Christmas to New Year – **3 rm** -/56.00 **s.**

Old Vicarage without rest., 66 Church Sq., TN31 7HF, ☏ 222119, Fax 227466, – ⇔ TV.
closed Christmas – **6 rm** 40.00/58.00 **st.**

Flushing Inn, 4 Market St., TN31 7LA, ☏ 223292, « 15C inn with 16C mural » – ⇔. AE VISA
closed Monday dinner, Tuesday and first 3 weeks January – **Meals** - Seafood 14.00/23.50 **t.** and a la carte 5.00.

Landgate Bistro, 5-6 Landgate, TN31 7LH, ☏ 222829 – AE VISA
closed Sunday, Monday, 1 week June, 1 week October and 1 week Christmas – **Meals** (dinner only) 15.50 **st.** and a la carte 4.00.

at Rye Foreign NW : 2 m. on A 268 – ✉ 01797 :

Broomhill Lodge, TN31 7UN, on A 268 ☏ 280421, Fax 280402, – ⇔ rest TV ☎ P
12 rm.

at Peasmarsh NW : 4 m. on A 268 – ✉ Rye – 01797 :

Flackley Ash, London Rd, TN31 6YH, ☏ 230651, Telex 957210, Fax 230510, – TV ☎ P – 100. AE VISA
Meals 14.15/25.15 **st.** – **30 rm** 69.00/98.00 **st.**, 2 suites – SB.

RYE FOREIGN E. Sussex – see Rye.

RYTON ON DUNSMORE W. Mids. 403 404 P 28 – see Coventry.

SAFFRON WALDEN Essex 404 U 27 **Great Britain G.** – pop. 14 019 – ECD : Thursday – 01799.
See : Audley End★★ *AC.*
1 Market Pl., Market Sq., CB10 1HR ☏ 510444.
♦London 46 – ♦Cambridge 15 – Chelmsford 25.

Saffron, 10-18 High St., CB10 1AY, ☏ 522676, Fax 513979 – TV ☎ – 80. AE VISA
Meals (see *Garden* below) – **20 rm** 30.00/85.00 **st.**

Garden (at Saffron H.), 10-18 High St., CB10 1AY, ☏ 522676, Fax 513979 – AE VISA
Meals 19.95 **st.** 4.00.

at Littlebury Green W : 4½ m. by B 1383 – ✉ Saffron Walden – 01763 :

Elmdon Lee, CB11 4XB, ☏ 838237, – TV P. VISA.
closed Christmas – **Meals** (by arrangement) (communal dining) 17.50 **s.** 3.50 – **3 rm** 27.50/55.00 **s.**

at Duddenhoe End W : 7½ m. by B 1052 and B 1383 off B 1039 – ✉ Saffron Walden – 01763 :

Duddenhoe End Farm without rest., CB11 4UU, ☏ 838258, – ⇔ P.
3 rm 22.00/44.00 **st.**

ATS Station Rd ☏ 521426

ST. AGNES Cornwall 403 E 33 **The West Country G.** – pop. 6 592 – ECD : Wednesday – 01872.
See : St. Agnes Beacon★★ (※★★).
Envir. : Portreath★, SW : 5½ m.
18 Perranporth, Budnic Hill ☏ 572454.
♦London 302 – Newquay 12 – Penzance 26 – Truro 9.

Rose-in-Vale , Mithian, TR5 0QD, E : 2 m. by B 3285 ☏ 552202, Fax 552700, heated, – ⇔ rest TV ☎ & P. AE VISA
Meals (bar lunch Monday to Saturday)/dinner 15.95 **t.** and a la carte 4.25 – **17 rm** 35.50/97.50 **t.** – SB.

ST. ALBANS Herts. 404 T 28 **Great Britain G.** – pop. 126 202 – ECD : Thursday – ☎ 01727.

See : City★ - Cathedral★ – Verulamium★ (Museum★ *AC*).

Envir. : Hatfield House★★ *AC*, E : 6 m. by A 1057.

Batchwood Drive ☏ 833349 – 18, 9 Kinsbourne Green Lane, Redbourn ☏ 793493.

Town Hall, Market Pl., AL3 5DJ ☏ 864511.

London 27 – Cambridge 41 – Luton 10.

- **Sopwell House**, Cottonmill Lane, AL1 2HQ, SE : 1 ½ m. by A 1081 and Mile House Lane ☏ 864477, Fax 844741, park – 400. AE VISA
Bejerano's Brasserie : **Meals** a la carte 8.95/21.20 **t.** 5.25 - (see also **Magnolia Conservatory** below) – 7.95 – **90 rm** 94.50/115.75 **t.**, 2 suites – SB.

- **Noke Thistle** (Mt. Charlotte Thistle) Watford Rd, AL2 3DS, SW : 2 ½ m. at junction of A 405 with B 4630 ☏ 854252, Telex 893834, Fax 841906, – rm – 50. AE VISA
Meals 17.50/21.00 **st.** and a la carte 5.75 – 8.75 – **109 rm** 80.00/90.00 **st.**, 2 suites – SB.

- **St. Michael's Manor,** Fishpool St., AL3 4RY, ☏ 864444, Fax 848909, « Manor house, lake, ≤ garden », park – – 35. AE VISA.
closed 27 to 30 December – **Meals** 12.00/20.00 **t.** and a la carte 5.95 – **22 rm** 50.00/104.00 **st.**

- **Ardmore House,** 54 Lemsford Rd, AL1 3PR, ☏ 859313, Fax 859313, – rm . AE VISA
Meals (dinner only) a la carte 10.00/18.00 **t.** 4.95 – **27 rm** 47.00/57.00 **t.** – SB.

- **Melford House** without rest., 24 Woodstock Rd North, AL1 4QQ, ☏ 853642, Fax 853642, –
12 rm 24.00/45.00 **st.**

- XXX **Magnolia Conservatory** (at Sopwell House H.), Cottonmill Lane, AL1 2HQ, SE : 1 ½ m. by A 1081 and Mile House Lane ☏ 864477, Fax 844741 – . AE VISA
closed Saturday lunch and Sunday dinner – **Meals** 16.95/21.50 **t.** and a la carte 6.25.

- XX **Cinta,** 20-26 High St., AL3 4EN, ☏ 837606. AE VISA JCB
closed Mondays except Bank Holidays – **Meals** - Chinese rest. 10.50/28.00 **t.** and a la carte 4.90.

ATS Grimston Rd ☏ 835174 — ATS Lyon Way, Hatfield Rd ☏ 852314

ST. AUSTELL Cornwall 403 F 32 **The West Country G.** – pop. 20 267 – ECD : Thursday – ☎ 01726.

See : Holy Trinity Church★.

Envir. : St. Austell Bay★★ (Gribbin Head★★) E : by A 390 and A 3082 – Carthew : Wheal Martyn Museum★★ *AC*, N : 2 m. by A 391 – Mevagissey★★, S : 5 m. by B 3273 – Charlestown★, SE : 2 m. by A 390.

Exc. : Trewithen★★★ *AC*, NE : 7 m. by A 390 – Lanhydrock★★, NE : 11 m. by A 390 and B 3269 – Polkerris★, E : 7 m. by A 390 and A 3082.

18 Carlyon Bay ☏ 814250.

London 281 – Newquay 16 – Plymouth 38 – Truro 14.

- **White Hart,** Church St., PL25 4AT, ☏ 72100, Fax 74705 – – 45. AE VISA
closed 25 and 26 December – **Meals** 7.95/12.00 **t.** 3.75 – **18 rm** 40.00/53.00 **t.** – SB.

at Tregrehan E : 2½ m. by A 390 – ✉ St. Austell – ☎ 01726 :

- **Boscundle Manor,** PL25 3RL, ☏ 813557, Fax 814997, « Tastefully converted 18C manor, gardens », heated, park – rest . VISA
April-October – **Meals** *(closed Sunday to non-residents)* (dinner only) 22.50 **st.** 5.00 – **9 rm** 65.00/110.00 **st.**, 1 suite.

at Carlyon Bay E : 2½ m. by A 3601 – ✉ St. Austell – ☎ 01726 :

- **Carlyon Bay,** PL25 3RD, ☏ 812304, Fax 814938, ≤ Carlyon Bay, « Extensive gardens », heated, 18, – – 50. AE VISA.
Meals *(closed 25 December)* 10.50/20.00 **t.** and a la carte 5.50 – **73 rm** 62.00/118.00 **t.** – SB.

- **Wheal Lodge,** 91 Sea Rd, PL25 3SH, ☏ 815543, Fax 815543, – .
closed Christmas – **Meals** 17.50 **st.** 3.50 – **6 rm** 35.00/70.00 **st.** – SB.

at Charlestown SE : 2 m. by A 390 – ✉ St. Austell – ☎ 01726 :

- **Pier House,** PL25 3NJ, ☏ 67955, Fax 69246, ≤ – . VISA.
Meals *(closed 25 December)* a la carte 8.15/26.15 **t.** 6.45 – **12 rm** 30.00/78.00 **t.**

- **Rashleigh Arms,** PL25 3NJ, ☏ 73635, Fax 69246, – . VISA.
Meals 7.50/10.20 **st.** and a la carte – **5 rm** 24.00/48.00 **t.**

ATS Gover Rd ☏ 65685/6

Plans de ville : *Les rues sont sélectionnées en fonction de leur importance pour la circulation et le repérage des établissements cités.*

Les rues secondaires ne sont qu'amorcées.

ST. BLAZEY Cornwall 403 F 32 – pop. 8 208 – ECD : Thursday – 01726.

London 276 – Newquay 21 – Plymouth 33 – Truro 19.

Nanscawen House, Prideaux Rd, PL24 2SR, W : 3/4 m. 814488, Fax 814488, <, heated, – TV P. VISA.
April-September – **Meals** (dinner only) 22.50 **s.** 4.00 – **3 rm** 35.00/72.00 **s.**

ST. HELENS Mersey. 402 403 L 23 – 01744.

Sherdley Park 813149.

London 207 – Liverpool 12 – Manchester 27.

Chalon Court, Chalon Way, Linkway West, WA10 1NG, 453444, Fax 454655, – rm TV P – 220. AE VISA
(dancing Friday and Saturday evening) – ***The Renaissance :*** **Meals** (dinner only) 19.95 **st.** 4.75 – 8.50 – **81 rm** 79.50 **st.**, 3 suites – SB.

Waterside, East Lancashire Rd, WA11 7LX, N : 1 3/4 m. at junction of A 580 with A 571 23333, Fax 454231 – TV P
43 rm.

The Griffin (Premier), Church Lane, Eccleston, WA10 5AD, W : 3 m. by A 570 on B 5201 27907, Fax 453475, TV P
11 rm.

ATS Sutton Rd 613434 ATS Blackbrook Rd, Blackbrook 54175/6

ST. HILARY Cornwall – see Marazion.

ST. IVES Cambs. 404 T 27 – pop. 15 312 – ECD : Thursday – Huntingdon – 01480 :

London 75 – Cambridge 14 – Huntingdon 6.

Slepe Hall, Ramsey Rd, PE17 4RB, 463122, Fax 300706 – TV P – 40. AE VISA
closed 25 to 28 December – **Meals** 13.95 **t.** and a la carte 4.25 – **15 rm** 49.50/59.50 **t.** – SB.

Dolphin, Bridge Foot, London Rd, PE17 4EP, 466966, Fax 495597 – TV P – 150. AE VISA.
Meals 15.00/17.50 **st.** and a la carte 3.00 – **47 rm** 55.00/65.00 **st.**

at Holywell E : 3 m. by A 1123 – Huntingdon – 01480 :

Old Ferryboat Inn, PE17 3TG, 463227, Fax 494885, – TV P. VISA.
accommodation closed 25 December – **Meals** (in bar) a la carte 10.70/22.15 **t.** – **7 rm** 39.99/68.00 **t.** – SB.

ATS East St. 465572

ST. IVES Cornwall 403 D 33 **The West Country G.** – pop. 9 439 – ECD : Thursday – 01736.

See : Town★★ – Barbara Hepworth Museum★★ *AC* Y **M1** – Tate Gallery ★★ – St. Nicholas Chapel (<★★) Y – St. Ia★ Y **A.**

Envir. : S : Penwith★★ Y.

Exc. : St. Michael's Mount★★ (<★★) S : 10 m. by B 3306 - Y - B 3311, B 3309 and A 30.

Tregenna Castle Hotel 795254 ext: 121 Y – West Cornwall, Lelant 753401 – Lakeside Lodge, Fen Rd, Pidley (01487) 740540.

The Guildhall, Street-an-Pol, TR26 2QS 796297.

London 319 – Penzance 10 – Truro 25.

Plan on next page

Porthminster, The Terrace, TR26 2BN, 795221, Fax 797043, <, heated, , – TV P. AE VISA Y **s**
Meals (buffet lunch)/dinner 17.50 **st.** and a la carte 4.95 – **46 rm** 59.50/134.00 **st.** – SB.

Pedn-Olva, The Warren, Porthminster Beach, TR26 2EA, 796222, Fax 797710, < coastline – TV P. VISA Y **n**
Meals 15.00 **t.** and a la carte 4.95 – **35 rm** 39.00/78.00 – SB.

Countryman, Old Coach Rd, TR26 3JQ, S : 2 1/2 m. by B 3306 and B 3311 on Hayle rd 797571, – TV P. AE VISA. Y
Meals (bar lunch)/dinner 17.00 **t.** and a la carte 6.25 – **8 rm.**

Skidden House, Skidden Hill, TR26 2DU, 796899, Fax 798619 – TV P. AE VISA JCB Y **e**
Meals *(restricted service January to March)* (bar lunch)/dinner 17.50 **st.** and a la carte 6.00 – **7 rm** 39.00/66.00 **st.** – SB.

Old Vicarage without rest., Parc-an-Creet, TR26 2ET, 796124, – TV P. AE VISA Y **i**
March-October – **8 rm** 20.00/46.00 **t.**

Blue Hayes, Trelyon Av., TR26 2AD, 797129, <, – rest TV P. VISA Y **c**
Early March-October – **Meals** 14.50 **st.** 3.00 – **9 rm** 31.50/76.00 **st.** – SB.

Pondarosa, 10 Porthminster Terr., TR26 2DQ, 795875 – TV P. AE VISA. Y **r**
Meals (by arrangement) 8.00 **st.** 2.95 – **10 rm** 13.00/40.00 **st.** – SB.

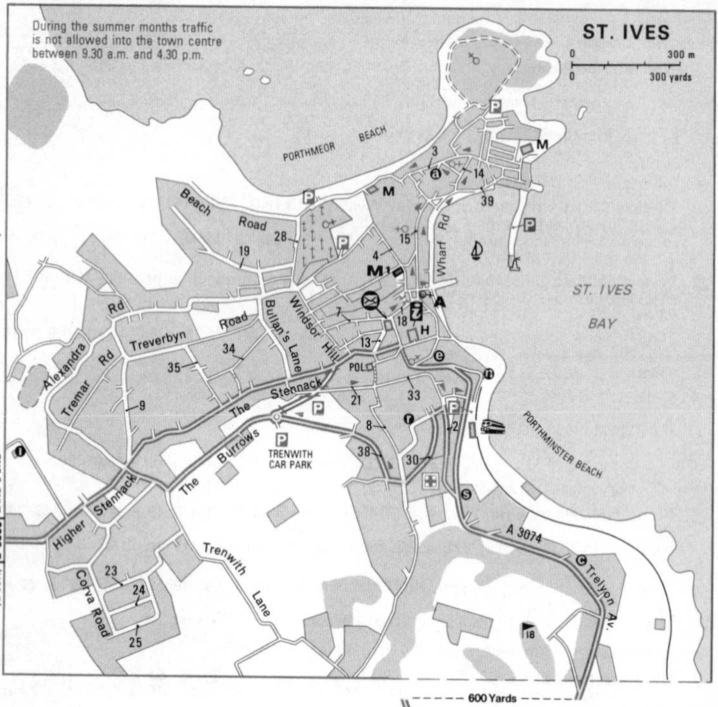

During the summer months traffic is not allowed into the town centre between 9.30 a.m. and 4.30 p.m.

ST. IVES

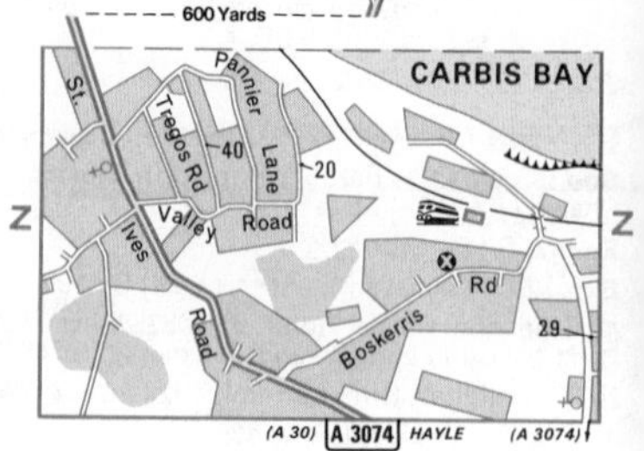

- Fore Street . . . . . . Y 15
- High Street . . . . . . Y 18

- Albert Road. . . . . . Y 2
- Back Road West . Y 3
- Barnoon Hill . . . . . Y 4
- Bedford Road . . . . Y 7
- Bishop's Road. . . . Y 8
- Carnellis Road. . . . Y 9
- Chapel Street . . . . Y 13
- Fish Street. . . . . . . Y 14
- Orange Lane. . . . . Y 19
- Parc Owles . . . . . . Z 20
- Park Av. . . . . Y 21
- Penwith Road . . . . Y 23
- Porthia Crescent . . . . . . Y 24
- Porthia Road . . . . . Y 25
- Porthmeor Hill. . . . Y 28
- Porthrepta Road . . Z 29
- Talland Road. . . . . Y 30
- Tregenna Terrace . . . . Y 33
- Trelawney Road . . Y 34
- Trerice Road . . . . . Y 35
- Trewidden Road . . Y 38
- Wharf (The). . . . . . Y 39
- Wheal Whidden . . Z 40

✕ **Pig'n'Fish,** Norway Lane, TR26 1LZ, ✆ 794204 – VISA — Y **a**
closed Sunday and November to February – **Meals** *(Mondays July and August only)* 17.50 **t.** (lunch) and a la carte 19.20/26.20.

at Carbis Bay S : 1 ¾ m. on A 3074 – ✉ St. Ives – ☎ 01736.

Boskerris, Boskerris Rd, TR26 2NQ, ✆ 795295, Fax 798632, ≤, heated, – rest TV ☎ **P**. VISA — Z **x**
Easter-October – **Meals** (bar lunch)/dinner 16.00 **st.** – **19 rm** 30.00/80.00 **st.** – SB.

ST. JUST Cornwall 403 C 33 **The West Country G.** – pop. 4 424 – ECD : Thursday – ☎ 01736.

See : Church★.

Envir. : Penwith★★ – Sancreed - Church★★ (Celtic Crosses★★) SE : 3 m. by A 3071 – Trengwainton Garden★★ (≤★★) *AC*, E : 4½ m. by A 3071 – St. Buryan★★ (Church Tower★★) SE : 5½ m. by B 3306 and A 30 – Land's End★ (cliff scenery★★★) S : 5½ m. by B 3306 and A 30 – Cape Cornwall★ (≤★★) W : 1½ m. – Geevor Tin Mine★ *AC*, N : 3 m. by B 3306 – Carn Euny★, SE : 3 m. by A 3071.

Cape Cornwall, ℘ 788611.

♦London 325 – Penzance 7.5 – Truro 35.

Boscean Country ⑤, TR19 7QP, by Boswedden Rd ℘ 788748, ≤, – ⓟ. VISA. ✱
April-October – **Meals** (dinner only)(residents only) 11.00 **t.** – **12 rm** ☐ 23.00/40.00 **t.**

ST. JUST IN ROSELAND Cornwall – see St. Mawes.

ST. KEVERNE Cornwall 403 E 33 – ✉ Helston – ☎ 01326.

Volnay, Porthoustock, TR12 6QW, NE : 1 m. ℘ 280183 – ⓟ
closed Monday – **Meals** (booking essential) (dinner only) a la carte 18.25/22.50 **t.** 4.00.

ST. LEONARDS Dorset 403 404 O 31 – see Ringwood (Hants.).

ST. LEONARDS E. Sussex 404 V 31 – see Hastings and St. Leonards.

ST. MARGARET'S AT CLIFFE Kent 404 Y 30 – see Dover.

ST. MARTINS Cornwall 403 ㉚ – see Scilly (Isles of).

ST. MARY'S Cornwall 403 ㉚ – see Scilly (Isles of).

ST. MAWES Cornwall 403 E 33 **The West Country G.** – ✉ Truro – ☎ 01326.

See : Town★ - Castle★ *AC* (≤★).

Envir. : St. Just in Roseland Church★★, N : 2½ m. by A 3078.

♦London 299 – ♦Plymouth 56 – Truro 18.

Tresanton ⑤, 27 Lower Castle Rd, TR2 5DR, ℘ 270544, Fax 270002, ≤ estuary, – TV ☎ ⓟ. AE ① VISA JCB
March-October and Christmas-New Year – **Meals** (bar lunch)/dinner a la carte 16.65/23.25 **t.** 5.20 – **20 rm** ☐ (dinner included) 63.00/130.00 **t.**, 1 suite.

Idle Rocks, Tredenham Rd, TR2 5AN, ℘ 270771, Fax 270062, ≤ harbour and estuary – TV ☎. VISA
Meals (bar lunch)/dinner 25.00 **st.** and a la carte 4.95 – **24 rm** ☐ (dinner included) 76.00/152.00 **st.** – SB.

Rising Sun, The Square, TR2 5DJ, ℘ 270233 – TV ☎ ⓟ. AE ① VISA. ✱
Meals (bar lunch Monday to Saturday)/dinner a la carte 16.00/26.00 **t.** 5.75 – **11 rm** ☐ 32.00/64.00 – SB.

St. Mawes, The Seafront, TR2 5DW, ℘ 270266, ≤ – TV ☎. VISA
closed December and January – **Meals** 12.50/24.00 **st.** 4.50 – **7 rm** ☐ (dinner included) 55.00/108.00 **st.** – SB.

at St. Just in Roseland N : 2½ m. on A 3078 – ✉ Truro – ☎ 01326 :

Rose da Mar ⑤, TR2 5JB, N : ¼ m. on B 3289 ℘ 270450, ≤, – ⓟ. ✱
mid March-September – **Meals** (dinner only) 15.50 **t.** 6.00 – **8 rm** ☐ 27.00/60.00 **t.**

ST. MICHAELS-ON-WYRE Lancs. 402 L 22 – ☎ 01995.

♦London 235 – ♦Blackpool 24 – Burnley 35 – ♦Manchester 43.

Mallards, Garstang Rd, PR3 0TE, ℘ 679661 – ⓟ. VISA
closed Sunday dinner, 1 week January and 2 weeks August – **Meals** (dinner only and Sunday lunch)/dinner 17.95 **t.** 4.50.

ST. NEOTS Cambs. 404 T 27 – pop. 12 468 – ☎ 01480.

Abbotsley, Eynesbury Hardwicke ℘ 474000 – Wyboston Lakes, Wyboston ℘ 212501.

♦London 60 – Bedford 11 – ♦Cambridge 17 – Huntingdon 9.

Eaton Oak, Crosshall Rd, PE19 4AG, NW : 1 m. on B 1048 at junction with A 1 ℘ 219555, Fax 407520 – TV ☎ ⓟ. AE VISA. ✱
Meals 15.00 **t.** and a la carte – **9 rm** ☐ 45.00/55.00 **t.**

Chequers Inn, St. Mary's St., Eynesbury, PE19 2TA, S : ½ m. on B 1043 ℘ 472116, – ⓟ. AE ① VISA
Meals a la carte 19.70/31.50 **t.** 4.00.

at Wyboston (Beds.) SW : 2½ m. by B 1428 on A 1 – ✉ Bedford – ☎ 01480 :

Wyboston Lakes Motel without rest., Great North Rd, MK44 3AL, N : ½ m. at junction of A 45 with A 1 ℘ 219949, Fax 407349 – TV ⓟ
38 rm.

ATS Brook St. ℘ 472920

SALCOMBE Devon 403 I 33 **The West Country G.** – pop. 2 189 – ECD : Thursday – ☎ 01548.

Envir. : Sharpitor (Overbecks Museum and garden) (<★★) *AC*, S : 2 m. by South Sands Z.

Exc. : Prawle Point (<★★★) E : 16 m. around coast by A 381 – Y - and A 379.

ℹ Council Hall, Market St., TQ8 8DE ☏ 842736/843927 (summer only).

♦London 243 – Exeter 43 – ♦Plymouth 27 – Torquay 28.

SALCOMBE

Fore Street	Y
Allenhayes Road	Y 2
Bonaventure Road	Y 3
Buckley Street	Y 4
Camperdown Road	Y 7
Church Street	Y 8
Coronation Road	Y 9
Devon Road	Y 13
Fortescue Road	Z 14
Grenville Road	Y 15
Herbert Road	Z 18
Knowle Road	Y 19
Moult Road	Z 20
Newton Road	Y 23
Sandhills Road	Z 24
Shadycombe Road	Y 25

Town plans
roads most used by traffic and those on which guide listed hotels and restaurants stand are fully drawn; the beginning only of lesser roads is indicated.

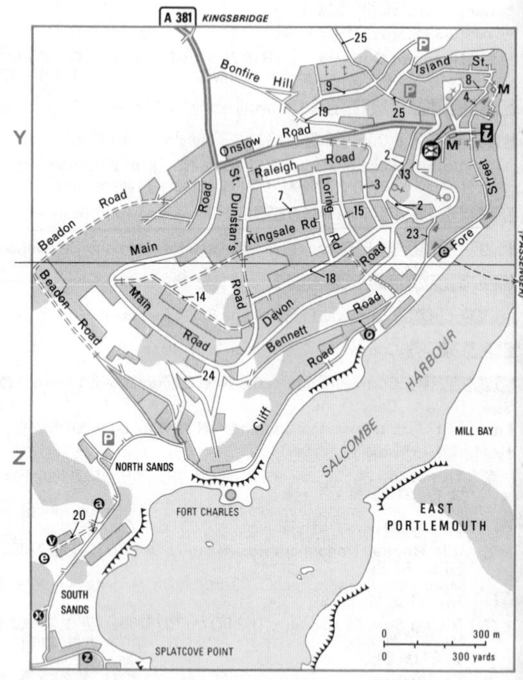

🏨 **Tides Reach,** South Sands, TQ8 8LJ, ☏ 843466, Fax 843954, < estuary, Ⓕ, ⓢ, ◻, ☼, squash – ⎘ ▢ ☎ ⓟ. ◻ AE ⓓ VISA — Z **x**
March-October – **Meals** (bar lunch)/dinner 19.75 **t.** and a la carte ⓘ 5.45 – **38 rm** ▭ (dinner included) 82.00/172.00 **st.** – SB.

🏨 **Marine,** Cliff Rd, TQ8 8JH, ☏ 844444, Fax 843109, < estuary, ⓢ, ◻ – ⎘ ⊬ ▢ ☎ ⓟ. ◻ AE ⓓ VISA — Y **e**
Meals (bar lunch Monday to Saturday)/dinner 22.00 **t.** and a la carte ⓘ 8.75 – **51 rm** ▭ (dinner inlcluded) 82.50/165.00 **t.**, 1 suite – SB.

🏨 **Bolt Head** ⓢ, South Sands, TQ8 8LL, ☏ 843751, Fax 843060, < estuary, ◻ heated – ▤ rest ▢ ☎ ⓟ. ◻ AE ⓓ VISA — Z **z**
17 March-5 November – **Meals** (buffet lunch)/dinner 22.00/40.00 **t.** – **28 rm** ▭ (dinner included) 82.00/184.00 **t.** – SB.

🏨 **Grafton Towers,** Moult Rd, TQ8 8LG, ☏ 842882, < estuary, ☼ – ⊬ rest ▢ ⓟ. ◻ VISA — Z **v**
April-October – **Meals** (dinner only) 19.00 ⓘ 4.50 – **13 rm** ▭ 45.00/90.00 – SB.

⌂ **The Wood** ⓢ, De Courcy Rd, Moult Hill, TQ8 8LQ, by Moult Rd ☏ 842778, Fax 844277, < estuary, ☼ – ⊬ rest ▢ ⓟ. AE — Z **e**
April-October – **Meals** (by arrangement) ⓘ 4.50 – **5 rm** ▭ 25.00/74.00 **t.** – SB.

⌂ **Bay View** without rest., Bennett Rd, TQ8 8JJ, ☏ 842238, < estuary – ⓟ. ◻ VISA. ✗ — Z **o**
April-September – **3 rm** ▭-/56.00 **st.**

at Soar Mill Cove SW : 4 ¼ m. by A 381 via Malborough village – Y – ✉ Salcombe – ☎ 01548 :

🏨 **Soar Mill Cove** ⓢ, TQ7 3DS, ☏ 561566, Fax 561223, <, ◻, ◻, ☼, ✗ – ⊬ rest ▢ ☎ ⓟ. ◻ VISA. ✗
closed November-9 February – **Meals** (light lunch)/dinner 37.00 **t.** and a la carte ⓘ 6.00 – **16 rm** ▭ 96.00/192.00 **t.** – SB.

at Hope Cove W : 4 m. by A 381 via Malborough village – Y – ✉ Kingsbridge – ☎ 01548 :

Lantern Lodge ⛺, TQ7 3HE, by Grand View Rd ☎ 561280, Fax 561736, ≤, ⛱, ▣, ☘ – ⊬ rest ▣ ☎ Ⓟ. ▣ VISA. ✂
March-November – **Meals** (dinner only) 14.50 **t.** ⅄ 4.00 – **14 rm** ▭ 54.45/99.00 **t.** – SB.

Port Light ⛺, Bolberry Down, TQ7 3DY, SE : 2¼ m. via Inner Hope ☎ 561384, ≤, ☘ – ▣ Ⓟ. ▣ VISA
closed January – **Meals** 12.00/17.00 **t.** and dinner a la carte ⅄ 3.95 – **5 rm** ▭ (dinner included) 45.00/70.00 **t.** – SB.

SALE Gtr. Manchester 402 403 404 N 23 – pop. 57 993 – ECD : Wednesday – ✉ Manchester – ☎ 0161.

⛳18 Sale Lodge, Golf Rd ☎ 973 3404.

♦London 212 – ♦Liverpool 36 – ♦Manchester 6 – ♦Sheffield 43.

Amblehurst, 44 Washway Rd, M33 1QZ, on A 56 ☎ 973 8800, Fax 905 1697, ☘ – ⊬ rm ▣ ☎ Ⓟ. ▣ AE VISA. ✂
closed 24 to 30 December – **Meals** *(closed Saturday lunch and Sunday dinner)* 11.95/13.95 **t.** and a la carte ⅄ 3.50 – **39 rm** ▭ 60.00/70.00 **t.** – SB.

Lennox Lea, Irlam Rd, M33 2BH, ☎ 973 1764, Fax 969 6059, ☘ – ⊬ rest ▣ ☎ Ⓟ
30 rm.

Cornerstones, 230 Washway Rd, M33 4RA, ☎ 962 6909, Fax 962 6909, ☘ – ⊬ ▣ ☎ Ⓟ. ▣ VISA. ✂
closed Christmas – **Meals** *(closed Friday to Sunday)* (dinner only) 15.00 **t.** ⅄ 3.50 – **9 rm** ▭ 21.50/38.00 **s.**

XXX **Summer Palace,** 11-15 Tatton Rd, M33 1EB, ☎ 973 9980, Fax 973 9958 – ▤. ▣ AE ⓓ VISA
Meals - Chinese (Peking) (dinner only) 10.00 **t.** and a la carte ⅄ 5.00.

Ask your bookseller for the catalogue of ***Michelin Publications.***

SALFORDS Surrey 404 T 30 – see Redhill.

SALISBURY Wilts. 403 404 O 30 **The West Country G.** – pop. 36 890 – ECD : Wednesday – ☎ 01722.

See : City★★ - Cathedral★★★ *AC* Z – Salisbury and South Wiltshire Museum★★ *AC* Z **M2** – Close★ Z : Mompesson House★ *AC* Z **A**, Museum of the Duke of Edinburgh's Royal Regiment★ *AC* Z **M1** – Sarum St. Thomas Church★ Y **B.**

Envir. : Wilton Village (Wilton House★★★ *AC*, Royal Wilton Carpet Factory★ *AC*) W : 3 m. by A 30 Y – Old Sarum★ *AC*, N : 2 m. by A 345 Y – Woodford (Heale House Garden★) *AC*, NW : 4½ m. by Stratford Rd Y.

Exc. : Stonehenge★★★ *AC*, NW : 10 m. by A 345 - Y - and A 303 – Wardour Castle★ *AC*, W : 15 m. by A 30 Y.

⛳18, ⛳9 Salisbury & South Wilts., Netherhampton ☎ 742645 – ⛳18 High Post, Great Durnford ☎ 782231.

ℹ Fish Row, SP1 1EJ ☎ 334956.

♦London 91 – Bournemouth 28 – ♦Bristol 53 – ♦Southampton 23.

Plan on next page

Milford Hall, 206 Castle St., SP1 3TE, ☎ 417411, Fax 419444 – ⊬ rest ▣ ☎ ♿ Ⓟ – 🏛 70. ▣ AE ⓓ VISA — Y **a**
Meals 16.50 **st.** and a la carte ⅄ 4.50 – **35 rm** ▭ 42.50/62.50 **st.** – SB.

White Hart (Forte), 1 St. John's St., SP1 2SD, ☎ 327476, Fax 412761 – ⊬ ▣ ☎ Ⓟ – 🏛 80. ▣ AE ⓓ VISA JCB — Z **s**
Meals 9.95/16.95 **t.** and a la carte ⅄ 6.95 – ▭ 8.50 – **68 rm** 70.00/80.00 **t.** – SB.

Trafalgar, 33 Milford St., SP1 2AP, ☎ 338686, Fax 414496 – ▣ ☎ – 🏛 35. ▣ AE ⓓ VISA — Y **v**
Meals (grill rest.) 9.95 **t.** – **18 rm** ▭ 50.00/60.00 **st.** – SB.

Byways House without rest., 31 Fowlers Rd, off Milford Hill, SP1 2QP, ☎ 328364, Fax 322146, ☘ – ▣ Ⓟ. ▣ VISA — Z **e**
closed Christmas and New Year – **23 rm** ▭ 30.50/56.00 **st.**

Stratford Lodge, 4 Park Lane, Castle Rd, SP1 3NP, ☎ 325177, Fax 412699, ☘ – ⊬ ▣ ☎ Ⓟ. ▣ VISA. ✂ — Y
closed Christmas – **Meals** 17.00 **t.** ⅄ 4.00 – **9 rm** ▭ 35.00/60.00 **t.** – SB.

Cricket Field Cottage without rest., Wilton Rd, SP2 7NS, W : 1¼ m. on A 36 - Y - ☎ 322595, ☘ – ⊬ ▣ Ⓟ. ✂
5 rm ▭ 25.00/38.00.

Victoria Lodge, 61 Castle Rd, SP1 3RH, ☎ 320586, Fax 414507 – ▣ Ⓟ — Y **e**
Meals (by arrangement) 11.25 **t.** ⅄ 3.00 – **13 rm** ▭ 20.00/40.00 **t.** – SB.

Glen Lyn without rest., 6 Bellamy Lane, Milford Hill, SP1 2SP, ☎ 327880 – ⊬ ▣ Ⓟ. ✂
9 rm ▭ 19.00/40.00 **st.** — YZ **x**

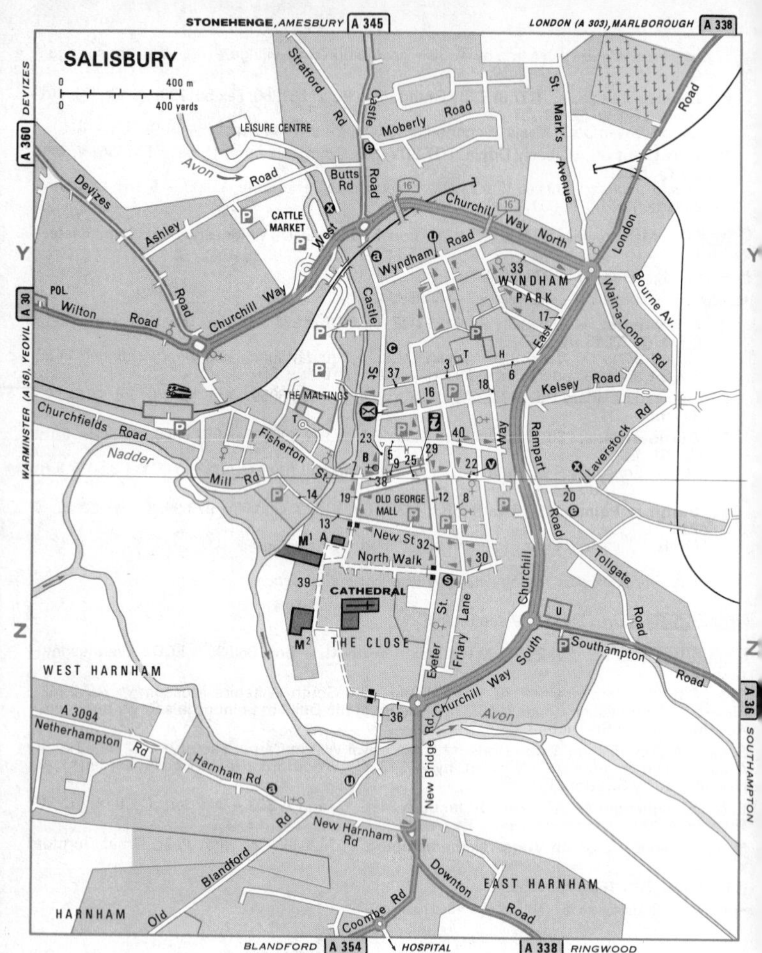

Butcher Row . . . . Y 9	Bedwin Street . . . . Y 3	Milford Hill . . . . Z 20
Catherine Street . . . . Z 12	Blue Boar Row . . . . Y 5	Milford Street . . . . Y 22
High Street . . . . Z 19	Bourne Hill . . . . Y 6	Queen Street . . . . Y 29
Maltings (The) Shopping Centre . . . . Y	Bridge Street . . . . YZ 7	St. Ann Street . . . . Z 30
Minster Street . . . . Y 23	Brown Street . . . . Z 8	St. John Street . . . . Z 32
New Canal . . . . Z 25	Crane Street . . . . Z 13	St. Mark's Road . . . . Y 33
Old George Mall Shopping Centre . . . . Z	Crane Bridge Road . . . . Z 14	St. Nicholas Road . . . . Z 36
Silver Street . . . . YZ 38	Endless Street . . . . Y 16	Scots Lane . . . . Y 37
	Estcourt Road . . . . Y 17	West Walk . . . . Z 39
	Greencroft Street . . . . Y 18	Winchester Street . . . . Y 40

Malvern without rest., 31 Hulse Rd, SP1 3LU, ☎ 327995, – TV. — Y **x**
3 rm ☕ 25.00/35.00 **st.**

Wyndham Park Lodge without rest., 51 Wyndham Rd, SP1 3AB, ☎ 328851, Fax 328851 – TV **P** — Y **u**
4 rm ☕ 15.00/36.00.

Just Brahm's, 68 Castle St., SP1 3TS, ☎ 328402, Fax 328593 – AE VISA — Y **c**
closed Sunday, 25 to 28 December, 1 January and Bank Holiday Mondays – **Meals** 10.45 **t.** and a la carte 4.75.

at Pitton E : 6 m. by A 30 – Y – ✉ Salisbury – 01722 :

Silver Plough, White Hill, SP5 1DZ, ☎ 712266 – **P**. AE VISA
Meals a la carte 9.95/18.45 **t.** 3.95.

at Whiteparish SE : 7 ½ m. by A 36 on A 27 – ✉ Salisbury – ☎ 01794 :

Newton Farmhouse, Southampton Rd, SP5 2QL, SE : 1 ½ m. on A 36 ℘ 884416, ⛱, ⛉ – ⛝ 📺 Ⓟ. ⛝
Meals (by arrangement) 12.50 **s.** – **8 rm** ☐ 30.00/40.00 **s.**

at Downton S : 6 m. by A 338 – Z – on B 3080 – ✉ Downton – ☎ 01725 :

Warren without rest., 15 High St., SP5 3PG, ℘ 510263, ⛉ – Ⓟ
closed Christmas – **6 rm** ☐ 30.00/45.00 **st.**

at Woodfalls S : 7 ¾ m. by A 338 – Z – on B 3080 – ✉ Salisbury – ☎ 01725 :

Woodfalls Inn, The Ridge, SP5 2LN, ℘ 513222, Fax 513220 – 📺 ☎ Ⓟ – 🚶 80. ⛝ AE VISA. ⛝
Meals 9.95/14.95 **st.** and a la carte 🍷 6.95 – **7 rm** ☐ (dinner included) 32.50/65.00 **st.**, 1 suite – SB.

at Harnham SW : 1 ½ m. by A 3094 – ✉ Salisbury – ☎ 01722 :

Rose and Crown (Q.M.H.), Harnham Rd, SP2 8JQ, ℘ 327908, Fax 339816, ≤, « Part 13C inn, riverside setting », ⛉ – 📺 ☎ Ⓟ – 🚶 80 Z **u**
28 rm.

Grasmere, 70 Harnham Rd, SP2 8JN, ℘ 338388, Fax 333710, ≤, ⛉ – ⛝ 📺 ☎ Ⓟ. ⛝ AE VISA JCB. ⛝ Z **a**
Meals 9.50/18.50 **st.** and a la carte 🍷 4.95 – **5 rm** ☐ 45.00/85.00 **st.** – SB.

at Broad Chalke SW : 8 m. by A 354 and Broad Chalke Valley Rd – Z – ✉ Salisbury – ☎ 01722 :

Queens Head, SP5 5EN, ℘ 780344 – 📺 ☎ Ⓟ. ⛝ VISA. ⛝
Meals 10.00/25.00 **t.** 🍷 5.00 – **4 rm** ☐ 25.00/45.00 **t.**

Stoke Farm ⛝, SP5 5EF, E : ¾ m. ℘ 780209, Fax 781041, « Working farm », ⛝, ⛉, ⛝ – ⛝ rm 📺 Ⓟ. ⛝
March-October – **Meals** (by arrangement) 14.50 **s.** – **3 rm** ☐ 22.00/44.00 **s.**

at Teffont W : 10 ¼ m. by A 36 – Z – and A 30 on B 3089 – ✉ Salisbury – ☎ 01722 :

Howard's House ⛝ with rm Teffont Evias, SP3 5RJ, on lane opposite Black Horse ℘ 716392, Fax 716820, ≤, « Part 17C former dower house », ⛉ – ⛝ rest 📺 ☎ Ⓟ. ⛝ AE ⛝ VISA
Meals (dinner only and Sunday lunch)/dinner 29.50/32.50 **st.** 🍷 6.25 – **9 rm** ☐ 87.50/107.50 **st.** – SB.

at Little Langford NW : 8 m. by A 36 and Great Wishford rd – ✉ Salisbury – ☎ 01722 :

Little Langford Farmhouse without rest., SP3 4NR, ℘ 790205, ≤, « Working farm », ⛉, park – ⛝ Ⓟ. ⛝
closed 24 to 26 and 31 December – **3 rm** ☐ 26.00/40.00 **st.**

ATS 155 Wilton Rd ℘ 336789 ATS 28 St. Edmund's Church St. ℘ 322390/322451

SALTASH Cornwall 403 H 32 **The West Country G.** – pop. 14 139 – ☎ 01752.

Exc. : St. Germans Church★, SW : 7 m. by A 38 and B 3249.

18, 18 St. Mellion ℘ (01579) 50101 – 18 China Fleet C.C. ℘ 848668.

Service Area, Carkeel Roundabout ℘ 849526.

♦London 246 – Exeter 38 – ♦Plymouth 5 – Truro 49.

Granada Lodge without rest., Callington Rd, Carkeel, PL12 6LF, NW : 1 ½ m. by A 388 on A 38 at Saltash Service Area ℘ 848408, Reservations (Freephone) 0800 555300 – ⛝ 📺 ☎ ♿ Ⓟ. ⛝ AE VISA. ⛝
☐ 4.00 – **31 rm** 39.95 **st.**

ATS 99 St. Stephens Rd ℘ 848469

SALTFORD Avon 403 404 M 29 – see Bristol.

SAMLESBURY Lancs. 402 M 22 – see Preston.

SAMPFORD PEVERELL Devon 403 J 31 – ✉ Tiverton – ☎ 01884.

♦London 184 – Barnstaple 34 – Exeter 20 – Taunton 19.

Parkway House, EX16 7BJ, ℘ 820255, Fax 820780, ⛉ – 📺 ☎ Ⓟ – 🚶 145. ⛝ AE VISA
Meals 12.00 **t.** and a la carte – **10 rm** ☐ 35.00/45.00 **st.**

Old Cottage Inn, ✉ Uffculme, EX15 3ES, E : 1 ¾ m. by A 361 on A 38 ℘ 840328 – ⛝ 📺 Ⓟ. ⛝ AE ⛝ VISA. ⛝
Meals (in bar) approx. 9.00 – **11 rm** ☐ 33.50 **t.**

"Short Breaks" (SB)

Molti alberghi propongono delle condizioni vantaggiose
per un soggiorno di due notti
comprendente la camera, la cena e la prima colazione.

SAMPFORD PEVERELL SERVICE AREA Devon 403 J 31 – ✉ Tiverton – ☎ 01884.
♦London 184 – Barnstaple 34 – Exeter 20 – Taunton 19.

- **Forte Travelodge** without rest., EX16 7HD, M 5 junction 27 ☎ 821087, Reservations (Freephone) 0800 850950 – TV ♿ P. AE VISA.
40 rm 33.50 **t.**

SANDBACH Ches. 402 403 404 M 24 – pop. 15 839 – ECD : Tuesday – ☎ 01270.
Malkins Bank ☎ 765931.
Motorway Service Area, M 6 (northbound), CW11 0TD ☎ 760460.
♦London 177 – ♦Liverpool 44 – ♦Manchester 28 – ♦Stoke-on-Trent 16.

- **Chimney House** (Country Club), Congleton Rd, CW11 0ST, E : 1 ½ m. on A 534 ☎ 764141, Fax 768916, – rm TV ☎ P – 70. AE VISA.
Meals 11.00/17.00 **t.** and a la carte 5.95 – 7.50 – **48 rm** 65.00/110.00 **st.** – SB.
- **Old Hall**, Newcastle Rd, CW11 0AL, ☎ 761221, Fax 762551, « 17C coaching inn », – TV ☎ P. AE VISA
Meals *(closed Sunday dinner and Bank Holidays)* (dinner only and Sunday lunch)/dinner 14.50 **st.** and a la carte 8.45 – **13 rm** 59.00/85.00 **st.** – SB.
- **Saxon Cross**, Holmes Chapel Rd, CW11 9SE, ☎ 763281, Fax 768723 – TV ☎ P – 50. AE VISA
Meals *(closed Saturday lunch, Sunday dinner and Bank Holidays)* 8.60/14.50 **st.** and a la carte 5.50 – **52 rm** 51.50/58.00 **st.** – SB.

SANDIACRE Derbs. 402 403 404 Q 25 – see Nottingham (Notts.).

SANDIWAY Ches. – ✉ Northwich – ☎ 01606.
♦London 191 – ♦Liverpool 34 – ♦Manchester 22 – ♦Stoke-on-Trent 26.

- **Nunsmere Hall** , Tarporley Rd, CW8 2ES, SW : 1 ½ m. by A 556 on A 49 ☎ 889100, Fax 889055, ≤, « Part Victorian house on wooded peninsula », , park – TV ☎ P – 50. AE VISA JCB.
Meals 17.50/45.00 **st.** and dinner a la carte – **31 rm** 82.50/130.00 **st.**, 1 suite – SB.

SANDPLACE Cornwall – see Looe.

SANDRINGHAM Norfolk 402 404 V 25 **Great Britain G.** – pop. 430 – ✉ King's Lynn – ☎ 01485.
See : Sandringham House★ *AC.*
♦London 111 – King's Lynn 8 – ♦Norwich 50.

- **Park House** , PE35 6EH, ☎ 543000, Fax 540663, « Former Royal residence » Restricted to physically disabled and their companions, heated, , park – rm TV ☎ ♿ P. AE VISA.
closed 9 to 21 December – **Meals** (buffet lunch)/dinner 12.50 **st.** 4.50 – **16 rm** 71.00/124.00 **st.**

at Wolferton W : 2 ¼ m. by King's Lynn rd – ✉ King's Lynn – ☎ 01485 :

- **Old Rectory** , PE31 6HF, ☎ 540496, , – P.
closed mid December to mid January – **Meals** (residents only) (communal dining) (booking essential) (unlicensed) 25.00 **s.** – **3 rm** 35.00/60.00 **s.**

SANDWICH Kent 404 Y 30 **Great Britain G.** – pop. 4 729 – ECD : Wednesday – ☎ 01304.
See : Town★.
The Guildhall, Cattle Market, CT13 9AH ☎ 613565 (summer only).
♦London 72 – Canterbury 13 – ♦Dover 12 – Maidstone 41 – Margate 9.

- **Bell**, The Quay, CT13 9EF, ☎ 613388, Fax 615308 – rm TV ☎ P – 120. AE VISA
Meals 9.95/29.50 **t.** and a la carte – **29 rm** 68.00/130.00 **t.** – SB.

SANDY Beds. 404 T 27 – pop. 8 989 – ECD : Thursday – ☎ 01767.
18, 18 John O'Gaunt, Sutton Park, Biggleswade ☎ 260360.
♦London 49 – Bedford 8 – ♦Cambridge 24 – Peterborough 35.

- Sandy, Girtford Bridge, London Rd, SG19 1DH, W : ¾ m. by B 1042 at junction of A 1 with A 603 ☎ 692220, Fax 680452 – TV ♿ P – 200
56 rm.

SANDYPARK Devon 403 I 31 – see Chagford.

SARISBURY Hants. 403 404 Q 31 – pop. 5 805 – ✉ Southampton – ☎ 01489.
♦London 90 – ♦Portsmouth 16 – ♦Southampton 6.

- **Dormy House**, 21 Barnes Lane, Sarisbury Green, SO3 6DA, S : 1 m. ☎ 572626 – rm TV P. AE VISA.
Meals (by arrangement) 10.95 3.95 – **12 rm** 36.50/45.00 **st.**

SAUNTON Devon 403 H 30 – ✉ Braunton – ☎ 01271.

♦London 230 – Barnstaple 8 – Exeter 48.

Preston House, EX33 1LG, ☎ 890472, Fax 890555, ≤ Saunton Sands, heated, – TV ☎ P. VISA.
March to November – **Meals** (bar lunch)/dinner 17.50 4.50 – **15 rm** 35.00/85.00 **t.**

SAWBRIDGEWORTH Herts. 404 U 28 – pop. 7 901 – ECD : Thursday and Saturday – ☎ 01279.

♦London 26 – ♦Cambridge 32 – Chelmsford 17.

The Manor of Groves, High Wych, CM21 0LA, SW : 1 ½ m. by A 1184 ☎ 600777, Fax 726972, ≤, heated, 18, park, – TV ☎ P – 70. AE VISA
Meals *(closed Saturday lunch and Sunday dinner)* 10.95/13.95 **t.** and a la carte 9.95 – **32 rm** 75.00/100.00 **st.** – SB.

SAWLEY Lancs. 402 M 22 – pop. 237 – ☎ 01765.

♦London 242 – ♦Blackpool 39 – ♦Leeds 44 – ♦Liverpool 54.

Spread Eagle, BB7 4NH, ☎ (01200) 441202, Fax 441973 – TV ☎ P. AE VISA.
Meals 19.95 **t.** (dinner) and lunch a la carte 5.50 – **10 rm** 45.00/55.00 **t.** – SB.

SCALBY N. Yorks. 402 S 21 – see Scarborough.

SCARBOROUGH N. Yorks. 402 S 21 – pop. 36 665 – ECD : Monday and Wednesday – ☎ 01723.

18 Scarborough North Cliff, North Cliff Av., ☎ 360786, NW : 2 m. by A 165 Y – 18 Scarborough South Cliff, Deepdale Av., off Filey Rd ☎ 360522, S : 1 m. by A 165 Z.

St. Nicholas Cliff, YO11 2EP ☎ 373333.

♦London 253 – ♦Kingston-upon-Hull 47 – ♦Leeds 67 – ♦Middlesbrough 52.

Plan on next page

Crown (Forte), 7-11 Esplanade, YO11 2AG, ☎ 373491, Fax 362271 – TV ☎ – 200. AE VISA JCB — Z i
Meals 16.95 **st.** and a la carte 5.75 – 8.50 – **77 rm** 65.00/80.00 **st.**, 1 suite – SB.

Palm Court, St. Nicholas Cliff, YO11 2ES, ☎ 368161, Fax 371547, – TV ☎ – 100 — Z e
46 rm, 1 suite.

Bradley Court, 7-9 Filey Rd, YO11 2SE, ☎ 360476, Fax 376661 – TV ☎ P – 120. AE VISA — Z r
Meals 7.50/15.50 **t.** 5.50 – **40 rm** 30.00/70.00 **t.** – SB.

Pickwick Inn without rest., Huntriss Row, YO11 2ED, ☎ 375787, Fax 374284 – TV ☎. AE VISA. — Z c
10 rm 27.00/44.00 **t.**

Old Mill, Mill St., YO11 1SZ, by Victoria Rd ☎ 372735, « Restored 18C windmill » – rest TV P — Z u
11 rm.

Jade Garden, 121 Falsgrave Rd, YO12 5EG, ☎ 369099 — Z v
Meals - Chinese.

at Scalby NW : 3 m. by A 171 – Z – ✉ Scarborough – ☎ 01723 :

Wrea Head, YO13 0PB, by Barmoor Lane ☎ 378211, Fax 371780, ≤, « Victorian country house », park – TV ☎ P – 25. AE VISA
Meals 12.50/21.50 **t.** 7.95 – **20 rm** 52.50/125.00 **st.**, 1 suite – SB.

at Hackness NW : 7 m. by A 171 – Z – ✉ Scarborough – ☎ 01723 :

Hackness Grange, YO13 0JW, ☎ 882345, Fax 882391, « 18C country house », park, – rest TV ☎ P. AE VISA.
Meals 20.00/35.00 **st.** 6.95 – **27 rm** 63.00/178.00 **st.**, 1 suite – SB.

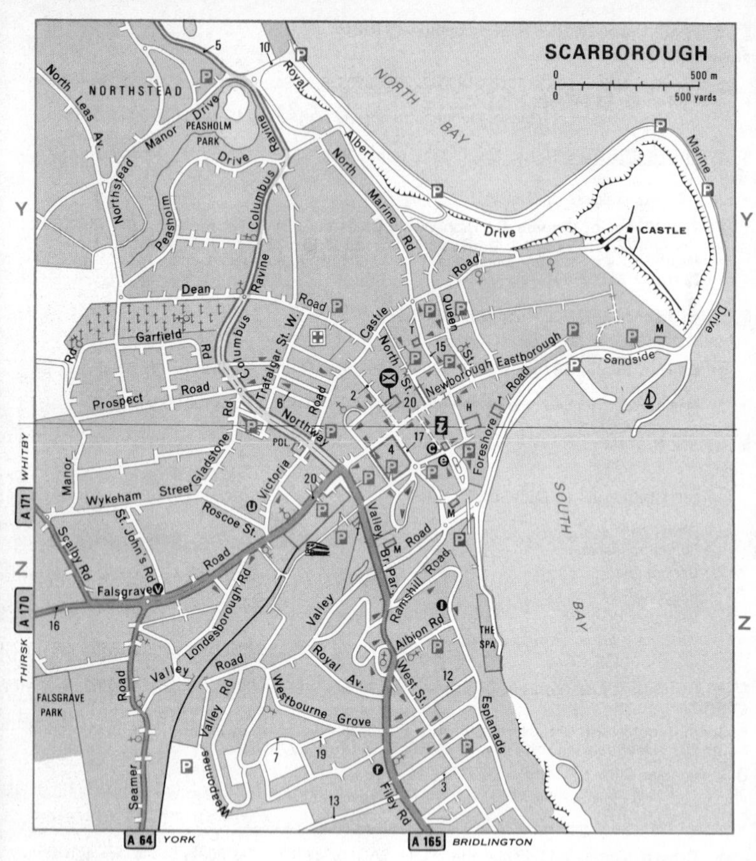

Aberdeen Walk .... Y 2	Westborough .... YZ 20	Peasholm Road .... Y 10
Brunswick Pavillon Shopping Centre .... Z 4	Avenue Victoria .... Z 3	Prince of Wales Terrace ..... Z 12
Eastborough .... Y	Burniston Road .... Y 5	Queen Margaret's Road ..... Z 13
Falsgrave Road .... Z	Cambridge Street .... Y 6	St. Thomas Street .... Y 15
Newborough .... Y	Oriel Crescent .... Z 7	Stepney Road .... Z 16
Victoria Road .... YZ	Peasholm Gap .... Y 8	Vernon Rd .... Z 17
		Westbourne Road .... Z 19

SCILLY (Isles of) Cornwall 403 ⑩ **The West Country G.** – pop. 2 048.

See : Islands★ - The Archipelago (⩽★★★).

Envir. : St. Agnes : Horsepoint★.

Helicopter service from St. Mary's and Tresco to Penzance : ℰ 0736 (Penzance) 63871.

✈ St. Mary's Airport : ℰ (01720) 422677, E : 1 ½ m. from Hugh Town.

⛴ from Hugh Town to Penzance (Isles of Scilly Steamship Co. Ltd) (summer only) (2 h 40 mn).

ℹ Porthcressa Bank, St. Mary's, TR21 0JY ℰ 01720 (Scillonia) 422536.

Bryher **The West Country G.** – pop. 66 – ✉ Scillonia – ☎ 01720.

See : Watch Hill (⩽★) – Hell Bay★.

Hell Bay ⛰, TR23 0PR, ℰ 422947, Fax 423004, ⛱ – ✗ rest TV. VISA. ✗
mid March to early October – **Meals** (bar lunch)/dinner 20.00 **t.** 4.75 –, **10 suites** 56.00/140.00 **t.** – SB.

Bank Cottage ⛰, TR23 0PR, ℰ 422612, Fax 422612, ⩽, ⛱ – ✗
March - October – **5 rm** (dinner included) 34.00/72.00 **st.**

St. Martin's The West Country G. – ✉ St. Martin's – ☎ 01720.

See : Viewpoint★★.

St. Martin's ⑤, TR25 0QW, ☎ 422092, Fax 422298, ≤ Tean Sound and islands, « Idyllic island setting », ⛱, 🌳 – ⇔ rest TV ☎. AE ① VISA. ✂
closed November-mid December – **Meals** (bar lunch)/dinner 29.50 **st.** 5.75 – **22 rm** ▭ 71.50/143.00 **st.**, 2 suites – SB.

St. Mary's The West Country G. – pop. 2 106 – ECD : Wednesday – ✉ St. Mary's – ☎ 01720.

See : Garrison Walk★ (≤★★) – Peninnis Head★.

⛳9 ☎ 422692,.

Tregarthen's, Hugh Town, TR21 0PP, ☎ 422540, Fax 422089, ≤ – TV ☎. AE ① VISA. ✂
April-October – **Meals** (bar lunch)/dinner 18.25 **st.** 5.50 – **29 rm** ▭ (dinner included) 52.00/136.00 **st.**

Star Castle ⑤, TR21 0JA, ☎ 422317, Fax 422343, « Elizabethan fortress », ⛱, 🌳, ✂ – ⇔ rest TV ☎. ① VISA
mid March-mid October – **Meals** (bar lunch)/dinner 28.00 **t.** and a la carte – **28 rm** ▭ 49.00/80.00 **t.** – SB.

Atlantic, Hugh St., Hugh Town, TR21 0PL, ☎ 422417, Fax 423009, ≤ St. Mary's Harbour – ⇔ TV ☎. VISA
closed December and January – **Meals** (dinner only) 18.50 **st.** 7.50 – **23 rm** ▭ (dinner included) 65.00/140.00 **st.** – SB.

Carnwethers ⑤, Pelistry Bay, TR21 0NX, ☎ 422415, ≦s, ⛱ heated, 🌳 – ⇔ TV. ✂
9 April-6 October – **Meals** 14.00 **st.** 3.40 – **10 rm** ▭ (dinner included) 50.00/92.00 **st.**

Tremellyn, Church Rd, Hugh Town, TR21 0NA, ☎ 422656, 🌳 – ⇔ rest TV P. ✂
March-October – **Meals** (by arrangement) 10.50 **st.** 3.95 – **8 rm** ▭ (dinner included) 36.00/77.00 **st.** – SB.

Tresco The West Country G. – pop. 285 – ✉ New Grimsby – ☎ 01720.

See : Island★ - Abbey Gardens★ *AC* (Lighthouse Way ≤★★).

Island ⑤, Old Grimsby, TR24 0PU, ☎ 422883, Fax 423008, ≤ St. Martin's and islands, « Idyllic island setting, sub-tropical gardens », ⛱ heated, park, ✂ – TV ☎. AE VISA. ✂
March-October – **Meals** (bar lunch)/dinner 29.00 **t.** and a la carte – **39 rm** ▭ (dinner included) 60.00/220.00 **t.**, 1 suite.

New Inn, TR24 0QQ, ☎ 422844, ≤, ⛱ heated, 🌳 – TV ☎. VISA. ✂
Meals (bar lunch)/dinner 16.50/25.50 **st.** – **12 rm** ▭ (dinner included) 59.00/118.00 **st.** – SB.

SCOLE Norfolk 404 X 26 – see Diss.

SCOTCH CORNER N. Yorks. 402 P 20 – ✉ Richmond – ☎ 01748.

ℹ Pavilion Service Area, A 1, DL10 6PQ ☎ 377677 (summer only).

♦London 235 – ♦Carlisle 70 – ♦Middlesbrough 25 – Newcastle upon Tyne 43.

Pavilion Lodge without rest., Middleton Tyas Lane, D10 6PQ, ☎ (01325) 377177, Fax 377890 – ⇔ TV ♿ P
50 rm.

Forte Travelodge without rest., Skeeby, DL10 5EQ, S : 1 m. on A 1 (northbound carriageway) ☎ 823768, Reservations (Freephone) 0800 850950 – TV ♿ P. AE VISA. ✂
40 rm 33.50 **t.**

SCUNTHORPE Humbs. 402 S 23 – pop. 61 555 – ECD : Wednesday – ☎ 01724.

⛳18 Ashby Decoy, Burringham Rd ☎ 842913 – ⛳9 Kingsway ☎ 840945 – ⛳9 Grange Park, Butterwick Rd, Messingham ☎ 762945.

✈ Humberside Airport : ☎ (01652) 688456, E : 15 m. by A 18.

♦London 167 – ♦Leeds 54 – Lincoln 30 – ♦Sheffield 45.

Wortley House, Rowland Rd, DN16 1SU, ☎ 842223, Fax 280646 – TV ☎ P – 🎪 250. AE ① VISA
Meals (bar lunch Monday to Saturday)/dinner 18.50 **st.** and a la carte 4.00 – **38 rm** ▭ 65.00/75.00 **st.** – SB.

Royal (Forte), 74 Doncaster Rd, DN15 7DE, ☎ 282233, Fax 281826 – ⇔ TV ☎ P – 🎪 240
33 rm.

at Broughton E : 7 m. by A 18 – ✉ Scunthorpe – ☎ 01652 :

Briggate Lodge Inn, Ermine St., DN20 0AQ, S : 1 m. ☎ 650770, Fax 650495, 🌳 – |♦| ⇔ rm TV ☎ ♿ P – 🎪 60. AE ① VISA JCB. ✂
Meals 15.50 **t.** and a la carte 5.25 – **48 rm** ▭ 77.00/85.00 **t.**, 2 suites.

ATS Grange Lane North ☎ 868191

SEACROFT W. Yorks. 402 ⑩ – see Leeds.

SEAFORD E. Sussex 404 U 31 – pop. 20 933 – ECD : Wednesday – ☎ 01323.

Southdown Rd ℘ 890139.

Station Approach, BN25 2AR ℘ 897426.

♦London 65 – ♦Brighton 14 – Folkestone 64.

XX **Quincy's,** 42 High St., BN25 1PL, ℘ 895490 – VISA JCB
closed Sunday dinner and Monday – **Meals** (dinner only and Sunday lunch)/dinner 17.95/21.45 **t.** 4.75.

at Westdean E : 3¼ m by A 259 – ☎ 01323 :

Old Parsonage without rest., BN25 4AL, ℘ 870432, ←, « 13C King John house », – .
closed Christmas and New Year – **3 rm** 42.50/65.00 **s.**

SEAHOUSES Northd 401 402 P 17 Great Britain G. – pop. 1 709 (inc. North Sunderland) – ECD : Wednesday – ☎ 01665.

Envir. : Farne Islands★ (by boat from harbour).

Beadnell Rd ℘ 720794.

Car Park, Seafield Rd, NE68 7SR ℘ 720884 (summer only).

♦London 328 – ♦Edinburgh 80 – ♦Newcastle upon Tyne 46.

Olde Ship, 9 Main St., NE68 7RD, ℘ 720200, Fax 721383, « Nautical memorabilia » – . VISA.
closed December and January – **Meals** (bar lunch)/dinner 13.00 4.60 – **15 rm** 33.00/66.00 – SB.

Beach House, 12a St. Aidans, Seafront, NE68 7SR, ℘ 720337, Fax 720921, ←, – rest . VISA
April-October – **Meals** (dinner only) 19.25 – **14 rm** 29.50/80.00 **t.** – SB.

SEATOLLER Cumbria – see Keswick.

SEATON BURN Tyne and Wear 402 P 18 – see Newcastle upon Tyne.

SEATON CAREW Cleveland 402 Q 20 – see Hartlepool.

SEAVIEW I.O.W. 403 404 Q 31 – see Wight (Isle of).

SEAVINGTON ST. MARY Somerset 403 L 31 The West Country G. – pop. 367 – ✉ Ilminster – ☎ 01460.

Envir. : Ilminster★ - St. Mary's★★, W : 2 m.

♦London 142 – Taunton 14 – Yeovil 11.

Pheasant, Water St., TA19 0QH, ℘ 240502, Fax 242388, – . VISA.
Meals *(closed Sunday dinner)* (dinner only and Sunday lunch)/dinner a la carte 16.50/21.50 **t.** 4.50 – **8 rm** 50.00/70.00 **t.** – SB.

SEDBERGH Cumbria 402 M 21 – pop. 3 088 – ☎ 0153 96.

Catholes-Abbot Holme ℘ 21551.

♦London 270 – ♦Carlisle 51 – Kendal 10 – Lancaster 27.

Oakdene Country, Garsdale Rd, LA10 5JN, E : 1¼ m. on A 684 ℘ 20280, Fax 21501, ←, – . VISA.
closed January – **Meals** (dinner only) 15.00 **st.** 5.30 – **6 rm** 25.00/50.00 **st.** – SB.

SEDGEFORD Norfolk 404 V 25 – pop. 464 – ✉ Hunstanton – ☎ 01485.

♦London 122 – ♦Cambridge 59 – ♦Norwich 43.

Sedgeford Hall , PE36 5LT, SE : ¾ m. on Fring rd ℘ 570902, Fax 570941, « Queen Anne house », , , park –
closed Christmas-New Year – **Meals** (booking essential) (residents only) (communal dining) (dinner only) 23.00 **st.** 4.00 – **3 rm** 40.00/76.00 **st.**

SEDGEMOOR SERVICE AREA Somerset – ☎ 01934.

Somerset Visitor Centre, M 5 South, BS26 2UF ℘ 750833.

Forte Travelodge without rest., BS24 0JL, M 5 (northbound carriageway) between junctions 22 and 21 ℘ 750831, Fax 750450, Reservations (Freephone) 0800 850950 – . VISA.
40 rm 33.50 **t.**

SEDLESCOMBE E. Sussex 404 V 31 – pop. 1 631 – ✉ Battle – ☎ 01424.

♦London 56 – Hastings 7 – Lewes 26 – Maidstone 27.

Brickwall, The Green, TN33 0QA, ℘ 870253, Fax 870785, heated, – . VISA
Meals 14.00/17.00 **t.** 4.95 – **23 rm** 42.00/70.00 **t.** – SB.

SELBY N. Yorks. 402 Q 22 **Great Britain G.** – pop. 12 600 – ☎ 01757.
See : Abbey Church★.
ℹ Park St., YO8 0AA ☎ 703263.
♦London 202 – ♦Kingston-upon-Hull 36 – ♦Leeds 23 – York 14.

Londesborough Arms, Market Pl., YO8 0NS, ☎ 707355, Fax 701607 – TV ☎ P – 45. AE VISA.
Meals a la carte 11.20/17.05 **st.** – **27 rm** 45.00/55.00 **st.**

ATS Unit 1, Canal Rd (off Bawtry Rd) ☎ 703245/702147

SELLING Kent 404 W 30 – pop. 687 – ✉ Faversham – ☎ 01795.
♦London 56 – Canterbury 10 – ♦Dover 28 – Maidstone 25.

Parkfield House without rest., Hogben's Hill, ME13 9QU, NW : ½ m. ☎ (01227) 752898, – P.
closed 24 to 26 December – **5 rm** 17.50/35.00 **s.**

SELSIDE Cumbria – see Kendal.

SEMINGTON Wilts. 403 404 N 29 – see Trowbridge.

SEMLEY Dorset 403 404 N 30 – see Shaftesbury.

SENNEN Cornwall 403 C 33 **The West Country G.** – ✉ Penzance – ☎ 01736.
See : Wayside Cross★ – Sennen Cove★ (≤★).
Envir. : Land's End★ (cliff scenery★★★) W : ½ m. – Penwith★★ – St. Buryan★★ (Church Tower★★) E : 5½ m. by B 3315 and B 3283 – Porthcurno★, SE : 3 m. by B 3315.
♦London 330 – Penzance 11 – Truro 40.

Old Success Inn, Sennen Cove, TR19 7DG, W : ¾ m. ☎ 871232, Fax 788354, ≤ – TV P. VISA
Meals 10.00/12.00 **t.** and dinner a la carte 3.75 – **12 rm** 26.00/80.00 **t.** – SB.

SETTLE N. Yorks. 402 N 21 – pop. 2 730 – ECD : Wednesday – ☎ 01729.
Giggleswick ☎ 825288.
ℹ Town Hall, Cheapside, BD24 9EJ ☎ 825192.
♦London 238 – Bradford 34 – Kendal 30 – ♦Leeds 41.

Falcon Manor, Skipton Rd, BD24 9BD, ☎ 823814, Fax 822087, – rest TV ☎ P. VISA
Meals (bar lunch Monday to Saturday)/dinner 19.50 **st.** and a la carte 4.35 – **19 rm** 55.00/105.00 **st.** – SB.

Royal Oak, Market Pl., BD24 9ED, ☎ 822561 – TV ☎ P.
accommodation closed 25 December – **Meals** 10.80/13.75 **st.** and a la carte 5.00 – **6 rm** 29.95/49.90 **st.**

SEVENOAKS Kent 404 U 30 **Great Britain G.** – pop. 19 617 – ECD : Wednesday – ☎ 01732.
Envir. : Knole★★ *AC*, SE ½m. – Ightham Mote★ *AC*, E : 5 m. by A 25.
18 Woodlands , Tinkerpot Lane ☎ (01959) 523805 – 18 Darenth Valley, Station Rd, Shoreham ☎ (01959) 522944.
ℹ Buckhurst Lane, TN13 1LQ ☎ 450305.
♦London 26 – Guildford 40 – Maidstone 17.

Royal Oak, Upper High St., TN13 1HY, ☎ 451109, Fax 740187, – rest TV ☎ P – 35. AE VISA
Meals 10.95/13.95 **t.** and a la carte 4.50 – 6.95 – **37 rm** 60.00/80.00 **t.** – SB.

at Ivy Hatch E : 4¾ m. by A 25 on Coach Rd – ✉ Sevenoaks – ☎ 01732 :

The Plough, TN15 0NL, ☎ 810268, – P. VISA
closed Sunday dinner – **Meals** a la carte 13.20/20.45 **t.** 4.00.

SEVERN VIEW SERVICE AREA Avon – ✉ Bristol – ☎ 01454.

Pavilion Lodge without rest., BS12 3BJ, M 4 junction 21 ☎ 633313, Fax 633819 – TV P
51 rm.

SHAFTESBURY Dorset 403 404 N 30 **The West Country G.** – pop. 6 203 – ECD : Wednesday and Saturday – ☎ 01747.
See : Gold Hill★ (≤★) – Local History Museum★ *AC*.
Envir. : Wardour Castle★ *AC*, NE : 5 m..
ℹ 8 Bell St., SP7 8AE ☎ 853514.
♦London 115 – Bournemouth 31 – ♦Bristol 47 – Dorchester 29 – Salisbury 20.

Royal Chase, Royal Chase Roundabout, SP7 8DB, SE : at junction of A 30 with A 350 ☎ 853355, Fax 851969, , – TV ☎ P – 190. AE VISA
Meals 8.80/25.00 **t.** and a la carte 6.00 – 7.95 – **34 rm** 58.25/74.50 **t.** – SB.

XX **La Fleur de Lys,** 25 Salisbury St., SP7 8EL, ℘ 853717 – AE VISA
closed Monday lunch and Sunday dinner – **Meals** 18.95 **t.** and a la carte 4.50.

X **Jesters,** 4 Bell St., SP7 8AR, ℘ 854444 – . VISA
closed 2 weeks February – **Meals** *(closed Sunday dinner and Monday)* a la carte 10.45/19.70 **t.** 4.75.

at Semley N : 3 ½ m. by A 350 – ✉ Shaftesbury – 01747 :

Benett Arms, SP7 9AS, ℘ 830221, Fax 830152 – TV . AE VISA
Meals a la carte 12.85/21.90 **st.** 4.00 – **5 rm** 29.00/44.00 **t.** – SB.

at Compton Abbas S : 4 m. on A 350 – ✉ Shaftesbury – 01747.

Old Forge without rest., Chapel Hill, SP7 0NQ, ℘ 811881, « Blacksmiths forge museum », –
3 rm 25.00/40.00 **s.**

at Motcombe NW : 2 ½ m. by B 3081 – ✉ Shaftesbury – 01747 :

Coppleridge Inn , SP7 9HW, N : 1 m. on Mere rd ℘ 851980, Fax 851858, , park, – TV . AE VISA
Meals 10.00 **t.** and a la carte 4.50 – **10 rm** 37.50/60.00 **t.** – SB.

SHALDON Devon 403 J 32 – see Teignmouth.

SHANKLIN I.O.W. 403 404 Q 32 – see Wight (Isle of).

SHAW Wilts. 403 404 N 29 – see Melksham.

SHAWBURY Shrops. 402 403 404 M 25 – pop. 2 457 – ✉ Shrewsbury – 01939.
♦London 159 – ♦Birmingham 43 – Chester 39 – ♦Stoke-on-Trent 29 – Shrewsbury 7.

The Sett , Stanton-upon-Hine-Heath, SY4 4LR, NE : 2 ¼ m. by B 5063 ℘ 250391, « Working farm » – . VISA
closed Christmas and New Year – **Meals** 14.00 **s.** – **3 rm** 22.00/44.00 **s.**

SHEDFIELD Hants. 403 404 Q 31 – pop. 1 447 – ✉ Southampton – 01329.
18, 9 Meon Valley Hotel, Sandy Lane, ℘ 833455, off A 334.
♦London 75 – ♦Portsmouth 13 – ♦Southampton 10.

Meon Valley H. Golf & Country Club (Country Club), Sandy Lane, SO3 2HQ, off A 334 ℘ 833455, Fax 834411, , , , 18, park, , squash – TV – 100. AE VISA.
Meals 22.00/42.00 **t.** 4.50 – 9.00 – **83 rm** 75.00/105.00 **t.** – SB.

SHEEPWASH Devon 403 H 31 – see Hatherleigh.

SHEERNESS Kent 404 W 29 – pop. 11 653 – ECD : Wednesday – 01795.
Bridge Rd Car Park, ME12 1RH ℘ 665324.
♦London 52 – Canterbury 24 – Maidstone 20.

Hotels and Restaurants see : Maidstone SW : 20 m.

SHEFFIELD S. Yorks. 402 403 404 P 23 **Great Britain G.** – pop. 501 202 – ECD : Thursday – 0114.
See : Cutlers' Hall★ CZ **A** – Cathedral Church of SS. Peter and Paul CZ **B** : Shrewsbury Chapel (Tomb★).
18 Tinsley Park, Darnall ℘ 2560237, BY – 18 Beauchief Municipal, Abbey Lane ℘ 2620648/2620040, AZ – 18 Birley Wood, Birley Lane ℘ 2647262, BZ – 18 Concord Park, Shiregreen Lane ℘ 2570274/2570053, BY – 18 Hillsborough, Worrall Rd ℘ 2343608, AY – 18 Abbeydale, Twentywell Lane, Dore ℘ 2360763, AZ – 18 Lees Hall, Hemsworth Rd, Norton ℘ 2554402, AZ.
Peace Gdns, S1 2HH ℘ 273 4671/2 – Railway Station, Sheaf St., S1 2BP ℘ 279 5901.
♦London 174 – ♦Leeds 36 – ♦Liverpool 80 – ♦Manchester 41 – ♦Nottingham 44.

Plans on following pages

Holiday Inn Sheffield, Victoria Station Rd, S4 7YE, ℘ 276 8822, Fax 272 4519 – rm TV – 350. AE VISA JCB DY **a**
Meals 9.95/15.95 **st.** and a la carte 4.95 – 9.95 – **100 rm** 67.00/89.00 **st.** – SB.

Charnwood, 10 Sharrow Lane, S11 8AA, ℘ 258 9411, Fax 255 5107 – TV – 80. AE VISA. CZ **u**
accommodation closed Christmas – ***Brasserie Leo* : Meals** 11.00/25.00 **t.** and a la carte 4.75 – ***Henfrey's* : Meals** *(closed Sunday and Monday)* (dinner only) 25.00 **t.** 4.75 – **22 rm** 74.00/90.00 **st.** – SB.

Swallow, Kenwood Rd, S7 1NQ, ℘ 258 3811, Fax 250 0138, , , , , , park – rm TV – 200. AE VISA AZ **r**
Meals 12.25/19.00 **st.** and a la carte 5.75 – **117 rm** 87.00/128.00 **st.** – SB.

Beauchief (Country Club), 161 Abbeydale Rd South, S7 2QW, SW : 3 ½ m. on A 621 ℘ 262 0500, Fax 235 0197, , – rm TV – 100. AE VISA. on A 625 AZ
Meals 7.75/14.00 **t.** and a la carte 5.95 – 7.50 – **41 rm** 65.00/95.00 **t.** – SB.

SHEFFIELD

BUILT UP AREA

Meadowhall Shopping Centre .... **BY**

Barrow Road............. **BY** 4
Bawtry Road............ **BY** 5
Bradfield Road .... **AY** 7
Brocco Bank .... **AZ** 8
Broughton Lane .... **BY** 10
Burngreave Road .... **AY** 12
Handsworth Road........ **BZ** 24
Holywell Road........... **BY** 29
Main Road.............. **BZ** 32
Meadow Hall Road....... **BY** 33
Middlewood Road .... **AY** 34
Newhall Road .... **BY** 36
Westbourne Road........ **AZ** 47
Western Bank........... **AZ** 48
Whitham Road .... **AZ** 49
Woodbourn Road....... **BYZ** 50
Woodhouse Road........ **BZ** 51

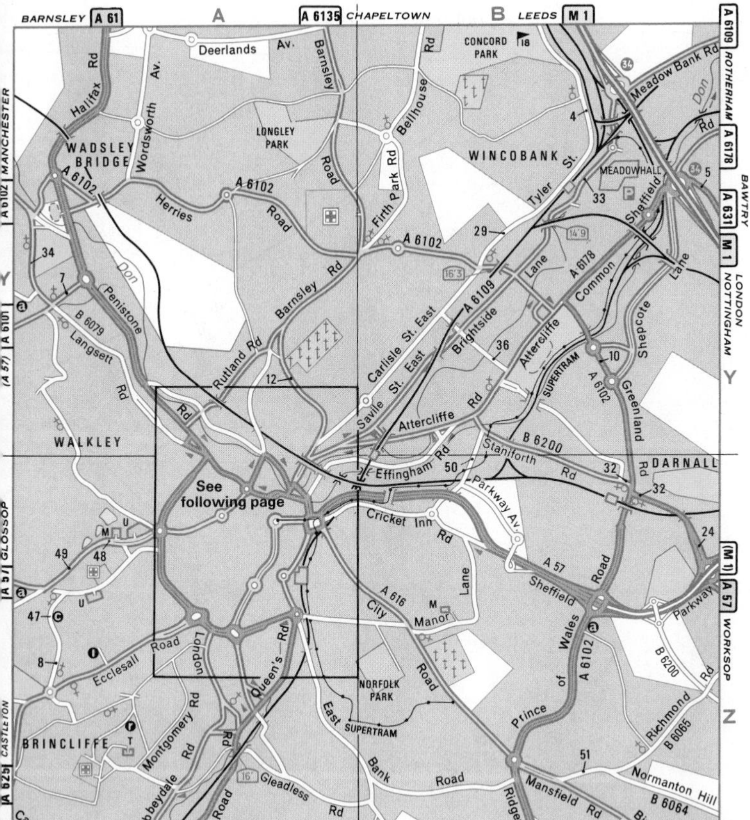

See following page

Ne confondez pas :

Confort des hôtels : 🏨🏨🏨🏨🏨 ... 🏨, 🏨, ⌂
Confort des restaurants : ✗✗✗✗✗ ..... ✗
Qualité de la table : ✿✿✿, ✿✿, ✿, **Meals**

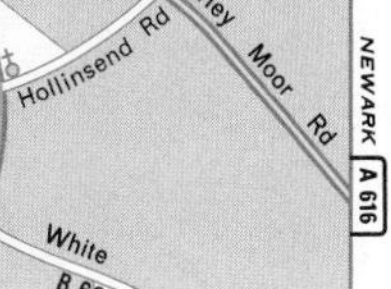

SHEFFIELD

CENTRE

Angel Street . . . . DY 3
Commercial Street . . . . DZ 16
Fargate . . . . CZ
High Street . . . . DZ
Leopold Street . . . . CZ 31
West Street . . . . CZ

Blonk Street . . . . DY 6
Castle Gate . . . . DY 13
Charter Row . . . . CZ 14
Church Street . . . . CZ 15
Cumberland Street . . . . CZ 17
Fitzwilliam Gate . . . . CZ 19
Flat Street . . . . DZ 20
Furnival Gate . . . . CZ 21
Furnival Street . . . . CZ 22
Haymarket . . . . DY 25
Moorfields . . . . CY 35
Pinstone Street . . . . CZ 37
Queen Street . . . . CY 38
St. Mary's Gate . . . . CZ 40
Shalesmoor . . . . CY 41
Snig Hill . . . . DY 42
Waingate . . . . DY 44
West Bar Green . . . . CY 45

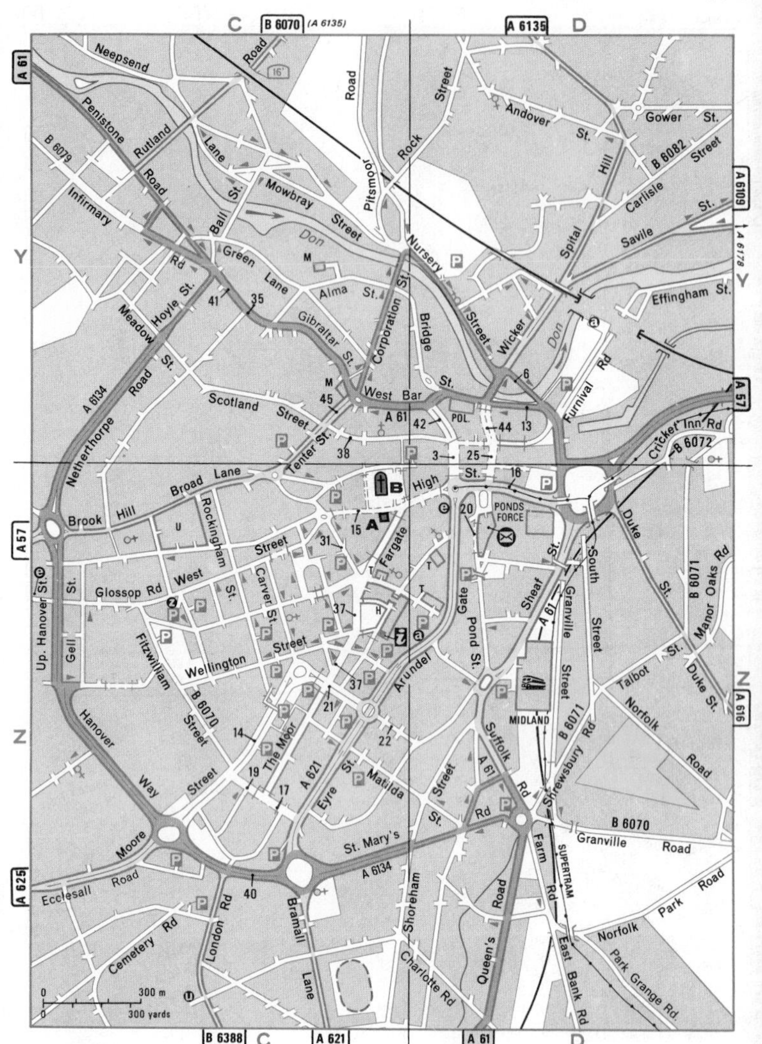

🏨 **Forte Posthouse,** Manchester Rd, Hallam, S10 5DX, ✆ 267 0067, Fax 268 2620, ≤, ⛳, ⛱, 🏊 – 🛗 ⚟ rm 📺 ☎ 🅟 – 🎭 300. 💳 AE ⓓ VISA JCB AZ **a**
Meals a la carte approx. 15.00 **t.** 🍷 5.50 – **133 rm** 56.00/69.50 **st.**, 2 suites.

🏨 **Harley,** 334 Glossop Rd, S10 2HW, ✆ 275 2288, Fax 272 2383 – ⚟ rm ▤ rest 📺 ☎ – 🎭 30. 💳 AE ⓓ VISA. ⚟ – *closed 25 December* – **Meals** *(closed Saturday lunch, Sunday and Bank Holidays)* (dancing Friday and Saturday evenings) 14.50/15.00 **st.** and a la carte 🍷 6.25 – ☕ 3.50 – **22 rm** 50.00/75.00 **st.** CZ **e**

Novotel, Arundel Gate, S1 2PR, ✆ 278 1781, Telex 548261, Fax 278 7744, – rm – 250. AE VISA DZ **a**
Meals 12.00/35.00 **st.** and a la carte 4.95 – 7.50 – **144 rm** 49.50/95.00 **st.**

Granada, 340 Prince of Wales Rd, S2 1FF, ✆ 253 0935, Fax 264 2731 – rm – 80. AE VISA BZ **a**
Meals *(closed Saturday lunch and 25 December)* (grill rest.) 12.95 **st.** and a la carte 5.95 – 7.25 – **60 rm** 52.50 **st.**

Comfort Inn without rest., George St., S1 2PF, ✆ 273 9939, Fax 276 8332 – AE VISA DZ **e**
closed 24 December-1 January – 5.95 – **50 rm** 39.95/44.95 **st.**

Westbourne House without rest., 25 Westbourne Rd, S10 2QQ, ✆ 266 0109, Fax 266 7778, – . AE VISA JCB AZ **c**
9 rm 40.00/55.00 **st.**

Millingtons without rest., 70 Broomgrove Rd, S10 2NA, ✆ 266 9549 – . AZ **i**
6 rm 23.00/42.00 **st.**

Coniston without rest., 90 Beechwood Rd, Hillsborough, S6 4LQ, ✆ 233 9680 – AY **a**
4 rm.

Le Neptune, 141 West St., S1 4EW, ✆ 279 6677 – AE VISA CZ **z**
Meals - French *(closed Saturday lunch, Sunday and 2 weeks Christmas)* 13.75/16.75 **t.** and a la carte 4.75.

Rafters, 220 Oakbrook Rd, Nether Green, S11 7ED, SW : 2 ½ m. by A 625 – AZ ✆ 230 4819. AE
closed Sunday, Tuesday and 14 to 28 August – **Meals** (dinner only) 15.95 **t.**

at Grenoside N : 4 ½ m. on A 61 – AY – ✉ Sheffield – 0114 :

Holme Lane Farm without rest., 38 Halifax Rd, S30 3PB, ✆ 246 8858, – . VISA.
7 rm 26.00/45.00 **st.**

at Whitley N : 5 m. by A 6135 - AY – ✉ Sheffield – 0114 :

Whitley Hall, Elliot Lane, Grenoside, S30 3NR, off Whitley Lane ✆ 245 4444, Fax 245 5414, , park – – 70. AE VISA
Meals *(closed Saturday lunch and Bank Holidays)* 12.00/22.00 **t.** and a la carte – **15 rm** 58.00/95.00 **t.**

at Chapeltown N : 6 m. on A 6135 – AY – ✉ Sheffield – 0114 :

Staindrop Lodge, Lane End, S30 4UH, NW : ½ m. on High Green rd ✆ 284 6727, Fax 284 6783 – – 80. AE VISA.
Meals *(closed lunch Saturday and Monday and Sunday dinner)* 8.10/17.90 **t.** and a la carte 4.00 – **13 rm** 55.00/69.00 **t.** – SB.

Greenhead House, 84 Burncross Rd, S30 4SF, ✆ 246 9004 – . VISA
closed Sunday, Monday, 2 weeks Easter, 2 weeks mid August and Christmas to New Year – **Meals** (booking essential) (dinner only) 30.00 **st.** 4.75.

at Ridgeway (Derbs.) SE : 6 ¾ m. by A 616 off B 6054 – BZ – ✉ Sheffield – 0114 :

Old Vicarage, Ridgeway Moor, S12 3XW, on Marsh Lane rd ✆ 247 5814, Fax 247 7079, – . AE VISA
closed Sunday dinner, Monday and 1 to 7 January – **Meals** (lunch booking essential) 33.00 **t.** 6.00.

at Meadow Head S : 5 ¼ m. on A 61 - AZ – ✉ Sheffield – 0114 :

Sheffield Moat House (Q.M.H.), Chesterfield Rd South, S8 8BW, ✆ 237 5376, Fax 237 8140, , , – rm rest – 500
89 rm, 5 suites.

ATS 87/91 Clifton St., Attercliffe ✆ 244 9750/ 244 9759 ATS Herries Rd ✆ 234 3986/7

SHELLEY W. Yorks. 402 404 O 23 – ✉ Huddersfield – 01484.

♦London 193 – ♦Leeds 22 – ♦Manchester 30 – ♦Sheffield 20.

Three Acres Inn, Roydhouse, HD8 8LR, NE : 1 ½ m. on Flockton rd ✆ 602606, Fax 608411 – rm . AE VISA.
Meals *(closed Saturday lunch)* 10.95/20.00 **st.** and dinner a la carte 4.95 – **20 rm** 47.50/57.50 **st.** – SB.

SHENINGTON Oxon. – see Banbury.

SHEPPERTON Surrey 404 S 29 – pop. 11 589 – 01932.

♦London 25.

Plan : see Greater London (South-West)

Edwinns, Church Sq., TW17 9JT, S : 1 m. ✆ 223543, Fax 253562 – AE VISA
closed lunch Saturday and Bank Holidays, Sunday dinner and 25 to 27 December – **Meals** 16.25/16.95 **t.** 5.65. AZ

SHEPTON MALLET Somerset 403 404 M 30 **The West Country G.** – pop. 7 581 – ECD : Wednesday – ☎ 01749.

See : Town★ - SS. Peter and Paul's Church★.

Envir. : Evercreech (Church Tower★) SE : 4 m. by A 371 and B 3081 – Downside Abbey★ (Abbey Church★) N : 5½ m. by A 37 and A 367.

Exc. : Longleat House★★★ *AC*, E : 15 m. by A 361 and B 3092 – Wells★★ - Cathedral★★★, Vicars' Close★, Bishop's Palace★ *AC* (≤★★) W : 6 m. by A 371 – Wookey Hole★★ (Caves★ *AC*, Papermill★, Fairground Collection★) W : 6½ m. by B 371 – Glastonbury★★ - Abbey★★★ (Abbots Kitchen★) *AC*, St. John the Baptist★★, Somerset Rural Life Museum★ *AC* – Glastonbury Tor★ (≤★★★) SW : 9 m. by B 3136 and A 361 - Nunney★, E : 8½ m. by A 361.

18 Mendip, Gurney Slade ✆ 840570.

♦London 127 – ♦Bristol 20 – ♦Southampton 63 – Taunton 31.

- **Thatched Cottage Inn,** 63-67 Charlton Rd, BA4 5QF, ✆ 342058, Fax 343265 rest TV ☎ P. VISA.
  Meals 10.00/30.00 **t.** 3.95 – **8 rm** 45.50/69.50 **t.** – SB.
- **Shrubbery,** Commercial Rd, BA4 5BV, ✆ 346671, Fax 346581, – TV ☎ P. VISA
  Meals 10.95/12.45 **t.** and a la carte – **8 rm** 42.00/60.00 **st.**
- XXX **Bowlish House** with rm, Wells Rd, BA4 5JD, W : ½ m. on A 371 ✆ 342022, – TV P. VISA
  Meals (booking essential)(dinner only) 22.50 **st.** 4.25 – 3.50 – **3 rm** 48.00 **st.**
- X **Blostin's,** 29 Waterloo Rd, BA4 5HH, ✆ 343648 – VISA
  closed Sunday, Monday, 2 weeks January and 2 weeks June – **Meals** (dinner only) 14.95 **t.** and a la carte 5.95.

at Doulting E : 1½ m. on A 361 – ✉ Shepton Mallet – ☎ 01749 :

- XXX **Brottens Lodge** with rm, BA4 4RB, S : 1 m. turning right at Abbey Barn Inn, following sign for Evercreech ✆ 880352, Fax 880601, ≤, – TV ☎ P. VISA.
  Meals *(closed Monday and Saturday lunch and Sunday)* 16.50/19.50 **t.** 4.00 – **3 rm** 45.00/75.00 **st.** – SB.

at Evercreech SE : 4 m. by A 371 on B 3081 – ✉ Shepton Mallet – ☎ 01749 :

- **Pecking Mill,** BA4 6PG, W : 1 m. on A 371 ✆ 830336, Fax 831316 – TV ☎ P. AE VISA.
  closed 25 and 26 December – **Meals** *(closed Monday lunch)* 12.00/18.00 **t.** and a la carte 4.00 – **6 rm** 33.00/44.00 **st.** – SB.

SHERBORNE Dorset 403 404 M 31 **The West Country G.** – pop. 7 606 – ECD : Wednesday – ☎ 01935.

See : Town★ - Abbey★★ – Castle★ *AC*.

Envir. : Sandford Orcas Manor House★ *AC*, NW : 4 m. by B 3148 – Purse Caundle Manor★ *AC*, NE : 5 m. by A 30.

Exc. : Cadbury Castle (≤★★) N : 8 m. by A 30.

18 Clatcombe ✆ 812475.

3 Tilton Court, Digby Rd, DT9 3LW ✆ 815341.

♦London 128 – Bournemouth 39 – Dorchester 19 – Salisbury 36 – Taunton 31.

- Eastbury, Long St., DT9 3BY, ✆ 813131, Fax 817296, – TV ☎ P – 60
  14 rm.
- **Antelope,** Greenhill, DT9 4EP, ✆ 812077, Fax 816473 – TV ☎ P – 80. AE VISA.
  Meals 10.95/15.00 **st.** and a la carte 4.95 – **19 rm** 39.95/65.00 **t.** – SB.
- **Quinns,** Marston Rd, DT9 4BL, ✆ 815008 – TV P
  Meals (by arrangement) (communal dining) 14.00 **s.** – **3 rm** 25.00/50.00 **s.** – SB.
- XX **Pheasants** with rm, 24 Greenhill, DT9 4EW, ✆ 815252, Fax 815252 – TV P. VISA.
  closed 2 weeks mid January – **Meals** *(closed Sunday dinner and Monday to non-residents)* 12.00/23.00 **t.** and a la carte 4.20 – **5 rm** 27.50/50.00 **st.** – SB.

at Oborne NE : 2 m. by A 30 – ✉ Sherborne – ☎ 01935 :

- XX **Grange** with rm, DT9 4LA, ✆ 813463, Fax 817464, ≤, – TV ☎ P. AE VISA.
  Meals - Italian *(closed Sunday dinner and Bank Holidays)* (dinner only and Sunday lunch)/dinner 17.50 **t.** and a la carte 3.95 – **5 rm** 45.00/60.00 **st.** – SB.

at Hermitage S : 7½ m. by A 352 – ✉ Sherborne – ☎ 01963 :

- **Almshouse Farm** without rest., DT9 6HA, ✆ 210296, ≤, « Former monastery, working farm », – P
  closed Christmas – **3 rm** 16.00/36.00 **s.**

at Yetminster SW : 5½ m. by A 352 and Yetminster rd – ✉ Sherborne – ☎ 01935 :

- **Manor Farmhouse,** DT9 6LF, ✆ 872247, « 17C farmhouse », – rest TV P. VISA.
  Meals (by arrangement) 15.00 – **3 rm** 27.50/50.00 **t.**

SHERBOURNE Warks. – see Warwick.

SHERE Surrey 404 S 30 – see Guildford.

SHERIFF HUTTON N. Yorks. 402 Q 21 – pop. 2 299 – ✉ York – ☎ 01347.
◆London 313 – York 10.

- **Rangers House** , The Park, YO6 1RH, S : 1 ¼ m. by Strensall rd ☎ 878397, Fax 878666, – ℗.
Meals 20.00 ℓ 4.00 – **6 rm** 35.00/70.00 – SB.

SHERINGHAM Norfolk 404 X 25 – pop. 5 870 – ECD : Wednesday – ☎ 01263.
18 Sheringham ☎ 822038.
Station Approach, NR26 8RA ☎ 824329 (summer only).
◆London 128 – Cromer 4 – ◆Norwich 27.

- **Beacon,** 1 Nelson Rd, NR26 8BT, ☎ 822019, – ℗. VISA.
May-September – **Meals** (by arrangement) 10.00 – **6 rm** 22.00/50.00 **st.** – SB.

SHIFNAL Shrops. 402 403 404 M 25 – pop. 6 516 – ECD : Thursday – ✉ Telford – ☎ 01952.
◆London 150 – ◆Birmingham 28 – Shrewsbury 16.

- **Park House,** Park St., TF11 9BA, ☎ 460128, Fax 461658, – TV ☎ ℗ – 180. AE VISA
Meals (bar lunch Saturday) 10.50/18.00 **st.** and a la carte ℓ 5.00 – **52 rm** 80.00/99.50 **st.**, 2 suites.

SHINFIELD Berks. 404 R 29 – see Reading.

SHIPHAM Somerset 403 L 30 **The West Country G.** – pop. 1 094 – ✉ Winscombe – ☎ 01934.
Envir. : Cheddar Gorge★★ (Gorge★★, Caves★★, Jacobs's Ladder ★) - St. Andrew's Church★, S : 2½m.
18, 9 Mendip Spring, Honeyhall Lane, Congresbury, Avon ☎ 853337/852322.
◆London 135 – ◆Bristol 14 – Taunton 20.

- **Daneswood House,** Cuck Hill, BS25 1RD, ☎ 843145, Fax 843824, ≤, – TV ☎ ℗. AE VISA.
closed 25 December-5 January – **Meals** *(closed Sunday dinner to non-residents)* 17.50/21.50 **st.** ℓ 4.50 – **9 rm** 57.50/79.50 **st.**, 3 suites – SB.

SHIPLEY W. Yorks. 402 O 22 – pop. 29 753 – ECD : Wednesday – ☎ 01274.
18 Northcliffe, High Bank Lane ☎ 584085.
◆London 216 – Bradford 4 – ◆Leeds 12.

- Hollings Hall (Country Club) , Hollins Hill, Baildon, BD17 7QW, NE : 2 ½ m. on A 6038 ☎ 530053, Fax 530187, , park – rm TV ☎ ℗ – 200. AE VISA.
Meals a la carte 14.70/20.70 **t.** – **58 rm**, 1 suite.
- **Aagrah,** 27 Westgate, BD18 3QX, ☎ 594660 – AE VISA
closed 25 December – **Meals** - Indian (booking essential) (dinner only) 11.55/17.85 **t.** and a la carte ℓ 4.00.

SHIPTON GORGE Dorset – see Bridport.

SHIPTON-UNDER-WYCHWOOD Oxon. 403 404 P 28 – pop. 1 154 – ECD : Wednesday – ☎ 01993.
◆London 81 – ◆Birmingham 50 – Gloucester 37 – ◆Oxford 25.

- **Lamb Inn,** High St., OX7 6DQ, ☎ 830465 – rest TV ℗. AE VISA.
Meals *(closed Monday)* (buffet lunch)/dinner 19.50 **t.** ℓ 4.50 – **5 rm** 48.00/65.00 **t.**

SHIRLEY W. Mids. 403 404 O 26 – see Solihull.

SHRAWLEY Heref. and Worcs. 403 404 N 27 – pop. 379 – ✉ Worcester – ☎ 01905.
◆London 152 – ◆Birmingham 45 – Leominster 33.

- **Lenchford,** WR6 6TB, SE : ½ m. on B 4196 ☎ 620229, Fax 621125, ≤, « Riverside setting », – TV ☎ ℗ – 80. AE VISA.
closed 25 to 31 December – **Meals** *(closed Sunday dinner)* (bar lunch)/dinner 9.25 **st.** and a la carte – **15 rm** 39.50/55.00 **st.** – SB.

SHREWLEY Warks. 403 404 P 27 – see Warwick.

SHREWSBURY Shrops. 402 403 L 25 **Great Britain G.** – pop. 91 749 – ECD : Thursday – ☎ 01743.

See : Abbey★ **D.**

Exc. : Ironbridge Gorge Museum★★ *AC* (The Iron Bridge★★ - Coalport China Museum★★ - Blists Hill Open Air Museum★★ – Museum of the River and Visitor Centre★) SE : 12 m. by A 5 and B 4380.

Condover ☎ 872976 – Meole Brace ☎ 364050.

The Music Hall, The Square, SY1 1LH ☎ 350761.

♦London 164 – ♦Birmingham 48 – ♦Cardiff 10 – Chester 43 – Derby 67 – Gloucester 93 – ♦Manchester 68 – ♦Stoke-on-Trent 39 – ♦Swansea 124.

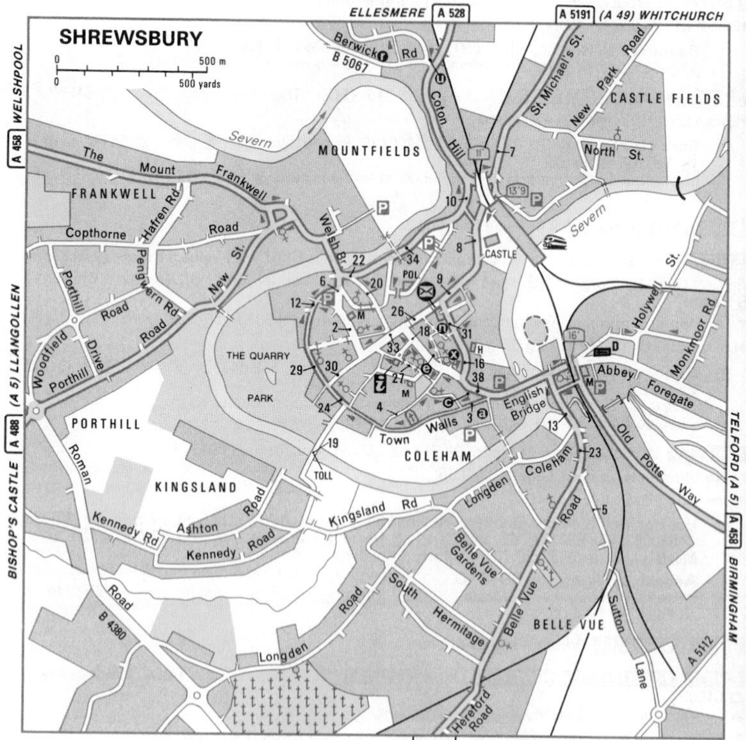

High Street 18
Pride Hill 26
Shoplatch 33

Barker Street 2
Beeches Lane 3
Belmont 4
Betton Street 5
Bridge Street 6

Castle Foregate 7
Castle Gates 8
Castle Street 9
Chester Street 10
Claremont Bank 12
Coleham Head 13
Dogpole 16
Kingsland Bridge 19
Mardol 20

Mardol Quay 22
Moreton Crescent 23
Murivance 24
Princess Street 27
St. Chad's Terrace 29
St. John's Hill 30
St. Mary's Street 31
Smithfield Road 34
Wyle Cop 38

Lion (Forte), Wyle Cop, SY1 1UY, ☎ 353107, Fax 352744 – 200. AE VISA JCB **c**
Meals (bar lunch Monday to Saturday)/dinner 16.95 **st.** and a la carte 6.70 – 8.50 – **59 rm** 55.00/80.00 **st.** – SB.

Prince Rupert (Q.M.H.), Butcher Row, SY1 1UQ, ☎ 236000, Fax 357306 – rest – 70. AE VISA. **n**
Meals 17.00 **t.** (dinner) and a la carte 23.80/32.10 **t.** 6.00 – 8.75 – **62 rm** 65.00/75.00 **t.**, 3 suites – SB.

Pinewood House without rest., Shelton Park, The Mount, SY3 8BL, NW : 1 ½ m. on A 458 ☎ 364200, –
4 rm 30.00/44.00 **s.**

Fieldside without rest., 38 London Rd, SY2 6NX, E : 1 ¼ m. by Abbey Foregate on A 5064 (via Shirehall) ☎ 353143, – . AE. – **6 rm** 28.00/42.00 **st.**

Cromwells, 11 Dogpole, SY1 1EN, ☎ 361440 – TV. VISA x
Meals a la carte 7.05/17.00 **t.** – **7 rm** 23.00/40.00 **t.**

Sandford House without rest., St. Julians Friars, SY1 1XL, ☎ 343829, – TV. VISA a
11 rm 23.00/43.50 **st.**

Tudor House without rest., 2 Fish St., SY1 1UR, ☎ 351735, « 15C house » – TV. e
closed 24 to 26 December – **3 rm** 28.00/46.00 **st.**

Sydney House, Coton Cres., off Coton Hill, SY1 2LJ, ☎ 354681, Fax 354681 – rest TV u
☎ P. AE VISA.
closed 24 to 1 January – **Meals** 12.00 **st.** 4.00 – **7 rm** 32.00/60.00 **st.**

Roseville, 12 Berwick Rd, SY1 2LN, ☎ 236470 – P. r
closed 16 December-9 February – **Meals** (by arrangement) 10.00 **s.** – **3 rm** 19.00/40.00 **s.** – SB.

at Albrighton N : 3 m. on A 528 – ✉ Shrewsbury – ☎ 01939 :

Albrighton Hall, Ellesmere Rd, SY4 3AG, ☎ 291000, Fax 291123, , , park, squash – rm TV ☎ P – 300. AE VISA
Meals *(closed Saturday lunch)* 9.50/18.75 **t.** and a la carte 7.00 – 5.95 – **39 rm** 75.00/135.00 **st.** – SB.

Albright Hussey , Ellesmere Rd, SY4 3AF, ☎ 290571, Fax 291143, <, « 16C moated manor house », – TV ☎ P. AE VISA.
Meals 12.00/17.50 **t.** and a la carte 5.95 – **5 rm** 65.00/120.00 **t.** – SB.

at Dorrington S : 7 m. on A 49 – ✉ Shrewsbury – ☎ 01743 :

Country Friends with rm, SY5 7JD, ☎ 718707, – P. AE VISA.
closed 2 weeks late July, 1 week October and 25 to 26 December – **Meals** *(closed Sunday and Monday)* 25.50 **t.** – **3 rm** (dinner included) 65.00/105.00 **t.**

at Longnor S : 8 ¼ m. by A 49 – ✉ Shrewsbury – ☎ 01743 :

Moat House , SY5 7PP, on No Through rd ☎ 718434, Fax 718434, <, « Timber framed medieval manor house », – rm P. AE VISA.
March-November – **Meals** (residents only)(booking essential) 27.00 **s.** – **3 rm** 38.00/64.00 **s.**

at Hanwood SW : 4 m. on A 488 – ✉ Shrewsbury – ☎ 01743 :

White House, SY5 8LP, ☎ 860414, – rm P.
Meals (by arrangement) 16.00 **s.** 4.00 – **6 rm** 20.00/50.00 **s.** – SB.

Old School House without rest., SY5 8LJ, ☎ 860694, – TV P.
3 rm 17.00/23.00 **st.**

at Alberbury W : 7 ½ m. by A 458 – ✉ Shrewsbury – ☎ 01743 :

Rowton Castle, SY5 9EP, SW : ½ m. off A 458 ☎ 884044, Fax 884949, <, , park – TV ☎ P – 110. AE VISA
Meals (bar lunch)/dinner 17.50 **t.** and a la carte 5.00 – **19 rm** 59.50/175.00 **t.** – SB.

ATS Lancaster Rd, Harlescott ☎ 343954/232231

SHURDINGTON Glos. 403 404 N 28 – see Cheltenham.

SIBSON Leics. – see Nuneaton (Warks.).

SIDFORD Devon 403 K 31 – see Sidmouth.

SIDMOUTH Devon 403 K 31 **The West Country G.** – pop. 12 982 – ECD : Thursday – ☎ 01395.

Envir. : Bicton★ (Gardens★) *AC*, SW : 5 m.

18 Cotmaton Rd ☎ 513023.

Ham Lane, EX10 8XR ☎ 516441.

♦London 170 – Exeter 14 – Taunton 27 – Weymouth 45.

Victoria, The Esplanade, Peak Hill, EX10 8RY, ☎ 512651, Fax 579154, <, , heated, , , – TV ☎ P
58 rm, 3 suites.

Riviera, The Esplanade, EX10 8AY, ☎ 515201, Fax 577775, < – rest TV ☎ – 85. AE VISA
Meals 11.50/18.50 **t.** and a la carte 4.40 – **27 rm** 63.00/168.00 **t.** – SB.

Belmont, The Esplanade, EX10 8RX, ☎ 512555, Fax 579101, <, – TV ☎ P. AE VISA
Meals (dancing Saturday evening) 10.95/19.50 **t.** and a la carte 4.75 – **54 rm** (dinner included) 83.00/206.00 **t.** – SB.

Salcombe Hill House , Beatlands Rd, EX10 8JQ, ☎ 514697, Fax 578310, heated, , – rest TV ☎ P. VISA.
March-October – **Meals** (bar lunch Monday to Saturday)/dinner 15.00 **t.** and a la carte – **30 rm** (dinner included) 56.00/112.00 **t.** – SB.

Littlecourt, Seafield Rd, EX10 8HF, ℘ 515279, heated, – rest. VISA
late March-late October – **Meals** (bar lunch)/dinner 14.00 **t.** 3.90 – **20 rm** (dinner included) 46.50/93.00 **t.** – SB.

Abbeydale, Manor Rd, EX10 8RP, ℘ 512060, – rest.
April-October – **Meals** (bar lunch)/dinner 14.00 **t.** – **18 rm** (dinner included) 35.00/100.00 **t.**

Mount Pleasant, Salcombe Rd, EX10 8JA, ℘ 514694, –
closed December and January – **Meals** (residents only) (dinner only) 13.50 **st.** 5.50 – **16 rm** (dinner included) 42.50/85.00 **st.** – SB.

Woodlands, Station Rd, Cotmaton Cross, EX10 8HG, ℘ 513120, – rest
29 rm.

Broad Oak without rest., Sid Rd, EX10 8QP, ℘ 513713, – .
3 rm 20.00/50.00 **s.**

Salcombe Cottage without rest., Hillside Rd, EX10 8JF, ℘ 516829, « 18C thatched cottage », –
4 rm 18.50/34.50 **st.**

at Sidford N : 2 m. – ✉ Sidmouth – 01395 :

Salty Monk, Church St., EX10 9QP, on A 3052 ℘ 513174, – rest. VISA
Restricted service in February – **Meals** *(closed Monday lunch)* 6.95/15.95 **st.** and a la carte 4.95 – **7 rm** 15.00/40.00 **st.** – SB.

ATS Vicarage Rd ℘ 512433

SILCHESTER Hants. 403 404 Q 29 – pop. 1 428 – ✉ Reading (Berks.) – 01734.
♦London 62 – Basingstoke 8 – Reading 14 – Winchester 26.

Romans, Little London Rd, RG7 2PN, ℘ 700421, Fax 700691, heated, , – – 40. VISA
closed 24 December-3 January – **Meals** *(closed Saturday lunch)* 17.00/21.50 **t.** 6.50 – **25 rm** 70.00/95.00 **t.** – SB.

SILVERDALE Lancs. 402 L 21 – ✉ Carnforth – 01524.
♦London 257 – ♦Carlisle 60 – Kendal 12 – Lancaster 13.

Lindeth House without rest., Lindeth Rd, LA5 0TX, by Shore rd ℘ 701238, – .
closed January-mid February – **3 rm** 30.00/45.00.

SIMONSBATH Somerset 403 I 30 The West Country G. – ✉ Minehead – 0164 383.
Envir. : Exmoor National Park★★ – Exford (Church★) E : 5½ m. by B 3223 and B 3224.
♦London 200 – Exeter 40 – Minehead 19 – Taunton 38.

Simonsbath House, TA24 7SH, ℘ 259, ←, « 17C country house », – rest. VISA.
closed December and January – **Meals** (dinner only) 20.50 **t.** 4.25 – **7 rm** 50.00/90.00 **t.** – SB.

SINDLESHAM Berks. – see Reading.

SISSINGHURST Kent 404 V 30 – see Cranbrook.

SIX MILE BOTTOM Cambs. – see Newmarket (Suffolk).

SKELTON N. Yorks. 402 Q 22 – see York.

SKELWITH BRIDGE Cumbria 402 K 20 – see Ambleside.

SKIPTON N. Yorks. 402 N 22 **Great Britain G.** – pop. 13 583 – ECD : Tuesday – ☎ 01756.

See : Castle★ *AC* – 18 ℘ 795657.

Old Town Hall, 9 Sheep St. BD23 1JH ℘ 792809.

♦London 217 – Kendal 45 – ♦Leeds 26 – Preston 36 – York 43.

- **Randell's,** Keighley Rd, BD23 2TA, S : 1 ¼ m. on A 629 ℘ 700100, Fax 700107, Ⅰ₆, ≘s, ▢, squash – |¢| ⇔ rm ▢ ☎ & ⓟ – 🔏 400. ▢ AE ⓞ VISA
  Meals (bar lunch Monday to Saturday)/dinner 15.95 **st.** – **76 rm** ▭ 72.50/115.00 **st.** – SB.
- **Bridge Hill,** Chapel Hill, BD23 1ML, ℘ 796676, Fax 796725 – ▢ ☎ ⓟ. ▢ VISA. ✻
  Meals *(closed Sunday and Monday)* 7.50/10.95 **t.** and dinner a la carte – **5 rm** ▭ 48.00/58.00 **t.** – SB.
- **Unicorn,** Devonshire Pl., Keighley Rd, BD23 2LP, ℘ 794146, Fax 793376 – ▢ ☎. ▢ AE VISA. ✻
  Meals (residents only) (dinner only) a la carte approx. 9.50 **st.** ⅱ 4.50 – **9 rm** ▭ 40.00/47.00 **st.**
- **Forte Travelodge** without rest., Gargrave Rd, BD23 1UD, W : 1 ¾ m. by Water St. at A 65/A 59 roundabout ℘ 798091, Reservations (Freephone) 0800 850950 – ▢ & ⓟ. ▢ AE VISA. ✻
  32 rm 33.50 **t.**

at Elslack W : 4 ½ m. by A 59 off A 56 – ✉ Skipton – ☎ 01282 :

- **Tempest Arms,** BD23 3AY, ℘ 842450, Fax 843331 – ▢ ☎ ⓟ – 🔏 80. ▢ AE VISA. ✻
  Meals 8.25/13.45 **st.** ⅱ 5.00 – **10 rm** ▭ 46.00/52.00 **st.**

ATS Carleton Rd Garage, Carleton Rd ℘ 795741/2

SLAIDBURN Lancs. 402 M 22 – pop. 302 – ✉ Clitheroe – ☎ 01200.

♦London 249 – Burnley 21 – Lancaster 19 – ♦Leeds 48 – Preston 27.

- **Parrock Head** ⑤, BB7 3AH, NW : 1 m. ℘ 446614, Fax 446313, ≤ Bowland Fells, ⛲ – ⇔ rest ▢ ☎ ⓟ. ▢ AE ⓞ VISA. ✻
  Meals (bar lunch Monday to Saturday)/dinner 14.50/18.50 **t.** ⅱ 5.00 – **9 rm** ▭ 40.00/65.00 **t.** – SB.

En haute saison, et surtout dans les stations, il est prudent de retenir à l'avance.

SLEAFORD Lincs. 402 404 S 25 – pop. 13 853 – ECD : Thursday – ☎ 01529.

18 South Rauceby ℘ 488275.

The Mill, Money's Yard, Carre St., NG35 9TW ℘ 414294.

♦London 119 – ♦Leicester 45 – Lincoln 17 – ♦Nottingham 39.

- **Lincolnshire Oak,** East Rd, NG34 7EQ, NE : ¾ m. on B 1517 ℘ 413807, Fax 413710, ⛲ – ⇔ rest ▢ ☎ ⓟ – 🔏 140. ▢ AE VISA. ✻
  Meals a la carte 13.85/18.20 **t.** – **14 rm** ▭ 39.00/65.00 **t.** – SB.
- **Forte Travelodge** without rest, NG34 8NP, NW : 1 m. on A 15 at junction with A 17 ℘ 414752, Reservation (Freephone) 0800 850950 – ▢ & ⓟ. ▢ AE VISA. ✻
  40 rm 33.50 **t.**
- **Tally Ho Inn,** Aswarby, NG34 8SA, S : 4 ½ m. on A 15 ℘ 455205, ≤, ⛲ – ▢ ⓟ. ▢ VISA. ✻
  closed 25-26 December and 1 January – **Meals** (in bar Sunday dinner) a la carte 11.95/18.40 **t.** ⅱ 3.50 – **6 rm** ▭ 30.00/45.00 **t.**

ATS 40 Albion Terr., off Boston Rd ℘ 302908

SLINFOLD W. Sussex – see Horsham.

SLOUGH Berks. 404 S 29 – pop. 101 066 – ECD : Wednesday – ☎ 01753.

18 Farnham Park, Park Rd, Stoke Poges ℘ 643332 – 18, 9, 9 Wexham Park, Wexham St., Wexham ℘ 663271 – 9 Hollow Hill Lane, Iver ℘ 655615.

♦London 29 – ♦Oxford 39 – Reading 19.

- **Copthorne,** Cippenham Lane, SL1 2YE, SW : 1 ¼ m. by A 4 on A 355 ℘ 516222, Telex 220250, Fax 516237, Ⅰ₆, ≘s, ▢ – |¢| ⇔ rm ▤ ▢ ☎ & ⓟ – 🔏 200. ▢ AE ⓞ VISA JCB. ✻
  ***Veranda* : Meals** (dancing Saturday evening) 14.50/18.50 **st.** and dinner a la carte ⅱ 6.50 – ***Reflections* : Meals** *(closed Sunday)* (dinner only) 29.00 **st.** ⅱ 6.50 – ▭ 10.25 – **217 rm** 115.00/185.00 **st.**, 2 suites – SB.
- **Heathrow/Slough Marriott,** Ditton Rd, Langley, SL3 8PT, SE : 2 ½ m. on A 4 ℘ 544244, Fax 540272, Ⅰ₆, ≘s, ▢, ✂ – |¢| ⇔ rm ▤ ▢ ☎ & ⓟ – 🔏 300. ▢ AE ⓞ VISA JCB. ✻
  Meals 15.25/19.95 **t.** and dinner a la carte ⅱ 7.95 – ▭ 11.85 – **348 rm** 110.00 **st.**, 1 suite – SB.
- **Courtyard by Marriott,** Church St., Chalvey, SL1 2NH, SW : 1 ¼ m. by A 4 on A 355 ℘ 551551, Fax 553333, Ⅰ₆ – |¢| ⇔ rm ▤ ▢ ☎ & ⓟ – 🔏 40. ▢ AE ⓞ VISA JCB. ✻
  Meals a la carte 14.25/19.45 and a la carte ⅱ 5.50 – ▭ 7.75 – **148 rm** 75.00 **t.** – SB.

ATS 1A Furnival Av. ℘ 524214

SMITE Heref. and Worcs. – see Droitwich.

SOAR MILL COVE Devon – see Salcombe.

SOHAM Cambs. 404 V 26 **Great Britain G.** – pop. 7 690 – ☏ 01353.
Envir. : Wicken Fen★, SW : 5 m. by A 142 and A 1123.
♦London 69 – ♦Cambridge 19.

Soham By-Pass Motel, CB7 5DF, NE : ½ m. on A 142 ☏ 720324, Fax 720324 – TV ☎ P
12 rm.

SOLIHULL W. Mids. 403 404 O 26 – pop. 199 859 – ECD : Wednesday – ☏ 0121.
Central Library, Homer Rd, B91 3RG ☏ 704 6130/704 6134.
♦London 109 – ♦Birmingham 7 – ♦Coventry 13 – Warwick 13.

Solihull Moat House (Q.M.H.), Homer Rd, B91 3QD, ☏ 711 4700, Fax 711 2696, – rm rest TV ☎ P – 200. AE VISA
Meals 11.75/17.50 **st.** and a la carte – 9.50 – **109 rm** 93.00/116.00 **st.**, 6 suites – SB.

St. John's Swallow, 651 Warwick Rd, B91 1AT, ☏ 711 3000, Fax 705 6629, – rm rest TV ☎ P – 800. AE VISA
Meals *(closed Saturday lunch)* (dancing Saturday evening) 12.50/19.00 **st.** and a la carte – **176 rm** 90.00/101.00 **st.**, 1 suite – SB.

Jarvis George, The Square, B91 3RF, ☏ 711 2121, Fax 711 3374 – rm TV ☎ P – 200. AE VISA
Meals 9.45/14.50 **st.** and a la carte – 8.00 – **117 rm** 85.00/105.00 **st.**, 10 suites – SB.

at Shirley W : 2½ m. by B 4025 – ✉ Solihull – ☏ 0121 :

Regency, Stratford Rd, B90 4EB, SE : 2 m. on A 34 ☏ 745 6119, Fax 733 3801, – rm rest TV ☎ P – 150. AE VISA
Meals 11.95/15.95 **t.** and dinner a la carte 5.75 – **110 rm** 93.00/100.00 **t.**, 2 suites – SB.

Travel Inn, Stratford Rd, B90 4PT, SE : 2½ m. on A 34 ☏ 744 2942, Fax 733 7075 – rm TV P. AE VISA.
Meals (Beefeater grill) a la carte approx. 16.00 **t.** – 4.95 – **51 rm** 33.50 **t.**

XX **Chez Julien,** 1036 Stratford Rd, Monkspath, B90 4EE, SE : 2½ m. on A 34 ☏ 744 7232, Fax 745 4775 – P. AE VISA
closed Saturday lunch, Sunday and Bank Holidays – **Meals** - French 11.80 **st.** and a la carte 4.90.

SOMERTON Somerset 403 L 30 **The West Country G.** – pop. 4 489 – ECD : Wednesday – ☏ 01458.
See : Town★ - Market Place★ (cross★) – St. Michael's Church★.
Envir. : Long Sutton★ (Church★★) SW : 2½m. by B 3165 – Huish Episcopi (St. Mary's Church Tower★★) SW : 4½m. by B 3153 – Lytes Cary★, SE : 3½m. by B 3151.
Exc. : Muchelney★★ (Parish Church★★) SW : 6½m. by B 3153 and A 372 – High Ham (≤★★, St. Andrew's★) NW : 6½m. by B 3153 – Midelney Manor★ *AC*, SW : 9 m. by B 3153 and A 378.
♦London 138 – ♦Bristol 32 – Taunton 17.

Lynch Country House without rest., 4 Behind Berry, TA11 7PD, ☏ 272316, Fax 272590, ≤, « Attractively converted Regency house », park – rest TV ☎ P. VISA.
5 rm 35.00/65.00 **t.**

ATS Bancombe Rd, Trading Est. ☏ 273467

SONNING-ON-THAMES Berks. 404 R 29 – pop. 1 354 – ECD : Wednesday – ☎ 01734.

♦London 48 – Reading 4.

Great House at Sonning, Thames St., RG4 0UT, ☎ 692277, Fax 441296, ⚐, ✂ – TV ☎ P – 80. AE VISA
Meals a la carte 16.75/25.00 **t.** 5.50 – 8.50 – **33 rm** 89.50/119.50 **st.**, 3 suites – SB.

XXX **French Horn** with rm, Thames St., RG4 0TN, ☎ 692204, Fax 442210, ≤ River Thames and gardens – TV ☎ P. AE VISA.
closed Good Friday and 26 December – **Meals** (booking essential) 16.00/40.00 **st.** and a la carte 7.75 – **11 rm** 75.00/85.00 **st.**, 4 suites.

SOURTON Devon 403 H 31 – see Okehampton.

SOUTHAMPTON Hants. 403 404 P 31 **Great Britain G.** – pop. 196 864 – ☎ 01703.

See : Old Southampton AZ : Bargate★ **B** - Tudor House Museum★ **M1**.

18, 9 Southampton Municipal, Golf Course Rd, Bassett ☎ 768407, AY – 18 Stoneham, Bassett Green Rd, Bassett ☎ 768151, AY – 9 Southampton Manor, Manor Farm, Botley, Chilworth ☎ 740544, AY.

Southampton/Eastleigh Airport : ☎ 629600, N : 4 m. BY.

to France (Cherbourg) (Stena Sealink Line) 1-2 daily (5 h) – to the Isle of Wight (East and West Cowes) (Red Funnel Ferries) frequent services daily.

Above Bar, SO9 4XF ☎ 221106.

♦London 87 – ♦Bristol 79 – ♦Plymouth 161.

Plans on following pages

De Vere Grand Harbour, West Quay Rd, SO15 1AG, ☎ 633033, Fax 633066, ⚒, ≘s, – TV ☎ P – 450. AE VISA. AZ **a**
Meals 10.00/30.00 **st.** and a la carte 5.50 – **169 rm** 110.00/120.00 **st.** 3 suites – SB.

Hilton National, Bracken Pl., Chilworth, SO16 3RB, ☎ 702700, Telex 47594, Fax 767233, ⚒, ≘s, – rm ▤ rest TV ☎ ♿ P – 200. AE VISA AY **e**
Meals *(closed Saturday lunch)* 12.95/17.95 **t.** 5.65 – 9.25 – **133 rm** 78.75/99.75 **st.**, 2 suites – SB.

Southampton Park, 12-13 Cumberland Pl., SO15 2WY, ☎ 223467, Fax 332538, ⚒, ≘s, – rm ▤ rest TV ☎ – 200. AE VISA AZ **u**
closed 24 to 27 December – **Meals** 15.95 **t.** – 7.50 – **72 rm** 52.50 **t.** – SB.

Novotel, 1 West Quay Rd, SO1 0RA, ☎ 330550, Fax 222158, ≤, ⚒, ≘s, – rm ▤ TV ☎ ♿ P – 450. AE VISA AZ **x**
Meals 9.95/13.95 **st.** and a la carte 4.95 – 7.50 – **121 rm** 49.50 **st.**

Polygon (Forte), Cumberland Pl., SO15 2WQ, ☎ 330055, Fax 332435 – rm TV ☎ P – 500. AE VISA JCB AZ **n**
Meals *(closed Saturday lunch)* a la carte 15.15/20.00 **st.** 6.25 – 8.50 – **91 rm** 39.50 **st.**, 2 suites – SB.

Southampton Moat House (Q.M.H.), 119 Highfield Lane, Portswood, SO17 1AQ, ☎ 559555, Fax 583910, ⚒, ≘s – TV ☎ P – 200. AE VISA BY **e**
Meals *(closed Saturday lunch)* 14.50 **st.** and a la carte 6.00 – **66 rm** – SB.

Dolphin (Forte), 35 High St., SO9 2DS, ☎ 339955, Fax 333650 – rm TV ☎ P – 75. AE VISA JCB AZ **i**
Meals (bar lunch Monday to Saturday)/dinner 15.95 **st.** and a la carte 6.70 – 8.50 – **71 rm** 50.00/60.00 **st.**, 2 suites – SB.

Forte Posthouse, Herbert Walker Av., SO1 0HJ, ☎ 330777, Fax 332510, ≤, ⚒, ≘s, – rm TV ☎ P – 150. AE VISA AZ **o**
Meals a la carte approx. 15.00 **t.** 5.50 – **128 rm** 56.00/69.50 **st.**

Star, 26-27 High St., SO14 2NA, ☎ 339939, Fax 335291 – rm TV ☎ P – 70. AE VISA AZ **z**
closed 24 to 28 December – **Meals** *(closed lunch Saturday and Bank Holidays)* 7.95/9.95 **t.** and a la carte 4.50 – 5.00 – **45 rm** 39.50/55.550 **t.** – SB.

Rosida Garden, 25-27 Hill Lane, S01 5AB, ☎ 228501, Fax 635501, heated, ⚐ – TV ☎ ♿ P. AE VISA AZ **r**
closed 24 to 31 December – **Meals** (dinner only) a la carte 10.00/16.00 **t.** 3.00 – **27 rm** 40.00/60.00 **t.**

Travel Inn, Romsey Rd, Nursling, SO1 9XJ, NW : 4 m. on A 3057 ☎ 732262 – rm TV ♿ P. AE VISA. AY **a**
Meals (Beefeater grill) a la carte approx. 16.00 **t.** – 4.95 – **32 rm** 33.50 **t.**

Hunters Lodge, 25 Landguard Rd, SO1 5DL, ☎ 227919, Fax 230913 – rm TV ☎ P. AE VISA. AZ **v**
closed Christmas and New Year – **Meals** (by arrangement) 9.50 **s.** 5.00 – **15 rm** 23.50/52.20 **t.** – SB.

XX **Kuti's Brasserie**, 39 Oxford St., SO1 1DP, ☎ 221585 – ▤. AE VISA AZ **e**
closed 25 and 26 December – **Meals** - Indian a la carte 10.55/15.20 **t.**

MICHELIN Distribution Centre, Test Lane, SO1 9JX, ☎ 872344, Fax 663617 AY

ATS West Quay Rd ☎ 333231 ATS 88-94 Portswood Rd ☎ 582727

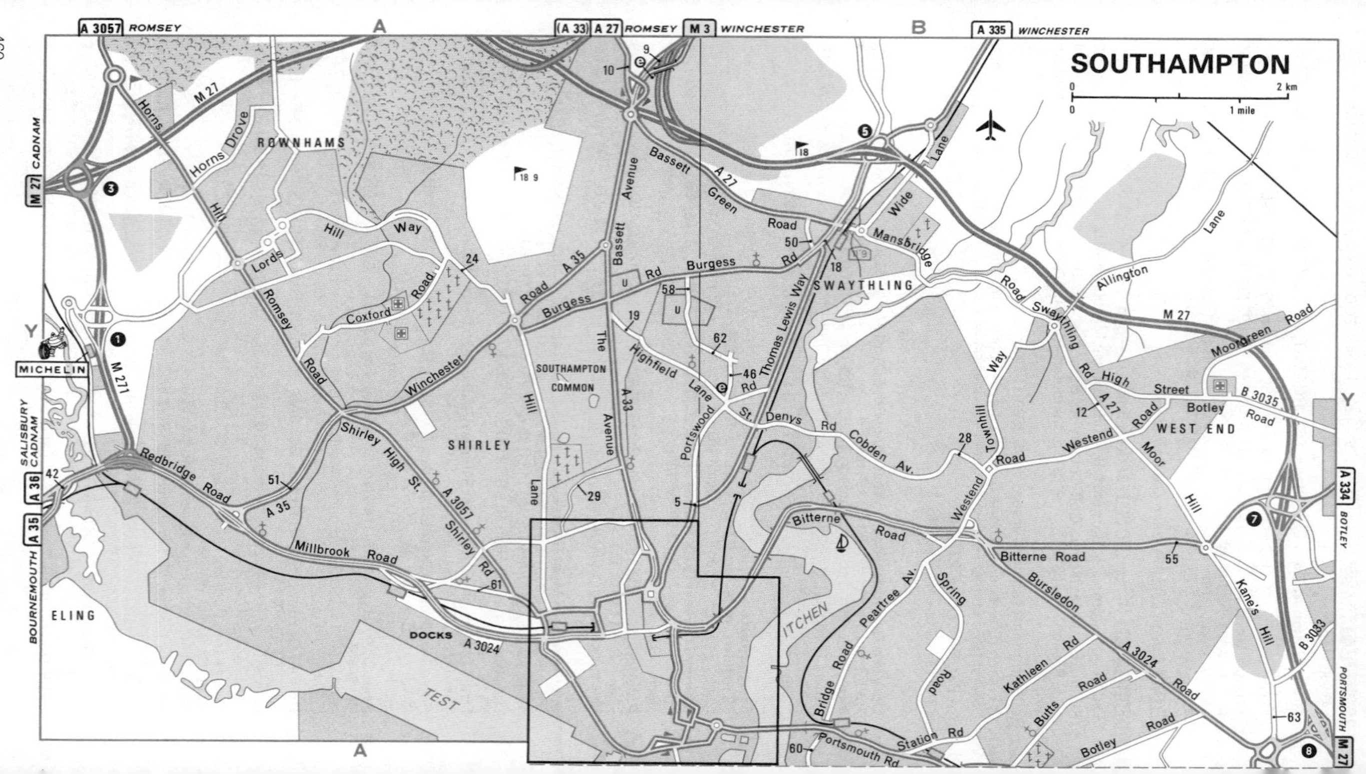
SOUTHAMPTON
0 2 km
0 1 mile
A 3057 ROMSEY
(A 33) A 27 ROMSEY
M 3 WINCHESTER
A 335 WINCHESTER
M 27 CADNAM
A 36 SALISBURY CADNAM
A 35 BOURNEMOUTH
A 334 BOTLEY
M 27 PORTSMOUTH
MICHELIN
ROWNHAMS
SWAYTHLING
SHIRLEY
WEST END
ELING
DOCKS
SOUTHAMPTON COMMON
ITCHEN
TEST
Horns Hill
Horns Drove
Lords Hill Way
Romsey Road
Coxford Road
Winchester Road
Hill Lane
Burgess Rd
Bassett Avenue
Bassett Green Road
The Avenue
Highfield Lane
Portswood Rd
Thomas Lewis Way
St. Denys Rd
Cobden Av.
Wide Lane
Mansbridge
Allington Lane
Swaythling Road
High Street
Moorgreen Road
Botley Road
Westend Road
Townhill Way
Moor Hill
Bitterne Road
Bursledon Road
Kane's Hill
Spring Road
Peartree Av.
Bridge Road
Kathleen Rd
Butts Road
Botley Road
Station Rd
Portsmouth Rd
Redbridge Road
Millbrook Road
Shirley High St.
Shirley Rd
M 27
M 271
A 27
A 33
A 35
A 3057
A 3024
B 3035
B 3033

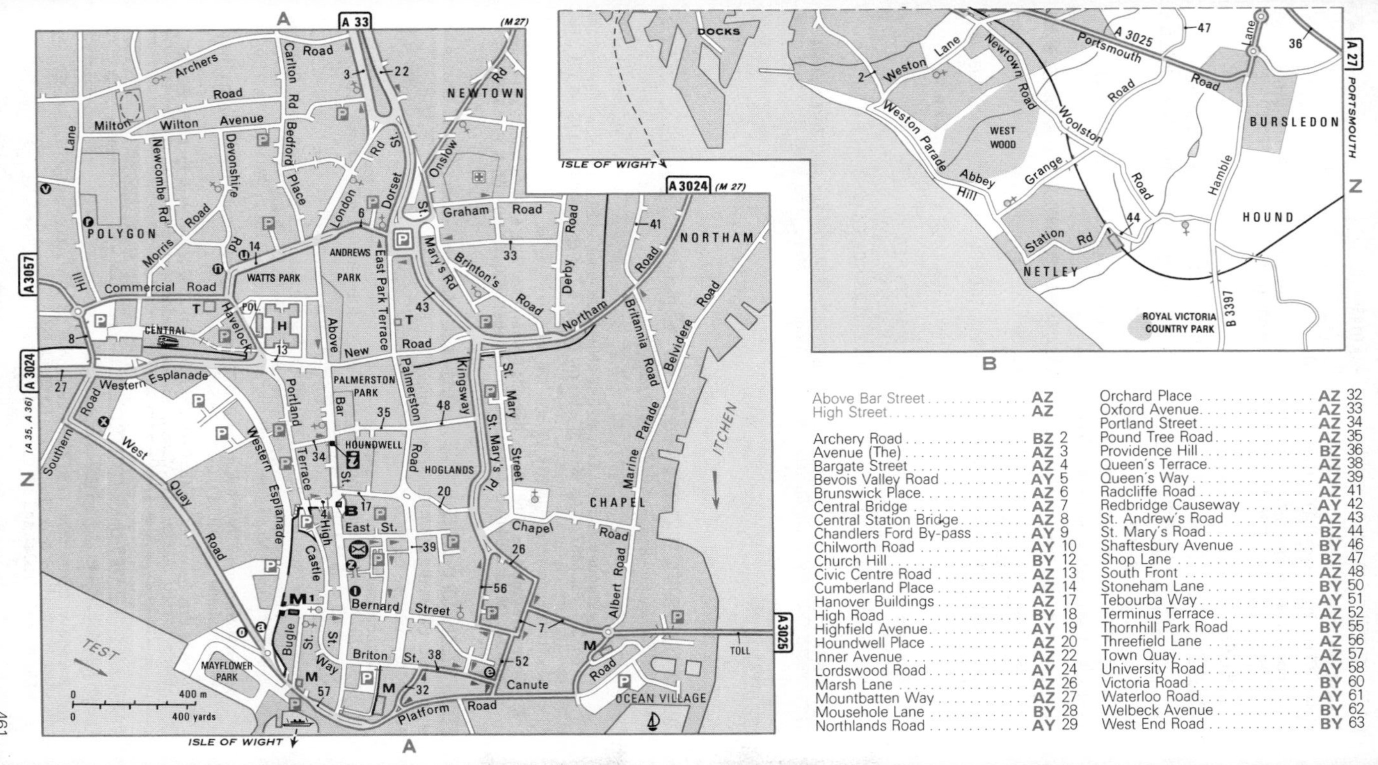

Street	Grid	No.
Above Bar Street	AZ	
High Street	AZ	
Archery Road	BZ	2
Avenue (The)	AZ	3
Bargate Street	AZ	4
Bevois Valley Road	AY	5
Brunswick Place	AZ	6
Central Bridge	AZ	7
Central Station Bridge	AZ	8
Chandlers Ford By-pass	AY	9
Chilworth Road	AY	10
Church Hill	BY	12
Civic Centre Road	AZ	13
Cumberland Place	AZ	14
Hanover Buildings	AZ	17
High Road	BY	18
Highfield Avenue	AY	19
Houndwell Place	AZ	20
Inner Avenue	AZ	22
Lordswood Road	AY	24
Marsh Lane	AZ	26
Mountbatten Way	AZ	27
Mousehole Lane	BY	28
Northlands Road	AY	29
Orchard Place	AZ	32
Oxford Avenue	AZ	33
Portland Street	AZ	34
Pound Tree Road	AZ	35
Providence Hill	BZ	36
Queen's Terrace	AZ	38
Queen's Way	AZ	39
Radcliffe Road	AZ	41
Redbridge Causeway	AY	42
St. Andrew's Road	AZ	43
St. Mary's Road	BZ	44
Shaftesbury Avenue	BY	46
Shop Lane	BZ	47
South Front	AZ	48
Stoneham Lane	BY	50
Tebourba Way	AY	51
Terminus Terrace	AZ	52
Thornhill Park Road	BY	55
Threefield Lane	AZ	56
Town Quay	AZ	57
University Road	AY	58
Victoria Road	BY	60
Waterloo Road	AY	61
Welbeck Avenue	BY	62
West End Road	BY	63

SOUTH CAVE Humbs. 402 S 22 – pop. 3 339 – ☎ 01430.

Cave Castle Hotel ✆ 421286/422245.

London 176 – Kingston-upon-Hull 12 – Leeds 40 – York 30.

- **Forte Travelodge** without rest., Beacon Service Area, HU15 1RZ, SW : 2 ½ m. on A 63 (eastbound carriageway) ✆ 424455, Reservations (Freephone) 0800 850950 – TV ♿ P. VISA.
  40 rm 33.50 **t.**

SOUTHEND-ON-SEA Essex 404 W 29 – pop. 158 517 – ECD : Wednesday – ☎ 01702.

Belfairs Park, Eastwood Rd North, Leigh-on-Sea ✆ 525345 – Ballards Gore, Gore Rd, Canewdon, Rochford ✆ 258917.

Southend-on-Sea Airport : ✆ 340201, N : 2 m.

High St. Precinct, SS1 1DZ ✆ 355120 – Civic Centre, Victoria Av., SS2 6ER ✆ 215120.

London 39 – Cambridge 69 – Croydon 46 – Dover 85.

- **Camelia,** 178 Eastern Esplanade, SS1 3AA, ✆ 587917, Fax 585704 – rest TV ☎. AE VISA
  Meals (dinner only and Sunday lunch)/dinner 12.95 **st.** and a la carte 4.00 – **16 rm** 39.50/80.00 **st.** – SB.
- **Balmoral,** 34-36 Valkyrie Rd, Westcliff-on-Sea, SS0 8BU, ✆ 342947, Fax 337828, – TV ☎ P. AE VISA
  Meals *(closed Sunday dinner)* 9.00 **st.** and dinner a la carte 5.25 – **22 rm** 35.00/48.00 **st.** – SB.
- **Pebbles,** 190 Eastern Esplanade, SS1 3AA, ✆ 582329 – TV.
  Meals (by arrangement) 9.50 **s.** – **5 rm** 24.00/36.00 **s.**
- Ilfracombe House, 11-13 Wilson Rd, SS1 1HG, ✆ 351000 – TV ☎
  13 rm.
- XX **Paris,** 719 London Rd, Westcliff-on-Sea, SS0 9ST, ✆ 344077, Fax 344077 – AE VISA
  closed Saturday lunch, Sunday dinner and Monday – **Meals** 14.50/26.95 **st.** and a la carte 4.95.

SOUTH KILVINGTON N. Yorks. – see Thirsk.

SOUTH LOPHAM Norfolk 404 X 26 – see Diss.

SOUTH MIMMS SERVICE AREA Herts. 404 T 28 – ✉ Potters Bar – ☎ 01707.

M 25 Motorway Services, EN6 3QQ ✆ 643233.

London 21 – Luton 17.

- **Forte Posthouse,** Bignells Corner, EN6 3NH, M 25 junction 23 at junction with A 1 (M) ✆ 643311, Fax 646728, – rm rest TV ☎ P – 170. AE VISA JCB.
  Meals a la carte approx. 15.00 **t.** 5.50 – **120 rm** 59.50/69.50 **st.**
- **Forte Travelodge** without rest., Bignells Corner, EN6 3QQ, M 25 junction 23 at junction with A 1 (M) ✆ 665440, Reservations (Freephone) 0800 850950 – TV ♿ P. AE VISA.
  52 rm 33.50 **st.**

SOUTH MOLTON Devon 403 I 30 – pop. 4 066 – ECD : Wednesday – ☎ 01769.

1 East St., EX36 3BU ✆ 574122 (summer only).

London 210 – Exeter 35 – Taunton 39.

- **Whitechapel Manor**, EX36 3EG, E : 4 m. by B 3227 and Whitechapel rd ✆ 573377, Fax 573797, ≤, « Elizabethan manor house built by Robert de Bassett », , park – rest TV ☎ P. AE VISA JCB.
  Meals (booking essential) 26.00/32.00 **t.** 7.50 – **9 rm** 65.00/160.00 **st.**, 1 suite – SB.
- **Park House**, EX36 3ED, N : ½ m. on North Molton rd ✆ 572610, ≤, « Victorian country house, gardens », , park – rest TV P. AE VISA.
  closed February – **Meals** (light lunch)/dinner 18.50 4.10 – **7 rm** 49.00/88.00 **t.** – SB.

at East Buckland NW : 6 ¼ m. by B 3226 and Filleigh rd, turning right at Stags Head – ✉ Barnstaple – ☎ 01598 :

- XX **Lower Pitt** with rm, EX32 0TD, ✆ 760243, Fax 760243, – P. AE VISA.
  Meals *(closed Sunday and Monday to non residents)* (booking essential) (dinner only) a la carte 14.75/18.70 **st.** 4.50 – **3 rm** 55.00/100.00 **st.** – SB.

SOUTH NORMANTON Derbs. 402 403 404 Q 24 – pop. 8 034 – ECD : Wednesday – ☎ 01773.

London 130 – Derby 17 – Nottingham 15 – Sheffield 31.

- **Swallow,** Carter Lane East, DE55 2EH, on A 38 ✆ 812000, Fax 580032, – rm rest TV ☎ ♿ P – 200. AE VISA
  Meals 12.50/19.50 **st.** and a la carte – **161 rm** 90.00/110.00 **st.** – SB.

SOUTH PETHERTON Somerset 403 L 31 **The West Country G.** – pop. 3 094 – ☎ 01460.

Envir. : Barrington Court Garden★ *AC*, W : 5½ m. by A 303.

♦London 138 – ♦Bristol 41 – Exeter 41 – Taunton 19 – Yeovil 7.5.

XX **Le Tire Bouchon at Oaklands House** with rm, 8 Palmer St., TA13 5DB, ℘ 240272, heated, – ☎ P. AE VISA
March-October – **Meals** - French *(closed Sunday and Monday)* (dinner only and Sunday lunch)/dinner 20.25 **t.** 4.95 – 3.50 – **5 rm** 40.00/75.00 **t.** – SB.

SOUTHPORT Mersey. 402 K 23 – pop. 88 596 – ECD : Tuesday – ☎ 01704.

18 Southport Municipal, Park Rd ℘ 535286 – 18 Park Rd ℘ 530435.

112 Lord St., PR8 1NY ℘ 533333.

♦London 221 – ♦Liverpool 20 – ♦Manchester 38 – Preston 19.

Scarisbrick, 239 Lord St., PR8 1NZ, ℘ 543000, Fax 533335 – TV ☎ P – 200. AE VISA
Meals (dancing Saturday evening) 7.45/14.50 **t.** and a la carte 4.75 – **77 rm** 65.00/95.00 **t.** – SB.

Stutelea, Alexandra Rd, PR9 0NB, ℘ 544220, Fax 500232, , , – TV ☎ P. AE VISA.
Meals (bar lunch)/dinner a la carte 9.70/16.80 **st.** 4.00 – **22 rm** 45.00/75.00 **st.** – SB.

Cambridge House, 4 Cambridge Rd, PR9 9NG, NE : 1 m. on A 565 ℘ 538372, Fax 547183, – TV ☎ P. AE VISA
Meals 12.95 **t.** and a la carte 5.55 – **18 rm** 28.00/49.00 **t.** – SB.

Radley, Promenade, PR8 1QU, ℘ 530310 – TV P. VISA.
closed 12 days January – **Meals** (dinner only) 8.00 **st.** 3.50 – **22 rm** 25.00/45.00 **st.** – SB.

Ambassador, 13 Bath St., PR9 0DP, ℘ 543998, Fax 536269 – TV P. VISA
closed Christmas-2 January – **Meals** 8.00 3.00 – **8 rm** 25.00/46.00 **st.** – SB.

Gilton, 7 Leicester St., PR9 0ER, ℘ 530646, Fax 533791, , – TV P. AE
closed January – **Meals** (by arrangement) 10.50 **st.** 3.60 – **13 rm** 25.00/40.00 – SB.

ATS 69 Shakespeare St. ℘ 534434

SOUTHSEA Hants. 403 404 Q 31 – see Portsmouth and Southsea.

SOUTH SHIELDS Tyne and Wear 401 402 P 19 – pop. 86 488 – ECD : Wednesday – ☎ 0191.

18 Cleadon Hills ℘ 456 0475 – 18 Whitburn, Lizard Lane ℘ 529 2144.

Amphitheatre, Sea Rd, NE33 2LD ℘ 455 7411 (summer only) – Museum and Art Gallery, Ocean Rd, NE33 2HZ ℘ 454 6612.

♦London 284 – ♦Newcastle upon Tyne 9.5 – Sunderland 6.

Sea, Sea Rd, NE33 2LD, ℘ 427 0999, Fax 454 0500 – TV ☎ P. AE VISA
Meals 8.50/10.95 **st.** and a la carte 4.25 – **33 rm** 58.00/73.00 **st.** – SB.

ATS Western Approach ℘ 454 1060/4247

SOUTHWAITE SERVICE AREA Cumbria 401 402 L 19 – ✉ Carlisle – ☎ 0169 74.

M 6 Service Area, CA4 0NS ℘ 73445/73446.

♦London 300 – ♦Carlisle 14 – Lancaster 58 – Workington 48.

Granada Lodge without rest., CA4 0NT, on M 6 ℘ 73131, Fax 73669, Reservations (Freephone) 0800 555300 – TV ☎ P. AE VISA.
4.00 – **39 rm** 39.95 **st.**

SOUTH WALSHAM Norfolk 404 Y 26 **Great Britain G.** – pop. 1 612 – ✉ Norwich – ☎ 01603.

Envir. : The Broads★.

♦London 120 – Great Yarmouth 11 – ♦Norwich 9.

South Walsham Hall H. & Country Club , South Walsham Rd, NR13 6DQ, ℘ 270378, Fax 270519, , heated, , , park, , squash – TV ☎ P. AE VISA.
closed first 2 weeks January – **Meals** 12.50/18.50 **t.** and a la carte 4.50 – **17 rm** 40.00/120.00 **st.** – SB.

SOUTHWELL Notts. 402 404 R 24 **Great Britain G.** – pop. 6 958 – ECD : Thursday – ☎ 01636.

See : Minster★★ *AC*.

♦London 135 – Lincoln 24 – ♦Nottingham 14 – ♦Sheffield 34.

Saracen's Head (Forte), Market Pl., NG25 0HE, ℘ 812701, Fax 815408 – TV ☎ P – 100
27 rm.

Old Forge without rest., 2 Burgage Lane, NG25 0ER, ℘ 812809, – TV ☎ P. VISA
5 rm 28.00/46.00.

SOUTHWOLD Suffolk 404 Z 27 – pop. 5 951 – ECD : Wednesday – ☎ 01502.

The Common ☎ 723234 – Town Hall, Market Pl., IP18 6EF ☎ 724729 (summer only).

London 108 – Great Yarmouth 24 – Ipswich 35 – Norwich 34.

- Swan, Market Pl., IP18 6EG, ☎ 722186, Fax 724800, – rest – 40 **43 rm**, 2 suites.
- **Crown,** 90 High St., IP18 6DP, ☎ 722275, Fax 724805 – – 40. AE VISA. *closed first week January* – **Meals** 14.75/19.25 **t.** – 4.50 – **12 rm** 38.00/58.00 **t.**

at Reydon NW : 1 m. by A 1095 on B 1126 – ✉ Southwold – ☎ 01502 :

- **Cricketers,** Wangford Rd, IP18 6PZ, ☎ 723603, Fax 722194, – . VISA **Meals** (in bar) 9.75/12.10 **t.** 4.50 – **9 rm** 35.00/53.00 **t.**

SOUTH WOODHAM FERRERS Essex 404 V 29 – pop. 6 975 – ✉ Chelmsford – ☎ 01245.

London 36 – Chelmsford 12 – Colchester 34 – Southend-on-Sea 13.

- Oakland, 2-6 Reeves Way, by Merchant St., CM3 5XE, ☎ 322811, Fax 329201 – **41 rm.**

SPALDING Lincs. 402 404 T 25 – pop. 19 561 – ☎ 01775.

Ayscoughfee Hall, Churchgate, PE11 2RA ☎ 725468/761161.

London 111 – Lincoln 40 – Leicester 56 – Norwich 65.

- **Queensgate,** Westlode St., PE11 2AF, ☎ 711929, Fax 724205 – . AE VISA. **Meals** (carving lunch) 13.00/25.00 6.95 – **11 rm** 40.00/49.00 **st.** – SB.
- **Bedford Court,** 10 London Rd, PE11 2TA, ☎ 722377, Fax 722377, – . **Meals** (by arrangement) – **4 rm** 25.00/40.00.

ATS 10 Gosberton Rd ☎ 680251

SPARK BRIDGE Cumbria – see Ulverston.

SPEEN Berks. – see Newbury.

SPEEN Bucks. – ✉ Princes Risborough – ☎ 01494.

London 41 – Aylesbury 15 – Oxford 33 – Reading 25.

- **Old Plow Inn** (Restaurant), Flowers Bottom, HP27 0PZ, W : ½ m. by Chapel Hill and Highwood Bottom ☎ 488300, – . AE VISA *closed Sunday dinner, Monday, 5 days at Christmas and Bank Holidays* – **Meals** 15.95/25.00 **t.** 7.50.

SPORLE Norfolk – see Swaffham.

SPRATTON Northants. 404 R 27 – see Northampton.

STADDLEBRIDGE N. Yorks. – see Northallerton.

STAFFORD Staffs. 402 403 404 N 25 – pop. 117 788 – ECD : Wednesday – ☎ 01785.

Brocton Hall, Brocton ☎ 662627 – Stafford Castle, Newport Rd ☎ 223821.

The Ancient High House, Greengate St., ST16 2JA ☎ 40204.

London 142 – Birmingham 26 – Derby 32 – Shrewsbury 31 – Stoke-on-Trent 17.

- **De Vere Tillington Hall,** Eccleshall Rd, ST16 1JJ, NW : 1 ½ m. on A 5013 ☎ 53531, Fax 59223, , , , – rm rest – 200. AE VISA **Meals** *(closed Saturday lunch)* 8.95/14.75 **st.** and a la carte – **90 rm** 80.00/110.00 **st.** – SB.
- **Garth,** Moss Pit, ST17 9JR, S : 2 m. on A 449 ☎ 56124, Fax 55152, – rm rest – 120. AE VISA **Meals** *(closed Saturday lunch)* 20.00 **t.** – **60 rm** 61.00 **st.** – SB.
- Vine, Salter St., ST16 2JU, ☎ 44112, Fax 46612 – . **Meals** (in bar) – **26 rm.**

ATS Kenworthy Rd, Astonfields Ind. Est. ☎ 223832/58118

STAINES Middx. 404 S 29 – pop. 51 949 – ECD : Thursday – ☎ 01784.

London 26 – Reading 25.

- **Thames Lodge** (Forte), Thames St., TW18 4SF, ☎ 464433, Fax 454858, – rest – 50. AE VISA JCB **Meals** (bar lunch Monday to Saturday)/dinner a la carte 13.40/21.30 **t.** 6.70 – 8.50 – **44 rm** 85.00/95.00 **t.** – SB.

STAITHES N. Yorks. – ✉ Saltburn (Cleveland) – ☎ 01947.

London 269 – Middlesbrough 22 – Scarborough 31.

- **Endeavour,** 1 High St., TS13 5BH, ☎ 840825 – *closed Sunday, except dinner in Summer, mid January-mid March and 25 to 26 December* – **Meals** - Seafood (lunch by arrangement)/dinner a la carte 16.15/21.95 **t.**

STAMFORD Lincs. 402 404 S 26 **Great Britain G.** – pop. 13 566 – ECD : Thursday – ☎ 01780.

See : Town★★ - St. Martin's Church★ – Lord Burghley's Hospital★ – Browne's Hospital★ *AC*.

Envir. : Burghley House★★ *AC*, SE : 1½ m. by B 1443.

Luffenham Heath, Ketton ℘ 720205.

Stamford Arts Centre, 27 St. Mary's St., PE9 2DL ℘ 55611.

♦London 92 – ♦Leicester 31 – Lincoln 50 – ♦Nottingham 45.

The George of Stamford, 71 St. Martin's, PE9 2LB, ℘ 55171, Fax 57070, « Part 16C coaching inn with walled monastic garden » – TV ☎ P – 50. AE VISA
Meals 18.50 **st.** (lunch) and a la carte 25.20/32.20 – **46 rm** 75.00/154.00 **st.**, 1 suite – SB.

Lady Anne's, 37-38 High St., St. Martin's Without, PE9 2LJ, ℘ 481184, Fax 65422, – rest TV ☎ P – 130. AE VISA
Meals (bar lunch)/dinner 14.50 **t.** and a la carte 5.75 – **29 rm** 49.50/78.25 **t.** – SB.

Ram Jam Inn, Great North Rd, Stretton, LE15 7QX, NW : 8 m. by B 1081 on A 1 (northbound carriageway) ℘ 410776, Fax 410361, – TV ☎ P – 30. AE VISA.
closed Christmas Day – **Meals** a la carte 10.00/17.95 **t.** 6.25 – 4.10 – **7 rm** 39.00/49.00 **t.**

Garden House, 42 High St., St. Martin's, PE9 2LP, ℘ 63359, Fax 63339, – rm TV ☎ P. AE VISA
Meals (bar dinner Sunday) 15.00/26.10 **st.** and a la carte 4.75 – **20 rm** 49.75/99.00 **st.** – SB.

Raj of India, 2 All Saints St., PE9 2PA, ℘ 53556 – . AE VISA
closed Christmas Day – **Meals** - Indian a la carte 7.45/10.40 **t.** 4.25.

L'Incontro, The Old Barn Passage, St. Mary's St., PE9 2HG, ℘ 51675, « 16C barn » – AE VISA JCB
closed Monday lunch, Sunday and Bank Holidays – **Meals** - Italian a la carte 14.65/18.90 **t.** 5.45.

at Empingham (Leics.) W : 5¾ m. on A 606 – ✉ Oakham – ☎ 01780 :

White Horse, 2 Main St., LE15 8PR, ℘ 460221, Fax 460521, – TV ☎ P – 60. AE VISA
Meals (bar dinner Sunday) 9.95/24.00 **t.** and dinner a la carte 3.75 – **14 rm** 30.00/60.00 **t.** – SB.

at Normanton Park (Leics.) W : 6½ m. by A 606 on Edith Weston Rd – ✉ Oakham – ☎ 01780 :

Normanton Park , South Shore, LE15 8RP, ℘ 720315, Fax 721086, <, , – rest TV ☎ P – 30. VISA
Meals a la carte 14.00/24.95 **st.** 3.95 – **23 rm** 49.50/79.50 **st.** – SB.

STANDISH Gtr. Manchester 402 404 M 23 – pop. 11 504 – ECD : Wednesday – ✉ Wigan – ☎ 01257.

♦London 210 – ♦Liverpool 22 – ♦Manchester 21 – Preston 15.

Kilhey Court, Chorley Rd, Worthington, WN1 2XN, E : 1¾ m. by B 5239 on A 5106 ℘ 472100, Fax 422401, , – rm rest TV ☎ P – 180. AE VISA.
***Laureate* : Meals** *(closed Saturday lunch)* 11.95/19.95 **st.** – 7.50 – **54 rm** 70.00/120.00 **st.** – SB.

Almond Brook Moat House (Q.M.H.), Almond Brook Rd, WN6 0SR, W : 1 m. on A 5209 ℘ 425588, Fax 427327, , , – rm rest TV ☎ P – 150. AE VISA
Meals 12.50 **st.** and a la carte – 7.75 – **121 rm** 65.00/85.00 **st.** – SB.

Wrightington, Moss Lane, Wrightington (Lancs.), WN6 9PB, W : 1¾ m. by A 5209 ℘ 425803, Fax 425830, , , , squash – TV ☎ P – 60. AE VISA JCB
Meals 6.95/12.95 **t.** and a la carte 3.95 – **47 rm** 56.00/75.00 **t.** – SB.

The Beeches, School Lane, WN6 0TD, on A 5209 ℘ 426432, Fax 427503, – P. AE VISA
***Restaurant* : Meals** *(closed Sunday dinner and Monday)* (dinner only and Sunday lunch)/dinner 11.95 **t.** and a la carte.
Stable Brasserie, Meals 5.95/11.95 **t.** and a la carte.

ATS 23 Market St. ℘ 423146/423732

STANDON Herts. 404 U 28 – pop. 3 496 – ✉ Ware – ☎ 01920.

♦London 31 – ♦Cambridge 23 – Luton 30.

No. 28, 28 High St., SG11 1LA, ℘ 821035, Fax 822630 – .

STANNERSBURN Northd. 401 402 M 18 – ✉ Hexham – ☎ 01434.

♦London 363 – ♦Carlisle 56 – ♦Newcastle upon Tyne 46.

Pheasant Inn , Falstone, NE48 1DD, ℘ 240382, Fax 240024 – TV P
closed 25-26 December – **Meals** 11.50/15.50 **t.** and a la carte 3.95 – **8 rm** 30.00/52.00 **t.** – SB.

STANSTEAD ABBOTS Herts. 404 U 28 – pop. 1 909 – ✉ Ware – ☎ 01279.

Briggens House Hotel, Briggens Park, Stanstead Rd ☎ 793742.

♦London 22 – ♦Cambridge 37 – Luton 32 – ♦Ipswich 66.

Briggens (Q.M.H.), Stanstead Rd, SG12 8LD, E : 2 m. by A 414 ☎ 792416, Fax 793685, ≤, heated, park, – – 100
53 rm, 1 suite.

STANSTED AIRPORT Essex 404 U 28 – ✉ Stansted Mountfitchet – ☎ 01279.

♦London 37 – ♦Cambridge 29 – Chelmsford 18 – Colchester 29.

Hilton National, Round Coppice Rd, CM24 8SE, ☎ 680800, Fax 680890, – rest – 250. AE VISA JCB
Meals 13.50/14.50 **t.** and a la carte 5.00 – 9.75 – **238 rm** 90.00/140.00 **st.** – SB.

at Broxted NE : 3¾ m. by Broxted rd – ✉ Great Dunmow – ☎ 01279 :

Whitehall, Church End, CM6 2BZ, on B 1051 ☎ 850603, Fax 850385, ≤, « Part 12C and 15C manor house, walled garden », – – 120. AE VISA.
closed 26 to 31 December – **Meals** (see below) – **25 rm** 75.00/155.00 **t.**

XXX **Whitehall,** (at Whitehall H.) Church End, CM6 2BZ, on B 1051 ☎ 850603, Fax 850385 – .
AE VISA
closed 26 to 31 December – **Meals** 22.50/37.50 **t.** 8.50.

STANTON FITZWARREN Wilts. – see Swindon.

STANTON HARCOURT Oxon 403 404 P 28 – pop. 908 – ✉ Oxford – ☎ 01865.

♦London 71 – Gloucester 45 – ♦Oxford 13 – Swindon 27.

X **Harcourt Arms,** OX8 1RJ, ☎ 881931 – . AE VISA
closed 26 December and 1 January – **Meals** 11.50 **t.** (dinner) and a la carte 5.50.

STANTON WICK Avon 403 404 M 29 – see Bristol.

STARBOTTON N. Yorks. – see Kettlewell.

STAVERTON Devon 403 I 32 – pop. 682 – ✉ Totnes – ☎ 01803.

♦London 220 – Exeter 20 – Torquay 33.

Sea Trout Inn, TQ9 6PA, ☎ 762274, Fax 762506, – . AE VISA
accommodation closed 24 to 26 December – **Meals** *(closed Sunday dinner)* (bar lunch Monday to Saturday)/dinner 16.50 **t.** and a la carte 4.25 – **10 rm** 39.50/54.00 **t.** – SB.

STAVERTON Glos. – see Cheltenham.

STEDHAM W. Sussex 404 R 31 – see Midhurst.

STEEPLE ASTON Oxon. 403 404 Q 28 – pop. 874 – ECD : Saturday – ✉ Bicester – ☎ 01869.

♦London 69 – ♦Coventry 38 – ♦Oxford 10.

Hopcrofts Holt (Mt Charlotte Thistle), OX6 3QQ, SW : 1¼ m. at junction of A 4260 with B 4030 ☎ 340259, Fax 340865, – rm – 100. AE VISA JCB
Meals *(closed Saturday lunch)* (carving lunch Sunday) 11.95/17.95 **t.** and a la carte 5.10 – **88 rm** 65.00/95.00 **t.** – SB.

Westfield Farm Motel, Fenway, OX6 3SS, ☎ 340591, – . VISA
Meals (by arrangement) 15.00 **t.** – **6 rm** 32.00/48.00 **st.** – SB.

X Red Lion, South St., OX6 3RY, ☎ 40225 – .

STEVENAGE Herts. 404 T 28 **Great Britain G.** – pop. 75 147 – ECD : Monday and Wednesday – ☎ 01438.

Envir. : Knebworth House★ *AC*, S : 2½ m.

18, 9 Aston Lane ☎ 880424 – 18, 9 Chesfield Downs Family Golf Centre, Jack's Hill, Graveley ☎ (01462) 482929.

Central Library, Southgate, SG1 1HD ☎ 369441.

♦London 36 – Bedford 25 – ♦Cambridge 27.

Stevenage Moat House (Q.M.H.), High St., Old Town, SG1 3AZ, ☎ 359111, Fax 742169, – rm – 200. AE VISA
Meals (bar lunch Saturday) 12.75 **t.** and a la carte 6.75 – 8.75 – **56 rm** 80.00/87.50 **t.** – SB.

Hertfordpark (Q.M.H.), Danestrete, SG1 1EJ, ☎ 350661, Fax 741880 – rm – 170. AE VISA
Meals *(closed lunch Saturday, Sunday and Bank Holidays)* 12.50 **st.** and a la carte 5.25 – 8.75 – **98 rm** 49.50 **st.** – SB.

Novotel Stevenage, Knebworth Park, SG1 2AX, SW : 1½ m. by A 602 at junction with A 1 (M) ☎ 742299, Fax 723872, heated – rm rest – 120. AE VISA JCB
Meals 14.50 **st.** and a la carte 4.95 – 7.50 – **100 rm** 49.50 – SB.

Travel Inn, Corey's Mill Lane, SG1 4AA, NW : 2 m. on A 602 ℘ 351318, Fax 74609 – rm.
Meals (Beefeater grill) a la carte approx. 16.00 **t.** – 4.95 – **39 rm** 33.50 **t.**

at Broadwater S : 1 ¾ m. by A 602 on B 197 – ✉ Stevenage – 01438 :

Forte Posthouse, Old London Rd, SG2 8DS, ℘ 365444, Fax 741308, – rm – 50.
Meals a la carte approx. 15.00 **t.** 5.50 – **54 rm** 56.00 **st.**

ATS 4-8 Norton Rd ℘ 313262

STEYNING W. Sussex 404 T 31 – pop. 5 629 – ECD : Thursday – 01903.

♦London 52 – ♦Brighton 12 – Worthing 10.

Old Tollgate, The Street, Bramber, BN44 3WE, SW : 1 m. ℘ 879494, Fax 813399 –
Meals (carving rest.) 14.25/17.25 **t.** – 5.95 – **31 rm** 57.00/77.00 **t.** – SB.

Springwells without rest., 9 High St., BN44 3GG, ℘ 812446, heated, –
closed 24 December-2 January – **11 rm** 40.00/75.00 **t.**

STILTON Cambs. 404 T 26 – pop. 3 765 – ✉ Peterborough – 01733.

♦London 76 – ♦Cambridge 30 – Northampton 43 – Peterborough 6.

Bell Inn, Great North Rd, PE7 3RA, ℘ 241066, Fax 245173, « Part 16C inn », – rm – 100.
closed 25-26 December and 1 January – **Meals** 15.50/21.50 **t.** and dinner a la carte 6.00 – **19 rm** 59.00/64.00 **t.** – SB.

STOCKBRIDGE Hants. 403 404 P 30 – pop. 524 – ECD : Wednesday – 01264.

♦London 75 – Salisbury 14 – Winchester 9.

Carbery, Salisbury Hill, SO20 6EZ, on A 30 ℘ 810771, Fax 811022, heated, –
closed 2 weeks January – **Meals** (by arrangement) – **11 rm** 22.00/48.00 **st.**

at Longstock N : 1 ½ m. by Longstock rd – ✉ Stockbridge – 01264 :

Peat Spade Inn, SO20 6DR, ℘ 810612, Fax 810612, –
closed Sunday dinner, 25-26 December and 3 weeks January-February – **Meals** 16.50 **t.** and a la carte.

STOCKPORT Gtr. Manchester 402 403 404 N 23 – pop. 284 395 – ECD : Thursday – 0161.

Heaton Moor, Mauldeth Rd, Heaton, Mersey ℘ 432 2134 - Romiley, Goosehouse Green ℘ 430 2392 – Ladythorn Rd, Bramhall ℘ 439 4057 – Davenport, Middlewood Rd, Poynton ℘ (01625) 877321 – Hazel Grove ℘ 483 3217 – Offerton Rd, Offerton ℘ 427 2001.

Graylaw House, Chestergate, SK1 1NM ℘ 474 3320/1.

♦London 201 – ♦Liverpool 42 – ♦Manchester 6 – ♦Sheffield 37 – ♦Stoke-on-Trent 34.

Saxon Holme, 230 Wellington Rd North, SK4 2QN, N : 1 m. on A 6 ℘ 432 2335, Fax 431 8076 –
Meals (dinner only) 12.50 **st.** and a la carte 3.50 – **33 rm** 43.50/55.00 **st.** – SB.

Old Rectory, Churchgate, SK1 1YG, E : ¼ m. by Wellington St. ℘ 429 0060 – rm
Meals (grill rest.) – **30 rm.**

Alma Lodge (Jarvis), 149 Buxton Rd, SK2 6EL, S : 1 ¼ m. on A 6 ℘ 483 4431, Fax 483 1983 – rm – 200
56 rm.

Travel Inn, Buxton Rd, SK2 6NB, S : 1 m. on A 6 ℘ 480 2968, Fax 477 8320 – rm
Meals (Beefeater grill) a la carte approx. 16.00 **t.** – 4.95 – **41 rm** 33.50 **t.**

ATS Hollingworth Rd, Bredbury ℘ 430 5221

STOCKTON-ON-TEES Cleveland 402 P 20 – pop. 173 912 – ECD : Thursday – 01642.

Eaglescliffe, Yarm Rd ℘ 780098 – Knotty Hill, Sedgefield ℘ 620320 – Norton, Junction Rd ℘ 676385/612452/674636.

Teesside Airport : ℘ (01325) 332811, SW : 6 m. by A 1027, A 135 and A 67.

Theatre Yard, off High St., TS18 1AT ℘ 615080.

♦London 251 – ♦Leeds 61 – ♦Middlesbrough 4.

Swallow, 10 John Walker Sq., TS18 1AQ, ℘ 679721, Fax 601714, – rm rest – 300.
Meals 12.50/17.95 **st.** and a la carte 4.50 – **125 rm** 85.00/96.00 **st.** – SB.

at Eaglescliffe S : 3 ½ m. on A 135 – ✉ Stockton-on-Tees – 01642 :

Parkmore, 636 Yarm Rd, TS16 0DH, ℘ 786815, Fax 790485, – – 140.
Meals 12.50/17.50 **t.** and a la carte 3.75 – **56 rm** 57.00/80.00 **st.** – SB.

ATS 18 Brunswick St. ℘ 675733 ATS 112 Norton Rd ℘ 604477

STOKE BRUERNE Northants. 404 R 27 – pop. 347 – ✉ Towcester – ☎ 01604.
♦London 69 – ♦Coventry 33 – Northampton 9 – ♦Oxford 33.

✗ **Bruerne's Lock,** 5 Canalside, NN12 7SB, ☎ 863654, « Attractive canalside setting » – AE VISA
closed Saturday lunch, Sunday dinner, Monday, 1 week October and 1 week December – **Meals** 16.00 **t.** (lunch) and a la carte 19.95/27.95 **t.** 5.95.

STOKE BY NAYLAND Essex 404 W 28 – see Colchester.

STOKE D'ABERNON Surrey 404 ㊷ – see Cobham.

STOKE FLEMING Devon 403 J 33 – see Dartmouth.

STOKE GABRIEL Devon 403 J 32 – see Totnes.

STOKE-ON-TERN Shrops. 402 403 404 M 25 – see Hodnet.

STOKE-ON-TRENT Staffs. 402 403 404 N 24 **Great Britain G.** – pop. 244 637 – ECD : Thursday – ☎ 01782.
See : Museum and Art Gallery★ Y **M** – Gladstone Pottery Museum★ *AC* V.
Envir. : Wedgwood Visitor's Centre★ *AC*, S : 5½ m. by A 500 and A 34 V.
Exc. : Little Moreton Hall★★ *AC*, N : 8½ m. by A 500 on A 34 U.
Greenway Hall, Stockton Brook ☎ 503158, U – Parkhall, Hulme Rd, Weston Coyney ☎ 599584, V.
Potteries Shopping Centre, Quadrant Rd, Hanley, ST1 1RZ ☎ 284600.
♦London 162 – ♦Birmingham 46 – ♦Leicester 59 – ♦Liverpool 58 – ♦Manchester 41 – ♦Sheffield 53.

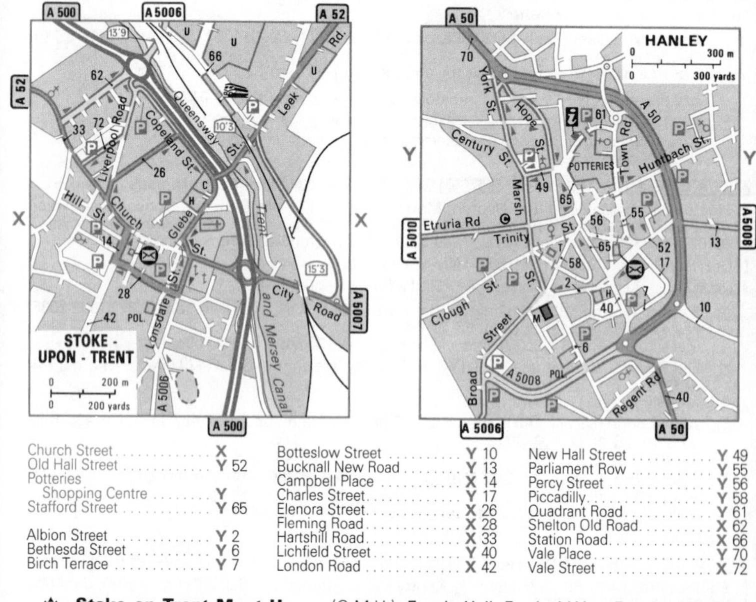

Church Street	X		Botteslow Street	Y 10		New Hall Street	Y 49
Old Hall Street	Y 52		Bucknall New Road	Y 13		Parliament Row	Y 55
Potteries Shopping Centre	Y		Campbell Place	X 14		Percy Street	Y 56
Stafford Street	Y 65		Charles Street	Y 17		Piccadilly	Y 58
			Elenora Street	X 26		Quadrant Road	Y 61
Albion Street	Y 2		Fleming Road	X 28		Shelton Old Road	X 62
Bethesda Street	Y 6		Hartshill Road	X 33		Station Road	X 66
Birch Terrace	Y 7		Lichfield Street	Y 40		Vale Place	Y 70
			London Road	X 42		Vale Street	X 72

Stoke-on-Trent Moat House (Q.M.H.), Etruria Hall, Festival Way, Etruria, ST1 5BQ, ☎ 219000, Fax 284500, rm rest – 600. AE VISA
Meals (bar lunch Saturday) 10.75/17.35 **st.** and a la carte – 8.50 – **143 rm** 85.00/145.00 **st.** U **n**

Stakis Stoke-on-Trent, 66 Trinity St., Hanley, ST1 5NB, ☎ 202361, Fax 286464, rm – 300. AE VISA Y **c**
***Chatterley's* : Meals** (bar lunch Saturday) (carving lunch) 11.00/14.00 **st.** – **123 rm** 77.00/89.00 **st.**, 4 suites – SB.

at Basford NW : 1¾ m. by A 500 off A 53 – ✉ Stoke-on-Trent – ☎ 01782 :

Haydon House, Haydon St., ST4 6JD, ☎ 711311, Fax 717470 – – 80. AE VISA U **a**
closed first week January – ***Clock* : Meals** *(closed Saturday lunch and Sunday)* 10.50/14.90 **t.** and a la carte – 6.00 – **21 rm** 50.00/62.00 **t.**, 6 suites – SB.

STOKE-ON-TRENT
NEWCASTLE-UNDER-LYME
BUILT UP AREA

Alexandra Road	U	3
Bedford Road	U	4
Brownhills Road	U	12
Church Lane	U	19
Cobridge Road	U	21
Davenport Street	U	23
Elder Road	U	24
Etruria Vale Road	U	27
Grove Road	V	30
Hanley Road	U	31
Heron Street	V	34
High Street	U	35
Higherland	V	37
Manor Street	V	44
Mayne Street	V	45
Moorland Road	U	48
Park Hall Road	V	54
Porthill Road	U	59
Snow Hill	U	63
Stoke Road	U	68
Strand (The)	V	69
Victoria Park Road	U	75
Watlands View	U	76
Williamson Street	U	77

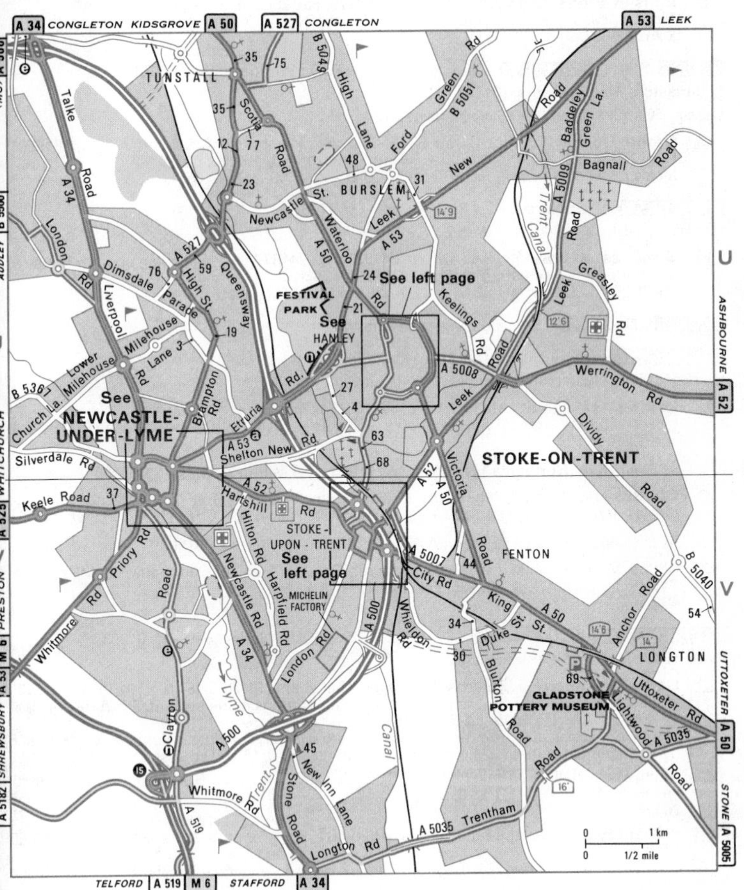

at *Talke* NW : 4 m. on A 500 at junction with A 34 – ✉ Stoke-on-Trent – ☎ 01782 :

Granada, Newcastle Rd, ST7 1UP, ☎ 777000, Fax 777162 – ⇔ rm ▤ rest TV ☎ ♿ P – 🚣 40. AE ⓓ VISA. ✻ U e
Meals *(closed 25-26 December)* 10.00 **st.** and a la carte 6.00 – ☕ 10.50 – **62 rm** 57.50/65.00 – SB.

ATS 25 Smithpool Rd, Fenton ☎ 47081

ATS 87/89 Waterloo Rd, Burslem ☎ 838493/836591

STOKE ST. GREGORY Somerset 403 L 30 – ✉ Taunton – ☎ 01823.

♦London 147 – ♦Bristol 39 – Taunton 8.

Slough Court without rest., Slough Lane, TA3 6JQ, ☎ 490311, « 14C moated manor house, working farm », , – TV P. ✻
March-October – **3 rm** ☕ 28.00/50.00 **st.**

STOKESLEY N. Yorks. 402 Q 20 – ✉ Middlesbrough (Cleveland) – ☎ 01642.

♦London 239 – ♦Leeds 59 – ♦Middlesbrough 8 – York 52.

Chapter's with rm, 27 High St., TS9 5AD, ℘ 711888, Fax 713387 – TV ☎. AE VISA
Meals *(closed Sunday lunch)* a la carte 13.50/24.50 **t.** 4.95 – **13 rm** 45.00/59.00 **t.**

STONE Glos. 403 404 M 29 – pop. 704 – ✉ Berkeley – ☎ 01454.

♦London 130 – ♦Bristol 17 – Gloucester 18.

Elms at Stone, GL13 9JX, on A 38 ℘ 260279, Fax 260279, – TV ☎ P. VISA
Meals *(closed Sunday dinner to non-residents)* 9.95/14.95 **t.** and lunch a la carte 4.50 – **8 rm** 38.00/48.00 **t.** – SB.

STONE Staffs. 402 403 404 N 25 – pop. 12 645 – ECD : Wednesday – ☎ 01785.

18 Barlaston, Meaford Rd ℘ (01782) 372795.

♦London 150 – ♦Birmingham 36 – ♦Stoke-on-Trent 9.

Stone House (Country Club), ST15 0BQ, S : 1 ¼ m. by A 520 on A 34 ℘ 815531, Fax 814764, , , , , – rm TV ☎ P – 150. AE VISA
Meals *(closed Saturday lunch)* 10.50/18.00 **st.** – 7.50 – **47 rm** 65.00 – SB.

STON EASTON Somerset – ✉ Bath (Avon) – ☎ 01761.

♦London 131 – Bath 12 – ♦Bristol 11 – Wells 7.

Ston Easton Park , BA3 4DF, ℘ 241631, Fax 241377, ≤, « Palladian country house », , park, – rest TV ☎ P. AE VISA.
Meals 26.00/38.00 **st.** 7.50 – 8.50 – **19 rm** 95.00/320.00 **st.**, 2 suites.

STONOR Oxon. 404 R 29 – see Henley-on-Thames.

STONY STRATFORD Bucks. 404 R 27 – ☎ 01908.

♦London 58 – ♦Birmingham 68 – Northampton 14 – ♦Oxford 32.

Peking, 117 High St., MK11 1AT, ℘ 563120, Fax 560084 – . AE VISA
closed Sunday and 25-26 December – **Meals** - Chinese (Peking, Szechuan) 25.00 **t.** and a la carte.

at Cosgrove (Northants.) N : 2½ m. by A 508 – ✉ Milton Keynes – ☎ 01908 :

Old Bakery, Main St., MK19 7JL, ℘ 262255, Fax 263620 – TV ☎ P. VISA.
Meals (dinner only) a la carte 10.15/17.70 **st.** 4.00 – 6.50 – **8 rm** 36.00/43.50 **st.** – SB.

at Deanshanger SW : 2 m. on A 422 – ✉ Milton Keynes – ☎ 01908 :

Shires Motel without rest., Open Pastures Service Area, Buckingham Rd, MK19 6AA, SW : ½ m. on A 422 ℘ 262925, Fax 263642 – TV P
48 rm.

STORRINGTON W. Sussex 404 S 31 – pop. 4 670 – ECD : Wednesday – ☎ 01903.

♦London 54 – ♦Brighton 20 – ♦Portsmouth 36.

Little Thakeham , Merrywood Lane, Thakeham, RH20 3HE, N : 1 ¾ m. by B 2139 ℘ 744416, Fax 745022, ≤, « Lutyens house with gardens in the style of Gertrude Jekyll », heated, – TV ☎ P. AE VISA.
closed Christmas and New Year – **Meals** *(closed Monday lunch and Sunday dinner)* (lunch by arrangement)/dinner 32.50 **st.** 5.00 – **7 rm** 95.00/150.00 **st.**, 2 suites.

Abingworth Hall , Thakeham Rd, RH20 3EF, N : 1 ¾ m. on B 2139 ℘ (01798) 813636, Fax 813914, , – TV ☎ P – 50
20 rm.

Manley's (Löderer), Manley's Hill, RH20 4BT, E : ¼ m. on A 283 ℘ 742331 – P. AE VISA
closed Sunday dinner, Monday and first 2 weeks January – **Meals** 18.60/28.50 **t.** and dinner a la carte 34.00/35.30 **t.** 6.90
Spec. Sauté de coquilles St. Jacques aux tagliolini, ail rôti et crème de piment, Magret de canard mariné à l'Orientale et chou blanc au gingembre, Kaiser-schmarrn mit himber saft.

Old Forge, 6a Church St., RH20 4LA, ℘ 743402, Fax 743402 – AE VISA
closed lunch Tuesday and Saturday, Sunday dinner, Monday, 2 weeks late spring and 3 weeks October – **Meals** 12.00/20.50 **t.** and a la carte 19.00/25.50 **t.** 4.50.

STOURBRIDGE W. Mids. 403 404 N26 – pop. 55136 – ECD : Thursday – ☎ 01384.

Kinver, Travellers Joy, 47 High St., DY7 6HE ℘ 872940.

♦London 147 – ♦Birmingham 14 – Wolverhampton 10 – Worcester 21.

Plan : see Birmingham p. 2

Talbot, High St., DY8 1DW, ℘ 394350, Fax 371318 – TV ☎ P – 150 AU **a**
25 rm.

Limes, 260 Hagley Rd, Pedmore, DY9 0RW, SE : 1½ m. on A 491 ℘ (01562) 882689, – TV ☎ P. AE VISA AU **z**
Meals (by arrangement) 6.90 **st.** 2.25 – **10 rm** 28.50/35.25 **st.** – SB.

at Hagley S : 2½ m. by A 491 – ✉ Stourbridge – ☎ 01562.

Travel Inn, Birmingham Rd, DY9 9JS, NE : 1 ½ m. on A 456 (eastbound) ℘ 883120, Fax 884416 – rm. AU r
Meals (Beefeater grill) a la carte 16.00 **t.** – 4.95 – **40 rm** 33.50 **t.**

at Kinver (Staffs.) W : 5 m. by A 458 – AU – ✉ Stourbridge – ☎ 01384.

Berkley's (Piano Room), 5-6 High St., DY7 6HG, ℘ 873679 –
closed Sunday, first 2 weeks February, 26 to 30 December and Bank Holidays – **Meals** (dinner only) 25.85 **t.** and a la carte 4.05.

STOURPORT-ON-SEVERN Heref. and Worcs. 403 404 N 26 – pop. 18 739 – ECD : Wednesday – ☎ 01299.

London 137 – Birmingham 21 – Worcester 12.

Stourport Moat House (Q.M.H.), 35 Hartlebury Rd, DY13 9LT, E : 1 ¼ m. on B 4193 ℘ 827733, Fax 878520, park, squash – rm – 400.
Meals *(closed Saturday lunch)* 9.95/14.25 **st.** and dinner a la carte 5.25 – 8.50 – **65 rm** 47.50/57.50 **st.**, 3 suites – SB.

STOWMARKET Suffolk 404 W/X 27 – pop. 13 229 – ECD : Tuesday – ☎ 01449.

Wilkes Way, IP14 1DE ℘ 676800.

London 81 – Cambridge 42 – Ipswich 12 – Norwich 38.

Forte Travelodge without rest., IP14 3PY, NW : 2 m. by A 1038 on A 45 (westbound) ℘ 615347, Reservations (Freephone) 0800 850950 –
40 rm 33.50 **st.**

at Mendlesham Green NE : 6 ¼ m. by B 1115, A 1120 and Mendlesham rd – ✉ Stowmarket – ☎ 01449 :

Cherry Tree Farm, IP14 5RQ, ℘ 766376,
closed Christmas and January – **Meals** (by arrangement) (communal dining) 14.00 **st.** – **3 rm** 30.00/46.00 **st.** – SB.

at Wetherden NW : 4 ¼ m. by A 45 – ✉ Stowmarket – ☎ 01359 :

Old Rectory without rest., IP14 3RE, E : ½ m. on Bacton rd ℘ 240144, park –
closed December to February – **3 rm** 25.00/40.00 **st.**

STOW-ON-THE-WOLD Glos. 403 404 O 28 **Great Britain G.** – pop. 1 999 – ECD : Wednesday – ☎ 01451.

Exc. : Chastleton House★★, NE : 6½ m. by A 436 and A 44.

Hollis House, The Square, Gl54 1AF ℘ 831082.

London 86 – Birmingham 44 – Gloucester 27 – Oxford 30.

Wyck Hill House, GL54 1HY, S : 2¼ m. by A 429 on A 424 ℘ 831936, Fax 832243, « Part Victorian country house », park – rest – 50.
Meals 13.95/32.00 **t.** and dinner a la carte – **30 rm** 75.00/130.00 **st.**, 1 suite – SB.

Grapevine, Sheep St., GL54 1AU, ℘ 830344, Fax 832278, « Mature grapevine in restaurant » – rest
closed 23 December-11 January – **Meals** (bar lunch Monday to Saturday)/dinner 17.95/25.95 **t.** 4.85 – **23 rm** (dinner included) 69.00/138.00 **t.** – SB.

Fosse Manor, Fosse Way, GL54 1JX, S : 1 ¼ m. on A 429 ℘ 830354, Fax 832486, – rest – 40.
closed 23 to 29 December – **Meals** 12.95/15.95 **t.** and a la carte 4.75 – **20 rm** 49.00/140.00 **t.** – SB.

Unicorn (Forte), Sheep St., GL54 1HQ, ℘ 830257, Fax 831090 –
Meals 11.95/16.95 **st.** and a la carte 7.20 – 8.50 – **20 rm** 70.00/85.00 **st.** – SB.

Stow Lodge, The Square, GL54 1AB, ℘ 830485,
closed one month January-February – **Meals** (bar lunch)/dinner 14.25 **t.** and a la carte – **22 rm** 57.00/100.00 **t.** – SB.

Bretton House, Fosseway, GL54 1JU, S : ½ m. on A 429 ℘ 830388, – rm
Meals (by arrangement) 12.50 **st.** – **3 rm** -/42.00 **st.** – SB.

Wyck Hill Lodge without rest., Wyck Hill, GL54 1HT, S : 2 m. by A 429 on A 424 ℘ 830141,
closed Christmas – **3 rm** 30.00/44.00 **st.**

Limes without rest., Evesham Rd, GL54 1EJ, ℘ 830034,
closed 24 to 27 December – **3 rm** 25.00/37.00.

Cross Keys Cottage without rest., Park St., GL54 1AQ, ℘ 831128 –
closed 24 to 26 December – **3 rm** 36.00/45.00 **st.**

at Broadwell NE : 1 ¾ m. by A 429 – ✉ Moreton-in-Marsh – ☎ 01451 :

College House, Chapel St., GL56 0TW, ℘ 832351, « 17C house »,
closed Christmas – **Meals** (by arrangement) (communal dining) 14.50 **st.** – **3 rm** 30.00/50.00 **st.**

at Upper Oddington E : 2 ¼ m. by A 436 – ✉ Moreton-in-Marsh – ☎ 01451 :

Horse and Groom Inn, GL56 OXH, ☏ 830584, – TV P. VISA.
Meals (bar lunch Monday to Saturday)/dinner a la carte 9.70/19.00 **t.** – **8 rm** 30.00/50.00 **t.** – SB.

at Bledington SE : 4 m. by A 436 on B 4450 – ✉ Kingham – ☎ 01608 :

Kings Head, OX7 6HD, ☏ 658365, Fax 658365 – rm TV ☎ P. VISA.
closed Christmas Day – **Meals** (bar lunch)/dinner a la carte 10.90/14.25 **st.** 3.50 – **12 rm** 32.00/60.00 **st.** – SB.

at Nether Westcote SE : 4 ¾ m. by A 429 off A 424 – ✉ Kingham – ☎ 01993 :

Lavender Hill, OX7 6SD, ☏ 831872, ← – TV P
Meals (by arrangement) 13.00 **st.** – **3 rm** 28.00/48.00 **st.** – SB.

at Lower Swell W : 1 ¼ m. on B 4068 – ✉ Stow-on-the-Wold – ☎ 01451 :

Old Farmhouse, GL54 1LF, ☏ 830232, Fax 870962, – TV ☎ P. VISA
closed 2 weeks February – **Meals** (bar lunch Monday to Saturday)/dinner 14.95 **st.** 5.00 – **13 rm** 40.00/64.00 **st.**, 1 suite – SB.

STRATFIELD TURGIS Hants. – pop. 94 – ✉ Basingstoke – ☎ 01256.

◆London 46 – Basingstoke 8 – Reading 11.

Wellington Arms, RG27 0AS, on A 33 ☏ 882214, Fax 882934, – TV ☎ P – 60. AE VISA
Meals *(closed Saturday lunch and Sunday dinner)* 18.95 **t.** and a la carte 5.50 – **33 rm** 55.00/75.00 **t.**, 2 suites.

STRATFORD-UPON-AVON Warks. 403 404 P 27 **Great Britain G.** – pop. 105 586 – ECD : Thursday – ☎ 01789.

See : Town★ - Shakespeare's Birthplace★ *AC*, AB.

Envir. : Mary Arden's House★ *AC*, NW : 4 m. by A 3400 A.

Exc. : Ragley Hall★ *AC*, W : 9 m. by A 422 A.

18 Tiddington Rd ☏ 297296, B – 18 Welcombe Hotel, Warwick Rd ☏ 299021, B – 18 Stratford Oaks, Bearley Rd, Snitterfield ☏ 731571, B.

Bridgefoot, CV37 6GW ☏ 293127.

◆London 96 – ◆Birmingham 23 – ◆Coventry 18 – ◆Oxford 40.

STRATFORD-UPON-AVON

Bridge Street . . . . . B 8
Henley Street . . . . . A 29
High Street . . . . . A 31
Sheep Street . . . . . AB 35
Wood Street . . . . . A 47

Banbury Road . . . . . B 2
Benson Road . . . . . B 3
Bridge Foot . . . . . B 6
Chapel Lane . . . . . A 13
Chapel Street . . . . . A 14
Church Street . . . . . A 16
Clopton Bridge . . . . . B 18
College Lane . . . . . A 19
Ely Street . . . . . A 22
Evesham Place . . . . . A 24
Great William Street . . . . . A 25
Greenhill Street . . . . . A 27
Guild Street . . . . . A 28
Rother Street . . . . . A 32
Scholars Lane . . . . . A 33
Tiddington Road . . . . . B 38
Trinity Street . . . . . A 40
Warwick Road . . . . . B 42
Waterside . . . . . B 43
Windsor Street . . . . . A 45

Town plans : *the names of main shopping streets are indicated in red at the beginning of the list of streets.*

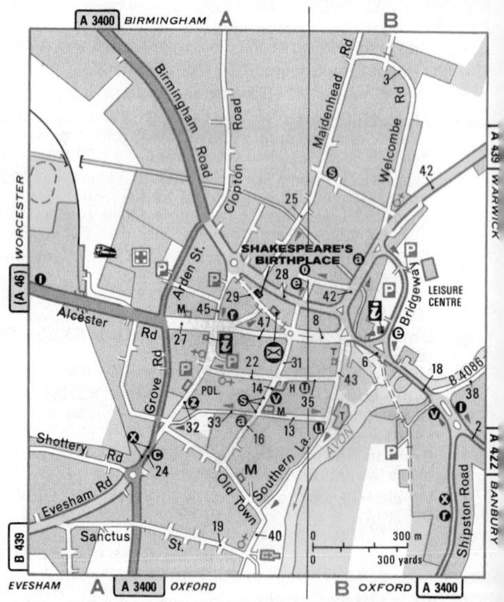

Welcombe H. & Golf Course, Warwick Rd, CV37 0NR, NE : 1 ½ m. on A 439 ☏ 295252, Telex 31347, Fax 414666, ←, « 19C Jacobean style mansion in park », 18, – TV ☎ P – 150. AE VISA JCB B
closed 29 December-3 January – **Meals** 16.50/28.50 **st.** and a la carte 8.50 – **67 rm** 95.00/210.00 **st.**, 8 suites.

Ettington Park, Alderminster, CV37 8BS, SE : 6 ¼ m. on A 3400 450123, Fax 450472, « Victorian Gothic mansion », park – 65. B
Meals 15.75/28.00 **st.** and a la carte – **43 rm** 115.00/160.00 **st.**, 5 suites – SB.

Moat House International (Q.M.H.), Bridgefoot, CV37 6YR, 414411, Fax 298589, – rm – 450. B **e**
Meals 11.75/14.50 **t.** – 7.75 – **245 rm** 55.00 **st.**, 2 suites – SB.

Shakespeare (Forte), Chapel St., CV37 6ER, 294771, Fax 415411, « 17C timbered inn » – – 100. A **v**
David Garrick : **Meals** 15.95/25.95 **t.** and a la carte – 10.00 – **62 rm** 95.00/125.00 **t.**, 1 suite – SB.

Alveston Manor (Forte), Clopton Bridge, CV37 7HP, 204581, Fax 414095, « Part Elizabethan house », – rm – 150. B **i**
Manor : **Meals** (bar lunch Monday to Saturday)/dinner 21.50 **t.** and a la carte 8.50 – 9.75 – **105 rm** 80.00/95.00 **t.**, 1 suite – SB.

Arden Thistle (Mt. Charlotte Thistle), 44 Waterside, CV37 6BA, 294949, Fax 415874, – rm – 50. B **u**
Bards : **Meals** 9.50/15.75 **st.** and a la carte 6.30 – 8.50 – **63 rm** 65.00/95.00 **st.** – SB.

Windmill Park, Warwick Rd, CV37 0PY, NE : 3 m. on A 439 731173, Fax 731131, park, – rm rest – 360. B
Meals 11.50/25.00 **st.** and a la carte – **103 rm** 82.50/98.00 **st.** – SB.

Grosvenor, 12-14 Warwick Rd, CV37 6YT, 269213, Fax 266087 – rest – 60. B **a**
Meals 19.75 **t.** and a la carte 4.50 – **38 rm** 72.00/95.00 **t.**, 2 suites – SB.

Falcon (Q.M.H.), Chapel St., CV37 6HA, 205777, Fax 414260 – rm – 200. A **s**
Meals 14.00/19.00 **st.** and a la carte 7.00 – **73 rm** 74.00/99.00 **t.** – SB.

White Swan (Forte), Rother St., CV37 6NH, 297022, Fax 268773, « Part 16C inn » – – 40. A **r**
Meals (bar lunch Monday to Saturday)/dinner 21.00 **st.** and a la carte 6.00 – 8.95 – **37 rm** 80.00/90.00 **st.** – SB.

Dukes, Payton St., CV37 6UA, 269300, Fax 414700, – . AB **o**
closed Christmas and New Year – **Meals** *(closed Sunday)* a la carte 17.70/26.40 **t.** 4.95 – **22 rm** 50.00/120.00 **t.** – SB.

Forte Posthouse, Bridgefoot, CV37 7LT, 266761, Fax 414547, – rm – 150. B **v**
Meals a la carte approx. 15.00 **t.** 5.50 – **60 rm** 56.00/69.50 **st.**

Stratford House, 18 Sheep St., CV37 6EF, 268288, Fax 295580 – . AB **u**
Shepherd's : **Meals** *(closed Monday lunch)* a la carte approx. 25.00 **t.** – **11 rm** 65.00/88.00 **t.**

Caterham House, 58-59 Rother St., CV37 6LT, 267309 – . A **z**
Le Bonaparte : **Meals** - French *(closed Saturday lunch, Sunday dinner, Monday, 1 week February and last 2 weeks August)* 14.00 **st.** and a la carte – **11 rm** 50.00/62.50 **st.**

Sequoia House without rest., 51-53 Shipston Rd, CV37 7LN, 268852, Fax 414559, – – 40. B **r**
closed 18 to 26 December – **21 rm** 39.00/72.00 **t.**

Stratheden without rest., 5 Chapel St., CV37 6EP, 297119, Fax 297119 – . A **s**
closed Christmas-New Year – **9 rm** 32.00/56.00 **t.**

Moonraker House without rest., 40 Alcester Rd, CV37 9DB, 267115, Fax 295504, – . A **i**
24 rm 28.00/59.00 **st.**

Twelfth Night without rest., Evesham Pl., CV37 6HT, 414595 – . A **x**
7 rm 27.00/56.00 **s.**

Payton without rest., 6 John St., CV37 6UB, 266442, Fax 266442 – . A **e**
closed 24 to 26 December – **5 rm** 38.00/60.00 **s.**

Virginia Lodge without rest., 12 Evesham Pl., CV37 6HT, 292157, – A **x**
closed 24 to 28 December – **8 rm** 20.00/48.00.

Carlton without rest., 22 Evesham Pl., CV37 6HT, 293548 – . A **c**
5 rm 23.00/46.00 **st.**

Victoria Spa without rest., Bishopton Lane, CV37 9QY, NW : 2 m. by A 3400 on Bishopton Lane turning left at roundabout with A 46 267985, Fax 204728, – . A
7 rm 45.00/50.00 **t.**

Melita without rest., 37 Shipston Rd, CV37 7LN, 292432, Fax 204867, – . B **x**
closed Christmas – **12 rm** 40.00/68.00 **t.**

Hardwick House without rest., 1 Avenue Rd, CV37 6UY, 204307, Fax 296760 – . B **s**
closed Christmas – **14 rm** 23.00/60.00 **t.**

XX **Hussains,** 6a Chapel St., CV37 6EP, ✆ 267506 – ▤. VISA A s
closed Christmas Day – **Meals** - Indian 7.50/15.00 **t.** and a la carte 4.50.

X **Sir Toby's,** 8 Church St., CV37 6HB, ✆ 268822 – ▤. VISA A a
closed Sunday to Tuesday and 1 month May-June – **Meals** (dinner only) a la carte 16.55/20.75 **t.** 4.75.

at Charlecote E : 4 ¾ m. by B 4086 on B 4088 – B – ✉ Stratford-upon-Avon – ☎ 01789 :

Charlecote Pheasant (Q.M.H.), CV35 9EW, ✆ 470333, Fax 470222, heated, – rm – 120. VISA
Meals 10.95/14.25 **st.** and dinner a la carte – 8.00 – **67 rm** 70.00/135.00 **t.**

at Wellesbourne E : 5 ¾ m. on B 4086 – B – ✉ Warwick – ☎ 01789 :

Chadley House, Loxley Rd, CV35 9JL, SW : 1 ¼ m. by A 429 ✆ 840994, Fax 842977, « Part Georgian farmhouse », – . VISA.
closed 25 and 26 December – **Meals** (dinner only and Sunday lunch) (Sunday dinner residents only) a la carte 15.75/20.25 **t.** 4.95 – **9 rm** 40.00/70.00 **t.** – SB.

Kings Head, Warwick Rd, CV35 9LX, ✆ 840206 – . VISA.
Meals (a la carte) 8.45/11.20 **t. 9 rm** 32.50/48.50.

at Ettington SE : 6 m. on A 422 – ✉ Stratford-upon-Avon – ☎ 01789 :

Ettington Manor, Rodgers Lane, CV37 7SX, ✆ 740216, « Part 13C and 16C manor house », –
3 rm.

at Long Marston SW : 7 m. by A 3400 – B – off B 4632 – ✉ Stratford-upon-Avon – ☎ 01789 :

Kings Lodge without rest., CV37 8RL, ✆ 720705, –
closed December and January – **3 rm** 25.00/50.00 **st.**

at Billesley W : 4 ½ m. by A 422 – A – off A 46 – ✉ Stratford-upon-Avon – ☎ 01789 :

Billesley Manor (Q.M.H.), B49 6NF, ✆ 400888, Fax 764145, ≤, « Part Elizabethan manor, topiary garden », , park, – – 90
39 rm, 2 suites.

at Wilmcote NW : 3 ½ m. by A 3400 – A – ✉ Stratford-upon-Avon – ☎ 01789 :

Pear Tree Cottage without rest., Church Rd, CV37 9UX, ✆ 205889, Fax 262862, –
closed 19 December-2 January – **7 rm** 30.00/45.00 **st.**

ATS Western Rd ✆ 205591

STRATTON Glos. 403 404 O 28 – see Cirencester.

STREATLEY Berks. 403 404 Q 29 **Great Britain G.** – pop. 986 – ✉ Goring – ☎ 01491.
Envir. : Basildon Park★ *AC*, SE : 2 ½ m. by A 329 – Mapledurham★ *AC*, E : 6 m. by A 329, B 471 and B 4526 – **Exc.** : Ridgeway Path★★.
18 Goring & Streatley, Rectory Rd ✆ 872688.
♦London 56 – ♦Oxford 16 – Reading 11.

Swan Diplomat, High St., RG8 9HR, ✆ 873737, Telex 848259, Fax 872554, « ≤ Thames-side setting », , , , – rm – 100. VISA
Meals (see ***Riverside*** below) – 9.50 – **45 rm** 86.50/126.00 **t.**, 1 suite – SB.

XXX **Riverside** (at Swan Diplomat H.), High St., RG8 9HR, ✆ 873737, Telex 848259, Fax 872554, « ≤ Thames-side setting », – . VISA
closed Saturday lunch – **Meals** 19.25/35.00 **t.** and a la carte 6.95.

STREET Somerset 403 L 30 **The West Country G.** – pop. 9 563 – ECD : Wednesday – ☎ 01458.
See : The Shoe Museum★.
Envir. : Glastonbury★★ - Abbey★★★ (Abbots Kitchen★) *AC*, St. John the Baptist★★, Somerset Rural Life Museum★ *AC*, Glastonbury Tor★ (≤★★★) NE : 2 m. by A 39.
♦London 138 – ♦Bristol 28 – Taunton 20.

Bear, 53 High St., BA16 0EF, ✆ 42021, Fax 840007, – rm – 80. VISA.
Meals a la carte 7.70/21.15 **t.** – **17 rm** 50.00/60.00 **st.**, 1 suite.

STRETTON Ches. 402 403 404 M 23 – see Warrington.

STRETTON Staffs. 402 403 404 P 25 – see Burton-upon-Trent.

STRETTON UNDER FOSSE Warks. 403 404 Q 26 – see Rugby.

STROUD Glos. 403 404 N 28 – pop. 37 791 – ECD : Thursday – ☎ 01453.
18, 18 Minchinhampton ✆ 832642 (old course) 833866 (new course) – 18 Painswick ✆ 812180.
Subscription Rooms, George St., GL5 1AE ✆ 765768.
♦London 113 – ♦Bristol 30 – Gloucester 9.

Stonehouse Court, Bristol Rd, Stonehouse, GL10 3RA, W : 3¼ m. on A 419 ℘ 825155, Fax 824611, – ▣ ☎ Ⓟ – 150. AE VISA
Meals *(closed Saturday lunch)* 11.95/19.00 **st.** and a la carte 6.75 – **35 rm** 55.00/85.00 **st.**, 1 suite.

Old Nelson, Stratford Lodge, Stratford Rd, GL5 4AF, N : ½ m. by A 46 ℘ 765821, Fax 765964 – rm ▣ ☎ Ⓟ. AE VISA.
Meals (grill rest.) a la carte approx. 12.00 – 3.45 – **32 rm** 39.50 **t.** – SB.

Imperial, Station Rd, GL5 3AP, ℘ 764077, Fax 751314 – ▣ ☎ Ⓟ
25 rm.

London, 30-31 London Rd, GL5 2AJ, ℘ 759992, Fax 753363 – ▣ ☎ Ⓟ. AE VISA.
Meals 12.95 **st.** and a la carte 3.75 – **12 rm** 39.00/59.00 **st.** – SB.

Old Vicarage, 167 Slad Rd, GL5 1RD, ℘ 752315, – ▣ ☎ Ⓟ.
closed January – **Meals** 15.00 **st.** – **3 rm** 30.00/39.00 **st.**

XX **Oakes** (Oakes), 169 Slad Rd, GL5 1RG, ℘ 759950, Fax 766441 – Ⓟ. AE VISA
closed Sunday dinner and Monday – **Meals** a la carte 21.00/33.00 **t.** 5.50
Spec. Sautéed chicken livers with bacon and a red wine dressing, Fillet of grey mullet with fried tomatoes and a creamy garlic dressing, Hot pistachio soufflé served with Chantilly cream.

at Brimscombe SE : 2¼ m. on A 419 – ✉ Stroud – 01453 :

Burleigh Court, Burleigh Lane, GL5 2PF, S : ½ m. by Burleigh rd via The Roundabouts ℘ 883804, Fax 886870, ←, heated, – ▣ ☎ Ⓟ. AE VISA.
Meals (buffet dinner Sunday) a la carte 17.70/21.75 **st.** 4.00 – **17 rm** 64.00/96.00 **t.** – SB.

at Rodborough S : ¾ m. by A 46 – ✉ Stroud – 01453 :

Bear of Rodborough (Forte), Rodborough Common, GL5 5DE, SE : 1½ m. on Minchinhampton rd ℘ 878522, Fax 872523, – ▣ ☎ Ⓟ – 70. AE VISA
Meals (bar lunch Monday to Saturday)/dinner 16.95 **st.** and a la carte 6.95 – 8.50 – **47 rm** 60.00/80.00 **t.** – SB.

at Amberley S : 3 m. by A 46 – ✉ Stroud – 01453 :

Amberley Inn, GL5 5AF, ℘ 872565, Fax 872738, – ▣ ☎ Ⓟ. AE VISA
Meals 7.75/19.95 **st.** and a la carte – **14 rm** 55.00/80.00 **st.** – SB.

ATS Dudbridge Rd ℘ 758156/752191

To visit a town or region: use the Michelin Green Guides.

STUCKTON Hants. – see Fordingbridge.

STUDLEY Warks. 403 404 O 27 – pop. 5 883 – ✉ Redditch – 01527.
London 109 – Birmingham 15 – Coventry 33 – Gloucester 39.

XX **Pepper's,** 45 High St., B80 7HN, ℘ 853183 – ▤. AE VISA
closed Sunday lunch and 25 to 26 December – **Meals** - Indian a la carte 8.75/16.00 **t.**

STURMINSTER NEWTON Dorset 403 404 N 31 **The West Country G.** – pop. 2 579 – 01258.
See : Mill★ *AC.*
London 123 – Bournemouth 30 – Bristol 49 – Salisbury 28 – Taunton 41.

Stourcastle Lodge, Gough's Close, DT10 1BU, (off the Market Place) ℘ 472320, Fax 473381, – rest ▣ ☎ Ⓟ. VISA.
Meals 15.00 **st.** – **5 rm** 20.00/64.00 **st.**

XXX **Plumber Manor** with rm, DT10 2AF, SW : 1¾ m. by A 357 on Hazelbury Bryan rd ℘ 472507, Fax 473370, ←, « 18C manor house », , park, – ▣ ☎ Ⓟ. AE VISA
closed February – **Meals** (dinner only and Sunday lunch)/dinner 20.00/27.50 **st.** 5.00 – **16 rm** 65.00/115.00 **st.** – SB.

SUDBURY Suffolk 404 W 27 **Great Britain G.** – pop. 11 291 – ECD : Wednesday – 01787.
See : Gainsborough's House★ *AC.*
Town Hall, Market Hill, CO10 6TL ℘ 881320 (summer only).
London 59 – Cambridge 37 – Colchester 15 – Ipswich 21.

Hill Lodge, Newton Rd, CO10 6RG, on A 134 (Colchester rd) ℘ 377568 – rest ▣ Ⓟ – 60. .
closed 1 week Christmas – **Meals** (by arrangement) 8.00 – **17 rm** 23.00/38.00 **s.**

X **Mabey's Brasserie,** 47 Gainsborough St., CO10 7SS, ℘ 374298 – AE VISA
closed Sunday, Monday, 25-26 December, 1 January and Bank Holidays – **Meals** a la carte 14.15/18.15 **t.** 5.25.

at Belchamp Walter (Essex) W : 5 m. by A 131 and Belchamps rd – ✉ Sudbury – 01787 :

St. Mary Hall, CO10 7BB, SW : 1½ m. on Great Yeldham rd ℘ 237202, , – Ⓟ. VISA.
Meals (by arrangement) (communal dining) 20.00 **st.** – **3 rm** 26.00/56.00.

ATS Edgeworth Rd ℘ 374227

SUNDERLAND

Fawcett Street	B	
High Street West	B	15
Holmeside	B	
John Street	B	16
The Bridges	B	
Albion Place	B	2
Barnes Park Road	A	3
Bedford Street	B	4
Borough Road	B	5
Bridge Street	B	6
Charlton Road	A	8
Chester Road	B	10
Crowtree Road	B	11
Derwent Street	B	12
Harbour View	A	14
Kayll Road	A	17
Livingstone Road	B	18
New Durham Road	B	19
Ormonde Street	A	21
Pallion Road	A	22
Park Lane	B	23
Queens Road	A	24
Roker Terrace	A	25
St. Luke's Terrace	A	26
St. Mary's Way	B	27
Shields Road	A	29
Southwick Road	B	30
Station Road	A	32
Trimdon Street	A	35
Vine Place	B	36
Wessington Way	A	38

Plans de villes :
Le nom des principales voies commerçantes est inscrit en rouge au début des légendes-rues.

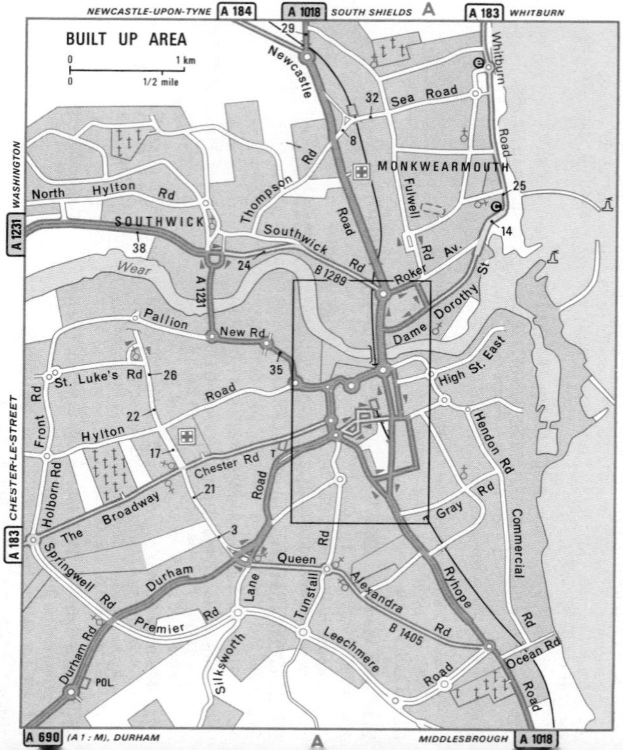

BUILT UP AREA
0 1 km
0 1/2 mile
NEWCASTLE-UPON-TYNE
A 184
A 1018
SOUTH SHIELDS
A
A 183
WHITBURN
WASHINGTON
A 1231
CHESTER-LE-STREET
A 183
A 690
(A 1 : M). DURHAM
MIDDLESBROUGH
A 1018
Newcastle
Sea Road
Whitburn
Road
MONKWEARMOUTH
Thompson Rd
North Hylton Rd
SOUTHWICK
Southwick Rd
Fulwell Rd
Roker Av.
Dame Dorothy St
B 1289
Wear
A 1231
Pallion
New Rd
St. Luke's Rd
Hylton Road
High St. East
Hendon Rd
Gray Rd
Commercial Rd
Front Rd
Holborn Rd
Chester Rd
The Broadway
Road
Queen
Durham Rd
Springwell Rd
Premier Rd
Lane
Tunstall Rd
Alexandra Rd
B 1405
Ryhope Road
Leechmere Road
Silksworth
Durham Rd
POL
Ocean Rd

CENTRE
0 300 m
0 300 yards
B
B 1289
A 1018
A 183
A 1231
A 183
A 690
A 1018
Roker Av.
Dame Dorothy St.
Bridge St.
North
Wear
POL
St. Michael's Way
CROWTREE LEISURE CENTRE
THE BRIDGES
Fawcett St.
Holmeside
MOWBRAY PARK
Burdon Road
Toward Rd
Derby St.
St. Michael's Way
Belvedere Rd
Park Rd
Thornhill Ter.
Thornholme Rd
Tunstall
Mowbray
Ryhope Rd
Road

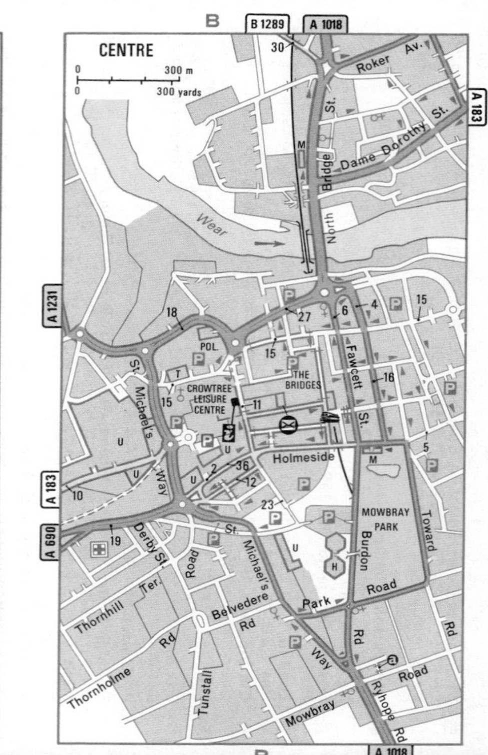

SUNDERLAND Tyne and Wear 401 402 P 19 – pop. 289 040 – ECD : Wednesday – ☎ 0191.

Whitburn, Lizard Lane ℘ 529 2144, A – Ryhope, Leechmere Way, Hollycarrside ℘ 521 3811/523 7333 A.

Unit 3, Crowtree Rd, SR1 3EL ℘ 565 0960/565 0990.

◆London 272 – ◆Leeds 92 – ◆Middlesbrough 29 – ◆Newcastle upon Tyne 12.

Plan on preceding page

Swallow Sunderland, Queens Par., Seaburn, SR6 8DB, ℘ 529 2041, Fax 529 4227, ≤, – rm – 300. VISA A e
Meals 13.50/21.50 **st.** and a la carte 5.00 – **65 rm** 90.00/150.00 **st.** – SB.

Roker, Roker Terrace, Roker, SR6 0PH, ℘ 567 1786, Fax 510 0289, ≤ – A c
45 rm.

Gelt House, 23 St. Bedes Terr., SR2 8HS, ℘ 567 2990, Fax 510 0724 – rest . VISA. B a
closed 23 December-16 January – **Meals** (by arrangement Friday to Sunday) (dinner only) 8.50 2.90 – **13 rm** 36.00/42.00 **t.**

Travel Inn, Wessington Way, SR5 3HR, ℘ 548 9384, Fax 584 4148 – rm – 25. VISA. by A 1231 A
Meals (grill rest.) a la carte approx. 16.00 **t.** – 4.95 – **40 rm** 33.50 **t.**

ATS Monkwearmouth Bridge ℘ 565 7694

SUNNINGHILL Berks. 404 S 29 – see Ascot.

SUTTON W. Sussex – see Petworth.

SUTTON COLDFIELD W. Mids. 403 404 O 26 – pop. 101 886 – ☎ 0121.

Pype Hayes, Eachelhurst Rd, Walmley ℘ 351 1014, DT – Boldmere, Monmouth Drive ℘ 354 3379, DT – 110 Thornhill Rd ℘ 353 2014 DT – , The Belfry, Wishaw ℘ (01675) 470301 DT.

◆London 124 – ◆Birmingham 8 – ◆Coventry 29 – ◆Nottingham 47 – ◆Stoke-on-Trent 40.

Plan : see Birmingham pp. 2 and 3

De Vere Belfry, Lichfield Rd, Wishaw, B76 9PR, E : 6 ½ m. by A 453 on A 446 ℘ (01675) 470301, Fax 470178, ≤, , park, , squash – rm rest – 300. VISA. by A 446 DT
Meals 14.95/25.50 **st.** and a la carte 8.50 – **209 rm** 120.00/155.00 **st.**, 10 suites – SB.

New Hall (Mt. Charlotte Thistle), Walmley Rd, B76 8QX, SE : 1 ½ m. by Coleshill St., Coleshill Rd and Reddicap Hill on B 4148 ℘ 378 2442, Fax 378 4637, ≤, « Part 13C moated manor house », , park, – rest – 45. VISA JCB
Meals *(closed Saturday lunch)* 25.00/28.80 **t.** and a la carte 6.20 – 9.65 – **55 rm** 93.00/165.00 **t.**, 5 suites – SB. DT i

Penns Hall (Jarvis), Penns Lane, Walmley, B76 1LH, SE : 2 ¾ m. by A 5127 ℘ 351 3111, Fax 313 1297, , , park, squash – rm – 400. VISA. DT v
Meals *(closed Saturday lunch)* 10.50/16.50 **t.** and a la carte 6.00 – 8.50 – **109 rm** 98.00/115.00 **st.**, 5 suites – SB.

Moor Hall, Moor Hall Drive, B75 6LN, NE : 2 m. by A 453 and Weeford Rd ℘ 308 3751, Telex 335127, Fax 308 8974, , – rm – 200. VISA JCB. DT r
Meals (carving lunch)/dinner 20.50 **st.** 6.00 – **75 rm** 82.00/150.00 **st.** – SB.

Royal, High St., B72 1UD, ℘ 355 8222, Fax 355 1837 – – 60. VISA.
Meals (grill rest.) a la carte 9.50/14.50 **st.** 3.50 – **22 rm** 35.95/49.95 **st.** DT c

Sutton Court, 60-66 Lichfield Rd, B74 2NA, N : ½ m. at junction of A 5127 with A 453 ℘ 355 6071, Fax 355 0083 – rm – 90. VISA JCB DT x
Meals (bar lunch Monday to Saturday)/dinner 16.95 **t.** and a la carte – 9.50 – **64 rm** 65.00/90.00 **st.** – SB.

Forte Travelodge, Boldmere Rd, B72 5UP, SW : 1 ¼ m. by A 5127 and A 453 on B 4142 ℘ 355 0017, Reservations (Freephone) 0800 850950 – rm . VISA.
Meals (Harvester grill) a la carte approx. 16.00 – 5.50 – **32 rm** 33.50 **t.** DT n

Parson and Clerk, Chester Rd North, Streetly, B73 6SP, W : 3 ½ m. by A 453 on A 452 ℘ 353 1747, Fax 352 1340 – . CT s
36 rm.

La Truffe, 65 Birmingham Rd, B72 1QF, ℘ 355 5836 – VISA DT u
closed Saturday lunch, Sunday, Monday, first week January, 2 weeks Easter and last week August – **Meals** 8.95/25.50 **t.** and a la carte 6.10.

at Curdworth SE : 6 ½ m. by A 5127, A 452 and A 38 on A 4097 – ✉ Sutton Coldfield – ☎ 01675 :

Old School House without rest., B76 9DR, on A 4097 ℘ 470177 –
6 rm 32.50/42.50 **t.**

Die Preise Einzelheiten über die in diesem Führer angegebenen Preise finden Sie in der Einleitung.

SUTTON COURTENAY Oxon. 403 404 Q 29 – ✉ Abingdon – ☎ 01235.

♦London 24 – ♦Oxford 12 – Reading 22 – Swindon 28.

✗ **The Fish,** 4 Appleford Rd, OX14 4NQ, ☏ 848242, Fax 484242 – Ⓟ. AE VISA
Meals a la carte 18.85/27.85 **t.**

SUTTON-ON-SEA Lincs. 402 404 U 24 – ☎ 01507.

♦London 151 – Boston 32 – Great Grimsby 30 – Lincoln 45.

Athelstone Lodge, 25 Trusthorpe Rd, LN12 2LR, ☏ 441521 – rest TV Ⓟ
March-October – **Meals** 10.00 **st.** – **6 rm** 18.00/36.00 **st.** – SB.

SUTTON SCOTNEY SERVICE AREA Hants. 403 404 P 30 – ✉ Winchester – ☎ 01962.

♦London 66 – Reading 32 – Salisbury 21 – ♦Southampton 19.

Forte Travelodge without rest., SO21 3JY, on A 34, ☏ 761016 (northside), 760779 (southside), Reservations (Freephone) 0800 850950 – TV Ⓟ. AE VISA.
71 rm 33.50 **t.**

SWAFFHAM Norfolk 404 W 26 **Great Britain G.** – pop. 5 855 – ECD : Thursday – ☎ 01760.

Exc. : Oxburgh Hall★★ *AC*, SW : 7½ m.

♦London 97 – ♦Cambridge 46 – King's Lynn 16 – ♦Norwich 27.

Strattons, Ash Close, PE37 7NH, off Market Sq. ☏ 723845, Fax 720458, « Part Queen Anne house », – rest TV ☎ Ⓟ. AE VISA
Meals (booking essential to non-residents) (dinner only) 24.00 **t.** 5.50 – **7 rm** 55.00/80.00 **st.**

George, Station St., PE37 7LJ, ☏ 721238, Fax 725333 – TV ☎ Ⓟ – 150. AE VISA.
Meals 14.50 3.95 – **31 rm** 45.00/59.00 **t.** – SB.

at Sporle NE : 3 m. by A 47 – ✉ King's Lynn – ☎ 01760 :

Corfield House, PE32 2EA, on Necton rd ☏ 723636, – TV Ⓟ. VISA.
closed Christmas-March – **Meals** 12.50 **st.** 3.50 – **5 rm** 23.00/43.00 **st.**

ATS Unit 2a, Tower Meadow (off Station St.) ☏ 722543

I prezzi — Per ogni chiarimento sui prezzi qui riportati, consultate le spiegazioni alle pagine dell'introduzione.

SWANAGE Dorset 403 404 O 32 **The West Country G.** – pop. 9 037 – ECD : Thursday – ☎ 01929.

See : Town★.

Envir. : St. Aldhelm's Head★★ (≤★★★) SW : 4 m. by B 3069 – Durlston Country Park (≤★★) S : 1 m. – Studland (Old Harry Rocks★★, St. Nicholas Church★) N : 3 m. – Worth Matravers (Anvil Point Lighthouse ≤★★) S : 2 m. – Great Globe★, S : 1¼ m.

Exc. : Corfe Castle★★ (≤★★) *AC*, NW : 6 m. by A 351.

18, 9 Isle of Purbeck, Studland ☏ 450354.

The White House, Shore Rd, BH19 1LB ☏ 422885.

♦London 130 – Bournemouth 22 – Dorchester 26 – ♦Southampton 52.

Havenhurst, 3 Cranborne Rd, BH19 1EA, ☏ 424224 – rest Ⓟ.
Meals 20.00 **t.** – **17 rm** 28.50/57.00 **t.** – SB.

Crowthorne, 24 Cluny Cres., BH19 2BT, by Stafford Rd ☏ 422108 – Ⓟ. VISA.
closed January – **Meals** 10.00 – **8 rm** 18.00/44.00 – SB.

✗ **Cauldron Bistro,** 5 High St., BH19 2LN, ☏ 422671. AE VISA JCB
Meals - Seafood *(closed Monday and Tuesday lunch)* 7.50/22.00 **t.** and a la carte.

✗ **The Galley,** 9 High St., BH19 2LN, ☏ 427299. AE VISA JCB
closed 1 January-14 February and 2 weeks November – **Meals** (dinner only) 14.50/20.00 **st.** 5.70.

SWAVESEY SERVICE AREA Cambs. 404 U 27 – see Cambridge.

SWINDON Wilts. 403 404 O 29 **The West Country G.** – pop. 127 348 – ECD : Wednesday – ☎ 01793.

See : Great Western Railway Museum★ *AC* – Railway Village Museum★ *AC* Y **M.**

Envir. : Lydiard Park (St. Mary's★) W : 4 m. U.

Exc. : Ridgeway Path★★, S : 8½ m. by A 4361 – Whitehorse (≤★) E : 7½ m. by A 4312, A 420 and B 400 off B 4057.

18, 9 Broome Manor, Pipers Way ☏ 532403 – 18 Shrivenham Park, Penny Hooks ☏ 783853, Fax 782999 – 18 Wootton Bassett ☏ 849999 – 18 Wrag Barn, Shrivenham Rd, Highworth ☏ 861327.

37 Regent Street, SN1 1JN ☏ 530328.

♦London 83 – Bournemouth 69 – ♦Bristol 40 – ♦Coventry 66 – ♦Oxford 29 – Reading 40 – ♦Southampton 65.

SWINDON

Beechcroft Road . . . . U 4
Bridge End Road . . . . U 6
Cheney Manor Road . . . . U 10
Cirencester Way . . . . U 12
Devises Road . . . . V 18
Gipsy Lane . . . . U 25
Kingsdown Road . . . . U 30
Moredon Road . . . . U 34
Newport Street . . . . V 36
Oxford Road . . . . U 42
Park Lane . . . . U 43
Rodbourne Road . . . . U 48
Slade Drive . . . . U 51
Swindon Road . . . . U 57
Vicarage Road . . . . U 61
Westcott Place . . . . U 64
Whitworth Road . . . . U 66
Wootton Basset Road . . . . . . U 69

De Vere, Shaw Ridge Leisure Park, Whitehill Way, SN5 7DW, W : 2¾ m. by A 3102 and Tewkesbury Way (at Mannington junction) ☎ 878785, Fax 877822, – rm rest – 400. VISA U e
Meals (carving lunch) 14.50/19.50 **st.** and dinner a la carte 4.75 – **146 rm** 100.00/150.00 **st.**, 8 suites – SB.

Swindon Marriott, Pipers Way, SN3 1SH, SE : 1½ m. by Marlborough Road off B 4006 ☎ 512121, Fax 513114, squash – rm – 250. VISA JCB V s
Meals 17.50 **st.** (dinner) and a la carte – 10.25 – **153 rm** 92.00/180.00 **st.** – SB.

Hilton National, Lydiard Fields, Great Western Way, SN5 8UZ, M4, Junction 16 ☎ 881777, Fax 881881, – rm – 350. VISA JCB. V a
Meals (bar lunch Saturday) 12.95/17.75 **st.** and a la carte 5.50 – 10.50 – **150 rm** 85.00/220.00 **st.** – SB.

SWINDON

Brunel Shopping Centre. YZ
Regent Street . . . . YZ 46

Beckhampton Street . . . . . Y 3
Bridge Street . . . . Y 7
Canal Walk. . . . . Y 9
Cricklade Street . . . . Z 13
Cross Street . . . . Z 15
Deacon Street . . . . Z 16
Dryden Street. . . . . Z 19
Edmund Street. . . . . Z 21
Faringdon Road . . . . Y 22
Farnsby Street. . . . . YZ 24
High Street. . . . . Z 27
Islington Street . . . . Y 28
London Street . . . . Y 31
Milton Road. . . . . YZ 33
North Star Avenue . . . . . . Y 37
North Street . . . . Z 39
Ocotal Way . . . . Y 40
Prospect Hill. . . . . Z 45
Sheppard Street . . . . Y 49
South Street. . . . . Z 52
Southampton Street . . . . . Y 54
Spring Gardens . . . . Y 55
The Parade. . . . . Y 58
Upham Road . . . . Z 60
Warwick Road . . . . Z 63
Wood Street. . . . . Z 67

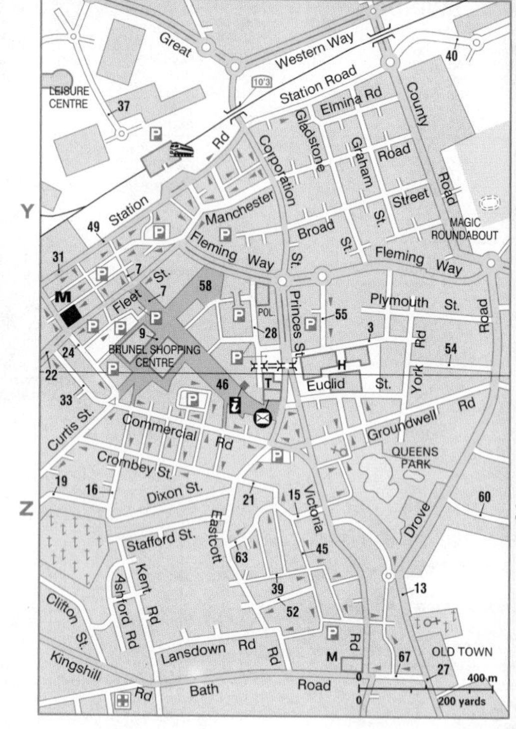

Forte Posthouse, Marlborough Rd, SN3 6AQ, SE : 2 ¾ m. on A 4259 ℘ 524601, Fax 512887, ... – rm ... – 80. ... VISA — V **b**
Meals a la carte approx. 15.00 **t.** 5.50 – **98 rm** 56.00/69.50 **st.**

at Blunsdon N : 4 ½ m. on A 419 – U – ✉ Swindon – ☎ 01793 :

Blunsdon House, The Ridge, SN2 4AD, ℘ 721701, Fax 721056, ..., park, ..., squash – ... rm ... – 300. ... VISA. — U **a**
Meals 10.75/11.75 **st.** and a la carte – **87 rm** 77.50/99.50 **st.**, 1 suite – SB.

at Stanton Fitzwarren NE : 5 ¼ m. by A 4312 and A 419 off A 361 – ✉ Swindon – ☎ 01793 :

Stanton House, The Avenue, SN6 7SD, ℘ 861777, Fax 861857, ... – ... rest ... – 110. ... VISA JCB. — U **c**
Meals - Japanese a la carte 16.50/25.00 **t.** – **86 rm** 65.00/90.00 **t.**

at Wroughton S : 3 ¼ m. on A 4361 – V – ✉ Swindon – ☎ 01793 :

Moormead, Moormead Rd, SN4 9BY, ℘ 814744, Fax 814119 – ... – 60 — V **h**
34 rm.

at Chiseldon S : 6 ¼ m. by A 4312, A 4259 and A 345 on B 4005 – V – ✉ Swindon – ☎ 01793 :

Chiseldon House ..., New Rd, SN4 0NE, ℘ 741010, Fax 741059, ... heated, ... – ... — V **d**
21 rm.

at Wootton Bassett W : 6 ¼ m. on A 3102 – ✉ Swindon – ☎ 01793 :

Marsh Farm, Coped Hall, SN4 8ER, N : 1 m. by A 3102 on Purton rd ℘ 848044, Fax 851528, ... – ... – 120. ... VISA
Meals 12.50 **t.** and a la carte 5.50 – **28 rm** 50.00/85.00 **t.**

at Hook W : 6 ¼ m. by A 3102, B 4534 and Hook rd – ✉ Swindon – ☎ 01793 :

School House, Hook St., SN4 8EF, ℘ 851198, Fax 851025, ... – ... VISA. ...
Meals *(closed Saturday lunch and Sunday)* 15.50/29.95 **st.** and a la carte 5.95 – **12 rm** 67.00/75.00 **st.** – SB.

ATS Cheney Manor Ind. Est. ℘ 521171 — ATS 86 Beatrice St. ℘ 534867/431620

SWINTON Gtr.Manchester 402 403 404 N 23 – see Manchester.

SYMONDS YAT WEST Heref. and Worcs. 403 404 M 28 **Great Britain G.** – ✉ Ross-on-Wye – ☎ 01600.

See : Town★ – Yat Rock (≤★).

Envir. : S : Wye Valley★.

♦London 126 – Gloucester 23 – Hereford 17 – Newport 31.

- Norton House, Whitchurch, HR9 6DJ, ☎ 890046, – TV P
  Meals (by arrangement) – **3 rm.**
- **Cedars,** Llangrove Rd, Whitchurch, HR9 6DQ, NW : ¾ m. ☎ 890351, – TV.
  Meals (by arrangement) 16.50 **st.** – **7 rm** 17.00/38.00 **st.** – SB.
- **Woodlea**, HR9 6BL, ☎ 890206, Fax 890206, – rest ☎ P. VISA
  Meals 13.50 **t.** 3.50 – **9 rm** 22.00/55.00 **t.**

TADWORTH Surrey 404 T 30 – ☎ 01737.

♦London 23 – ♦Brighton 36 – Guildford 22 – Maidstone 41.

- XX **Gemini,** Station Approach, KT20 5AH, ☎ 812179. VISA
  closed Saturday lunch, Sunday dinner, Monday, first two weeks January and 2 weeks June – **Meals** 10.50/21.50 **t.**

TALKE Staffs. 402 403 404 N 24 – see Stoke-on-Trent.

TALKIN Cumbria 401 402 L 19 – see Brampton.

TALLAND BAY Cornwall 403 G 32 – see Looe.

TAMWORTH Staffs. 402 403 404 O 26 – pop. 70 065 – ECD : Wednesday – ☎ 01827.

18 Eagle Drive, Amington ☎ 53850.

Town Hall, Market St., B79 7LY ☎ 59134.

♦London 128 – ♦Birmingham 12 – ♦Coventry 29 – ♦Leicester 31 – ♦Stoke-on-Trent 37.

- **Travel Inn,** Bitterscote, Bonehill Rd, B78 3HQ, on A 51 ☎ 54414, Fax 310420 – rm TV P. AE VISA.
  Meals (Beefeater grill) a la carte approx. 16.00 **t.** – 4.95 – **40 rm** 33.50 **t.**

at Bodymoor Heath S : 6¾ m. by A 4091 – ✉ Sutton Coldfield – ☎ 01827 :

- **Marston Farm,** B76 9JD, ☎ 872133, Fax 875043, park, – rest TV ☎ P – 50. AE VISA
  Meals 12.50/15.75 **t.** and a la carte 5.50 – **37 rm** 75.00/90.00 **st.** – SB.

ATS Tame Valley Ind. Est., Watling St., Wilnecote ☎ 281983

TAMWORTH SERVICE AREA Staffs. – ✉ Tamworth – ☎ 01827.

- **Granada Lodge** without rest., Green Lane, B77 6PS, A 5 / M 42 junction 10 ☎ 260120, Fax 260145, Reservations (Freephone) 0800 555300 – TV ☎ P. AE VISA.
  4.00 – **63 rm** 39.95 **st.**

TANSLEY Derbs. – see Matlock.

TAPLOW Berks. 404 R 29 – ☎ 01628.

♦London 33 – Maidenhead 2 – Reading 12.

- **Cliveden**, SL6 0JF, N : 2 m. by Berry Hill ☎ 668561, Fax 661837, « Mid-Victorian stately home, ≤ National Trust Gardens, parterre and River Thames », heated, park, squash – rest TV ☎ P – 40. AE VISA
  Terrace : **Meals** 26.00/35.00 **t.** and a la carte 30.00/53.00 **st.** 10.00 – (see also ***Waldo's*** below) – 14.50 – **32 rm** 225.00/375.00 **t.**, 5 suites – SB.
- XXXX ✿ **Waldo's** (at Cliveden H.), SL6 0JF, N : 2 m. by Berry Hill ☎ 668561, Fax 661837 – P. AE VISA
  closed Sunday and Monday – **Meals** (dinner only) 40.00/60.00 **t.** 10.00
  Spec. Cornish crab with lime, pimentos, scallops and a potato and chive salad, Char grilled fillet of Scotch beef with smoked foie gras, Hot apricot soufflé with a wild strawberry ice cream.

When visiting Great Britain,
use the ***Michelin Green Guide "Great Britain".***

- *Detailed descriptions of places of interest*
- *Touring programmes*
- *Maps and street plans*
- *The history of the country*
- *Photographs and drawings of monuments, beauty spots, houses...*

TARPORLEY Ches. 402 403 404 M 24 – pop. 2 308 – ☎ 01829.

Portal, Cobblers Cross ☏ 733933.

♦London 186 – Chester 11 – ♦Liverpool 36 – Shrewsbury 36.

Swan, 50 High St., CW6 0AG, ☏ 733838, Fax 732932 – TV ☎ P – 100. VISA.
Meals 14.95 **t.** and a la carte – **13 rm** 44.95/52.95 **t.** – SB.

TARRANT MONKTON Dorset 403 404 N 31 – see Blandford Forum.

TATTENHALL Ches. 402 403 404 L 24 – pop. 3 263 – ☎ 01829.

♦London 200 – ♦Birmingham 71 – Chester 10 – ♦Manchester 38 – ♦Stoke-on-Trent 30.

Higher Huxley Hall, CH3 9BZ, N : 2 ¼ m. on Huxley rd ☏ 781484, Fax 781142, ≤, « Part 14C manor house, working farm », – TV P. VISA.
Meals (communal dining) 20.00 **s.** 5.00 – **3 rm** 35.00/70.00.

Newton Hall without rest., CH3 9AY, N : 1 m. by Huxley Rd ☏ 70153, « Working farm », – P.
closed Christmas and New Year – **3 rm** 20.00/40.00 **s.**

TAUNTON Somerset 403 K 30 **The West Country G.** – pop. 41 545 – ECD : Thursday – ☎ 01823.

See : Town★ – St. Mary Magdalene★ – Somerset County Museum★ *AC* – St. James★ – Hammett St.★ – The Crescent★ – Bath Alley★.

Envir. : Trull (Church★) S : 2½ m. by A 38.

Exc. : Bishops Lydeard★ (Church★) NW : 6 m. – Wellington : Church★, Wellington Monument (≤★★) SW : 7½ m. by A 38 – Combe Florey★, NW : 8 m. – Gaulden Manor★ *AC*, NW : 10 m. by A 358 and B 3227.

Taunton Vale, Creech Heathfield ☏ 412220 – Vivary Park ☏ 289274 – Taunton and Pickeridge, Corfe ☏ 421537.

The Library, Corporation St., TA1 4AN ☏ 274785.

♦London 168 – Bournemouth 69 – ♦Bristol 50 – Exeter 37 – ♦Plymouth 78 – ♦Southampton 93 – Weymouth 50.

❁ **Castle,** Castle Green, TA1 1NF, ☏ 272671, Fax 336066, « Part 12C castle with Norman garden » – rest TV ☎ P – 100. VISA
Meals (restricted menu Sunday dinner) 16.50/32.50 **st.** 5.60 – **35 rm** 65.00/150.00 **st.** – SB
Spec. Baked crab tart, Braised shoulder of lamb, Honey cheesecake

Forte Posthouse, Deane Gate Av., TA1 2UA, E : 2½ m. by A 358 at junction with M 5 ☏ 332222, Fax 332266, – rm rest TV ☎ P – 200. VISA
Meals a la carte approx. 15.00 **t.** 5.50 – **97 rm** 56.00 **st.**

Orchard House without rest., Fons George, Middleway, TA1 3JS, off Wilton St. ☏ 351783, Fax 351785, – TV P. VISA.
6 rm 35.00/55.00 **t.**

Travel Inn, 81 Bridgwater Rd, TA1 2DU, E : 1 ¾ m. by A 358 ☏ 321112, Fax 322054 – rm TV P. VISA.
Meals (Beefeater grill) a la carte approx. 16.00 **t.** – 4.95 – **40 rm** 33.50 **t.**

Forde House without rest., 9 Upper High St., TA1 3PX, ☏ 279042, – TV P.
closed Christmas and New Year – **5 rm** 27.00/48.00 **s.**

at Hatch Beauchamp SE : 6 m. by A358 – ✉ Taunton – ☎ 01823 :

Farthings, TA3 6SG, ☏ 480664, Fax 481118, « Georgian country house », – rest TV ☎ P. VISA
Meals (lunch by arrangement)/dinner 8.00/15.00 **t.** 4.60 – **9 rm** 50.00/80.00.

Frog Street Farm, Beercrocombe, TA3 6AF, SE : 1 ¼ m. by Beercrocombe Rd ☏ 480430, « 15C farmhouse, working farm », heated, – rm P.
March-October – **Meals** (by arrangement) (communal dining) 15.00 **t.** – **3 rm** 27.00/54.00 **st.**

XX **Nightingales,** Bath House Farm, Lower West Hatch, TA3 5RH, W : 1 m. by A 358 ☏ 480806, – P. VISA
closed Sunday and Monday – **Meals** (dinner only and Sunday lunch)/dinner 24.00 **t.**

at Bishop's Hull W : 1 ¾ m. by A 38 – ✉ Taunton – ☎ 01823 :

Meryan House, Bishop's Hull Rd, TA1 5EG, ☏ 337445, Fax 322355, – TV ☎ P. VISA
Meals *(in bar Sunday)* (dinner only) 14.00 **st.** 4.50 – **12 rm** 36.00/53.00 **st.** – SB.

at West Bagborough NW : 10½ m. by A 358 – ✉ Taunton – ☎ 01323 :

Bashfords Farmhouse without rest., TA4 3EF, ☏ 432015, – TV P.
3 rm 17.00/37.50.

ATS 138 Bridgwater Rd, Bathpool ☏ 412826

TAUNTON DEANE SERVICE AREA Somerset 403 K 31 – ✉ Taunton – ☎ 01823.

Road Chef Lodge without rest., TA3 7PF, ☏ 332228, Fax 338131 – TV ☎ P
39 rm.

TAVISTOCK Devon 403 H 32 **The West Country G.** – pop. 10 222 – ECD : Wednesday – ☎ 01822.

Envir. : Morwellham★ *AC*, SW : 4½ m.

Exc. : E : Dartmoor National Park★★ (Brent Tor ≤★★, Haytor Rocks ≤★) – Buckland Abbey★★ *AC*, S : 7 m. by A 386 – Lydford★★ (Lydford Gorge★★) N : 8½ m. by A 386.

Down Rd ☎ 612049 – Hurdwick, Tavistock Hamlets ☎ 612746.

Town Hall, Bedford Sq., PL19 0AE ☎ 612938 (summer only).

London 239 – Exeter 38 – Plymouth 15.

Bedford (Forte), 1 Plymouth Rd, PL19 8BB, ☎ 613221, Fax 618034 – TV ☎ P – 45. AE VISA
Meals (bar lunch Monday to Saturday)/dinner 16.95 **t.** and a la carte 6.70 – 8.50 – **30 rm** 55.00/65.00 **t.** – SB.

Neils, 27 King St., PL19 0DT, ☎ 615550 – AE VISA
closed Sunday and Monday – **Meals** (dinner only) 16.00 **t.** and a la carte 8.00.

at Mary Tavy N : 3¾ m. on A 386 – ✉ Tavistock – ☎ 01822 :

Stannary with rm, PL19 9QB, ☎ 810897, Fax 810898, – TV P. AE VISA.
Meals - Vegetarian *(closed Sunday and Monday)* (dinner only) 30.00 **s.** 4.50 – **3 rm** (dinner included) 70.00/120.00 **s.** – SB.

at Gulworthy W : 3 m. on A 390 – ✉ Tavistock – ☎ 01822 :

Horn of Plenty with rm, PL19 8JD, ☎ 832528, Fax 832528, ≤ Tamar Valley and Bodmin Moor, – TV ☎ P. AE VISA
closed 25 and 26 December – **Meals** *(closed Monday lunch)* 14.50/26.50 **s.** 6.90 – 5.00 – **7 rm** 78.00/98.00 **t.**

ATS 2 Parkwood Rd ☎ 612545

Pour visiter une ville ou une région : utilisez les Guides Verts Michelin.

TEESSIDE AIRPORT Durham 402 P 20 – see Darlington.

TEFFONT Wilts. – see Salisbury.

TEIGNMOUTH Devon 403 J 32 – pop. 13 403 – ECD : Thursday – ☎ 01626.

The Den, Sea Front, TQ14 8BE ☎ 779769.

London 216 – Exeter 16 – Torquay 8.

London, Bank St., TQ14 8AW, ☎ 776336, Fax 778457, – TV ☎ – 150. AE VISA
Meals 12.00 **st.** (dinner) and a la carte 4.00 – **30 rm** 35.00/80.00 **t.** – SB.

Cliffden, Dawlish Rd, TQ14 8TE, ☎ 770052, Fax 770594, ≤, Restricted to the blind and their companions, – TV ☎ P. VISA
Meals (residents only) – **21 rm.**

Thomas Luny House, Teign St., TQ14 8EG, ☎ 772976, « Georgian house built by Thomas Luny », – rest TV ☎ P.
closed January – **Meals** (residents only) (communal dining) (dinner only) 16.50 6.50 – **4 rm** 30.00/60.00 **st.** – SB.

at Shaldon S : 1 m. on B 3199 – ✉ Teignmouth – ☎ 01626 :

Ness House, Marine Par., TQ14 0HP, ☎ 873480, Fax 873486, ≤, – TV ☎ P. AE VISA.
Meals 12.50 **t.** and a la carte 5.50 – **12 rm** 40.00/80.00 **t.** – SB.

Glenside, Ringmore Rd, TQ14 0EP, W : ½ m. on B 3195 ☎ 872448, – rest TV P
closed January – **Meals** 13.00 **t.** 5.00 – **10 rm** 17.00/36.00 **t.** – SB.

TELFORD Shrops. 402 403 404 M 25 **Great Britain G.** – pop. 76 330 – ☎ 01952.

Envir. : Ironbridge Gorge Museum★★ *AC* (The Iron Bridge★★, Coalport China Museum★★, Blists Hill Open Air Museum★★, Museum of the River and Visitor Centre★) S : 5 m. by B 4373.

Exc. : Weston Park★★ *AC*, E : 7 m. by A 5.

18, 9 Telford Hotel, Great Hay, Sutton Hill ☎ 585642 – 18 Wrekin, Wellington ☎ 244032 – 18, 9, 9, 9 The Shropshire, Muxton Grange ☎ 677866.

The Telford Centre, Management Suite, TF3 4BX ☎ 291370.

London 152 – Birmingham 33 – Shrewsbury 12 – Stoke-on-Trent 29.

Holiday Inn, Telford International Centre, St. Quentin Gate, TF3 4EH, SE : ½ m. ☎ 292500, Fax 291949, squash – rm rest TV ☎ P – 300. AE VISA
accommodation closed 25 and 26 December – **Meals** 10.50/15.95 **st.** and a la carte 5.95 – 9.95 – **100 rm** 89.00/135.00 **st.** – SB.

Telford H. Golf & Country Club (Q.M.H.), Great Hay, Sutton Hill, TF7 4DT, S : 4½ m. by A 442 ☎ 585642, Fax 586602, ≤, 9, 18, squash – rest TV ☎ P – 240. AE VISA
Meals *(closed Saturday lunch)* 13.20/19.95 **t.** and a la carte 5.50 – **85 rm** 91.00/108.00 **st.**, 1 suite – SB.

Telford Moat House (Q.M.H.), Forgegate, Telford Centre, TF3 4NA, ✆ 291291, Fax 292012, – rm rest – 400.
closed 25 to 30 December – **Meals** *(closed lunch Saturday and Bank Holidays)* (carving lunch) 9.50/25.00 **st.** and dinner a la carte 5.50 – 8.50 – **144 rm** 79.95/95.00 **t.**, 4 suites – SB.

Madeley Court, Castlefields Way, Madeley, TF7 5DW, S : 4½ m. by A 442 and A 4169 on B 4373 ✆ 680068, Fax 684275, « Part 16C manor house », – – 200
47 rm.

Forte Travelodge, Shawbirch Crossroads, Shawbirch, TF1 3QA, NW : 5½ m. by A 442 at junction with B 5063 ✆ 251244, Reservations (Freephone) 0800 850950 – .
Meals (Harvester grill) a la carte approx. 16.00 **t.** – 5.50 – **40 rm** 33.50 **t.**

White House, Wellington Rd, Muxton, TF2 8NG, N : 4 ½ m. by A 442 off A 578 ✆ 604276, Fax 670336, – .
Meals *(closed Saturday lunch)* 12.50 **t.** and a la carte – **30 rm** 49.50/67.50 **t.** – SB.

at Norton S : 7 m. on A 442 – ✉ Shifnal – 01952 :

Hundred House, Bridgnorth Rd, TF11 9EE, ✆ 730353, Fax 730355, « Tastefully decorated inn, antiques », – .
Meals 12.95/25.00 **t.** and a la carte 6.25 – **10 rm** 52.00/69.00 **st.** – SB.

at Wellington W : 6 m. by M 54 on B 5061 – ✉ Telford – 01952 :

Buckatree Hall, The Wrekin, Buckatree, TF6 5AL, SE : 2¾ m. by B 5061 ✆ 641821, Fax 247540, – rm – 170.
Meals 8.50/16.95 **t.** and a la carte – **60 rm** 69.00/85.00 **t.**, 2 suites – SB.

Charlton Arms (Premier), Church St., TF1 1DG, ✆ 251351, Fax 222077, – rm – 150
23 rm.

ATS Queen St., Madeley ✆ 582820

ATS Kensington Way, Oakengates ✆ 613810/612198

TEMPLE SOWERBY Cumbria 401 402 M 20 – pop. 329 – ECD : Thursday – ✉ Penrith – 0176 83.
London 297 – Carlisle 31 – Kendal 38.

Temple Sowerby House, CA10 1RZ, ✆ 61578, Fax 61958, – rest .
Meals (light lunch Monday to Saturday)/dinner 23.00 **t.** 4.50 – **12 rm** 48.00/70.00 **t.** – SB.

TENBURY WELLS Heref. and Worcs. 403 404 M 27 – 01584.
London 144 – Birmingham 36 – Hereford 20 – Shrewsbury 37 – Worcester 28.

Cadmore Lodge, St. Michaels, WR15 8TQ, SW : 2¾ m. by A 4112 turning right opposite Cloisters College ✆ 810044, Fax 810044, , park, – rm – 100.
Meals 10.00/14.50 **t.** and a la carte – **8 rm** 34.50/57.50 **t.** – SB.

TENTERDEN Kent 404 W 30 – pop. 7 005 – ECD : Wednesday – 01580.
Town Hall, High St., TN30 6AN ✆ 763572 (summer only).
London 57 – Folkestone 26 – Hastings 21 – Maidstone 19.

Jarvis White Lion, 57 High St., TN30 6BD, ✆ 765077, Fax 764157 – rm – 50.
Meals 8.50/12.95 **st.** – **15 rm** 55.00/85.00 **st.** – SB.

Little Silver Country, Ashford Rd, St. Michaels, TN30 6SP, N : 2 m. on A 28 ✆ (01233) 850321, Fax 850647, – – 150.
Meals (dinner only) (booking essential) 22.00 **st.** and a la carte 5.50 – **10 rm** 60.00/100.00 **st.** – SB.

Brattle House, Cranbrook Rd, TN30 6UL, W : 1 m. by A 28 ✆ 763565, – .
closed Christmas and New Year – **Meals** (by arrangement) (communal dining) 16.00 **s.** – **3 rm** 41.00/55.00 **s.**

Collina House, 5 East Hill, TN30 6RL, ✆ 764852 – rm .
Meals 21.00 **st.** 4.50 – **17 rm** 28.00/45.00 **st.**

TETBURY Glos. 403 404 N 29 **Great Britain G.** – pop. 5 065 – ECD : Thursday – 01666.
Envir. : Westonbirt Arboretum★ *AC*, SW : 2½ m. by A 433 – Westonbirt ✆ (0166 88) 242.
The Old Court House, 63 Long St., GL8 8AA ✆ 503552 (summer only).
London 113 – Bristol 27 – Gloucester 19 – Swindon 24.

The Close, 8 Long St., GL8 8AQ, ✆ 502272, Fax 504401, « 16C town house with walled garden » – rest – 30.
Meals 16.50/26.50 **t.** and a la carte 7.50 – **15 rm** 82.00/155.00 **t.** – SB.

Snooty Fox, Market Pl., GL8 8DD, ✆ 502436, Fax 503479 – .
12 rm.

XX **Number Sixty Five,** 65 Long St., GL8 8AA, ✆ 503346 –
closed Sunday dinner – **Meals** 19.25 **t.** and a la carte 5.25.

at Westonbirt SW : 2 ½ m. on A 433 – ✉ Tetbury – ☎ 01666 :

Hare and Hounds, GL8 8QL, ☎ 880233, Fax 880241, ⛲, 🎾, squash – TV ☎ P – 🅰 150. VISA JCB
Meals 11.00/19.00 **st.** and a la carte 3.75 – **30 rm** 58.00/88.00 **st.**

at Willesley SW : 4 m. on A 433 – ✉ Tetbury – ☎ 01666 :

Tavern House without rest., GL8 8QU, ☎ 880444, Fax 880254, « Part 17C former inn and staging post », – TV ☎ P. VISA.
4 rm 37.50/63.00.

at Calcot W : 3 ½ m. on A 4135 – ✉ Tetbury – ☎ 01666 :

Calcot Manor, GL8 8YJ, ☎ 890391, Fax 890394, « Converted Cotswold farm buildings », heated, 🎾 – rest TV ☎ P. VISA.
Meals a la carte 15.45/25.85 **t.** 6.50 – **20 rm** 75.00/125.00 **t.**

Wenn Sie ein ruhiges Hotel suchen,
benutzen Sie zuerst die Karte in der Einleitung
oder wählen Sie im Text ein Hotel mit dem Zeichen oder .

TEWKESBURY Glos. 403 404 N 28 **Great Britain G.** – pop. 9 546 – ECD : Thursday – ☎ 01684.

See : Town★ – Abbey★★ (Nave★★, vault★).

Envir. : St. Mary's, Deerhurst★, SW : 4 m. by A 38 and B 4213.

18 Tewkesbury Park Hotel, Lincoln Green Lane ☎ 295405.

64 Barton St., GL20 5PX ☎ 295027.

London 108 – Birmingham 39 – Gloucester 11.

Tewkesbury Park H. Golf & Country Club (Country Club), Lincoln Green Lane, GL20 7DN, S : 1 ¼ m. by A 38 ☎ 295405, Fax 292386, ←, 18, park, 🎾, squash – TV ☎ P – 🅰 150. VISA.
Meals (bar lunch Saturday) 12.00/19.50 **st.** and dinner a la carte – 9.00 – **78 rm** 75.00/100.00 **st.** – SB.

Royal Hop Pole (Forte), Church St., GL20 5RT, ☎ 293236, Fax 296680, – TV ☎ P. VISA JCB
Meals 10.95/17.95 **t.** and dinner a la carte 6.70 – 8.50 – **29 rm** 60.00/75.00 **t.** – SB.

Bell, Church St., GL20 5SA, ☎ 293293, Fax 295938 – TV ☎ P – 🅰 40. VISA.
Meals (bar lunch Monday to Saturday)/dinner 16.95 **st.** and a la carte – **25 rm** 58.00/85.00 – SB.

Jessop House, 65 Church St., GL20 5RZ, ☎ 292017, Fax 273076 – TV ☎ P. VISA.
closed 24 December - 2 January – **Meals** *(closed Sunday)* (bar lunch)/dinner a la carte 12.80/20.30 **st.** 3.60 – **8 rm** 55.00/75.00 **st.** – SB.

Bistrot André, 78 Church St., GL20 5RX, ☎ 290357, – VISA
closed February – **Meals** - French *(closed Sunday)* (dinner only) a la carte 12.30/20.25 **st.**

at Puckrup N : 2 ½ m. on A 38 – ✉ Tewkesbury – ☎ 01684 :

Puckrup Hall, GL20 6EL, ☎ 296200, Fax 850788, ←, 18, park – rm TV ☎ P – 🅰 200. VISA
Meals 25.00 **t.** (dinner) and a la carte 12.90/21.95 **t.** 6.00 – 6.00 – **82 rm** 75.50/95.00 **t.**, 2 suites – SB.

at Bredons Norton NE : 4 ¾ m. by B 4080 – ✉ Tewkesbury – ☎ 01684 :

Home Farm, GL20 7HA, NE : ¾ m. taking right turn at village hall ☎ 72322, « Working farm », park – P
3 rm.

at Corse Lawn SW : 6 m. by A 38 and A 438 on B 4211 – ✉ Gloucester – ☎ 01452 :

Corse Lawn House, GL19 4LZ, ☎ 780771, Fax 780840, « Queen Anne house », heated, 🎾 – TV ☎ P – 🅰 40. VISA
Meals - (see *Corse Lawn House* below) – **17 rm** 70.00/90.00 **st.**, 2 suites – SB.

Corse Lawn House (at Corse Lawn House), GL19 4LZ, ☎ 780771, Fax 780840, – P. VISA
Meals 15.95/23.95 **st.** and a la carte 5.00.

at Kemerton NW : 8 ¼ m. by A 438 – ✉ Tewkesbury – ☎ 01386 :

Upper Court, GL20 7HY, take turning at stone cross in village ☎ 725351, Fax 725472, ←, « Georgian manor house, antique furnishings, gardens », heated, park, 🎾 – TV P
Meals (booking essential) (residents only) (communal dining) – **6 rm.**

ATS Oldbury Rd ☎ 292461

THAME Oxon. 404 R 28 **The West Country G.** – pop. 10 806 – ECD : Wednesday – ☎ 01844.
Exc. : Ridgeway Path★★.
Town Hall, OX9 3DP ☎ 212834.
London 48 – Aylesbury 9 – Oxford 13.

- **Spread Eagle,** 16 Cornmarket, OX9 2BW, ☎ 213661, Fax 261380 – TV ☎ P – 250. AE VISA JCB.
closed 28 to 30 December – **Meals** *(closed lunch Bank Holiday Mondays)* 16.95/19.95 **st.** and a la carte 4.50 – 7.45 – **33 rm** 67.95/89.95 **st.**, 2 suites.
- **Essex House,** Chinnor Rd, OX9 3LS, ☎ 217567, Fax 216420 – TV ☎ P. AE VISA.
Meals *(closed Sunday and Bank Holidays)* (dinner only) a la carte approx. 15.00 **st.** – **13 rm** 43.00/58.00 **st.**
- XX **Thatchers,** 29-30 Lower High St., OX9 2AA, ☎ 212146, Fax 217413 – P. VISA
closed Saturday lunch and Sunday – **Meals** 9.50/22.95 **t.** and a la carte 3.75.

at Towersey E : 2 m. by A 4129 – ✉ Thame – ☎ 01844 :

- **Upper Green Farm** without rest., Manor Rd, OX9 3QR, ☎ 212496, Fax 260399, « Part 15C and 16C thatched farmhouse, 17C barn », – TV P.
8 rm 30.00/50.00 **st.**

THATCHAM Berks. 403 404 Q 29 – pop. 15 818 – ✉ Newbury – ☎ 01635.
London 69 – Bristol 68 – Oxford 30 – Reading 15 – Southampton 40.

- **Regency Park,** Bowling Green Rd, RG13 3RP, NW : 1 ¾ m. by A 4 by Northfield Rd ☎ 871555, Fax 871571, – rest TV ☎ P – 60. AE VISA
Meals 13.95/19.95 **st.** and a la carte 6.95 – 8.95 – **49 rm** 75.00/90.00 **st.**, 1 suite – SB.

THAXTED Essex 404 V 28 – pop. 2 681 – ☎ 01371.
London 44 – Cambridge 24 – Colchester 31 – Chelmsford 20.

- **Four Seasons,** Walden Rd, CM6 2RE, NW : ½ m. on B 184 ☎ 830129, Fax 830835 – TV ☎ P. AE VISA.
Meals *(closed dinner Sunday and Bank Holidays)* a la carte 16.25/25.50 **t.** 4.00 – **9 rm** 50.00/65.00 **t.** – SB.
- **Farmhouse Inn,** Monk St., CM6 2NR, S : 1 ½ m. by B 184 ☎ 830864, Fax 831196 – TV ☎ P. AE VISA.
Meals (bar lunch Monday to Saturday)/dinner a la carte 9.40/16.70 **t.** 4.00 – **11 rm** 29.50/39.50 **t.**
- **Folly House,** Watling Lane, CM6 2QY, ☎ 830618, – TV P.
Meals (by arrangement) (communal dining) 20.00 – **3 rm** 25.00/45.00 **s.**

THELBRIDGE Devon 403 I 31 – ✉ Tiverton – ☎ 01884.
London 220 – Barnstaple 21 – Exeter 20 – Taunton 34.

- **Thelbridge Cross Inn,** Thelbridge Cross, EX17 4SQ, on B 3042 ☎ 860316, Fax 860316, – rest TV ☎ P. AE VISA.
Meals a la carte 8.40/16.50 **t.** 4.75 – **8 rm** 35.00/70.00 **t.** – SB.

THETFORD Norfolk 404 W 26 – pop. 19 901 – ECD : Wednesday – ☎ 01842.
London 83 – Cambridge 32 – Ipswich 33 – King's Lynn 30 – Norwich 29.

- **Bell** (Forte), King St., IP24 2AZ, ☎ 754455, Fax 755552 – TV ☎ P – 80. AE VISA JCB
Meals *(closed Saturday lunch)* 12.95/18.95 **st.** and a la carte 6.70 – 8.50 – **46 rm** 55.00/80.00 **st.**, 1 suite – SB.
- **The Historical Thomas Paine,** 33 White Hart St., IP24 1AA, ☎ 755631, Fax 766505 – TV ☎ P. AE VISA JCB.
Meals *(closed Saturday lunch)* 10.75/15.50 **st.** and a la carte 4.75 – **13 rm** 47.00/60.00 **st.** – SB.

ATS Canterbury Way ☎ 755529

THIRSK N. Yorks. 402 P 21 – pop. 4 162 – ECD : Wednesday – ☎ 01845.
Thornton-Le-Street ☎ 522170.
14 Kirkgate, YO7 1PQ ☎ 522755 (summer only).
London 227 – Leeds 37 – Middlesbrough 24 – York 24.

- **Sheppard's,** Front St., Sowerby, YO7 1JF, S : ½ m. ☎ 523655, Fax 524720 – rm TV ☎ P. VISA.
Meals (in bar Sunday dinner, Monday and lunchtime) a la carte 14.80/22.95 **t.** 5.15 – **8 rm** 54.00/80.00 **t.**
- **Spital Hill**, YO7 3AE, SE : 1 ¾ m. on A 19, entrance between 2 white posts ☎ 522273, , park – ☎ P. VISA.
Meals (by arrangement) (communal dinning) 17.00 **st.** 2.60 – **3 rm** 36.00/60.00 **st.**
- **St. James House** without rest., 36 The Green, YO7 1AQ, ☎ 524120 – TV.
April to October – **6 rm** 25.00/40.00.
- **Brook House** without rest., Ingramgate, YO7 1DD, at far end of drive ☎ 522240, Fax 525585, – TV P.
closed 2 weeks Christmas-New Year – **3 rm** 24.00/32.00 **s.**

at South Kilvington N : 1 ½ m. on A 61 – ✉ Thirsk – ☎ 01845 :

Thornborough House Farm, YO7 2NP, N : ¼ m., entrance between roundabout and A 19 junction ✆ 522103, Fax 522103, – TV P. VISA
Meals (by arrangement) (communal dining) 8.50 **st.** – **3 rm** 15.00/34.00 **t.** – SB.

at Asenby SW : 5 ¼ m. by A 168 – ✉ Thirsk – ☎ 01845 :

Crab and Lobster, YO7 3QL, ✆ 577286, Fax 577109, « Thatched inn, memorabilia », – P. AE VISA
closed Sunday dinner – **Meals** (booking essential) 12.95/19.95 **t.** and a la carte **t.** 4.00.

ATS Long St. ✆ 522982/522923

THORALBY N. Yorks. 402 N/O 21 – pop. 160 – ✉ Leyburn – ☎ 01969.
London 245 – Kendal 41 – Leeds 64 – York 57.

Littleburn, DL8 3BE, W : ½ m. by unmarked lane taking left fork after ¼ m. ✆ 663621, ←, « 17C country house », – P
closed 1 week Christmas – **Meals** (by arrangement) (communal dining) 18.00 **s.** – **3 rm** 30.00/60.00 **s.**

Low Green House, DL8 3SZ, SE : ¼ m. on unmarked lane ✆ 663623, – TV P
closed 1 week Christmas – **Meals** (by arrangement) 12.00 **s.** – **4 rm** 23.00/38.00 **s.**

THORNABY-ON-TEES Cleveland 402 Q 20 – pop. 26 319 – ✉ Middlesbrough – ☎ 01642.
18 Tees-Side, Acklam Rd ✆ 676249.
London 250 – Leeds 62 – Middlesbrough 3 – York 49.

Forte Posthouse, Low Lane, Stainton Village, TS17 9LW, SE : 3 ½ m. by A 1045 on A 1044 ✆ 591213, Fax 594989, , – rm TV ☎ P – 100. AE VISA
Meals a la carte approx. 15.00 **t.** 5.50 – **135 rm** 56.00/69.50 **st.**

THORNBURY Avon 403 404 M 29 – pop. 12 617 – ECD : Thursday – ✉ Bristol – ☎ 01454.
London 128 – Bristol 12 – Gloucester 23 – Swindon 43.

Thornbury Castle, Castle St., BS12 1HH, ✆ 281182, Fax 416188, « 16C castle, gardens », park – rest TV ☎ P. AE VISA.
closed 2 days January – **Meals** 18.50/31.00 **t.** 7.50 – 8.95 – **16 rm** 75.00/200.00 **t.**, 1 suite.

THORNTHWAITE Cumbria 402 K 20 – see Keswick.

THORNTON CLEVELEYS Lancs. 402 L 22 – pop. 26 615 – ☎ 01253.
London 244 – Blackpool 6 – Lancaster 20 – Manchester 44.

Victorian House with rm, Trunnah Rd, Thornton, FY5 4HF, ✆ 860619, Fax 865350, « Victoriana », – TV ☎ P. VISA
closed last week January – **Meals** *(closed Monday lunch and Sunday)* 11.00/21.00 **st.** and lunch a la carte 5.50 – **3 rm** 49.50/75.00 **st.**

THORPE Derbs. 402 403 404 O 24 **Great Britain G.** – pop. 201 – ✉ Ashbourne – ☎ 01335.
See : Dovedale** (Ilam Rock*).
London 151 – Derby 16 – Sheffield 33 – Stoke-on-Trent 26.

Peveril of the Peak (Forte), DE6 2AW, ✆ 350333, Fax 350507, ←, , – TV ☎ P – 60
47 rm.

THORPE MARKET Norfolk 404 X 25 – pop. 303 – ✉ North Walsham – ☎ 01263.
London 130 – Norwich 21.

Green Farm, North Walsham Rd, NR11 8TH, ✆ 833602, Fax 833163 – TV ☎ P. AE VISA
Meals (bar lunch)/dinner 16.95 **t.** and a la carte 5.00 – **9 rm** 48.00/62.50 **t.** – SB.

THORPE ST. ANDREW Norfolk 404 Y 26 – see Norwich.

THRAPSTON SERVICE AREA Northants. 404 S 26 – ✉ Kettering – ☎ 01832.

Forte Travelodge without rest., NN14 4UR, at junction of A 14 with A 605 and A 45 ✆ 735199, Reservations (Freephone) 0800 850950 – TV P. AE VISA
40 rm 33.50 **t.**

THREE BRIDGES W. Sussex – see Crawley.

THRELKELD Cumbria 402 K 20 – see Keswick.

THRUSSINGTON Leics. 402 403 404 Q 25 – see Leicester.

THURLESTONE Devon 403 I 33 – see Kingsbridge.

THURROCK SERVICE AREA Essex 404 V 29 – ✉ West Thurrock – ☎ 01708.
18 Belhus Park, South Ockendon ☎ 854260.
ℹ Granada Motorway Service Area (M 25), RM16 3BG ☎ 863733.

Granada Lodge without rest., RM16 3BG, ☎ 891111, Fax 860971, Reservations (Freephone) 0800 555300 – TV ☎ P. AE VISA.
4.00 – **44 rm** 39.95 **st.**

ATS Units 13/14, Eastern Av., Waterglade Ind. Park, West Thurrock, Grays ☎ 862237

TICEHURST E. Sussex 404 V 30 – ✉ Wadhurst – ☎ 01580.
18 Dale Hill Hotel, Ticehurst ☎ 200112.

Dale Hill Golf H., TN5 7DQ, NE : ½ m. on A 268 ☎ 200112, Fax 201249, 18, park – TV ☎ P – 30. AE VISA
Meals 8.50/15.00 **st.** and a la carte 5.10 – 3.00 – **31 rm** 60.00/130.00 **t.**, 1 suite.

TICKTON Humbs. – see Beverley.

TILSTON Ches. 402 403 L 24 – see Malpas.

TINTAGEL Cornwall 403 F 32 **The West Country G.** – pop. 1 721 – ECD : Wednesday except summer – ☎ 01840.
See : Arthur's Castle (site★★★) *AC* – Tintagel Church★ – Old Post Office★ *AC.*
Envir. : Delabole Quarry★ *AC,* SE : 4½ m. by B 3263.
Exc. : Camelford★, SE : 6½ m. by B 3263 and B 3266.
♦London 264 – Exeter 63 – ♦Plymouth 49 – Truro 41.

Wootons Country, Fore St., PL34 0DD, ☎ 770170, Fax 770978 – TV ☎ P. VISA.
Meals (bar lunch)/dinner 14.50 **t.** and a la carte 3.75 – **11 rm** 25.00/80.00 **t.** – SB.

Trebrea Lodge, Trenale, PL34 0HR, SE : 1 m. by Boscastle Rd (B 3263) and Trenale Lane on Trewarmett rd ☎ 770410, ←, « Part 18C manor house, 14C origins », – TV ☎ P. AE VISA
Meals (dinner only) 16.00 **t.** 4.10 – **7 rm** 45.00/72.00 **t.**

Bossiney House, Bossiney Rd, PL34 0AX, NE : ½ m. on B 3263 ☎ 770240, Fax 770501, – P. AE VISA
April-October – **Meals** (bar lunch)/dinner 13.00 **st.** 4.15 – **19 rm** 29.00/52.00 **t.** – SB.

Trewarmett Lodge, Trewarmett, PL34 0ET, S : 1½ m. on B 3263 ☎ 770460 – rm P. AE VISA
April to October – **Meals** 12.95 **t.** and a la carte 4.60 – **6 rm** 18.00/38.00 **t.** – SB.

Old Millfloor, Trebarwith, PL34 0HA, S : 1¾ m. by B 3263 ☎ 770234, « Former flour mill », park – TV P.
March-November – **Meals** (by arrangement) 11.00 – **3 rm** 17.00/34.00.

Old Borough House, Bossiney Rd, PL34 0AY, NE : ½ m. on B 3263 ☎ 770475 – rest P.
Meals 10.00 **s.** – **5 rm** 29.50/39.00 **s.**

TODDINGTON SERVICE AREA Beds. 404 S 28 – pop. 3 999 – ✉ Luton – ☎ 01525.

Granada Lodge without rest., LU5 6HR, M 1 junction 12 (southbound carriageway) ☎ 875150, Fax 878452, Reservations (Freephone) 0800 555300 – TV ☎ P. AE VISA.
4.00 – **40 rm** 39.95 **st.**

TODWICK S. Yorks. – pop. 1 639 – ✉ Sheffield – ☎ 01909.
♦London 161 – ♦Nottingham 35 – ♦Sheffield 10.

Red Lion, Worksop Rd, S31 0DJ, on A 57 ☎ 771654, Fax 773704 – rm TV ☎ P – 70. VISA
Meals 8.95/19.45 **t.** and a la carte – 5.00 – **30 rm** 39.95 **t.**

TONBRIDGE Kent 404 U 30 – pop. 34 407 – ECD : Wednesday – ☎ 01732.
18 Poult Wood, Higham Lane ☎ 364039.
ℹ Tonbridge Castle, Castle St., TN9 1BG ☎ 770929.
♦London 33 – ♦Brighton 37 – Hastings 31 – Maidstone 14.

Rose and Crown (Forte), 125 High St., TN9 1DD, ☎ 357966, Fax 357194 – TV ☎ P – 100. AE VISA JCB
Meals 11.95/15.95 **t.** and a la carte 6.70 – 8.50 – **48 rm** 55.00/70.00 **st.** – SB.

The Office, 163 High St., TN9 1BX, ☎ 353660 – AE VISA JCB
closed Sunday and Bank Holidays – **Meals** a la carte 11.60/14.30 **t.**

at Golden Green NE : 4 m. by Three Elm Lane off A 26 – ✉ Tonbridge – ☎ 01732 :

Goldhill Mill without rest., TN11 0BA, ☎ 851626, Fax 851881, « Part Tudor and Georgian water mill », park, – TV ☎ P. VISA.
closed 16 July-31 August and 25-26 December – **3 rm** 55.00/72.50 **st.**

ATS 61/63 Pembury Rd ☎ 353800/352231

TORCROSS Devon 403 J 33 – see Kingsbridge.

TORQUAY Devon 403 J 32 **The West Country G.** – pop. 54 430 – ECD : Wednesday and Saturday – ☎ 01803.

See : Torbay★ – Kent's Cavern★ *AC* CX A – **Envir.** : Cockington★, W : 1 m. AX.

Petitor Rd, St. Marychurch ☎ 314591, B.

Vaughan Parade, TQ2 5JG ☎ 297428.

♦London 223 – Exeter 23 – ♦Plymouth 32.

Plans on following pages

Imperial (Forte), Parkhill Rd, TQ1 2DG, ☎ 294301, Telex 42849, Fax 298293, ≤ Torbay, heated, , squash – rm rest – 350. AE VISA JCB CZ **a**
Meals 17.00/32.00 **t.** and dinner a la carte 7.50 – 10.00 – **150 rm** 125.00/145.00 **t.**, 17 suites – SB.

Grand, Seafront, TQ2 6NT, ☎ 296677, Fax 213462, ≤, heated, – rm – 300. AE VISA BZ **z**
Meals (dancing Saturday evening) 13.50/18.50 **st.** and a la carte – **101 rm** 75.00/120.00 **st.**, 11 suites – SB.

Palace, Babbacombe Rd, TQ1 3TG, ☎ 200200, Fax 299899, « Extensive gardens », heated, park, squash – rm – 350. AE VISA CX **u**
Meals 13.50/20.50 **t.** and a la carte 5.80 – **134 rm** (dinner included) 63.00/126.00 **t.**, 6 suites – SB.

Corbyn Head, Seafront, TQ2 6RH, ☎ 213611, Fax 296152, ≤, heated – AE VISA BX **a**
Meals (bar lunch)/dinner 18.50 **st.** and a la carte 4.95 – **51 rm** 50.00/130.00 **t.** – SB.

Osborne, Hesketh Cres., Meadfoot, TQ1 2LL, ☎ 213311, Fax 296788, ≤, heated, – – 80. AE VISA CX **n**
Raffles : **Meals** (in bar) a la carte 10.25/16.15 **t.** 4.85 – (see also *Langtry's* below) – **23 rm** (dinner included) 65.00/180.00 **st.** – SB.

Abbey Lawn, Scarborough Rd, TQ2 5UQ, ☎ 299199, Fax 291460, ≤, heated, – – 80 CY **c**
54 rm, 1 suite.

Livermead Cliff, Seafront, TQ2 6RQ, ☎ 299666, Telex 42424, Fax 294496, ≤, heated, – – 70. AE VISA BX **r**
Meals 7.95/17.00 **st.** and a la carte 4.95 – **64 rm** 34.00/110.00 **st.** – SB.

Livermead House, Seafront, TQ2 6QJ, ☎ 294361, Fax 200758, ≤, heated, squash – – 80. AE VISA BZ **e**
Meals 10.00/21.00 **st.** and a la carte 4.75 – **64 rm** (dinner included) 60.00/120.00 **st.** – SB.

Homers, Warren Rd, TQ2 5TN, ☎ 213456, Fax 213458, ≤ Torbay, – rest CZ **n**
13 rm, 1 suite.

Albaston House, 27 St. Marychurch Rd, TQ1 3JF, ☎ 296758 – VISA JCB
closed December – **Meals** 10.00/15.00 **st.** and dinner a la carte 4.00 – **13 rm** 27.00/54.00 **st.** CY **a**

Fairmount House, Herbert Rd, Chelston, TQ2 6RW, ☎ 605446, Fax 605446, – rest AE VISA AX **a**
early March-early November – **Meals** *(closed Sunday dinner)* (bar lunch)/dinner 11.00 **t.** 4.85 – **8 rm** 29.00/58.00 **t.** – SB.

Glenorleigh, 26 Cleveland Rd, TQ2 5BE, ☎ 292135, Fax 292135, heated, – rest VISA BY **n**
mid January-mid October – **Meals** (by arrangement) 2.50 – **16 rm** 20.00/40.00 **st.** – SB.

Cranborne, 58 Belgrave Rd, TQ2 5HY, ☎ 298046 – rest VISA BY **i**
closed December – **Meals** (by arrangement) – **12 rm** (dinner included) 20.00/58.00 **st.** – SB.

Belmont, 66 Belgrave Rd, TQ2 5HY, ☎ 295028, Fax 295028 – AE VISA
Meals 8.50 **t.** – **13 rm** 14.00/38.00 **t.** – SB. BY **i**

Langtry's (at Osborne H.), Hesketh Cres., Meadfoot, TQ1 2LL, ☎ 213311, Fax 296788, ≤ – AE VISA CX **n**
Meals *(closed Sundays November - February)* (dinner only) a la carte 21.75/22.50 **st.** 4.85.

Remy's, 3 Croft Rd, TQ2 5UF, ☎ 292359 – VISA CY **x**
closed Sunday, Monday and 1 week Christmas – **Meals** - French (booking essential) (dinner only) 12.85 **t.** 5.00.

Mulberry Room with rm, 1 Scarborough Rd, TQ2 5UJ, ☎ 213639 – CY **x**
Meals *(closed Monday and Tuesday)* 9.50/16.50 **st.** and lunch a la carte 5.50 – **3 rm** 25.00/42.00 **st.** – SB.

Village Brasserie, 5 Ilsham Rd, Wellswood, TQ1 2JG, ☎ 290855 – AE VISA CX **r**
closed Saturday lunch and Sunday except lunch November-March – **Meals** a la carte 7.00/12.00 **st.** and a la carte 4.25.

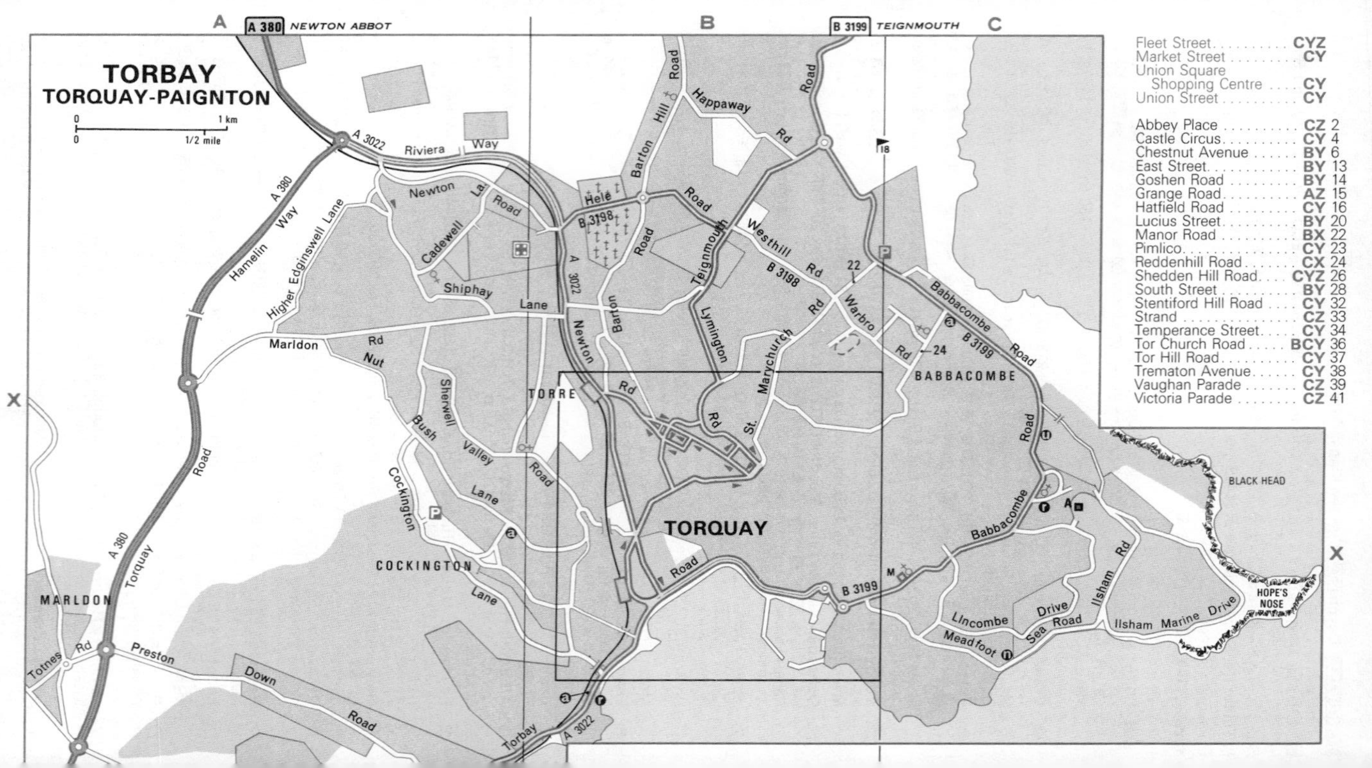
TORBAY
TORQUAY-PAIGNTON
0 1 km
0 1/2 mile
A
B
C
X
A 380 NEWTON ABBOT
B 3199 TEIGNMOUTH
18
TORQUAY
BABBACOMBE
TORRE
COCKINGTON
MARLDON
BLACK HEAD
HOPE'S NOSE
Fleet Street CYZ
Market Street CY
Union Square Shopping Centre CY
Union Street CY
Abbey Place CZ 2
Castle Circus CY 4
Chestnut Avenue BY 6
East Street BY 13
Goshen Road BY 14
Grange Road AZ 15
Hatfield Road CY 16
Lucius Street BY 20
Manor Road BX 22
Pimlico CY 23
Reddenhill Road CX 24
Shedden Hill Road CYZ 26
South Street BY 28
Stentiford Hill Road CY 32
Strand CZ 33
Temperance Street CY 34
Tor Church Road BCY 36
Tor Hill Road CY 37
Trematon Avenue CY 38
Vaughan Parade CZ 39
Victoria Parade CZ 41

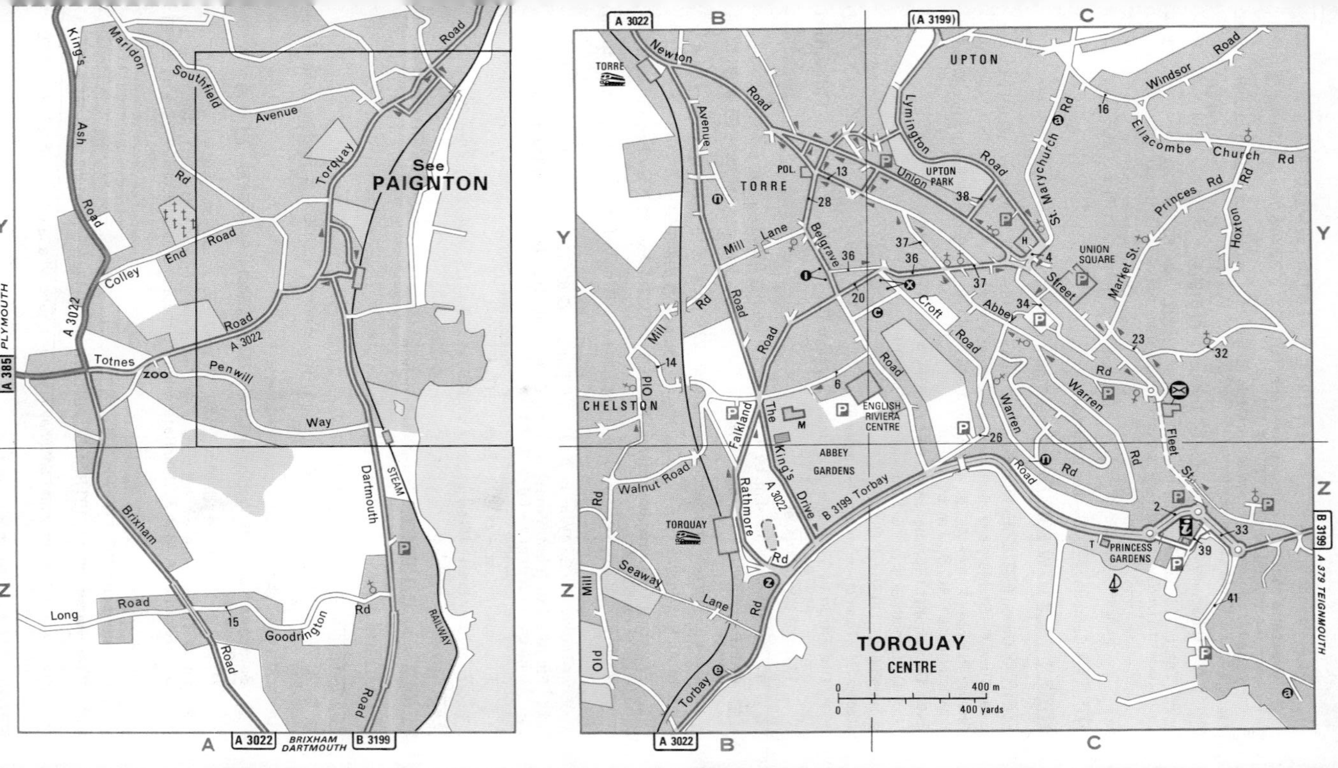

See PAIGNTON
TORQUAY CENTRE
A 385 PLYMOUTH
A 3022 BRIXHAM DARTMOUTH B 3199
A 3022
(A 3199)
B 3199 A 379 TEIGNMOUTH
King's Ash Road
Marldon Rd
Southfield Avenue
Torquay Road
Colley End Road
Totnes Road
A 3022
ZOO
Penwill Way
Dartmouth Road
STEAM RAILWAY
Brixham Road
Long Road
Goodrington Rd
TORRE
Newton Road
Avenue Road
UPTON
Lymington Road
Union
UPTON PARK
POL.
Mill Lane
Belgrave Road
Croft Road
Abbey Road
Street
UNION SQUARE
St. Marychurch Rd
Windsor Road
Ellacombe Church Rd
Princes Rd
Hoxton Rd
Market St.
Warren Rd
Fleet St.
CHELSTON
Old Mill Rd
Falkland
The King's Drive
A 3022
ENGLISH RIVIERA CENTRE
ABBEY GARDENS
B 3199 Torbay Road
Rathmore Rd
Walnut Road
TORQUAY
Seaway Lane
Torbay Rd
PRINCESS GARDENS
0 400 m
0 400 yards

at Maidencombe N : 3 ½ m. by B 3199 – BX – ✉ Torquay – ☎ 01803 :

Orestone Manor ⛺, Rockhouse Lane, TQ1 4SX, ✆ 328098, Fax 328336, ←, heated, – rest TV ☎ P. AE VISA. closed 2 January - 4 February – **Meals** (dinner only and Sunday lunch)/dinner 27.50 **st.** 5.00 – **18 rm** (dinner included) 80.00/200.00 **st.** – SB.

at Babbacombe NE : 1 ½ m. – ✉ Torquay – ☎ 01803 :

XX **Table,** 135 Babbacombe Rd, TQ1 3SR, ✆ 324292 – . VISA CX **a**
closed Monday, 1 to 18 February and 1 to 18 September – **Meals** (booking essential) (dinner only) 26.00/28.00 **t.** 5.00.

ATS 20 Tor Church Rd ✆ 293985 ATS 100 Teignmouth Rd ✆ 329495

TORVER Cumbria 402 K 20 – see Coniston.

TOTLAND BAY I.O.W. 403 404 P 31 – see Wight (Isle of).

TOTNES Devon 403 I 32 **The West Country G.** – pop. 7 018 – ECD : Thursday – ☎ 01803.

See : Town★ – St. Mary's★ – Butterwalk★ – Castle (←★★★) *AC.*

Envir. : Paignton Zoo★★ *AC*, E : 4 ½ m. by A 385 and A 3022 – British Photographic Museum, Bowden House★ *AC*, S : 1 m. by A 381.

Exc. : Dartmouth★★ (Castle ←★★★) SE : 12 m. by A 381 and A 3122.

18, 9 Dartmouth Golf & C C, Blackawton ✆ 7421686.

The Plains, TQ9 5EJ ✆ 863168.

London 224 – Exeter 24 – Plymouth 23 – Torquay 9.

Old Forge at Totnes without rest., Seymour Pl., TQ9 5AY, ✆ 862174, « 14C working forge », – TV P. VISA.
10 rm 30.00/60.00 **st.**

at Stoke Gabriel SE : 4 m. by A 385 – ✉ Totnes – ☎ 01803 :

Gabriel Court ⛺, TQ9 6SF, ✆ 782206, Fax 782333, heated, , – TV ☎ P. AE VISA
Meals (dinner only and Sunday lunch)/dinner 22.00 **st.** 4.60 – **19 rm** 53.00/77.00 **st.**

at Ashprington S : 3 ½ m. by A 381 – ✉ Totnes – ☎ 01803 :

Waterman's Arms, Bow Bridge, TQ9 7EG, ✆ 732214, Fax 732214, « Part 15C inn », – TV ☎ P. VISA
Meals (bar lunch Monday to Saturday)/dinner a la carte 11.40/18.65 **t.** 4.00 – **10 rm** 35.00/66.00 – SB.

at Tuckenhay S : 4 ¼ m. by A 381 – ✉ Totnes – ☎ 01803 :

XX **Floyd's Inn (sometimes)** with rm, Bow Creek, TQ9 7EQ, ✆ 732350, Fax 732651, ←, « Riverside setting » – TV ☎ P. VISA
closed 23 December - 1 January – **Meals** – ***Restaurant*** *: (closed Saturday lunch, Sunday and Tuesday)* 37.50 **st.** – 9.00 – **3 rm** 125.00/175.00 **st.**

X **The Canteen** – **Meals** (in bar) 7.50/32.00 **st.** and a la carte 24.50/31.50 **st.**

ATS Babbage Rd ✆ 862086

TOTON Notts. 402 403 404 Q 25 – see Nottingham.

TOTTENHILL Norfolk – see King's Lynn.

TOWCESTER Northants. 403 404 R 27 – pop. 7 006 – ☎ 01327.

18, 18, 9 West Park G. & C.C., Whittlebury, Towcester ✆ 858092 – 18 Farthingstone Hotel ✆ 361533.

London 70 – Birmingham 50 – Northampton 9 – Oxford 36.

Saracens Head, 219 Watling St., NN12 7BX, ✆ 350414, Fax 359879 – TV ☎ P – 30. AE VISA.
Meals 9.95/19.95 **t.** and a la carte 5.50 – **21 rm** 55.00/75.00 **st.** – SB.

Forte Travelodge without rest., East Towcester bypass, NN12 6TQ, SW : ½ m. by Brackley rd on A 43 ✆ 359105, Reservations (Freephone) 0800 850950 – TV P. AE VISA.
33 rm 33.50 **t.**

at Paulerspury SE : 3 ¼ m. by A 5 – ✉ Towcester – ☎ 01327 :

XX **Vine House** with rm, 100 High St., NN12 7NA, ✆ 811267, Fax 811309, – TV ☎ P. VISA.
Meals *(closed Monday and Saturday lunch and Sunday)* a la carte 13.95/23.50 **t.** 5.00 – **6 rm** 38.80/61.10 **st.**

TOWERSEY Oxon. 404 R 28 – see Thame.

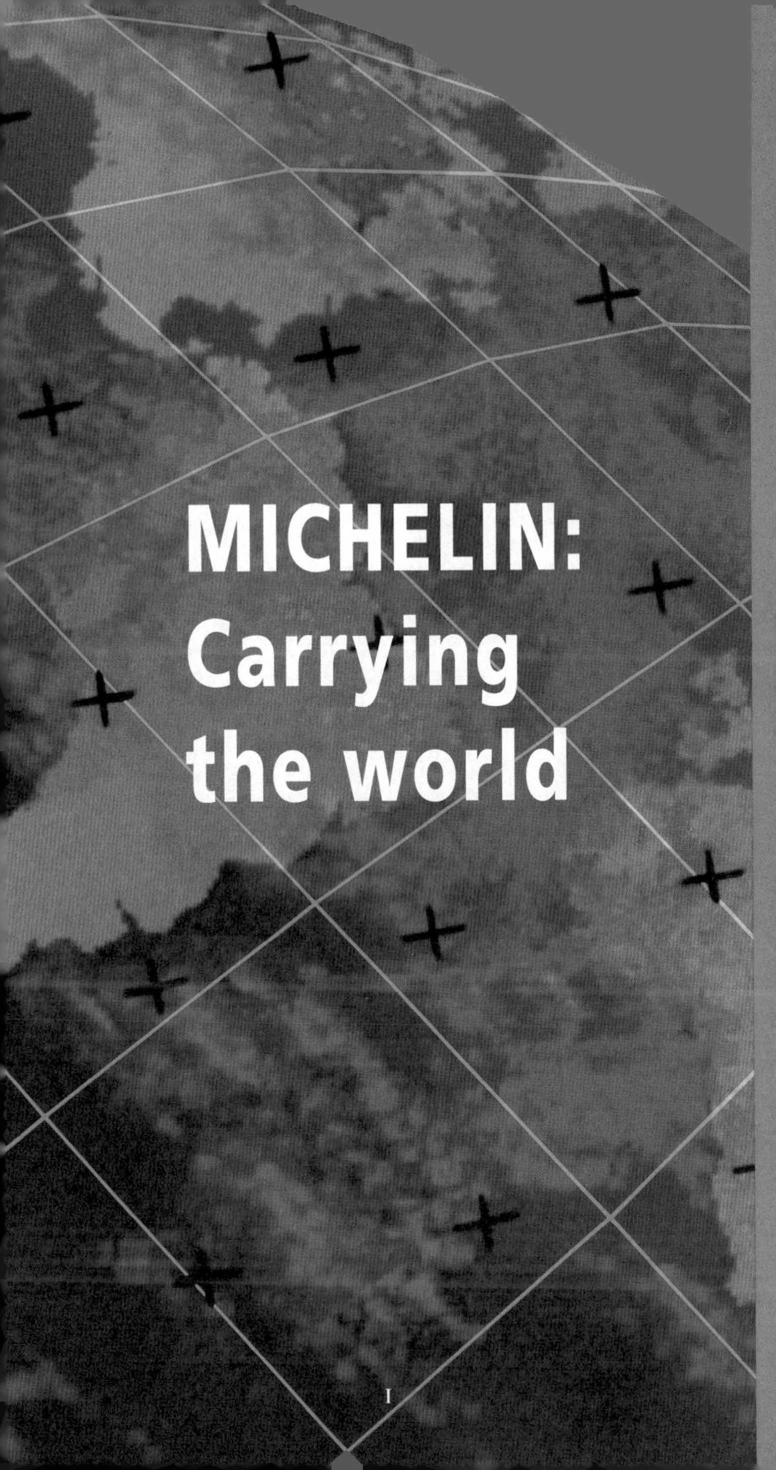
MICHELIN:
Carrying
the world

In every kind of weather, in every type of vehicle, people all over the world are making their way with Michelin.

Michelin is the world's number one tyre manufacturer and since it produced the first detachable pneumatic bicycle tyre in rural France in 1889, the company has expanded to cover more than 150 countries, with 125,000 employees making, selling and distributing 655,000 tyres every day. In addition, Michelin is a European leader in travel publishing and every day thousands of travellers reach their destinations thanks to Michelin Maps and Guides.

Michelin has total commitment to the quality of its products and a single-minded dedication to people on the move. That is why it spends more on Research and Development than any other tyre company, and not surprisingly has an outstanding record for innovation. In 1995, this record is set to continue with the revolutionary new Michelin Energy tyre, saving millions of pounds on fuel and helping to significantly reduce exhaust emissions.

As vehicles develop, there will be even more need for the highest quality tyres to meet the new demands of the road. Which is why Michelin continues to work closely with manufacturers in anticipation of the vehicles of tomorrow, carrying the public and the transport industry safely into the future.

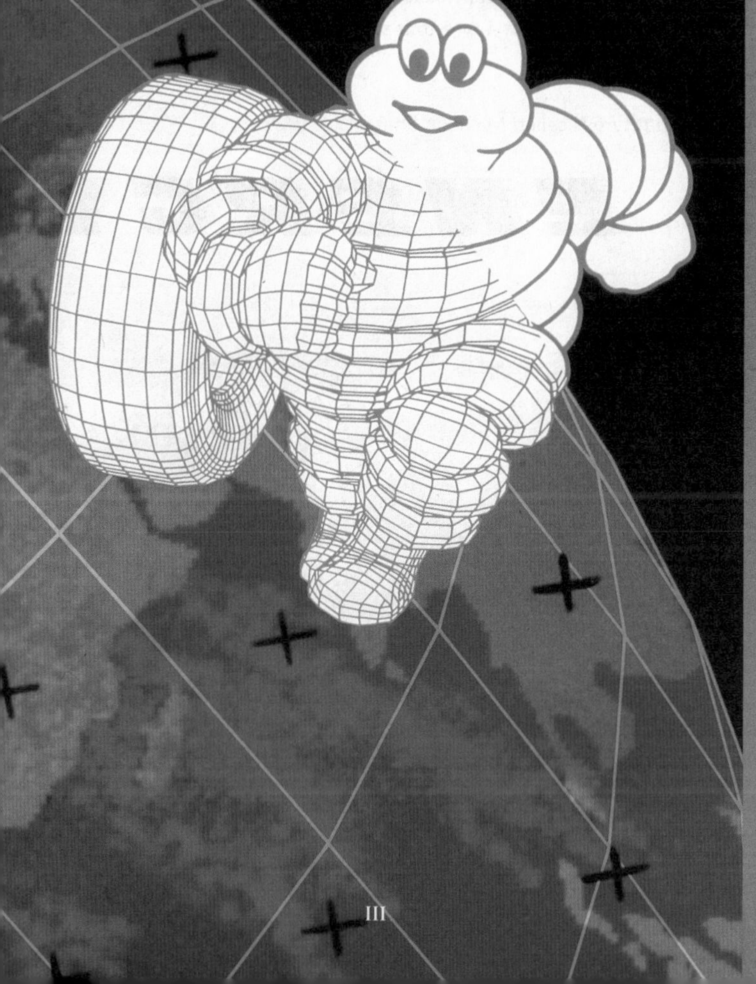

DRIVING FOR A BETTER FUTURE

As cars improve and roads develop, motorists are clocking up more miles than ever before.

As a result, safety and comfort are of prime importance, while at the same time there is a growing need to save fuel, to cut the cost of travel and help reduce exhaust emissions.

To meet these challenges, drivers need a tyre that improves fuel economy, but also provides maximum grip and ride quality. And thanks to Michelin, that concept is now a reality with the launch of a tyre that sets new standards for safety and economy.

That tyre is called Michelin Energy.

ENERGY

Michelin Energy improves fuel consumption by 5% by reducing the resistance caused by the tyre on the road. In other words, the car rolls more easily and less fuel is needed to drive it forward. However, when it comes to braking and cornering, Michelin Energy maintains the superb grip and reassuring handling that is true of all Michelin tyres. Never before have such levels of high performance been incorporated into such a fuel-efficient tyre.

5%

Michelin Energy is a major innovation for drivers, allowing them to economise on fuel and reduce pollution without compromising safety. In time, this advanced technology will be applied to other Michelin tyres, and wherever you see the Energy name you will find a practical solution to the problems of the environment as well as the superb driving capability you expect from Michelin.

Michelin Energy. Your choice for a better future.

COMMITTED TO CHOICE

The new Michelin Energy range gives drivers more choice for their vehicles, combining top performance with maximum efficiency. In recent years, Michelin has become committed to offering greater choice, ensuring that for every type of driver, there is a Michelin tyre to suit.

For example, the need for quality at the right price is satisfied by the new range of Michelin Classic tyres. They embody the traditional Michelin values of long life and superior grip and are offered at a price to suit the most cost-conscious motorist.

High performance drivers also have more options with Michelin, and the three tyres in the Pilot range allow them to make their vehicle more sporty, comfortable or stable over long distances, depending on their individual preference.

MICHELIN Pilot

Whatever car you drive, Michelin creates the perfect balance between your needs as a driver and the capability of your vehicle to give the smoothest and safest ride possible.

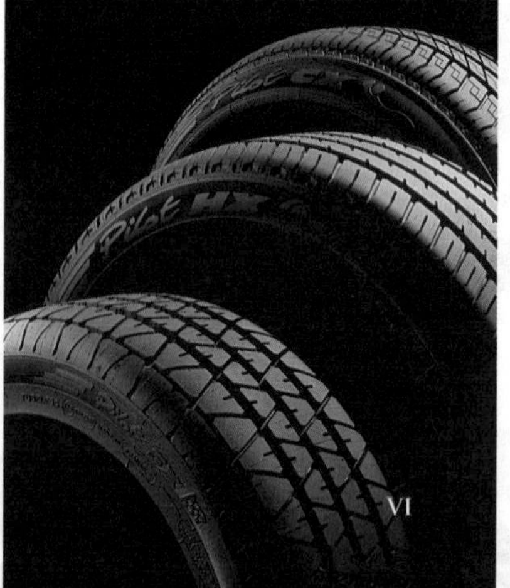

For full details of these and the many other Michelin tyres available for your car, contact your local tyre dealer.

LEADING THE WAY

For nearly 100 years, Michelin Maps and Guides have been showing travellers the clearest routes and essential sights at destinations all over the world. Today, Michelin is one of the largest travel publishers in Europe with a range of over 250 regularly updated titles.

Before and during a trip, motorists find the best plans for the journey ahead laid out in Michelin road maps and atlases. These range from large scale route planners to detailed local maps and are well known for their quality and accuracy.

On arrival, the dilemma of what to do is solved by Michelin Green Guides. These easy-to-follow tourist guides cover Western Europe and North America and provide detailed information on local geography and history, with town plans, lists of museums and opening times of many civic amenities.

At the end of the day when you want a bite to eat and a place to sleep, Michelin Red Hotel and Restaurant Guides provide reviews of literally thousands of establishments from low cost inns to luxury hotels. And when you are travelling with children, Michelin I-Spy books will keep them occupied for hours with a vast range of topics from airports to zoos.

Used together, Michelin Maps and Guides provide everything you need to get the most from your visit. They make sense of even the longest journey and are widely available at bookshops or directly from Michelin.

RACING FOR CHANGE

Few things are tougher on tyres than the race track. In fact, Michelin uses motorsport to develop better tyres for the road, and in 1994, Michelin race tyres were being pushed harder than ever.

In the British Touring Car Championship, Michelin shod cars took the driver, manufacturer and team titles using tyres very similar to the Pilot range for road use. Meanwhile, in the British Rally Championships, Michelin Pilot Team Ford drivers Malcolm Wilson and Stephen Finlay secured first and second places respectively.

Michelin also made its mark on the World Rally Championship, entering its 21st year in the competition with Mitsubishi, Ford and last year's winners Toyota all choosing Michelin tyres.

Of course, Michelin's domination of the racing world is not limited to four wheels and from the roar of Mick Doohan's world championship motorcycle victory to the sweat of the professional cycle circuit, Michelin tyres could be seen leading the field.

With Michelin, success improves the product and throughout 1995, as Michelin winners continue to take the chequered flag, the real winners will be the thousands of private drivers and riders who use Michelin tyres everyday.

TREGONY Cornwall 403 F 33 **The West Country G.** – pop. 670 – ✉ Truro – ☎ 01872.
Envir. : Trewithen*** *AC*, N : 2½ m.
♦London 291 – Newquay 18 – Plymouth 53 – Truro 10.

- **Tregony House,** 15 Fore St., TR2 5RN, ☎ 530671, – P.
March-October – **Meals** (by arrangement) **st.** – **6 rm** 19.25/44.50 **st.**

TREGREHAN Cornwall 403 F 32 – see St. Austell.

TRERICE Cornwall 403 E 32 – see Newquay.

TRESCO Cornwall 403 ㉚ – see Scilly (Isles of).

TREYARNON BAY Cornwall 403 E 32 – see Padstow.

TRING Herts. 404 S 28 – pop. 10 610 – ECD : Wednesday – ☎ 01442.
♦London 38 – Aylesbury 7 – Luton 14.

- Pendley Manor, Cow Lane, HP23 5QY, E : 1½ m. by B 4635 off B 4251 ☎ 891891, Fax 890687, park, – TV ☎ P – 200
71 rm.
- **Rose and Crown,** High St., HP23 5AH, ☎ 824071, Fax 890735 – rm TV ☎ P – 70. AE VISA.
Meals (bar lunch Saturday) 9.95/15.95 **t.** and a la carte 5.50 – **27 rm** 59.50/85.00 **t.** – SB.
- **Travel Inn,** Tring Hill, HP23 4LD, W : 1½ m. on A 41 ☎ 824819, Fax 890787 – rm TV P. AE VISA.
closed 24 to 26 December – **Meals** (Beefeater grill) a la carte approx. 16.00 **t.** – 4.95 – **30 rm** 33.50 **t.**

Michelin n'accroche pas de panonceau aux hôtels et restaurants qu'il signale.

TROTTON W. Sussex – see Midhurst.

TROUTBECK Cumbria 402 L 20 – see Windermere.

TROWBRIDGE Wilts. 403 404 N 30 **The West Country G.** – pop. 25 279 – ECD : Wednesday – ☎ 01225.
Envir. : Westwood Manor*, NW : 3 m. by A 363 – Farleigh Hungerford Castle* (St. Leonard's Chapel*) *AC*, W : 4 m.
Exc. : Longleat House*** *AC*, SW : 12 m. by A 363, A 350 and A 362 - Bratton Castle (≤**) SE : 7½ m. by A 363 and B 3098 – Steeple Ashton* (The Green*) E : 6 m. – Edington (St. Mary, St. Katherine and All Saints*) SE : 7½ m.
St. Stephen's Pl., BA14 8AH ☎ 777054.
♦London 115 – ♦Bristol 27 – ♦Southampton 55 – Swindon 32.

- **Old Manor**, Trowle, BA14 9BL, NW : 1 m. on A 363 ☎ 777393, Fax 765443, « Queen Anne house of 15C origin », – TV ☎ P. AE VISA JCB.
closed Christmas-New Year – **Meals** *(closed Sunday)* (residents only) (dinner only) a la carte 13.15/22.40 **t.** 3.75 – **14 rm** 45.00/65.00 **t.**
- **Hilbury Court,** Hilperton Rd, BA14 7JW, NE : ¼ m. on A 361 ☎ 752949, Fax 777990, – rest TV ☎ P. VISA.
closed 24 December-1 January – **Meals** *(closed dinner Friday to Sunday and Bank Holidays)* (residents only) (bar lunch)/dinner 14.00 **st.** 4.40 – **13 rm** 36.00/52.00 **st.**
- **Brookfield House** without rest., Vaggs Hill, Wingfield, BA14 9NA, SW : 4 m. by A 366 on B 3109 ☎ 830615, « Working farm », park – rm TV P.
closed 1 week Christmas – **3 rm** 25.00/40.00 **st.**

at Hilperton NE : 1¾ m. on A 361 – ✉ Trowbridge – ☎ 01225 :

- Lion and Fiddle, BA14 7QQ, ☎ 776392, – TV ☎ P
5 rm.

at Semington NE : 3 m. by A 361 on A 350 – ✉ Trowbridge – ☎ 01380 :

- **Highfield House,** BA14 6JN, on A 350 ☎ 870554 – P. AE VISA
closed Monday lunch and Sunday dinner – **Meals** 10.25/15.00 **t.** 4.75.

ATS Canal Rd, Ladydown Trading Est. ☎ 753469

TRURO Cornwall 403 E 33 **The West Country G.** – pop. 16 522 – ECD : Thursday – ☎ 01872.
See : Royal Cornwall Museum* *AC*.
Envir. : Trelissick garden** (≤**) *AC*, S : 4 m. by A 39 – Feock (Church*) S : 5 m. by A 39 and B 3289.
Exc. : Trewithen***, NE : 7½ m. by A 39 and A 390.
18 Treliske ☎ 72640.
Municipal Buildings, Boscawen St., TR1 2NE ☎ 74555.
♦London 295 – Exeter 87 – Penzance 26 – ♦Plymouth 52.

Alverton Manor, Tregolls Rd, TR1 1XQ, ✆ 76633, Fax 222989, « Mid 19C manor house, former Bishop's residence and convent », – rest – 150.
Meals 9.95/16.95 **st.** and dinner a la carte 4.95 – **34 rm** 59.00/120.00 **st.** – SB.

Royal, Lemon St., TR1 2QB, ✆ 70345, Fax 42453 – rm – 40.
Meals a la carte 10.15/18.40 **t.** – **34 rm** 49.00/65.00 **st.** – SB.

Laniley House without rest., Newquay Rd, nr. Trispen, TR4 9AU, NE : 3½ m. by A 39 and A 3076 on Frogmore rd ✆ 75201, – .
closed Christmas and New Year – **3 rm** 25.00/36.00.

Blue Haze without rest., The Parade, Malpas Rd, TR1 1QE, ✆ 223553, Fax 223553, – .
3 rm 20.00/36.00.

Conifers without rest., 36 Tregolls Rd, TR1 1LA, ✆ 79925 – .
4 rm 17.00/34.00.

at Blackwater W : 7 m. by A 390 – ✉ Truro – ☎ 01872 :

Pennypots (Viner), TR4 8EY, SW : ¾ m. ✆ (01209) 820347 – .
closed Sunday, Monday and 4 weeks winter – **Meals** (dinner only) a la carte 21.20/27.50 **t.**
Spec. Pan fried scallops with a garlic and herb beurre blanc, Roast sea bass fillets on a soy sauce flavoured with coriander and ginger, A chocolate, orange and crème fraîche flavoured dessert, cherry coulis.

ATS Tabernacle St. ✆ 74083 ATS Newham Rd ✆ 40353

Piante di città : *le vie sono selezionate in funzione della loro importanza per la circolazione e l'ubicazione degli edifici citati.*

Non indichiamo che l'inizio delle vie secondarie.

TRUSHAM Devon – ✉ Newton Abbot – ☎ 01626.

Cridford Inn, TQ13 0NR, ✆ 853694, « 11C former hall house » – rest .
closed 2 weeks January and 1 week June – **Meals** *(closed Sunday and Monday dinner)* (booking essential) (bar lunch)/dinner 15.75 **st.** 3.75 – **4 rm** 37.50/55.00 **st.** – SB.

TUCKENHAY Devon – see Totnes.

TUNBRIDGE WELLS Kent 404 U 30 – see Royal Tunbridge Wells.

TURNERS HILL W. Sussex 404 T 30 – ☎ 01342.
London 33 – Brighton 24 – Crawley 7.

Alexander House , RH10 4QD, E : 1 m. on B 2110 ✆ 714914, Fax 717328, ←, « Part 17C country house in extensive parkland », – rest .
Meals 14.75/30.00 **t.** and a la carte 7.50 – 12.50 – **9 rm** 95.00/125.00 **t.**, 6 suites.

TUTBURY Staffs. 402 403 404 O 25 **Great Britain G.** – pop. 3 805 (inc. Hatton) – ECD : Wednesday – ✉ Burton-upon-Trent – ☎ 01283.
Envir. : Sudbury Hall★★ *AC*, NW : 5½m. by A 50.
London 132 – Birmingham 33 – Derby 11 – Stoke-on-Trent 27.

Ye Olde Dog and Partridge, High St., DE13 9LS, ✆ 813030, Fax 813178, « Part 15C timbered inn », – .
accommodation closed 25 December and 1 January – **Meals** (carving rest.) 9.50/15.65 **t.** 4.75 – **17 rm** 52.50/78.00 **t.**

Mill House without rest., Cornmill Lane, DE13 9HA, SE : ½ m. ✆ 813634, « Georgian house and watermill », – .
closed 25 and 26 December – **3 rm** 35.00/55.00 **st.**

TWO BRIDGES Devon 403 I 32 **The West Country G.** – ✉ Yelverton – ☎ 01822.
Envir. : Dartmoor National Park★★ (Brent Tor ←★★, Haytor Rocks ←★).
London 226 – Exeter 25 – Plymouth 17.

Prince Hall , PL20 6SA, E : 1 m. on B 3357 ✆ 890403, Fax 890676, ←, – rest .
closed mid December-mid January – **Meals** (dinner only) 19.50 **t.** 4.45 – **8 rm** (dinner included) 47.50/95.00 **t.** – SB.

TWO MILLS Ches. – see Chester.

TYNEMOUTH Tyne and Wear 401 402 P 18 – pop. 8 921 – ECD : Wednesday – ☎ 0191.
London 290 – Newcastle upon Tyne 8 – Sunderland 7.

Hope House, 47 Percy Gdns, NE30 4HH, ✆ 257 1989, Fax 257 1989, ←, « Tastefully furnished Victorian house » – .
Meals (communal dining) (unlicensed) (dinner only) 13.50 **s.** and a la carte – **3 rm** 35.00/47.50 **s.** – SB.

UCKFIELD E. Sussex 404 U 31 – pop. 12 087 – ECD : Wednesday – 01825.

London 45 – Brighton 17 – Eastbourne 20 – Maidstone 34.

Horsted Place, Little Horsted, TN22 5TS, S : 2 ½ m. by B 2102 and A 22 on A 26 750581, Fax 750459, ≤, « Victorian Gothic country house and gardens », 18, park, – rest – 100. AE VISA
Meals 14.95/30.00 **t.** and a la carte 5.75 – 7.50 – **3 rm** 130.00/180.00 **t.**, **14 suites** 250.00/325.00 **t.** – SB.

Hooke Hall, 250 High St., TN22 1EN, 761578, Fax 768025, « Queen Anne town house », – . VISA.
closed 23 December - 1 January – **Meals** *(closed Saturday lunch and Sunday)* a la carte 20.00/25.50 **t.** and a la carte 4.75 – 7.00 – **9 rm** 40.00/115.00 **st.**

ULLINGSWICK Heref. and Worcs. – pop. 237 – Hereford – 01432.

London 134 – Hereford 12 – Shrewsbury 52 – Worcester 19.

Steppes Country House, HR1 3JG, 820424, « Converted farmhouse of 14C origins », – . AE VISA
closed 3 weeks January and 2 weeks December – **Meals** (booking essential) (bar lunch)/dinner 22.50 **st.** and a la carte 5.50 – **6 rm** 45.00/76.00 – SB.

ULLSWATER Cumbria 402 L 20 – Penrith – 0176 84.

Main Car Park, Glenridding, CA11 0PA 82414 (summer only) – The Square, Pooley Bridge, CA10 2NP 86530 (summer only).

London 296 – Carlisle 25 – Kendal 31 – Penrith 6.

at Howtown SW : 4 m. of Pooley Bridge – Penrith – 0176 84 :

Howtown, CA10 2ND, 86514, ≤, –
April-October – **Meals** 8.00/12.00 **t.** – **13 rm** 36.50/73.00 **t.**

at Pooley Bridge on B 5320 – Penrith – 0176 84 :

Sharrow Bay Country House, CA10 2LZ, S : 2 m. on Howtown rd 86301, Fax 86349, ≤ Ullswater and fells, « Lakeside setting, gardens, tasteful decor », – rest .
closed December to late February – **Meals** (booking essential) 29.75/39.75 **st.** and a la carte 31.50/41.50 **st.** – **22 rm** (dinner included) 125.00/250.00 **st.**, 6 suites.

at Watermillock on A 592 – Penrith – 0176 84 :

Leeming House (Forte), CA11 0JJ, on A 592 86622, Fax 86443, ≤, « Lakeside country house and gardens », park – . AE VISA JCB
Meals 28.50 **t.** (dinner) and lunch a la carte 15.80/27.40 **t.** 9.90 – 10.50 – **39 rm** 75.00/155.00 **t.** – SB.

Old Church, CA11 0JN, 86204, Fax 86368, ≤ Ullswater and fells, « Lakeside setting », , – rest . VISA.
April-October – **Meals** (booking essential) (dinner only)(closed Sunday) 22.50 **st.** 6.50 – **10 rm** 45.00/150.00 **st.**

Rampsbeck House, CA11 0LP, 86442, Fax 86688, ≤, , park – . VISA.
closed 4 January-mid February – **Meals** (lunch by arrangement)/dinner 25.00 **t.** 4.50 – **20 rm** 48.00/120.00 **t.**, 1 suite – SB.

Knotts Mill, CA11 0JN, 86472, Fax 86699, ≤, – rest . VISA.
closed 1 week Christmas – **Meals** 10.00 **st.** 4.50 – **9 rm** 32.00/52.00 **st.** – SB.

ULVERSTON Cumbria 402 K 21 – pop. 11 866 – ECD : Wednesday – 01229.

18 Bardsea Park 582824.

Coronation Hall, County Sq., LA12 7LZ 587120.

London 278 – Kendal 25 – Lancaster 36.

Trinity House, 1 Princes St., LA12 7NB, off A 590 587639, Fax 587639 – . AE VISA JCB
Meals *(closed Sunday to non residents)* (dinner only) 14.95 **t.** 4.50 – **6 rm** 43.00/65.00 **t.**

Church Walk House, Church Walk, LA12 7EW, 582211 – .
closed Christmas and New Year – **Meals** (by arrangement) 8.50/12.00 **s.** 3.00 – **3 rm** 15.00/38.00 **st.**

Bay Horse Inn with rm, Canal Foot, LA12 9EL, E : 2¼ m. by A 5087, Morecambe Rd and beyond Industrial area, on the coast 583972, Fax 580502, ≤ Morecambe bay – rest . VISA
closed 2 January-2 February – **Meals** *(closed lunch Sunday and Monday)* (booking essential) 14.50 **t.** (lunch) and a la carte 18.45/23.15 5.55 – **6 rm** (dinner included) 80.00/140.00 **t.** – SB.

at Spark Bridge N : 5 ½ m. by A 590 off A 5092 – ✉ Ulverston – ☎ 01229 :

XX **Bridgefield House** with rm, LA12 8DA, NW : 1 m. on Nibthwaite rd (first left after bridge) ☎ 885239, Fax 885379, ←, – rest ☎ P. VISA
closed 25 December – **Meals** (booking essential) (dinner only) 20.00 **t.** – **5 rm** 30.00/60.00 **t.** – SB.

ATS The Gill ☎ 583442

UMBERLEIGH Devon 403 I 31 – ☎ 01769.
♦London 218 – Barnstaple 7 – Exeter 31 – Taunton 49.

Rising Sun, EX37 9DU, on A 377 ☎ 60447, Fax 60764, – TV ☎ P. VISA
Meals 9.95/15.95 **st.** and a la carte 4.95 – **11 rm** 36.00/66.00 **st.** – SB.

UP HOLLAND Lancs. 402 M 23 – see Wigan.

UPLYME Devon 403 L 31 – see Lyme Regis.

UPPER BENEFIELD Northants. – see Oundle.

UPPER ODDINGTON Glos. – see Stow-on-the-Wold.

UPPER SLAUGHTER Glos. 403 404 O 28 – see Bourton-on-the-Water.

UPPINGHAM Leics. 404 R 26 – pop. 3 143 – ECD : Thursday – ☎ 01572.
♦London 101 – ♦Leicester 19 – Northampton 28 – ♦Nottingham 35.

Rutland House without rest., 61 High St. East, LE15 9PY, ☎ 822497, Fax 822497, – TV P. VISA
4 rm 29.00/39.00 **st.**

XX **Lake Isle** with rm, 16 High St. East, LE15 9PZ, ☎ 822951, Fax 822951 – TV ☎. AE VISA
Meals *(closed Monday lunch and Sunday dinner to non-residents)* 13.50/21.00 **t.** 5.90 – **10 rm** 45.00/66.00 **t.**, 2 suites – SB.

at Morcott Service Area E : 4 ¼ m. by A 6003 on A 47 – ✉ Uppingham – ☎ 01572 :

Forte Travelodge without rest., Glaston Rd, LE15 8SA, ☎ 87719, Reservations (Freephone) 0800 850950 – TV & P. AE VISA.
40 rm 33.50 **t.**

UPTON ST. LEONARDS Glos. – see Gloucester.

UPTON SNODSBURY Heref. and Worcs. 403 404 N 27 – see Worcester.

UPTON-UPON-SEVERN Heref. and Worcs. 403 404 N 27 – pop. 2 561 – ECD : Thursday – ☎ 01684.
Pepperpot, Church St., WR8 0HT ☎ 594200 (summer only).
♦London 116 – Hereford 25 – Stratford-upon-Avon 29 – Worcester 11.

White Lion, High St., WR8 0HJ, ☎ 592551, Fax 592551 – TV ☎ P. AE VISA
closed 25 and 26 December – **Meals** 15.25 **t.** and a la carte 4.95 – **10 rm** 54.50/74.50 **t.** – SB.

Pool House without rest., Hanley Rd, WR8 0PA, NW : ½ m. on B 4211 ☎ 592151, ←, , – P. VISA.
closed Christmas and New Year – **9 rm** 31.50/56.00 **s.**

UTTOXETER Staffs. 402 403 404 O 25 **Great Britain G.** – pop. 11 707 – ECD : Thursday – ☎ 01889.
Envir. : Sudbury Hall★★ *AC*, E : 5 m. by A 518 and A 50.
18 Wood Lane ☎ 565108.
♦London 145 – ♦Birmingham 33 – Derby 19 – Stafford 13 – ♦Stoke-on-Trent 16.

White Hart, Carter St., ST14 8EU, ☎ 562437, Fax 565099 – TV ☎ P – 50
Meals (grill rest.) a la carte 7.30/18.55 **t.** 5.00 – 5.00 – **21 rm** 33.00/55.00 **t.**

Bank House, Church St., ST14 8AG, ☎ 566922, Fax 567565 – TV ☎ P – 40
15 rm.

Forte Travelodge without rest., Ashbourne Rd, ST14 5AA, at junction of A 50 with B 5030 ☎ 562043, Reservations (Freephone) 0800 850950 – TV & P. AE VISA.
32 rm 33.50 **t.**

ATS Smithfield Rd ☎ 563848/565201

VENN OTTERY Devon 403 K 31 – ✉ Ottery St. Mary – ☎ 01404.
♦London 209 – Exeter 11 – Sidmouth 5.

Venn Ottery Barton , EX11 1RZ, ☎ 812733, – rest P. VISA
Meals 15.00 **st.** 3.50 – **16 rm** 21.00/51.00 **t.** – SB.

VENTNOR I.O.W. 403 404 Q 32 – see Wight (Isle of).

VERYAN Cornwall 403 F 33 **The West Country G.** – pop. 877 – ✉ Truro – ☎ 01872.
See : Village★.
♦London 291 – St. Austell 13 – Truro 13.

Nare ⑤, Carne Beach, TR2 5PF, SW : 1 ¼ m. ℘ 501279, Fax 501856, ≤ Carne Bay, heated, – ☎ ⓟ. VISA
closed 6 weeks January-February – **Meals** 11.50/26.00 **t.** and a la carte – **34 rm** 70.00/180.00 **t.**, 2 suites.

at Ruan High Lanes W : 1 ¼ m. on A 3078 – ✉ Truro – ☎ 01872 :

Hundred House, TR2 5JR, ℘ 501336, – rest ☎ ⓟ. VISA
March-October – **Meals** (dinner only) 98.50 4.50 – **10 rm** 33.00/66.00 **t.** – SB.

WADDESDON Bucks. 404 R 28 – ☎ 01296.
♦London 51 – Aylesbury 5 – Northampton 32 – ♦Oxford 31.

Five Arrows, High St., HP18 0JE, ℘ 651727, Fax 658596, – rm ☎ ⓟ. VISA.
Meals a la carte 12.40/18.40 **t.** 7.00 – **6 rm** 50.00/65.00 **st.**

WADDINGTON Lancs. 402 M 22 – see Clitheroe.

WADHURST E. Sussex 404 U 30 – pop. 4 499 – ECD : Wednesday – ☎ 01892.
♦ London 44 – Hastings 21 – Maidstone 24 – Royal Tunbridge Wells 6.

Spindlewood ⑤, Wallcrouch, TN5 7JG, SE : 2 ¼ m. on B 2099 ℘ (01580) 200430, Fax 201132, ≤, – ☎ ⓟ. VISA.
closed 4 days at Christmas – **Meals** *(closed Bank Holiday lunch)* 25.00 **t.** (dinner) and lunch a la carte 17.20/23.30 **t.** 3.95 – **9 rm** 46.00/65.00 **t.** – SB.

Newbarn ⑤ without rest., Wards Lane, TN5 6HP, E : 3 m. by B 2099 ℘ 782042, ≤ Bewl Water and countryside, – ⓟ.
3 rm 22.00/44.00.

Kirkstone without rest., Mayfield Lane, TN5 6HX, ℘ 783204, – ⓟ
3 rm 18.00/34.00 **st.**

WAKEFIELD W. Yorks. 402 P 22 **Great Britain G.** – pop. 74 764 – ECD : Wednesday – ☎ 01924.
Envir. : Nostell Priory★ *AC*, SE : 4 ½ m. by A 638.
City of Wakefield, Lupset Park, Horbury Rd ℘ 367442 – 28 Woodthorpe Lane, Woodthorpe ℘ 255104 – Low Laithes, Parkmill Lane, Flushdyke, Ossett ℘ 273275 – Normanton, Snydale Rd ℘ 892943 – Painthorpe House, Painthorpe Lane, Crigglestone ℘ 255083.
Town Hall, Wood St., WF1 2HQ ℘ 295000/295001.
♦London 188 – ♦Leeds 9 – ♦Manchester 38 – ♦Sheffield 23.

Cedar Court, Denby Dale Rd., Calder Grove, WF4 3QZ, SW : 3 m. on A 636 ℘ 276310, Telex 557647, Fax 280221 – rm ☎ ⓟ – 400. AE VISA
Meals 9.75/20.00 **st.** and a la carte – 7.95 – **144 rm** 75.00 **t.**, 5 suites – SB.

Swallow, Queen St., WF1 1JU, ℘ 372111, Fax 383648 – rm rest ☎ ⓟ – 250. AE VISA
Meals (light lunch)/dinner 15.00 **st.** and a la carte 6.75 – **63 rm** 78.00/110.00 **st.** – SB.

Forte Posthouse, Queen's Drive, Ossett, WF5 9BE, W : 2 ½ m. on A 638 ℘ 276388, Fax 276437 – rm rest ☎ ⓟ – 150. AE VISA JCB.
Meals a la carte approx. 15.00 **t.** 5.50 – **99 rm** 56.00/69.50 **st.**

at Newmillerdam S : 3 ½ m. on A 61 – ✉ Wakefield – ☎ 01924 :

St. Pierre, Barnsley Rd, WF2 6QG, ℘ 255596, Fax 252746 – rm rest ☎ ⓟ – 40. AE VISA
Meals 9.95 **st.** (dinner) and a la carte 10.00/16.00 **st.** 4.95 – 5.75 – **42 rm** 47.50 **st.**, 2 suites – SB.

ATS Bethel Pl., Thornes Lane ℘ 371638

WALBERSWICK Suffolk 404 Y 27 – ✉ Southwold – ☎ 01502.
♦London 97 – Great Yarmouth 28 – ♦Ipswich 32 – ♦Norwich 32.

Anchor, The Street, IP18 6UA, ℘ 722112, Fax 722283, – rest ⓟ
13 rm.

WALBERTON W. Sussex – see Arundel.

WALKINGTON Humbs. 402 S 22 – see Beverley.

Plan Guide **Le Tunnel sous la Manche**

260 *Version française*

avec les curiosités touristiques en Angleterre

261 *Version anglaise*

avec les curiosités touristiques sur le continent

WALLINGFORD Oxon. 403 404 Q 29 **The West Country G.** – pop. 6 616 – ECD : Wednesday – 01491.

Exc. : Ridgeway Path★★.

Town Hall, Market Place, OX10 0EJ 826972.

London 54 – Oxford 12 – Reading 16.

George (Mt. Charlotte Thistle), 84 High St., OX10 0BS, 836665, Fax 825359 – rm – 120.
Meals *(closed Saturday lunch)* 12.95/16.95 **st.** and a la carte 4.75 – **39 rm** 69.00/89.00 **t.** – SB.

at North Stoke S : 2 ¾ m. by A 4130 and A 4074 on B 4009 – Wallingford – 01491 :

Springs, Wallingford Rd, OX10 6BE, 836687, Fax 836877, heated, park, – – 50.
Meals 17.00/24.00 **t.** and a la carte 6.00 – **34 rm** 85.00/140.00 **st.**, 2 suites – SB.

WALMERSLEY Gtr. Manchester – see Bury.

WALSALL W. Mids. 403 404 O 26 – pop. 259 488 – ECD : Thursday – 01922.

Calderfields, Aldridge Rd 640540 CT.

London 126 – Birmingham 9 – Coventry 29 – Shrewsbury 36.

Plan of enlarged area : see Birmingham pp. 2 and 3

Friendly, 20 Wolverhampton Rd West, Bentley, WS2 0BS, W : 2 ½ m. on A 454 724444, Fax 723148, – rm – 180. BT **a**
Meals *(closed Saturday lunch)* (carving rest.) 13.50 **st.** and a la carte 5.50 – 6.75 – **155 rm** 57.75/94.00 **st.** – SB.

Boundary (Forte), Birmingham Rd, WS5 3AB, SE : 1 ½ m. on A 34 33555, Fax 612034, – rm rest – 65. CT **e**
Meals (bar lunch Saturday) 12.00/13.95 **st.** and a la carte 3.95 – 8.95 – **94 rm** 55.00/70.00 **st.** – SB.

ATS Leamore Trading Est., Fryers Rd, Bloxwich 478631

WALSGRAVE ON SOWE W. Mids. – see Coventry.

WALTHAM ABBEY Essex 404 U 28 – pop. 11 207 – 01992.

London 15 – Cambridge 44 – Ipswich 66 – Luton 30 – Southend-on-Sea 35.

Swallow, Old Shire Lane, EN9 3LX, SE : 1 ½ m. on A 121 717170, Fax 711841, – rm rest – 220.
Meals 14.75/22.50 **st.** and a la carte 4.00 – **163 rm** 75.00/175.00 **st.** – SB.

ATS Unit 17, Lea Rd, Ind. Park 788050

WALTON-ON-THAMES Surrey 404 S 29 – ECD : Wednesday – 01932.

London 23 – Brighton 54 – Portsmouth 61 – Southampton 65.

Ashley Park, Ashley Park Rd, KT12 1JP, 220196, Fax 248721 – – 60
29 rm.

WANSFORD Cambs. 404 S 26 – see Peterborough.

WARE Herts. 404 T 28 – pop. 17 069 – ECD : Thursday – 01920.

Whitehill, Dane End 438495.

London 24 – Cambridge 30 – Luton 22.

Hanbury Manor, Thundridge, SG12 0SD, N : 1 ¾ m. by A 1170 on A 10 487722, Fax 487692, « Jacobean style mansion in extensive grounds, walled garden », squash – rest – 140.
Meals 19.00/27.00 **st.** and a la carte 7.00 – (see also **Zodiac Room** below) – **90 rm** 145.00/235.00 **st.**, 5 suites – SB.

Ware Moat House (Q.M.H.), Baldock St., SG12 9DR, N : ½ m. on A 1170 465011, Telex 817417, Fax 468016 – rm rest – 150
49 rm.

XXXX **Zodiac Room** (at Hanbury Manor H.), Thundridge, SG12 0SD, N : 1 ¾ m. by A 1170 on A 10 487722, Fax 487692 – .
closed Sunday dinner – **Meals** (dinner only and Sunday lunch)/dinner 28.00/48.00 **st.** and a la carte 7.00.

at Puckeridge N : 5 ½ m. by A 1170 and A 10 at junction with A 120 – Ware – 01920.

Vintage Court, SG11 1SA, 822722, Fax 822877, – rm – 90.
25 rm 60.45/67.40 **t.**

WAREHAM Dorset 403 404 N 31 The West Country G. – pop. 5 644 – ECD : Wednesday – ☎ 01929.

See : Town★ – St. Martin's★★.

Envir. : Blue Pool★ *AC*, S : 3½ m. by A 351 – Bovington★ (Bovington Camp Tank Museum★ *AC*, Woolbridge Manor★) W : 5 m. by A 352.

Exc. : Moreton Church★★, W : 9½ m. by A 352 – Corfe Castle★★ (≤★★) *AC*, SE : 6 m. by A 351 – Lulworth Cove★, SW : 10 m. by A 352 and B 3070.

Hyde ☎ 472244/472272.

Town Hall, East St., BH20 4NN ☎ 552740.

London 123 – Bournemouth 13 – Weymouth 19.

Priory ⛪, Church Green, BH20 4ND, ☎ 551666, Fax 554519, ≤, « Part 16C priory, riverside gardens », – TV ☎ P. AE VISA.
Meals 12.95/28.50 **t.** and a la carte 7.00 – **17 rm** 70.00/185.00 **t.**, 2 suites – SB.

Springfield Country, Grange Rd, Stoborough, BH20 5AL, S : 1 m. by South St. and West Lane ☎ 552177, Fax 551862, heated, squash – TV ☎ P – 75. AE VISA
Meals (bar lunch Monday to Saturday)/dinner 15.00 **t.** and a la carte 4.50 – **32 rm** 58.00/100.00 **t.**

Kemps Country House, East Stoke, BH20 6AL, W : 2 ¾ m. on A 352 ☎ 462563, Fax 405287, – rest TV ☎ P – 70. AE VISA.
Meals *(closed Saturday lunch)* 9.95/20.00 **t.** and a la carte – **14 rm** 48.00/104.00 **st.** – SB.

WAREN MILL Northd. – see Bamburgh.

WARMINSTER Wilts. 403 404 N 30 The West Country G. – pop. 16 267 – ECD : Wednesday – ☎ 01985.

Envir. : Longleat House★★★ *AC*, SW : 3 m.

Exc. : Stonehenge★★★ *AC*, E : 18 m. by A 36 and A 303 – Bratton Castle (≤★★) NE : 6 m. by A 350 and B 3098.

Central Car Park, BA12 9BT ☎ 218548.

London 111 – Bristol 29 – Exeter 74 – Southampton 47.

Bishopstrow House, Boreham Rd, BA12 9HH, SE : 1 ½ m. on B 3414 ☎ 212312, Fax 216769, ≤, heated, park, – rest TV ☎ P – 70. AE VISA
Meals 25.00/36.00 **t.** and a la carte – **29 rm** 98.00/175.00 **t.**, 3 suites.

Granada Lodge without rest., BA12 7RU, NW : 1 ¼ m. by B 3414 ☎ 219539, Fax 214380, Reservations (Freephone) 0800 555300 – TV ☎ P. AE VISA.
4.00 – **32 rm** 39.95 **st.**

at Heytesbury SE : 3 ¾ m. by B 3414 – ✉ Warminster – ☎ 01985 :

Angel, High St., BA12 0ED, ☎ 840330, Fax 840931, « 17C inn » TV ☎. VISA
closed 25 December – **Meals** 16.00/21.50 **t.** and a la carte 4.50 – **4 rm** 36.00/50.00 **t.**

at Crockerton S : 1 ¾ m. by A 350 – ✉ Warminster – ☎ 01985 :

Springfield House, BA12 8AU, on Potters Hill rd ☎ 213696, – P.
Meals (by arrangement) 18.00 **st.** – **3 rm** 26.00/42.00 **st.**

at Horningsham SW : 5 m. by A 362 – ✉ Warminster – ☎ 01985 :

Bath Arms, BA12 7LY, ☎ 844308, Fax 844150, – TV P. VISA
Meals 17.50/25.00 **t.** and a la carte 4.00 – **7 rm** 32.00/52.00 **t.**

WARREN STREET Kent 404 W 30 – ✉ Maidstone – ☎ 01622.

London 51 – Folkestone 28 – Maidstone 12.

Harrow Inn, ME17 2ED, ☎ 858727, Fax 850026, – TV ☎ P. AE VISA.
closed 24 and 25 December – **Meals** a la carte 16.15/24.85 **t.** – **15 rm** 45.00/58.00 **st.** – SB.

WARRINGTON Ches. 402 403 404 M 23 – pop. 81 366 – ECD : Thursday – ☎ 01925.

Hill Warren, Appleton ☎ 261620 – Walton Hall, Warrington Rd, Higher Walton ☎ 266775 – Kelvin Close, Birchwood ☎ 818819 – Leigh, Kenyon Hall, Culcheth ☎ 763130.

21 Rylands St., WA1 1EJ ☎ 442180/444400.

London 195 – Chester 20 – Liverpool 18 – Manchester 21 – Preston 28.

Village H. & Leisure Club, Centre Park, WA1 1QA, ☎ 240000, Fax 445240, squash – rm TV ☎ – 250. AE VISA.
Meals (grill rest.) (bar lunch Saturday) 8.00/12.00 **st.** and a la carte 4.95 – **87 rm** 33.50/80.00 **st.**

Holiday Inn Garden Court, Woolston Grange Av., Woolston, WA1 4PX, E : 3¼ m. by A 57 at junction 21 of M 6 on B 5210 ℘ 838779, Fax 838859 – rm rest . VISA JCB.
Meals (dinner only) 13.50 **st.** and a la carte 5.50 – 7.95 – **99 rm** 58.00 **st.** – SB.

Fir Grove, Knutsford Old Rd, WA4 2LD, SE : 2 m. by A 50 ℘ 267471, Fax 601092 – – 200. VISA.
Meals *(closed Saturday lunch and Bank Holidays)* 8.00/15.00 **t.** and a la carte 5.25 – **40 rm** 59.00/70.00 **t.**

Travel Inn, Calver Rd, Winwick Quay Industrial Estate, WA2 8RN, N : 2¼ m. on A 49 ℘ 414417, Fax 414544 – . VISA.
Meals (grill rest.) a la carte approx. 16.00 **t.** – 4.95 – **40 rm** 33.50 **t.**

at Stretton S : 3½ m. by A 49 on B 5356 – ✉ Warrington – 01925 :

Park Royal International, Stretton Rd, WA4 4NS, ℘ 730706, Fax 730740, – – 450. VISA JCB
Meals 10.75/14.85 **st.** and a la carte 8.00 – 8.50 – **100 rm** 73.00/123.00 **st.** – SB.

ATS Grange Av., Latchford ℘ 632613

We suggest:

For a successful tour, that you prepare it in advance.

***Michelin maps** and **guides** will give you much useful information on route planning, places of interest, accommodation, prices etc.*

WARWICK Warks. 403 404 P 27 **Great Britain G.** – pop. 21 701 – ECD : Thursday – 01926.

See : Town★ - Castle★★ *AC* Y – Leycester Hospital★ *AC* Y **B** – Collegiate Church of St. Mary★ (Tomb★) Y **A.**

Warwick Racecourse ℘ 494316 Y.

The Court House, Jury St., CV34 4EW ℘ 492212.

♦London 96 – ♦Birmingham 20 – ♦Coventry 11 – ♦Oxford 43.

Plan opposite

Old Fourpenny Shop, 27-29 Crompton St., CV34 6HJ, ℘ 491360, Fax 491360 – . VISA. Y **a**
Meals *(closed Sunday to non-residents)* (bar lunch)/dinner 10.00 **st.** and a la carte 2.95 – **12 rm** 32.50/55.00 **st.** – SB.

Park Cottage without rest., 113 West St., CV34 6AH, ℘ 410319, Fax 410319 – . Y **e**
closed Christmas and New Year – **4 rm** 38.00/50.00 **st.**

at Barford S : 3½ m. on A 429 – Z – ✉ Warwick – 01926 :

Glebe House, Church St., CV35 8BS, on B 4462 ℘ 624218, Fax 624625, , , , – rest – 130
39 rm, 2 suites.

at Longbridge SW : 2 m. on A 429 – Z – ✉ Warwick – 01926 :

Hilton National, Stratford Rd, CV34 6RE, at junction of A 429 with M 40 ℘ 499555, Fax 410020, , , – rm – 300. VISA.
Meals *(closed Saturday lunch)* (carving lunch) 12.95/19.95 **t.** and a la carte 6.50 – 10.95 – **181 rm** 90.00 **t.** – SB.

at Sherbourne SW : 2¾ m. by A 429 – Z – ✉ Warwick – 01926 :

Old Rectory, Vicarage Lane, CV35 8AB, at junction with A 46 ℘ 624562, – . VISA
closed 3 days Christmas – **Meals** (in lounge) (dinner only) 8.00/15.45 **st.** – **14 rm** 31.50/50.00 **st.** – SB.

at Hatton NW : 3½ m. by A 425 on A 4177 – Z – ✉ Warwick – 01926 :

Northleigh House, Five Ways Rd, CV35 7HZ, NW : 2½ m. by A 4177, turning left at roundabout with A 4141 ℘ 484203, – . VISA
closed mid December-31 January – **Meals** (by arrangement) 14.50 – **7 rm** 30.00/55.00 **st.**

at Shrewley NW : 4¾ m. by A 425 and A 4177 - Z - on B 4439 – ✉ Warwick – 01926 :

Shrewley House, CV35 7AT, ℘ 842549, Fax 842216, – . VISA
Meals (by arrangement) 15.00 **s.** – **4 rm** 37.00/62.00 **s.**

at Honiley NW : 6¾ by A 425 on A 4177 – Z – ✉ Warwick – 01926.

Honiley Court (Country Club), CV8 1NP, on A 4177 ℘ 484234, Fax 484474 – rm – 150. VISA
Meals 8.50/20.00 **st.** and a la carte – 7.50 – **62 rm** 59.00 **st.** – SB.

WARWICK
ROYAL LEAMINGTON SPA

High Street	Y	23
Jury Street	Y	
Market Place	Y	29
Smith Street	Y	
Swan Street	Y	46
Birmingham Road	Z	7
Bowling Green Street	Y	9
Brook Street	Y	12
Butts (The)	Y	13
Castle Hill	Y	15
Church Street	Y	17
Lakin Road	Y	25
Linen Street	Y	26
North Rock	Y	32
Old Square	Y	35
Old Warwick Road	Z	36
Radford Road	Z	39
St. John's Road	Y	42
St. Nicholas Church Street	Y	43
Theatre Street	Y	48
West Street	Y	50

Les plans de villes sont disposés le Nord en haut.

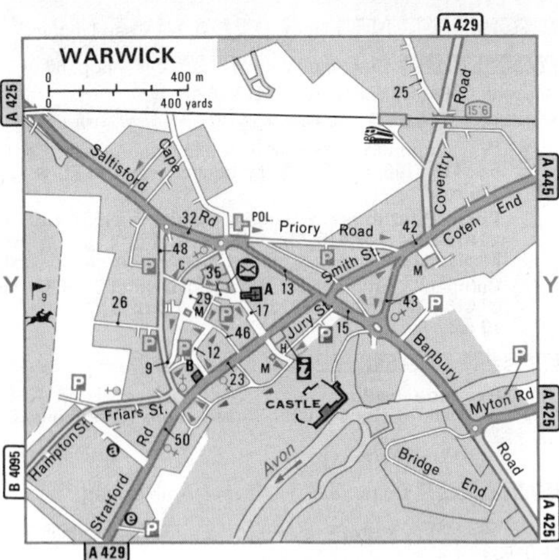

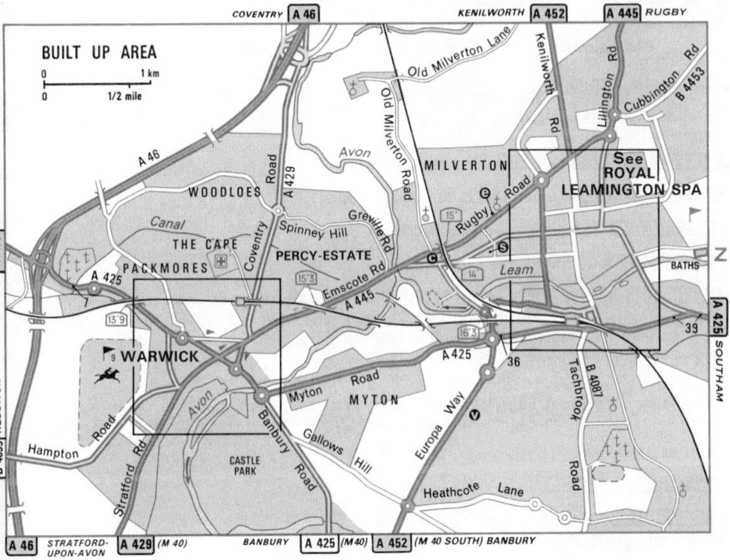

WARWICK
0 400 m
0 400 yards
A 429
A 425
A 445
B 4095
Saltisford
Cape
Rd
Priory Road
Smith St.
Coten End
Coventry Road
Jury St.
Banbury Road
Myton Rd
Bridge End
Avon
CASTLE
Friars St.
Hampton St.
Stratford Rd
POL.
Y

BUILT UP AREA
0 1 km
0 1/2 mile
COVENTRY A 46
KENILWORTH A 452
A 445 RUGBY
Old Milverton Lane
Old Milverton Road
Kenilworth Rd
Lillington Rd
Cubbington Rd
B 4453
MILVERTON
See ROYAL LEAMINGTON SPA
WOODLOES
Avon
Rugby Road
Spinney Hill
Greville Rd
THE CAPE
PERCY-ESTATE
PACKMORES
Canal
Coventry Road
A 429
A 46
A 425
Emscote Rd
A 445
Leam
BATHS
Z
WARWICK
Myton Road
MYTON
Europa Way
Tachbrook Road
B 4087
Banbury Road
Gallows Hill
CASTLE PARK
Hampton Road
Stratford Rd
Heathcote Lane
A 425
SOUTHAM
A 46 STRATFORD-UPON-AVON A 429 (M 40) BANBURY A 425 (M40) A 452 (M 40 SOUTH) BANBURY

WASDALE HEAD Cumbria 402 K 20 – ✉ Gosforth – ☎ 0194 67.

♦London 324 – Kendal 72 – Workington 30.

⌂ **Wasdale Head Inn** 🐎, CA20 1EX, ☏ 26229, Fax 26334, ← Wasdale Head – ☎ Ⓟ. 🅂 VISA
closed mid January-mid February and mid November-28 December – **Meals** (bar lunch)/ dinner a la carte 15.00/21.45 **t.** 🍷 4.25 – **9 rm** ☕ 29.00/58.00 **t.**

WASHFORD Somerset The West Country G. – ✉ Watchet – ☎ 01984.

See : Cleeve Abbey★★ *AC*.

Envir. : Dunster★★ – Castle★★ *AC* (upper rooms ←★) Water Mill★ *AC*, St. George's Church★, Dovecote★, NW : 3½ m. by A 39.

♦London 178 – ♦Bristol 55 – Taunton 16.

⌂ Langtry Country House without rest., TA23 0NT, on A 39 ☏ 40484, 🌳 – ⊁ TV Ⓟ
6 rm.

WASHINGBOROUGH Lincs. 402 404 S 24 – see Lincoln.

WASHINGTON Tyne and Wear 401 402 P 19 – pop. 60 012 – ECD : Wednesday – 0191.

18 Stone Cellar Rd , Usworth 417 2626.

London 278 – Durham 13 – Middlesbrough 32 – Newcastle upon Tyne 7.

Washington Moat House (Q.M.H.), Stone Cellar Rd, District 12, NE37 1PH, 417 2626, Fax 415 1166, 18, squash – rm – 200
105 rm.

Forte Posthouse, Emerson, District 5, NE37 1LB, at junction of A 1 (M) with A 195 416 2264, Fax 415 3371 – rm – 100. AE VISA
Meals a la carte approx. 15.00 **t.** 5.50 – **138 rm** 56.00 **st.**

Campanile, Emerson Rd, Emerson, District 5, NE37 1LE, at junction of A 1(M) with A 195 416 5010, Fax 416 5023 – rm – 25
79 rm.

WASHINGTON SERVICE AREA Tyne and Wear – Washington – 0191.

Granada Lodge without rest., DH3 2SJ, on A 1 (M) (southbound carriageway) 410 0076, Fax 410 0057, Reservations (Freephone) 0800 555300 – . AE VISA.
4.00 – **35 rm** 39.95 **st.**

WATERHEAD Cumbria 402 L 20 – see Ambleside.

WATERHOUSES Staffs. 402 403 404 O 24 **Great Britain G.** – pop. 1 182 – Stoke-on-Trent – 01538.

Envir. : Dovedale★★ (Ilam Rock★) E : 6 m. by A 523.

London 115 – Birmingham 63 – Derby 23 – Manchester 39 – Stoke-on-Trent 17.

XX ✪ **Old Beams** (Wallis) with rm, Leek Rd, ST10 3HW, 308254, Fax 308157, – rest . AE VISA.
Meals *(closed Saturday lunch, Sunday dinner and Monday)* (booking essential) 17.50/30.50 **t.** 8.45 – **5 rm** 52.00/87.00 **t.**
Spec. Duet of sea bass and lobster with a ginger beurre blanc, Open tart of thinly sliced pigeon garnished with wild forest mushrooms, Caramelised mango served with sweet spicy ice cream.

WATERINGBURY Kent 404 V 30 – see Maidstone.

WATERMILLOCK Cumbria 402 L 20 – see Ullswater.

WATERROW Somerset – see Wiveliscombe.

WATER YEAT Cumbria – see Coniston.

WATFORD Herts. 404 S 29 – pop. 74 566 – ECD : Wednesday – 01923.

18, 9 Bushey, High St. (0181) 950 2283, BT – 18 Bushey Hall, Bushey Hall Drive 225802, BT – 9, 18 Oxhey Park, Prestwick Rd, South Oxhey 248312, AT.

London 21 – Aylesbury 23.

Plan : see Greater London (North-West)

Hilton National, Elton Way, WD2 8HA, Watford bypass, E : 3½ m. on A 41 at junction with B 462 235881, Fax 220836, – rm rest – 375. AE VISA JCB. BT **e**
Meals *(closed Saturday lunch)* 14.75/18.75 11.75 – 10.25 – **194 rm** 90.00 **st.**, 1 suite.

WATH-IN-NIDDERDALE N. Yorks. – see Pateley Bridge.

WEAVERHAM Ches. 402 403 404 M 24 – pop. 6 604 – 01606.

London 191 – Chester 15 – Liverpool 28 – Manchester 28.

Oaklands, Millington Lane, Gorstage, CW8 2SU, SW : 2 m. by A 49 853249, Fax 852419, – . VISA.
Meals 12.95/17.50 **st.** and a la carte 5.20 – **11 rm** 49.00/55.00 **st.** – SB.

Tall Trees Lodge without rest., Tarporley Rd, Lower Whitley, WA4 4EZ, N : 2 ¾ m. on A 49 at junction with A 533 790824, Fax 791330 – – 40. AE VISA
20 rm 33.50 **st.**

WEEDON BEC Northants. 403 404 Q 27 – pop. 2 363 – ECD : Wednesday – Northampton – 01327.

London 74 – Coventry 18 – Northampton 8 – Oxford 41.

Heyford Manor (Country Club), Flore, NN7 4LP, E : 1 ½ m. on A 45 349022, Fax 349017, – rm – 80. AE VISA.
Meals *(closed Saturday lunch)* 10.65/20.45 **t.** and a la carte 4.95 – 7.50 – **53 rm** 59.00 **t.** – SB.

WELLAND Heref. and Worcs. 403 404 N 27 – see Great Malvern.

WELLESBOURNE Warks. 403 404 P 27 – pop. 3 998 – see Stratford-upon-Avon.

WELLINGBOROUGH Northants. 404 R 27 – pop. 67 789 – ECD : Thursday – ☎ 01933.

ℹ Wellingborough Library, Pebble Lane, NN8 1AS ☎ 228101.

London 73 – Cambridge 43 – Leicester 34 – Northampton 10.

- **Hind** (Q.M.H.), Sheep St., NN8 1BY, ☎ 222827, Fax 441921 – rest TV ☎ P – 80. AE VISA
  Meals 12.95/15.00 **st.** and a la carte 4.95 – 8.75 – **34 rm** 55.00/65.00 **st.** – SB.

WELLINGTON Shrops. 402 403 404 M 25 – see Telford.

WELLINGTON Somerset 403 K 31 – ☎ 01823.

- **Pinksmoor Millhouse**, Pinksmoor, TA21 0HD, SW : 2 3/4 m. by A 38 ☎ 672361, ≤, « Working farm », – rm TV P.
  closed Christmas – **Meals** (by arrangement) (communal dining) 11.50 **st.** – **3 rm** 20.50/37.00 **st.**

WELLINGTON HEATH Heref. and Worcs. 403 404 M 27 – see Ledbury.

WELLS Somerset 403 404 M 30 **The West Country G.** – pop. 9 763 – ECD : Wednesday – ☎ 01749.

See : City★★ – Cathedral★★★ – Vicars' Close★ – Bishop's Palace★ (≤★★) *AC*.

Envir. : Glastonbury★★ – Abbey★★★ (Abbots Kitchen★) *AC*, St. John the Baptist★★, Somerset Rural Life Museum★ *AC*, Glastonbury Tor★ (≤★★★) SW : 5 1/2 m. by A 39 – Wookey Hole★★ (Caves★ *AC*, Papermill★, Fairground Collection★) NW : 2 m.

Exc. : Cheddar Gorge★★ (Gorge★★, Caves★★, Jacob's Ladder ✻★) St. Andrew's Church★, NW : 7 m. by A 371 – Axbridge★★ (King John's Hunting Lodge★, St. John the Baptist Church★) NW : 8 1/2 m. by A 371.

18 East Horrington Rd ☎ 672868.

ℹ Town Hall, Market Pl., BA5 2RB ☎ 672552.

London 132 – Bristol 20 – Southampton 68 – Taunton 28.

- **Swan,** 11 Sadler St., BA5 2RX, ☎ 678877, Fax 677647, squash – TV ☎ P – 150. AE VISA
  Meals 12.25/16.50 **t.** 5.35 – **38 rm** 62.50/83.50 **t.** – SB.
- **Beryl**, BA5 3JP, E : 1 1/4 m. by B 3139 off Hawkers Lane ☎ 678738, Fax 670508, ≤, « Victorian Gothic country house, antique furniture », heated, park – TV ☎ P
  closed 24 to 26 December – **Meals** *(closed Sunday)* (residents only) (communal dining) (booking essential) (dinner only) 18.00 **st.** 5.00 – **7 rm** 45.00/75.00.
- **White Hart,** Sadler St., BA5 2RR, ☎ 672056, Fax 672056 – TV ☎ P – 60. AE VISA
  Meals 12.95/14.50 **t.** and a la carte 4.00 – **15 rm** 45.00/60.00 **t.** – SB.
- **Star,** 18 High St., BA5 2SQ, ☎ 670500, Fax 672654 – TV ☎. AE VISA JCB
  Meals (in bar) a la carte 6.95/11.50 **t.** and a la carte – 5.00 – **12 rm** 450.00/80.00 **st.**
- **Infield House** without rest., 36 Portway, BA5 2BN, ☎ 670989, Fax 679093, – TV P.
  3 rm 29.00/42.00 **st.**
- **Littlewell Farm,** Coxley, BA5 1QP, SW : 1 1/2 m. on A 39 ☎ 677914, – TV P
  Meals (by arrangement) (communal dining) 15.00 **st.** 4.95 – **5 rm** 21.00/44.00 **st.** – SB.

at Wookey Hole NW : 1 3/4 m. by A 371 – ✉ Wells – ☎ 01749 :

- **Glencot House,** Glencot Lane, BA5 1BH, ☎ 677160, Fax 670210, , park – rest TV ☎ P – 40. VISA
  Meals *(closed Sunday and Monday to non-residents)* (dinner only) 21.50 **t.** 5.10 – **12 rm** 45.00/80.00 **t.** – SB.

at Priddy NW : 6 1/4 m. by A 39 – ✉ Wells – ☎ 01749 :

- **Highcroft** without rest., Wells Rd, BA5 3AU, SE : 1 1/4 m. ☎ 673446, ≤, , park – P
  closed Christmas-New Year – **4 rm** 16.00/34.00.

WELLS-NEXT-THE-SEA Norfolk 404 W 25 **Great Britain G.** – pop. 2 808 – ECD : Thursday – ☎ 01328.

Envir. : Holkham Hall★★ *AC*, W : 2 m. by A 149.

ℹ Staithe St., NR23 1AN ☎ 710885 (summer only).

London 117 – King's Lynn 31 – Norwich 36.

- **Scarborough House,** Clubbs Lane, NR23 1DP, ☎ 710309 – TV P. AE VISA
  Meals (dinner only) 10.95 **t.** 3.50 – **14 rm** 29.00/58.00 – SB.
- **The Cobblers,** Standard Rd, NR23 1JU, ☎ 710155, – TV P.
  closed 1 week Christmas – **Meals** (by arrangement) 8.95 **st.** 2.45 – **8 rm** 18.00/40.00 **st.**
- **Moorings,** 6 Freeman St., NR23 1BA, ☎ 710949 –
  closed Thursday lunch, Tuesday, Wednesday, 4 to 22 June and 4 to 21 December – **Meals** - Seafood (booking essential) 14.95/22.95 **t.** 4.40.

WELWYN Herts. 404 T 28 – ☎ 01438.
◆London 31 – Bedford 31 – ◆Cambridge 31.

Tewin Bury Farm, AL6 0JB, SE : 3½ m. by A 1000 on B 1000 ℘ 717793, Fax 840440, – **16 rm.**

WELWYN GARDEN CITY Herts. 404 T 28 – pop. 40 665 – ECD : Wednesday – ☎ 01707.
Panshanger, Old Herns Lane, ℘ 339507.
Campus West, The Campus, AL8 6BX ℘ 390653/322880.
◆London 28 – Bedford 34 – ◆Cambridge 34.

Homestead Court (Forte), Homestead Lane, AL7 4LX, SW : 1 ¼ m. by B 195 and Heronswood Rd off Cole Green Lane ℘ 324336, Fax 326447, – rm – 80. AE VISA JCB
Meals (bar lunch Monday to Saturday)/dinner 13.80 **st.** and a la carte 7.50 – 8.95 – **58 rm** 62.50 **st.** – SB.

ATS 17 Tewin Rd ℘ 371619

WEM Shrops. 402 403 L 25 – Shrewsbury – ☎ 01939.
◆London 167 – ◆Birmingham 50 – Chester 32 – ◆Stoke-on-Trent 36 – Shrewsbury 8.

Soulton Hall, SY4 5RS, E : 2 m. on B 5065 ℘ 232786, Fax 234097, « 16C manor house, working farm », , park – . VISA.
Meals (by arrangement) 17.50 **st.** 4.85 – **6 rm** 27.00/59.00 **st.** – SB.

WENDLING Norfolk 404 W 25 - see East Dereham.

WENTBRIDGE W. Yorks. 402 404 Q 23 – Pontefract – ☎ 01977.
◆London 183 – ◆Leeds 19 – ◆Nottingham 55 – ◆Sheffield 28.

Wentbridge House, Old Great North Rd, WF8 3JJ, ℘ 620444, Fax 620148, – – 120. AE VISA.
closed 25 December – **Meals** 14.50/19.75 **t.** and a la carte 6.25 – **13 rm** 65.00/98.00 **t.**

WEOBLEY Heref. and Worcs. 403 L 27 – pop. 1 076 – Hereford – ☎ 01544.
◆London 145 – Brecon 30 – Hereford 12 – Leominster 9.

Red Lion, HR4 8SE, ℘ 318220, « 14C former inn » – – **5 rm.**

XX **Ye Olde Salutation Inn** with rm, Market Pitch, HR4 8SJ, ℘ 318443, Fax 318216 – . AE VISA.
closed 25 December – **Meals** *(closed Sunday dinner and Monday)* a la carte 15.60/25.20 **t.** 4.95 – **4 rm** 32.50/60.00 **t.**

WEST BAGBOROUGH Somerset 403 K 30 – see Taunton.

WEST BEXINGTON Dorset – Dorchester – ☎ 01308.
◆London 150 – Bournemouth 43 – Bridport 6 – Weymouth 13.

Manor, Beach Rd, DT2 9DF, ℘ 897616, Fax 897035, ←, – . AE VISA.
Meals 13.50/20.85 **t.** – **13 rm** 48.00/78.00 **st.** – SB.

WEST BRIDGFORD Notts. 403 404 Q 25 – see Nottingham.

WEST BROMWICH W. Mids. 403 404 O 26 – see Birmingham.

WEST CHILTINGTON W. Sussex 404 S 31 see Pulborough.

WEST COKER Somerset 403 404 M 31 – see Yeovil.

WESTDEAN E. Sussex – see Seaford.

WEST DOWN Devon 403 H 30 – ☎ 01271.
◆London 221 – Exeter 52 – Taunton 59.

Long House, The Square, EX34 8NF, ℘ 863242, Fax 863242, – rest . VISA.
March-October – **Meals** 10.00/15.50 **st.** and a la carte 3.50 – **4 rm** 30.00/53.00 **st.**

WESTERHAM Kent 404 U 30 **Great Britain G.** – pop. 3 686 – ECD : Wednesday – ☎ 01959.
Envir. : Chartwell★ *AC*, S : 2 m. by B 2026.
◆London 24 – ◆Brighton 45 – Maidstone 22.

Kings Arms, Market Sq., TN16 1AN, ℘ 562990, Fax 561240 – . AE VISA
closed 25-31 December – **Meals** *(closed Saturday lunch)* 15.75/20.00 **st.** and a la carte 6.50 – 7.50 – **16 rm** 65.00/95.00 **st.** – SB.

WESTGATE Durham 401 402 N 19 – Weardale – ☎ 01388.
◆London 278 – ◆Carlisle 49 – ◆Middlesbrough 50 – ◆Newcastle upon Tyne 42.

Breckon Hill , DL13 1PD, E : ½ m. on A 689 ℘ 517228, ←, – .
March - October – **Meals** (communal dining) 12.50 **t.** 2.90 – **6 rm** 27.00/40.00 **t.**

WEST HADDON Northants. 403 404 Q 26 – see Rugby.

WESTLETON Suffolk 404 Y 27 – pop. 1 317 – ECD : Wednesday – ✉ Saxmundham – ☎ 01728.

♦London 97 – ♦Cambridge 72 – ♦Ipswich 28 – ♦Norwich 31.

- **Crown,** IP17 3AD, ☎ 648777, Fax 648239, – TV ☎ P. VISA
  closed 25 and 26 December – **Meals** 16.50 **t.** and a la carte – **19 rm** 49.50/89.50 **t.** – SB.

WEST LULWORTH Dorset 403 404 N 32 **The West Country G.** – pop. 838 – ECD : Wednesday – ✉ Wareham – ☎ 01929.

See : Lulworth Cove★.

♦London 129 – Bournemouth 21 – Dorchester 17 – Weymouth 19.

- **Cromwell House,** Main Rd, BH20 5RJ, ☎ 400253, Fax 400566, ≤, heated, – TV ☎ P. AE VISA
  closed 19 to 28 December – **Meals** (dinner only) 20.00 **t.** and a la carte 4.50 – **14 rm** 28.50/57.00 – SB.
- **Gatton House,** Main Rd, BH20 5RU, ☎ 400252, Fax 400252, – rest TV P. VISA
  March-mid November – **Meals** (residents only) (dinner only) 14.50 **t.** 3.50 – **8 rm** 37.00/56.00 **t.** – SB.

__En saison,__ surtout dans les stations fréquentées, il est prudent de retenir à l'avance. Cependant, si vous ne pouvez pas occuper la chambre que vous avez retenue, prévenez immédiatement l'hôtelier.

Si vous écrivez à un hôtel à l'étranger, joignez à votre lettre un coupon-réponse international (disponible dans les bureaux de poste).

WEST MALLING Kent 404 V 30 – pop. 2 479 – ☎ 01732.

♦London 27 – ♦Brighton 47 – Hastings 40 – Maidstone 6.

- **Heavers Farm** , Chapel St., Ryarsh, ME19 5JU, NW : 2 ½ m. by A 20 ☎ 842074, Fax 842074, – P.
  closed Christmas and New Year – **Meals** (by arrangement) – **3 rm** 20.00/34.00 **st.**

WEST MERSEA Essex 404 W 28 – pop. 6 602 – ✉ Colchester – ☎ 01206.

♦London 58 – Chelmsford 27 – Colchester 9.5.

- XX **Le Champenois, Blackwater H.** with rm, 20-22 Church Rd, CO5 8QH, ☎ 383338 – TV P. AE VISA.
  closed first 3 weeks January – **Meals** *(closed Tuesday lunch and Sunday dinner)* 17.80 **t.** and a la carte 3.90 – **7 rm** 25.00/62.00 **t.** – SB.

WESTONBIRT Glos. 403 404 N 29 – see Tetbury.

WESTON-ON-THE-GREEN Oxon. 403 404 Q 28 – pop. 460 – ✉ Bletchington – ☎ 01869.

♦London 65 – ♦Birmingham 61 – Northampton 33 – ♦Oxford 8.

- **Weston Manor,** OX6 8QL, on B 430 ☎ 350621, Fax 350901, heated, , park, squash – TV ☎ P – 40. AE VISA.
  Meals *(closed Sunday lunch)* 16.50/25.00 5.25 – **34 rm** 80.00/95.00 **st.**, 1 suite – SB.

WESTON-SUPER-MARE Avon 403 K 29 **The West Country G.** – pop. 64 935 – ECD : Thursday – ☎ 01934.

See : Seafront (≤★★) BZ.

Exc. : Axbridge★★ (King John's Hunting Lodge★, St. John the Baptist Church★) SE : 9 m. by A 371 - BY - and A 38 – Cheddar Gorge★★ (Gorge★★, Caves★★, Jacob's Ladder ★) – St. Andrew's Church★, SE : 10½ m. by A 371.

18 Worlebury, Monks Hill ☎ 623214, BY – 18 Uphill Rd North ☎ 621360 AZ.

Beach Lawns, BS23 1AT ☎ 626838.

♦London 147 – ♦Bristol 24 – Taunton 32.

Plan on next page

- **Grand Atlantic** (Forte), Beach Rd, BS23 1BA, ☎ 626543, Fax 415048, ≤, , , – TV ☎ P – 200. AE VISA JCB BZ **e**
  Meals (bar lunch Monday to Saturday)/dinner 16.95 **st.** and a la carte 6.95 – 8.75 – **76 rm** 50.00/90.00 **st.** – SB.
- Old Colonial, 30 Knightstone Rd, BS23 2AW, ☎ 620739, Fax 642725, ≤ – TV ☎ P
  9 rm. BZ **a**
- Royal Pier, 55-57 Birnbeck Rd, BS23 2EJ, ☎ 626644, Fax 624169, ≤ Weston Bay and Bristol Channel – TV ☎ P – 70 AY **a**
  40 rm.
- **Commodore,** Beach Rd, Sand Bay, Kewstoke, BS22 9UZ, by Kewstoke rd (toll) ☎ 415778, Fax 636483 – TV ☎ P – 120. AE VISA. AY **e**
  closed first 2 weeks January – **Meals** (bar lunch Monday to Saturday)/dinner a la carte 11.95/15.90 **st.** 3.70 – **18 rm** 49.00/65.00 **st.** – SB.

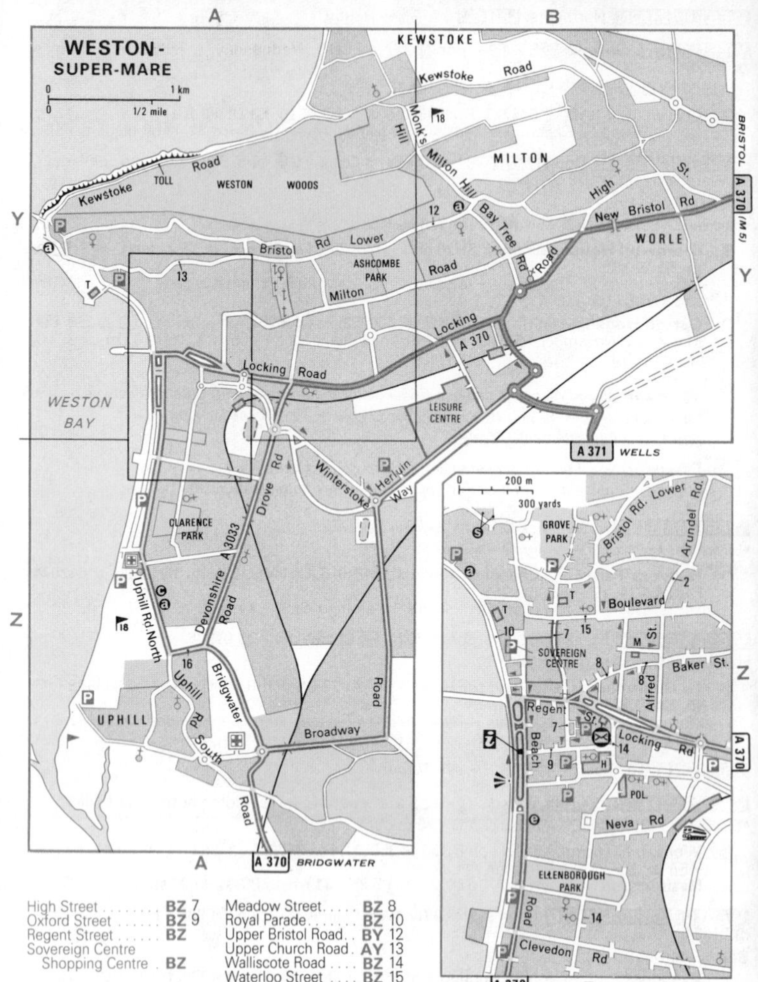

High Street . . . . BZ 7
Oxford Street . . . . BZ 9
Regent Street . . . . BZ
Sovereign Centre
Shopping Centre . BZ

Albert Quadrant . . . . BZ 2
Meadow Street. . . . . BZ 8
Royal Parade . . . . BZ 10
Upper Bristol Road. . BY 12
Upper Church Road . AY 13
Walliscote Road . . . . BZ 14
Waterloo Street . . . . BZ 15
Windwhistle Road . . AZ 16

Beachlands, 17 Uphill Rd North, BS23 4NG, ℘ 621401, Fax 621966, – TV ☎ **P**. AE VISA — AZ **c**
closed 24 December-1 January – **Meals** (dinner only and Sunday lunch)/dinner 12.00 **t.** 5.50 – **18 rm** 31.00/62.00 **t.** – SB.

Queenswood, Victoria Park, BS23 2HZ, off Upper Church Rd ℘ 416141, Fax 621759 – rest rest TV ☎. AE VISA — BZ **s**
Meals 8.50/17.50 4.50 – **17 rm** 35.75/71.50 **t.** – SB.

Ormonde House without rest., 19 Uphill Rd North, BS23 4NG, ℘ 412315, , , – TV **P**. VISA. — AZ **a**
7 rm 22.50/37.00 **st.**

Braeside, 2 Victoria Park, BS23 2HZ, off Upper Church Rd ℘ 626642 – rest TV
Meals 8.50 **st.** – **9 rm** 22.50/45.00 **st.** – SB. — BZ **s**

Duets, 103 Upper Bristol Rd, BS22 8ND, ℘ 413428 – VISA — BY **a**
closed Sunday dinner, Monday, 1 week January and 2 weeks June – **Meals** (lunch by arrangement)/dinner 14.95 **t.** and a la carte 5.75.

WEST PENNARD Somerset 403 M 30 – see Glastonbury.

WEST RUNTON Norfolk 404 X 25 – ECD : Wednesday – ✉ Cromer – ☎ 01263.

Links Country Park Hotel, ✆ 838383.

♦London 135 – King's Lynn 42 – ♦Norwich 24.

Links Country Park, Sandy Lane, NR27 9QH, ✆ 838383, Fax 838264, ≘s, ⌧, 9, ⛱, ℜ – |¢| ▤ rest TV ☎ P – 🅐 200. AE VISA
Meals (dinner only and Sunday lunch)/dinner 19.00 **st.** and a la carte ₰ 5.20 – **40 rm** ⊒ 52.50/125.00 **st.** – SB.

Dormy House, Cromer Rd, NR27 9QA, on A 149 ✆ 837537, ⛱ – |¢| ⇆ rest TV ☎ P. AE VISA. ⚘
Meals 8.50/16.50 **t.** and dinner a la carte ₰ 3.95 – **14 rm** ⊒ 56.000/96.00 **t.** – SB.

WEST SCRAFTON N. Yorks. – see Middleham.

WEST STOUR Dorset – pop. 159 – ✉ Gillingham – ☎ 01747.

♦London 119 – Bournemouth 35 – Salisbury 28 – Yeovil 15.

Ship Inn, SP8 5RP, on A 30 ✆ 838640, ⛱ – TV P. VISA. ⚘
Meals (in bar lunchtime and Sunday to Tuesday dinner)/dinner a la carte ₰ 4.95 – **6 rm** ⊒ 28.00/42.00 **t.**

WEST WITTON N. Yorks. 402 O 21 – pop. 325 – ✉ Leyburn – ☎ 01969.

♦London 241 – Kendal 39 – ♦Leeds 60 – York 53.

Wensleydale Heifer, Main St., DL8 4LS, ✆ 22322, Fax 24183, ⛱ – TV ☎ P. AE ⓓ VISA
Meals 12.50/22.50 **st.** and a la carte ₰ 4.95 – **20 rm** ⊒ 49.00/85.00 **st.** – SB.

WETHERAL Cumbria 401 402 L 19 – see Carlisle.

WETHERBY W. Yorks. 402 P 22 **Great Britain G.** – pop. 24 656 – ECD : Wednesday – ☎ 01937.

Envir. : Harewood House** (The Gallery*) *AC*, SW : 5½m. by A 58 and A 659.

18 Linton Lane ✆ 580089 – 🛈 Council Offices, 24 Westgate, LS22 6NL ✆ 582706.

♦London 208 – Harrogate 8 – ♦Leeds 13 – York 14.

Wood Hall ⑤, Trip Lane, Linton, LS22 4JA, SW : 3 m. by A 661 and Linton Rd ✆ 587271, Fax 584353, ≤, « Part Jacobean and Georgian country house in park », ⅓, ≘s, ⌧, ⚲, ⛱ – |¢| TV ☎ P – 🅐 140. AE VISA
Meals (closed Saturday lunch) 13.95/22.95 **t.** and dinner a la carte ₰ 6.00 – **43 rm** ⊒ 90.00/245.00 **t.** – SB.

Linton Springs ⑤, Sicklinghall Rd, LS22 4AF, W : 1 ¾ m. by A 661 ✆ 585353, Fax 587579, ⛱, park, ℜ – TV ☎ P – 🅐 30. AE ⓓ VISA. ⚘
Meals a la carte 14.40/18.90 **t.** ₰ 4.95 – ⊒ 7.50 – **10 rm** 58.00/75.00 **st.**, 2 suites.

WETHERDEN Suffolk 404 W 27 – see Stowmarket.

WETHERSFIELD Essex 404 V 28 – pop. 1 204 – ✉ Braintree – ☎ 01371.

♦London 52 – ♦Cambridge 31 – Chelmsford 19 – Colchester 22.

XX **Dicken's,** The Green, CM7 4BS, ✆ 850723, « Part 17C house » – P. VISA
closed Sunday dinner, Monday and Tuesday – **Meals** (lunch by arrangement)/dinner a la carte 18.40/23.40 **t.** ₰ 7.85.

WEYBRIDGE Surrey 404 S 29 – pop. 50 031 (inc. Walton-on-Thames) – ECD : Wednesday – ☎ 01932.

♦London 23 – Crawley 27 – Guildford 17 – Reading 33.

Plan : see Greater London (South-West)

Oatlands Park, Oatlands Drive, KT13 9HB, NE : ¾ m. by A 317 on A 3050 ✆ 847242, Telex 915123, Fax 842252, ⛱, park, ℜ – |¢| ⇆ rm TV ☎ P – 🅐 300. AE ⓓ VISA AY
Meals (bar lunch Saturday) 15.00/17.50 **t.** and a la carte ₰ 5.50 – **112 rm** ⊒ 97.00/128.00 **st.**, 4 suites – SB.

Ship Thistle (Mt. Charlotte Thistle), Monument Green, High St., KT13 8BQ, ✆ 848364, Fax 857153 – ⇆ rm ▤ rest TV ☎ P – 🅐 150. AE ⓓ VISA JCB. ⚘
Meals (bar lunch Saturday) 13.75/15.95 **t.** and dinner a la carte ₰ 7.50 – ⊒ 8.25 – **39 rm** 89.00/115.00 **st.** – SB. by A 3050 AY

XXX **Casa Romana,** 2 Temple Hall, Monument Hill, KT13 8RH, ✆ 843470 – ▤ P. AE ⓓ VISA by A 3050 AY
Meals - Italian 16.50 **t.** and a la carte ₰ 4.95.

In alta stagione, *e soprattutto nelle stazioni turistiche,*
è prudente prenotare con un certo anticipo.
Avvertite immediatamente l'albergatore se non potete più
occupare la camera prenotata.

Se scrivete ad un albergo all'estero, allegate alla vostra
lettera un tagliando-risposta internazionale (disponibile presso gli uffici postali).

WEYMOUTH Dorset 403 404 M 32 **The West Country G.** – pop. 38 384 – ECD : Wednesday – 01305.

See : Town★ – Timewalk★ *AC* – Nothe Fort (≤★) *AC* – Boat Trip★ (Weymouth Bay and Portland Harbour) *AC*.

Envir. : Chesil Beach★★ – Portland★ – Portland Bill (★★) S : 2½ m. by A 354.

Exc. : Maiden Castle★★ (≤★) N : 6½ m. by A 354 – Abbotsbury★★ (Swannery★ *AC*, Sub-Tropical Gardens★ *AC*, St. Catherine's Chapel★) NW : 9 m. by B 3157.

18 Links Road, ℘ 773981.

to Channel Islands : Guernsey (St. Peter Port) and Jersey (St. Helier) (Condor Ltd : hydrofoil) 2 daily.

The King's Statue, The Esplanade, DT4 7AN ℘ 765221/765223.

♦London 142 – Bournemouth 35 – ♦Bristol 68 – Exeter 59 – Swindon 94.

Rex, 29 The Esplanade, DT4 8DN, ℘ 760400, Fax 760500 – TV. AE VISA
closed Christmas – **Meals** (bar lunch)/dinner 12.50 **t.** and a la carte 4.60 – **31 rm** 46.00/82.00 **t.** – SB.

Streamside, 29 Preston Rd, Overcombe, DT3 6PX, NE : 2 m. on A 353 ℘ 833121, Fax 832043, – TV. AE VISA
Meals 7.75/11.75 **t.** and a la carte **t.** – **15 rm** 45.00/76.00 **t.** – SB.

Bay Lodge, 27 Greenhill, DT4 7SW, ℘ 782419, Fax 782828 – TV. AE VISA.
Meals (dinner only) 13.75 **st.** and a la carte 4.00 – **12 rm** 26.00/59.00 **st.** – SB.

Chatsworth, 14 The Esplanade, DT4 8EB, ℘ 785012, Fax 766342 – rest TV. AE VISA
Meals 12.00 **st.** 3.50 – **8 rm** 20.00/54.00 **st.** – SB.

Sou'West Lodge, Rodwell Rd, DT4 8QT, ℘ 783749 – rest TV
closed 21 December-3 January – **Meals** (by arrangement) 7.00 **st.** – **8 rm** 21.00/45.00 **st.**

Perry's, The Harbourside, 4 Trinity Rd, DT4 8TJ, ℘ 785799 – VISA
closed lunch Monday and Saturday, Sunday dinner September-May and 26 to 28 December – **Meals** 15.50 **t.** and dinner a la carte 18.00/24.00 **t.** 5.50.

Die Preise Einzelheiten über die in diesem Führer angegebenen Preise finden Sie in der Einleitung.

WHALLEY Lancs. 402 M 22 – pop. 3 195 – Blackburn – 01254.

9 Long Leese Barn, Clerkhill ℘ 822236.

♦London 233 – ♦Blackpool 32 – Burnley 12 – ♦Manchester 28 – Preston 15.

Foxfields, Whalley Rd, Billington, BB6 9HY, SW : 1¼ m. ℘ 822556, Fax 824613 – rm TV – 150. AE VISA.
Meals (see **Foxfields** below) – **18 rm** 60.00/85.00 **t.**, **26 suites** – SB.

Mytton Fold Farm, Whalley Rd, Langho, BB6 8AB, SW : 1½ m. ℘ 240662, Fax 248119, 18, – rest TV – 250. AE VISA.
Meals (bar lunch Monday to Saturday)/dinner 13.50 **t.** and a la carte 5.15 – **27 rm** 45.00/67.00 – SB.

Foxfields, (at Foxfields H.) Whalley Rd, Billington, BB6 9HY, SW : 1¼ m. ℘ 822556, Fax 824613 – . AE VISA
Meals *(closed Saturday lunch)* 11.95/14.50 **t.** and a la carte 4.95 – SB.

WHAPLODE Lincs. 402 404 T 25 – pop. 1 929 – Spalding – 01406.

♦London 106 – Lincoln 45 – ♦Leicester 61 – ♦Norwich 60.

Guy Wells, Eastgate, PE12 6TZ, E : ½ m. by A 151 ℘ 422239, « Queen Anne house », – .
closed 3 days Christmas – **Meals** (by arrangement) 12.00 **s.** – **3 rm** 20.00/38.00 **s.** – SB.

WHARRAM-LE-STREET N. Yorks. – see Malton.

WHEATLEY Oxon. 403 404 Q 28 – see Oxford.

WHICKHAM Tyne and Wear 401 402 O 19 – see Newcastle upon Tyne.

WHIMPLE Devon 403 J 31 – see Exeter.

WHITBY N. Yorks. 402 S 20 – pop. 13 640 – ECD : Wednesday – 01947.

18 Low Straggleton ℘ 602768.

Langborne Rd, YO21 1YN ℘ 602674.

♦London 257 – ♦Middlesbrough 31 – Scarborough 21 – York 45.

Larpool Hall Country House, Larpool Lane, YO22 4ND, SE : 1 m. by A 171 ℘ 602737, Fax 602737, ≤, , park – TV. VISA.
Meals 9.95/19.00 **t.** and dinner a la carte 5.25 – **14 rm** 37.50/100.00 **t.** – SB.

at Dunsley W : 3¼ m. by A 171 – Whitby – 01947 :

Dunsley Hall, YO21 3TL, ℘ 893437, Fax 893505, ≤, , , , – rest TV
7 rm.

WHITEHAVEN Cumbria 402 J 20 – ☎ 01946.

St. Bees, Rhoda Grove, Rheda, Frizington ℘ 812105.

Market Hall, Market Pl., CA28 7JG ℘ 695678.

Ennerdale, Cleator, CA23 3DT, SE : 6 m. by A 5094 and A 595 on A 5086 ℘ 813907, Fax 815260, – TV ☎ P – 80. AE VISA
Meals 10.50/18.50 **st.** and dinner a la carte 4.95 **20 rm** 69.00/99.00 **st.** – SB.

ATS Meadow Rd ℘ 692576

WHITEPARISH Wilts. 403 404 P 30 – see Salisbury.

WHITEWELL Lancs. 402 M 22 – pop. 3 577 – ✉ Clitheroe – ☎ 01200.

♦London 281 – Lancaster 31 – ♦Leeds 55 – ♦Manchester 41 – Preston 13.

Inn at Whitewell, Forest of Bowland, BB7 3AT, ℘ 448222, Fax 448298, ≤, « Antiques and memorabilia », – TV ☎ P. AE VISA
Meals (bar lunch)/dinner a la carte 14.00/20.90 **t.** 5.50 – **9 rm** 38.00/67.00 **t.**, 1 suite.

WHITLEY S. Yorks. – see Sheffield.

WHITLEY BAY Tyne and Wear 401 402 P 18 – ☎ 0191 – Park Rd, NE26 1EJ ℘ 252 4494.

♦London 295 – ♦Newcastle upon Tyne 10 – Sunderland 10.

Windsor, South Par., NE26 2RF, ℘ 251 8888, Fax 297 0272 – rest TV ☎ – 100. AE VISA JCB
Meals (bar lunch)/dinner 13.00 **st.** and a la carte 4.30 – **64 rm** 53.00/60.00 **st.**

Ambassador, South Par., NE26 2RQ, ℘ 253 1218, Fax 297 0089 – TV ☎ P. AE VISA JCB
Meals (dinner only) 9.95 **t.** and a la carte 4.95 – **27 rm** 46.00/56.00 **t.** – SB.

ATS John St., Cullercoats ℘ 253 3903

WHITNEY-ON-WYE Heref. and Worcs. 403 K 27 – ✉ Hereford – ☎ 01497.

♦London 150 – ♦Birmingham 56 – ♦Cardiff 73 – Hereford 17.

Rhydspence Inn, HR3 6EU, W : 1½ m. on A 438 ℘ 831262, « Part 14C inn », – TV P. AE VISA
Meals a la carte 17.25/24.45 **t.** – **5 rm** 27.50/55.00 **t.** – SB.

WHITSTABLE Kent 404 X 29 – ✉ Whitstable – ☎ 01227.

Whitstable Oyster Fishery Co., Royal Native Oyster Stores, The Horsebridg, CT5 1BU, ℘ 276856, Fax 770666, ≤, « Converted warehouse ». AE VISA JCB
closed Sunday dinner, Monday and 25-26 December – **Meals** - Seafood rest. a la carte 15.40/20.40 **t.**

WHITTLE-LE-WOODS Lancs. 402 M 23 – see Chorley.

WICKHAM Hants. 403 404 Q 31 – pop. 2 941 – ECD : Wednesday – ☎ 01329.

♦London 74 – ♦Portsmouth 12 – ♦Southampton 11 – Winchester 16.

Old House, The Square, PO17 5JG, ℘ 833049, Fax 833672, « Queen Anne house », – TV ☎ P. AE VISA.
closed 2 weeks August and 2 weeks December – **Meals** *(closed lunch Monday and Saturday and Sunday)* 25.00 **st.** 5.75 – 8.00 – **12 rm** 62.00/69.00 **st.** – SB.

WIDEGATES Cornwall 403 G 32 – see Looe.

WIDNES Ches. 402 403 404 L 23 – pop. 55 973 – ECD : Thursday – ☎ 0151.

Highfield Rd ℘ 424 2440 – Widnes Municipal, Dundalk Rd ℘ 424 6230.

Municipal Building, Kingsway, WA8 7QF ℘ 424 2061.

♦London 205 – ♦Liverpool 19 – ♦Manchester 27 – ♦Stoke-on-Trent 42.

Everglades Park, Derby Rd, WA8 0UJ, NE : 3 m. by A 568 on A 5080 ℘ 495 2040, Fax 424 6536 – rest TV ☎ P – 200. AE VISA JCB.
Meals 10.95 **t.** (dinner) and a la carte 7.50/21.50 **t.** 4.50 – **32 rm** 50.00/65.00 **st.** – SB.

at Cronton NW : 2 m. by A 568 on A 5080 – ✉ Widnes – ☎ 0151 :

Hillcrest, Cronton Lane, WA8 9AR, ℘ 424 1616, Fax 495 1348 – TV ☎ P – 120. AE VISA
closed 26 to 29 December – **Meals** *(closed lunch Bank Holidays)* (bar lunch Saturday) 9.95/12.75 **t.** and dinner a la carte 4.95 – **50 rm** 39.50/92.50 **st.**

ATS Tanhouse Lane ℘ 424 3011/2945

WIGAN Lancs. 402 M 23 – ☎ 01942.

♦London 203 – ♦Liverpool 18 – ♦Manchester 24 – Preston 18.

Wigan Oak, Riverway, WN1 3SS, access by Orchard St. ℘ 826888, Fax 825800 – rm TV ☎ P – 140. AE VISA.
6.25 – **88 rm** 55.00/65.00 **t.** – SB.

at Up Holland W : 1¼ m. on A 577 – ✉ Wigan – ☎ 01695 :

🏨 **Lancashire Manor,** Prescott Rd, WN8 9PU, SW : 2¾ m. by A 577 and Stannanought Rd ✆ 720401, Fax 50953 – ⇔ rm TV ☎ ♿ P – 🏆 200. AE VISA
Meals *(closed Saturday lunch)* 17.50 **st.** and a la carte 5.00 – **55 rm** 53.00/90.00 **st.** – SB.

ATS 98 Warrington Rd, Newtown ✆ (01942) 42017/42442

WIGHT (Isle of) 403 404 PQ 31 32 **Great Britain G.** – pop. 118 594.

See : Island★★.

Envir. : Osborne House, East Cowes★★ *AC* – Carisbrooke Castle, Newport★★ *AC* (Keep ≤★) – Brading★ (Roman Villa★ *AC*, St. Mary's Church★, Nunwell House★ *AC*) – Shorwell : St. Peter's Church★ (wall paintings★).

from East and West Cowes to Southampton (Red Funnel Ferries) frequent services daily – from Yarmouth to Lymington (Wightlink Ltd) frequent services daily (30 mn) – from Fishbourne to Portsmouth (Wightlink Ltd) frequent services daily (35 mn).

from Ryde to Portsmouth (Hovertravel Ltd) frequent services daily (10 mn) – from Ryde to Portsmouth (Wightlink Ltd) frequent services daily (15 mn).

Alverstone – ✉ Isle of Wight – ☎ 01983.

Grange 🐦, PO36 0EZ, ✆ 403729, – ⇔ rest P. ✗
closed December and January – **Meals** 13.50 **st.** – **6 rm** 18.50/48.00 **st.**

Chale – pop. 561 – ECD : Thursday – ✉ Isle of Wight – ☎ 01983.

Newport 9.

🏨 **Clarendon H. and Wight Mouse Inn,** Newport Rd, PO38 2HA, ✆ 730431, Fax 730431, ≤, – TV P. VISA
Meals 7.00/15.00 **st.** and a la carte 4.00 – **12 rm** 30.00/65.00 **t.**, 1 suite – SB.

Cowes – pop. 16 371 – ECD : Wednesday – ✉ Isle of Wight – ☎ 01983.

Osborne, East Cowes ✆ 295421.

The Arcade, Fountain Quay, PO31 7AR ✆ 291914.

Newport 4.

🏨 **New Holmwood,** Queens Rd, Egypt Point, PO31 8BW, ✆ 292508, Fax 295020, ≤, heated – TV ☎ P – 🏆 150. AE VISA
Meals 7.50/15.00 **t.** and a la carte – **23 rm** 60.00/85.00 **t.**, 2 suites – SB.

🏨 Fountain, High St., PO31 7AW, ✆ 292397, Fax 299554 – TV ☎
20 rm.

Freshwater – pop. 5 073 – ECD : Thursday – ✉ Isle of Wight – ☎ 01983.

Newport 13.

Yarlands Country House 🐦, Victoria Rd, PO40 9PP, ✆ 752574, – ⇔ TV P. ✗
April - September – **Meals** (dinner only) 12.00 **st.** 3.50 – **6 rm** 31.00/52.00 **st.**

Blenheim House without rest., Gate Lane, Freshwater Bay, PO40 9QD, S : 1 m. ✆ 752858, heated – TV P. ✗
June - September – **Meals** (by arrangement) **8 rm** 21.00/42.00 **st.**

Newport – pop. 19 758 – ECD : Thursday – ✉ Isle of Wight – ☎ 01983.

St. George's Down, Shide ✆ 525076.

The Car Park, South Street, PO30 1JU ✆ 525450.

ATS 44/50 South St. ✆ 522881

Niton – ✉ Isle of Wight – ☎ 01983.

Windcliffe Manor 🐦, Sandrock Rd, Undercliff, PO38 2NG, ✆ 730215, heated, – ⇔ rest TV ☎ P. AE VISA
Meals (light lunch)/dinner 16.95/26.95 **t.** 4.30 – **14 rm** (dinner included) 45.00/90.00 **t.** – SB.

Pine Ridge, The Undercliff, PO38 2LY, ✆ 730802, Fax 731001, – ⇔ rest TV ☎ P. VISA
Meals 14.95 **st.** 3.50 – **9 rm** 25.00/60.00 **st.** – SB.

Seaview – ✉ Isle of Wight – ☎ 01983.

🏨 **Seaview,** High St., PO34 5EX, ✆ 612711, Fax 613729 – TV ☎ P. AE VISA
Meals *(closed Sunday dinner except Bank Holidays)* a la carte 18.85/26.85 **t.** 3.80 – **16 rm** 40.00/60.00 **t.**, 1 suite – SB.

Shanklin – pop. 8 109 – ECD : Wednesday – ✉ Isle of Wight – ☎ 01983.

Fairway Lake, Sandown ☎ 403217.

67 High St., PO37 6JJ ☎ 862942.

Newport 9.

Brunswick, Queens Rd, PO37 6AN, ☎ 863245, heated, – rest. VISA
March - October – **Meals** (bar lunch)/dinner 14.00 **t.** – **32 rm** 36.00/62.00 **t.** – SB.

Fern Bank, Highfield Rd, PO37 6PP, ☎ 862790, Fax 864412, – rest. VISA.
Meals (bar lunch Monday to Saturday)/dinner 13.50 **t.** and a la carte 4.00 – **24 rm** 35.00/91.00 **t.** – SB.

Bourne Hall Country, Luccombe Rd, PO37 6RR, ☎ 862820, Fax 865138, heated, – AE VISA.
closed January – **Meals** (bar lunch)/dinner 14.00 **t.** and a la carte 4.95 – **30 rm** (dinner included) 54.80/97.00 **t.** – SB.

Queensmead, 12 Queens Rd, PO37 6AN, ☎ 862342, heated, – rest. AE VISA
mid March-October and Christmas – **Meals** (bar lunch)/dinner 15.30 **st.** 3.95 – **30 rm** 37.00/80.00 **t.** – SB.

Chine Lodge, Eastcliff Rd, PO37 6AA, ☎ 862358, – rest.
closed November - January – **Meals** (booking essential) (residents only) (dinner only) 8.50 **st.** 4.00 – **7 rm** 21.00/55.00 **st.** – SB.

Luccombe Chine Country House, Luccombe Chine, PO37 6RH, S : 2 ¼ m. by A 3055 ☎ 862037, ≤, – VISA.
closed December and January – **Meals** (dinner only) 12.50 **t.** 4.25 – **6 rm** 59.00/82.00 **t.** – SB.

Delphi Cliff, 7 St. Boniface Cliff Rd, PO37 6ET, ☎ 862179, ≤, – rest. VISA.
April-October – **Meals** (by arrangement) – **10 rm** (dinner included) 22.00/50.00 **t.**

Cavendish House without rest., Eastmount Rd, PO37 6DN, ☎ 862460 – VISA.
closed 2 weeks February and Christmas - New Year – **3 rm** 25.00/45.00 **st.**

Totland – pop. 2 316 – ECD : Wednesday – ✉ Isle of Wight – ☎ 01983.

Newport 13.

Sentry Mead, Madeira Rd, PO39 0BJ, ☎ 753212, – rest. AE VISA
closed 23 December - 3 January – **Meals** (bar lunch)/dinner 12.50 **t.** – **14 rm** 30.00/60.00 **t.** – SB.

Rockstone Cottage, Colwell Chine Rd, PO40 9NR, NE : ¾ m. by A 3054 ☎ 753723, – rest
Meals (by arrangement) 12.00 **st.** 3.00 – **5 rm** 22.00/44.00 **st.**

Littledene Lodge, Granville Rd, PO39 0AX, ☎ 752411 – rest
March-November – **Meals** (by arrangement) 9.50 2.95 – **6 rm** 30.00/40.00 **s.** – SB.

Ventnor – pop. 7 956 – ECD : Wednesday – ✉ Isle of Wight – ☎ 01983.

Steephill Down Rd ☎ 853326.

34 High St., PO38 1RZ ☎ 853625 (summer only).

Newport 10.

Madeira Hall without rest., Trinity Rd, PO38 1NS, ☎ 852624, Fax 854906, heated, – VISA.
8 rm 28.00/65.00 **s.**

Hillside, Mitchell Av., PO38 1DR, ☎ 852271, ≤, – rest. AE VISA
Meals (by arrangement) 8.50 **st.** 3.20 – **11 rm** (dinner included) 30.00/60.00 **st.** – SB.

at Bonchurch – ✉ Isle of Wight – ☎ 01983 :

Peacock Vane Country House, Bonchurch Village Rd, PO38 1RJ, ☎ 852019, Fax 854796, « Victoriana », – rest. VISA
closed January - March – **Meals** *(closed lunch Monday and Tuesday)* 7.95/22.45 **t.** 4.80 – **11 rm** 50.00/85.00 **t.**, 1 suite – SB.

Winterbourne, PO38 1RQ, via Bonchurch Shute ☎ 852535, Fax 853056, « Country house ≤ gardens and sea », heated – rest. AE VISA
April to October and weekends in winter – **Meals** (light lunch by arrangement)/dinner 15.95 **t.** 6.00 – **17 rm** (dinner included) 57.00/144.00 **t.**

Highfield, 87 Leeson Rd, Upper Bonchurch, PO38 1PU, on A 3055 ☏ 852800, ←, – rest TV ☎ P. VISA
April - November – **Meals** 8.50/14.95 **st.** and dinner a la carte 4.00 – **12 rm** (dinner included) 38.00/69.00 **t.** – SB.

Lake, Shore Rd, PO38 1RF, ☏ 852613, Fax 852613, – rest P
March-October – **Meals** (dinner only) 10.00 3.50 – **21 rm** 18.50/47.00 **t.** – SB.

Horseshoe Bay without rest., Shore Rd, PO38 1RN, ☏ 852487, ← – P
3 rm.

WIGSTON FIELDS Leics. 402 403 404 Q 26 – see Leicester.

WILLERBY Humbs. 402 S 22 – see Kingston-upon-Hull.

WILLERSEY Heref. and Worcs. 403 404 O 27 – see Broadway.

WILLERSEY HILL Glos. 403 404 O 27 – see Broadway (Heref. and Worcs.).

WILLESLEY Glos. 403 404 N 29 – see Tetbury.

WILLITON Somerset 403 K 30 **The West Country G.** – pop. 2 410 – ECD : Saturday – ✉ Taunton – ☏ 01984.

Envir. : Cleeve Abbey★★ *AC*, W : 2 m. by A 39.

London 177 – Minehead 8 – Taunton 16.

White House, 11 Long St., TA4 4QW, ☏ 632306 – TV ☎ P.
mid May-October – **Meals** (dinner only) 33.00 6.90 – **12 rm** 39.00/78.00 **st.** – SB.

Fairfield House, 51 Long St., TA4 4QY, ☏ 632636 – P. VISA.
March-October – **Meals** (dinner only) 11.50 **st.** and a la carte 5.00 – **5 rm** 25.00/45.00 **st.** – SB.

Curdon Mill, Lower Vellow, TA4 4LS, SE : 2 ½ m. by A 358 on Stogumber rd ☏ 656522, Fax 656197, ←, « Converted water mill on working farm », heated, park – TV P. VISA.
closed 1 to 14 February – **Meals** (by arrangement) 19.50 – **6 rm** 30.00/60.00 **st.**

WILMCOTE Warks. 403 404 O 27 – see Stratford-upon-Avon.

WILMINGTON Devon 403 K 31 – see Honiton.

WILMINGTON East Sussex 404 U 31 – see Eastbourne.

WILMSLOW Ches. 402 403 404 N 24 – pop. 28 827 – ECD : Wednesday – ☏ 01625.

18 Great Warford, Mobberley ☏ (01565) 872148.

London 189 – Liverpool 38 – Manchester 12 – Stoke-on-Trent 27.

Stanneylands, Stanneylands Rd, SK9 4EY, N : 1 m. by A 34 ☏ 525225, Fax 537282, « Gardens » – rest TV ☎ P – 100. AE VISA.
Meals *(closed dinner Sunday, Good Friday, 25 December and 1 January)* 12.50/25.00 **t.** and a la carte 5.25 – **32 rm** 79.00/120.00 **t.**

Wilmslow Moat House (Q.M.H.), Oversley Ford, Altrincham Rd, SK9 4LR, NW : 2¾ m. on A 538 ☏ 529201, Fax 531876, squash – rm TV ☎ P – 300. AE VISA
Meals *(closed Saturday lunch)* 12.00/15.95 **t.** and a la carte 4.95 – 8.75 – **125 rm** 80.00/92.50 **st.** – SB.

at Handforth N : 3 m. on A 34 – ✉ Wilmslow – ☏ 01625 :

Pinewood (Mt. Charlotte Thistle), 180 Wilmslow Rd, SK9 3LG, S : 1 m. on A 34 ☏ 529211, – rm TV ☎ P – 200
58 rm.

Belfry, Stanley Rd, SK9 3LD, ☏ (0161) 437 0511, Fax 499 0597 – TV ☎ P – 120. AE VISA.
closed 25 December and 1 January – **Meals** (dancing Friday evening) 21.50 **t.** and a la carte 6.00 – **77 rm** 77.00/99.00 **t.**, 3 suites.

WIMBORNE MINSTER Dorset 403 404 O 31 **The West Country G.** – pop. 6 9083 – ECD : Wednesday – ☏ 01202.

See : Town★ – Priest's House Museum★ *AC*.

Envir. : Kingston Lacy★★ *AC*, NW : 3 m. by B 3082.

29 High St., BH21 1HR ☏ 886116.

London 112 – Bournemouth 10 – Dorchester 23 – Salisbury 27 – Southampton 30.

Beechleas, 17 Poole Rd, BH21 1QA, ☏ 841684, « Georgian townhouse » – TV ☎ P. AE VISA.
1 to 23 January – **Meals** *(closed Sunday and Monday to non-residents)* (dinner only) 18.50 **t.** – 8.50 – **9 rm** 53.00/83.00 **st.** – SB.

Stour Lodge, 21 Julians Rd, BH21 1EF, on A 31 (Dorchester rd) 888003, Fax 888003, –
closed 21 December-5 January – **Meals** (by arrangement) 10.00 – **3 rm** 25.00/45.00 **st.** – SB.

Les Bouviers, Oakley Hill, Merley, BH21 1RJ, S : 1 ¼ m. on A 349 889555 –
Meals *(closed Saturday lunch)* 11.95/22.95 **st.** and a la carte 7.25.

at Horton N : 6 m. by B 3078 – Wimborne Minster – 01258 :

Northill House, BH21 7HL, NW : ½ m. 840407, – rest .
closed 20 December-15 February – **Meals** (bar lunch)/dinner 13.00 **st.** 4.00 – **9 rm** 37.00/65.00 **st.**

WINCANTON Somerset 403 404 M 30 – 01963.

London 125 – Bristol 34 – Taunton 37 – Yeovil 18.

Lower Church Farm without rest., Rectory Lane, Charlton Musgrove, BA9 8ES, NE : 1 ½ m. by B 3081 and Charlton Musgrove rd 32307, ≤, « Working farm », , park –
closed 20 December-2 January **3 rm** 17.00/30.00 **st.**

ATS Bennetts Field Trading Est., Southgate Rd 33846

In alta stagione, e soprattutto nelle stazioni turistiche,
è prudente prenotare con un certo anticipo.

WINCHCOMBE Glos. 403 404 O 28 – 01242.

London 100 – Birmingham 43 – Gloucester 26 – Oxford 43.

White Lion, 37 North St., GL54 5PS, 603300, Fax 221969, « Part 15C inn », – . VISA
Meals (bar lunch Monday to Saturday)/dinner a la carte 13.00/21.00 **t.** – **6 rm** 30.00/65.00 **st.** – SB.

Sudeley Hill Farm without rest., GL54 5JB, E : 1 m. by Castle St. 602344, ≤, « Part 15C house, working farm », , park –
closed Christmas – **3 rm** 25.00/40.00 **s.**

Wesley House with rm, High St., GL54 5LJ, 602366, « Part 15C house » – rm . AE VISA.
closed 16 January-10 February – **Meals** *(closed Sunday dinner except Bank Holidays)* 18.00/30.00 **t.** and lunch a la carte 4.50 – **6 rm** 25.00/65.00 **t.** – SB.

WINCHELSEA E. Sussex 404 W 31 **Great Britain G.** – 01797.

See : Town★ – St. Thomas Church (effigies★).

London 64 – Brighton 46 – Folkestone 30.

Strand House, TN36 4JT, E : ¼ m. on A 259 226276, « Part 14C and 15C house », – rest . VISA
Meals (by arrangement) 16.00 **st.** 4.00 – **10 rm** 28.00/50.00 **t.** – SB.

WINCHESTER Hants. 403 404 P 30 **Great Britain G.** – pop. 96 386 – ECD : Thursday – 01962.

See : City★★ - Cathedral★★★ *AC* B – Winchester College★ *AC* B **B** – Castle Great Hall★ B **D** – God Begot House★ B **A.**

Envir. : St. Cross Hospital★★ *AC* A.

Guildhall, The Broadway, SO23 9LJ 840500/848180.

London 72 – Bristol 76 – Oxford 52 – Southampton 12.

Plan on next page

Lainston House, Sparsholt, SO21 2LT, NW : 3 ½ m. by A 272 863588, Fax 772672, ≤, « 17C manor house », , park, – – 80. AE VISA JCB A
Meals 14.50/25.50 **t.** and a la carte 6.50 – 10.00 – **37 rm** 95.00/225.00, 1 suite – SB.

Forte Crest, Paternoster Row, SO23 9LQ, 861611, Fax 841503, ≤ – rm – 100 B **c**
93 rm, 1 suite.

Winchester Moat House (Q.M.H.), Worthy Lane, SO23 7AB, 868102, Fax 840862, , , – – 250. AE VISA B **e**
Meals 13.50/17.50 **st.** and a la carte 4.75 – 8.75 – **72 rm** 69.50/79.50 **t.** – SB.

Hotel du Vin and Bistro, 14 Southgate St., SO23 9EF, 841414, Fax 842458, « Wine memorabilia », – – 30. AE VISA. B **i**
Meals 15.00/30.00 **t.** and a la carte 5.00 – **13 rm** 60.00/80.00 **t.** – SB.

Royal, St. Peter St., SO23 8BS, 840840, Fax 841582, – rm – 100. AE VISA JCB B **n**
Meals 12.25/17.50 **t.** and dinner a la carte 4.75 – 8.95 – **75 rm** 69.00/109.00 **t.** – SB.

WINCHESTER

High Street . . . . B

Alresford Road . . . . A 2
Andover Road . . . . B 3
Bereweeke Road . . . . A 5
Bridge Street . . . . B 6
Broadway (The) . . . . B 8
Chilbolton Avenue . . . . A 9
City Road . . . . B 10
Clifton Terrace . . . . B 12
East Hill . . . . B 15
Eastgate Street . . . . B 16
Easton Lane . . . . A 18
Friarsgate . . . . B 19
Garnier Road . . . . A 20
Kingsgate Road . . . . A 22
Magdalen Hill . . . . B 23
Middle Brook Street . . . . B 24
Morestead Road . . . . A 25
Park Road . . . . A 26
Quarry Road . . . . A 29
St. George's Street . . . . B 32
St. Paul's Hill . . . . B 33
St. Peter's Street . . . . B 34
Southgate Street . . . . B 35
Stoney Lane . . . . A 36
Stockbridge Road . . . . B 37
Sussex Street . . . . B 38
Union Street . . . . B 39
Upper High Street . . . . B 40

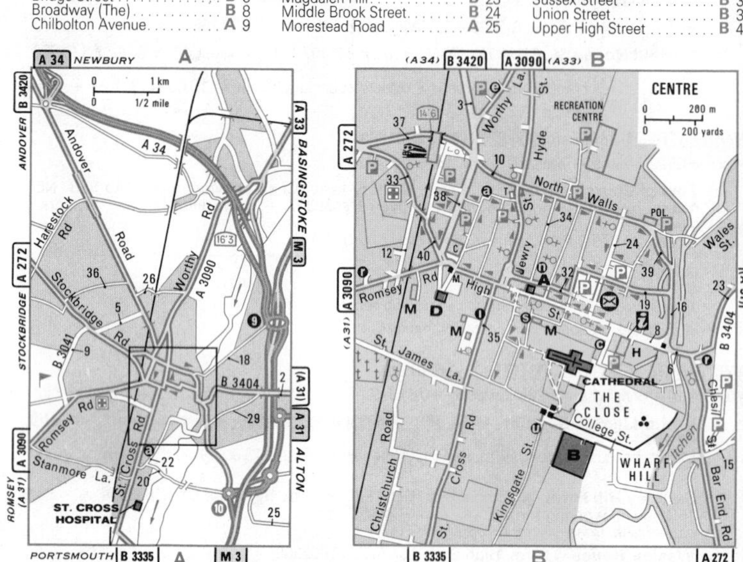

Wykeham Arms, 75 Kingsgate St., SO23 9PE, ✆ 853834, Fax 854411, « Traditional 18C inn, memorabilia », – TV ☎ P. AE VISA — B u
Meals *(closed Sunday)* (in bar) a la carte 15.85/19.85 **t.** 4.35 – **7 rm** 65.00/75.00 **st.**

East View without rest., 16 Clifton Hill, SO22 5BL, ✆ 862986, ≤, – TV P. VISA — B r
3 rm 35.00/45.00 **st.**

Florum House, 47 St. Cross Rd, SO23 9PS, ✆ 840427, Fax 840427, – rest TV P. VISA — A a
Meals (by arrangement) 12.70 **st.** 4.80 – **9 rm** 36.00/52.00 **st.** – SB.

Portland House without rest., 63 Tower St., SO23 8TA, ✆ 865195 – TV. — B a
4 rm 38.00/48.00 **st.**

XX **Nine The Square,** 9 Great Minster St., The Square, SO23 9HA, ✆ 864004, Fax 879586 – AE VISA — B s
closed Sunday and 1 week January – **Meals** a la carte 12.40/25.40 **t.**

X **Old Chesil Rectory,** Chesil St., SO23 8HV, ✆ 851555, « 15C » – VISA — B r
closed Sunday, Monday, 2 weeks August and 2 weeks Christmas-New Year 17.00 **t.** (lunch) and a la carte 5.00.

at Marwell Zoological Park SE : 7 ¼ m. by A 33 - B - and B 3335 on B 2177 – ✉ Winchester – 01962 :

Marwell Safari Lodge, SO21 1JY, ✆ 777681, Fax 777625, , park – TV ☎ & P – 180. AE VISA
Meals (buffet lunch)/dinner 12.95 **t.** and a la carte 5.95 – 7.50 – **68 rm** 65.00/75.00 **st.** – SB.

ATS 61 Bar End Rd ✆ 865021

WINDERMERE Cumbria 402 L 20 **Great Britain G.** – pop. 7 932 – ECD : Thursday – 0153 94.

Envir. : Lake Windermere★★ – Brockhole National Park Centre★ *AC*, NW : 2 m. by A 591.

18 Cleabarrow ✆ 43123, E : 1 ½ m. by A 5074 – Z – on B 5284.

Victoria St., LA23 1AD ✆ 46499 at Bowness, Glebe Rd, LA23 3HJ ✆ 42895 (summer only).

◆London 274 – ◆Blackpool 55 – ◆Carlisle 46 – Kendal 10.

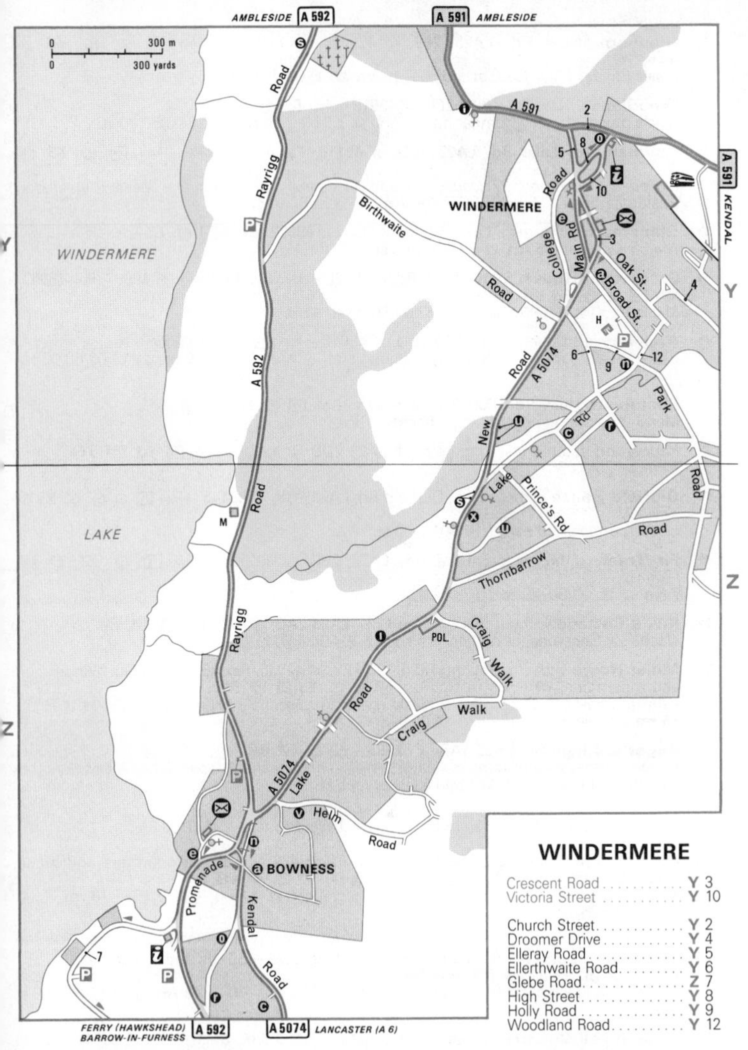

Langdale Chase ⊗, LA23 1LW, NW : 3 m. on A 591 ☎ 32201, Fax 32604, ≤ Lake Windermere and mountains, « Lakeside setting », ⊗, ⊗, ⊗ – ⊗ rest TV ☎ P. ⊗ AE ⊕ VISA Y
Meals 13.50/23.00 **t.** and dinner a la carte 10.90 – **32 rm** ⊗ 46.20/143.00 **t.**

Holbeck Ghyll ⊗, Holbeck Lane, LA23 1LU, NW : 3¼ m. by A 591 ☎ 32375, Fax 34743, ≤ Lake Windermere and mountains, « Former hunting lodge », ⊗, ⊗ – ⊗ rest TV ☎ P. ⊗ AE ⊕ VISA Y
Meals (dinner only) 32.50 **t.** – **14 rm** ⊗ (dinner included) 77.50/230.00 **t.** – SB.

Merewood Country House ⊗, Ecclerigg, LA23 1LH, NW : 2 ½ m. on A 591 ☎ 46484, Fax 42128, ≤, ⊗, park – ⊗ TV ☎ P – ⊗ 80 – **20 rm.** Y

Quarry Garth Country House, Troutbeck Bridge, LA23 1LF, NW : 2 m. on A 591 ☎ 88282, Fax 46584, ⊗, park – ⊗ rest TV ☎ P. ⊗ AE ⊕ VISA Y
Meals (dinner only) 19.50 **st.** 6.00 – **10 rm** ⊗ (dinner included) 65.00/130.00 **st.** – SB.

Cedar Manor, Ambleside Rd, LA23 1AX, ☎ 43192, Fax 45970, ⊗ – ⊗ rest TV ☎ P. ⊗ VISA Y i
Meals (dinner only) 22.50 **t.** 5.50 – **12 rm** ⊗ (dinner included) 51.00/92.00 **t.** – SB.

Glenburn, New Rd, LA23 2EE, ✆ 42649, Fax 88998 – TV ☎ P. VISA JCB. Y u
Meals (dinner only) 15.00 **st.** 5.50 – **16 rm** 35.00/60.00 **st.**

Woodlands, New Rd, LA23 2EE, ✆ 43915 – TV P. VISA. Y u
Meals (residents only) (dinner only) 13.50 **st.** 3.50 – **14 rm** 20.00/56.00 **st.**

Hawksmoor, Lake Rd, LA23 2EQ, ✆ 42110, Fax 42110, – TV P. VISA. Z s
closed 20 November-27 December and 11 January-12 February – **Meals** (dinner only) (residents only) 10.50 **st.** 3.50 – **10 rm** 25.00/52.00 **st.**

Glencree without rest., Lake Rd, LA23 2EQ, ✆ 45822 – TV P. VISA. Z s
March-October – **5 rm** 29.00/60.00 **st.**

Braemount House, Sunny Bank Rd, LA23 2EN, by Queens Drive ✆ 45967, Fax 45967 – TV ☎ P. VISA. Z u
Meals 15.50 **st.** 5.90 – **6 rm** 37.00/80.00 **st.** – SB.

Archway, 13 College Rd, LA23 1BU, ✆ 45613 – TV ☎. AE VISA. Y e
closed 10-20 January – **Meals** (by arrangement) 11.00 **st.** 6.95 – **5 rm** 24.00/50.00 **st.** – SB.

Beaumont, Holly Rd, LA23 2AF, ✆ 47075 – TV P. AE VISA. Y n
Meals (by arrangement) 12.50 – **10 rm** 35.00/56.00 **st.**

Kirkwood without rest., Prince's Rd, LA23 2DD, ✆ 43907 – TV. VISA JCB Y r
7 rm 25.00/50.00 **s.**

Oldfield House without rest., Oldfield Rd, LA23 2BY, ✆ 88445 – TV ☎ P. AE VISA JCB. Y c
closed January – **8 rm** 27.00/50.00 **st.**

Fir Trees without rest., Lake Rd, LA23 2EQ, ✆ 42272 – TV P. AE VISA. Z x
7 rm 35.00/50720 **st.**

Kay's Cottage without rest., 7 Broad St., LA23 2AB, ✆ 44146 – TV. VISA. Y a
closed 22 December-3 January – **4 rm** 30.00/34.00 **t.**

Miller Howe with rm, Rayrigg Rd, LA23 1EY, ✆ 42536, Fax 45664, ≤ Lake Windermere and mountains, – rest rest TV ☎ P. AE VISA Y s
early March-early December – **Meals** (booking essential) (dinner only) 32.00 **t.** 7.50 – **13 rm** (dinner included) 75.00/250.00 **t.**

Roger's, 4 High St., LA23 1AF, ✆ 44954 – AE VISA Y o
closed Sunday except Bank Holidays, 1 week January and 1 week July – **Meals** (lunch by arrangement)/dinner 17.00 **t.** and a la carte 5.95.

at Bowness-on-Windermere S : 1 m. – ✉ Windermere – 0153 94 :

Old England (Forte), LA23 3DF, ✆ 42444, Fax 43432, ≤ Lake Windermere and mountains, heated, – TV ☎ P – 90. AE VISA JCB Z e
Meals (bar lunch Monday to Saturday)/dinner 19.50 **st.** 6.00 – 7.95 – **76 rm** 60.00/120.00 **st.**, 2 suites – SB.

Linthwaite House, Crook Rd, LA23 3JA, S : ¾ m. by A 5074 on B 5284 ✆ 88600, Fax 88601, ≤ Lake Windermere and fells, « Extensive grounds and private lake », – TV ☎ P. AE VISA JCB. Z
Meals (light lunch Monday to Saturday)/dinner 27.00 **st.** 7.00 – **18 rm** 75.00/160.00 **st.** – SB.

Lindeth Fell Country House, Kendal Rd, LA23 3JP, S : 1 m. on A 5074 ✆ 43286, ≤ Lake Windermere and mountains, « Country house atmosphere, gardens », park, – rest TV ☎ P. VISA. Z
mid March-mid November – **Meals** (light lunch)/dinner 19.00 **t.** 4.50 – **14 rm** (dinner included) 51.00/115.00 **t.**

Craig Manor, Lake Rd, LA23 3AR, ✆ 88877, Fax 88878, ≤ – TV ☎ P. AE VISA Z i
Meals (bar lunch Monday to Saturday)/dinner 20.00 and a la carte 6.00 – **16 rm** 40.00/100.00 **st.** – SB.

Burnside, Kendal Rd, LA23 3EP, ✆ 42211, Fax 43824, , , , , squash – TV ☎ P – 90. AE VISA Z c
Meals (bar lunch Monday to Saturday)/dinner 19.00 **t.** and a la carte 4.60 – **55 rm** 47.50/95.00 **st.**, 2 suites.

Belsfield (Forte), Back Belsfield Rd, LA23 3EL, ✆ 42448, Fax 46397, ≤, , , , – TV ☎ P – 130. AE VISA JCB Z o
Meals (bar lunch)/dinner 16.50 **st.** and a la carte 7.45 – 8.75 – **62 rm** 70.00/105.00 **st.**, 2 suites – SB.

Burn How, Back Belsfield Rd, LA23 3HH, ℘ 46226, Fax 47000, – rest TV ☎ P. AE VISA. Z r
Meals (bar lunch)/dinner 18.50 **st.** and a la carte 5.00 – **26 rm** 48.00/84.00 **st.** – SB.

Wild Boar, Crook Rd, LA23 3NF, SE : 4 m. by A 5074 on B 5284 ℘ 45225, Fax 42498, – TV ☎ P – 40. AE VISA Z
Meals 11.65/25.85 **st.** 4.95 – **36 rm** 55.00/114.00 **st.** – SB.

Crag Brow Cottage, Helm Rd, LA23 3BU, ℘ 44080, Fax 46003, – rest TV ☎ P. VISA JCB. Z v
Meals 9.95/21.95 **st.** and a la carte – **11 rm** 45.00/80.00 **st.** – SB.

Bordriggs Country House, Longtail Hill, LA23 3LD, S : 1 m. by A 592 on B 5284 ℘ 43567, Fax 46949, heated, – TV ☎ P. Z
Meals (residents only) (dinner only) 14.00 **st.** 3.50 – **10 rm** 27.50/65.00 **t.**

White Foss without rest., Longtail Hill, LA23 3JD, S : ¾ m. by A 592 on B 5284 ℘ 46593, ≤, – P. Y
April-October – **3 rm** 40.00/46.00 **st.**

Laurel Cottage without rest., St. Martins Sq., LA23 3EF, ℘ 45594 – TV. Z a
closed Christmas – **15 rm** 21.00/52.00 **st.**

Gilpin Lodge with rm, Crook Rd, LA23 3NE, SE : 2½ m. by A 5074 on B 5284 ℘ (01539) 488818, Fax 488058, ≤, – rest TV ☎ P. AE VISA JCB. Z
Meals 11.50/26.00 **st.** and lunch a la carte **st.** 5.00 – **9 rm** 50.00/120.00 **st.** – SB.

Porthole Eating House, 3 Ash St., LA23 3EB, ℘ 42793, Fax 88675 Z n

Brown Horse Inn, Winster, LA23 3NR, SE : 3 m. on A 5074 ℘ 43443 – P
closed mid November-mid December – **Meals** a la carte 9.00/14.25 **st.** 3.50.

at Troutbeck N : 4 m. by A 592 – Y – ✉ Windermere – 0153 94 :

Mortal Man, LA23 1PL, ℘ 33193, Fax 31261, ≤ Garburn Hill and Troutbeck Valley, – rest TV ☎ P
mid February-mid November – **Meals** (dinner only and Sunday lunch)/dinner 20.00 **st.** 5.50 – **12 rm** (dinner included) 55.00/110.00 **st.** – SB.

WINDSOR Berks. 404 S 29 **Great Britain G.** – pop. 30 832 (inc. Eton) – ECD : Wednesday – 01753.

See : Town★ – Castle★★★ : St. George's Chapel★★★ *AC* (stalls★★★), State Apartments★★ *AC*, North Terrace (≤★★) Z – Eton College★★ *AC* (College Chapel★★, Wall paintings★) Z.

Envir. : Windsor Park★ *AC* Y.

Central Station, Thames St., SL4 1PJ ℘ 852010.

London 28 – Reading 19 – Southampton 59.

Plan on next page

Oakley Court (Q.M.H.), Windsor Rd, Water Oakley, SL4 5UR, W : 3 m. on A 308 ℘ (01628) 74141, Telex 849958, Fax 37011, ≤, « Part Gothic mansion on banks of River Thames », , park – rm TV ☎ P – 100. AE VISA JCB. Y
Meals 19.75/29.50 **t.** and a la carte 6.95 – 13.50 – **91 rm** 136.50/191.00 **t.**, 1 suite – SB.

Castle (Forte), High St., SL4 1LJ, ℘ 851011, Fax 830244 – rm TV ☎ P – 420. AE VISA Z c
Meals 16.50/25.00 **t.** and a la carte – 11.50 – **101 rm** 99.00/145.00 **st.**, 3 suites – SB.

Aurora Garden, 14 Bolton Av., SL4 3JF, ℘ 868686, Fax 831394, – TV ☎ P – 90. AE VISA Z a
Meals *(closed dinner 25 and 26 December)* 10.00/13.95 **t.** and a la carte 4.50 – **14 rm** 60.00/80.00 **st.** – SB.

Dorset without rest., 4 Dorset Rd, SL4 3BA, ℘ 852669 – TV P Z e
5 rm.

Fairlight Lodge, 41 Frances Rd, SL4 3AQ, ℘ 861207, Fax 865963, – TV ☎ P. AE VISA. Z z
Meals a la carte 9.00/16.50 **st.** 4.00 – **10 rm** 37.00/60.00 **st.**

WINDSOR

High Street	Z 14
King Edward Court Centre	Z
Peascod Street	Z
Thames Street	Z 25
Bexley Street	Z 2
Bolton Road	Y 3
Castle Hill	Z 4
Claremont Road	Z 6
Clarence Crescent	Z 7
Clewer Crescent Road	Z 8
Datchet Rd	Z 9
Goswell Road	Z 10
Grove Road	Z 12
High Street (DATCHET)	Y 13
Horton Road	Y 16
Keats Lane	Z 17
Peascod Street	Z 18
Ragstone Road	Y 20
River Street	Z 22
Stovell Road	Z 23
Thames Avenue	Z 24
Trinity Place	Z 27
Windsor Bridge	Z 28
Windsor Road	Y 29

North is at the top on all town plans.

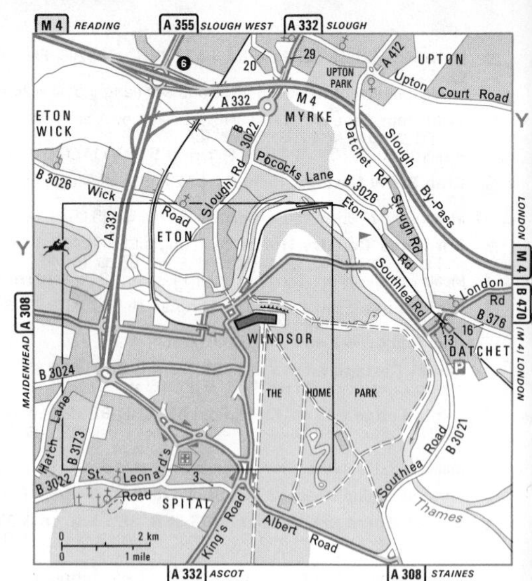

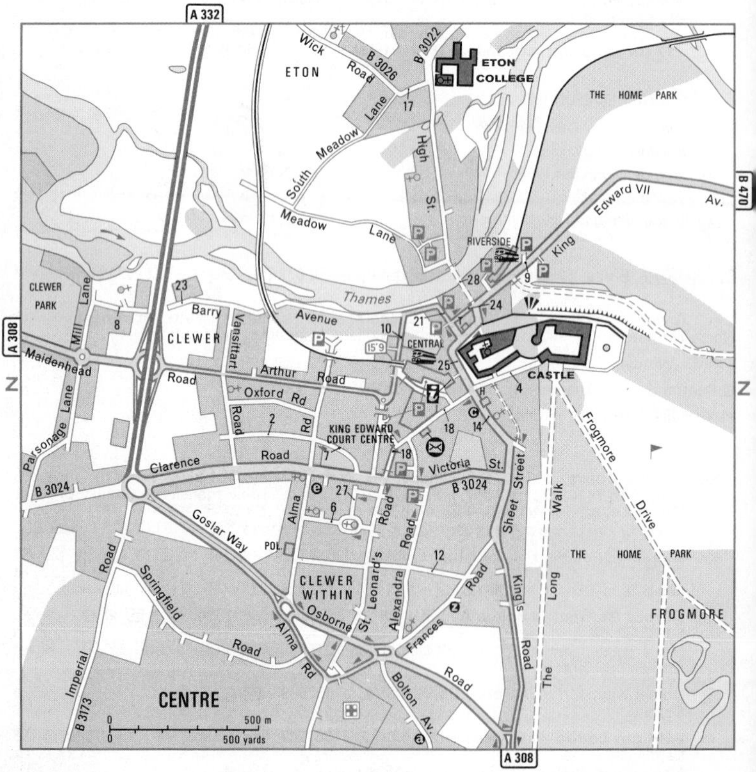

WINEHAM W. Sussex 404 T 31 – see Henfield.

WINGHAM Kent 404 X 30 – pop. 1 553 – ☎ 01227.
♦London 66 – Canterbury 7 – ♦Dover 19 – Margate 14.

✗ **Four Seasons,** 109 High St., CT3 1BU, ℘ 720286, ⌂ – ⊡ VISA
closed Sunday dinner, 1 week January and 2 weeks October – **Meals** (dinner only and Sunday lunch)/dinner 16.95 **t.** ₰ 3.95.

WINKTON Dorset – see Christchurch.

WINSCOMBE Avon 403 L 30 – ☎ 01934.
♦London 137 – ♦Bristol 16 – Taunton 22.

Sidcot Arms (Premier), Bridgwater Rd, BS25 1NN, on A 38 ℘ 844145, Fax 844192 – ⇆ rest TV ☎ ♿ P
31 rm, 1 suite.

WINSFORD Somerset 403 J 30 **The West Country G.** pop. 270 – ECD : Thursday – ✉ Minehead – ☎ 0164 385 (3 fig.) and 01643 (6 fig.).
See : Village★.
Envir. : Exmoor National Park★★.
♦London 194 – Exeter 31 – Minehead 10 – Taunton 32.

Royal Oak Inn, TA24 7JE, ℘ 455, Fax 388, « Attractive part 12C thatched inn », ⌂ – TV ☎ P. ⊡ AE ⊙ VISA
Meals (bar lunch Monday to Saturday)/dinner 15.00/25.00 **t.** – **14 rm** ⊇ 37.50/53.75 **t.** – SB.

Karslake House, TA24 7JE, ℘ 851242, ⌂ – ⇆ TV P
closed 1-15 July and November-March – **Meals** 14.50 **st.** ₰ 4.60 – **7 rm** ⊇ 29.50/59.00 **st.**

WINSLEY Wilts. 403 404 N 29 – see Bath (Avon).

WINSTER Derbs. 402 403 404 P 24 – ☎ 01629.
♦London 157 – Derby 21 – ♦Manchester 46 – ♦Nottingham 28 – ♦Sheffield 28.

Dower House without rest., Main St., DE4 2DH, ℘ 650213, Fax 650894, « Elizabethan house », ⌂ – ⇆ TV P
March-October – **3 rm** ⊇ 20.00/55.00 **s.**

WINTERBOURNE Avon 403 404 M 29 – see Bristol.

WINTERINGHAM Humbs. 402 S 22 – pop. 4 714 – ✉ Scunthorpe – ☎ 01724.
♦London 176 – ♦Kingston-upon-Hull 16 – ♦Sheffield 67.

XXXX ✿ **Winteringham Fields** (Schwab) with rm, DN15 9PF, ℘ 733096, Fax 733898, « Part 16C manor house », ⌂ – ⇆ TV ☎ P. ⊡ AE VISA. ✻
closed first week August and 2 weeks Chritmas – **Meals** *(closed lunch Saturday to Monday and Sunday dinner)* 15.75/29.00 **st.** and dinner a la carte 33.00/42.00 **st.** ₰ 5.50 – ⊇ 7.00 – **6 rm** 65.00/95.00 **st.**, 1 suite
Spec. Pan fried scallops and monkfish layered with semolina, Rolled rack of Lincolnshire lamb with roast garlic, Winteringham corn tart.

WISBECH Cambs. 404 U 25 – ☎ 01945.
♦London 103 – ♦Cambridge 43 – ♦Norwich 58.

White Lion, South Brink, PE13 1JD, ℘ 63060, Fax 63069 – ⇆ rest TV ☎ P – 🔬 120. ⊡ VISA
Meals - Italian approx. 16.00 **t.** ₰ 4.95 – ⊇ 4.95 – **14 rm** 39.00/100.00 **st.** – SB.

ATS North End ℘ 583214

WITCOMBE Glos. – see Gloucester.

WITHAM Essex 404 V 28 – pop. 26 872 – ECD : Wednesday – ☎ 01376.
♦London 42 – ♦Cambridge 46 – Chelmsford 9 – Colchester 13.

Jarvis Rivenhall, Rivenhall End, CM8 3BH, NE : 1 ½ m. by B 1389 on A 12 (southbound carriageway) ℘ 516969, Fax 513674, Ⅎ₆, ≘s, ▣, squash – ⇆ rm TV ☎ P – 🔬 185. ⊡ AE ⊙ VISA
Meals *(closed Saturday lunch)* 11.50/15.50 **st.** and a la carte ₰ 5.25 – ⊇ 7.50 – **55 rm** 58.00/68.00 **st.** – SB.

ATS Unit 15, Moss Rd Ind. Est. East ℘ 518360/515671

WITHERSLACK Cumbria 402 L 21 – see Grange-over-Sands.

WITHINGTON Glos. 403 404 O 28 – pop. 486 – ☎ 01242.
♦London 91 – Gloucester 15 – ♦Oxford 35 – Swindon 24.

Halewell ⑤, GL54 4BN, ℘ 890238, Fax 890332, ≤, « Part 15C monastery, country house atmosphere », ⛆ heated, ⌇, ⌂, park – ⇆ rest TV P. ⊡ AE VISA. ✻
Meals (booking essential) (residents only) (communal dining) (dinner only) 19.50 **st.** – **6 rm** ⊇ 49.50/77.00 **st.**

WITHYPOOL Somerset 403 J 30 **The West Country G.** – pop. 196 – ECD : Thursday – ✉ Minehead – ☎ 0164 383.

Envir. : Exmoor National Park★★ – Exford (Church★) NE : 4 m. by B 3223 and B 3224.

♦London 204 – Exeter 34 – Taunton 36.

- **Westerclose Country House** ⑤, TA24 7QR, NW : ¼ m. ℘ 302, ≤, ⛱, park – ⇔ rest TV P. VISA
  closed 31 December-February – **Meals** (*closed Monday to non-residents except Bank Holidays*) 19.00 **t.** and a la carte 4.50 – **10 rm** ⊐ 27.00/74.00 **t.** – SB.
- **Royal Oak Inn**, TA24 7QP, ℘ 506, Fax 659, « Part 17C inn », – TV ☎ P. AE VISA
  closed 25 and 26 December – **Meals** (bar lunch Monday to Saturday)/dinner 19.50 **t.** and a la carte 4.60 – **8 rm** ⊐ 30.00/72.00 **t.** – SB.

WITNEY Oxon 403 404 P 28 – pop. 19 041 – ECD : Tuesday – ☎ 01993.

ℹ Town Hall, Market Sq., OX8 6AG ℘ 775802.

♦London 69 – Gloucester 39 – ♦Oxford 13.

- **Witney Lodge**, Ducklington Lane, OX8 7TJ, S : 1 ½ m. on A 415 ℘ 779777, Fax 703467, Fö, ≘s, ⊠ – ⇔ rm TV ☎ & P – 160. AE VISA.
  Meals 8.75/11.50 **st.** and a la carte 4.50 – ⊐ 5.95 – **74 rm** 63.00/82.00 **st.** – SB.

at Hailey N : 1 ¼ m. on B 4022 – ✉ Witney – ☎ 01993 :

- **Bird in Hand**, OX8 5XP, N : 1 m. on B 4022 ℘ 868321, Fax 868702 – ⇔ rm TV ☎ & P. VISA
  Meals a la carte 12.20/17.90 **t.** 5.35 – ⊐ 7.50 – **16 rm** 37.50 **t.** – SB.

at Barnard Gate E : 3 ¼ m. by B 4022 off A 40 – ✉ Eynsham – ☎ 01865 :

- **Boot Inn**, OX8 6AE, ℘ 881231, Fax 881834 – P. VISA
  Meals a la carte 12.85/22.40.

ATS Orchard Way, off Corn St. ℘ 704273

WITTERSHAM Kent 404 W 30 – ✉ Tenterden – ☎ 01797.

♦London 59 – ♦Brighton 54 – Folkestone 22 – Maidstone 28.

- **Wittersham Court** ⑤, TN30 7EA, ℘ 270425, ⛱, squash – ⇔ rm P. VISA
  closed Christmas and New Year – **Meals** (by arrangement) 17.00 – **3 rm** ⊐ 45.00/55.00 – SB.

WIVELISCOMBE Somerset 403 K 30 **The West Country G.** – pop. 2 394 – ECD : Thursday – ✉ Taunton – ☎ 01984.

Envir. : Gaulden Manor★ *AC*, NE : 3 m. by B 3188.

♦London 185 – Barnstaple 38 – Exeter 37 – Taunton 14.

- **Langley House**, Langley Marsh, TA4 2UF, NW : ½ m. ℘ 623318, Fax 624573, ⛱ – ⇔ rest TV ☎ P. AE VISA
  Meals (booking essential) (dinner only) 24.50/28.50 **st.** 4.75 – **8 rm** ⊐ 64.50/110.00 **st.** – SB.
- **Jews Farm House** ⑤, Huish Champflower, TA4 2HL, NW : 2 ½ m. turning right opposite postbox in wall onto rd marked as unsuitable for heavy vehicles; 2nd on left ℘ 624218, ≤, « 13C farmhouse », ⛱, park – ⇔ rm P.
  closed December and January – **Meals** (by arrangement) (communal dining) 18.00 – **3 rm** ⊐ 40.00/60.00 **st.**
- **Deepleigh** ⑤ without rest., Langley Marsh, TA4 2UU, NW : 1 m. on Whitefield rd ℘ 623379, « Converted 16C farmhouse », ⛱ – ⇔ TV P.
  3 rm ⊐ 26.00/40.00 **t.**

at Waterrow SW : 2½ m. on B 3227 – ✉ Taunton – ☎ 01984 :

- Hurstone ⑤ without rest., TA4 2AT, E : ½ m. ℘ 623441, ≤ Tone Valley, « Converted farmhouse », ⛱, park – ⇔ TV ☎ P
  5 rm.

WOBURN Beds. 404 S 28 **Great Britain G.** – pop. 1 534 – ECD : Wednesday – ✉ Milton Keynes – ☎ 01525.

See : Woburn Abbey★★.

♦London 49 – Bedford 13 – Luton 13 – Northampton 24.

- **Bedford Arms** (Mt. Charlotte Thistle), 1 George St., MK17 9PX, ℘ 290441, Fax 290432 – ⇔ rm TV ☎ P – 60. AE VISA
  Meals 15.95/18.50 **st.** and a la carte – ⊐ 8.50 – **54 rm** 70.00/99.00 **st.**, 1 suite – SB.
- **Bell Inn**, 34-35 Bedford St., MK17 9QD, ℘ 290280, Fax 290017 – TV ☎ P. AE VISA
  Meals (see **Bell Inn** below) – **27 rm** ⊐ 58.00/77.00 **st.** – SB.
- XXX **Paris House**, Woburn Park, MK17 9QP, SE : 2 ¼ m. on A 4012 ℘ 290692, Fax 290471, « Reconstructed timbered house in park », ⛱ – P. AE VISA
  closed Sunday dinner, Monday and February – **Meals** 23.00/40.00 **t.** 5.00.
- XX **Bell Inn**, (at Bell Inn H.) 21 Bedford St., MK17 9QD, ℘ 290280, Fax 290017 – P. AE VISA
  closed Saturday lunch, Sunday dinner and 25 to 30 December – **Meals** 17.95 **t.** 5.95.

WOKINGHAM Berks. 404 R 29 – pop. 30 773 – ECD : Wednesday – ☎ 01734.

Easthampstead Park ℘ (01344) 424066 – 18, 9 Sandford Lane, Hurst ℘ 344355.

◆London 43 – Reading 7 – ◆Southampton 52.

Stakis Bracknell, London Rd, RG11 1ST, E : 1½ m. on A 329 ℘ 772550, Fax 772526, park, – rm rest – 280. VISA JCB
Meals *(closed Saturday lunch)* (carving lunch) 14.95/19.75 **t.** and dinner a la carte – 9.75 – **125 rm** 115.00/150.00 **st.**, 3 suites – SB.

Edward Court, Wellington Rd, RG11 2AN, ℘ 775886, Fax 772018 – . VISA
Meals 11.50/13.95 **t.** and a la carte 4.50 – 7.00 – **25 rm** 49.00/56.00 **t.** – SB.

WOLFERTON Norfolk 402 404 V 25 – see Sandringham.

When travelling for business or pleasure
in ***England, Wales, Scotland*** *and* ***Ireland****:*

– use the series of five maps
(nos 401, 402, 403, 404 and 405) at a scale of 1:400 000

– they are the perfect complement to this Guide

WOLVERHAMPTON

Darlington Street B
Mander Centre B
Victoria Street B 24
Wulfrun Centre B

Alfred Squire Road A 2
Birmingham New Road A 3
Bridgnorth Road A 6
Cleveland Street B 7
Garrick Street B 8
High Street A 9
Lichfield Road A 10

Lichfield Street B 12
Market Street B 14
Princess Street B 15
Queen Square B 17
Railway Drive B 20
Salop Street B 22
Thompson Avenue A 23

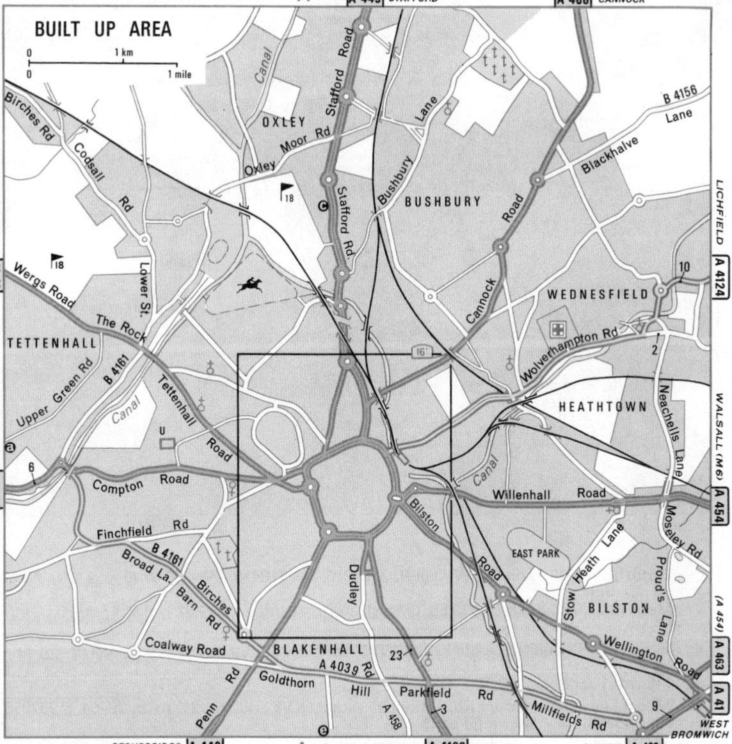

WOLVERHAMPTON W. Mids. 402 403 404 N 26 – pop. 242 190 – ECD : Thursday – ☏ 01902.

⛳ Oxley Park, Stafford Rd, Bushbury ℰ 20506, A – ⛳ Wergs, Keepers Lane, Tettenhall ℰ 742225, A – ⛳ Perton Park, Wrottesley Park Rd ℰ 380103/380073, A.

ℹ 18 Queen Sq., WV1 1TQ ℰ 312051.

◆London 132 – ◆Birmingham 15 – ◆Liverpool 89 – Shrewsbury 30.

Plan of Enlarged Area : see Birmingham pp. 2 and 3

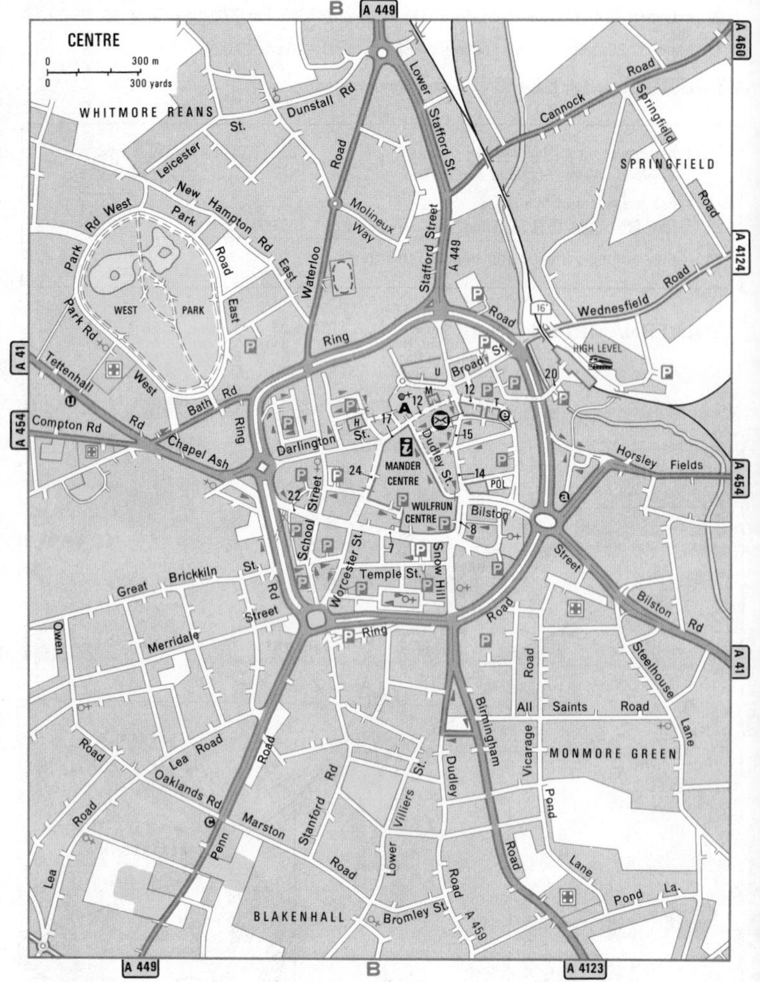

🏨 **Goldthorn,** 126 Penn Rd, WV3 0ER, ℰ 29216, Fax 710419 – ⇔ 📺 ☎ **P** – 🎤 140. AE ⓓ VISA JCB — B **c**
Meals (bar lunch Saturday) 10.50/16.95 **st.** and a la carte 🍷 4.95 – **92 rm** ☕ 47.00/85.00 **st.** – SB.

🏨 Victoria H. Periquito, Lichfield St., WV1 4DB, ℰ 29922, Fax 29923 – |‡| ⇔ rm 📺 ☎ – 🎤 210 — B **e**
116 rm, 1 suite.

🏨 Mount (Jarvis) 🌿, Mount Rd, Tettenhall Wood, WV6 8HL, W : 2½ m. by A 454 ℰ 752055, Fax 745263, 🌳 – ⇔ rm 📺 ☎ **P** – 🎤 160 — A **a**
55 rm, 1 suite.

Novotel, Union St., WV1 3JN, ✆ 871100, Fax 870054, heated – rm TV – 200. AE VISA B a
Meals 10.00/15.00 **st.** and dinner a la carte 4.95 – 7.50 – **132 rm** 49.50 **st.** – SB.

Jarvis Park Hall, Park Drive, Ednam Rd, WV4 5AJ, off Goldthorn Hill ✆ 331121, Fax 344760, – TV – 400. AE VISA A e
Meals (bar lunch) 9.85 **t.** and dinner a la carte – 7.60 – **56 rm** 45.00/55.00 **st.**, 1 suite – SB.

Castlecroft House, Castlecroft Rd, Castlecroft, WV3 8NA, W : 3 ¾ m. by A 454 – A – Windmill Lane and Castlecroft Av. ✆ 764040, Fax 380111, – TV – 40. VISA
Meals *(closed Sunday dinner)* (bar lunch Monday to Saturday)/dinner 18.00 **t.** and a la carte 4.95 – **30 rm** 55.00/65.00 **t.**

Ely House, 53 Tettenhall Rd, WV3 9NB, ✆ 311311, Fax 21098 – TV . AE VISA B u
closed 24 to 30 December – **Meals** 11.95 **t.** and a la carte 4.95 – **18 rm** 40.00/68.00 **t.**

Wheaton House without rest., 285 Stafford Rd, Oxley, WV10 6DQ, N : 1 ½ m. on A 449 ✆ 28841 – TV A c
4 rm 17.50/28.00.

ATS 35-39 Wednesfield Rd ✆ 455055 ATS 2 Willenhall Rd ✆ 871417

WOOBURN COMMON Bucks. – see Beaconsfield.

WOODBRIDGE Suffolk 404 X 27 – pop. 7 449 – ECD : Wednesday – 01394.
Cretingham, Grove Farm ✆ (01728) 685275 – Seckford Hall Rd, Great Bealings ✆ 388000.
London 81 – Great Yarmouth 45 – Ipswich 8 – Norwich 47.

Seckford Hall , IP13 6NU, SW : 1 ¼ m. by A 12 ✆ 385678, Fax 380610, ←, « Part Tudor country house », , park – rm rest TV – 100. AE VISA
closed 25 December – **Meals** 13.00 **st.** (lunch) and a la carte 22.15/33.45 5.00 – **25 rm** 79.00/120.00 **st.**, 7 suites – SB.

Crown (Forte), Thoroughfare, IP12 1AD, ✆ 384242, Fax 387192 – rm TV . AE VISA
Meals 10.95/17.95 **t.** and a la carte 6.95 – 8.50 – **20 rm** 60.00/70.00 **t.** – SB.

Grove, 39 Grove Rd, IP12 4LG, on A 12 ✆ 382202, – rest TV . VISA
Meals 11.20 **s.** – **9 rm** 19.00/42.00 **s.** – SB.

WOODFALLS Wilts. – see Salisbury.

WOODFORD Gtr. Manchester – see Bramhall.

WOODGREEN Hants. – see Fordingbridge.

WOODHALL SPA Lincs. 402 404 T 24 **Great Britain G.** – pop. 3 266 – ECD : Wednesday – 01526.
Envir. : Tattershall Castle★ *AC*, SE : 4 m. by B 1192 and A 153 – Woodhall Spa ✆ 352511.
The Cottage Museum, Iddlesleigh Rd, LN10 6SH ✆ 353775 (summer only).
London 138 – Lincoln 18.

Petwood House Stixwould Rd, LN10 6QF, ✆ 352411, Fax 353473, ←, « Gardens », park – TV – 150. AE VISA
Meals (bar lunch Monday to Saturday)/dinner a la carte 13.00/21.95 **st.** 5.50 – **46 rm** 70.00/120.00 **st.** – SB.

Golf, The Broadway, LN10 6SG, ✆ 353535, Fax 353096, – TV – 150. AE VISA
Meals (bar lunch Monday to Saturday)/dinner 13.50 **t.** and a la carte 4.95 – **50 rm** 57.50/85.00 **t.** – SB.

Dower House , Manor Estate, via Spa Rd, LN10 6PY, ✆ 352588, Fax 354045, – TV . AE VISA.
Meals (lunch by arrangement)/dinner 12.50 **st.** and a la carte 3.65 – **7 rm** 42.00/64.00 **st.** – SB.

Pitchaway, The Broadway, LN10 6SQ, ✆ 352969 – TV .
Meals (by arrangement) 10.00 – **7 rm** 17.00/45.00 – SB.

Oglee, 16 Stanhope Av., LN10 6SP, ✆ 353512, Fax 353512, – TV . VISA.
Meals (by arrangement) 12.50 **t.** 5.00 – **5 rm** 20.00/38.00 **st.**

WOODSEAVES Staffs. 402 403 404 N 25 – 01785.
London 155 – Birmingham 38 – Shrewsbury 23 – Stoke-on-Trent 15.

Old Parsonage with rm, High Offley, ST20 0NE, W : 1¼ m. ✆ 284446, Fax 284446, ←, – rm TV . AE VISA
Meals 12.50/22.50 **t.** and a la carte 5.95 – 5.00 – **4 rm** 40.00 **st.** – SB.

Royal Oak, Grubb St., High Offley, ST20 0NE, W : 1 ¼ m. ✆ 284579 – . VISA
closed Sunday dinner, Monday to Wednesday and Bank Holidays – **Meals** (dinner only and Sunday lunch)/dinner 18.50 **t.** 4.95.

WOODSTOCK Oxon. 403 404 P 28 **Great Britain G.** – pop. 2 898 – ECD : Wednesday – ☏ 01993.

See : Blenheim Palace★★★ (The Grounds★★★) *AC.*

ℹ Hensington Rd, OX20 1JQ ✆ 811038 (summer only).

♦London 65 – Gloucester 47 – ♦Oxford 8.

Bear (Forte), Park St., OX20 1SZ, ✆ 811511, Fax 813380, « Part 16C inn » – TV ☎ P – 70. AE VISA
Meals 18.50/25.95 **st.** – 8.95 – **41 rm** 95.00/115.00 **st.**, 4 suites – SB.

Feathers, Market St., OX20 1SX, ✆ 812291, Fax 813158, « Tastefully furnished 17C houses » – TV ☎. AE VISA JCB
Meals 16.50/26.50 **t.** and a la carte – 7.50 – **16 rm** 75.00/145.00, 1 suite – SB.

WOODY BAY Devon 403 I 30 – see Lynton.

WOOKEY HOLE Somerset 403 L 30 – see Wells.

WOOLACOMBE Devon 403 H 30 **The West Country G.** – pop. 1 171 – ECD : Wednesday – ☏ 01271.

Envir. : Mortehoe★★ (St. Mary's Church★, Morte Point★, Vantage Point★) N : ½ m.

ℹ Hall 70, Beach Rd, EX34 7BT ✆ 870553 (summer only).

♦London 237 – Barnstaple 15 – Exeter 55.

Woolacombe Bay, EX34 7BN, ✆ 870388, Fax 870613, ≤, heated, squash – TV ☎ P – 200. AE VISA.
closed 2 January-9 February – **Meals** (dancing Tuesday evening) (light lunch Monday to Saturday)/dinner 17.00 **st.** and a la carte 4.50 – **59 rm** (dinner included) 65.00/200.00 **t.** – SB.

Little Beach, The Esplanade, EX34 7DJ, ✆ 870398, ≤ – rest TV ☎ P. VISA
March-October – **Meals** (dinner only) 14.50 **st.** 3.95 – **10 rm** 27.00/60.00 **st.**

at Mortehoe N : ½ m. – ✉ Woolacombe – ☏ 01271 :

Watersmeet, The Esplanade, EX34 7EB, ✆ 870333, Fax 870890, ≤ Morte Bay, heated, – rest TV ☎ P. AE VISA.
closed December and January – **Meals** (bar lunch)/dinner 25.50 **st.** and a la carte 4.75 – **24 rm** (dinner included) 61.00/174.00 **st.** – SB.

Cleeve House, EX34 7ED, ✆ 870719 – TV P.
April-September – **Meals** (dinner only) 15.00 **s.** – **6 rm** (dinner included) 45.00/74.00 **s.** – SB.

Sunnycliffe, Chapel Hill, EX34 7EB, ✆ 870597, ≤ Morte Bay – TV P.
February-October – **Meals** 15.00 – **8 rm** 25.00/64.00 **st.** – SB.

WOOLER Northd 401 402 N 17 – ☏ 01668.

♦London 321 – ♦Edinburgh 64 – Newcastle-upon-Tyne 45.

Ryecroft, NE11 6AB, ✆ 281459, Fax 282214, – ☎ P. VISA
Meals (light lunch Monday to Saturday)/dinner 15.00 **st.** 4.75 – **9 rm** 22.50/45.00 **st.** – SB.

WOOLLEY EDGE SERVICE AREA W. Yorks. – ✉ Wakefield – ☏ 01924.

Granada Lodge without rest., WF4 4LQ, M 1 between junctions 38 and 39 ✆ 830569, Fax 830609, Reservations (Freephone) 0800 555300 – TV ☎ ♿ P. AE VISA.
4.00 – **31 rm** 39.95 **st.**

WOOLSTONE Glos. – see Cheltenham.

WOOLTON Mersey. 402 403 L 23 – see Liverpool.

WOOLTON HILL Berks. – see Newbury.

WOOTTON BASSETT Wilts. 403 404 O 29 – see Swindon.

WORCESTER Heref. and Worcs. 403 404 N 27 **Great Britain G.** – pop. 81 755 – ECD : Thursday – ☏ 01905.

See : City★ – Cathedral★★ – Royal Worcester Porcelain Works★ (Dyson Perrins Museum★) **M.**

Exc. : The Elgar Trail★.

9 The Fairway, Tolladine Rd ✆ 21074 – 9, 18 Perdiswell Municipal, Bilford Rd ✆ 754668.

ℹ The Guildhall, High St., WR1 2EY ✆ 726311/723471.

♦London 124 – ♦Birmingham 26 – ♦Bristol 61 – ♦Cardiff 74.

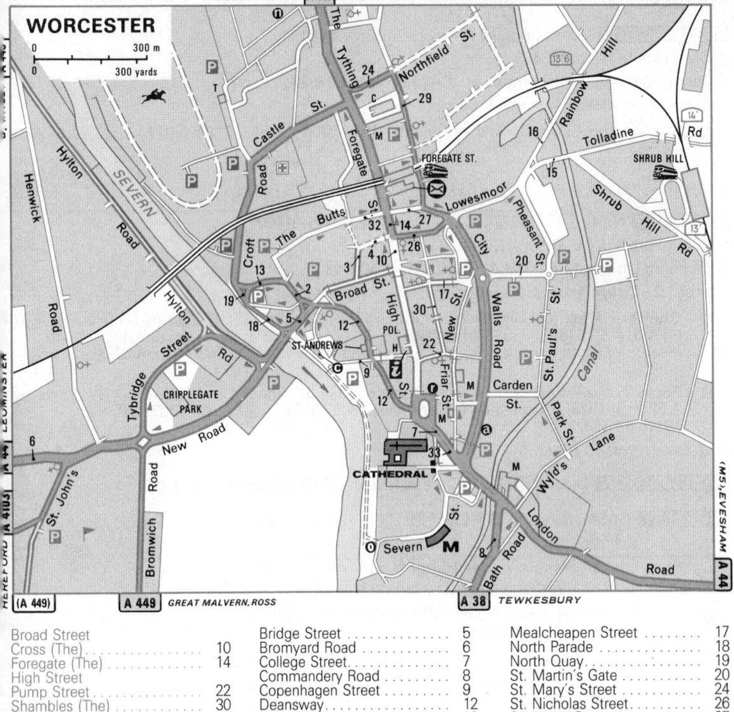

Broad Street
Cross (The) 10
Foregate (The) 14
High Street
Pump Street 22
Shambles (The) 30

All Saints Road 2
Angel Place 3
Angel Street 4
Bridge Street 5
Bromyard Road 6
College Street 7
Commandery Road 8
Copenhagen Street 9
Deansway 12
Dolday 13
Lowesmoor Place 15
Lowesmoor Terrace 16
Mealcheapen Street 17
North Parade 18
North Quay 19
St. Martin's Gate 20
St. Mary's Street 24
St. Nicholas Street 26
Sansome Street 27
Sansome Walk 29
Shaw Street 32
Sidbury 33

Fownes, City Walls Rd, WR1 2AP, ✆ 613151, Fax 23742, « Converted glove factory » – 120. a
Meals *(closed Saturday lunch)* 9.95/16.95 **st.** and a la carte – 7.50 – **58 rm** 75.00/85.00 **t.**, 3 suites – SB.

Giffard (Forte), High St., WR1 2QR, ✆ 726262, Fax 723458 – rm – 150. r
Meals (bar lunch Monday to Saturday)/dinner 14.95 **st.** and a la carte 5.95 – 7.95 – **100 rm** 50.00/60.00 **st.**, 3 suites – SB.

Diglis House, Severn St., WR1 2NF, ✆ 353518, Fax 767772, ≤, « Georgian house on banks of River Severn », – . o
Meals 8.00/13.00 **t.** and a la carte 5.95 – **11 rm** 49.00/120.00 **t.** – SB.

Number 40 without rest., 40 Britannia Sq., WR1 3DN, ✆ 611920, Fax 27152, « Regency townhouse » – n
5 rm 35.00/45.00 **st.**

Hillcrest House, 1 The Hill Av., WR5 2AW, by Bath Rd ✆ 354937, –
4 rm.

Heathside, 172 Droitwich Rd, Fernhill Heath, WR3 7UA, NE : 3 m. by A 449 on A 38 ✆ 458245, – .
Meals (by arrangement) 10.00 – **9 rm** 18.00/44.00 – SB.

Brown's, 24 Quay St., WR1 2JJ, ✆ 26263, « Converted riverside corn mill » – . c
closed Saturday lunch, Sunday dinner, 1 week Christmas and Bank Holiday Mondays – **Meals** 15.00/30.00 **st.** 5.00.

at Upton Snodsbury E : 6 m. by A 44 on A 422 – ✉ Worcester – 01905 :

Upton House, WR7 4NR, on B 4082 (beside church) ✆ 381226, « Tastefully furnished timbered house », – .
closed Christmas and New Year – **Meals** (by arrangement) (communal dining) 23.50 – **3 rm** 30.00/65.00 **st.**

ATS Little London, Barbourne ✆ 24009/28543

WORFIELD Shrops. – see Bridgnorth.

WORKINGTON Cumbria 402 J 20 – pop. 26 938 – 01900.

Branthwaite Rd 603460.

Central Car Park, Washington St., CA14 3AW 602923.

London 313 – Carlisle 33 – Keswick 20.

Washington Central, Washington St., CA14 3AW, 65772, Fax 68770 – 180.
40 rm.

ATS Annie Pit Lane, Clay Flatts Trading Est. 602352

WORKSOP Notts. 402 403 404 C 24 – pop. 38 222 – 01909.

Kilton Forest, Blyth Rd 472488.

Worksop Library, Memorial Av., S80 2BP 501148.

London 163 – Derby 47 – Lincoln 28 – Nottingham 30 – Sheffield 19.

Clumber Park (Country Club), Clumber Park, S80 3PA, SE : 6½ m. by B 6040 and A 57 on A 614 (01623) 835333, Fax 835525, – – 220.
Meals (bar lunch Saturday) 11.00/15.00 **st.** and a la carte – 7.50 – **47 rm** 59.00 **st.**, 1 suite – SB.

Forte Travelodge without rest., Dukeries Mill, St. Annes Drive, S80 3QD, W : ½ m. by A 57 501528, Reservation (Freephone) 0800 850950 – .
40 rm 33.50 **t.**

ATS 44-46 Carlton Rd 501818

WORMINGTON Glos. 403 404 O 27 – see Broadway (Heref and Worcs.).

WORSLEY Gtr. Manchester 402 403 404 MN 23 – see Manchester.

Es ist empfehlenswert, ***in der Hauptsaison*** *und vor allem in Urlaubsorten, Hotelzimmer im voraus zu bestellen. Benachrichtigen Sie sofort das Hotel, wenn Sie ein bestelltes Zimmer nicht belegen können.*

Wenn Sie an ein Hotel im Ausland schreiben, fügen Sie Ihrem Brief einen internationalen Antwortschein bei (im Postamt erhältlich).

WORTHING W. Sussex 404 S 31 – pop. 96 157 – ECD : Wednesday – 01903.

Hill Barn, Hill Barn Lane 237301, BY – , Links Rd 260801 AY.

Shoreham Airport : (01273) 452304, E : 4 m. by A 27 BY.

Chapel Rd, BN11 1HL 210022 – Marine Parade, East of Pier 210022 (summer only).

London 59 – Brighton 11 – Southampton 50.

Plan opposite

Beach, Marine Par., BN11 3QJ, 234001, Fax 234567, – – 80. AZ **e**
Meals 18.50 **t.** (dinner) and a la carte15.95/22.50 4.25 – **77 rm** 51.00/81.50 **t.**, 3 suites – SB.

Chatsworth, Steyne, BN11 3DU, 236103, Fax 823726 – – 150. BZ **x**
Meals (carving lunch) 9.95/14.95 3.95 – **107 rm** 49.90/81.00 **t.** – SB.

Windsor House, 14-20 Windsor Rd, BN11 2LX, 239655, Fax 210763, – rest – 130. BY **i**
Meals (bar lunch)/dinner 13.95 **t.** 4.75 – **30 rm** 39.50/75.00 – SB.

Kingsway, 117-119 Marine Par., BN11 3QQ, 237542, Fax 204173 – . AZ **i**
Meals (carving rest.) 8.75/13.95 **t.** and a la carte 5.30 – **29 rm** 47.50/80.00 **t.** – SB.

Cavendish, 115/116 Marine Par., BN11 3QG, 236767, Fax 823840 – – 50. AZ **u**
Meals *(closed Sunday dinner)* 9.95/16.95 **st.** 4.50 – **21 rm** 35.00/65.00 **st.** – SB.

Bonchurch House, 1 Winchester Rd, BN11 4DJ, 202492 – rest . AZ **v**
closed October-15 December – **Meals** 10.50 **st.** 4.00 – **6 rm** 20.00/40.00 **st.** – SB.

Beacons, 18 Shelley Rd, BN11 1TU, 230948 – rest . BZ **e**
Meals 11.50 2.75 – **6 rm** 25.00/44.00 **s.**

Madeira Lodge without rest., 1 Madeira Av., BN11 2AT, 212364 – BY **e**
4 rm.

Upton Farm without rest., Upper Brighton Rd, Sompting Village, BN14 9JU, 233706, – . BY **a**
3 rm 20.00/35.00 **st.**

WORTHING

Chapel Road . . . . BZ
Guildbourne Centre. . . . . BZ
Montague Street. . . . . BZ
Montague Centre
Shopping Centre. . . . . . . BZ
South Street (WORTHING). BZ

Broadwater Road . . . . BZ 3
Broadwater Street West. . . BY 5
Broadway (The). . . . . BZ 6
Brougham Road . . . . BY 7
Brunswick Road . . . . AZ 8
Church Road. . . . . AY 12
Cowper Road . . . . AZ 13
Crockhurst Hill . . . . AY 14
Durrington Hill. . . . . AY 15
Eriswell Road . . . . ABZ 16
Goring Street. . . . . AY 17
Goring Way. . . . . AY 18
Grafton Road. . . . . BZ 20
High Street . . . . BZ 21
Liverpool Road . . . . BZ 22
Mulberry Lane. . . . . AY 24
Portland Road . . . . BZ 25
Rectory Road . . . . AY 26
Reigate Road. . . . . AY 27
Sompting Avenue. . . . . BY 28
Sompting Road. . . . . BY 29
South Street
(WEST TARRING) . . AY, AZ 30
Southfarm Road. . . . . ABZ 31
Steyne (The) . . . . BZ 32
Steyne Garden . . . . BZ 33
Stoke Abbot Road . . . . BZ 34
Tennyson Road. . . . . AZ 36
Thorn Road . . . . AZ 37
Union Place . . . . BZ 38
Warwick Road. . . . . BZ 40
Warwick Street . . . . BZ 41
West Street . . . . BZ 42
Western Place . . . . BZ 44
Wykeham Road. . . . . AZ 45

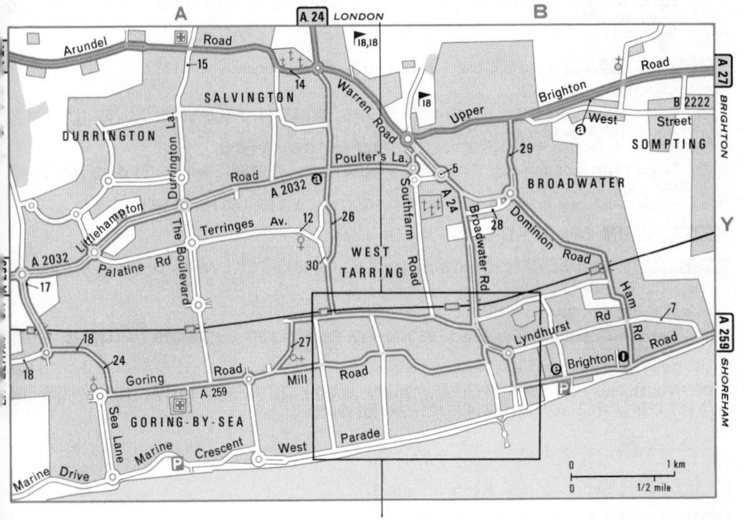

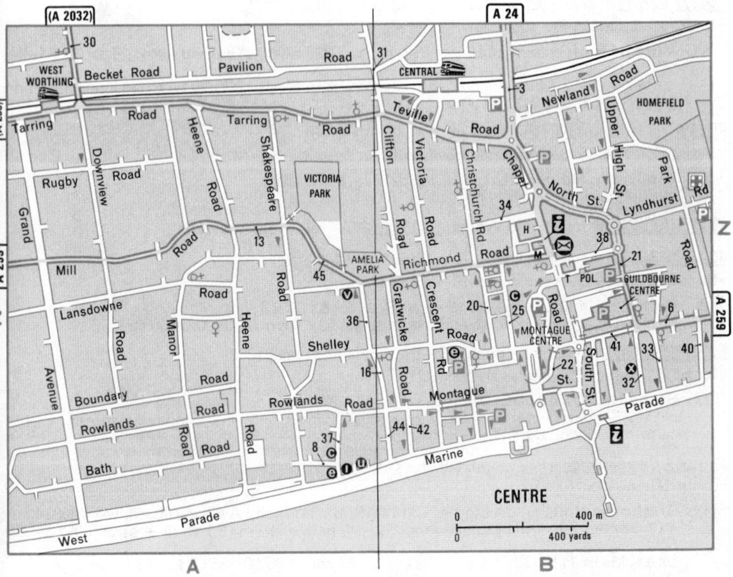

(A 2032)
A 24
WEST WORTHING
CENTRAL
Becket Road
Pavilion Road
Tarring Road
Teville Road
Newland Road
HOMEFIELD PARK
Upper High St.
Park Rd
Downview Road
Rugby Road
Heene Road
Shakespeare Road
VICTORIA PARK
Clifton Road
Victoria Road
Christchurch Rd
Chapel Road
North St.
Lyndhurst Road
Grand Avenue
Mill Road
AMELIA PARK
Richmond Road
GUILDBOURNE CENTRE
A 259
Z
Lansdowne Road
Manor Road
Heene Road
Shelley Road
Gratwicke Road
Crescent Road
MONTAGUE CENTRE
South St.
Boundary Road
Rowlands Road
Montague St.
Parade
Bath Road
Marine Parade
West Parade
CENTRE
400 m
400 yards
A
B

XX **Trenchers,** 118-120 Portland Rd, BN11 1QA, ✆ 820287 – VISA BZ c
closed Sunday dinner – **Meals** 15.50/19.50 **t.** and dinner a la carte 4.75.

XX **Paragon,** 9-10 Brunswick Rd, BN11 3NG, ✆ 233367 – AE VISA AZ c
closed Sunday and Bank Holidays – **Meals** 14.00/18.00 **st.** and a la carte 4.75.

XX **Beijing,** 1 Littlehampton Rd, BN13 1PY, ✆ 694508 – AE VISA AY a
Meals - Chinese (Peking, Szechuan) 10.00/16.00 **st.** and a la carte.

ATS 34 Thorn Rd ✆ 237640

WRESSLE N. Yorks. 402 R 22 – ✉ Selby – 01757.
London 208 – Kingston-upon-Hull 31 – Leeds 31 – York 19.

Loftsome Bridge Coaching House, YO8 7EN, S : ½ m. ✆ 630070, Fax 630070, – TV P. VISA
Meals (dinner only and Sunday lunch)/dinner 14.50 **st.** 3.90 – **15 rm** 35.00/45.00.

WROTHAM HEATH Kent 404 U 30 – pop. 1 767 – ✉ Sevenoaks – 01732.
London 35 – Maidstone 10.

Forte Posthouse, London Rd, TN15 7RS, ✆ 883311, Fax 885850, – rm TV P – 60. AE VISA
Meals a la carte approx. 15.00 **t.** 5.50 – **107 rm** 59.50/69.50 **st.**

Travel Inn, London Rd, TN15 7RX, ✆ 884214, Fax 780368 – rm TV P. AE VISA.
Meals (Beefeater grill) a la carte approx. 16.00 **t.** – 4.95 – **40 rm** 33.50 **t.**

WROUGHTON Wilts. 403 404 O 29 – see Swindon.

WROXHAM Norfolk 404 Y 25 **Great Britain G.** – pop. 1 494 – ECD : Wednesday – 01603.
Envir. : The Broads★.
London 118 – Great Yarmouth 21 – Norwich 7.

Garden Cottage without rest., 96 Norwich Rd, NR12 8RY, ✆ 784376 – TV P. AE VISA.
3 rm 30.00/42.00 **st.**

Staitheway House without rest., Staitheway Rd, The Avenue, NR12 8TH, SW : ¾ m. by A 1151 ✆ 782148, Fax 782148, – TV P.
3 rm 22.00/42.00.

WROXTON Oxon. 403 404 P 27 – see Banbury.

WYBOSTON Beds. – see St. Neots (Cambs.).

WYCH CROSS E. Sussex 404 U 30 – see Forest Row.

WYE Kent 404 W 30 – ✉ Ashford – 01233.
London 60 – Canterbury 10 – Dover 28 – Hastings 34.

XX **Wife of Bath** with rm, 4 Upper Bridge St., TN25 5AW, ✆ 812540, – TV P. VISA.
closed Sunday, Monday and first week January – **Meals** 12.75/22.95 **t.** and lunch a la carte 4.75 – **2 rm** 30.00/40.00 **t.**

WYLAM Northd. 401 402 O 19 – pop. 2 142 – 01661.
London 266 – Carlisle 48 – Newcastle upon Tyne 10.

XX **Laburnum House,** NE41 8AJ, ✆ 852185 – AE VISA
closed Sunday – **Meals** (dinner only) 15.50 **t.** and a la carte.

WYNDS POINT Heref. and Worcs. 403 404 M 27 – see Great Malvern.

YARCOMBE Devon 403 K 31 – ✉ Honiton – 01404.
London 180 – Exeter 25 – Southampton 95 – Taunton 12.

Belfry, EX14 9BD, on A 30, ≤ – TV P. AE VISA
Meals (dinner only) 12.75 **st.** and a la carte 4.50 – **6 rm** 45.00/69.00 **st.** – SB.

YARLINGTON Somerset – pop. 117 – ✉ Wincanton – 01963.
London 127 – Bristol 32 – Taunton 30 – Yeovil 12.

XX **Stags Head,** BA9 8DG, ✆ 440393 – . VISA
closed Sunday dinner and Monday – **Meals** (dinner only and Sunday lunch)/dinner a la carte 19.20/22.50 **t.** 4.30.

YARM Cleveland 402 P 20 – pop. 8 929 – 01642.
London 242 – Middlesbrough 8.

Crathorne Hall, Crathorne, TS15 0AR, S : 3½ m. by A 67 ✆ 700398, Fax 700814, ≤, « Converted Edwardian mansion », , park – rm TV P – 200. AE VISA
Leven : **Meals** 14.50/22.75 **t.** and a la carte – **37 rm** 95.00/135.00 **t.** – SB.

YATELEY Surrey 404 R 29 – pop. 14 121 – ECD : Wednesday – ✉ Camberley – ☎ 01252.
♦London 37 – Reading 12 – ♦Southampton 58.

Casa Dei Cesari, Handford Lane, Cricket Hill, GU17 7BA, ℘ 873275, Fax 870614, – TV ☎ P. AE VISA.
Meals - Italian 15.50 **t.** and a la carte 4.50 – **36 rm** 60.00/80.00 **st.**, 2 suites.

YATTENDON Berks. 403 404 Q 29 – ✉ Newbury – ☎ 01635.
♦London 61 – ♦Oxford 23 – Reading 12.

Royal Oak with rm, The Square, RG16 0UF, ℘ 201325, Fax 201926, – rest TV ☎ P. AE VISA.
Meals *(closed Sunday dinner)* (booking essential) 19.50/29.50 **t.** – **5 rm** 70.00/80.00 **t.**

YATTON Heref. and Worcs. – see Ross-on-Wye.

YELVERTON Devon 403 H 32 **The West Country G.** – pop. 3 297 (inc. Horrabridge) – ☎ 01822.
See : Yelverton Paperweight Centre*.
Envir. : Buckland Abbey** *AC*, SW : 2 m.
Exc. : E : Dartmoor National Park** (Brent Tor ≤**, Haytor Rocks ≤*).
Golf Links Rd ℘ 853618.
♦London 234 – Exeter 33 – ♦Plymouth 9.

Moorland Links, PL20 6DA, S : 2 m. on A 386 ℘ 852245, Fax 855004, ≤, , – rm TV ☎ P – 50. AE VISA
Meals *(closed lunch Saturday and Bank Holidays)* 13.45/17.25 **t.** – **44 rm** 64.95/77.00 **t.**, 1 suite – SB.

Harrabeer Country House, Harrowbeer Lane, PL20 6EA, ℘ 853302, – TV ☎ P. AE VISA
closed 23 December-2 January – **Meals** 12.50 **s.** 3.50 – **7 rm** 22.00/51.00 **s.** – SB.

Overcombe, Horrabridge, PL20 7RN, N : 1¼ m. on A 386 ℘ 853501, ≤, – TV ☎ P. VISA
Meals (dinner only) 11.50 **t.** 4.15 – **11 rm** 21.00/47.00 **t.**

YEOVIL Somerset 403 404 M 31 **The West Country G.** – pop. 28 317 – ECD : Monday and Thursday – ☎ 01935.
See : St. John the Baptist*.
Envir. : Monacute House** *AC*, W : 4 m. on A 3088 – Fleet Air Arm Museum, Yeovilton** *AC*, NW : 5 m. by A 37 – Tintinhull House Garden* *AC*, NW: 5½ m. – Ham Hill (≤**) W : 5½ m. by A 3088 – Stoke sub-Hamdon (parish church*) W : 5¼ m. by A 3088.
Exc. : Muchelney** (Parish Church**) NW : 14 m. by A 3088, A 303 and B 3165 – Lytes Cary*, N : 7½ m. by A 37, B 3151 and A 372 – Sandford Orcas Manor House*, NW : 8 m. by A 359 – Cadbury Castle (≤**) NE : 10½ m. by A 359 – East Lambrook Manor* *AC*, W : 12 m. by A 3088 and A 303.
Sherborne Rd ℘ 75949.
Petter's House, Petter's Way, BA20 1SH ℘ 71279 – at Podimore, Somerset Visitor Centre, Forte Services (A 303), BA22 8JG ℘ 841302 (summer only).
♦London 136 – Exeter 48 – ♦Southampton 72 – Taunton 26.

Manor (Forte), Hendford, BA20 1TG, ℘ 23116, Fax 706607 – TV ☎ P – 60. AE VISA JCB
Meals 9.95/16.95 **st.** 6.50 – 8.50 – **41 rm** 60.00/90.00 **st.** – SB.

Yeovil Court, West Coker Rd., BA20 2NE, SW : 2 m. on A 30 ℘ 863746, Fax 863990 – TV ☎ P – 50. AE VISA
Meals *(closed Saturday lunch and Sunday dinner)* a la carte 13.40/19.85 **st.** 3.75 – **17 rm** 59.00/69.00 **st.**, 1 suite – SB.

at Podimore N : 9½ m. by A 37 off A 303 – ✉ Yeovil – ☎ 01935 :

Forte Travelodge without rest., BA22 8JG, W : ½ m. ℘ 840074, Reservations (Freephone) 0800 850950 – TV P. AE VISA.
31 rm 33.50 **t.**

at Barwick S : 2 m. by A 30 off A 37 – ✉ Yeovil – ☎ 01935 :

Little Barwick House with rm, BA22 9TD, ℘ 23902, Fax 20908, « Georgian dower house », – rest TV ☎ P. AE VISA
closed first 3 weeks January – **Meals** *(closed Sunday to non-residents)* (booking essential) (dinner only) 24.90 **t.** 4.60 – **6 rm** 48.00/76.00 – SB.

at West Coker SW : 3½ m. on A 30 – ✉ West Coker – ☎ 01935 :

Four Acres, High St., BA22 9AJ, ℘ 862555, Fax 863929, – rest TV ☎ P – 100. AE VISA.
Meals 13.50 **st.** 4.00 – **25 rm** 65.00/79.00 **st.** – SB.

Skittles, 1 Church St., BA22 9AH, ℘ 863986 – . AE VISA
closed Sunday dinner – **Meals** a la carte 9.50/19.50 **t.** 3.50.

at Montacute W : 5 ½ m. on A 3088 – ✉ Martock – ☎ 01935 :

Kings Arms, Bishopston, TA15 6UU, ℘ 822513, Fax 826549, – TV ☎ P. AE VISA.
Meals (buffet lunch)/dinner 12.00 **st.** and a la carte 4.10 – **11 rm** ☐ 46.00/79.00 **st.** – SB.

XX **Milk House** with rm, The Borough Sq., TA15 6XB, ℘ 823823, – TV. VISA.
Meals *(closed Sunday dinner, Monday and Tuesday to non residents)* (dinner only and Sunday lunch)/dinner 21.00 **st.** and a la carte – ☐ 5.00 – **2 rm** 40.00/58.00 **st.**

ATS Penmill Trading Est., Lyde Rd ℘ 75580/71780

YETMINSTER Dorset 403 404 M 31 – see Sherborne.

YORK N. Yorks. 402 Q 22 **Great Britain G.** – pop. 98 745 – ☎ 01904.

See : City★★★ – Minster★★★ (Stained Glass★★★, Chapter House★★, Choir Screen★★) CDY – National Railway Museum★★★ CY – The Walls★★ CDXYZ – Castle Museum★ *AC* DZ **M2** – Jorvik Viking Centre★ *AC* DY **M1** – Fairfax House★ *AC* DY **A** – The Shambles★ DY **54** – 18 Lords Moor Lane, Stronsall ℘ 491840, BY – 9 Heworth, Muncaster House, Muncastergate ℘ 424618 BY.

De Grey Rooms, Exhibition Sq., YO1 2HB ℘ 621756/7 – York Railway Station, Outer Concourse, YO2 2JA ℘ 643700 – TIC Travel Office, 6 Rougier St., YO2 1AJ ℘ 620557.

♦London 203 – ♦Kingston-upon-Hull 38 – ♦Leeds 26 – ♦Middlesbrough 51 – ♦Nottingham 88 – ♦Sheffield 62.

Plan opposite

Middlethorpe Hall, Bishopthorpe Rd, YO2 1QB, S : 1 m. ℘ 641241, Fax 620176, ≤, « William and Mary house, gardens », park – rest TV ☎ P – 60. AE VISA. by A 19 BZ
Meals 14.90/35.75 **st.** and dinner a la carte 5.50 – ***Grill* : Meals** *(May-September)* (dinner only Friday and Saturday and Sunday lunch) 24.95 **st.** 5.50 – ☐ 9.95 – **23 rm** 83.00/129.00 **st.**, 7 suites – SB.

Swallow, Tadcaster Rd, YO2 2QQ, ℘ 701000, Fax 702308, – rm TV ☎ P – 170. AE VISA AZ **a**
Meals 13.75/18.95 **st.** and a la carte 6.00 – **111 rm** ☐ 92.00/107.00 **st.**, 1 suite – SB.

Viking (Q.M.H.), North St., YO1 1JF, ℘ 659822, Fax 641793, ≤, – rm rest TV ☎ P – 300. AE VISA. CY **n**
Meals (carving lunch) 12.00/18.00 **t.** and dinner a la carte 5.50 – ☐ 9.25 – **186 rm** 93.00/118.00 **t.**, 1 suite – SB.

Mount Royale, The Mount, YO2 2DA, ℘ 628856, Fax 611171, « Tasteful decor and furnishings », heated, – TV ☎ P. AE VISA JCB. AZ **s**
closed 24 to 30 December – **Meals** (dinner only) 35.00 **t.** 5.95 – **20 rm** ☐ 65.00/110.00 **t.**, 1 suite – SB.

The Grange, Clifton, YO3 6AA, ℘ 644744, Fax 612453, « Regency town house » – TV ☎ P – 45. AE VISA CX **u**
Meals 12.50/19.00 **st.** 4.50 – **30 rm** ☐ 86.00/165.00 **st.** – SB.

Ambassador, 123-125 The Mount, YO2 2DA, ℘ 641316, Fax 640259, – rest TV ☎ P – 50. AE VISA. AZ **c**
Meals (bar lunch)/dinner 22.50 **t.** 4.75 – **24 rm** ☐ 79.00/98.50 **t.** – SB.

York Pavilion, 45 Main St., Fulford, YO1 4PJ, S : 1 m. on A 19 ℘ 622099, Fax 626939, – rest TV ☎ P – 30. AE VISA JCB. B
closed 25 and 26 December – **Meals** 9.95/17.95 **st.** and a la carte 6.50 – **23 rm** ☐ 78.00/98.00 **st.** – SB.

Judges' Lodging, 9 Lendal, YO1 2AQ, ℘ 638733, Fax 679947 – TV ☎ P. AE VISA CY **x**
Meals (bar lunch Monday to Saturday)/dinner 9.95 **t.** and a la carte 5.25 – **12 rm** ☐ 65.00/120.00 **t.** – SB.

Novotel, Fishergate, YO1 4AD, ℘ 611660, Telex 57556, Fax 610925, – rm rest TV ☎ P – 210. AE VISA DZ **o**
Meals (bar lunch)/dinner 14.00 **st.** 4.95 – ☐ 7.50 – **124 rm** 53.50/69.50 **st.**

Forte Posthouse, Tadcaster Rd, YO2 2QF, ℘ 707921, Telex 57798, Fax 702804, – rm TV ☎ P – 100. AE VISA AZ **r**
Meals a la carte approx. 15.00 **t.** 5.50 – **139 rm** 56.00/69.50 **st.**

Monkbar, St. Maurice's Rd, YO3 7JA, ℘ 638086, Fax 629195 – TV ☎ P – 70. AE VISA DX **a**
Meals 9.50/14.95 **st.** and a la carte 4.75 – **47 rm** ☐ 69.00/119.00 **st.** – SB.

4 South Parade without rest., 4 South Par., YO2 2BA, ℘ 628229, Fax 628229, « Georgian town house » – TV ☎. CZ **n**
3 rm ☐ 68.00/85.00.

Holmwood House without rest., 114 Holgate Rd, YO2 4BB, ℘ 626183, Fax 670899 – TV ☎ P. AE VISA. AZ **x**
12 rm ☐ 48.00/60.00 **st.**

Arndale without rest., 290 Tadcaster Rd, YO2 2ET, ℘ 702424, – TV P. AZ **i**
closed Christmas and New Year – **10 rm** ☐ 35.00/59.00 **st.**

Curzon Lodge and Stable Cottages without rest., 23 Tadcaster Rd, YO2 2QG, ℘ 703157, – TV P. VISA. AZ **a**
closed Christmas and New Year – **10 rm** ☐ 38.00/58.00 **st.**

YORK

Blake Street . . . . . CY 5
Coney Street . . . . . CY 13
Davygate . . . . . CY 16
Lendal . . . . . CY 32
Parliament Street . . . . . DY 42
Shambles (The) . . . . . DY 54
Stonegate . . . . . CY 58

Bishopgate Street . . . . . CZ 3
Bishophill Senior . . . . . CZ 4
Campleshon Road . . . . . AZ 7
Church Street . . . . . DY 8
Clifford Street . . . . . DY 10
Colliergate . . . . . DY 12
Cromwell Road . . . . . CZ 15
Deangate . . . . . DY 18
Duncombe Place . . . . . CY 20
Fawcett Street . . . . . DZ 21
Fetter Lane . . . . . CY 22
Goodramgate . . . . . DY 25
High Ousegate . . . . . DY 26
High Petergate . . . . . CY 28
Knavesmire Road . . . . . AZ 29
Leeman Road . . . . . AY, CY 30
Lord Mayor's Walk . . . . . DX 33
Low Petergate . . . . . DY 35
Melrosegate . . . . . BY 36
Museum Street . . . . . CY 39
Pavement . . . . . DY 43
Peasholme Green . . . . . DY 45
Penley's Grove Street . . . . . DX 46
Queen Street . . . . . CZ 49
St. Helen's Road . . . . . AZ 50
St. Leonard's Place . . . . . CY 52
St. Maurice's Road . . . . . DXY 53
Station Road . . . . . CY 55
Stonebow (The) . . . . . DY 56
Tower Street . . . . . DZ 59
University Road . . . . . BZ 60

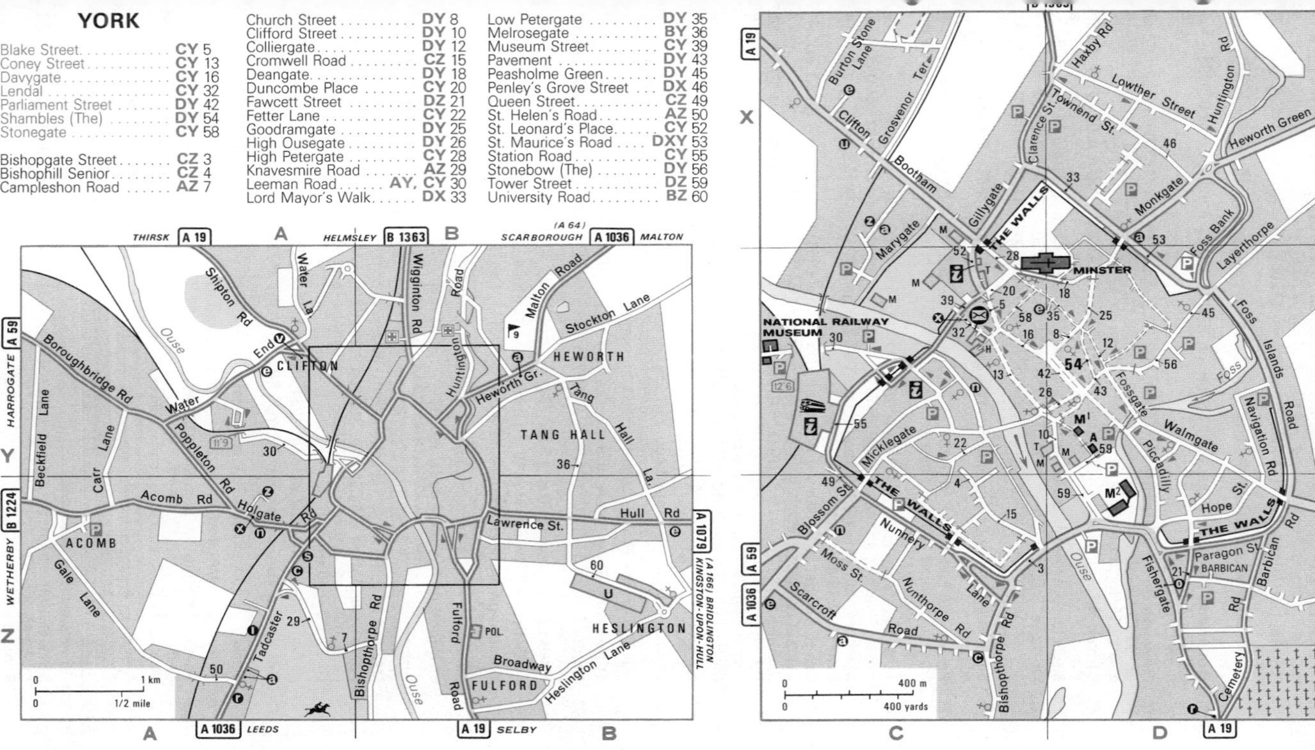

23 St.Mary's without rest., 23 St. Marys, Bootham, YO3 7DD, ☎ 622738 – *closed Christmas and New Year* – **9 rm** 34.00/60.00 **t.** CX **a**

Kilima, 129 Holgate Rd, YO2 4DE, ☎ 625787, Fax 612083, – rest AZ **n**
Meals (lunch by arrangement)/dinner 17.95 **t.** and a la carte 4.95 – **15 rm** 47.25/84.50 **t.** – SB.

Grasmead House without rest., 1 Scarcroft Hill, YO2 1DF, ☎ 629996, Fax 629996 – CZ **a**
6 rm 58.00 **st.**

Heworth Court, 76-78 Heworth Green, YO3 7TQ, ☎ 425156, Fax 415290 – rest BY **a**
Meals 7.95/16.00 **t.** and a la carte 5.95 – **25 rm** 42.00/82.00 **t.** – SB.

Clifton Bridge, Water End, YO3 6LL, ☎ 610510, Fax 640208 – rest AY **e**
Meals (bar lunch)/dinner 14.35 **st.** and a la carte 4.95 – **14 rm** 40.00/64.00 **st.** – SB.

Cottage, 3 Clifton Green, YO3 6LH, ☎ 643711, Fax 611230 – *closed Christmas* – **Meals** (dinner only) 11.50 **t.** and a la carte 4.95 – **19 rm** 30.00/60.00 **t.** – SB. AY **v**

Black Bull Country Lodge, Hull Rd, YO1 3LF, ☎ 411856, Fax 430667 –
40 rm. BZ **e**

Priory, 126 Fulford Rd, YO1 4BE, ☎ 625280, Fax 625280, – *closed Christmas* – **Meals** (dinner only) a la carte 9.50/16.50 **st.** and a la carte 4.50 – **20 rm** 28.00/45.00 **t.** – SB. DZ **r**

18 St.Paul's Square, 18 St. Pauls Sq., YO2 4BD, ☎ 629884, – AZ **z**
closed Christmas and New Year – **Meals** (by arrangement) 17.50 **s.** – **3 rm** 35.00/60.00 **s.**

Ashbury without rest., 103 The Mount, YO2 2AX, ☎ 647339 – CZ **e**
5 rm 35.00/50.00 **st.**

Crook Lodge, 26 St. Mary's, Bootham, YO3 7DD, ☎ 655614 – rest
closed Christmas – **Meals** 10.50 **st.** 3.75 – **7 rm** 23.50/45.00 **st.** – SB. CX **z**

Hobbits without rest., 9 St. Peter's Grove, Clifton, YO3 6AQ, ☎ 624538 – CX **e**
closed 24 to 30 December – **6 rm** 27.00/54.00 **st.**

Melton's, 7 Scarcroft Rd, YO2 1ND, ☎ 634341, Fax 629233 – CZ **c**
closed Monday lunch, Sunday dinner, last week August and 24 December-13 January – **Meals** (booking essential) 14.00/23.50 **st.** (lunch) and a la carte 7.00.

19 Grape Lane, 19 Grape Lane, YO1 2HU, ☎ 636366 – CY **e**
closed Sunday, Monday, last week January, first 2 weeks February, last 2 weeks September and Christmas – **Meals** - English 19.95 **t.** (dinner) and a la carte 21.25/25.75.

at Kexby E : 6 ¾ m. on A 1079 - B – York – 01759 :

Kexby Bridge, Hull Rd, YO4 5LD, ☎ 388223, Fax 388822, – – 100.
Meals (dinner only) 17.00 **st.** 6.95 – **32 rm** 50.00/75.00 **st.** – SB.

at Escrick S : 5 ¾ m. on A 19 - B – York – 01904 :

Parsonage Country House, YO4 6LF, ☎ 728111, Fax 728151, – rest – 160.
Meals 9.50/18.50 **t.** and a la carte 4.50 – **13 rm** 57.50/97.50 **t.** – SB.

at Bilbrough SW : 5 ½ m. by A 1036 – AZ – off A 64 – York – 01937 :

Bilbrough Manor, YO2 3PH, ☎ 834002, Fax 834724, « Tastefully decorated Victorian manor », , park – rest
Meals 14.50/30.00 **t.** and a la carte 6.15 – **12 rm** 65.00/150.00 **t.** – SB.

Forte Travelodge without rest., Steeton, LS24 8EG, SW : ¾ m. by A 1036 –AZ- on A 64 (eastbound carriageway) ☎ 531823, Reservations (Freephone) 0800 850950 – – **40 rm** 33.50 **t.**

at Long Marston W : 7 m. on B 1224 –AZ – York – 01904 :

Gill House Farm, Tockwith Rd, YO5 8PJ, N : ½ m. ☎ 738379, « Working farm », –
Meals (by arrangement) 10.00 **st.** – **4 rm** 30.00/40.00 **st.**

at Skelton NW : 3 m. on A 19 - A – York – 01904 :

Fairfield Manor, Shipton Rd, YO3 6XW, ☎ 670222, Fax 670311, – rest – 200.
Meals 9.95/15.95 **st.** and a la carte – **84 rm** 69.00/95.00 **st.**, 6 suites – SB.

ATS 2 James St. ☎ 412372/410375
ATS 36 Holgate Rd ☎ 654411
ATS 110 Layerthorpe ☎ 628479/625884

YOXFORD Suffolk 404 Y 27 – pop. 784 – Saxmundham – 01728.

London 95 – Ipswich 25 – Norwich 55.

Sans Souci without rest., Main Rd, IP17 3EX, on A 12 ☎ 668268, Fax 668268, –
3 rm 24.00/38.00 **s.**

Wales

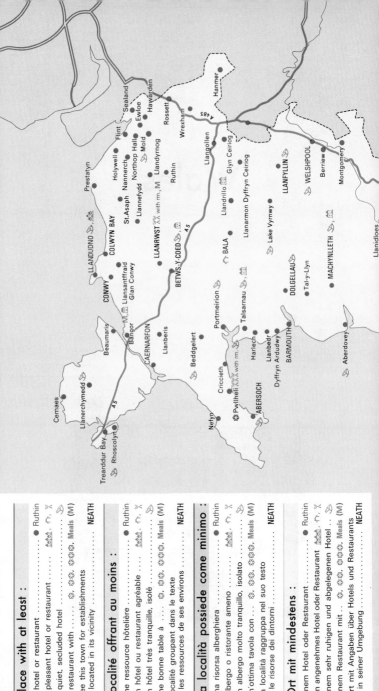

Place with at least :

a hotel or restaurant .... ● Ruthin
a pleasant hotel or restaurant ...... 🏨, ⌂, ✕
a quiet, secluded hotel .... ♨
a restaurant with ...... ✿, ✿✿, ✿✿✿, **Meals** (M)
See this town for establishments located in its vicinity .... **NEATH**

Localité offrant au moins :

une ressource hôtelière .... ● Ruthin
un hôtel ou restaurant agréable .... 🏨, ⌂, ✕
un hôtel très tranquille, isolé .... ♨
une bonne table à .... ✿, ✿✿, ✿✿✿, **Meals** (M)
Localité groupant dans le texte les ressources de ses environs .... **NEATH**

La località possiede come minimo :

una risorsa alberghiera .... ● Ruthin
Albergo o ristorante ameno .... 🏨, ⌂, ✕
un albergo molto tranquillo, isolato .... ♨
un'ottima tavola con ... ✿, ✿✿, ✿✿✿, **Meals** (M)
La località raggruppa nel suo testo le risorse dei dintorni .... **NEATH**

Ort mit mindestens :

einem Hotel oder Restaurant .... ● Ruthin
ein angenehmes Hotel oder Restaurant 🏨, ⌂, ✕
einem sehr ruhigen und abgelegenen Hotel .. ♨
einem Restaurant mit .. ✿, ✿✿, ✿✿✿, **Meals** (M)
Ort mit Angaben über Hotels und Restaurants in seiner Umgebung .... **NEATH**

ABERYSTWYTH
Llangurig
Knighton
Rhayader
Presteigne
A 483
New Quay
LLANDRINDOD WELLS
ABERPORTH
Rhydlewis
Llanwrtyd Wells
CARDIGAN
Llangammarch Wells
Pumsaint
HAY-ON-WYE
Crug-y-bar
Cynghordy
Newport
Three Cocks
FISHGUARD
Boncath
Llyswen
Crymmych
Brechfa
Talgarth
with rm.
Brecon
ST. DAVIDS
Wolf's Castle
Llangorse
A 40
Llandeilo
Whitland
CRICKHOWELL
Haverfordwest
St. Clears
A 48
MONMOUTH
ABERGAVENNY
Merthyr Tydfil
Cross Hands
Laugharne
Raglan
Milford Haven
Saundersfoot
Aberdare
Swansea S.A.
PEMBROKE
TENBY
Pontypool
USK
Tintern
NEATH
Llantrisant
SWANSEA
Cwmbran
Chepstow
Porth
Port Talbot
Pontypridd
Magor S.A.
M 4
NEWPORT
Sarn Park S.A.
Miskin
Cardiff West S. A.
BRIDGEND
St. Brides-Super-Ely
PORTHCAWL
Cowbridge
CARDIFF
Llantwit Major
Barry

ABERDARE (Aberdâr) M. Glam. 403 J 28 – ☎ 01685.

Ty Newydd, Penderyn Rd, Hirwaun, CF44 9SX, NW : 5 m. on A 4059 ✆ 813433, Fax 813139, – TV ☎ P – 200
28 rm, 1 suite.

ATS Canal Rd, Cwmbach ✆ 873914/875491

ABERDOVEY (Aberdyfi) Gwynedd 403 H 26 – pop. 869 – ECD : Wednesday – ☎ 01654.

18 Aberdovey ✆ 767210.

London 230 – Dolgellau 25 – Shrewsbury 66.

Plas Penhelig, LL35 0NA, E : 1 m. by A 493 ✆ 767676, Fax 767783, ≤, « Terraced gardens », park – TV ☎ P – 35. VISA JCB.
9 March-December – **Meals** 18.50 (dinner) – **11 rm** 40.00/112.00 **t.** – SB.

Trefeddian, Tywyn Rd, LL35 0SB, W : 1 m. on A 493 ✆ 767213, Fax 767777, ≤ golf course and sea, , park, – rest TV ☎ P. VISA
10 March-1 January – **Meals** 7.75/15.75 **t.** 4.00 – **46 rm** 40.00/200.00 **t.** – SB.

Penhelig Arms, LL35 0LT, ✆ 767215, Fax 767690, ≤, « Part 18C inn » – rm TV ☎ P. VISA JCB
closed 25 and 26 December – **Meals** (bar lunch Monday to Saturday)/dinner 18.50 **t.** – **11 rm** 38.00/78.00 **t.** – SB.

Harbour, LL35 0EB, ✆ 767250, Fax 767078, ≤ – TV. AE VISA
Meals a la carte 9.50/16.00 **st.** 3.50 – **8 rm** 45.00/70.00 **st.**, 1 suite – SB.

Maybank, LL35 0PT, E : 1 m. on A 493 ✆ 767500, ≤ – rm TV P. VISA.
closed January-13 February and 10 November-22 December – **Meals** (booking essential) (dinner only) 17.95 **st.** – **5 rm** 35.95/51.90 **st.** – SB.

Brodawel, Tywyn Rd, LL35 0SA, W : 1¼ m. on A 493 ✆ 767347, ≤, – TV P
March-November – **Meals** (by arrangement) 14.00 **st.** 3.50 – **6 rm** 20.00/40.00 **s.**

The Guide is updated annually so renew your Guide every year.

ABERGAVENNY (Y-Fenni) Gwent 403 L 28 **Great Britain G.** – pop. 9 593 – ECD : Thursday – ☎ 01873.

Exc. : Raglan Castle★ *AC*, SE : 9 m. by A 40.

18 Monmouthshire, Llanfoist ✆ 853171.

Swan Meadow, Monmouth Road, NP7 5HH ✆ 857588 (summer only).

London 163 – Gloucester 43 – Newport 19 – Swansea 49.

Llansantffraed Court, Llanvihangel Gobion, NP7 9BA, SE : 6½ m. by A 40, B 4598 and Raglan rd ✆ 840678, Fax 840674, ≤, , park – rm TV ☎ P. AE VISA
Meals (lunch by arrangement Monday to Saturday)/dinner 19.95 **st.** 4.95 – **21 rm** 59.00/130.00 **st.** – SB.

Halidon House without rest., 63 Monmouth Rd, NP7 5HR, ✆ 857855, ≤, – P.
April-October – **4 rm** 15.00/35.00 **st.**

Balti House, 35 Frogmore St., NP7 5AN, ✆ 857389
Meals - Indian.

at Llanfihangel Crucorney N : 6½ m. by A 40 on A 465 – ✉ Abergavenny – ☎ 01873 :

Penyclawdd Court, NP7 7LB, S: ¼m. by Pantygelli rd ✆ 890719, Fax 890848, ≤, « Tudor manor house », – rm TV P. VISA.
Meals (by arrangement) (communal dining) 20.00 **st.** – **3 rm** 45.00/60.00 **st.**

at Govilon W : 5¼ m. by A 465 on B 4246 – ✉ Abergavenny – ☎ 01873 :

Llanwenarth House, NP7 9SF, N : 1 m. on B 4246 ✆ 830289, Fax 832199, ≤, « 16C manor house », – rest TV P
closed mid January-February – **Meals** (by arrangement) (residents only) (communal dining) (dinner only) 21.00 **s.** 6.60 – **5 rm** 50.00/72.00 **s.**

at Llanwenarth NW : 3 m. on A 40 – ✉ Abergavenny – ☎ 01873 :

Llanwenarth Arms, Brecon Rd, NP8 1EP, ✆ 810550, Fax 811880, ≤, – TV ☎ P. AE VISA.
Meals a la carte 11.45/24.35 **st.** 3.95 – **18 rm** 49.00/59.00 **st.**

ATS 11 Monmouth Rd ✆ 854348/855829

ABERPORTH Dyfed 403 G 27 – pop. 2 147 – ECD : Wednesday – ✉ Cardigan – ☎ 01239.

London 249 – Carmarthen 29 – Fishguard 26.

Penrallt, SA43 2BS, SW : 1 m. by B 4333 ✆ 810227, Fax 811375, ≤, , , heated, 9, , – TV ☎ P. AE VISA
closed 25 to 1 January – **Meals** (bar lunch)/dinner 15.00 **st.** and a la carte 4.50 – **16 rm** 48.00/75.00 **st.** – SB.

at Tresaith NE : 1¾ m. – ✉ Cardigan – ☎ 01239 :

Glandwr Manor, SA43 2JH, ✆ 810197, – P.
March-October – **Meals** *(closed Sunday to non residents)* (dinner only) 12.00 **t.** and a la carte 3.70 – **7 rm** 28.00/56.00 **t.**

ABERSOCH Gwynedd 402 403 G 25 – ECD : Wednesday – ✉ Pwllheli – ☎ 01758.

Abersoch ☏ 712622.

♦London 265 – Caernarfon 28 – Shrewsbury 101.

Abersoch Harbour, Lon Engan, LL53 7HR, ☏ 712406, ← – TV ☎ P. VISA.
Meals (bar lunch Monday to Saturday)/dinner 14.50 **t.** and a la carte – **14 rm** 32.00/125.00 **t.** – SB.

Riverside, LL53 7HW, ☏ 712419, Fax 712671, – TV ☎ P. AE VISA.
mid February-mid November – **Meals** (bar lunch)/dinner 22.00 **st.** 4.50 – **12 rm** 40.00/80.00 **st.** – SB.

White House, LL53 7AG, ☏ 713427, Fax 713512, ←, – TV ☎ P – 120. VISA
Meals *(closed lunch to non-residents)* (bar lunch residents only) 16.50 **t.** and a la carte 5.50 – **14 rm** 30.50/70.00 **t.** – SB.

Neigwl, Lon Sarn Bach, LL53 7DY, ☏ 712363, Fax 712363, ← Cardigan Bay – TV P. VISA
Meals (dinner only) 18.50 **st.** 4.50 – **9 rm** 36.00/60.00 **st.** – SB.

Tudor Court, Lon Sarn Bach, LL53 7EB, ☏ 713354, Fax 713354 – TV P. VISA.
Meals 9.50/11.00 **t.** and a la carte 4.50 – **10 rm** 25.00/60.00 **st.** – SB.

at Bwlchtocyn S : 2 m. – ✉ Pwllheli – ☎ 01758 :

Porth Tocyn , LL53 7BU, ☏ 713303, Fax 713538, ← Cardigan Bay and mountains, heated, , – TV ☎ P.
Easter-mid November – **Meals** (bar lunch Monday to Saturday)/dinner 25.00 **t.** 4.50 – 3.50 – **17 rm** 54.00/99.00 **t.** – SB.

Crowrach Isaf , LL53 7BY, ☏ 712860, ←, , park – TV P.
closed January – **Meals** 12.50 **st.** – **3 rm** 19.00/38.00 **st.** – SB.

ABERYSTWYTH Dyfed 403 H 26 **Great Britain G.** – pop. 8 359 – ECD : Wednesday – ☎ 01970.

See : Town★ - ←★ from the National Library of Wales.

Exc. : Devil's Bridge (Pontarfynach)★, E : 12 m. by A 4120 – Strata Florida★ *AC*, SE : 15 m. by B 4340.

Bryn-y-Mor ☏ 615104.

Terrace Rd, SY23 2AG ☏ 612125.

♦London 238 – Chester 98 – Fishguard 58 – Shrewsbury 74.

Belle Vue Royal, Marine Terrace, SY23 2BA, ☏ 617558, Fax 612190, ← – rm TV ☎ P – 40. AE VISA.
closed 24 to 26 December – **Meals** 12.50/17.50 **t.** and a la carte 10.50/19.00 **t.** 6.25 – **37 rm** 47.50/73.50 **st.**

Four Seasons, 50-54 Portland St., SY23 2DX, ☏ 612120, Fax 627458 – rest TV ☎ P. AE VISA.
closed 24 December-3 January – **Meals** *(closed Sunday dinner to non-residents)* (bar lunch Monday to Saturday)/dinner 18.00 **st.** 4.50 – **14 rm** 45.00/65.00 **st.** – SB.

Groves, 44-46 North Par., SY23 2NF, ☏ 617623, Fax 627068 – TV ☎ P. AE VISA.
Meals (bar lunch)/dinner a la carte 13.95/18.30 **st.** 5.50 – **9 rm** 45.00/75.00 **st.** – SB.

Sinclair, 43 Portland St., SY23 2DX, ☏ 615158 – TV.
Meals 10.00 **st.** – **3 rm** 25.00/40.00 **st.**

at Chancery (Rhydgaled) S : 4 m. on A 487 – ✉ Aberystwyth – ☎ 01970 :

Conrah Country , SY23 4DF, ☏ 617941, Fax 624546, ←, « 18C country house », , , park – rest TV ☎ P – 50. AE VISA.
closed 22 December-5 January – **Meals** 16.00/25.00 **t.** and a la carte 5.50 – **20 rm** 58.00/103.00 **t.** – SB.

ATS Glanyrafon Ind. Est., Llanbadarn ☏ 611166

ARTHOG Gwynedd 402 403 I 25 – see Dolgellau.

BALA Gwynedd 402 403 J 25 – pop. 1 922 – ECD : Wednesday – 01678.

Bala Lake Hotel 520344.

Pensarn Road, LL23 7NH 521021 (Winter open Fri to Sun only).

London 216 – Chester 46 – Dolgellau 18 – Shrewsbury 52.

- **White Lion Royal,** 61 High St., LL23 7AE, 520314 – TV P. VISA
  closed 25 December – **Meals** 7.95/11.25 **st.** 5.25 – **26 rm** 36.00/64.00 **st.** – SB.
- **Fron Feuno Hall**, LL23 7YF, SW : 1 m. on A 494 521115, Fax 521151, Bala Lake, park, – P.
  April-October – **Meals** (by arrangement) (communal dining) 16.00 **st.** – **3 rm** 30.00/56.00 **st.** – SB.
- **Melin Meloch,** LL23 7DP, E : 1¾ m. by A 494 on B 4401 520101, « Part 13C converted water mill », – TV P.
  closed December – **Meals** (by arrangement) (communal dining) 12.00 **s.** – **4 rm** 35.00/40.00 **s.**
- **Llidiardau Mawr** without rest., Llidiardau, LL23 7SG, NW : 4 ¼ m. by A 4212 520555, « 17C stone-built mill house », – P.
  Easter-September – **3 rm** 20.00/40.00 **st.**

at Fron-Goch NW : 2¾ m. on A 4212 – Bala – 01678 :

- **Fferm Fron-Goch,** LL23 7NT, 520483, « 17C Farmhouse, working farm », park – TV P.
  Meals (by arrangement) 9.50 **s.** – **3 rm** 16.00/34.00 **s.** – SB.
- Cysgod Y Garn, LL23 7NT, 520483 – TV P
  4 rm.

BANGOR Gwynedd 402 403 H 24 – pop. 11 173 – ECD : Wednesday – 01248.

St. Deiniol, Pentryn 353098.

Theatr Gwynedd, Deiniol Rd, LL57 2TL 352786 (summer only).

London 247 – Birkenhead 68 – Holyhead 23 – Shrewsbury 83.

- **Menai Court,** Craig-y-Don Rd, LL57 2BG, 354200, Fax 354200, – TV P – 60. VISA JCB
  Meals *(closed lunch Saturday and Sunday)* (lunch by arrangement)/dinner 14.95 **t.** and a la carte – **14 rm** 40.00/68.00 – SB.
- **Travelodge,** One Stop Services, Llandegai, LL57 4BG, SE : 2½ m. by A 5122, at junction of A 5 with A 55 370345 – rm TV P. VISA.
  Meals (grill rest.) a la carte approx. 10.00 **t.** 3.45 – 5.95 – **30 rm** 33.50 **st.**

FRON-GOCH Gwynedd 402 403 J 25 – see Bala.

BARMOUTH (Abermaw) Gwynedd 402 403 H 25 – pop. 2 386 – ECD : Wednesday – 01341.

The Old Library, Station Rd, LL42 1LU 280787 (summer only).

London 231 – Chester 74 – Dolgellau 10 – Shrewsbury 67.

- **Ty'r Graig Castle,** Llanaber Rd, LL42 1YN, on A 496 280470, Fax 280470, – rest TV P. VISA JCB.
  March-November – **Meals** (bar lunch Monday to Saturday)/dinner 15.50 **t.** and a la carte 5.50 – **12 rm** 38.00/71.00 **t.** – SB.
- **Cranbourne,** 9 Marine Par., LL42 1NA, 280202 – rest TV. VISA.
  closed 24-28 December – **Meals** 8.50 3.00 – **10 rm** 15.00/48.00.

at Llanaber NW : 1½ m. on A 496 – Barmouth – 01341 :

- **Llwyndû Farmhouse**, LL42 1RR, N : ¾ m. on A 496 280144, Fax 280144, « Part 17C », – TV P
  Meals 19.50 **st.** – **7 rm** 45.00/54.00 **st.** – SB.

BARRY (Barri) S. Glam. 403 K 29 – pop. 46 368 – ECD : Wednesday – 01446.

Brynhill Port Rd, Colcot 735061 – RAF, St. Athan 751043.

The Triangle, Paget Rd, Barry Island, CF6 8TJ 747171 (summer only).

London 167 – Cardiff 10 – Swansea 39.

- **Egerton Grey,** CF62 3BZ, SW : 4½ m. by A 4226 and Porthkerry rd via Cardiff Airport 711666, Fax 711690, « Country house atmosphere », park, – rest TV P – 40. VISA
  Meals 12.50/21.00 **st.** 4.75 – **10 rm** 55.00/120.00 **st.** – SB.
- **Mount Sorrel,** Porthkerry Rd, CF62 7XY, 740069, Fax 746600, – TV P – 150. VISA
  Meals (bar lunch)/dinner 15.50/17.50 **st.** 5.70 – **46 rm** 60.00/90.00 – SB.
- **Aberthaw House,** 28 Porthkerry Rd, CF62 8AX, 737314, Fax 732376 – TV. VISA
  closed 23 December-10 January – **Meals** *(closed Sunday)* (dinner only) 14.50 **t.** and a la carte 3.95 – 6.95 – **9 rm** 29.95/49.95 **t.**
- **Cwm Ciddy Toby,** Airport Rd, CF6 9BA, NW : 1½ m. by B 4266 700075, Fax 700075 – TV P. VISA.
  closed 25-26 December – **Meals** (grill rest.) 7.95 **t.** and a la carte – **14 rm** 49.00/59.00 **t.**

BEAUMARIS Gwynedd 402 403 H 24 **Great Britain G.** – pop. 2 050 – ECD : Wednesday – ☎ 01248.

See : Castle★★ *AC*.

Envir. : Isle of Anglesey★★.

Exc. : Plas Newydd★★ *AC*, SW : 7 m. by A 545 and A 4080.

Baron Hill ☎ 810231.

♦London 253 – Birkenhead 74 – Holyhead 25.

- **Ye Olde Bull's Head Inn,** Castle St., LL58 8AP, ☎ 810329, Fax 811294 – rm. VISA
  closed 25-26 December and 1 January – **Meals** (see below) – **11 rm** 43.00/73.00 – SB.
- **Bishopsgate House,** 54 Castle St., LL58 8BB, ☎ 810302, Fax 810166 – rest. VISA
  closed January – **Meals** *(closed lunch October-May)* (bar lunch Monday to Saturday)/dinner 13.50 **t.** 5.25 – **12 rm** 32.00/56.00 **t.** – SB.
- Plas Cichle, LL58 8PS, NW : 2 ½ m. by B 5109 and Llanfaes Rd ☎ 810488, «, Working farm », park –
  3 rm.
- **Ye Olde Bull's Head Inn** (at Ye Olde Bull's Head Inn H.), Castle St., LL58 8AP, ☎ 810329, Fax 811294 –. VISA
  closed 25-26 December and 1 January – **Meals** (bar lunch Monday to Saturday)/dinner 18.95 **t.** and a la carte 6.50.

BEDDGELERT Gwynedd 402 403 H 24 **Great Britain G.** – pop. 535 – ECD : Wednesday – ☎ 01766.

Exc. : Snowdon★★★ (★★★ from summit) N : by marked footpaths or by Snowdon Mountain Railway from Llanberis.

♦London 249 – Caernarfon 13 – Chester 73.

- **Royal Goat,** LL55 4YE, ☎ 890224, Fax 890422, –. AE VISA
  Meals 11.00/17.00 **st.** and a la carte 5.50 – **28 rm** 42.00/68.00 **st.**, 2 suites – SB.
- **Sygun Fawr Country House**, LL55 4NE, NE : ¾ m. by A 498 ☎ 890258, mountains and valley, « Part 16C stone built house », park –
  closed January – **Meals** 15.00 **st.** 4.10 – **7 rm** 30.00/50.00 **st.** – SB.

BEREA Dyfed – see St. Davids.

BERRIEW (Aberriw) Powys 402 403 K 26 – pop. 1 305 – ✉ Welshpool – ☎ 01686.

♦London 190 – Chester 49 – Shrewsbury 26.

- **Lion,** SY21 8PQ, ☎ 640452, Fax 640604, « Part 17C inn » –. AE VISA JCB.
  Meals (booking essential) (bar lunch Monday to Saturday)/dinner a la carte 15.75/20.45 **t.** 5.00 – **7 rm** 45.00/85.00 **t.** – SB.

BETWS-Y-COED Gwynedd 402 403 I 24 **Great Britain G.** – pop. 848 – ECD : Thursday – ☎ 01690.

See : Town★.

Envir. : Swallow Falls★, NW : 2 m. by A 5.

Clubhouse ☎ 710556.

Royal Oak Stables, LL24 0AH ☎ 710426.

♦London 226 – Holyhead 44 – Shrewsbury 62.

- **Royal Oak,** Holyhead Rd, LL24 0AY, ☎ 710219, Fax 710603 –. AE VISA.
  Meals 10.00/20.00 **t.** and a la carte 3.00 – **27 rm** 49.00/78.00 **t.** – SB.
- **Waterloo,** LL24 0AR, on A 5 ☎ 710411, Fax 710411, –. AE VISA.
  closed 24 and 25 December – **Meals** (bar lunch Monday to Saturday)/dinner 16.50 **t.** and a la carte 5.95 – **39 rm** 48.25/84.00 **t.** – SB.
- **Tan-y-Foel**, LL26 ORE, E : 4 m. by A 5 and A 470 on Nebo rd ☎ 710507, Fax 710681, Vale of Conwy and Snowdonia, « Part 16C manor house », park –. AE VISA JCB.
  closed Christmas – **Meals** (residents only) (dinner only) 23.00 **st.** 5.50 – **7 rm** 69.50/110.00 **st.** – SB.
- **Ty Gwyn,** LL24 OSG, SE : ½ m. on A 5 ☎ 710383, Fax 710383, « 17C inn » –. VISA
  Meals (lunch by arrangement Monday to Saturday)/dinner 17.95 **t.** 5.50 – **13 rm** 20.00/80.00 **t.**
- **Park Hill,** Llanrwst Rd, LL24 0HD, NE : 1 m. by A 5 on A 470 ☎ 710540, Fax 710540, Vale of Conwy, – rest. AE VISA.
  Meals (dinner only) 14.50 **t.** 3.95 – **11 rm** 18.50/62.00 **t.** – SB.
- **Bryn Bella** without rest., Llanrwst Rd, LL24 0HD, ☎ 710627, –.
  4 rm 22.50/36.00 **st.**

at Penmachno SW : 4¾ m. by A 5 on B 4406 – ✉ Betws-y-Coed – ☎ 01690 :

- **Penmachno Hall**, LL24 0PU, ☎ 760207, – rest. VISA.
  closed 24 December-5 January – **Meals** 16.00 **st.** 2.95 – **4 rm** 30.00/50.00 **st.**

BONCATH Dyfed 403 G 27 – ☎ 01239.

♦London 247 – Carmarthen 27 – Fishguard 17.

Pantyderi Mansion, SA37 0JB, W : 2 ¾ m. by B 4332 ☎ 841227, Fax 841670, ≤, « Working farm », heated, park –
8 rm.

BONTDDU Gwynedd 402 403 I 25 – see Dolgellau.

BRECHFA Dyfed 403 H 28 – ✉ Carmarthen – ☎ 01267.

♦London 223 – Carmarthen 11 – ♦Swansea 30.

XX **Ty Mawr Country House** with rm, Abergorlech Rd, SA32 7RA, ☎ 202332, Fax 202437, « Part 15C and 16C house », – . AE VISA
closed last 2 weeks January, last week November-first week December and 25-26 December – **Meals** *(closed Tuesday dinner to non-residents)* 14.00/20.00 **st.** 8.45 – **5 rm** 48.00/76.00 **st.** – SB.

BRECON **(Aberhonddu)** Powys 403 J 28 **Great Britain G.** – pop. 7 523 – ECD : Wednesday – ☎ 01874.

Exc. : Dan-yr-Ogof Caves** *AC*, SW : 18 m. by A 40 and A 4067.

18 Penoyre Park, Cradoc ☎ 623658 – 9 Llanfaes ☎ 622004.

Cattle Market Car Park, LD3 9DA ☎ 622485.

♦London 171 – ♦Cardiff 40 – Carmarthen 31 – Gloucester 65.

Peterstone Court, Llanhamlach, LD3 7YB, SE : 3 ¼ m. on A 40 ☎ 665387, Fax 665376, ≤, « Georgian manor house », heated, – . AE VISA
Meals 11.95/30.95 **st.** and a la carte 5.25 – **12 rm** 79.50/130.00 **st.** – SB.

ATS The Watton ☎ 624496/624163

BRIDGEND **(Pen-y-Bont)** Mid Glam. 403 J 29 – pop. 14 311 – ECD : Wednesday – ☎ 01656.

♦London 177 – ♦Cardiff 20 – ♦Swansea 23.

Heronston, Ewenny Rd, CF35 5AW, S : 2 m. on B 4265 ☎ 668811, Fax 767391, heated, – – 120. AE VISA JCB
Meals 15.00/25.00 **t.** 5.25 – **76 rm** 65.00/125.00 **t.** – SB.

at Pencoed NE : 4 ½ m. by A 473 – ✉ Pencoed – ☎ 01656 :

Forte Travelodge, CF3 5HU, E : 1 ¼ m. by Felindre rd ☎ 864404, Reservations (Freephone) 0800 850950 – . AE VISA
Meals (Harvester grill) a la carte approx. 16.00 **st.** – 5.50 – **40 rm** 33.50 **t.**

at Coychurch (Llangrallo) E : 2 ¼ m. by A 473 – ✉ Bridgend – ☎ 01656 :

Coed-y-Mwstwr, CF35 6AF, N : 1 m. ☎ 860621, Fax 863122, ≤, heated, park, – – 120. AE VISA
Meals 12.50/26.00 **t.** and a la carte – **22 rm** 78.00/100.00 **t.**, 1 suites – SB.

at Southerndown SW : 5 ½ m. by A 4265 – ✉ Bridgend – ☎ 01656 :

X **Frolics,** Beach Rd, CF32 0RP, ☎ 880127 – VISA
closed Sunday dinner and Monday – **Meals** (dinner only and Sunday lunch)/dinner 13.95 **t.** and a la carte.

at Laleston W : 2 m. on A 473 – ✉ Bridgend – ☎ 01656 :

XX **Great House** with rm, CF32 0HP, on A 473 ☎ 657644, Fax 668892, – . AE VISA.
Meals *(closed Saturday lunch, Sunday dinner and 1 January)* 13.00 **t.** and dinner a la carte 5.25 – **7 rm** 65.00/85.00 **t.** – SB.

ATS 122 Coity Rd ☎ 658775/6

BWLCHTOCYN Gwynedd 402 403 G 25 – see Abersoch.

CADOXTON W. Glam. 403 I 29 – see Neath.

CAERNARFON Gwynedd 402 403 H 24 **Great Britain G.** – pop. 9 695 – ECD : Thursday – ☎ 01286.

See : Town*** – Castle*** *AC*.

18 Llanfaglan ☎ 673783.

Oriel Pendeitsh, Castle St., LL55 2PB ☎ 672232.

♦London 249 – Birkenhead 76 – Chester 68 – Holyhead 30 – Shrewsbury 85.

Seiont Manor, Llanrug, LL55 2AQ, E : 3 m. on A 4086 ☎ 673366, Fax 672840, , park – – 100. AE VISA
Meals 11.50/22.50 – **28 rm** 72.50/145.00 **st.** – SB.

Pengwern, Saron, LL54 5UH, SW : 3 ¼ m. by A 487 on Llandwrog rd 830717, « Working farm », park – rest .
closed December and January – **Meals** (by arrangement) 9.50 **st.** – **3 rm** 22.00/44.00 **st.**, 1 suite – SB.

Isfryn, 11 Church St., LL55 1SW, 675628 – rest
March-October – **Meals** (by arrangement) 15.50 **s.** – **6 rm** 17.00/38.00.

at Seion NE : 5 ½ m. by A 406 and B 4366 on Seion rd – Caernarfon – 01248 :

Ty'n Rhos Country House, Llanddeiniolen, LL55 3AE, SW : ¼ m. 670489, Fax 670079, park – rest VISA.
closed 24 December-5 January – **Meals** (dinner only) (by arrangement) 18.50 **t.** 5.75 – **11 rm** 39.00/80.00 **t.** – SB.

ATS Bangor Rd 673110

CARDIFF (Caerdydd) S. Glam. 403 K 29 **Great Britain G.** – pop. 279 055 – ECD : Wednesday – 01222.

See : City★ – Castle★ (interiors★) *AC* BZ – National Museum of Wales★ (Picture Collection★) *AC* BY – Llandaff Cathedral★ *AC* AV **B.**

Envir. : Welsh Folk Museum, St. Fagan's★★ *AC,* by St. Fagan's Rd AV – Castell Coch★ *AC,* NW : 4 ½ m. by A 470 AV.

Exc. : Caerphilly Castle★★ *AC,* N : 7 m. by A 469 AV.

18 Dinas Powis 512727, AX.

Cardiff (Wales) Airport : (01446) 711111, SW : 8 m. by A 48 AX – **Terminal** : Central Bus Station.

Central Station, Central Square, CF1 1QY 227281.

London 155 – Birmingham 110 – Bristol 46 – Coventry 124.

Plans on following pages

Copthorne, Copthorne Way, Culverhouse Cross, CF5 6XJ, W : 4 ¾ m. by A 4161 and A 48 at junction with A 4232 599100, Fax 599080, – rm rest – 300. VISA AX
Meals (in bar Sunday dinner) 17.00 **st.** and a la carte 5.95 – 9.95 – **134 rm** 92.00/102.00 **st.**, 1 suite – SB.

Cardiff Marriott, Mill Lane, CF1 1EZ, 399944, Fax 395578, squash – rm – 300. VISA JCB. BZ **s**
Meals 15.50 **st.** and a la carte 7.25 – 10.25 – **178 rm** 79.00/84.00 **st.**, 4 suites – SB.

Angel (Q.M.H.), Castle St., CF1 2QZ, 232633, Telex 498132, Fax 396212, – – 300 BZ **a**
89 rm, 2 suites.

Park (Mt. Charlotte Thistle), Park Pl., CF1 3UD, 383471, Telex 497195, Fax 399309 – rm – 300 BZ **c**
115 rm, 4 suites.

Cardiff International, Mary Ann St., CF1 2EQ, 341441, Telex 498005, Fax 223742 – rm rest – 40. VISA. BZ **a**
Meals (bar lunch Saturday) 11.50/14.95 **st.** and a la carte 4.25 – 8.95 – **140 rm** 75.00/90.00 **st.**, 3 suites – SB.

Cardiff Moat House (Q.M.H.), Circle Way East, Llanedeyrn, CF3 7XF, NE : 3 m. by A 48 732520, Telex 497582, Fax 549092, – rm rest – 300
133 rm, 2 suites. AV **n**

Forte Crest, Castle St., CF1 2XB, 388681, Fax 371495 – rm – 150
153 rm, 1 suite. BZ **i**

Friendly, Merthyr Rd, CF4 7LD, NW : 5 m. by A 470 at junction with M 4 529988, Fax 529977, – rm rest – 180. VISA
Meals *(closed Saturday lunch)* (carving rest.) 13.50 **st.** (dinner) and a la carte 5.50 – 6.75 – **95 rm** 70.50/94.00 **st.** – SB. by A 470 AV

Churchills, Cardiff Rd, CF5 2AD, 562372, Fax 568347 – rest – 110. VISA AV **v**
Meals (bar lunch Saturday) 8.50/16.50 **st.** and a la carte 3.95 – 6.90 – **28 rm** 60.00/70.00 **st.**, 7 suites – SB.

Forte Posthouse, Pentwyn Rd, CF2 7XA, NE : 4 m. by A 48 731212, Fax 549147, – rm rest – 120. VISA JCB AV
Meals a la carte approx. 15.00 **st.** 5.50 – **142 rm** 56.00/69.50 **st.**

Masons Arms (Toby), 21-23 Tyn-y-Parc Rd, CF4 6BG, NW : 3 ½ m. by A 470 692554, Fax 693724 – rm – 120 AV **s**
30 rm.

Forte Travelodge, Circle Way East, Llanedeyrn, CF3 7ND, on Coed-y-Gores rd 549564, Reservations (Freephone) 0800 850950 – . VISA. AV **c**
Meals (Harvester grill) a la carte approx. 16.00 **t.** – **32 rm** 33.50 **t.**

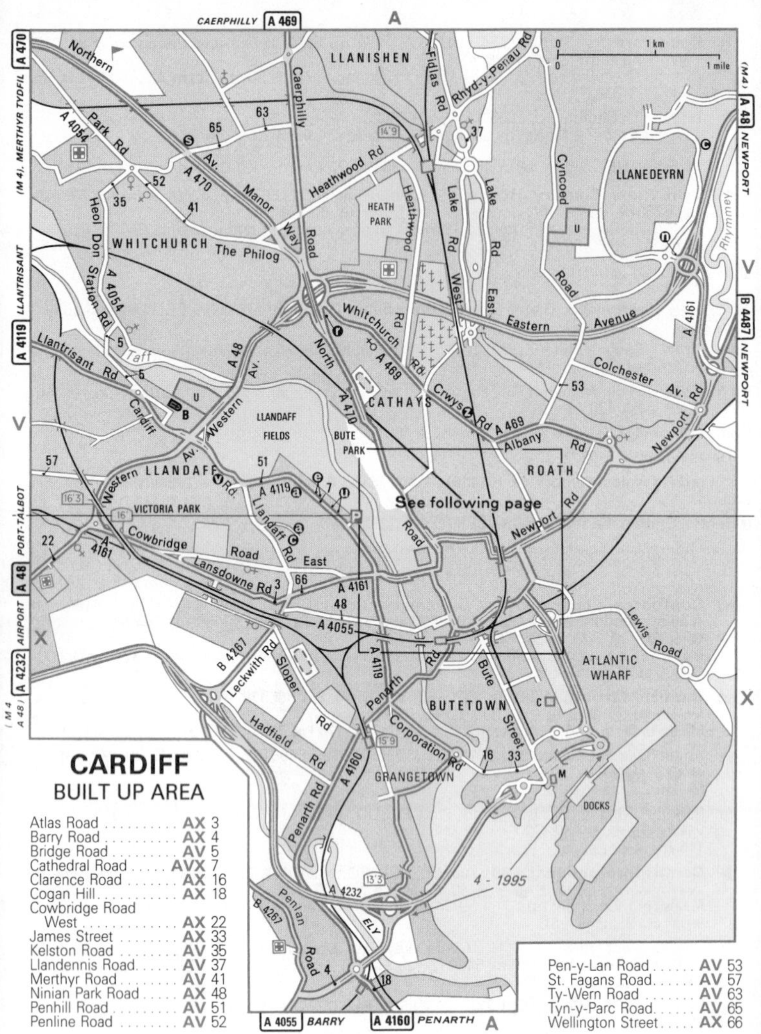

Townhouse without rest., 70 Cathedral Rd, CF1 9LL, ℰ 239399, Fax 223214 – TV ☎ P. VISA — AV **u**
6 rm ☐ 35.00/45.00 **st.**

Willows, 126-128 Cathedral Rd, CF1 9LQ, ℰ 340881, Fax 230122 – TV ☎. AE VISA.
Meals (by arrangement) 9.95 **13 rm** 22.00/38.00 **s.** – SB. — AV **e**

Ferrier's without rest., 130-132 Cathedral Rd, CF1 9LQ, ℰ 383413, Fax 383413 – TV ☎ P. AE VISA — AV **e**
closed 2 weeks Christmas-New Year – **26 rm** ☐ 20.00/48.00 **t.**

Annedd Lon without rest., 3 Dyfrig St., off Cathedral Rd, CF1 9LR, ℰ 223349 – TV. — AV **u**
6 rm ☐ 18.00/38.00 **s.**

Georgian without rest., 179 Cathedral Rd, CF1 9PL, ℰ 232594, Fax 232594 – TV. VISA. — AV **a**
8 rm ☐ 20.00/40.00 **st.**

CARDIFF

Duke Street . . . . **BZ** 26
High Street . . . . **BZ**
Queen Street . . . . **BZ**
Queens Arcade
  Shopping Centre . . . . **BZ** 54
St. David's
  Shopping Centre . . . . **BZ**
St. Mary Street . . . . **BZ**
Working Street . . . . **BZ** 67

Castle Street . . . . **BZ** 9
Cathays Terrace . . . . **BY** 10
Central Square . . . . **BZ** 12
Church Street . . . . **BZ** 14
City Hall Road . . . . **BY** 15
College Road . . . . **BY** 20
Corbett Road . . . . **BY** 21
Customhouse Street . . . . . . **BZ** 23
David Street . . . . **BZ** 25
Dumfries Place . . . . **BY** 28
Greyfriars Road . . . . **BY** 29

Guilford Street . . . . **BZ** 30
Hayes (The) . . . . **BZ** 32
King Edward VII Avenue . . **BY** 36
Mary Ann Street . . . . **BZ** 39
Moira Terrace . . . . **BZ** 42
Nantes (Boulevard de) . . . . **BY** 44
Penarth Road . . . . **BZ** 49
St. Andrews Place . . . . **BY** 56
St. John Street . . . . **BZ** 58
Station Terrace . . . . **BZ** 61
Stuttgart Street . . . . **BY** 62

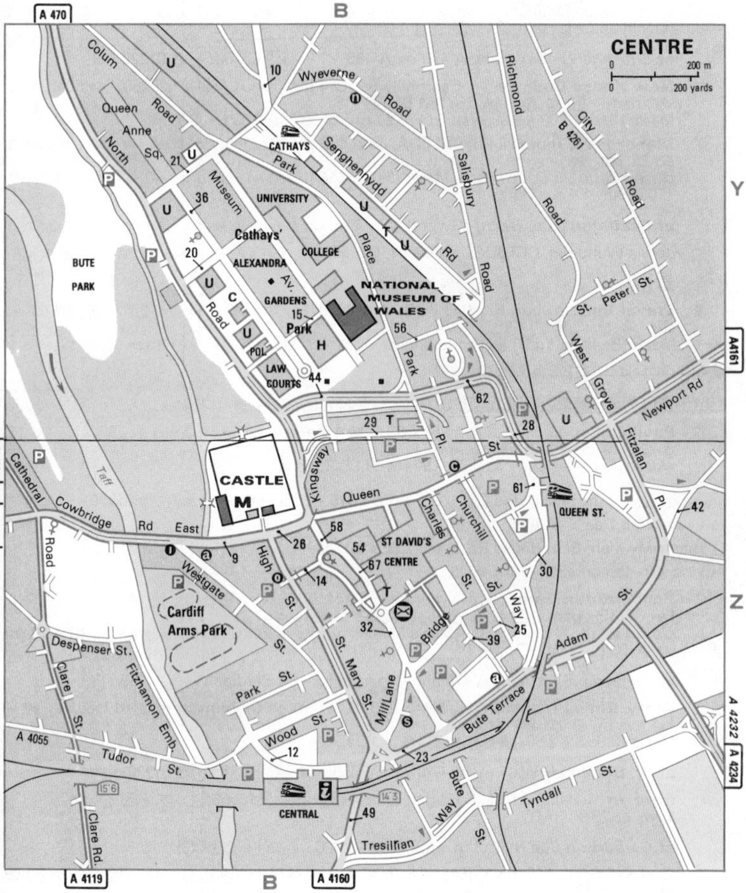

XXXX **De Courcey's,** Tyla Morris Av., Pentyrch, CF4 8QN, NW : 6 m. by A 4119 on Pentyrch rd ☎ 892232, Fax 891949 – Ⓟ. AE ① VISA — AV
closed Sunday, Monday and 25-30 December – **Meals** (dinner only) 18.95/29.45 **st.** and a la carte 5.00.

XX **Indian Ocean,** 290 North Rd, Gabalfa, CF4 3BN, ☎ 621349 – ▤. AE ① VISA — AV **r**
Meals - Indian 9.50 **t.** and a la carte.

X **Le Cassoulet,** 5 Romilly Cres., Canton, CF1 9NP, ☎ 221905. AE VISA — AX **c**
closed Saturday lunch, Sunday, Monday, August and 2 weeks Christmas – **Meals** - French 18.00/23.00 **t.** 4.50.

X **Quayle's,** 6-8 Romilly Cres., Canton, CF1 9NR, ☎ 341264 – AE VISA — AX **a**
closed Sunday dinner, Tuesday, 26 December and Bank Holidays – **Meals** - Bistro 9.95/11.95 **t.** and a la carte 4.95.

✗ **Blas-ar-Gymru (A Taste of Wales),** 48 Crwys Rd, CF2 4NN, ✆ 382132, Fax 565062 – P. VISA AV **z**
closed Saturday lunch, Sunday, lunch 1-14 January and Bank Holiday Mondays – **Meals** 18.95 **t.** and lunch a la carte 4.50.

✗ **Thai House,** 23 High St., CF1 2BZ, ✆ 387404, Fax 640810 – VISA BZ **o**
closed Sunday – **Meals** - Thai 7.00/29.99.

✗ **Armless Dragon,** 97 Wyeverne Rd, Cathays, CF2 4BG, ✆ 382357 – VISA BY **n**
closed Saturday lunch, Sunday, Monday, 25-26 December and 1 January – **Meals** 9.90 **t.** (lunch) and a la carte 13.70/21.70 4.00.

at Thornhill N : 5 ¼ m. by A 470 on A 469 – AV – ✉ Cardiff – ☎ 01222 :

New House Country ⑤, Caerphilly Rd, CF4 5UA, on A 469 ✆ 520280, Fax 520324, ←, park – TV ☎ P – 250. VISA
Meals 10.00/25.00 6.95 – 5.00 – **20 rm** 58.00/80.00 **t.** – SB.

Manor Parc, Thornhill Rd, CF4 5UA, on A 469 ✆ 693723, Fax 614624, – TV ☎ P. VISA.
closed 24 to 26 December – **Meals** 15.00/16.95 **t.** and a la carte 7.00 – **12 rm** 57.50/110.00 **st.**

at Castleton (Cas-Bach) (Gwent) NE : 7 m. on A 48 – AV – ✉ Cardiff – ☎ 01633 :

Jarvis Wentloog, CF3 8UQ, ✆ 680591, Fax 681287, – rm rest TV ☎ P – 120
55 rm.

Travel Inn, Newport Rd, CF3 8UQ, ✆ 680070, Fax 681143 – rm TV P. VISA.
Meals (Beefeater grill) a la carte approx. 16.00 **t.** 5.00 – 4.95 – **47 rm** 33.50 **st.**

ATS Hadfield Rd ✆ 228251/226336

CARDIFF WEST SERVICE AREA S. Glam. – ✉ Pontycwn – ☎ 01222.

Pavilion Lodge without rest., CF7 8SA, M 4 junction 33 ✆ 892255, Fax 892497 – TV P – 30. VISA JCB
closed 25 December – 4.00 – **50 rm** 31.95/35.95 **st.**

CARDIGAN (Aberteifi) Dyfed 403 G 27 – pop. 3 815 – ECD : Wednesday – ☎ 01239.

18 Gwbert-on-Sea ✆ 612035.

Theatr Mwldan, Bath House Rd, SA43 2JY ✆ 613230.

London 250 – Carmarthen 30 – Fishguard 19.

Penbontbren Farm ⑤, Glynarthen, SA44 6PE, NE : 9 ½ m. by A 487 ✆ 810248, Fax 811129, park – TV ☎ P – 30. VISA JCB
closed 24 to 28 December – **Meals** (dinner only) a la carte 14.70 **t.** approx 4.10 – **10 rm** 40.00/68.00 **st.** – SB.

at Cilgerran S : 3 m. by A 478 and Cilgerran rd – ✉ Cardigan – ☎ 01239 :

Allt-y-Rheini Mansion ⑤, SA43 2TJ, S : ½ m. on Crymmych rd ✆ 612286, ←, – rest TV P. VISA.
Meals 13.95 **t.** 3.80 – **5 rm** 31.00/54.00 **t.**

at St. Dogmaels W : 1 m. by A 487 on B 4568 – ✉ Cardigan – ☎ 01239 :

Berwyn ⑤ without rest., Cardigan Rd, SA43 3HS, ✆ 613555, ←, – TV P.
3 rm 20.00/37.00.

at Gwbert on Sea NW : 3 m. on B 4548 – ✉ Cardigan – ☎ 01239 :

Gwbert, SA43 1PP, on B 4548 ✆ 612638, Fax 621474, ← Cardigan Bay – rm TV ☎ P. VISA.
Meals (bar lunch Monday to Saturday)/dinner 14.50 **st.** and a la carte 5.95 – **17 rm** 44.50/79.00 **t.** – SB.

ATS 4 Bath House Rd ✆ 612917

CASTLETON (Cas-Bach) Gwent 403 K 29 – see Cardiff (South Glam.).

CEMAES Gwynedd 402 403 G 23 **Great Britain G.** – ☎ 01407.

Envir. : Isle of Anglesey★★.

London 272 – Bangor 25 – Caernarfon 32 – Holyhead 16.

Hafod Country House, LL67 ODS, S : ½ m. on Llanfechell rd ✆ 710500, ←, – TV P.
March-October – **Meals** (by arrangement) 12.00 – **3 rm** 32.00/38.00 **t.** – SB.

CHANCERY (Rhydgaled) Dyfed 403 H 26 – see Aberystwyth.

CHEPSTOW Gwent 403 404 M 29 **Great Britain G.** – pop. 9 461 – ECD : Wednesday – ☎ 01291.

See : Castle★ *AC*.

Envir. : Wye Valley★ (Eagle's Nest Viewpoint, Windcliff★).

18, 18 St. Pierre ☎ 625261.

Castle Car Park, NP6 5EY ☎ 623772 (summer only).

London 131 – Bristol 17 – Cardiff 28 – Gloucester 34.

St. Pierre H. Golf & Country Club (Country Club), NP6 6YA, SW : 3 ½ m. on A 48 ☎ 625261, Fax 629975, ←, Fб, ≘s, 🔲, 18, park, ✗, squash – ⇔ TV ☎ P – 🏃 220. AE ⓓ VISA JCB. ✗
Meals (dinner only and Sunday lunch)/dinner 19.50 **st.** and a la carte 6.50 – ☐ 9.00 – **134 rm** 105.00 **st.**, 9 suites – SB.

George (Forte), Moor St., NP6 5DB, ☎ 625363, Fax 627418 – ⇔ TV ☎ P – 🏃 30. AE ⓓ VISA JCB
Meals (buffet lunch Monday to Saturday)/dinner 15.95 **st.** and a la carte 6.95 – ☐ 8.50 – **14 rm** 67.50/92.50 **st.** – SB.

Beaufort, Beaufort Sq., NP6 5EP, ☎ 622497, Fax 627389 – TV ☎ P – 🏃 30. AE ⓓ VISA. ✗
Meals (bar lunch)/dinner 10.95 **t.** and a la carte 4.00 – ☐ 4.95 – **18 rm** 36.00/47.00 **t.**

Castle View, 16 Bridge St., NP6 5EZ, ☎ 620349, Fax 627397, ☐ – ⇔ rest TV ☎. AE ⓓ VISA
Meals *(Sunday dinner residents only)* (bar lunch Monday to Saturday)/dinner 15.00/20.00 **t.** 5.95 – ☐ 4.95 – **13 rm** 35.00/56.50 **t.** – SB.

✗ Leadon's, 6 Station Rd, NP6 5EP, ☎ 627402.

CILGERRAN Dyfed 403 G 27 – see Cardigan.

COLWYN BAY (Bae Colwyn) Clwyd 402 403 I 24 **Great Britain G.** – pop. 27 002 – ECD : Wednesday – ☎ 01492.

Envir. : Bodnant Garden★★ *AC*, SW : 6 m. by A 55 and A 470.

18 Abergele and Pensarn, Tan-y-Goppa Rd, Abergele ☎ (01745) 824034 – 9 Old Colwyn, Woodland Av. ☎ 515581.

40 Station Rd, LL29 8BU ☎ 530478 – The Promenade, Rhos-on-sea ☎ 548778 (summer only).

London 237 – Birkenhead 50 – Chester 42 – Holyhead 41.

Norfolk House, 39 Princes Drive, LL29 8PF, ☎ 531757, Fax 533781, ☐ – |‡| ⇔ rm TV ☎ P – 🏃 35. AE ⓓ VISA
closed 24 December-2 January – **Meals** (bar lunch)/dinner 13.75 **t.** and a la carte 4.60 – **23 rm** ☐ 32.50/58.00 **t.** – SB.

Hopeside, 63-67 Princes Drive, West End, LL29 8PW, ☎ 533244, Fax 532850 – ⇔ TV ☎ P – 🏃 50. AE ⓓ VISA
Meals 10.00/25.00 **t.** and a la carte 4.50 – **19 rm** ☐ 35.00/50.00 **t.** – SB.

✗✗ **Café Niçoise,** 124 Abergele Rd, LL29 7PS, ☎ 531555 – AE ⓓ VISA
closed lunch Monday-Wednesday, Sunday, 1 week January and 1 week June – **Meals** 12.95 **t.** and a la carte 4.95.

at Rhos-on-Sea (Llandrillo-yn-Rhos) NW : 1 m. – ✉ Colwyn Bay – ☎ 01492 :

Ashmount, College Av., LL28 4NT, ☎ 544582, Fax 545479 – TV ☎ P. AE ⓓ VISA JCB
Meals (dinner only) 11.95 **st.** and a la carte 3.95 – **17 rm** ☐ 35.25/60.00 **st.** – SB.

CONWY Gwynedd 402 403 I 24 **Great Britain G.** – pop. 3 627 – ECD : Wednesday – ☎ 01492.

See : Town★ – Castle★★ *AC* – Town Walls★★ – Plas Mawr★★ *AC*.

Envir. : Sychnant Pass (←★★) – Bodnant Garden★★ *AC*, S : 6 m. by A 55 and A 470.

18 Morfa ☎ 593400 – 9 Penmaenmawr ☎ 623330.

Conwy Castle Visitor Centre, ☎ 592248.

London 241 – Caernarfon 22 – Chester 46 – Holyhead 37.

Castle (Forte), High St., LL32 8DB, ☎ 592324, Fax 583351 – ⇔ TV ☎ P – 🏃 30
29 rm.

Berthlwyd Hall ⛰, Llechwedd, LL32 8DQ, SW : 2¼ m. by B 5106 and Sychnant rd, off Hendre rd ☎ 592409, Fax 572290, ←, heated, ☐ – TV ☎ P. ⓓ VISA
closed January – **Meals** (dinner only and Sunday lunch)/dinner 18.50 **st.** and a la carte 6.25 – ☐ 4.00 – **9 rm** 47.50/95.50 **st.** – SB.

at Roewen S : 3 m. by B 5106 – ✉ Conwy – ☎ 01492 :

Tir-y-Coed ⛰, LL32 8TP, ☎ 650219, ←, ☐ – ⇔ rest TV P
March-October – **Meals** 11.00 **t.** 4.75 – **7 rm** ☐ 26.50/48.25 **t.** – SB.

at Tal-y-Bont S : 5¾ m. on B 5106 – ✉ Conwy – ☎ 01492 :

Lodge, LL32 8YX, ☎ 660766, Fax 660534 – ⇔ rm TV ☎ P – 🏃 30. AE VISA
Meals (closed Tuesday lunch) 5.75/14.95 **st.** and dinner a la carte 4.95 – **10 rm** ☐ 33.95/70.00 **st.** – SB.

COWBRIDGE S. Glam. 403 J 29 – pop. 6 167 – 01656.

♦London 167 – ♦Cardiff 12 – ♦Swansea 30.

Stembridge Farmhouse without rest., Llandow, CF7 7NT, SW : 3½ m. 890389, ←, – TV P.
closed 11 December-1 January – **3 rm** 25.00/55.00 **st.**

COYCHURCH (Llangrallo) M. Glam. 403 J 29 – see Bridgend.

CRICCIETH Gwynedd 402 403 H 25 – pop. 1 720 – ECD : Wednesday – 01766.

18 Ednyfed Hill 522154.

♦London 249 – Caernarfon 17 – Shrewsbury 85.

Mynydd Ednyfed, Caernarfon Rd, LL52 0PH, NW : ¾ m. on B 4411 523269, ←, , – TV P. AE VISA
closed 24-30 December – **Meals** *(closed Sunday to non-residents)* (dinner only) 18.95 3.75 – **9 rm** 32.50/58.00 **t.** – SB.

CRICKHOWELL Powys 403 K 28 – pop. 2 166 – ECD : Wednesday – 01873.

9 Old Rectory Hotel, Llangattock 810373.

♦London 169 – Abergavenny 6 – Brecon 14 – Newport 25.

Gliffaes Country House, NP8 1RH, W : 3 ¾ m. by A 40 (01874) 730371, Fax 730463, ←, « Country house and gardens on the banks of the River Usk », , park, – TV P. AE VISA JCB.
closed 5 January-24 February – **Meals** (bar lunch Monday to Saturday)/dinner 19.00 **st.** and a la carte – **22 rm** 33.50/99.00 **st.**

Bear, High St., NP8 1BW, 810408, Fax 811696 – TV P. AE VISA JCB
Meals (in bar Sunday) (lunch booking essential)/dinner a la carte 15.00/22.50 **t.** 3.95 – **28 rm** 42.00/70.00 **t.**

at Llangenny E : 3 m. by A 40 via Glangrwyney – ✉ Crickhowell – 01873 :

Gellirhydd Farm, NP8 1HF, N : 1 ½ m. taking unmarked road before bridge 810466, ←, , , park – P.
closed Christmas and New Year – **Meals** (by arrangement) (communal dining) 10.00 – **3 rm** 18.00/40.00 – SB.

at Llangattock SW : 1 ¼ m. by A 4077 and Llangynidr rd – ✉ Crickhowell – 01873 :

Ty Croeso, The Dardy, NP8 1PU, 810573, Fax 810573, ←, – TV P. AE VISA JCB
Meals (lunch by arrangement Monday to Saturday)/dinner 14.95 **t.** and a la carte 3.95 – **8 rm** 30.00/65.00 **t.** – SB.

CROSSGATES Powys 403 J 27 – see Llandrindod Wells.

CROSS HANDS Dyfed 403 H 28 – pop. 13 94 – 01269.

♦London 208 – Fishguard 63 – ♦Swansea 19.

Forte Travelodge without rest., SA14 6NW, on A 48 845700, Reservations (Freephone) 0800 850950 – TV P. AE VISA.
32 rm 33.50 **t.**

CRUG-Y-BAR Dyfed 403 I 27 – ECD : Saturday – ✉ Llanwrda – 01558.

♦London 213 – Carmarthen 26 – ♦Swansea 36.

Glanrannell Park, SA19 8SA, SW : ½ m. by B 4302 685230, Fax 685784, ←, , , park – rest P. VISA JCB
April-October – **Meals** *(closed Sunday lunch to non- residents)* (light lunch)/dinner 10.00/24.00 **t.** 3.00 – **8 rm** 36.00/62.00 **t.** – SB.

CRYMMYCH Dyfed 403 G 28 – ✉ Whitland – 01994.

♦London 245 – Carmarthen 25 – Fishguard 19.

Preseli Country House, SA34 0YP, S : 4 m. by A 478, on lane opposite disused quarry 419425, Fax 419425, ←, , park – TV P.
Meals (by arrangement)(communal dining) 15.00 **st.** 5.95 – **7 rm** 20.00/40.00 – SB.

CWMBRAN Gwent 403 K 29 – pop. 44 592 – ECD : Wednesday – 01633.

♦London 149 – ♦Bristol 35 – ♦Cardiff 17 – Newport 5.

Parkway, Cwmbran Drive, NP44 3UW, S : 1 m. by A 4051 871199, Telex 497887, Fax 869160, , , – rm TV P – 550. AE VISA
closed Christmas – **Meals** *(closed Saturday lunch)* 7.05/12.25 **st.** and a la carte 4.25 – 8.95 – **69 rm** 69.50/83.50 **st.**, 1 suite – SB.

ATS Station Rd 484964

CYNGHORDY Dyfed 403 I 27 – ✉ Llandovery – ☎ 015505.

◆London 210 – Carmarthen 31 – ◆Swansea 41.

- **Llanerchindda Farm** ⑤, SA20 0NB, N : 2½ m. by Station rd and under viaduct ℘ 274, Fax 274, ←, « Working farm », ⛱ – ⚡ rest TV P
  Meals 9.00 **st.** 3.00 – **7 rm** ⊒ 20.00/40.00 **st.**

DEGANWY Gwynedd 402 403 I 24 – see Llandudno.

DOLGELLAU Gwynedd 402 403 I 25 – pop. 2 621 – ECD : Wednesday – ☎ 01341.

Pencefn Rd ℘ 422603.

Ty Meirion, Eldon Sq., LL40 1PU ℘ 422888 (summer only).

◆London 221 – Birkenhead 72 – Chester 64 – Shrewsbury 57.

- **Penmaenuchaf Hall** ⑤, Penmaenpool, LL40 1YB, W : 1 ¾ m. on A 493 ℘ 422129, Fax 422129, ←, « Country house atmosphere », ⛱, park – ⚡ rest TV ☎ P – 🏛 70. AE VISA JCB.
  Meals 13.95/21.50 **t.** and lunch a la carte 6.00 – **14 rm** ⊒ 50.00/140.00 **t.** – SB.
- **Dolserau Hall** ⑤, LL40 2AG, NE : 2¾ m. by A 494 ℘ 422522, Fax 422400, ←, ⛱ – ⚡ TV ☎ P. VISA
  Meals (dinner only) 19.50 **s.** 4.95 – **14 rm** ⊒ 41.00/76.00 **t.** – SB.
- **George III,** Penmaenpool, LL40 1YD, W : 2 m. by A 493 ℘ 422525, Fax 423565, ← Mawddach estuary and mountains, – ⚡ rest TV ☎ P. VISA JCB
  Meals 11.50 **t.** (lunch) and a la carte 15.30/23.50 – **12 rm** ⊒ 48.00/92.00 **t.** – SB.

at Ganllwyd N : 5½ m. on A 470 – ✉ Dolgellau – ☎ 01341 :

- **Dolmelynllyn Hall** ⑤, LL40 2HP, ℘ 440273, Fax 440273, ←, ⛱, park – ⚡ TV ☎ P. AE VISA.
  closed December-January, and weekdays February – **Meals** (lunch by arrangement) 22.50 **st.** 6.25 – **11 rm** ⊒ 57.50/110.00 **st.** – SB.

at Llanfachreth NE : 3¾ m. – ✉ Dolgellau – ☎ 01341 :

- **Ty Isaf** ⑤, LL40 2EA, ℘ 423261, ←, « 17C longhouse », ⛱ – ⚡ P
  closed 3 weeks February-March and 3 weeks October-November – **Meals** (communal dining) 11.00 **st.** 3.50 – **3 rm** ⊒ 23.00/46.00 **st.**

at Arthog SW : 7 m. on A 493 – ✉ Dolgellau – ☎ 01341 :

- **Cyfannedd Uchaf** ⑤, LL39 1LX, S : 4½ m. by A 493 Cregennan Lakes rd, taking right turn at T. junction at end of road (gated roads) ℘ 250526, ← Barmouth, Mawddach estuary and mountains, park – ⚡ P.
  March-October – **3 rm** ⊒ 16.00/32.00 **st.**

at Bontddu W : 5 m. on A 496 (Barmouth Rd) – ✉ Dolgellau – ☎ 01341 :

- **Bontddu Hall,** LL40 2UF, ℘ 430661, Fax 430284, ← Mawddach estuary and mountains, « Victorian mansion in extensive gardens », park – ⚡ rest TV ☎ P. AE VISA JCB
  April-October – ***Garden :*** **Meals** 12.75/23.50 **t.** 5.75 – **17 rm** ⊒ 52.50/90.00 **t.**, 3 suites – SB.
- **Borthwnog Hall,** LL40 2TT, E : 1 m. on A 496 ℘ 430271, Fax 430682, ← Mawddach estuary and mountains, « Part Regency house, art gallery », ⛱, park – ⚡ rest TV P. VISA.
  closed 24 to 27 December – **Meals** (booking essential) (dinner only) 16.00 **t.** and a la carte – **3 rm** ⊒ 112.00 **st.** – SB.

DRENEWYDD YN NOTAIS **(Nottage)** M. Glam. – see Porthcawl.

DYFFRYN ARDUDWY Gwynedd 402 403 H 25 – pop. 1 489 (inc. Tal-y-bont) – ☎ 01341.

◆London 237 – Dolgellau 16 – Caernarfon 44.

- **Ael-Y-Bryn,** LL44 2BE, on A 496 ℘ 242701, Fax 242682, ←, ⛱, ✂ – TV P. VISA
  Meals (bar lunch Monday to Saturday)/dinner a la carte 8.85/15.15 4.95 – **8 rm** ⊒ 30.00/50.00 **st.** – SB.

EGLWYSFACH Dyfed 403 I 26 – see Machynlleth (Powys).

EWLOE Clwyd – ☎ 01244.

Autolodge Site, Gateway Services, A 55 Expressway westbound, Northophall, CH7 6HE ℘ 541597.

◆London 200 – ◆Chester 8.5 – Shrewsbury 48.

- **St David's Park,** St. David's Park, CH5 3YB, on B 5125 at junction with A 494 ℘ 520800, Fax 520930, Ⓕ, ≘, 🏊, 18, ⛱, ✂ – ⚡ rm ▤ rest TV ☎ ♿ P – 🏛 270. AE VISA JCB
  Fountains : **Meals** 16.95 **t.** and a la carte – ⊒ 8.95 – **121 rm** 79.00/135.00 **st.** – SB.

ATS Holywell Rd (Nr. Queensferry) ℘ 520380

FISHGUARD (Abergwaun) Dyfed 403 F 28 – pop. 3 128 – ECD : Wednesday – 01348.
to Republic of Ireland (Rosslare) (Stena Sealink Line) 2 daily (3 h 30 mn).
4 Hamilton St., SA65 9HL 873484.
London 265 – Cardiff 114 – Gloucester 176 – Holyhead 169 – Shrewsbury 136 – Swansea 76.

Manor House, 11 Main St., SA65 9HG, 873260, – TV. VISA
closed 23 to 29 December – **Meals** (dinner only) 16.00 **t.** 4.75 – **6 rm** 22.00/44.00 **t.** – SB.

Plas Glyn-Y-Mel without rest., Lower Town, SA65 9LY, 872296, ←, , , park – TV P
5 rm 37.00/70.00 **t.**

Three Main Street with rm., Main St., SA65 9HG, 874275 – .
closed February – **Meals** *(closed Monday in winter and Sunday)* (light lunch)/dinner a la carte 14.95/21.70 **t.** – **3 rm** 30.00/50.00 **t.** – SB.

at Pontfaen SE : 5½ m. by B 4313 – 01239 :

Tregynon Country Farmhouse , Gwaun Valley, SA65 9TU, E : 6¼ m. 820531, Fax 820808, , park – TV P – 25. VISA JCB.
closed 2 weeks winter – **Meals** (booking essential) (dinner only) 15.50 **t.** – **8 rm** 63.00 **t.** – SB.

Gellifawr Country House , SA65 9TX, E : 5 m. 820343, Fax 820128, heated, , park – P. VISA
Meals (bar lunch)/dinner 18.50 **st.** and a la carte 5.15 – **10 rm** 25.00/59.00 **st.** – SB.

at Letterston S : 5 m. by A 40 – Letterston – 01348 :

Heathfield Mansion , SA62 5EG, NW : 1½ m. by B 4331 840263 – P
March-October – **Meals** (by arrangement) 8.00 **st.** 3.50 – **3 rm** 25.00/36.00 **st.** – SB.

at Welsh Hook SW : 7½ m. by A 40 – Haverfordwest – 01348 :

Stone Hall with rm, SA62 5NS, 840212, Fax 840815, « Part 14C manor house with 17C extension », – TV P. AE VISA.
closed 2 weeks mid January – **Meals** *(closed Monday)* (dinner only) 16.00 **t.** and a la carte 4.75 – **5 rm** 46.00/63.00 **t.** – SB.

at Goodwick (Wdig) NW : 1½ m. – Fishguard – 01348 :

Ivybridge, Drim Mill, Dyffryn, SA64 0FT, E : ¾ m. by A 487 872623, Fax 875366, park – rest TV P
Meals 10.50 – **6 rm** 19.50/43.00 **st.** – SB.

ATS Scleddau 873522

FLINT (Fflint) Clwyd 402 403 K 24 – 01352.

Green's Lodge, Northop Rd, Flint Mountain, CH6 5QG, S : 1½ m. on A 5119 763127, Fax 763126, – TV P. AE VISA.
Meals (in bar Sunday dinner) 10.95/19.95 **t.** and a la carte 3.45 – **21 rm** 39.50/55.00 **t.** – SB.

ATS 31 Chester Rd 733401/734368

GANLLWYD Gwynedd 402 403 I 25 – see Dolgellau.

GLYN CEIRIOG Clwyd 402 403 K 25 – Llangollen – 0169 172.
London 194 – Shrewsbury 30 – Wrexham 17.

Golden Pheasant , Llwynmawr, LL20 7BB, SE : 1¾ m. by B 4500 718281, Fax 718479, ←, – TV P. AE VISA
Meals 10.95/12.95 **st.** 6.95 – **18 rm** (dinner included) 45.00/100.00 **st.** – SB.

GOODWICK (Wdig) Dyfed 403 F 27 – see Fishguard.

GOVILON Gwent – see Abergavenny.

GUILSFIELD Powys 402 403 K 26 – see Welshpool.

GWBERT ON SEA Dyfed 403 F 27 – see Cardigan.

HANMER Clwyd 402 403 L 25 – pop. 565 – Whitchurch – 0194 874.
London 237 – Chester 26 – Shrewsbury 27 – Stoke-on-Trent 28.

Hanmer Arms, SY13 3DE, 532, Fax 740, – TV P – 40. AE VISA
Meals a la carte 8.05/17.55 **t.** 4.30 – **18 rm** 42.00/52.00 **t.**, 7 suites – SB.

Great Britain and Ireland are covered entirely
at a scale of 16 miles to 1 inch by our map « Main roads » 986.

HARLECH Gwynedd 402 403 H 25 **Great Britain G.** – pop. 1 880 – ECD : Wednesday – ☎ 01766.
See : Castle★★ *AC*.
Royal St. David's ☎ 780203.
Gwyddfor House, High St., LL46 2YA ☎ 780658 (summer only).
London 241 – Chester 72 – Dolgellau 21.

Gwrach Ynys, LL47 6TS, N : 2¼ m. on A 496 ☎ 780742, Fax 780742, – rest TV ☎ P
7 rm.

Castle Cottage with rm, Pen Llech, LL46 2YL, off B 4573 ☎ 780479 – rest. VISA
Meals (booking essential)(dinner only and Sunday lunch)/dinner 17.95 **t.** 4.95 – **6 rm** 23.00/50.00 **t.** – SB.

HAVERFORDWEST **(Hwlffordd)** Dyfed 403 F 28 – pop. 11 099 – ECD : Thursday – ☎ 01437.
Arnolds Down ☎ 763565.
2 Old Bridge, SA61 2EZ ☎ 763110.
London 250 – Fishguard 15 – Swansea 57.

Mariners, Mariners Sq., SA61 2DU, ☎ 763353, Fax 764258 – TV ☎ P – 35
30 rm.

Wilton House, 6 Quay St., SA61 1BG, ☎ 760033, Fax 760297 – TV. AE VISA.
Meals a la carte 8.95/14.70 **st.** 3.25 – **6 rm** 25.00/45.00 **st.**

ATS Back Lane, Prendergast ☎ 763756/7

HAWARDEN **(Penarlâg)** Clwyd 402 403 K 24 – ☎ 01244.

Swiss Restaurant Imfeld, 68 The Highway, CH5 3DH, ☎ 534523. VISA
closed Monday and 30 January-12 February – **Meals** (dinner only) 19.50 5.50.

ATS Holywell Rd, Ewloe, Deeside ☎ 520380

HAY-ON-WYE Powys 403 K 27 – pop. 1 407 – ECD : Tuesday – ☎ 01497.
Rhosgoch, Builth Wells ☎ 851251.
London 154 – Brecon 16 – Hereford 21 – Newport 62.

Swan, Church St., HR3 5DQ, ☎ 821188, Fax 821424, – rest TV ☎ P – 160.
AE VISA
Meals (bar lunch Monday to Saturday)/dinner 22.50 **t.** and a la carte 4.25 – **18 rm** 50.00/80.00 **st.** – SB.

Old Black Lion, Lion St., HR3 5AD, ☎ 820841, « Part 13C and 17C inn » – rest TV ☎
P. AE VISA
Meals (bar lunch Monday to Saturday)/dinner a la carte 15.75/19.75 **t.** 4.95 – **10 rm** 18.95/41.90 **t.** – SB.

York House, Hardwick Rd, Cusop, HR3 5QX, E : ½ m. on B 4348 ☎ 820705, – TV
P. AE VISA
Meals (by arrangememt) 12.00 **st.** – **5 rm** 21.00/44.00 **st.**

at Llanigon SW : 2½ m. by B 4350 – ✉ Hay-on-Wye – ☎ 01497 :

Old Post Office without rest., HR3 5QA, ☎ 820008, « 17C house » – P
March-November – **3 rm** 17.00/40.00.

HOLYHEAD **(Caergybi)** Gwynedd 402 403 G 24 – pop. 12 569 – ECD : Tuesday – ☎ 01407.
to Republic of Ireland (Dun Laoghaire) (Stena Sealink Line) 2-4 daily (3 h 30 mn) – to Republic of Ireland (Dublin) (B & I Line) 2 daily (3 h 30 mn).
London 269 – Birkenhead 94 – Cardiff 215 – Chester 88 – Shrewsbury 105 – Swansea 190.

Hotel see : Rhoscolyn S : 5½ m.

HOLYWELL **(Treffynnon)** Clwyd 402 403 K 24 – pop. 6 084 – ECD : Wednesday – ☎ 01745.
Holywell, Brynford ☎ 710040/713937.
London 217 – Chester 19 – Liverpool 34.

Kinsale Hall, Llanerchymor, CH8 9DT, N : 3½ m. by B 5121 off A 548 ☎ 560001, Fax 561298, park – rest TV ☎ P – 400. AE VISA
Meals 16.50/35.00 **st.** and dinner a la carte – **27 rm** 60.00/70.00 **st.**, 2 suites – SB.

Stamford Gate, Halkyn Rd, CH8 7SJ, ☎ (01352) 712942, Fax 713309 – TV ☎ P. VISA.
Meals (dancing Friday and Saturday) 9.50/20.00 **st.** and a la carte 4.00 – 5.50 – **12 rm** 32.00/36.00 **st.**

Forte Travelodge without rest., Halkyn, CH8 8RF, SE : 3½ m. on A 55 (westbound carriageway) ☎ (01352) 780952, Reservations (Freephone) 0800 850950 – TV P. AE VISA.
31 rm 33.50 **t.**

HOWEY Powys – see Llandrindod Wells.

Les prix Pour toutes précisions sur les prix indiqués dans ce guide, reportez-vous à l'introduction.

KNIGHTON (Trefyclawdd) Powys 403 K 26 – pop. 2 851 – ☎ 01547.
Little Ffrydd Wood ☎ 528646.
The Offas Dyke Centre, West St., LD7 1EW ☎ 528753.
London 162 – Birmingham 59 – Hereford 31 – Shrewsbury 35.

Milebrook House, Ludlow Rd, Milebrook, LD7 1LT, E : 2 m. on A 4113 ☎ 528632, Fax 520509, – rest TV P. VISA JCB.
Meals *(closed Monday lunch)* (bar lunch)/dinner 19.50 **st.** and a la carte 5.50 – **6 rm** 44.80/62.00 **st.** – SB.

LAKE VYRNWY Powys 402 403 J 25 – ✉ Llanwddyn – ☎ 01691
Vyrnwy Craft Workshops, SY10 0IZ ☎ 73346.
London 204 – Chester 52 – Llanfyllin 10 – Shrewsbury 40.

Lake Vyrnwy, SY10 0LY, ☎ 870692, Fax 870259, Lake Vyrnwy, « Victorian sporting estate », park, – TV P – 80. AE VISA
Meals (lunch booking essential) 12.75/22.50 **t.** – **36 rm** 55.50/122.50 **t.**, 1 suite – SB.

LALESTON M. Glam. 403 J 29 – see Bridgend.

LAMPHEY Dyfed – see Pembroke.

LANGSTONE Gwent 403 L 29 – see Newport.

LAUGHARNE Dyfed 403 G 28 – pop. 1 272 – ☎ 01994.
London 233 – Carmarthen 13 – Fishguard 41.

Halldown without rest., SA33 4QS, N : 1 ½ m. on A 4066 ☎ 427452, – P
5 rm 16.00/32.00 **s.**

LETTERSTON Dyfed 403 F 28 – see Fishguard.

LLANABER Gwynedd 402 403 H 25 – see Barmouth.

La guida cambia, cambiate la guida ogni anno.

LLANARMON DYFFRYN CEIRIOG Clwyd 402 403 K 25 – pop. 1 349 – ✉ Llangollen – ☎ 0169 176.
London 196 – Chester 33 – Shrewsbury 32.

West Arms, LL20 7LD, ☎ 665, Fax 622, – P – 75. AE VISA
Meals (bar lunch Monday to Friday)/dinner 22.50 **t.** and a la carte 5.50 – **12 rm** (dinner included) 65.00/120.00 **t.**, 2 suites – SB.

LLANBEDR Gwynedd 402 403 H 25 – pop. 1 101 – ECD : Wednesday – ☎ 01341.
London 262 – Holyhead 54 – Shrewsbury 100.

Pensarn Hall, LL45 2HS, N : ¾ m. on A 496 ☎ 236236, – TV P. VISA
March-October – **Meals** (dinner only) 10.50 **st.** 3.00 – **8 rm** 25.00/45.00 **st.** – SB.

Victoria Inn, LL45 2LD, ☎ 23213, – rest TV P. VISA
Meals 8.95/14.00 **t.** 3.50 – **5 rm** 26.00/48.50 **st.**

LLANBERIS Gwynedd 403 H 24 **Great Britain G.** – pop. 1 986 – ECD : Wednesday – ☎ 01286.
Envir. : Snowdon★★★ (★★★ from summit) SE : by Snowdon Mountain Railway or by marked footpaths.
Amgueddfa'r Gogledd/Museum of the North, LL55 4UR ☎ 870765 (summer only).
London 243 – Caernarfon 7 – Chester 65 – Shrewsbury 78.

Y Bistro, 43-45 High St., LL55 4EU, ☎ 871278 – . VISA
closed Sunday – **Meals** (booking essential) (dinner only) 24.00 **t.**

LLANDEGLEY Powys – see Llandrindod Wells.

LLANDEILO Dyfed 403 I 28 – pop. 850 – ECD : Thursday – ☎ 01558.
Glynhir, Llandybie, nr Ammanford ☎ (01269) 850472.
London 218 – Brecon 34 – Carmarthen 15 – Swansea 25.

Plough Inn with rm, Rhosmaen, SA19 6NP, N : 1 m. on A 40 ☎ 823431, Fax 823969, – TV P – 45. VISA.
closed 25 and 26 December – **Meals** *(closed Sunday dinner to non-residents)* a la carte 12.00/20.50 **t.** 5.50 – 4.00 – **12 rm** 40.00/60.00 **t.**

ATS Towy Terr., Ffairfach ☎ 822567

LLANDRILLO Clwyd 402 403 J 25 – pop. 1 048 – ✉ Corwen – ☎ 0149 084.
London 210 – Chester 40 – Dolgellau 26 – Shrewsbury 46.

Tyddyn Llan Country House, LL21 0ST, ☎ 264, Fax 414, « Part Georgian country house », – P. VISA
closed February – **Meals** 12.75/25.50 **t.** – **10 rm** 64.00/99.00 **t. st.** – SB.

LLANDRINDOD WELLS Powys 403 J 27 **Great Britain G.** – pop. 4 943 – ECD : Wednesday – 01597.

Exc. : Elan Valley★★, NW : 12 m. by A 4081, A 470 and B 4518.

Llandrindod Wells ℘ 822010/823873.

Old Town Hall, Memorial Gardens, LD1 5DL ℘ 822600.

London 204 – Brecon 29 – Carmarthen 60 – Shrewsbury 58.

Metropole, Temple St., LD1 5DY, ℘ 823700, Fax 824828, – – 250. VISA
Meals 9.75/16.95 **t.** 4.50 – **120 rm** 59.50/79.50 **st.**, 2 suites – SB.

Dillraj, Emporium Building, Temple St., LD1 5DL, ℘ 823843
Meals - Indian.

Charis without rest., Pentrosfa, LD1 5NL, S : ¾ m. by A 470 ℘ 824732 – .
4 rm 20.00/32.00 **t.**

at Crossgates NE : 3 ½ m. at junction of A 483 with A 54 – Llandrindod Wells – 01597 :

Guidfa House, LD1 6RF, ℘ 851241, Fax 851875, – . VISA.
Meals 12.50 3.00 – **7 rm** 21.00/44.00 **st.** – SB.

at Llandegley E : 7 m. by A 483 on A 44 – Llandrindod Wells – 01597 :

Ffaldau Country House, LD1 5UD, ℘ 851421, – . VISA.
Meals (dinner only) 18.00 and a la carte 5.00 – **4 rm** 22.00/45.00.

at Howey S : 1 ½ m. by A 483 – Llandrindod Wells – 01597 :

Three Wells Farm, LD1 5PB, NE : ½ m. ℘ 824427, Fax 822484, ≤, « Working farm », – rest
Meals 10.00 **t.** 3.00 – **11 rm** 17.00/44.00 **st.**, 4 suites – SB.

Corven Hall, LD1 5RE, S : ½ m. by A 483 on Hundred House rd ℘ 823368, – rest
closed December and January – **Meals** (dinner only) 10.00 **t.** 3.00 – **10 rm** 24.00/36.00 **t.** – SB.

Holly Farm, LD1 5PP, W : ½ m. ℘ 822402, « Working farm », – rest .
May-October – **Meals** 8.00 **st.** – **3 rm** 18.00/36.00 **st.**

Die Preise Einzelheiten über die in diesem Führer angegebenen Preise finden Sie in der Einleitung.

LLANDUDNO Gwynedd 402 403 I 24 **Great Britain G.** – pop. 18 647 – ECD : Wednesday except summer – 01492.

Exc. : Bodnant Garden★★ *AC*, S : 7 m. by A 470.

Rhos-on-Sea, Pernrhyn Bay ℘ 549641, A – 72 Bryniau Rd, West Shore ℘ 875325 A – Hospital Rd ℘ 876450 B.

1-2 Chapel St., LL30 2YU ℘ 876413.

London 243 – Birkenhead 55 – Chester 47 – Holyhead 43.

Plan on next page

Bodysgallen Hall, LL30 1RS, SE : 2 m. on A 470 ℘ 584466, Fax 582519, ≤ gardens and mountains, « Part 17C and 18C hall with terraced gardens », park, – – 50. VISA. B
Meals (booking essential) 15.90/27.50 **st.** 5.90 – 9.95 – **19 rm** 85.00/120.00 **st.**, 9 suites – SB.

Imperial, The Promenade, LL30 1AP, ℘ 877466, Fax 878043, , , – – 150. VISA B **v**
Meals 10.50/19.50 **st.** – **97 rm** 55.00/85.00, 3 suites – SB.

Empire, 73 Church Walks, LL30 2HE, ℘ 860555, Fax 860791, « Collection of Russell Flint prints », , heated, – rest – 60. VISA JCB. A **e**
closed 18 to 29 December – **Meals** (bar lunch Monday to Friday)/dinner 19.00 **st.** and a la carte 4.95 – **43 rm** 50.00/100.00 **st.**, 7 suites – SB.

Empire (No 72), 72 Church Walks, LL30 2HE, ℘ 860555, Fax 860791, « Victoriana » – . VISA JCB.
closed 18 to 29 December – **8 rm** 60.00/95.00 **st.** – SB.

St. Tudno, North Parade, LL30 2LP, ℘ 874411, Fax 860407, ≤, – rest rest . VISA JCB. A **c**
Meals 14.25/26.00 **st.** 5.95 – **21 rm** 65.00/75.00 **st.** – SB.

Dunoon, Gloddaeth St., LL30 2DW, ℘ 860787, Fax 860031, – . VISA A **r**
mid March-October – **Meals** 8.50/16.00 **st.** 4.50 – **56 rm** 32.00/70.00 **st.** – SB.

Bedford, Promenade, Craig-y-Don, LL30 1BN, E : 1 m. on B 5115 – B ℘ 876647, Fax 860185 – . VISA
***Gigolos :* Meals** - Italian 9.50/14.50**st.** and a la carte 4.10 – **27 rm** 25.00/54.00 **st.** – SB.

LLANDUDNO

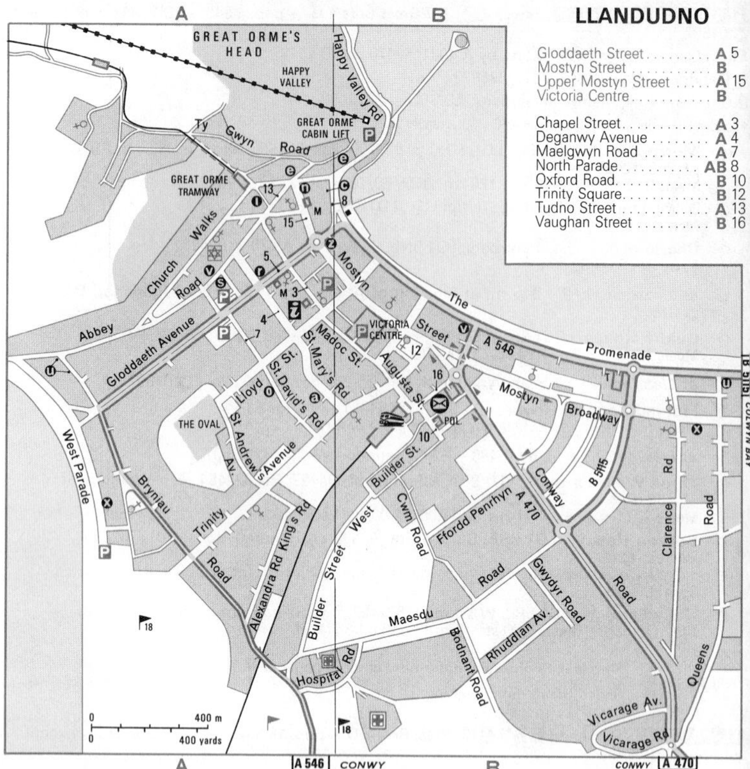

Bryn Derwen, Abbey Rd, LL30 2EE, ℘ 876804, ≤, 🌳 – ⊭ TV P. VISA. ✗ — A **v**
March-October – **Meals** 13.50 **t.** – **9 rm** ☐ 34.00/48.00 **t.** – SB.

Wilton, 14 South Par., LL30 2LN, ℘ 876086, Fax 876086 – ⊭ rest TV ☎ — AB **z**
closed December and January – **Meals** 10.00 **st.** 🍷 4.50 – **14 rm** ☐ 24.00/48.00 **st.**

Belle Vue, 26 North Par., LL30 2LP, ℘ 879547, ≤ – 🛗 TV ☎ P. AE ⓓ VISA — B **e**
March-October – **Meals** (bar lunch)/dinner 10.00 **t.** and a la carte 🍷 4.60 – **17 rm** ☐ 24.50/53.00 **t.** – SB.

Bromwell Court, Promenade, 6 Craig-y-Don Par., LL30 1BG, ℘ 878416, Fax 874142 – ⊭ rest TV ☎. VISA. ✗ — B **u**
April-October – **Meals** (dinner only) 8.50 🍷 4.25 – **11 rm** ☐ 18.50/42.00 – SB.

Epperstone, 15 Abbey Rd, LL30 2EE, ℘ 878746, Fax 871223 – ⊭ rest TV ☎ P. VISA — A **s**
closed January – **Meals** 10.00 **st.** 🍷 3.95 – **8 rm** ☐ 24.00/48.00 **st.** – SB.

Sunnymede, West Par., West Shore, LL30 2BD, ℘ 877130 – ⊭ rest TV P. VISA — A **x**
closed January-March – **Meals** 10.70 **st.** 🍷 4.00 – **18 rm** ☐ 31.00/69.00 **st.** – SB.

Hollybank, 9 St. David's Pl., LL30 2UG, ℘ 878521 – ⊭ TV. VISA — A **a**
March-October – **Meals** 7.00 🍷 3.50 – **7 rm** ☐ 21.00/38.00 **st.** – SB.

Craiglands, 7 Carmen Sylva Rd, LL30 1LZ, E : 1 m. by A 546 off B 5115 ℘ 875090 – ⊭ rest TV — B
April-October – **Meals** (by arrangement) – **6 rm** 18.50/44.00 **s.**

Tan Lan, Great Orme's Rd, West Shore, LL30 2AR, ℘ 860221, Fax 860221 – ⊭ rest TV P. VISA — A **u**
March-October – **Meals** 11.50 **t.** 🍷 3.75 – **18 rm** ☐ 22.00/46.00 **t.** – SB.

Banham House, 2 St. David's Rd, LL30 2UL, ℘ 875680, Fax 875680 – ⊭ rm TV P. ✗ — A **o**
Meals 9.95 **st.** 🍷 4.10 – **6 rm** ☐ 25.75/47.00 **st.**

Clontarf, 1 Great Orme's Rd, West Shore, LL30 2AR, ℘ 877621 – ⊭ P. ✗ — A **u**
March-October and 4 days at Christmas – **Meals** (by arrangement) – **9 rm** ☐ 20.50/41.00.

XX **Martin's,** 11 Mostyn Av., LL30 1YS, ℘ 870070 – VISA B **x**
closed Sunday dinner, Monday and January – **Meals** (dinner only and Sunday lunch)/dinner 21.00 **st.** and a la carte 4.00.

X **Richard's Bistro,** 7 Church Walks, LL30 2HD, ℘ 877924 – VISA A **n**
Meals (dinner only) a la carte 11.85/20.95 **st.**

X **No. 1,** 1 Old Rd, LL30 2HA, ℘ 875424, Fax 875424 – VISA A **i**
closed Monday lunch, Sunday and 25 to 26 December – **Meals** - Bistro 13.25 **st.** (dinner) and a la carte 5.95.

at Deganwy S : 2 ¾ m. on A 546 – A – ✉ Llandudno – ☎ 01492 :

X **Paysanne,** Station Rd, LL31 9EJ, ℘ 582079 – VISA
closed Sunday and Monday – **Meals** (booking essential)(dinner only) 9.50 **t.** and a la carte 4.50.

LLANDYRNOG Clwyd 402 403 J/K 24 – ✉ Denbigh – ☎ 01824.

Berllan Bach , Fford Las, LL16 4LR, SE : 1 ¼ m. by Police Station rd on Llangynhafel rd ℘ 790732, –
Meals 12.50 **s.** – **3 rm** 25.00/35.00 **s.** – SB.

LLANERCHYMEDD Gwynedd 402 403 G 24 **Great Britain G.** – pop. 613 – ☎ 01248.
Envir. : Isle of Anglesey★★.
♦London 262 – Bangor 18 – Caernarfon 23 – Holyhead 15.

Llwydiarth Fawr , LL71 8DF, N : ¾ m. on B 5111 ℘ 470321, ≤, « Georgian farmhouse », , , park – .
closed Christmas – **Meals** (by arrangement) 15.00 **st.** – **3 rm** 22.50/45.00 **st.**, 2 suites – SB.

Tre'r Ddol , LL71 7AR, SW : 3 ½ m. by B 5112 ℘ 470278, ≤, « 17C farmhouse », , park –
closed Christmas – **Meals** 10.00 **st.** – **4 rm** 20.00/38.00 **st.**

Drws-Y-Coed , LL71 8AD, E : 1 ½ m. by B 5111 on Benllech rd ℘ 470473, ≤, , park – .
closed December – **Meals** (by arrangement) 10.00 – **3 rm** 20.00/38.00 – SB.

LLANFACHRETH Gwynedd 402 403 I 25 – see Dolgellau.

LLANFIHANGEL Powys 402 403 J 25 – see Llanfyllin.

LLANFIHANGEL CRUCORNEY Gwent 403 L 28 – see Abergavenny.

LLANFYLLIN Powys 402 403 K 25 – pop. 1 267 – ECD : Friday – ☎ 01691.
Council Offices, High St., SY22 5DB ℘ 648868 (summer only).
♦London 188 – Chester 42 – Shrewsbury 24 – Welshpool 11.

Bodfach Hall , SY22 5HS, NW : ¼ m. on A 490 ℘ 648272, Fax 648272, ≤, , park – . VISA
March-October – **Meals** *(closed Sunday dinner to non-residents)* (bar lunch Monday to Saturday)/dinner 15.50 **st.** – **9 rm** 34.00/68.00 **t.** – SB.

X **Seeds,** 5 Penybryn Cottages, High St., SY22 5AP, ℘ 648604, « 16C cottages », – . VISA
closed Monday except Bank Holidays and September-May – **Meals** 17.75/22.25 **t.** and lunch a la carte 4.75.

at Llanfihangel SW : 5 m. by A 490 and B 4393 on B 4382 – ✉ Llanfyllin – ☎ 01691.

Cyfie Farm , SY22 5JE, S : 1 ½ m. by B 4382 ℘ 648451, ≤ Meifod valley, « Working farm, restored 17C longhouse », , park – .
Meals (communal dining) 10.00 – **2 rm** 18.50/41.00 **st.**, 3 suites – SB.

LLANGAMMARCH WELLS Powys 403 J 27 – ECD : Wednesday – ☎ 01591.
♦London 200 – Brecon 17 – Builth Wells 8.

Lake Country House , LD4 4BS, E : ¾ m. ℘ 620202, Fax 620457, ≤, « Country house in extensive grounds », , , park, – rest . VISA
Meals (lunch by arrangement)/dinner 21.50 **st.** 5.75 – **7 rm** 78.50/110.00 **st.**, 11 suites 125.00/135.00 – SB.

LLANGATTOCK Powys 403 K 28 – see Crickhowell.

LLANGENNY Powys 403 K 28 – see Crickhowell.

En saison, *surtout dans les stations fréquentées, il est prudent de retenir à l'avance. Cependant, si vous ne pouvez pas occuper la chambre que vous avez retenue, prévenez immédiatement l'hôtelier.*

Si vous écrivez à un hôtel à l'étranger, joignez à votre lettre un coupon-réponse international (disponible dans les bureaux de poste).

LLANGOLLEN Clwyd 402 403 K 25 **Great Britain G.** – pop. 3 267 – ECD : Thursday – ☎ 01978.
See : Plas Newydd★ *AC.*
Exc. : Chirk Castle★ *AC*, SE : 7½ m. by A 5.
⛳18 Vale of Llangollen, Holyhead Rd ☎ 860613.
ℹ Town Hall, Castle St., LL20 5PD ☎ 860828.
♦London 194 – Chester 23 – Holyhead 76 – Shrewsbury 30.

- Bryn Howel, LL20 7UW, E : 2¾ m. on A 539 ☎ 860331, Fax 860119, ≤, ≘s, ↘, ⚘ – |≡| TV ☎ P – 🏟 300
38 rm.
- **Royal** (Forte), Bridge St., LL20 8PG, ☎ 860202, Fax 861824, ≤ – ⇔ TV ☎ P – 🏟 60. AE ⓓ VISA JCB
Meals (bar lunch Monday to Saturday)/dinner 15.95 **t.** 6.75 – ☐ 8.50 – **33 rm** 55.00/80.00 **t.** – SB.
- **Gales Wine Bar,** 18 Bridge St., LL20 8PF, ☎ 860089, Fax 861313 – ⇔ rm TV ☎ P. VISA. ⛔
closed 25 December-1 January – **Meals** (closed Sunday) (in bar) a la carte 7.80/11.70 **t.** – **12 rm** ☐ 32.00/46.50 **t.**, 2 suites.

LLANGORSE Powys 403 K 28 – pop. 490 – ✉ Brecon – ☎ 01874.
♦London 177 – Abergavenny 15 – Brecon 5 – Newport 33.

- **Red Lion,** LD3 7TY, ☎ 84238 – TV P. ⛔
Meals *(closed lunch Monday to Friday November-March)* (bar lunch Monday to Saturday)/dinner 12.00 **t.** and a la carte 4.10 – **10 rm** 25.00/50.00 **t.** – SB.

LLANGURIG Powys 403 J 26 – pop. 680 – ECD : Thursday – ✉ Llanidloes – ☎ 0155 15.
♦London 188 – Aberystwyth 25 – Carmarthen 75 – Shrewsbury 53.

- **Old Vicarage,** SY18 6RN, ☎ 440280, Fax 440280 – ⇔ TV P
March-October – **Meals** 11.00 **st.** 3.95 – **4 rm** ☐ 28.00/40.00 **st.** – SB.

LLANGYBI Gwent – see Usk.

Se cercate un albergo tranquillo,
oltre a consultare le carte dell'introduzione,
rintracciate nell'elenco degli esercizi quelli con il simbolo 🐦 *o* 🐦.

LLANIDLOES Powys 403 J 26 – ☎ 01686.

- **Glyngynwydd** 🐦 without rest., Cwmbelan, SY18 6QQ, S : 2½ m. by B 4518 on A 470 ☎ 413854, « 17C farmhouse », ⚘ – ⇔ P
3 rm ☐ 18.50/36.00 **st.**

LLANIGON Powys 403 K 27 – see Hay-on-Wye.

LLANNEFYDD Clwyd 402 403 J 24 – pop. 567 – ✉ Denbigh – ☎ 01745.
♦London 225 – Chester 37 – Shrewsbury 63.

- **Hawk and Buckle Inn,** LL16 5ED, ☎ 79249, Fax 79316, ≤ – ⇔ rm TV ☎ P. VISA. ⛔
closed 25 December – **Meals** *(closed Sunday dinner)* (bar lunch and Sunday dinner)/dinner a la carte 10.85/19.30 **t.** and a la carte **t.** – **10 rm** ☐ 36.00/50.00 **t.** – SB.

LLANRHIDIAN W. Glam. – see Swansea.

LLANRWST Gwynedd 402 403 I 24 – pop. 3 012 – ECD : Thursday – ☎ 01492.
♦London 230 – Holyhead 50 – Shrewsbury 66.

- **Priory,** Maenan, LL26 0UL, N : 2½ m. on A 470 ☎ 660247, Fax 660734, ↘, ⚘ – TV ☎ P. AE ⓓ VISA
Meals (lunch booking essential)/dinner 10.00 **t.** and a la carte 5.85 – **12 rm** ☐ 39.00/49.00 **st.**
- **Bron Eirian** 🐦, Town Hill, LL26 0NF, ☎ 641741, ≤, ⚘ – ⇔ TV P
Meals (communal dining) 12.50 **st.** – **3 rm** ☐ 23.00/38.00 **st.**
- XX **Cae'r Berllan** 🐦 with rm, LL26 0PP, S : 1 m. on A 470 ☎ 640027, « 16C manor house », ⚘ – ⇔ TV P. VISA
closed January, February and November – **Meals** *(closed Sunday to Tuesday to non-residents)* (booking essential) (dinner only) a la carte 13.50/25.00 **t.** 4.50 – **2 rm** ☐ 37.50/65.00 **t.**

at Trefriw NW : 2 m. on B 5106 – ✉ Llanrwst – ☎ 01492 :

- **Hafod House,** LL27 0RQ, ☎ 640029, Fax 641351, ⚘ – ⇔ rest TV ☎ P. AE ⓓ VISA. ⛔
closed 3 weeks January – **Meals** *(closed Sunday to Tuesday)* (dinner only) 17.95 **st.** 3.95 – **7 rm** ☐ 34.50/69.00 **st.** – SB.
- X **Chandler's Brasserie,** LL27 0JH, ☎ 640991 – ⇔ P. VISA
closed Sunday, Monday, 3 weeks late January-mid February, 2 weeks October and Christmas – **Meals** (dinner only) a la carte 15.65/19.15 **t.**

LLANSANFFRAID GLAN CONWY Gwynedd 402 403 I24 **Great Britain G.** – pop. 2 194 – ✉ Aberconwy – ☎ 01492.

Envir. : Bodnant Garden** *AC*, S : 2½ m. by A 470.

♦London 241 – Colwyn Bay 4 – Holyhead 42.

Old Rectory ⚘, LL28 5LF, on A 470 ☎ 580611, Fax 584555, ≤ Conwy estuary, « Georgian country house with antique furnishings », – ⇔ TV ☎ P. AE VISA JCB.
closed 14 December-1 February – **Meals** (dinner only) 27.50 **st.** 6.90 – **6 rm** 72.00/104.00 **st.** – SB.

LLANTRISANT Gwent 403 L 28 – pop. 8 317 (inc. Pontyclun) – ✉ Usk – ☎ 01291.

♦London 148 – ♦Bristol 34 – Gloucester 43 – Newport 8.

Greyhound Inn, NP5 1LE, NE : ½ m. on Usk rd ☎ 672505, Fax 673255, – TV ☎ ♿ P. VISA.
Meals *(closed Sunday dinner)* 8.50/15.00 **t.** 4.25 – **10 rm** 50.00/65.00 **st.** – SB.

LLANTWIT MAJOR S. Glam. 403 J 29 – pop. 9 836 – ☎ 01446.

♦London 175 – ♦Cardiff 18 – ♦Swansea 33.

West House, West St., CF61 1SP, ☎ 792406, Fax 796147, – TV ☎ P. AE VISA
Meals 9.00/13.50 **t.** and a la carte 3.95 – **21 rm** 45.00/68.00 **t.** – SB.

LLANWENARTH Gwent – see Abergavenny.

LLANWRTYD WELLS Powys 403 J 27 – pop. 649 – ECD : Wednesday – ☎ 01591.

♦London 214 – Brecon 32 – Carmarthen 39.

Lasswade Country House, Station Rd, LD5 4RW, ☎ 610515, ≤, , – ⇔ TV ☎ P. VISA
Meals (dinner only and Sunday lunch)/dinner 14.95 **st.** 4.95 – **8 rm** 27.50/55.00 **st.** – SB.

LLYSWEN Powys 403 K 27 – pop. 168 – ✉ Brecon – ☎ 01874.

♦London 188 – Brecon 8 – ♦Cardiff 48 – Worcester 53.

Llangoed Hall ⚘, LD3 0YP, NW : 1 ¼ m. on A 470 ☎ 754525, Fax 754545, ≤, « Edwardian mansion by Sir Clough Williams-Ellis of 17C origins », , , – ⇔ rest TV ☎ P. AE VISA JCB.
Meals 17.00/35.50 **t.** and a la carte 32.50/42.00 **t.** 7.50 – **20 rm** 95.00/185.00 **t.**, 3 suites – SB.

Griffin Inn, LD3 0UR, on A 470 ☎ 754241, Fax 754592, « Part 15C inn », , – ⇔ rest ☎ P
8 rm.

MACHYNLLETH Powys 402 403 I 26 – pop. 1 110 – ECD : Thursday – ☎ 01654.

Ffordd Drenewydd ☎ 702000.

Canolfan Owain Glyndwr Centre, SY20 8EE ☎ 702401.

♦London 220 – Shrewsbury 56 – Welshpool 37.

Dolguog Hall ⚘, SY20 8UJ, E : 1½ m. by A 489 ☎ 702244, Fax 702530, ≤, « 17C country house », , , park – ⇔ TV ☎ P.
9 rm.

Bacheiddon Farm ⚘ without rest., Aberhosan, SY20 8SG, SE : 5¼ m. on Dylife rd, via Forge ☎ 702229, « Working farm » – P.
May-September – **3 rm** 36.00 **s.**

at Eglwysfach (Dyfed) SW : 6 m. on A 487 – ✉ Machynlleth (Powys) – ☎ 01654 :

Ynyshir Hall ⚘, SY20 8TA, ☎ 781209, Fax 781366, ≤, « Georgian country house, gardens », park – ⇔ TV ☎ P. AE VISA.
Meals (booking essential) 15.00/28.00 **st.** – **6 rm** 85.00/140.00 **st.**, 2 suites.

MAGOR SERVICE AREA Gwent – ✉ Newport – ☎ 01633.

Granada Lodge without rest., NP6 3YL, M 4 junction 23 ☎ 880111, Fax 881896, Reservations (Freephone) 0800 555300 – ⇔ TV ☎ ♿ P. AE VISA.
4.00 – **43 rm** 39.95 **st.**

MERTHYR TYDFIL M. Glam. 403 J 28 – pop. 59 317 – ECD : Thursday – ☎ 01685.

Morlais Castle, Pant, Dowlais ☎ 722822 – Cilsanws Mountain, Cefn Coed ☎ 723308.

14a Glebeland St., CF47 8AU ☎ 379884.

♦London 179 – ♦Cardiff 25 – Gloucester 59 – ♦Swansea 33.

Tregenna, Park Terr., CF47 8RF, ☎ 723627, Fax 721951 – TV ☎ P. AE VISA
Meals 7.50/17.25 **st.** and a la carte 5.00 – **24 rm** 39.00/60.00 **st.** – SB.

MILFORD HAVEN (Aberdaugleddau) Dyfed 403 E 28 – pop. 13 649 – ECD : Thursday – 01646.

18 Hubbertson 692368.

94 Charles St., SA73 2HL 690866 (summer only).

London 258 – Carmarthen 39 – Fishguard 23.

Lord Nelson, Hamilton Terr., SA73 3AL, 695341, Fax 694026, – TV. VISA.
closed 25 December – **Meals** (bar lunch)/dinner a la carte 11.05/17.70 **t.** 4.20 – **31 rm** 42.00/65.00 **t.**, 1 suite.

MISKIN M. Glam. – Cardiff – 01443.

London 169 – Cardiff 22 – Swansea 31.

Miskin Manor, CF7 8ND, E : 1 ¾ m. by A 4119 (Groes Faen rd) 224204, Fax 237606, <, park, squash – TV – 200. VISA.
Meals a la carte 20.65/30.65 **t.** – **31 rm** 80.00/1100.00 **t.**, 1 suite – SB.

MOLD (Yr Wyddgrug) Clwyd 402 403 K 24 – pop. 9 168 – ECD : Thursday – 01352.

18 Pantmywyn 740318/741513 – 18 Old Padeswood, Station Rd (01244) 547401 – 18 Padeswood & Buckley, The Caia, Station Lane, Padeswood (01244) 550537 – 9 Caerwys 720692.

Library, Earl Road, Ch7 1AP 759331.

London 211 – Chester 12 – Liverpool 29 – Shrewsbury 45.

Soughton Hall, CH7 6AB, N : 2½ m. by A 5119 840811, Fax 840382, <, « Early 18C Italianate mansion », – rest TV. VISA.
closed first 2 weeks January – **Meals** *(closed Sunday lunch)* 14.50/21.50 **st.** and a la carte 6.50 – **12 rm** 70.00/119.00 **st.** – SB.

Tower, Nercwys, CH7 4ED, S : 1 m. by B 5444 and Nercwys rd 700220, « 15C fortified house », park – TV. VISA
Meals (by arrangement) (communal dining) 25.00 – **3 rm** 40.00/60.00 **st.**

ATS Wrexham Rd 753682

MONMOUTH (Trefynwy) Gwent 403 L 28 **Great Britain G.** – pop. 8 204 – ECD : Thursday – 01600.

Envir. : S : Wye Valley★.

Exc. : Raglan Castle★ *AC*, SW : 8 m. by A 40.

18 The Rolls of Monmouth, The Hendre 715353 – 9 Leasebrook Lane 712212.

Shire Hall, Agincourt Sq., NP5 3DY 713899.

London 147 – Gloucester 26 – Newport 24 – Swansea 64.

Riverside, Cinderhill St., NP5 3EY, 715577 – TV – 150. VISA.
Meals (bar lunch Monday to Saturday)/dinner a la carte 10.50/22.50 **st.** 2.50 – **17 rm** 48.00/66.00 **st.** – SB.

at Whitebrook SE : 8½ m. by A 466 – Monmouth – 01600 :

Crown at Whitebrook with rm, NP5 4TX, 860254, Fax 860607, – rest TV. VISA JCB
closed 2 weeks January and 2 weeks August – **Meals** *(closed Monday lunch and Sunday dinner to non-residents)* 14.95/26.90 **t.** and lunch a la carte – **12 rm** 50.00/80.00 **t.** – SB.

ATS Wonastow Rd, Wonastow Ind. Est. 716832

MONTGOMERY (Trefaldwyn) Powys 403 K 26 **Great Britain G.** – pop. 1 059 – 01686.

See : Castle★.

London 194 – Birmingham 71 – Chester 53 – Shrewsbury 30.

Dragon, Town Square, SY15 6AA, 668359, Fax 668287, – rm TV.
14 rm.

Little Brompton Farm without rest., SY15 6HY, SE : 2 m. on B 4385 668371, « Working farm », park – TV.
3 rm 19.00/38.00.

MOYLGROVE Dyfed 403 F 27 – see Newport.

MUMBLES W. Glam. 403 I 29 – see Swansea.

NANNERCH Clwyd 402 403 K 24 – pop. 513 – Mold – 01352.

London 218 – Chester 19 – Liverpool 36 – Shrewsbury 52.

Old Mill, Melin-y-Wern, Denbigh Rd, CH7 5RH, NW : ¾ m. on A 451 741542, Fax 740254, « Converted stables to 19C corn mill », – TV. VISA JCB
closed February – **Meals** (residents only) (dinner only) 21.00 – **7 rm** 37.00/55.00 **st.** – SB.

NEATH (Castell-Ned) W. Glam. 403 I 29 – ☎ 01639.

Swansea Bay, Jersey Marine ☎ (01792) 814153/812198.

◆London 188 – ◆Cardiff 40 – ◆Swansea 8.

Castle, The Parade, SA11 1RB, ☎ 641119, Fax 641624, – rm – 140.
Meals 4.95/16.00 **st.** and a la carte 4.50 – **28 rm** 39.50/49.50 **st.** – SB.

at Cadoxton NW : 1 ½ m. by A 474 – ✉ Neath – ☎ 01639 :

Cwmbach Cottages, Cwmbach Rd, SA10 8AH, ☎ 639825, – rm.
Meals (by arrangement) – **5 rm** 25.00/40.00 **st.**

NEFYN Gwynedd 402 403 G 25 – pop. 2 548 – ECD : Wednesday – ☎ 01758.

Nefyn & District ☎ 720218.

◆London 265 – Caernarfon 20.

Caeau Capel, Rhodfar Mor, LL53 6EB, ☎ 720240, –.
Easter-October – **Meals** (bar lunch)/dinner 13.50 **st.** – **18 rm** 23.65/47.30 **st.** – SB.

NEWPORT Dyfed 403 F 27 – pop. 1 224 – ECD : Wednesday – ☎ 01239.

Newport ☎ 820244.

◆London 258 – Fishguard 7.

Llysmeddyg, East St., SA42 0SY, on A 487 ☎ 820008, –.
closed Christmas – **Meals** (by arrangement) 12.50 – **4 rm** 17.50/35.00 **st.**

Grove Park, Pen-y-bont, SA42 0LT, on Moylegrove rd ☎ 820122 –
Meals 12.00 **st.** 4.00 – **4 rm** 38.00/40.00 **st.** – SB.

Cnapan with rm, East St., SA42 0SY, on A 487 ☎ 820575, – rest.
closed February and 25-26 December – **Meals** *(closed Monday to Saturday lunch November-January and Tuesday March-October)* (booking essential) a la carte 14.45/19.50 **t.** 4.95 – **5 rm** 29.00/48.00 **t.**

at Moylgrove NE : 6 m. – ✉ Cardigan – ☎ 0123 986 :

Old Vicarage, SA43 3BN, S : ¼ m. on Glanrhyd rd ☎ 231, –.
Meals 12.50 **st.** 3.50 – **3 rm** 20.00/45.00 **st.**

NEWPORT (Casnewydd-Ar-Wysg) Gwent 403 L 29 **Great Britain G.** – pop. 115 896 – ECD : Thursday – ☎ 01633.

Envir. : Caerleon (Fortress Baths★, Roman Amphitheatre★ *AC*) NE : 3½m. on B 4596.

Tredegar Park, Bassaleg Rd ☎ 895219 – , Caerleon, Broadway ☎ 420342 – Parc, Church Lane, Coedkenew ☎ 680933.

Museum and Art Gallery, John Frost Sq., NP9 1HZ ☎ 842962 – Ffwrrwm Art & Craft Centre, High St., NP6 1AG ☎ 430777.

◆London 145 – ◆Bristol 31 – ◆Cardiff 12 – Gloucester 48.

Celtic Manor, Coldra Woods, NP6 2YA, E : 3 m. on A 48 ☎ 413000, Fax 412910, , park – rm – 300
Meals (see ***Hedley's*** below) – **73 rm.**

Hilton National, The Coldra, NP6 2YG, E : 3 m. on A 48 ☎ 412777, Fax 413087, – 350.
Meals *(closed Saturday lunch)* (carving rest.)/dinner 15.75 **st.** and a la carte 5.50 – 9.25 – **119 rm** 70.00 **st.** – SB.

Westgate, Commercial St., NP9 1TT, ☎ 244444, Fax 246616 – – 150.
Meals (closed Saturday and Bank Holiday lunch) 7.50/13.95 4.25 – 6.50 – **69 rm** 57.50/78.00 – SB.

Kings, High St., NP9 1QU, ☎ 842020, Fax 244667 – – 200.
closed 24-30 December – **Meals** (dinner only and Sunday lunch)/dinner a la carte 10.30/15.00 4.50 – 6.00 – **47 rm** 44.00/52.00 **st.** – SB.

Newport Lodge, 147 Bryn Bevan, Brynglas Rd, NP9 5QN, N : ¾ m. by A 4042 ☎ 821818, Fax 856360 –
27 rm.

Kepe Lodge without rest., 46a Caerau Rd, NP9 4HH, ☎ 262351, –.
8 rm.

Hedley's (at Celtic Manor H.), Coldra Woods, NP6 2YA, E : 3 m. on A 48 ☎ 413000, Fax 412910 –.

at Langstone E : 4 ½ m. on A 48 – ✉ Newport – ☎ 01633 :

Stakis Country Court, Chepstow Rd, NP6 2LX, ☎ 413737, Fax 413713, – rm rest – 80.
Meals *(closed Saturday lunch)* 13.50/17.25 **st.** and a la carte – 8.75 – **131 rm** 85.00/115.00 **st.**, 9 suites.

at Redwick SE : 9 ½ m. by M4 off B 4245 – ✉ Magor – ☎ 01633 :

Brick House, NP6 3DX, ☎ 880230, Fax 880230 –.
Meals (by arrangement) 10.00 – **7 rm** 25.00/40.00 **s.**

ATS 101 Corporation Rd ☎ 216115/216117

NEW QUAY (Ceinewydd) Dyfed 403 G 27 – pop. 915 – ECD : Wednesday – 01545.

Church St., SA45 9NZ ✆ 560865 (summer only).

London 234 – Aberystwyth 24 – Carmarthen 31 – Fishguard 39.

Park Hall, Cwmtydu, SA44 6LG, SW : 2¾ m. by A 486 and Llangrannog rd ✆ 560306, ←, – TV P. VISA
Meals (by arrangement) 19.50 **st.** 3.25 – **5 rm** 29.00/50.00 **st.** – SB.

NORTHOP HALL Clwyd 402 403 K 24 – pop. 4 155 (Northop) – 01244.

Autolodge Site, Gateway Services, CH7 6HE, A 55 (westbound) ✆ 541597.

London 220 – Chester 9 – Shrewsbury 52.

Autolodge, Gateway Services, A 55 (westbound carriageway), CH5 6HB, ✆ 550011, Fax 550763 – rm TV P – 40. AE VISA.
Meals (dinner only) 10.00/17.50 **st.** and a la carte 3.75 – 6.50 – **38 rm** 33.50/68.00 **st.** – SB.

Forte Travelodge without rest., CH7 6HB, A 55 (eastbound carriageway) ✆ 816473, Reservations (Freephone) 0800 850950 – TV P. AE VISA.
40 rm 33.50 **t.**

NOTTAGE (Drenewydd Yn Notais) M. Glam. 403 I 29 – see Porthcawl.

PANT MAWR Powys 403 I 26 – ✉ Llangurig – 0155 15.

London 219 – Aberystwyth 21 – Shrewsbury 55.

Glansevern Arms, SY18 6SY, on A 44 ✆ 240, ← – TV P
closed 1 week Christmas – **Meals** *(closed Sunday dinner)* (booking essential) (dinner only and Sunday lunch)/dinner 17.75 **t.** 5.00 – **7 rm** 35.00/55.00 **t.** – SB.

PEMBROKE (Penfro) Dyfed 403 F 28 **Great Britain G.** – pop. 15 881 – ECD : Wednesday – 01646.

See : Castle** *AC*.

Defensible Barracks, Pembroke Dock ✆ 683817.

to Republic of Ireland (Rosslare) (B & I Line) 1-2 daily (4 h 15 mn).

Pembroke Visitor Centre, Commons Road, SA71 4EA ✆ 622388.

London 252 – Carmarthen 32 – Fishguard 26.

Underdown Country House, Grove Hill, SA71 5PR, ✆ 683350, Fax 621229, « Antiques and gardens » – TV P. VISA.
Meals *(closed Sunday lunch)* (booking essential) a la carte 17.20/23.50 **t.** 3.25 – **6 rm** 35.00/75.00 **t.** – SB.

at Lamphey E : 1¾ m. on A 4139 – ✉ Pembroke – 01646 :

Court, SA71 5NT, ✆ 672273, Fax 672480, , park – TV P – 80. AE VISA.
Meals (light lunch)/dinner 14.95 **st.** and a la carte – **25 rm** 59.50/105.00 **st.**, 7 suites – SB.

Lamphey Hall, SA71 5NR, ✆ 672394, Fax 672369, – TV P. AE VISA
Meals 6.95/21.55 **t.** and a la carte 4.70 – **10 rm** 35.00/60.00 **t.** – SB.

at Pembroke Dock NW : 2 m. on A 4139 – ✉ 01646 :

Cleddau Bridge, Essex Rd, SA72 6UT, NE : 1 m. by A 4139 on A 477 (at Toll Bridge) ✆ 685961, Fax 685746, heated – TV P – 175
22 rm, 2 suites.

ATS Well Hill Garage, Well Hill ✆ 683217/683836

PENALLY (Penalun) Dyfed 403 F 29 – see Tenby.

PENCOED M. Glam. 403 J 29 – see Bridgend.

PENMACHNO Gwynedd 402 403 I 24 – see Betws-y-Coed.

PONTFAEN Dyfed – see Fishguard.

PONTYPOOL (Pontypwl) Gwent 403 K 28 – 01495.

Pentwyn Farm, Little Mill, NP4 0HQ, NE : 4½ m. by A 472 and A 4042 on A 472 ✆ 785249, Fax 785249, « 16C Longhouse », heated, – P.
closed 2 weeks Christmas – **Meals** (by arrangement) (communal dining) 10.00 – **3 rm** 19.00/36.00 **st.** – SB.

PONTYPRIDD M. Glam. 403 K 29 – 01443.

London 164 – Cardiff 9 – Swansea 40.

Llechwen Hall, Llanfabon, CF37 4HP, NE : 4¼ m. by A 4223 off A 4054 ✆ 742050, Fax 742189, – TV P – 80. AE VISA JCB
Meals 10.95/12.95 **st.** and dinner a la carte 3.95 – **11 rm** 48.50/95.00 **st.** – SB.

ATS Nile St., off Broadway ✆ 403796

PORTH M. Glam. 403 J 29 – ✉ Pontypridd – ☎ 01443.
♦London 168 – ♦Cardiff 13 – ♦Swansea 45.

Heritage Park, Coed Cae Rd, Trehafod, CF37 2NP, on A 4058 ☎ 687057, Fax 687060 – rest TV ☎ & P – 200
50 rm.

PORTHCAWL M. Glam. 403 I 29 – pop. 16 099 – ECD : Wednesday – ☎ 01656.
The Old Police Station, John St., CF36 3DT ☎ 786639/782211.
♦London 183 – ♦Cardiff 28 – ♦Swansea 18.

Atlantic, West Drive, CF36 3LT, ☎ 785011, Fax 771877, ← – TV ☎ P. AE VISA
Meals (in bar Sunday dinner and lunchtimes)/dinner 11.50 **t.** and a la carte 4.70 – **18 rm** 46.50/69.00 **t.** – SB.

at Nottage N : 1 m. by A 4229 – ✉ Porthcawl – ☎ 01656 :

Rose and Crown, Heol-y-Capel, CF36 3ST, N : 1 m. by A 4229 ☎ 784850, Fax 772345 – TV ☎ P. AE VISA.
Meals (carving rest.) 10.00 **t.** 4.65 – **8 rm** 35.95/39.95 **t.**

PORTHGAIN Dyfed 403 E 28 – see St. Davids.

PORTMEIRION Gwynedd 402 403 H 25 **Great Britain G.** – ☎ 01766.
See : Village ★ *AC.*
♦London 245 – Caernarfon 23 – Colwyn Bay 40 – Dolgellau 24.

Portmeirion , LL48 6ET, ☎ 770228, Fax 771331, ← village and estuary, « Private Italianate village, antiques », heated, , park, – rest TV ☎ P – 100. AE VISA.
closed 8 January-3 February – **Meals** *(closed Monday lunch)* 14.00/26.00 **st.** 5.00 – 8.50 – **26 rm** 70.00/115.00 **st.**, 8 suites – SB.

PORT TALBOT W. Glam. 403 I 29 – pop. 47 299 – ☎ 01639.
♦London 193 – ♦Cardiff 35 – ♦Swansea 11.

Travel Inn, Baglan Rd, SA12 8ES, M 4 Junction 42 ☎ 813017, Fax 823096 – rm TV & P. AE VISA.
Meals (Beefeater grill) a la carte approx. 16.00 **t.** 5.60 – 4.95 – **40 rm** 33.50 **st.**

ATS Afan Way ☎ 883895/885747

PRESTATYN Clwyd 402 403 J 23 – ☎ 01745.

Traeth Ganol, 41 Beach Rd West, LL19 7LL, ☎ 853594, Fax 886687 – TV & P. VISA.
Meals 12.50 **t.** 4.25 – **9 rm** 28.00/42.00 **t.** – SB.

PRESTEIGNE Powys 403 K 27 – pop. 2 141 – ECD : Thursday – ☎ 01544.
The Old Market Hall, Broad St., LD8 2AW ☎ 260193 (summer only).
♦London 159 – Llandrindod Wells 20 – Shrewsbury 39.

Radnorshire Arms (Forte), High St., LD8 2BE, ☎ 267406, Fax 260418, – TV ☎ P – 25
16 rm.

PUMSAINT Dyfed 403 I 27 – ☎ 01558.
♦London 208 – Carmarthen 28 – ♦Swansea 38.

Seguendo di Stagioni, Harford, SA19 8DT, NW : 2 m. on A 482 ☎ 650671, Fax 650671 – P. VISA
closed Monday and Tuesday – **Meals** - Italian (dinner only and Sunday lunch) 15.00 **t.** and a la carte 4.95.

PWLLHELI Gwynedd 402 403 G 25 – pop. 3 974 – ☎ 01758.
Golf road ☎ 701644.
Y Maes, Station Road, LL53 5HG ☎ 613000 (summer only).
♦London 261 – Aberystwyth 73 – Caernarfon 21.

Plas Bodegroes (Chown) with rm, LL53 5TH, NW : 1 3/4 m. on A 497 ☎ 612363, Fax 701247, « Georgian country house », , park – TV ☎ P. AE VISA
closed Monday except Bank Holidays and November-February – **Meals** (booking essential) (dinner only) 30.00/36.00 **t.** 5.50 – **8 rm** (dinner included) 75.00/180.00 **t.** – SB
Spec. Warm lambs tongues with mustard dressing, Turbot with herb crust, smoked prawn sauce, Figs in port with white chocolate ice cream.

RAGLAN Gwent 403 L 28 – ✉ Abergavenny – ☎ 01873.
♦London 154 – Gloucester 34 – Newport 18 – ♦Swansea 58.

Clytha Arms with rm, NP7 9BW, W : 3 m. on Clytha rd (old Abergavenny Rd) ☎ 840206, Fax 840206 – rest TV P. VISA
Meals *(closed Monday lunch)* (in bar Sunday dinner) a la carte 12.75/21.50 **st.** 3.65 – **3 rm** 35.00/60.00 **st.**

REDWICK Gwent 403 L 29 – see Newport.

RHAYADER (Rhaeadr) Powys 403 J 27 Great Britain G. – pop. 1 626 – ☎ 01597.

Envir. : Elan Valley★★, SW : by B 4518.

ℹ The Leisure Centre, North St., LD6 5BU ☎ 810591 (summer only)

◆London 180 – Brecon 34 – Hereford 46 – Shrewsbury 60.

Elan, West St., LD6 5AF, ☎ 810373 – TV ☎ P. AE VISA
Meals *(closed lunch Thursday and dinner Sunday and Monday to non residents)* (bar lunch)/dinner 8.95/11.95 ▮ 4.00 – **11 rm** ☐ 16.50/42.00 **t.** – SB.

RHOSCOLYN Gwynedd 402 403 G 24 Great Britain G. – pop. 539 – ✉ Holyhead – ☎ 01407.

Envir. : Isle of Anglesey★★.

◆London 269 – Bangor 25 – Caernarfon 30 – Holyhead 5.5.

Old Rectory ⑤, LL65 2DQ, ☎ 860214, ≤, ⚘ – ⊬ TV P. VISA
closed 21 to 3 January – **Meals** (communal dining) 15.00 **st.** – **5 rm** ☐ 31.50/51.00 **st.** – SB.

RHOS-ON-SEA (Llandrillo-Yn-Rhos) Clwyd 402 403 I 24 – see Colwyn Bay.

RHYDLEWIS Dyfed 403 G 27 – ✉ Llandysul – ☎ 01239.

◆London 235 – Carmarthen 26 – Fishguard 38.

Broniwan ⑤, SA44 5PF, NE : 1/4 m. by Plump rd, taking first turn right onto unmarked road ☎ 851261, « Working farm », ⚘, park – ⊬ P
Meals (by arrangement) 9.50 **s.** – **3 rm** ☐ 17.00/33.00.

ROEWEN Gwynedd – see Conwy.

I prezzi — Per ogni chiarimento sui prezzi qui riportati, consultate le spiegazioni alle pagine dell'introduzione.

ROSSETT (Yr Orsedd) Clwyd 402 403 L 24 – pop. 2 936 – ☎ 01244.

◆London 203 – Chester 8 – Shrewsbury 39.

Llyndir Hall ⑤, Llyndir Lane, LL12 0AY, N : 3/4 m. by B 5445 ☎ 571648, Fax 571258, « Part Strawberry Gothic country house », ♞, ▣, ⚘ – ⊬ rm TV ☎ ♿ P – ♚ 150. AE ⓪ VISA JCB. ✻
Meals (bar lunch Saturday) 14.95/28.50 **st.** and a la carte ▮ 7.00 – **37 rm** ☐ 74.00/110.00 **st.**, 1 suite – SB.

Rossett Hall, Chester Rd, LL12 0DE, ☎ 571000, Fax 571505, ⚘ – ⊬ rm TV ☎ ♿ P – ♚ 120. AE ⓪ VISA JCB. ✻
Meals (closed Saturday lunch) 19.95 **t.** ▮ 4.95 – **29 rm** ☐ 68.00/105.00 **t.**, 1 suite.

RUTHIN (Rhuthun) Clwyd 402 403 K 24 – pop. 5 029 – ECD : Thursday – ☎ 01824.

Ruthin-Pwllglas ☎ 702296.

ℹ Ruthin Craft Centre, Park Rd, LL15 1BB ☎ 703992.

◆London 210 – Birkenhead 31 – Chester 23 – Shrewsbury 46.

Ruthin Castle, Corwen Rd, LL15 2NU, ☎ 702664, Fax 705978, « Reconstructed Victorian and part medieval castle », ⚘, ⚘, park – ⧉ TV ☎ P – ♚ 140. AE ⓪ VISA. ✻
Meals 8.25/16.95 **t.** and dinner a la carte ▮ 6.25 – **62 rm** ☐ 65.00/85.00 **st.** – SB.

Eyarth Station ⑤, Llanfair Dyffryn Clwyd, LL15 2EE, S : 1 3/4 m. by A 525 off Pwllglas rd ☎ 703643, Fax 707464, ≤, ⚓ heated, ⚘ – ⊬ rm P. VISA
Meals 12.00 ▮ 4.00 – **6 rm** ☐ 25.00/44.00.

ST. ASAPH (Llanelwy) Clwyd 402 403 J 24 Great Britain G. – pop. 3 399 – ECD : Thursday – ☎ 01745.

See : Cathedral★.

Envir. : Rhuddlan Castle★★, N : 2 1/2 m. by A 525 and A 547 – Denbigh Castle★, S : 6 m. by A 525 and A 543.

◆London 225 – Chester 29 – Shrewsbury 59.

Oriel House, Upper Denbigh Rd, LL17 0LW, S : 3/4 m. on A 525 ☎ 582716, Fax 582716, ⚘ – TV ☎ P – ♚ 250. AE ⓪ VISA
Meals 10.00/21.00 **t.** and a la carte ▮ 3.50 – **19 rm** ☐ 40.00/66.00 **t.** – SB.

Plas Elwy, The Roe, LL17 0LT, N : 1/2 m. at junction of A 525 with A 55 ☎ 582263, Fax 583864 – TV ☎ P. AE ⓪ VISA. ✻
closed 26 to 30 December – **Meals** *(closed Sunday dinner to non residents)* (dinner only and Sunday lunch)/dinner 12.95 **t.** and a la carte ▮ 4.50 – **13 rm** ☐ 35.00/60.00 **t.**

ST.BRIDES-SUPER-ELY S. Glam. – pop. 85 – ☎ 01446.

◆London 155 – ◆Bristol 51 – ◆Cardiff 9 – Newport 22.

Sant-Y-Nyll ⑤ without rest., CF5 6EZ, ☎ 760209, Fax 760209, ≤, ⚘, park – TV P. AE. ✻
Meals (by arrangement) – **6 rm** ☐ 25.00/50.00 **st.** – SB.

ST. CLEARS (Sancler) Dyfed 403 G 28 – pop. 3 014 – ECD : Wednesday – ☎ 01994.
♦London 229 – Carmarthen 9 – Fishguard 37.

- **Forge Motel,** SA33 4NA, E : 1 m. on A 40 ☎ 230300, Fax 230300, – TV ☎ P. VISA
  closed 25 and 26 December – **Meals** (grill rest.) a la carte 5.65/16.75 **t.** 3.95 – **18 rm** 35.00/55.00 **t.**

ST. DAVIDS (Tyddewi) Dyfed 403 E 28 **Great Britain G.** – pop. 1 959 – ECD : Wednesday – ☎ 01437.
See : Town★ – Cathedral★★ – Bishops Palace★ *AC.*
St. Davids City, Whitesands Bay ☎ 721751.
♦London 266 – Carmarthen 46 – Fishguard 16.

- **Old Cross,** Cross Sq., SA62 6SP, ☎ 720387, – rm TV ☎ P. VISA
  March-October – **Meals** (dinner only) 14.50 **t.** and a la carte 3.50 – **16 rm** 35.00/65.00 **t.** – SB.
- **Ramsey House,** Lower Moor, SA62 6RP, SW : ½ m. on Porth Cleis Rd. ☎ 720321, –
  Meals 12.50 **st.** 4.05 – **7 rm** 45.00/73.00 **st.** – SB.

  at Berea NE : 4½ m. by A 487, B 4583 and Llanrian rd – ✉ St. Davids – ☎ 01348 :

- **Cwmwdig Water**, SA62 6DW, NE : ½ m. ☎ 831434, ←, – P. VISA
  Meals (by arrangement) 14.00 **st.** 4.10 – **12 rm** (dinner included) 34.00/68.00 **t.** – SB.

  at Porthgain NE : 7¾ m. by A 487 via Llanrian – ✉ Haverfordwest – ☎ 01348 :

- Harbour Lights, SA62 5BN, ☎ 831549.

ST.DOGMAELS Dyfed 403 G 27 – see Cardigan.

SARN PARK SERVICE AREA M. Glam. – ✉ Bridgend – ☎ 01656.
M 4, Junction 36, CF32 9SY ☎ 654906.
♦London 174 – ♦Cardiff 17 – ♦Swansea 20.

- **Forte Travelodge** without rest, CF32 9RW, M 4 junction 36 ☎ 659218, Reservations (Freephone) 0800 850950 – TV ♿ P. AE VISA.
  40 rm 33.50 **t.**

SAUNDERSFOOT Dyfed 403 F 28 – pop. 2 666 – ECD : Wednesday – ☎ 01834.
♦London 245 – Carmarthen 25 – Fishguard 34 – Tenby 3.

- **St. Brides,** St. Brides Hill, SA69 9NH, ☎ 812304, Fax 813303, ←, heated – rm rest TV ☎ P – 100. AE VISA
  closed 2 to 14 January – **Meals** 11.50/22.00 **st.** and a la carte 6.00 – **43 rm** 56.00/90.00 **st.**, 2 suites – SB.
- **Vine Farm,** The Ridgeway, SA69 9LA, ☎ 813543, – TV P
  April-October – **Meals** (by arrangement) – **5 rm** 20.00/43.00 **st.** – SB.

SEALAND Clwyd – ✉ Deeside – ☎ 01244.

- **Gateway to Wales,** Welsh Rd, CH5 2HX, at junction of A 550 with A 548 ☎ 830332, Fax 836190, – TV ☎ ♿ P – 140. AE VISA.
  Meals 7.00/14.50 **t.** and a la carte 4.50 – 6.95 – **38 rm** 45.00/60.00, 1 suite – SB.

SEION Gwynedd 402 403 H 24 see Caernarfon.

SOUTHERNDOWN M. Glam. 403 J 29 see Bridgend.

SWANSEA (Abertawe) W. Glam. 403 I 29 **Great Britain G.** – pop. 181 906 – ECD : Thursday – ☎ 01792.
See : Maritime Quarter★ B – Maritime and Industrial Museum★ B **M.**
Envir. : Gower Peninsula★ : Cefn Bryn (✱★★) – Rhossili (←★★★) W : by A 4067 A.
Morriston, 160 Clasemont Rd ☎ 771079, A – Clyne, 120 Owls Lodge Lane, Mayals ☎ 401989, A – Langland Bay ☎ 366023, A – Fairwood Park, Blackhills Lane, Upper Killay ☎ 203648, A – Inco, Clydach ☎ 844216, A.
to Republic of Ireland (Cork) (Swansea Cork Ferries) (10 h).
Singleton St., SA1 3QG ☎ 468321.
♦London 191 – ♦Birmingham 136 – ♦Bristol 82 – ♦Cardiff 40 – ♦Liverpool 187 – ♦Stoke-on-Trent 175.

Plan on next page

- **Swansea Marriott,** Maritime Quarter, SA1 3SS, ☎ 642020, Fax 650345, ←, – rm TV ☎ ♿ P – 250. AE VISA B **e**
  Meals 12.95/15.95 **s.** and a la carte 7.25 – 10.25 – **117 rm** 92.00/116.00 **st.** – SB.
- Forte Crest, 39 The Kingsway, SA1 5LS, ☎ 651074, Fax 456044, – rm TV ☎ P – 250 B **a**
  93 rm, 6 suites.

SWANSEA

Street	Square	No.
College Street	B	13
Kingsway (The)	B	
Oxford Street	B	
Parc Tawe Shopping Centre	B	
Princess Way	B	
Quadrant Centre	B	
St. David's Square	B	
Alexandra Road	B	2
Belle Vue Way	B	4
Carmarthen Road	B	7
Christina Street	B	9
Clarence Terrace	B	10
Clase Road	A	12
De La Beche Street	B	14
Dillwyn Street	B	15
East Bank Way	B	16
Fabian Way	B	17
Grove Place	B	18
Martin Street	A	19
Nelson Street	B	20
New Cut Bridge	B	21
Pen-y-Graig Road	A	22
Plasmarl By-Pass	A	23
Ravenhill Road	A	24
Station Road	A	25
St. Helen's Road	A	27
St. Mary's Square	B	28
Tawe Bridge	B	29
Terrace Road	A	30
Union Street	B	32
Uplands Crescent	A	34
Walter Road	A	36
Wellington Street	B	37
West Way	B	38
William Street	B	39
Woodfield Street	A	40

Zum besseren Verständnis der Stadpläne lesen Sie bitte die Zeichenerklärung in der Einleitung.

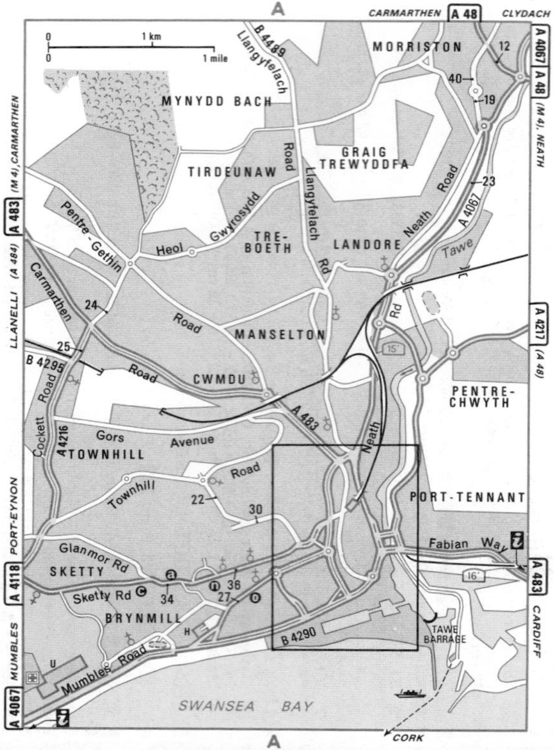

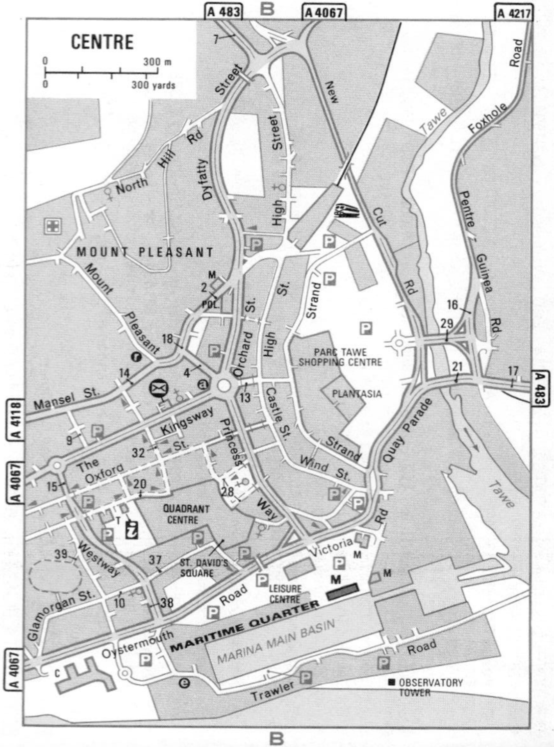

Fforest, Pontardulais Rd, Fforestfach, SA5 4BA, NW : 3 ½ m. on A 483 ℘ 588711, Fax 586219, – rm – 200. A
Meals *(closed Saturday lunch)* 10.00/20.00 **t.** and a la carte – **34 rm** 49.50/55.00 **t.** – SB.

Beaumont, 72-73 Walter Rd, SA1 4QA, ℘ 643956, Fax 643044 – . A **n**
Meals *(closed Sunday lunch)* (dinner only) (lunch by arrangement) 12.75/18.75 **t.** and a la carte 5.50 – **17 rm** 47.50/59.50 **t.**

Windsor Lodge, Mount Pleasant, SA1 6EG, ℘ 642158, Fax 648996 – . B **r**
closed 25 and 26 December – **Meals** (lunch and Sunday dinner by arrangement)/dinner 15.00/25.00 3.75 – **18 rm** 43.00/70.00 **t.** – SB.

Tredilion House, 26 Uplands Cres., Uplands, SA2 0PB, ℘ 470766, Fax 456064 – . A **a**
Meals (dinner only) 12.00 **st.** 3.50 – **7 rm** 34.00/48.00 **st.** – SB.

Alexander, 3 Sketty Rd, Uplands, SA2 0EU, ℘ 470045, Fax 476012 – rest . A **c**
closed 24 December-2 January – **Meals** (by arrangement) **6 rm** 30.00/42.00 **st.**

Annie's, 56 St. Helen's Rd, SA1 4BE, ℘ 655603 – A **o**
closed Monday except summer and Sunday – **Meals** (booking essential) (dinner only) 17.50/19.50 **st.** 4.45.

at Swansea Enterprise Park NE : 4 m. by A 4067 - A - off A 48 – ✉ Swansea – ☎ 01792 :

Hilton National, Phoenix Way, SA7 9EG, ℘ 310330, Fax 797535, – rm rest – 180.
Meals 11.00/17.50 **t.** and dinner a la carte – 9.25 – **118 rm** 55.00/65.00 **t.**, 2 suites –.

at Mumbles SW : 7 ¾ m. by A 4067 – ✉ Swansea – ☎ 01792 :

Norton House, 17 Norton Rd, SA3 5TQ, ℘ 404891, Fax 403210, – .
Meals (lunch by arrangement)/dinner 19.50/23.50 **t.** 4.95 – **15 rm** 55.00/80.00 **t.** – SB.

Osborne (Jarvis), Rotherslade Rd, Langland Bay, SA3 4QL, W : ¾ m. ℘ 366274, Fax 363100, – – 50.
Meals (bar lunch Monday to Saturday)/dinner 32.00 **t.** and a la carte 6.00 – **32 rm** 71.00/95.00 **t.** – SB.

Hillcrest, 1 Higher Lane, SA3 4NS, W : ¾ m. on Langland rd ℘ 363700, Fax 363768 – .
closed first 3 weeks January – **Meals** *(closed Sunday dinner and Monday to non-residents)* (dinner only and Sunday lunch)/dinner a la carte 15.25/21.70 **t.** 6.50 – **7 rm** 50.00/64.00 **t.**

Wittemberg, 2 Rotherslade Rd, Langland, SA3 4QN, W : ¾ m. ℘ 369696, Fax 366995 – .
closed January – **Meals** 10.50 **st.** 2.00 – **11 rm** 32.00/52.00 **st.** – SB.

at Llanrhidian W : 10 ½ m. by A 4118 – A – and B 4271 on B 4295 – ✉ Reynoldston – ☎ 01792 :

Fairyhill, Reynoldston, SA3 1BS, W : 2 ½ m. by B 4295 (Llangennith rd) ℘ 390139, Fax 391358, , park – – 35.
Meals 13.95/24.50 **st.** – **8 rm** 65.00/120.00 **st.** – SB.

ATS 139 Neath Rd, Hafod ℘ 456379

SWANSEA SERVICE AREA W. Glam. – ☎ 01792.

Pavilion Lodge without rest., Penllergaer, SA4 1GT, M 4 : junction 47 ℘ 894894, Fax 898806 – .
4.00 – **50 rm** 31.95/35.95 **st.**

TALGARTH Powys 403 K 28 – pop. 1 818 – ☎ 01874.

♦London 182 – Brecon 10 – Hereford 29 – ♦Swansea 53.

Olde Masons Arms, LD3 0BB, ℘ 711688 – .
Meals (bar lunch)/dinner 10.50 **st.** and a la carte 2.95 – **7 rm** 26.50/49.00 **st.** – SB.

TALSARNAU Gwynedd 402 403 H 25 – pop. 647 – ✉ Harlech – ☎ 01766.

♦London 236 – Caernafon 33 – Chester 67 – Dolgellau 25.

Maes-y-Neuadd, LL47 6YA, S : 1 ½ m. by A 496 off B 4573 ℘ 780200, Fax 780211, « Part 14C country house », , park – rest – 25.
Meals 14.00/21.00 **st.** 4.50 – **15 rm** (dinner included) 69.00/192.00 **st.**, 1 suite – SB.

Tegfan, Llandecwyn, LL47 6YG, N : 1 ¼ m. on A 496 ℘ 771354, – .
Meals (by arrangement) 10.00 **t.** – **3 rm** 14.00/32.00 **s.**, 1 suite.

TAL-Y-BONT Gwynedd 402 403 I 24 – see Conwy.

TAL-Y-LLYN Gwynedd 402 403 I 25 – pop. 623 (inc. Corris) – ✉ Tywyn – ☎ 01654.

♦London 224 – Dolgellau 9 – Shrewsbury 60.

- **Tynycornel,** LL36 9AJ, on B 4405 ✆ 782282, Fax 782679, ≤ Tal-y-Llyn lake and mountains, heated, – rest TV ☎ P. AE VISA
  Meals 10.00/17.50 **t.** 5.15 – **16 rm** 60.00/170.00 **t.**, 1 suite.

TENBY (Dinbych-Y-Pysgod) Dyfed 403 F 28 **Great Britain G.** – pop. 4 808 – ECD : Wednesday – ☎ 01834.

See : Town★ – Harbour and Seafront★★.

Envir. : Caldey Island★, S : by boat.

18 The Burrows ✆ 842787/842978.

The Croft, SA70 8AP ✆ 842402.

♦London 247 – Carmarthen 27 – Fishguard 36.

- **Waterwynch House**, Narberth Rd, SA70 8TJ, N : 1 ¾ m. on A 478 ✆ 842464, Fax 845076, ≤, , park – rest TV ☎ P
  mid March-mid November – **Meals** *(closed Sunday dinner)* (dinner only and Sunday lunch)/dinner 15.00 7.00 – **14 rm** 48.00/96.00 **t.**, 3 suites – SB.
- **Atlantic,** Esplanade, SA70 7DU, ✆ 842881, Fax 842881, , – TV ☎ P. AE VISA.
  closed 23 December-5 January – **Meals** (bar lunch Monday to Saturday)/dinner 16.00 **t.** and a la carte 5.40 – **40 rm** 51.00/90.00 **t.** – SB.
- **Fourcroft,** North Beach, SA70 8AP, ✆ 842886, Fax 842888, ≤, , heated, – TV ☎ – 80. VISA
  Meals (bar lunch)/dinner 18.00 **st.** 4.50 – **46 rm** 34.00/78.00 – SB.
- **Broadmead,** Heywood Lane, SA70 8DA, NW : ¾ m. ✆ 842641, Fax 845757, – TV ☎ P.
  closed January, February and November – **Meals** (bar lunch)/dinner 15.00 **t.** and a la carte 3.75 – **20 rm** 31.00/52.00 **st.** – SB.
- **Buckingham,** Esplanade, SA70 6DU, ✆ 842622, ≤ – rm TV. VISA
  April-October – **Meals** 9.50 **st.** 5.50 – **8 rm** 24.00/38.00 **st.** – SB.
- **Harbour Heights** without rest., 11 The Croft, SA70 8AP, ✆ 842132, ≤ – TV ☎. VISA
  March-November – **9 rm** 30.00/50.00 **st.**
- **Myrtle House,** St. Marys St., SA70 7HW, ✆ 842508 – TV. VISA.
  closed December – **Meals** 7.50 3.00 – **8 rm** (dinner included) 27.00/58.00 **s.** – SB.

at Penally (Penalun) SW : 2 m. by A 4139 – ✉ Tenby – ☎ 01834 :

- **Penally Abbey**, SA70 7PY, ✆ 843033, Fax 844714, ≤, TV ☎ P. VISA.
  Meals (dinner only) 22.00 **st.** and a la carte 4.95 – **12 rm** (dinner included) 80.00/140.00 **st.**

THORNHILL S. Glam. 403 K 29 – see Cardiff.

THREE COCKS (Aberllynfi) Powys 403 K 27 – ✉ Brecon – ☎ 01497.

♦London 184 – Brecon 11 – Hereford 25 – ♦Swansea 55.

- XX **Three Cocks** with rm, LD3 0SL, on A 438 ✆ 847215, « Part 15C inn », – P. VISA.
  closed December to 10 February – **Meals** *(closed Sunday lunch and Tuesday)* 24.00/32.00 **st.** and a la carte 4.00 – **7 rm** 40.00/62.00 **st.** – SB.

TINTERN (Tyndyrn) Gwent 403 404 L 28 **Great Britain G.** – pop. 749 – ECD : Wednesday – ✉ Chepstow – ☎ 01291.

See : Abbey★★ *AC*.

Envir. : Wye Valley★.

♦London 137 – ♦Bristol 23 – Gloucester 40 – Newport 22.

- **Beaufort** (Jarvis), NP6 6SF, on A 466 ✆ 689777, Fax 689727, – TV ☎ P – 100. AE VISA
  Meals (bar lunch Monday to Saturday)/dinner 17.75 **t.** 6.50 – **24 rm** 69.00/92.00 **t.** – SB.
- **Royal George,** NP6 6SF, on A 466 ✆ 689205, Fax 689448, – TV ☎ P. AE VISA JCB
  Meals (bar lunch)/dinner 16.50 **t.** and a la carte 5.95 – **19 rm** 59.60/86.50 **t.** – SB.
- XX **Parva Farmhouse** with rm, NP6 6SQ, on A 466 ✆ 689411, Fax 689557 – TV ☎ P. VISA
  Meals (dinner only) 16.00 **st.** and a la carte 4.80 – **9 rm** 39.00/58.00 **st.** – SB.

TREARDDUR BAY Gwynedd 402 403 G 24 – ✉ Holyhead – ☎ 01407.

- **Trearddur Bay,** LL65 2UN, ✆ 860301, Fax 861181, , – TV ☎ P – 120. AE VISA JCB
  Meals (bar lunch Monday to Saturday)/dinner 18.00 **t.** and a la carte 5.00 – **31 rm** 68.00/100.00 **t.** – SB.

TREFRIW Gwynedd 402 403 I 24 – see Llanrwst.

TRESAITH Dyfed – see Aberporth.

USK (Brynbuga) Gwent 403 L 28 **Great Britain G.** – pop. 2 187 – ECD : Wednesday – ☎ 01291.
Exc. : Raglan Castle★ *AC*, NE : 7 m. by A 472, A 449 and A 40.
Alice Springs, Bettws Newydd ☎ (01873) 880772.
◆London 144 – ◆Bristol 30 – Gloucester 39 – Newport 10.

- **Glen-yr-Afon House,** Pontypool Rd, NP5 1SY, ☎ 672302, Fax 672597, – – 200.
Meals 16.00 **t.** and a la carte 5.70 – **28 rm** 52.85/64.65 **t.**

at Llangybi S : 2½ m. on Llangybi rd – ✉ Usk – ☎ 01633 :

- **Cwrt Bleddyn,** NP5 1PG, S : 1 m. ☎ 450521, Fax 450220, park, squash – rm – 200.
Meals 14.95/22.50 **t.** and a la carte 6.50 – **32 rm** 73.50/102.00 **t.**, 4 suites – SB.

WELSH HOOK Dyfed – see Fishguard.

WELSHPOOL (Trallwng) Powys 402 403 K 26 **Great Britain G.** – pop. 5 900 – ECD : Thursday – ☎ 01938.
Envir. : Powis Castle★★, S : 1 m. by A 483.
Golfa Hill ☎ 83249.
The Flash Leisure Centre, Salop Road SY21 ☎ 552043.
◆London 182 – ◆Birmingham 64 – Chester 45 – Shrewsbury 19.

- **Royal Oak,** The Cross, SY21 7DG, ☎ 552217, Fax 552217 – – 150.
Meals 9.50/14.95 **t.** and a la carte 4.50 – **25 rm** 40.00/75.00 **t.** – SB.
- **Moat Farm** , SY21 8SE, S : 2¼ m. on A 483 ☎ 553179, « Working farm », park – rest
March-October – **Meals** (by arrangement) (communal dining) 11.00 **st.** – **3 rm** (dinner included) 34.00/60.00 **st.** – SB.

at Guilsfield N : 3 m. by A 490 on B 4392 – ✉ Welshpool – ☎ 01938 :

- **Lower Trelydan** , SY21 9PH, S : ¾ m. by B 4392 on unmarked rd ☎ 553105, « 16C farmhouse, working farm », park – rm
Meals (by arrangement) 11.00 **t.** 3.00 – **3 rm** 26.00/36.00 **t.**

WHITEBROOK Gwent – see Monmouth.

WHITLAND (Hendy-Gwyn) Dyfed 403 G 28 – pop. 1 518 – ECD : Wednesday – ☎ 01994.
◆London 235 – Carmarthen 15 – Haverfordwest 17.

- Cilpost Farm , SA34 0RP, N : 1 ¼ m. by North Rd ☎ 240280, ←, « Working dairy farm », –
7 rm.

ATS Emporium Garage, Market St. ☎ 240587

WOLF'S CASTLE (Cas-Blaidd) Dyfed 403 F 28 – ✉ Haverfordwest – ☎ 01437.
◆London 258 – Fishguard 7 – Haverfordwest 8.

- **Wolfscastle Country,** SA62 5LZ, on A 40 ☎ 741225, Fax 741383, squash – rest
Meals (lunch by arrangement Monday to Saturday)/dinner a la carte 13.85/21.15 **t.** 4.40 – **20 rm** 36.00/70.00 **t.** – SB.

WREXHAM (Wrecsam) Clwyd 402 403 L 24 **Great Britain G.** – pop. 39 929 – ECD : Wednesday – ☎ 01978.
See : St. Giles Church★.
Envir. : Erddig★ *AC*, SW : 2 m..
Holt Rd ☎ 261033 – Chirk G & C.C. ☎ (01691 774407).
Lambpit St., LL11 1AY ☎ 292015.
◆London 192 – Chester 12 – Shrewsbury 28.

- **Llwyn Onn** , Cefn Rd, LL13 0NY, 2½ m. by A 534 ☎ 261225, Telex 261225, Fax 261225, ←, – rm – 25.
Meals 13.50 **st.** and a la carte 3.75 – **13 rm** 52.00/90.00 **t.** – SB.
- **Cross Lanes,** Marchwiel, LL13 0TF, SE : 3½ m. on A 525 ☎ 780555, Fax 780568, park – – 100.
closed 25 and 26 December – **Meals** (bar lunch Saturday) 11.90/21.95 **st.** and a la carte 4.95 – 4.50 – **15 rm** 54.00/78.00 **st.** – SB.
- **Forte Travelodge** without rest., Croes-Foel roundabout, Rhostyllen, LL14 4EJ, SW : 2½ m. on A 483 (Wrexham bypass) ☎ 365705, Reservations (Freephone) 0800 850950 – **32 rm** 33.50 **t.**
- **Travel Inn,** Chester Rd, LL12 8PW, NE : 2½ m. by A 483 on B 5445 ☎ 853214 – rm
Meals (grill rest.) a la carte approx. 16.00 **t.** – 4.95 – **38 rm** 33.50 **t.**

ATS Dolydd Rd, Croesnewydd ☎ 352301/352928 ATS Eagles Meadow, Clwyd (ASDA) ☎ 366510

Scotland

Place with at least :

a hotel or restaurant .... ● Tongue
a pleasant hotel or restaurant .. 🏨, 🏠, ✕
a quiet, secluded hotel .... 🐎
a restaurant with .... ✿, ✿✿, ✿✿✿, **Meals** (**M**)
See this town for establishments located in its vicinity .... **ABERDEEN**

La località possiede come minimo :

una risorsa alberghiera .... ● Tongue
Albergo o ristorante ameno .... 🏨, 🏠, ✕
un albergo molto tranquillo, isolato ...... 🐎
un'ottima tavola con . ✿, ✿✿, ✿✿✿, **Meals** (**M**)
La località raggruppa nel suo testo le risorse dei dintorni .... **ABERDEEN**

Localité offrant au moins :

une ressource hôtelière .... ● Tongue
un hôtel ou restaurant agréable 🏨, 🏠, ✕
un hôtel très tranquille, isolé .... 🐎
une bonne table à ✿, ✿✿, ✿✿✿, **Meals** (**M**)
Localité groupant dans le texte les ressources de ses environs .. **ABERDEEN**

Ort mit mindestens :

einem Hotel oder Restaurant ..... ● Tongue
ein angenehmes Hotel oder Restaurant 🏨, 🏠, ✕
einem sehr ruhigen und abgelegenen Hotel 🐎
einem Restaurant mit ✿, ✿✿, ✿✿✿, **Meals** (**M**)
Ort mit Angaben über Hotels und Restaurants in seiner Umgebung .... **ABERDEEN**

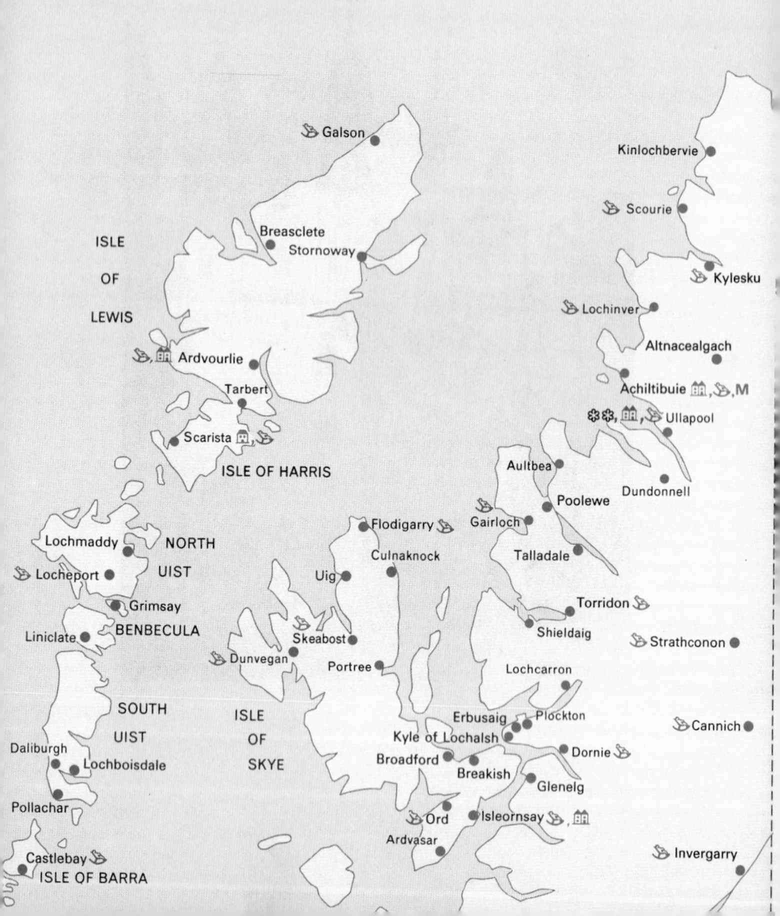

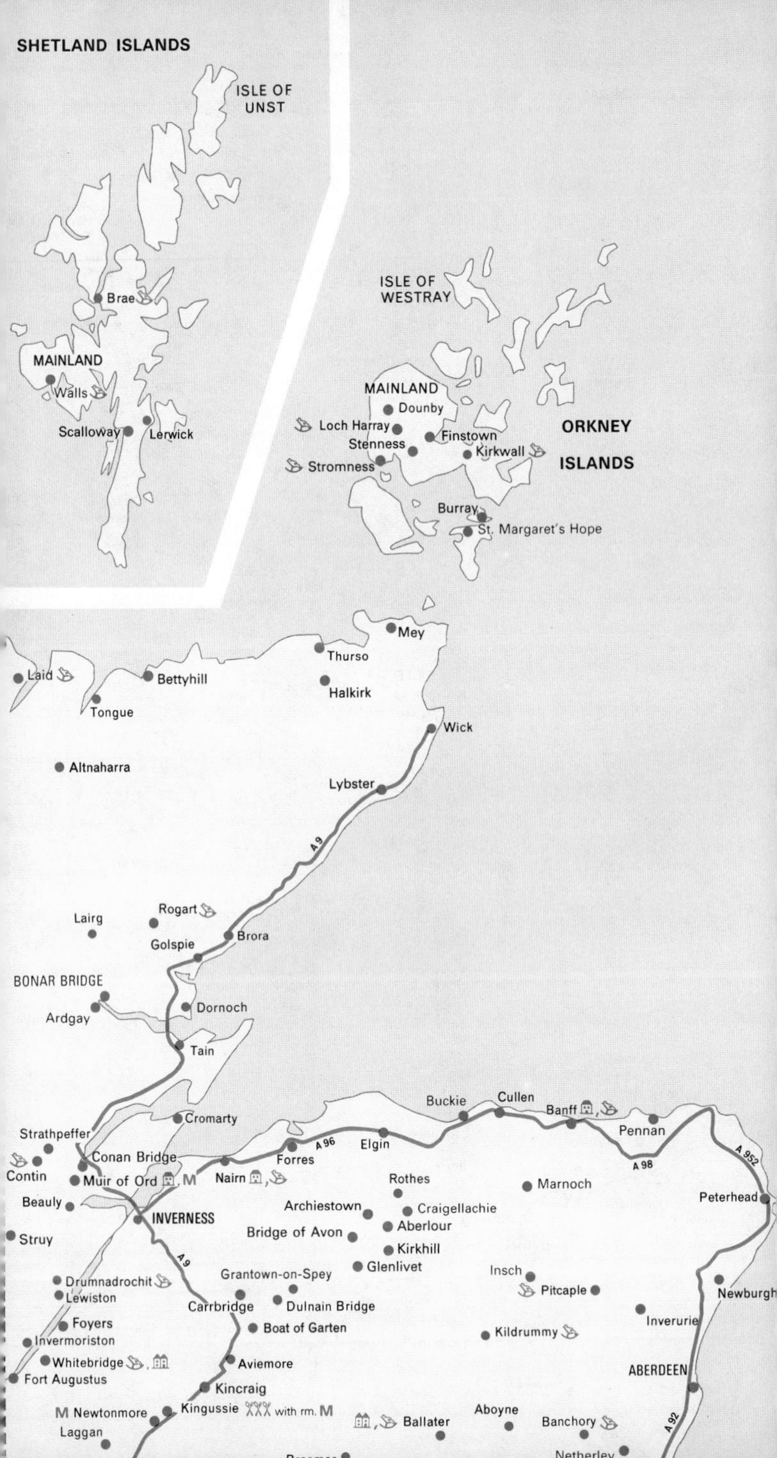

SHETLAND ISLANDS
ISLE OF UNST
Brae
MAINLAND
Walls
Scalloway
Lerwick
ISLE OF WESTRAY
MAINLAND
Dounby
Loch Harray
Finstown
Stenness
Kirkwall
Stromness
ORKNEY ISLANDS
Burray
St. Margaret's Hope
Mey
Thurso
Laid
Bettyhill
Halkirk
Tongue
Wick
Altnaharra
Lybster
A9
Rogart
Lairg
Brora
Golspie
BONAR BRIDGE
Ardgay
Dornoch
Tain
Buckie
Cullen
Banff
Pennan
Cromarty
Strathpeffer
A 96
Elgin
Forres
Conan Bridge
A 98
A 952
Contin
Muir of Ord
M
Nairn
Rothes
Marnoch
Beauly
Archiestown
Craigellachie
Peterhead
INVERNESS
Aberlour
Bridge of Avon
Struy
Kirkhill
A9
Glenlivet
Insch
Grantown-on-Spey
Drumnadrochit
Pitcaple
Newburgh
Lewiston
Carrbridge
Dulnain Bridge
Inverurie
Foyers
Boat of Garten
Kildrummy
Invermoriston
Whitebridge
Aviemore
ABERDEEN
Fort Augustus
Kincraig
M Newtonmore
Kingussie
with rm. M
Aboyne
Ballater
Banchory
A 92
Laggan
Netherley

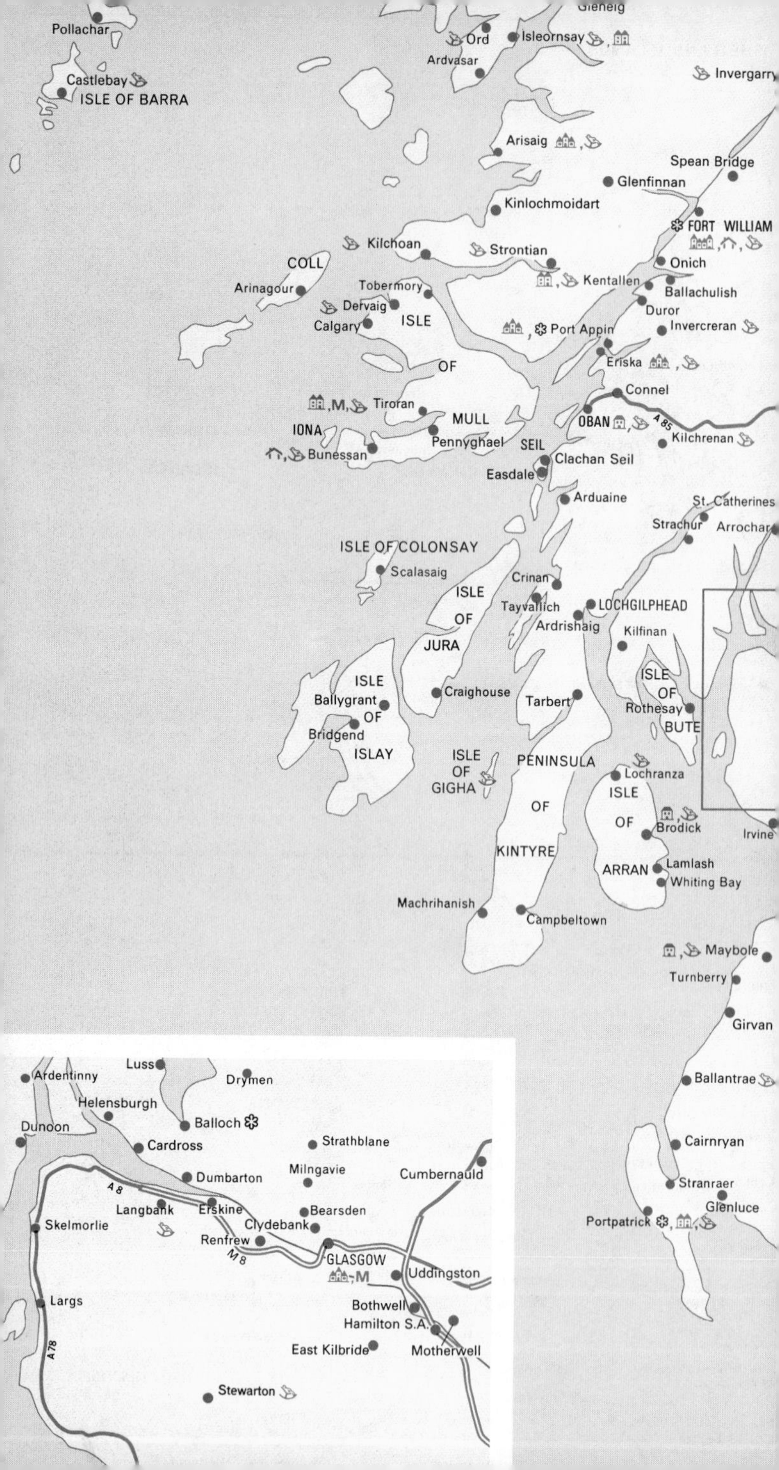

Pollachar
Castlebay
ISLE OF BARRA
Ord
Isleornsay
Ardvasar
Invergarry
Arisaig
Spean Bridge
Glenfinnan
Kinlochmoidart
FORT WILLIAM
Kilchoan
Strontian
Onich
COLL
Kentallen
Ballachulish
Arinagour
Tobermory
Duror
Dervaig
Calgary
ISLE
Port Appin
Invercreran
Eriska
OF
Connel
Tiroran
MULL
OBAN
A 85
IONA
Pennyghael
SEIL
Kilchrenan
Bunessan
Clachan Seil
Easdale
Arduaine
St. Catherines
Strachur
Arrochar
ISLE OF COLONSAY
Scalasaig
Crinan
ISLE
Tayvallich
LOCHGILPHEAD
OF
Ardrishaig
Kilfinan
JURA
ISLE
ISLE
OF
Craighouse
Tarbert
Rothesay
Ballygrant
OF
BUTE
Bridgend
ISLAY
ISLE
OF
GIGHA
PENINSULA
Lochranza
ISLE
OF
OF
Brodick
Irvine
KINTYRE
Lamlash
ARRAN
Whiting Bay
Machrihanish
Campbeltown
Maybole
Turnberry
Girvan
Ballantrae
Cairnryan
Stranraer
Glenluce
Portpatrick
Luss
Ardentinny
Drymen
Helensburgh
Dunoon
Balloch
Cardross
Strathblane
Milngavie
Cumbernauld
Dumbarton
A 8
Langbank
Erskine
Bearsden
Skelmorlie
Clydebank
Renfrew
M 8
GLASGOW
M
Uddingston
Largs
Bothwell
Hamilton S.A.
A 78
East Kilbride
Motherwell
Stewarton

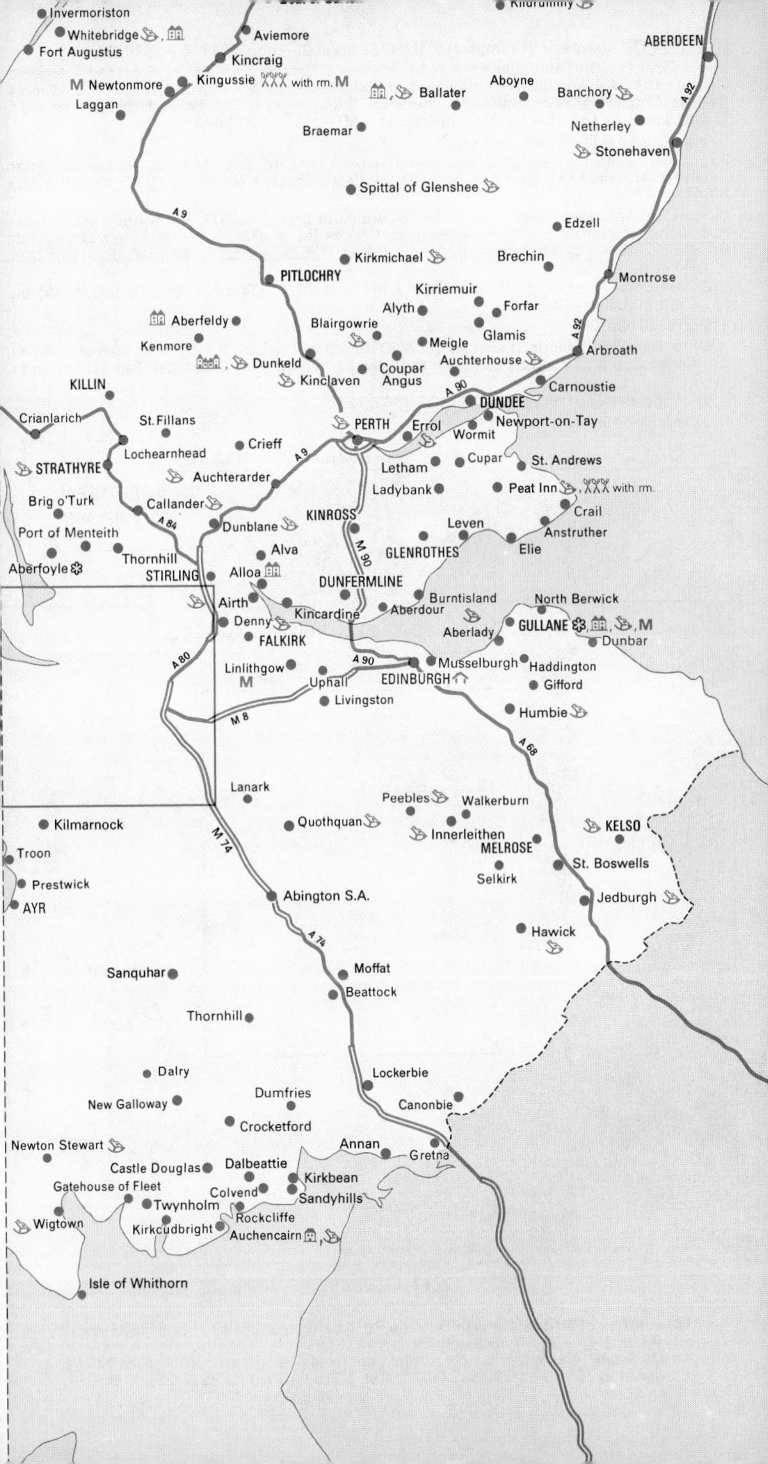
Invermoriston
Whitebridge
Fort Augustus
Aviemore
Kincraig
Newtonmore
Kingussie
with rm.
Laggan
Ballater
Aboyne
Banchory
ABERDEEN
A 92
Netherley
Braemar
Stonehaven
Spittal of Glenshee
A 9
Edzell
Kirkmichael
Brechin
PITLOCHRY
Montrose
Kirriemuir
Alyth
Forfar
Aberfeldy
Blairgowrie
Glamis
Kenmore
Meigle
A 92
Dunkeld
Coupar Angus
Auchterhouse
Arbroath
Kinclaven
KILLIN
Carnoustie
A 90
DUNDEE
Crianlarich
St. Fillans
PERTH
Errol
Newport-on-Tay
Wormit
Crieff
Lochearnhead
A 9
Cupar
St. Andrews
STRATHYRE
Letham
Auchterarder
Ladybank
Peat Inn
with rm.
Brig o'Turk
Callander
Crail
KINROSS
A 84
Leven
Port of Menteith
Dunblane
Anstruther
M 90
GLENROTHES
Elie
Alva
Thornhill
Aberfoyle
STIRLING
Alloa
DUNFERMLINE
Burntisland
North Berwick
Airth
Kincardine
Aberdour
GULLANE
M
Denny
Aberlady
Dunbar
FALKIRK
A 80
A 90
Linlithgow
Musselburgh
Haddington
M
Uphall
EDINBURGH
Gifford
Livingston
Humbie
M 8
A 68
Lanark
Peebles
Walkerburn
Kilmarnock
Quothquan
KELSO
Innerleithen
M 74
MELROSE
Troon
St. Boswells
Selkirk
Prestwick
Abington S.A.
Jedburgh
AYR
Hawick
A 74
Moffat
Sanquhar
Beattock
Thornhill
Lockerbie
Dalry
Dumfries
New Galloway
Canonbie
Crocketford
Newton Stewart
Annan
Gretna
Castle Douglas
Dalbeattie
Kirkbean
Gatehouse of Fleet
Colvend
Sandyhills
Twynholm
Wigtown
Rockcliffe
Kirkcudbright
Auchencairn
Isle of Whithorn

ABERDEEN Aberdeen. (Grampian) **401** N 12 **Scotland G.** – pop. 204 885 – ☎ 01224.

See : City★★ - Old Aberdeen★★ X – St. Machar's Cathedral★★ (West Front★★★, Heraldic Ceiling★★★) X **A** – Art Gallery★★ (Macdonald Collection★★) Y **M** – Mercat Cross★★ Y **B** – King's College Chapel★ (Crown Spire★★★, medieval fittings★★★) X **D** – Provost Skene's House★ (painted ceilings★★) Y **E** – Maritime Museum★ Z **M1** – Marischal College★ Y **U**.

Envir. : Brig o' Balgownie★, by Don St. X.

Exc. : SW : Deeside★★ - Crathes Castle★★ (Gardens★★★) *AC*, SW : 16 m. by A 93 X – Dunottar Castle★★ *AC* (site★★★), S : 18 m. by A 92 X – Castle Fraser★ (exterior★★) *AC*, W : 16 m. by A 944 X.

18, 18 Royal Aberdeen, Balgownie, Links Rd, Bridge of Don ☎ 702571, X – 18 Auchmill, Provost Rust Drive ☎ 714577, X – 18 Balnagask, St. Fitticks Rd ☎ 876407, X – 18 King's Links, Golf Rd ☎ 632269, X – 18 Portlethen, Badentoy Rd ☎ 782575, X – 18, 9 Murcar, Bridge of Don ☎ 704345, X.

✈ Aberdeen Airport : ☎ 722331, NW : 7 m. by A 96 X – **Terminal** : Bus Station, Guild St. (adjacent to Railway Station).

☎ 0345 090700.

⛴ to Shetland Islands (Lerwick) (P & O Scottish Ferries) (14 h) – to Orkney Islands (Stromness) (P & O Scottish Ferries) – to Norway (Bergen) (P & O Scottish Ferries) (summer only).

ℹ St. Nicholas House, Broad St. AB9 1DE ☎ 632727.

◆Edinburgh 130 – ◆Dundee 67.

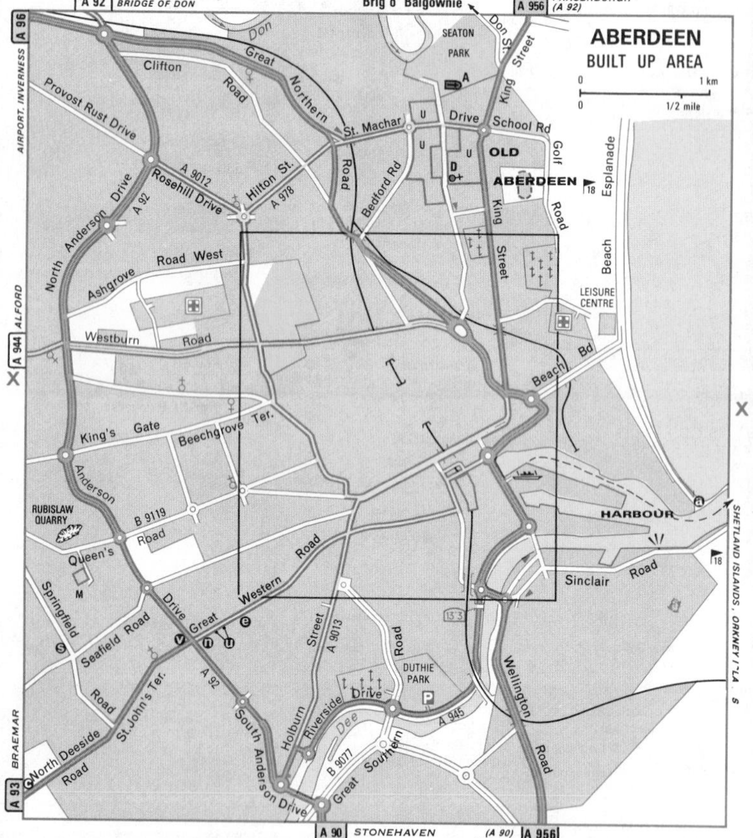

Marcliffe at Pitfodels, North Deeside Rd, AB1 9YA, ☎ 861000, Fax 868860, – ⛶ 📺 ☎ ♿ 🅿 – 90. AE VISA. X **a**
Invery Room : **Meals** *(closed Sunday)* (dinner only) a la carte 27.50/42.50 **st.** 6.00 – *Conservatory* : **Meals** a la carte 15.00/20.50 **st.** 6.00 – **42 rm** 95.00/265.00 **st.** – SB.

ABERDEEN

Street	Grid	No.
Bon Accord Centre	Y	
George Street	Y	
St. Nicholas Centre	Y	29
St. Nicholas Street	YZ	30
Trinity Centre	Z	
Union Street	Z	
Broad Street	Y	6
Castle Street	Y	7
College Street	Z	9
Craigie Loanings	Y	12
Denburn Road	YZ	14
East North Street	Y	16
Great Southern Road	Z	18
Guild Street	Z	19
Justice Street	Y	21
Millburn Street	Z	23
Rosemount Terrace	Y	25
Rosemount Viaduct	Y	26
St. Andrew Street	Y	28
School Hill	YZ	32
South Esplanade West	Z	33
South Mount Street	Y	34
Springbank Terrace	Z	35
Spring Garden	Y	36
Trinity Quay	Z	37
Union Terrace	Z	39
Upperkirkgate	Y	40
Victoria Street	Z	42
Waverley Place	Z	43
Wellington Place	Z	45
Wellington Road	Z	47
Woolmanhill	Y	48

Caledonian Thistle (Mt. Charlotte Thistle), 10-14 Union Terr., AB9 1HE, ☏ 640233, Telex 73758, Fax 641627, – rm TV ☎ P – 35. AE VISA Z i
Meals *(closed Saturday and Sunday lunch)* 10.25/19.50 **st.** and a la carte 6.95 – 10.25 – **78 rm** 99.00/130.00 **st.**, 2 suites – SB.

Stakis Aberdeen, 161 Springfield Rd, AB9 2QH, ☏ 313377, Fax 312028, – rm TV ☎ P – 900. AE VISA JCB. X s
Meals 10.00/12.00 **st.** and dinner a la carte 7.00 – 9.50 – **109 rm** 99.00/129.00 **st.**, 1 suite – SB.

Ardoe House, South Deeside Rd, Blairs, AB1 5YP, SW : 5 m. on B 9077 - ☏ 867355, Fax 861283, ≤, « Part 19C baronial mansion », park – TV ☎ P – 120. AE VISA X
Meals (closed Saturday lunch) 16.00/25.00 and a la carte 6.50 – 9.50 – **69 rm** 79.00/120.00 **t.**, 2 suites – SB.

Copthorne, 122 Huntly St., AB1 1SU, ☏ 630404, Fax 640573 – rm TV ☎ – 220. AE VISA Z a
Meals *(closed lunch Saturday and Sunday)* 16.00 **t.** and a la carte 7.25 – 9.75 – **89 rm** 90.00/115.00 **t.** – SB.

Quality, Bridge of Don, AB23 8BL, N : 3 m. on A 92 ℘ 706707, Fax 823923 – rm. AE VISA X
closed Christmas – **Meals** a la carte 12.60/18.00 **st.** – 8.50 – **123 rm** 56.00/125.00 **st.**

Amatola (Jarvis), 448 Great Western Rd, AB1 6NP, ℘ 318724, Fax 312716 – rm – 400. AE VISA X v
closed 26 and 27 December – **Meals** 8.95/12.95 **st.** and a la carte – 8.75 – **53 rm** 79.00/95.00 **st.** – SB.

Malacca, 349 Great Western Rd, AB1 6NW, ℘ 588901, Fax 571621 – . AE VISA. X u
Meals - Seafood 8.50/18.00 **t.** and a la carte 7.00 – **21 rm** 65.00/85.00 **t.** – SB.

Craiglynn, 36 Fonthill Rd, AB1 2UJ, ℘ 584050, Fax 584050 – . AE VISA. Z e
Meals (dinner only)/14.95 **st.** 5.00 – **9 rm** 45.00/62.50 **t.** – SB.

Cedars without rest., 339 Great Western Rd, AB1 6NW, ℘ 583225, Fax 583225 – . AE VISA. X e
13 rm 38.00/52.00 **st.**

Corner House, 385 Great Western Rd, AB1 6NY, ℘ 313063, Fax 313063 – rest . AE VISA. X u
Meals approx. 11.00 **st.** 3.75 – **17 rm** 48.00/56.00 **st.**

Manorville without rest., 252 Great Western Rd, AB1 6PJ, ℘ 594190, Fax 594190 – Z c
3 rm.

Fourways without rest., 435 Great Western Rd, AB1 6NJ, ℘ 310218, Fax 310218 – . AE VISA. X n
7 rm 25.00/40.00 **s.**

Rendez-vous, 210-212 George St., AB1 1BS, ℘ 633610, Fax 649389 – Y c
Meals - Chinese (Peking) and Thai.

Nargile, 77-79 Skene St., AB1 1QD, ℘ 636093, Fax 636202 – AE VISA Y a
closed 25 and 26 December, 1 January and third week August – **Meals** - Turkish (dinner only) 18.00 **st.** and a la carte 5.20.

Silver Darling, Pocra Quay, North Pier Rd, AB2 1DQ, ℘ 576229, Fax 626558 – AE VISA X a
closed Saturday lunch, Sunday, 2 weeks Christmas-New Year and Bank Holidays – **Meals** - French Seafood (booking essential) 20.85 **t.** (lunch) and a la carte 25.75/28.65.

at Murcar N : 4½ m. on A 92 – X – ✉ Aberdeen – 01224 :

Travel Inn without rest., AB2 8BP, on B 999 ℘ 821217, Fax 706869 – . AE VISA.
4.95 – **40 rm** 33.50 **t.**

at Altens S : 3 m. on A 956 – X – ✉ Aberdeen – 01224 :

Altens Skean Dhu (Mt. Charlotte Thistle), Souterhead Rd, AB1 4LF, ℘ 877000, Telex 739631, Fax 896964, heated – rm rest – 400. AE VISA
Meals *(closed Saturday lunch and Sunday)* 15.00/17.50 **st.** and a la carte 5.95 – 8.95 – **220 rm** 83.00/105.00 **t.**, 1 suite – SB.

at Cults SW : 4 m. on A 93 – X – ✉ Aberdeen – 01224 :

Faraday's, 2 Kirk Brae, AB1 9SQ, ℘ 869666 – . VISA
closed Monday lunch, Sunday and 26 December-10 January – **Meals** (booking essential) 25.50 **t.** (dinner) and lunch a la carte approx. 11.60 **t.** 7.10.

at Maryculter SW : 8 m. on B 9077 – X – ✉ Aberdeen – 01224 :

Maryculter House, South Deeside Rd, AB1 0BB, ℘ 732124, Fax 733510, « Part 13C house on River Dee », – – 30. AE VISA
Meals *(closed Sunday dinner)* (bar lunch)/dinner 30.00 **t.** – 9.50 – **23 rm** 108.00/110.00 **t.** – SB.

at Westhill W : 6½ m. by A 944 – X – ✉ Aberdeen – 01224 :

Courtyard, Elrick, AB32 6TL, W : ½ m. by A 944 (behind Broadstraik Inn) ℘ 742540, Fax 742796 – . AE VISA
closed Sunday, Monday, 25 to 26 December, 1 to 2 January and two weeks mid July – **Meals** a la carte 13.70/24.50 **t.** 6.00.

at Bucksburn NW : 4 m. by A 96 – X – on A 947 – ✉ Aberdeen – ☎ 01224 :

Holiday Inn Crown Plaza Aberdeen (Q.M.H.), Oldmeldrum Rd, AB2 9LN, ☎ 713911, Fax 714020, ⚲, ≘s, ⊠ – ⏚ ⇔ rm ▣ ☎ Ⓟ – 🛋 180. ⊠ AE ⓓ VISA JCB
Meals 9.75/20.00 **st.** and a la carte 🍷 5.95 – ☕ 9.95 – **144 rm** 105.00/130.00 **t.** – SB.

at Dyce NW : 5 ½ m. by A 96 – X – on A 947 – ✉ Aberdeen – ☎ 01224 :

Aberdeen Marriott, Riverview Drive, Farburn, AB2 0AZ, ☎ 770011, Fax 722347, ⚲, ≘s, ⊠ – ⇔ rm ▤ ▣ ☎ ♿ Ⓟ – 🛋 400. ⊠ AE ⓓ VISA. ✼
Meals 15.95/19.95 **st.** and a la carte 🍷 7.95 – ☕ 10.75 – **153 rm** 115.00/125.00 **st.**, 1 suite – SB.

at Aberdeen Airport NW : 6 m. by A 96 – X – ✉ Aberdeen – ☎ 01224 :

Aberdeen Airport Skean Dhu (Mt. Charlotte Thistle), Argyll Rd, AB2 0DU, ☎ 725252, Telex 739239, Fax 723745, ⊠ heated – ⇔ rm ▣ ☎ ♿ Ⓟ – 🛋 550. ⊠ AE ⓓ VISA JCB
Meals 12.00/18.50 **st.** and a la carte – ☕ 8.95 – **148 rm** 87.00/160.00 **st.** – SB.

Speedbird Inn, Argyll Rd, AB2 0AF, ☎ 772884, Fax 772560 – ⇔ rm ▣ ☎ ♿ Ⓟ. ⊠ AE ⓓ VISA
Meals a la carte approx. 9.10 **st.** 🍷 2.95 – ☕ 3.95 – **100 rm** 45.00 **st.**

ATS Beach Boulevard ☎ 592727 ATS 214 Hardgate ☎ 589461

ABERDOUR Fife. (Fife) 401 K 15 **Scotland G.** – pop. 1 832 – ECD : Wednesday – ☎ 01383.

See : Town★ – Aberdour Castle★ *AC*.

⛳18 Seaside Pl. ☎ 860080.

♦Edinburgh 17 – Dunfermline 7.

Woodside, 80 High St., KY3 0SW, ☎ 860328, Fax 860920, ≘s – ▣ ☎ Ⓟ. ⊠ AE ⓓ VISA
Meals (bar lunch)/dinner 17.50 **t.** and a la carte 🍷 4.15 – **20 rm** ☕ 53.00/65.00 **t.**, 1 suite – SB.

Prices For full details of the prices quoted in the guide, consult the introduction.

ABERFELDY Perth. (Tayside) 401 I 14 **Scotland G.** – pop. 4 083 – ECD : Wednesday – ☎ 01887.

See : Town★.

Envir. : St. Mary's Church (painted ceiling★) NE : 2 m. by A 827.

Exc. : Loch Tay★★, SW : 6 m. by A 827 – Ben Lawers★★, SW : 16 m. by A 827 – Blair Castle★★ *AC*, N : 20 ½ m. by A 827 and A 9.

⛳9 Taybridge Rd ☎ 820535.

ℹ The Square PH15 2DD ☎ 820276.

♦Edinburgh 76 – ♦Glasgow 73 – ♦Oban 77 – Perth 32.

Farleyer House ⛰, PH15 2JE, W : 2 m. on B 846 ☎ 820332, Fax 829430, ≤, ⚓, 🌳, park – ⇔ ▣ ☎ Ⓟ. ⊠ AE ⓓ VISA. ✼
***Menzies* : Meals** *(restricted opening Nov.-Mar.)* (dinner only) 27.50/32.00 **t.** 🍷 5.00 – ***Bistro* : Meals** a la carte 11.95/25.70 **t.** 🍷 4.50 – **11 rm** ☕ 70.00/160.00 **t.** – SB.

Guinach House ⛰, Urlar Rd, PH15 2ET, off Crieff Rd ☎ 820251, Fax 829607, ≤, 🌳 – ⇔ rest ▣ Ⓟ. ⊠ VISA
Meals (light lunch by arrangement)/dinner 21.00 **st.** 🍷 8.45 – **7 rm** ☕ 37.50/75.00 **st.**

ABERFOYLE Stirling (Central) 401 G 15 **Scotland G.** – pop. 936 – ECD : Wednesday – ✉ Stirling – ☎ 01877.

Envir. : The Trossachs★★★ (Loch Katherine★★) N : 5 m. by A 821 – Hilltop Viewpoint★★★ (✻★★★) N : 2 ½ m. by A 821 – Inchmahone Priory (double effigy★) *AC*, E : 4 m. by A 81.

Exc. : Ben Lomond★★, W : 16 m. by B 829.

⛳18 Braeval ☎ 382493.

ℹ Main St. ☎ 382352 (summer only).

♦Edinburgh 56 – ♦Glasgow 27.

✻ **Braeval Old Mill** (Nairn), FK8 3UY, E : 1 m. by A 821 on A 81 ☎ 382711, Fax 382400 – Ⓟ. ⊠ VISA
closed Sunday dinner, Monday, 1 week February and 1 week October/November – **Meals** (booking essential) (dinner only and Sunday lunch) 18.50/27.50 **t.**
Spec. Artichoke soup with smoked bacon, Baked fillet of hake with tomato, shallots and a pesto butter sauce, Passion fruit jelly with fresh fruits and lime syrup.

ABERLADY E. Lothian. (Lothian) 401 L 15 – pop. 1 033 – ECD : Wednesday – ☎ 01875.

♦Edinburgh 16 – Haddington 5 – North Berwick 7.5.

Green Craigs ⛰, EH32 0PY, SW : ¾ m. on A 198 ☎ 870301, Fax 870440, ≤, 🌳 – ▣ ☎ Ⓟ. ⊠ AE ⓓ VISA
closed 1 January – **Meals** 12.00/23.50 **t.** and a la carte 🍷 5.00 – **6 rm** ☕ 60.00/120.00 **t.** – SB.

Kilspindie House, Main St., EH32 0RE, ☎ 870682, Fax 870504 – ▣ ☎ Ⓟ. ⊠ VISA
Meals (bar lunch Monday to Saturday)/dinner 13.00 **t.** 🍷 4.50 – **26 rm** ☕ 36.00/68.00 **t.** – SB.

ABERLOUR Banff. (Grampian) 401 K 11 – ☎ 01340 Carron.
♦Edinburgh 192 – ♦Aberdeen 60 – Elgin 15 – ♦Inverness 55.

Dowans, AB38 9LS, SW : ¾ m. by A 95 ℘ 871488, Fax 871038, – ☎ P. VISA
closed January and February – **Meals** (bar lunch)/dinner 18.50 **st.** – **17 rm** 39.00/70.00 **st.**

ABINGTON SERVICE AREA Lanark. (Strathclyde) – ✉ Biggar – ☎ 0186 42.
♦Edinburgh 43 – Dumfries 37 – ♦Glasgow 38.

Forte Travelodge without rest., ML12 6RG, at junction of A 74 with M 74 ℘ 782, Reservations (Freephone) 0800 850950 – TV & P. AE VISA.
56 rm 33.50 **t.**

ABOYNE Aberdeen. (Grampian) 401 L 12 **Scotland G.** – pop. 3 793 – ECD : Thursday – ☎ 0133 98.
Exc. : Craigievar Castle★ *AC*, NE : 12 m. by B 9094, B 9119 and A 980.
Formanston Park ℘ 86328.
Ballater Road Car Park ℘ 86060 (summer only).
♦Edinburgh 131 – ♦Aberdeen 30 – ♦Dundee 68.

Birse Lodge, Charleston Rd, AB34 5EL, ℘ 86253, – TV ☎ P
16 rm.

Hazlehurst Lodge, Ballater Rd, AB34 5HY, ℘ 86921, Fax 86660, – P. AE VISA
closed January and February – **Meals** 25.00 **st.** 7.00 – **3 rm** 30.00/64.00 **st.** – SB.

ACHILTIBUIE Ross and Cromarty. (Highland) 401 D 9 – ☎ 01854.
♦Edinburgh 243 – ♦Inverness 84 – Ullapool 25.

Summer Isles, IV26 2YG, ℘ 622282, Fax 622251, « Picturesque setting ≤ Summer Isles », – rest ☎ P
Easter-mid October – **Meals** (booking essential) (dinner only) 33.00 **st.** – **11rm** 44.00/95.00 **st.**, 1 suite.

AIRTH Stirling. (Central) 401 I 15 – pop. 1 519 – ✉ Falkirk – ☎ 01324.
♦Edinburgh 30 – Dunfermline 14 – Falkirk 7 – Stirling 8.

Airth Castle, FK2 8JF, ℘ 831411, Telex 777975, Fax 831419, ≤, « Part 13C and 17C castle and stables in extensive grounds », , park – TV ☎ & P – 400. AE VISA.
Meals 11.95/17.50 **t.** and a la carte 4.90 – **75 rm** 77.00/100.00 **t.** – SB.

ALLOA Stirling. (Central) 401 I 15 **Scotland G.** – pop. 26 362 – ☎ 01259.
Exc. : Culross★★★ (Village★★★, Palace★★ *AC*, Study★ *AC*) SE : 7 m. by A 907, A 977 and B 9037 – Castle Campbell★ (site★★★, ≤★) *AC*, NE : 8 m. by A 908 and A 91 – Stirling★★, W : 8 m. by A 907.
Schawpark, Sauchie ℘ 722745 – Braehead, Cambus ℘ 722078.
♦Edinburgh 33 – ♦Dundee 48 – ♦Glasgow 35.

Gean House, Gean Park, Tullibody Rd, FK10 2HS, NW : 1 m. on B 9096 ℘ 219275, Fax 213827, ≤, – rest TV ☎ P – 60. AE VISA.
Meals (booking essential) 13.50/24.50 **st.** – **7 rm** 80.00/140.00 **t.** – SB.
ATS Union St. ℘ 724253

ALLOWAY Ayr. (Strathclyde) 401 402 G 17 – see Ayr.

ALTENS Aberdeen. (Grampian) – see Aberdeen.

ALTNACEALGACH Sutherland. (Highland) 401 F 9 – ✉ Lairg – ☎ 01854.
♦Edinburgh 235 – ♦Inverness 79 – Ullapool 20.

Altnacealgach, IV27 4HF, on A 837 ℘ 666220, ≤, – P.
Meals (in bar) (residents only) 10.00 **t.** – **7 rm** 20.00/40.00 **t.**

ALTNAHARRA Sutherland. (Highland) 401 G 9 **Scotland G.** – ✉ Lairg – ☎ 01549.
Exc. : Ben Loyal★★, N : 10 m. by A 836 – Ben Hope★ (≤★★★) NW : 14 m.
♦Edinburgh 239 – ♦Inverness 83 – Thurso 61.

Altnaharra, IV27 4UE, ℘ 411222, Fax 411222, ≤, – rest P. VISA
March-October – **Meals** (bar lunch)/dinner 18.50 **st.** 5.00 – **18 rm** 36.50/73.00 **st.** – SB.

ALVA Stirling.(Central) 401 I 15 – ☎ 01259.
♦Edinburgh 36 – ♦Dundee 46 – ♦Glasgow 35.

XX **Farriers** with rm, Woodland Park, Alva Stables, FK12 5HU, ℘ 762702, Fax 769782 – TV ☎ P. AE VISA
Meals 16.95/25.00 **st.** and a la carte 4.50 – **6 rm** 39.00/49.50 **t.**

Les prix Pour toutes précisions sur les prix indiqués dans ce guide, reportez-vous à l'introduction.

ALYTH Perth. (Tayside) 401 J 14 – pop. 4 650 – ☏ 01828.

Pitcrocknie ☏ 632268.

◆Edinburgh 63 – ◆Aberdeen 69 – ◆Dundee 16 – Perth 21.

Lands of Loyal , Loyal Rd, PH11 8JQ, N : ½ m. by B 952 ☏ 633151, Fax 633313, ←, – rest TV ☎ P. AE VISA
Meals 21.75 **t.** (dinner) and a la carte 10.20/19.40 5.95 – **14 rm** 40.00/65.00 **t.** – SB.

Drumnacree House, St. Ninians Rd, PH11 8AP, ☏ 632194, – TV P. VISA
April - 23 December – **Meals** *(closed Sunday and Monday to non-residents)* (booking essential)(dinner only) 24.00 **t.** 6.00 – **6 rm** (dinner included) 54.00/104.00 **t.** – SB.

ANNAN Dumfries (Dumfries and Galloway) 401 402 K 19 – ☏ 01461.

◆ Edinburgh 87 – Carlisle 15 – Dumfries 16 – ◆Glasgow 84.

Northfield House, DG12 5LL, N : 1 m. on B 722 (Eaglesfield rd) ☏ 202851, , – TV P
closed Christmas, New Year and January – **Meals** (by arrangement) (residents only) 25.00 **t.** – **3 rm** 50.00/80.00 **t.**

ANSTRUTHER Fife. (Fife) 401 L 15 **Scotland G.** – pop. 1 307 – ECD : Wednesday – ☏ 01333.

See : Scottish Fisheries Museum★★ *AC*.

Envir. : The East Neuk★★ – Crail★★ (Old Centre★★, Upper Crail★) NE : 4 m. by A 917.

Exc. : Kellie Castle★ *AC*, NW : 7 m. by B 9171, B 942 and A 917.

Marsfield Shore Rd ☏ 310956.

Harbour Head, KY10 3AB ☏ 311073 (summer only).

◆Edinburgh 46 – ◆Dundee 23 – Dunfermline 34.

Spindrift, Pittenweem Rd, KY10 3DT, ☏ 310573 – TV P. VISA.
closed 10 to 31 January – **Meals** 15.00 **st.** 4.80 – **8 rm** 30.00/55.00 **st.** – SB.

Cellar, 24 East Green, KY10 3AA, ☏ 310378 – . AE VISA
closed Sunday, Monday, 1 week May, 1 week November and Christmas – **Meals** - Seafood 28.50 **t.** (dinner) and lunch a la carte 12.50/19.50 7.50.

ARBROATH Angus. (Tayside) 401 M 14 **Scotland G.** – pop. 24 002 – ECD : Wednesday – ☏ 01241.

See : Town★ – Abbey★ *AC* – **Envir.** : St. Vigeans★, N : 1 ½ m. by A 92.

Arbroath, Elliot ☏ 872069/875837 – Market Pl., DD11 1HR ☏ 872609.

◆Edinburgh 72 – ◆Aberdeen 51 – ◆Dundee 16.

But n' Ben, Auchmithie, DD11 5SQ, NE : 3 m. by A 92 ☏ 877223, « Converted fishermens cottages » – . VISA
closed Sunday dinner and Tuesday – **Meals** (light lunch)/dinner a la carte 12.50/17.00 **t.** 4.50.

ARCHIESTOWN Moray. (Grampian) 401 K 11 – ✉ Aberlour (Banff) – ☏ 01340.

◆Edinburgh 194 – ◆Aberdeen 62 – ◆Inverness 49.

Archiestown (at Archiestown H.), AB38 7QX, ☏ 810218, Fax 810239, – TV ☎ P. AE VISA
early February-mid October – **Meals** (see below) – **8 rm** 27.50/80.00 **st.**

Archiestown, AB38 7QX, ☏ 810218, Fax 810239 – P. VISA
early February-mid October – **Meals** (bar lunch)/dinner 25.00 **st.** 5.50.

ARDENTINNY Argyll. (Strathclyde) 401 F 15 – ECD : Wednesday – ✉ Dunoon – ☏ 01369.

◆Edinburgh 107 – Dunoon 13 – ◆Glasgow 64 – ◆Oban 71.

Ardentinny , PA23 8TR, ☏ 810209, Fax 810345, ← Loch Long, – rest TV ☎ P. AE VISA
16 March-October – **Meals** (bar lunch)/dinner 22.00 **st.** and a la carte 4.95 – **11 rm** 51.00/134.00 **st.** – SB.

ARDEONAIG Perth. (Central) 401 H 14 – see Killin.

ARDGAY Sutherland. (Highland) 401 G10 – ☏ 0186 32.

◆Edinburgh 205 – ◆Inverness 49 – Wick 77.

Ardgay House, IV24 3DH, ☏ 345, – TV P.
March-November – **Meals** (residents only) (dinner only) 12.00 **st.** – **6 rm** -/48.00.

ARDRISHAIG Argyll. (Strathclyde) 401 D 15 – pop. 1 283 – ✉ Lochgilpead – ☏ 01546.

◆Edinburgh 132 – ◆Glasgow 86 – ◆Oban 40.

Allt-na-Craig, Tarbert Rd, PA30 8EP, on A 83 ☏ 603245, ←, – rest P
closed Christmas and New Year – **Meals** (by arrangement) 15.00 **st.** 3.50 – **6 rm** 24.00/56.00 **st.** – SB.

Fascadale House without rest., PA30 8EP, on A 83 ☏ 603845, ←, – P.
March-October – **3 rm** 20.00/44.00 **st.**

ARDUAINE Argyll. (Strathclyde) 401 D 15 **Scotland G.** – ECD : Wednesday – ✉ Oban – ☎ 01852.
Exc. : Loch Awe★★, E : 12 m. by A 816 and B 840.
♦Edinburgh 142 – ♦Oban 20.

Loch Melfort ⓢ, PA34 4XG, ☎ 200233, Fax 200214, ≤ Sound of Jura, 🌳, park – ⇆ rest TV ☎ P. VISA
closed 5 January-late February – **Meals** (bar lunch)/dinner 24.50 ⌂ 11.95 – **27 rm** ☐ 59.00/95.00 **st.** – SB.

ARDVASAR Inverness. (Highland) 401 C 12 – see Skye (Isle of).

ARDVOURLIE Western Isles (Outer Hebrides) 401 Z 10 – see Lewis and Harris (Isle of).

ARINAGOUR Argyll. (Strathclyde) 401 A 14 – see Coll (Isle of).

ARISAIG Inverness. (Highland) 401 C 13 **Scotland G.** – ECD : Thursday – ☎ 01687.
See : Village★.
Envir. : Silver Sands of Morar★, N : 5½ m. by A 830.
⛳9 Traigh, 5 Back of Keppoch ☎ 262.
♦Edinburgh 172 – ♦Inverness 102 – ♦Oban 88.

Arisaig House ⓢ, Beasdale, PH39 4NR, SE : 3 ¼ m. on A 830 ☎ 450622, Fax 450626, ≤ Loch nan Uamh and Roshven, « Gardens », park – ⇆ rest TV ☎ P. AE VISA. ⚔
12 April-5 November – **Meals** (booking essential) (light lunch)/dinner 38.50 **t.** ⌂ 7.00 – ☐ 7.50 – **12 rm** 60.00/215.00 **t.**, 2 suites.

Arisaig, PH39 4NH, ☎ 450210, Fax 450310, ≤ – ⇆ rest ☎ P. VISA
Meals (bar lunch Monday to Saturday)/dinner 16.50 **t.** ⌂ 4.30 – ☐ 8.50 – **15 rm** ☐ 22.00/57.00 **t.**

✗ **Old Library Lodge** with rm, High St., PH39 4NH, ☎ 450651, Fax 450219, ≤ Loch nan Ceall and Inner Hebridean Isles – TV ☎. VISA
April-October – **Meals** 21.00 **t.** and lunch a la carte – **6 rm** ☐ 45.00/62.00 **t.**

ARRAN (Isle of) Bute. (Strathclyde) 401 402 DE 16 17 **Scotland G.** – pop. 4 474.
See : Island★★ – Brodick Castle★★ *AC.*
⛴ from Brodick to Ardrossan (Caledonian MacBrayne Ltd) 4-5 daily (55 mn) – from Lochranza to Kintyre Peninsula (Claonaig) (Caledonian MacBrayne Ltd) frequent services daily (30 mn).
ℹ The Pier, Lochranza ☎ (01770) 830320 (summer only).

Brodick – pop. 884 – ECD : Wednesday – ✉ Brodick – ☎ 01770.
⛳18 Brodick ☎ 302349 – ⛳9 Machrie Bay ☎ 850261.
ℹ The Pier TA27 8AU ☎ 302140/302401.

Auchrannie Country House, KA27 8BZ, ☎ 302234, Fax 302812, Ⅎ6, ≘s, ⬚, 🌳 – ⇆ rest TV ☎ ♿ P. VISA. ⚔
Meals 21.00 **st.** (dinner) and a la carte 10.00/16.20 ⌂ 6.00 – **26 rm** ☐ 56.00/92.00 **st.**, 2 suites – SB.

Kilmichael Country House ⓢ, Glencloy, KA27 8BY, 1 m. by Shore Rd, taking left turn opposite Golf Club ☎ 302219, 🌳 – ⇆ TV ☎ P
closed Christmas – **Meals** *(closed Monday to non residents)* (dinner only) 24.50 **t.** ⌂ 3.75 – **5 rm** ☐ 45.00/89.00 **t.**, 1 suite.

Arran, Shore Rd, KA27 8AJ, ☎ 302265, Fax 302093, ≤, ≘s, ⬚, 🌳 – ⇆ rest TV ☎ P. VISA
Meals (bar lunch)/dinner a la carte 7.75/18.90 **t.** ⌂ 3.65 – **15 rm** ☐ 28.00/56.00 **t.**

Glen Cloy Farmhouse ⓢ, KA27 8DA, ☎ 302351, 🌳 – ⇆ rest TV P
March-October – **Meals** 18.50 – **5 rm** ☐ 22.50/50.00 **s.** – SB.

Dunvegan House, Shore Rd, KA27 8AJ, ☎ 302811, ≤, 🌳 – ⇆ rm TV P. ⚔
March-October – **Meals** 12.50 **st.** – **10 rm** ☐ 18.50/52.00 **st.**

Lamlash – pop. 908 – ECD : Wednesday except summer – ✉ Brodick – ☎ 01770.
⛳18 Lamlash ☎ 200296.

Glenisle, Shore Rd, KA27 8LS, ☎ 600559, ≤, 🌳 – TV ☎ P. VISA
closed January and February – **Meals** (bar lunch)/dinner 12.50 **st.** ⌂ 4.25 – **13 rm** ☐ 33.50/67.00 **st.** – SB.

✗✗ **Carraig Mhor,** Shore Rd, KA27 8LS, ☎ 600453 – ⇆. VISA
closed 8 to 31 January – **Meals** (dinner only) a la carte 16.50/27.85 **t.** ⌂ 3.00.

Lochranza – ✉ Lochranza – ☎ 01770.
⛳9 Lochranza ☎ 830273.
ℹ The Pier ☎ 830320 (summer only).

Apple Lodge, KA27 8HJ, ☎ 830229, Fax 830229, 🌳 – ⇆ rest TV P. ⚔
Meals 12.50 **st.** – **3 rm** ☐ -/50.00 **s.**

Butt Lodge ⓢ, KA27 8JF, SE : ½ m. by Brodick Rd ☎ 830240, ≤, 🌳 – ⇆ P. VISA. ⚔
April-October – **Meals** 12.50 **s.** – **5 rm** ☐ 30.00/50.00 **s.**

Whiting Bay – ECD : Wednesday except summer – ✉ Whiting Bay – ☎ 01770.
18 Whiting Bay ☎ 700487.

Royal, Shore Rd, KA27 8PZ, ☎ 700286, Fax 700286, ≤, – rest TV ☎ P
March-October – **Meals** 11.00 **st.** – **6 rm** 25.00/46.00 **st.**

ARROCHAR Dunbarton (Strathclyde) 401 F 15 **Scotland G.** – pop. 417 – ECD : Wednesday – ☎ 0130 12.
Envir. : E : Ben Lomond★★.
Exc. : S : Loch Lomond★★.
♦Edinburgh 83 – ♦Glasgow 35 – ♦Oban 57.

Succoth Farmhouse without rest., G83 7AL, N : 3/4 m. on Succoth rd ☎ 591, – P.
April-Octoober – **3 rm** 16.00/32.00.

AUCHENCAIRN Kirkcudbright. (Dumfries and Galloway) 401 402 I 19 – ✉ Castle Douglas – ☎ 0155 664.
♦Edinburgh 98 – ♦Dumfries 21 – Stranraer 62.

Collin House, DG7 1QN, N : 1 m. by A 711 ☎ 292, « Part 18C country house, ≤ Auchencairn Bay and Cumbrian Mountains », , park – rest TV ☎ P. VISA.
closed 2 weeks February – **Meals** (dinner only) 27.00 **st.** 4.05 – **6 rm** 57.00/84.00 **st.** – SB.

AUCHTERARDER Perth. (Tayside) 401 I 15 **Scotland G.** – pop. 3 910 – ECD : Wednesday – ☎ 01764.
Envir. : Tullibardine Chapel★, NW : 2 m.
18 Ochil Rd ☎ 662804 – 9 Rollo Park, Dunning ☎ 684747.
☐ 90 High St. PH3 1BJ ☎ 663450.
♦Edinburgh 55 – ♦Glasgow 45 – Perth 14.

Gleneagles, PH3 1NF, SW : 2 m. by A 824 on A 823 ☎ 662231, Telex 76105, Fax 662134, ≤, « Championship golf courses and extensive leisure facilities », 9, 18, , park, , squash – rm rest TV ☎ P – 360. AE VISA JCB
***Strathearn* : Meals** 27.00/39.50 **t.** and dinner a la carte – ***Dormy Grill* : Meals** (closed Monday and Tuesday October-Easter) (grill rest.) (dinner only) a la carte 18.75/24.75 **t.** 9.00 – **216 rm** 155.00/295.00 **t.**, 18 suites – SB.

Auchterarder House, PH3 1DZ, N : 1 1/2 m. on B 8062 ☎ 663646, Fax 662939, ≤, « Scottish Jacobean house », , park – rest TV ☎ P. AE VISA
Meals (booking essential) 15.00/27.50 **t.** 7.50 – **13 rm** 90.00/195.00 **t.**, 2 suites – SB.

Duchally House, PH3 1PN, S : 4 m. by A 824 off A 823 ☎ 663071, Fax 662464, ≤, , park – TV ☎ P – 50. AE VISA
Meals (lunch by arrangement)/dinner 22.50 **st.** and a la carte 3.95 – **13 rm** 55.00/85.00 **st.** – SB.

Collearn House, PH3 1DF, ☎ 663553, Fax 662376, – rm TV ☎ P – 60. AE VISA.
Meals 15.00/30.00 4.75 – **8 rm** 60.00/90.00 **t.** – SB.

AUCHTERHOUSE Angus. (Tayside) 401 K 14 – ✉ Dundee – ☎ 0182 626.
♦Edinburgh 69 – ♦Dundee 7 – Perth 24.

XXX **Old Mansion House** with rm, DD3 0QN, ☎ 366, Fax 400, ≤, « Part 15C and 17C country house », heated, , park, , squash – rest TV ☎ P. AE VISA
closed 24 December to 4 January – **Meals** 16.00/27.95 **t.** and a la carte 5.00 – **6 rm** 80.00/130.00 **st.**

AULTBEA Ross and Cromarty. (Highland) 401 D 10 **Scotland G.** – ECD : Wednesday – ☎ 01445.
Envir. : Inverewe Gardens★★★ *AC*, S : 5 1/2 m. by A 832.
Exc. : Loch Maree★★★, S : 10 m. by A 832.
♦Edinburgh 234 – ♦Inverness 79 – Kyle of Lochalsh 80.

Aultbea, IV22 2HX, ☎ 731201, Fax 731214, ≤, – TV ☎ P. VISA
Meals (bar lunch)/dinner 21.00 **st.** and a la carte 4.00 – **8 rm** 34.50/69.00 **st.** – SB.

AVIEMORE Inverness. (Highland) 401 I 12 **Scotland G.** – pop. 1 510 – ECD : Wednesday – Winter sports – ☎ 01479.
See : Town★.
Exc. : The Cairngorms★★ (≤★★★) – ★★★ from Cairn Gorm, SE : 11 m. by B 970 – Landmark Visitor Centre (The Highlander★) *AC*, N : 7 m. by A 9 – Highland Wildlife Park★ *AC*, SW : 7 m. by A 9.
☐ Grampian Rd TH22 1PP ☎ 810363.
♦Edinburgh 129 – ♦Inverness 29 – Perth 85.

Stakis Four Seasons, Aviemore Centre, PH22 1PF, ✆ 810681, Fax 810534, ≤ Cairngorms, Fø, ≘s, ▣ – |‡| ⇆ rm ▣ ☎ Ⓟ – 🏊 110. ▣ AE ⓪ VISA
Meals (dancing Saturday evening) 8.50/16.50 **st.** and a la carte 🍷 7.00 – ☐ 8.50 – **88 rm** 75.00/135.00 **st.** – SB.

Corrour House ⛺, Inverdruie, PH22 1QH, SE : 1 m. on B 970 ✆ 810220, Fax 811500, ≤, ⛺ – ⇆ rest ▣ ☎ Ⓟ. ▣ AE VISA
closed November-January – **Meals** (dinner only) 18.00 **t.** 🍷 3.50 – **8 rm** ☐ 30.00/60.00 **st.**

Lynwilg House, Lynwilg, PH22 1PZ, S : 2 m. by B 9152 on A 9 ✆ 811685, ≤, 🐟, ⛺ – ▣ Ⓟ. ▣ VISA. ⛺
closed November-27 December – **Meals** (by arrangement) 15.00 **st.** – **4 rm** ☐ 22.00/50.00 **st.**

AYR Ayr. (Strathclyde) 401 402 G 17 **Scotland G.** – pop. 47 872 – ECD : Wednesday – ☎ 01292.

Envir. : Alloway★ (Burns Cottage and Museum★ *AC*) S : 3 m. by B 7024 BZ.

Exc. : Culzean Castle★ *AC* (setting★★★, Oval Staircase★★) SW : 13 m. by A 719 BZ.

⛳18 Belleisle ✆ 441258, BZ – ⛳18 Dalmilling, Westwood Av., Whitletts ✆ 263893, BZ – ⛳9 Doon Valley, Hillside, Patna ✆ 531607, BZ.

ℹ Burns House, Burns Statue Square, KA7 1UD ✆ 288688.

♦Edinburgh 81 – ♦Glasgow 35.

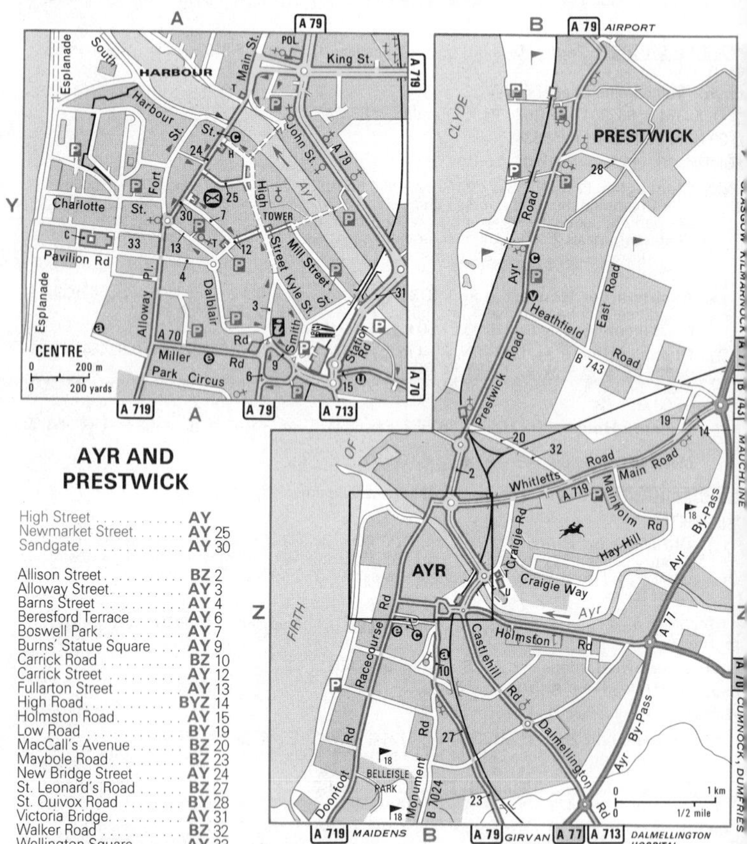

High Street	AY
Newmarket Street	AY 25
Sandgate	AY 30
Allison Street	BZ 2
Alloway Street	AY 3
Barns Street	AY 4
Beresford Terrace	AY 6
Boswell Park	AY 7
Burns' Statue Square	AY 9
Carrick Road	BZ 10
Carrick Street	AY 12
Fullarton Street	AY 13
High Road	BYZ 14
Holmston Road	AY 15
Low Road	BY 19
MacCall's Avenue	BZ 20
Maybole Road	BZ 23
New Bridge Street	AY 24
St. Leonard's Road	BZ 27
St. Quivox Road	BY 28
Victoria Bridge	AY 31
Walker Road	BZ 32
Wellington Square	AY 33

Fairfield House, 12 Fairfield Rd, KA7 2AR, ✆ 267461, Fax 261456, ≘s, ▣, ⛺ – ▣ ☎ Ⓟ. ▣ AE ⓪ VISA. ⛺ AY **a**
Meals 19.95/24.50 **st.** and dinner a la carte 🍷 5.95 – **34 rm** ☐ 75.00/125.00 **st.**, 1 suite – SB.

Kylestrome, 11 Miller Rd, KA7 2AX, ✆ 262474, Fax 260863 – TV ☎ P – 25. AE VISA. AY e
Meals 8.95/15.95 and a la carte 4.50 – **12 rm** 50.00/80.00 **st.** – SB.

Pickwick, 19 Racecourse Rd, KA7 2TD, ✆ 260111, Fax 285348 – TV ☎ P BZ e
15 rm.

Langley Bank without rest., 39 Carrick Rd, KA7 2RD, ✆ 264246, Fax 282628 – TV ☎ P. AE VISA. BZ a
6 rm 30.00/50.00 **st.**

Glenmore, 35 Bellevue Cres., KA7 2DP, ✆ 269830 – TV BZ c
Meals (by arrangement) 10.00 – **5 rm** 20.00/40.00 **st.**

Crescent without rest., 26 Bellevue Cres., KA7 2DR, ✆ 287329 – TV BZ c
closed December and January – **5 rm** 30.00/46.00.

Coila without rest., 10 Holmston Rd, KA7 3BB, ✆ 262642 – TV ☎ P. VISA AY u
4 rm 30.00/45.00 **s.**

Fouters, 2a Academy St., KA7 1HS, ✆ 261391 – AE VISA AY c
closed Sunday lunch, Monday, 3 days at Christmas and 1 to 3 January – **Meals** 8.95/13.95 **t.** and a la carte 4.50.

at Alloway S : 3 m. on B 7024 – BZ – ✉ Ayr – 01292 :

Northpark House, 2 Alloway, KA7 4NL, ✆ 442336, Fax 445572 – TV ☎ P. AE VISA
Meals 12.50/21.00 **t.** and a la carte 4.95 – **5 rm** 55.00/95.00 **t.** – SB.

Burns Monument, KA7 4PQ, ✆ 442466, Fax 443174, ←, – TV ☎. AE VISA
Meals 12.50 **st.** 6.00 **9 rm** 40.00/60.00 **st.**

BALLACHULISH Argyll. (Highland) 401 E 13 **Scotland G.** – ECD : Wednesday – 0185 52.

Exc. : Glen Coe★★, E : 6 m. by A 82.

PA39 4JR ✆ 296 (summer only).

♦Edinburgh 117 – ♦Inverness 80 – Kyle of Lochalsh 90 – ♦Oban 38.

Ballachulish, PA39 4JY, W : 2¼ m. by A 82 on A 828 ✆ 606, Fax 463, ←, – TV ☎ P. VISA
Meals (bar lunch)/dinner 22.50 **t.** and a la carte 5.50 – **30 rm** 47.50/82.00 **st.** – SB.

Isles of Glencoe, PA39 4HL, ✆ 602, Fax 770, ← Loch Leven and the Pap of Glencoe, , – rest TV ☎ P. VISA JCB
Meals 15.00/21.00 **st.** and a la carte 5.50 – **39 rm** 56.00/92.00 **st.** – SB.

Ballachulish House, PA39 4JX, W : 2½ m. by A 82 on A 828 ✆ 266, Fax 498, ←, – P. VISA.
closed Christmas and New Year – **Meals** 22.00 **st.** – **6 rm** 48.00/76.00 **st.**

Lyn Leven, White St., PA39 4JP, ✆ 392, Fax 600, ←, – rest TV P.
closed Christmas – **Meals** (by arrangement) – **8 rm** 25.00/37.00 **t.** – SB.

BALLANTRAE Ayr. (Strathclyde) 401 402 E 18 – ✉ Girvan – 01465.

♦Edinburgh 115 – ♦Ayr 33 – Stranraer 18.

Balkissock Lodge, KA26 0LP, E : 4 m. by A 77 (south) taking first turn left after bridge ✆ 831537, Fax 831537, – TV P. VISA.
April-October – **Meals** 14.75 **st.** – **3 rm** (dinner included) 57.50/75.00 **st.** – SB.

BALLATER Aberdeen. (Grampian) 401 K 12 – pop. 1 051 – ECD : Thursday – 0133 97.

18 Victoria Rd ✆ 55567.

Station Sq. ✆ 55306 (summer only).

♦Edinburgh 111 – ♦Aberdeen 41 – ♦Inverness 70 – Perth 67.

Craigendarroch H. & Country Club, Braemar Rd, AB35 5XA, on A 93 ✆ 55858, Fax 55447, ← Dee Valley and Grampians, , , , , , squash – TV ☎ P – 110. AE VISA.
Lochnagar* : Meals** *(closed Tuesday to Thursday)* (dinner only) 18.50 **t.** 5.50 – (see also ***Oaks below) – **49 rm** 105.00/160.00 **st.**, 1 suite – SB.

Tullich Lodge, AB35 5SB, E : 1½ m. on A 93 ✆ 55406, Fax 55397, ← Dee Valley and Grampians, « Country house atmosphere », – ☎ P. AE VISA
April-October – **Meals** (booking essential) (bar lunch)/dinner 23.00 **st.** 6.00 – **10 rm** (dinner included) 95.00/190.00 **st.** – SB.

Balgonie Country House, Braemar Pl., AB35 5RQ, W : 1 m. by A 93 ✆ 55482, Fax 55482, ←, – rest TV ☎ P. VISA
closed 10 January-28 February – **Meals** (lunch by arrangement Monday to Saturday)/dinner 21.50 **t.** 7.00 – **9 rm** 52.50/95.00 **t.** – SB.

Darroch Learg, Braemar Rd, AB35 5UX, ✆ 55443, Fax 55252, ← Dee Valley and Grampians, – TV ☎ P. VISA
closed January – **Meals** (light lunch Monday to Saturday)/dinner 21.75 **st.** 6.00 – **20 rm** 42.00/94.00 **st.**

Glen Lui, 14 Invercauld Rd, AB35 5RP, ☎ 55402, Fax 55545, ≤, 🌳 – ⅍ rest 📺 ☎ Ⓟ. AE VISA
Meals 12.00/19.50 **st.** and dinner a la carte 4.20 – **17 rm** 26.00/66.00 **st.**, 2 suites – SB.

Alexandra, 12 Bridge Sq., AB35 5QJ, ☎ 55376, Fax 55466 – 📺 ☎ Ⓟ. AE VISA
Meals 16.00/25.00 **t.** and dinner a la carte 4.50 – **7 rm** 30.00/60.00 **t.** – SB.

Auld Kirk, Braemar Rd, AB35 5RQ, ☎ 55762, Fax 55707, « Former 19C church » – 📺 ☎ Ⓟ. VISA
Meals 10.00/15.95 **st.** and a la carte 3.95 – **6 rm** 25.00/44.00 **st.**

Moorside House without rest., 26 Braemar Rd, AB35 5RL, ☎ 55492, 🌳 – 📺 Ⓟ. VISA
April-October – **9 rm** 29.00/36.00 **st.**

Morvada without rest., Braemar Rd, AB35 5RL, ☎ 55501, 🌳 – 📺 Ⓟ.
7 rm.

Highland without rest., 12 Invercauld Rd, AB35 5RP, ☎ 55468, 🌳 – ⅍ 📺 Ⓟ.
6 rm 18.00/46.00 **st.**

Oaklands without rest., 30 Braemar Rd, AB35 5RL, ☎ 55013, 🌳 – 📺 Ⓟ
May-September – **3 rm** 30.00/44.00 **st.**

XXX **Oaks** (at Craigendarroch H.), Braemar Rd, AB35 5XA, on A 93 ☎ 55858, Fax 55447 – ⅍ Ⓟ. AE VISA
Meals (dinner only and Sunday lunch)/dinner 25.00 **t.** and a la carte 5.50.

X **Green Inn** with rm, 9 Victoria Rd, AB35 5QQ, ☎ 55701, Fax 55701 – 📺. VISA
closed 25 December and 2 weeks November – **Meals** (closed Saturday lunch and lunch November to March) 12.50 **t.** (lunch) and dinner a la carte 17.25/24.50 **t.** – **3 rm** 30.00/50.00 **st.** – SB.

BALLOCH Dunbarton (Strathclyde) 401 G 15 **Scotland G.** – ✉ Alexandria – ☎ 01389.
Envir. : N : Loch Lomond★★.
The Old Station Building, Balloch Road JH3 8LQ ☎ 753533 (summer only).
♦Edinburgh 72 – ♦Glasgow 20 – Stirling 30.

Cameron House ⛰, Loch Lomond, G83 8QZ, NW : 1½ m. by A 811 on A 82 ☎ 755565, Fax 759522, ≤ Loch Lomond, « Lochside setting », 🏋, ≘s, 🏊, 🏌9, 🎣, 🌳, park, 🎾, squash – 🛗 ⅍ rest 📺 ☎ Ⓟ – 🏛 300. AE VISA.
Meals - ***Brasserie*** a la carte 10.95/24.60 **st.** – (see also ***Georgian Room*** below) – **63 rm** 125.00/150.00 **st.**, 5 suites – SB.

XXX ✿ **Georgian Room** (at Cameron House H.), Loch Lomond, G83 8QZ, ☎ 755565, Fax 759522, ≤ Loch Lomond, « Lochside setting », 🌳 – ⅍ Ⓟ. AE VISA
closed lunch Saturday and Sunday – **Meals** (booking essential) 16.50/32.50 **st.** and a la carte
Spec. Terrine of duck liver and morel mushrooms, Loin of lamb on a potato, apple and mint parcel, honey and raspberry jus, Hot pear soufflé infused with dark chocolate, eau de vie cream.

BALLYGRANT Argyll. (Strathclyde) 401 B 16 – see Islay (Isle of).

BALQUHIDDER Perth. (Central) 401 G 14 – see Strathyre.

BANAVIE Inverness. (Highland) 401 E 13 – see Fort William.

BANCHORY Kincardine. (Grampian) 401 M 12 **Scotland G.** – pop. 4 935 – ECD : Thursday – ☎ 01330.
Envir. : Crathes Castle★★ (Gardens★★★) *AC*, E : 3 m. by A 93.
Exc. : Dunnottar Castle★★ (site★★★) *AC*, SW : 15½ m. by A 93 and A 957 – Aberdeen★★, NE : 17 m. by A 93.
🏌18 Kinneskie ☎ 822365 – 🏌9 Torphins ☎ (013398) 82115.
Bridge St. AB31 3SX ☎ 822000.
♦Edinburgh 118 – ♦Aberdeen 17 – ♦Dundee 55 – ♦Inverness 94.

Raemoir House ⛰, AB31 4ED, N : 2½ m. on A 980 ☎ 824884, Fax 822171, ≤, « 18C mansion with 16C Ha-House », ≘s, 🌳, park, 🎾 – 📺 ☎ ♿ Ⓟ – 🏛 50. AE VISA.
closed first 2 weeks January – **Meals** (bar lunch Monday to Saturday)/dinner 24.50 **t.** and a la carte 6.00 – **19 rm** 52.50/125.00 **t.**, 4 suites – SB.

Banchory Lodge ⛰, Dee St., AB31 3HS, ☎ 822625, Fax 825019, ≤, « Part 18C house on River Dee », ≘s, 🎣, 🌳 – 📺 ☎ Ⓟ. AE VISA
Meals 15.00/25.50 **st.** – **22 rm** 65.00/105.00 **st.**

Tor-na-Coille, Inchmarlo Rd, AB31 4AB, ☎ 822242, Fax 824012, 🌳, squash – 🛗 📺 ☎ Ⓟ – 🏛 90. AE VISA
closed 25 to 27 December – **Meals** a la carte 18.20/27.65 **t.** – **23 rm** 55.00/95.00 **t.** – SB.

BANFF Banff. (Grampian) 401 M 10 **Scotland G.** – pop. 4 402 – ECD : Wednesday – ☎ 01261.
See : Town★ – Duff House★ (baroque exterior★) *AC* – Mercat Cross★.
🏌18 Royal Tarlair, Buchan St., Macduff ☎ 832548/832897 – 🏌18 Duff House Royal, The Barnyards ☎ 812062.
Collie Lodge AB45 1AU ☎ 812419 (summer only).
♦Edinburgh 177 – ♦Aberdeen 47 – Fraserburgh 26 – ♦Inverness 74.

Eden House, AB45 3NT, S : 5 m. by A 98 and A 947 on Scattertie Dunlugas rd ☎ 821282, ≤, « Part 18C former shooting lodge overlooking River Deveron Valley », park, – ⊁ P.
closed Christmas and New Year – **Meals** (booking essential) (communal dining) (dinner only) (unlicensed) 18.00 **st.** – **5 rm** 32.00/68.00 **st.**

ATS Carmelite St. ☎ 812234

BARRA (Isle of) Inverness (Western Isles) 401 X 12/13 – ✉ Castlebay – ☎ 01871.

Castlebay – ☎ 01871.

Isle of Barra, Tangusdale Beach, PA80 5XW, NW : 2 m. on A 888 ☎ 810383, Fax 810385, ≤ Tangusdale Beach – ⊁ rest TV ☎ P. VISA
May-September – **Meals** (bar lunch)/dinner 16.50 **st.** 4.50 – **30 rm** 40.00/65.00 – SB.

Castlebay, PA80 5XD, ☎ 810223, ≤, – TV ☎. VISA
Meals (bar lunch)/dinner 15.00 **st.** 4.50 – **13 rm** 27.50/60.00 **st.** – SB.

Faire Mhaoldonaich, Nask, PA80 5XN, W : 1½ m. by A 888 on Nask rd ☎ 810441, ≤ – P
Meals (communal dining) – **3 rm.**

Tigh na Mara, PA80 5XD, ☎ 810304 – ⊁
April-October – **Meals** 9.00 – **5 rm** 17.00/34.00 **st.**

BEARSDEN Dunbarton. (Strathclyde) 401 G 16 – pop. 40 612 – ECD : Tuesday and Saturday – ✉ Glasgow – ☎ 0141.
◆Edinburgh 51 – ◆Glasgow 5.

La Bavarde, 19 New Kirk Rd, G61 9JS, ☎ 942 2202 – AE VISA
closed Sunday, Monday, 3 weeks July and 2 weeks Christmas-New Year – **Meals** 6.75 **t.** (lunch) and dinner a la carte 13.45/23.00 **t.** 4.50.

BEATTOCK Dumfries. (Dumfries and Galloway) 401 402 J 18 **Scotland G.** – ✉ Moffat – ☎ 01683.
Exc. : Grey Mare's Tail★★, NE : 10½ m. by A 74, A 701 and A 708.
◆Edinburgh 60 – ◆Carlisle 41 – ◆Dumfries 20 – ◆Glasgow 59.

Auchen Castle, DG10 9SH, N : 2 m. by A 74 ☎ 30407, Fax 30667, ≤, park – TV ☎ P – 45. AE VISA
closed 3 weeks Christmas - New Year – **Meals** (bar lunch)/dinner 17.00 **st.** 4.20 – **25 rm** 48.00/75.00 **st.** – SB.

Broomlands Farm without rest., DG10 9PQ, S : ½ m. by A 74 ☎ 30320, « Working farm », – P
3 rm.

BEAULY Inverness. (Highland) 401 G 11 – pop. 1 135 – ECD : Thursday – ☎ 01463.
◆Edinburgh 169 – ◆Inverness 13 – ◆Wick 125.

Lovat Arms, IV4 7BS, ☎ 782313, Fax 782768 – ⊁ rest TV ☎ P. VISA
Meals (bar lunch Monday to Saturday)/dinner 19.00 **s.** 3.60 – **22 rm** 37.00/90.00 **t.** – SB.

Priory, The Square, IV4 7BX, ☎ 782309, Fax 782531 – TV ☎. AE VISA
Meals 15.50 **t.** and a la carte 3.00 – **23 rm** 39.50/69.50 **t.** – SB.

Chrialdon, Station Rd, IV4 7EH, ☎ 782336, – ⊁ rest TV P. VISA
March-October – **Meals** 17.50 **st.** 6.50 – **8 rm** 21.00/54.00 **st.**

BENBECULA Inverness. (Western Isles) 401 X 11 – see Uist (Isles of).

BETTYHILL Sutherland. (Highland) 401 H 8 – ✉ Thurso (Caithness) – ☎ 01641.
◆Edinburgh 262 – ◆Inverness 93 – Thurso 31.

Tigh Na Sgoil, Kirtomy, KW14 7TB, NE : 3¼ m. by A 836 on Kirtomy rd ☎ 521455, Fax 521457, – TV ☎ P.
Meals (communal dining) 11.00 **st.** 2.50 – **5 rm** 26.50/53.00 **st.**

BLAIRGOWRIE Perth. (Tayside) 401 J 14 **Scotland G.** – pop. 5 208 – ☎ 01250.
Exc. : Scone Palace★★ *AC*, S : 12 m. by A 93.
26 Wellmeadow PH10 6AS ☎ 872960/873701.
◆Edinburgh 60 – ◆Dundee 19 – Perth 16.

Kinloch House, PH10 6SG, W : 3 m. on A 923 ☎ 884237, Fax 884333, ≤, « Country house atmosphere », park – ⊁ rest TV ☎ P. AE VISA
closed 18 to 30 December – **Meals** 14.95/27.95 **st.** 5.75 – **21 rm** (dinner included) 75.00/186.00 **st.**

Altamount House, Coupar Angus Rd, PH10 6JN, on A 923 ☎ 873512, Fax 876200, – ⊁ rest TV ☎ P
7 rm.

Rosemount Golf, Golf Course Rd, PH10 6LJ, SE : 1 ¾ m. by A 923 ☎ 872604, Fax 874496, – TV ☎ P – 50. VISA
Meals 10.50 **st.** and a la carte 4.50 – **12 rm** 38.00/56.00 **st.** – SB.

Laurels, PH10 6LH, SW : 1¼ m. on A 93 ☎ 874920, – ⊁ rest P. AE VISA
closed December – **Meals** (by arrangement) 10.00 **s.** 3.50 – **6 rm** 17.50/35.00 **s.**

BLAIRLOGIE Stirling. (Central) – see Stirling.

BOAT OF GARTEN Inverness. (Highland) 401 I 12 – ECD : Thursday – ☎ 01479.

Boat of Garten ℘ 831282.

♦Edinburgh 133 – ♦Inverness 28 – ♦Perth 89.

- **The Boat,** PH24 3BH, ℘ 831258, Fax 831414, – TV ☎ P. AE VISA JCB
  closed 8 November-20 December – **Meals** (bar lunch Monday to Saturday)/dinner 21.00 **t.** 6.80 – **32 rm** -/84.00 **t.** – SB.
- **Heathbank House,** Spey Av., PH24 3BD, ℘ 831234, – P.
  closed November - 25 December – **Meals** 17.00 **s.** 4.70 – **7 rm** 30.00/60.00 **s.**

BONAR BRIDGE Sutherland. (Highland) 401 G 10 – pop. 480 – ECD : Wednesday – ✉ Ardgay – ☎ 01863.

℘ 2333 (summer only).

♦Edinburgh 206 – ♦Inverness 50 – ♦Wick 76.

- **Kyle House,** Dornoch Rd, IV24 3EB, ℘ 766360 – rest P
  closed December and January – **Meals** (by arrangement) 10.00 **s.** – **6 rm** 16.00/38.00 **s.**

at Invershin W : 3 m. on A 836 – ✉ Lairg – ☎ 01549 :

- **Gneiss House** without rest., Balchraggan, IV27 4ET, ℘ 421282, – P. AE VISA.
  Booking essential – **3 rm** 15.00/36.00.

BOTHWELL Lanark. (Strathclyde) 401 402 H 16 **Scotland G.** – ✉ Glasgow – ☎ 01698.

See : Castle★ *AC.*

Envir. : Blantyre (David Livingstone Museum★) *AC,* W : 2 m. by A 724.

♦Edinburgh 39 – ♦Glasgow 8.5.

- **Silvertrees,** 27-29 Silverwells Cres., G71 8DP, ℘ 852311, Fax 852311 ext : 200, – TV ☎ P – 120. AE VISA
  Meals *(closed Sunday dinner)* 10.50/14.50 **t.** and a la carte 5.50 – **24 rm** 50.00/65.00 **t.**, 2 suites.

BRAE Shetland. (Shetland Islands) 401 P 2 – see Shetland Islands (Mainland).

BRAEMAR Aberdeen. (Grampian) 401 J 12 **Scotland G.** – ECD : Thursday except summer – ☎ 0133 97.

Envir. : Lin O'Dee★, W : 5 m.

Cluniebank Rd ℘ 41618.

Fife Mews, Mar Rd ℘ 41600.

♦Edinburgh 85 – ♦Aberdeen 58 – ♦Dundee 51 – Perth 51.

- **Invercauld Arms** (Mt. Charlotte Thistle), Invercauld rd, AB35 5YR, ℘ 41605, Fax 41428 – TV ☎ P – 60. AE VISA JCB
  Meals 9.75/15.95 **t.** and dinner a la carte 5.75 – **68 rm** 65.00/90.00 **t.** – SB.
- **Braemar Lodge,** Glenshee Rd, AB35 5YQ, ℘ 41627, Fax 41627, – TV P. VISA
  closed November-January – **Meals** (dinner only) 19.50 **st.** 4.75 – **5 rm** 34.00/68.00 **st.** – SB.

BREAKISH Inverness (Highland) 401 C 12 – see Skye (Isle of).

BREASCLETE Western Isles (Outer Hebrides) 401 Z 9 – see Lewis and Harris (Isle of).

BRECHIN Angus (Tayside) 401 M 13 – ☎ 01307.

- **Blibberhill Farm,** DD9 6TH, SW : 5 m. by A 935 and B 9134 off Melgund rd ℘ 830225, « Working farm », – TV P.
  Meals (communal dining) 9.00 **s.** – **3 rm** 17.50/35.00 **s.**

BRIDGEND Argyll. (Strathclyde) 401 B 16 – see Islay (Isle of).

BRIDGE OF AVON Banff. (Highland) 401 J 11 – ✉ Ballindalloch – ☎ 01807.

♦Edinburgh 157 – ♦Inverness 50.

- **Delnashaugh Inn,** AB37 9AS, on A 95 ℘ 500255, Fax 500389, ≤ – TV ☎ P. VISA.
  closed 27 November-6 March – **Meals** (bar lunch)/dinner 21.00 **t.** – **9 rm** (dinner included) 50.00/130.00 **t.**

BRIG O'TURK Perth. (Central) 401 G 15 **Scotland G.** – ✉ Callander – ☎ 01877.

Envir. : The Trossachs★★★ (Loch Katherine★★) W : 2 m. by A 821 – Hilltop Viewpoint★★★ (✻★★★) SW : 3½ m. by A 821.

♦Edinburgh 58 – ♦Glasgow 36 – Perth 47.

- **Dundarroch Country House** without rest., Trossachs, FK17 8HT, ℘ 376200, Fax 376202, ≤, , park – TV ☎ P. VISA.
  mid March-October – **3 rm** 42.75/119.00 **t.**

BROADFORD Inverness (Highland) 401 C 12 – see Skye (Isle of).

BRODICK Bute. (Strathclyde) 401 402 E 17 – see Arran (Isle of).

BRORA Sutherland. (Highland) 401 I 9 – pop. 1 728 – ECD : Wednesday – 01408.
Golf Rd 621417.
Edinburgh 234 – Inverness 78 – Wick 49.

Links, Golf Rd, KW9 6QS, 621225, Fax 621383, ← – VISA
April-October – **Meals** a la carte 13.00/20.00 **t.** 5.00 – **23 rm** 50.00/90.00 **t.**, 1 suite – SB.

Royal Marine, Golf Rd, KW9 6QS, 621252, Fax 621181, – VISA
closed 25 December – **Meals** 15.00/25.00 **t.** and a la carte 5.00 – **11 rm** 50.00/90.00 **t.** – SB.

Lynwood, Golf Rd, KW9 6QS, 621226, – VISA
closed March-November – **Meals** (communal dining) 10.00 **st.** – **4 rm** 22.00/38.00 **st.** – SB.

Tigh Fada without rest., Golf Rd, KW9 6QS, 621332, Fax 621332, ←, –
closed December and January – **3 rm** 16.00/40.00.

BROUGHTY FERRY Angus. (Tayside) 401 L 14 – see Dundee.

BUCKIE Banff. (Grampian) 401 L 10 – pop. 8 324 – ECD : Wednesday – 01542.
Buckpool, Barhill Rd 832236 – Strathlene 831798.
Cluny Sq. 834853 (summer only).
Edinburgh 195 – Aberdeen 66 – Inverness 56.

XX **Old Monastery,** Drybridge, AB56 2JB, SE : 3½ m. by A 942 on Deskford rd 832660, ←, « Former chapel overlooking Spey Bay » – VISA
closed Sunday, Monday, 2 weeks November and 3 weeks January – **Meals** a la carte 14.00/25.00 **t.** 6.50.

BUCKSBURN Aberdeen. (Grampian) 401 N 12 – see Aberdeen.

BUNESSAN Argyll. (Strathclyde) 401 B 15 – see Mull (Isle of).

BURNTISLAND Fife. (Fife) 401 K 15 – pop. 4 432 – 01592.
Burntisland Golf House Club, Dodhead 873247 – Kinghorn, McDuff Cres. 890345.
4 Kirkgate KY3 9BB 872667.
Edinburgh 20 – Dunfermline 10 – Kirkcaldy 6.

Kingswood, Kinghorn Rd, KY3 9LL, 872329, Fax 873123 – 100. VISA
Meals (bar lunch)/dinner 14.50 **t.** and a la carte 3.50 – **10 rm** 48.00/70.00 **t.** – SB.

BURRAY Orkney. (Orkney Islands) 401 L 7 – see Orkney Islands.

BUSBY Lanark. (Strathclyde) 401 402 H 16 – see Glasgow.

BUTE (Isle of) Bute. (Strathclyde) 401 402 E 16 – pop. 7733.
from Rothesay to Wemyss Bay (Caledonian MacBrayne Ltd) frequent services daily (30 mn) – from Rhubodach to Colintraive (Caledonian MacBrayne Ltd) frequent services daily (5 mn).

Rothesay – Rothesay – 01700.
Canada Hill 502244.

Alamein House, 28 Battery Pl., Promenade, PA20 9DU, 502395, ← – rest
closed 2 weeks October-November and Christmas-New Year – **Meals** 9.00 **st.** – **7 rm** 19.50/47.00 **st.** – SB.

CAIRNBAAN Argyll. (Strathclyde) 401 D 15 – see Lochgilphead.

CAIRNRYAN Wigtown (Dumfries and Galloway) 401 402 E 19 – Stranraer – 0581.
Edinburgh 149 – Ayr 73 – Dumfries 88 – Stranraer 20.

Merchant's House, Main St., DG9 8QX, 200215, ← – rm VISA
Meals (by arrangement) 12.50 **t.** 4.75 – **3 rm** 18.00/36.00 **t.**

CALGARY Argyll. (Strathclyde) 401 C 14 – see Mull (Isle of).

CALLANDER Perth. (Central) 401 H 15 **Scotland G.** – pop. 3 268 – ECD : Wednesday except summer – ☎ 01877.

See : Town★.

Exc. : The Trossachs★★★ (Loch Katrine★★) – Hilltop Viewpoint★★★ (※★★★) W : 10 m. by A 821.

Aveland Rd ℘ 330090.

Rob Roy & Trossachs Visitor Centre, Ancaster Sq. PA28 6EF ℘ 330342 (summer only).

♦Edinburgh 52 – ♦Glasgow 43 – ♦Oban 71 – Perth 41.

- **Roman Camp**, Main St., FK17 8BG, ℘ 330003, Fax 331533, ≤, « 17C hunting lodge in extensive gardens », park – rest TV ☎ & P. AE VISA
  Meals 18.50/32.00 **t.** and a la carte 6.00 – **11 rm** 79.00/129.00 **t.**, 3 suites – SB.
- **Arran Lodge,** Leny Rd, FK17 8AJ, ℘ 330976, – TV P.
  closed 10 January to 10 February – **Meals** (unlicensed) (residents only) (dinner only) 17.50 **s.** – **4 rm** 34.40/64.00 **s.** – SB.
- **Invertrossachs Country House** without rest., Invertrossachs, FK17 8HG, SW : 5 ½ m. by A 81 and Invertrossachs rd taking no through road after 1 ¾ m. ℘ 331126, Fax 331229, ≤, « Edwardian hunting lodge in extensive grounds », – TV ☎ P. AE VISA
  closed 20 December-3 January – **3 rm** 45.00/140.00 **st.**
- **Lubnaig,** Leny Feus, FK17 8AS, ℘ 330376, Fax 330376, – TV P. VISA
  April-October – **Meals** (residents only) (dinner only) 18.00 **t.** – **10 rm** 40.00/58.00 **t.** – SB.
- **Dalgair,** Main St., FK17 8BQ, ℘ 330283, Fax 331114 – TV ☎ P. AE VISA.
  Meals (bar lunch Monday to Friday)/dinner 10.00 **st.** and a la carte 3.95 – **8 rm** 26.00/45.00 **st.** – SB.
- **Priory,** Bracklinn Rd, FK17 8EH, ℘ 330001, – rest TV P.
  April-October – **Meals** 10.50 **t.** – **8 rm** 26.50/53.00 **t.** – SB.
- **Brook Linn**, Leny Feus, FK17 8AU, ℘ 330103, ≤, – TV P
  mid March-October – **Meals** 12.00 4.00 – **7 rm** 19.00/48.00 **st.**
- **East Mains House,** Bridgend, FK17 8AG, ℘ 330535, – TV P
  mid March - mid October – **Meals** (by arrangement) 10.00 **s.** – **5 rm** 16.00/36.00 **s.**
- **Highland House,** 8 South Church St., FK17 8BN, ℘ 330269 – TV. AE VISA
  February-mid November – **Meals** 15.75 **st.** 3.50 – **9 rm** 22.50/45.00 **t.** – SB.

CAMPBELTOWN Argyll. (Strathclyde) 401 D 17 – see Kintyre (Peninsula).

CANNICH Inverness. (Highland) 401 F 11 – ✉ Beauly – ☎ 01456.

♦Edinburgh 184 – ♦Inverness 28 – Kyle of Lochalsh 54.

- **Cozac Lodge**, IV4 7LX, W : 8 ½ m. ℘ 415263, Fax 415263, ≤ Loch Sealbanach and Affric Hills, « Converted shooting lodge », – rm TV P. AE VISA
  Meals (residents only) (dinner only) 17.50 **t.** 5.00 – **6 rm** (dinner included) 59.00/100.00 **st.** – SB.

CANONBIE Dumfries. (Dumfries and Galloway) 401 402 L 18 – ☎ 0138 73.

♦Edinburgh 80 – ♦Carlisle 15 – ♦Dumfries 34.

- XX **Riverside Inn** with rm, DG14 0UX, ℘ 71295 – rest TV P. VISA.
  closed 25 and 26 December, 1-2 January, 2 weeks February and 2 weeks November – **Meals** *(closed Sunday)* (booking essential) (bar lunch)/dinner 23.50 **t.** and a la carte 3.95 – **6 rm** 55.00/78.00 **st.** – SB.

CARDROSS Dunbarton. (Strathclyde) 401 G 16 – ☎ 01389.

♦Edinburgh 63 – ♦Glasgow 17 – Helensburgh 5.

- **Kirkton House**, Darleith Rd, G82 5EZ, ℘ 841951, Fax 841868, ≤, – TV ☎ P. AE VISA
  closed 18 December-13 January – **Meals** 19.50 **st.** 3.25 – **6 rm** 31.00/57.00 **st.** – SB.

CARNOUSTIE Angus. (Tayside) 401 L 14 – pop. 12 337 – ☎ 01241.

Medal Starter's Box, Princes St., Monifieth ℘ (01382) 532767 – Buddon Links, Links Par. ℘ 853249 – Panmure, Barry ℘ 853120 – Burnside, Links Par. ℘ 855344.

The Library, High St. DD7 6AN ℘ 852258 (summer only).

♦Edinburgh 68 – ♦Aberdeen 59 – ♦Dundee 12.

- XX **11 Park Avenue,** 11 Park Av., DD7 7JA, ℘ 853336 – AE VISA
  closed Saturday lunch, Sunday, and Monday – **Meals** 12.95/20.95 **st.** and dinner a la carte 4.50.

Les prix Pour toutes précisions sur les prix indiqués dans ce guide, reportez-vous à l'introduction.

CARRBRIDGE Inverness. (Highland) 401 I 12 – ECD : Wednesday – ☎ 01479.

Carrbridge ℘ 841623.

Main St. ℘ 841630 (summer only).

◆Edinburgh 135 – ◆Aberdeen 92 – ◆Inverness 23.

Feith Mho'r Country House ⛱, Station Rd, PH23 3AP, W : 1¼ m. ℘ 841621, ≤, – rest TV P
Meals 11.00 **t.** – **6 rm** 18.00/42.00 **t.**

CASTLEBAY Inverness (Western Isles) 401 X 12/13 – see Barra (Isle of).

CASTLE DOUGLAS Kirkcudbright. (Dumfries and Galloway) 401 402 I 19 **Scotland G.** – pop. 4 187 – ECD : Thursday – ☎ 01556.

Envir. : Threave Garden★★ *AC*, SW : 2½m. by A 75 – Threave Castle★ *AC*, W : 1 m.

Abercromby Rd ℘ 502801/502099.

Markethill Car Park ℘ 502611 (summer only).

◆Edinburgh 98 – ◆Ayr 49 – ◆Dumfries 18 – Stranraer 57.

Longacre Manor ⛱, Ernespie Rd, DG7 1LE, NE : ¾ m. on A 745 ℘ 503576, – TV ☎ P. VISA.
Meals 15.00 **st.** 3.75 – **4 rm** 30.00/60.00.

ATS Station Yard ℘ 503121/2

CLACHAN SEIL Argyll. (Strathclyde) 401 D 15 – see Seil (Isle of).

CLEISH Fife. (Tayside) 401 J 15 – see Kinross.

CLYDEBANK Dunbarton. (Strathclyde) 401 G 16 – pop. 45 717 – ☎ 0141.

Clydebank Municipal, Overtoun Rd, Dalmuir ℘ 952 8698 – Hardgate ℘ (01389) 73289.

◆Edinburgh 52 – ◆Glasgow 6.

Patio, 1 South Av., Clydebank Business Park, G81 2RW, ℘ 951 1133, Fax 952 3713 – rm rest TV ☎ & P – 150. AE VISA
closed 26 to 28 December and 1 to 3 January – **Meals** *(closed lunch Saturday, Sunday and Bank Holidays)* 11.95/15.50 **st.** and a la carte 6.25 – 9.25 – **78 rm** 57.50/67.50 **st.**, 2 suites – SB.

COLL (Isle of) Argyll. (Strathclyde) 401 A 14 – pop. 172.

from Arinagour to Oban (Caledonian MacBrayne Ltd) 3 weekly (3 h 20 mn) – from Arinagour to Isle of Mull (Tobermory) (Caledonian MacBrayne Ltd) 3 weekly (1 h 20 mn).

Arinagour – ✉ Coll – ☎ 0187 93.

Tigh-na-Mara ⛱ without rest., PA78 6SY, ℘ 354, ≤ Mull and Treshnish Isles, « Idyllic Hebridean setting », – P
8 rm.

COLONSAY (Isle of) Argyll. (Strathclyde) 401 B 15 – pop. 106 – ☎ 0195 12.

Isle of Colonsay ℘ 316.

from Scalasaig to Oban via Port Askaig and Kennacraig (Caledonian MacBrayne Ltd) (2 h 15 mn).

Scalasaig – ECD : Wednesday – ✉ Colonsay – ☎ 01951.

Isle of Colonsay ⛱, PA61 7YP, ℘ 200316, Fax 200353, ≤, – rest TV P. AE VISA JCB
March-early November and Christmas to New Year – **Meals** (bar lunch)/dinner 19.50 **st.** 4.60 – **11 rm** (dinner included) 75.00/150.00 **st.** – SB.

COLVEND Kircudbright. (Dumfries and Galloway) **Scotland G.** – ✉ Dalbeattie – ☎ 01556.

Envir. : Kippford★, NW : 2 m. by A 710.

Sandyhills, Dalbeattie ℘ 630398.

◆Edinburgh 99 – ◆Dumfries 19.

Clonyard House, DG5 4QW, NW : 1 m. on A 710 ℘ 630372, Fax 630422, – TV ☎ & P. AE VISA JCB
Meals a la carte 10.00/17.00 **t.** 3.80 – **15 rm** 38.00/66.00 **t.** – SB.

CONAN BRIDGE Inverness 401 G 11 – ☎ 01349.

◆Edinburgh 168 – ◆Inverness 12.

Kinkell House ⛱, Easter Kinkell, IV7 8HY, E : 3 m. by B 9163 and A 835 on B 9169 ℘ 861270, ≤, – TV P. VISA
closed January and February – **Meals** (booking essential) a la carte 8.60/17.25 **st.** 4.75 – **3 rm** 42.00/64.00 – SB.

CONNEL Argyll. (Strathclyde) 401 D 14 – ⊠ Oban – ☎ 01631.
♦Edinburgh 118 – ♦Glasgow 88 – ♦Inverness 113 – ♦Oban 5.

- **Ards House,** PA37 1PT, ✆ 710255, ≤, – ⊁ P. VISA.
closed December and January – **Meals** 15.00 **t.** 4.50 – **6 rm** 30.00/54.00 **t.** – SB.
- **Ronebhal,** PA37 1PJ, ✆ 710310, ≤, – ⊁ P. VISA.
April-mid October – **Meals** a la carte approx. 10.25 – **6 rm** 16.00/52.00 – SB.

CONTIN Ross and Cromarty 401 G 11 – ⊠ Strathpeffer – ☎ 01997.
♦Edinburgh 175 – ♦Inverness 19.

- **Coul House**, IV14 9EY, ✆ 421487, Fax 421945, ≤, – TV ☎ P. AE VISA JCB
Meals (lunch by arrangement)/dinner 25.50 **t.** and a la carte – **21 rm** 45.00/90.00 **t.**
- **Contin House**, IV14 9EB, by Contin Burial Ground rd ✆ 421920, Fax 421841, ≤, « 18C former manse », – ⊁ TV ☎ P. VISA.
closed January and February – **Meals** (residents only)(dinner only) 26.00 **st.** – **5 rm** 80.00/110.00 **t.** – SB.

COUPAR ANGUS Perth. (Tayside) 401 K 14 – ⊠ Blairgowrie – ☎ 01828.

- **Moorfield House,** Myreiggs Rd, PH13 9HS, NW : 2 ½ m. by A 923 ✆ 627303, Fax 627339, – TV ☎ P – 120. AE VISA.
Meals (lunch by arrangement)/dinner 20.50 **t.** – **12 rm** 35.00/96.00 **t.** – SB.

CRAIGELLACHIE Banff. (Grampian) 401 K 11 **Scotland G.** – ☎ 01340.
Envir. : Glenfiddich Distillery★, SE : 5 m. by A 941.
♦Edinburgh 190 – ♦Aberdeen 58 – ♦Inverness 53.

- **Craigellachie,** Victoria St., AB38 9SR, ✆ 881204, Fax 881253, – ⊁ rest TV ☎ P. AE VISA
Meals (buffet lunch)/dinner 26.50 **t.** – **30 rm** 58.50/119.00 **t.** – SB.

CRAIGHOUSE Argyll. (Strathclyde) 401 C 16 – see Jura (Isle of).

CRAIL Fife. (Fife) 401 M 15 **Scotland G.** – pop. 1 537 – ECD : Wednesday – ☎ 01333.
See : Town★★ – Old Centre★★ – Upper Crail★.
Envir. : Scottish Fisheries Museum★★, NE : 4 m. by A 917 – The East Neuk★★, SW : 4 m. by A 917 – Kellie Castle★ *AC*, NE : 5½m. by B 9171 and A 917.
18 Crail Golfing Society, Balcomie Clubhouse ✆ 450278.
Museum & Heritage Centre, 62-64 Marketgate KY10 3TC ✆ 450869 (summer only).
♦Edinburgh 50 – ♦Dundee 23 – Dunfermline 38.

- **Caiplie,** 53 High St., KY10 3RA, ✆ 450564 ⊁ rest
March-October – **Meals** 13.00 **s.** 3.75 – **7 rm** 16.50/33.00.

CRIANLARICH Perth. (Central) 401 G 14 – ☎ 01838.
♦Edinburgh 82 – ♦Glasgow 52 – Perth 53.

- **Allt-Chaorain House**, FK20 8RU, NW : 1 m. on A 82 ✆ 300283, Fax 300238, ≤, – ⊁ TV ☎ P. VISA
March-October – **Meals** (residents only) (communal dining) (dinner only) 18.00 **t.** – **8 rm** 40.00/70.00 **t.** – SB.

CRIEFF Perth. (Tayside) 401 I 14 **Scotland G.** – pop. 6 096 – ECD : Wednesday – ☎ 01764.
See : Town★ – **Envir.** : Drummond Castle Gardens★ *AC*, S : 2 m. by A 822 – Comrie (Scottish Tartans Museum★) W : 6 m. by A 85.
Exc. : Scone Palace★★ *AC*, E : 16 m. by A 85 and A 93.
18, 9 Perth Rd ✆ 652909 – 9 Muthill, Peak Rd ✆ 681523.
Town Hall, High St. PH7 3HU ✆ 652578.
♦Edinburgh 60 – ♦Glasgow 50 – ♦Oban 76 – Perth 18.

- **Murraypark,** Connaught Terr., PH7 3DJ, ✆ 653731, Fax 655311, – ⊁ rest TV ☎ P – 25. AE VISA
Meals (bar lunch)/dinner 25.50 **t.** and a la carte 5.50 – **20 rm** 45.00/70.00 **t.**, 1 suite – SB.
- **Leven House,** Comrie Rd, PH7 4BA, on A 85 ✆ 652529, ≤ – ⊁ rest TV P
closed December and January – **Meals** 12.00 **st.** 3.00 – **12 rm** 16.00/40.00 **st.** – SB.

CRINAN Argyll. (Strathclyde) 401 D 15 **Scotland G.** – ⊠ Lochgilphead – ☎ 0154 683.
See : Hamlet★ – **Exc.** : Kilmory Knap (Macmillan's Cross★) SW : 14 m.
♦Edinburgh 137 – ♦Glasgow 91 – ♦Oban 36.

- **Crinan,** PA31 8SR, ✆ 261, Fax 292, « ≤ commanding setting overlooking Loch Crinan and Sound of Jura », – TV ☎ P. AE VISA
closed 1 week Christmas – **Meals** (bar lunch)/dinner 27.50 **t.** 4.50 – (see also ***Lock 16*** below) – **22 rm** 75.00/250.00 **t.** – SB.
- XX **Lock 16** (at Crinan H.), PA31 8SR, ✆ 261, Fax 292, « ≤ commanding setting overlooking Loch Crinan and Sound of Jura » – P. VISA
closed Sunday and Monday – **Meals** - Seafood (booking essential) (dinner only) 40.00 **t.** 4.50.

CROCKETFORD Dumfries. (Dumfries and Galloway) 401 402 I 18 – ✉ Dumfries – ☎ 01556.
♦Edinburgh 73 – ♦Ayr 51 – Dumfries 10.

Galloway Arms, DG2 8RA, ℘ 690248 – TV P. VISA
Meals (bar lunch)/dinner 18.00 **st.** and a la carte 4.50 – **13 rm** 30.00/60.00 **st.** – SB.

CROMARTY Ross and Cromarty. (Highland) 401 H 10 **Scotland G.** – pop. 865 – ECD : Wednesday – ☎ 01381.
Exc. : Fortrose (Cathedral Church setting★) SW : 10 m. by A 832.
18 Fortrose & Rosemarkie, Ness Road East ℘ 620529.
♦Edinburgh 182 – ♦Inverness 26 – ♦Wick 126.

Royal, Marine Terr., IV11 8YN, ℘ 600217, ← – TV P. AE VISA
Meals (closed Sunday dinner) 12.50/19.50 **st.** and dinner a la carte – **10 rm** 32.00/55.00 **st.**

CROSSFORD Fife. (Fife) 401 J 15 – see Dunfermline.

CULLEN Banff. (Grampian) 401 L 10 **Scotland G.** – pop. 1 522 – ECD : Wednesday – ☎ 01542.
See : Cullen Auld Kirk★ (Sacrament house★, panels★).
Envir. : Deskford Church (Sacrament house★) S : 4 m. by A 98 and B 9018 – Portsoy★, E : 5½ m. by A 98.
18 The Links ℘ 840685 – 20 Seafield St. AB56 2FH ℘ 840757 (summer only).
♦Edinburgh 189 – ♦Aberdeen 59 – Banff 12 – ♦Inverness 61.

Bayview, Seafield St., AB56 2SU, ℘ 841031, ← – TV ☎. VISA.
closed Christmas-mid March – **Meals** (bar lunch)/dinner a la carte 9.75/20.25 **st.** 4.00 – **6 rm** 35.00/60.00 **st.**

CULLODEN Inverness. (Highland) 401 H 11 – see Inverness.

CULNAKNOCK Inverness. (Highland) 401 B 11 – see Skye (Isle of).

CULTS Aberdeen. (Grampian) 401 N 12 – see Aberdeen.

CUMBERNAULD Lanark. (Strathclyde) 401 I 16 – pop. 62 412 – ☎ 01236.
18 Palacerigg Country Park ℘ 734969.
♦Edinburgh 40 – ♦Glasgow 11 – Stirling 13.

Westerwood, St. Andrews Drive, G68 0EW, N : 2 m. by A 8011 ℘ 457171, Fax 738478, 18, – rm TV ☎ P – 150
41 rm.

Travel Inn, 4 South Muirhead Rd, G67 1AX, off A 8011 ℘ 725339, Fax 736380 – rm TV P. AE VISA.
Meals (Beefeater grill) a la carte approx. 16.00 **t.** – 4.95 – **37 rm** 33.50 **st.**

CUPAR Fife. (Fife) 401 K 15 – pop. 8 174 – ECD : Thursday – ☎ 01334.
The Granary, Coal Road, PY15 5YQ ℘ 652874.
♦Edinburgh 45 – ♦Dundee 15 – Perth 23.

Ostler's Close, Bonnygate, KY15 4BU, ℘ 655574 – AE VISA
closed Sunday and Monday – **Meals** a la carte 13.00/26.65 **t.** 4.00.

ATS St. Catherine St. ℘ 654003

DALBEATTIE Kirkcudbright. (Dumfries and Galloway) 401 402 I 19 **Scotland G.** – pop. 4 421 – ☎ 01556.
Envir. : Kippford★, S : 5 m. by A 710.
9 Dalbeattie ℘ 611421 – Town Hall DJ5 ℘ 610117 (summer only).
♦Edinburgh 94 – ♦Ayr 56 – ♦Dumfries 14 – Stranraer 62.

Auchenskeoch Lodge , DG5 4PG, SE : 5 m. on B 793 ℘ (01387) 780277, Fax 780277, , park – rest P. VISA
Easter-October – **Meals** (by arrangement) 13.50 **st.** 5.00 – **5 rm** 31.00/50.00 **st.**

Briardale House, 17 Haugh Rd, DG5 4AR, ℘ 611468 – rm rest TV P
closed November and December – **Meals** (by arrangement) 11.00 **s.** – **3 rm** 27.00/38.00 **s.** – SB.

DALCROSS Inverness. (Highland) – see Inverness.

DALIBURGH Inverness. (Western Isles) 401 X 12 – see Uist (Isles of).

DALRY (ST. JOHN'S TOWN OF) Kirkcudbright. (Dumfries and Galloway) 401 402 H 18 – pop. 5 886 – ✉ Castle Douglas – ☎ 0164 43.
♦Edinburgh 82 – ♦Dumfries 27 – ♦Glasgow 66 – Stranraer 47.

Lochinvar, 3 Main St., DG7 3UP, ℘ 210, Fax 210 – TV P. AE VISA
Meals (bar lunch)/dinner 20.00 **st.** 3.50 – **15 rm** 16.00/30.00 **st.** – SB.

DENNY Stirling. (Central) 401 I 15 **Scotland G.** – pop. 23 172 – ☎ 01324.

Exc. : Stirling★★, N : 8 m. by A 872.

◆Edinburgh 34 – ◆Glasgow 25 – Stirling 7.

- **Topps Farm** ⛰, Fintry Rd, FK6 5JF, W : 4 m. on B 818 ☎ 822471, Fax 822471, ← – ⛔ TV ♿ P. VISA
  Meals (by arrangement) 14.00 **st.** 4.00 – **8 rm** ☐ 30.00/42.00 **st.** – SB.

DERVAIG Argyll. (Strathclyde) 401 B 14 – see Mull (Isle of).

DIRLETON E. Lothian. (Lothian) 401 402 L 15 – see Gullane.

DORNIE Ross and Cromarty. (Highland) 401 D 12 – ✉ Kyle of Lochalsh – ☎ 0159 985 (3 fig.) and 01599 (6 fig.).

◆Edinburgh 212 – ◆Inverness 74 – Kyle of Lochalsh 8.

- **Castle Inn,** IV40 8DT, ☎ 233, Fax 233 – TV P. VISA
  Meals (bar lunch)/dinner a la carte 8.40/17.85 **t.** – **12 rm** ☐ 24.50/59.00 **t.**
- **Conchra House** ⛰, Ardelve, IV40 8DZ, ☎ 555233, Fax 555233, ← Loch Long, « Part Georgian country house », 🌳 – ⛔ P. VISA
  Meals 15.00 – **6 rm** ☐ 30.00/50.00.

DORNOCH Sutherland. (Highland) 401 H 10 **Scotland G.** – pop. 2 042 – ECD : Thursday – ☎ 01862.

See : Town★.

18, 18 Royal Dornoch, Golf Rd ☎ 810219 – ℹ The Square, IV25 35D ☎ 810400.

◆Edinburgh 219 – ◆Inverness 63 – ◆Wick 65.

- **Highfield** without rest., Evelix Rd, IV25 3HR, ☎ 810909, 🌳 – ⛔ TV P
  3 rm ☐ 28.00/44.00 **s.**

DOUNBY Orkney. (Orkney Islands) 401 K 6 – see Orkney Islands (Mainland).

DRUMNADROCHIT Inverness. (Highland) 401 G 11 **Scotland G.** – pop. 542 – ✉ Milton – ☎ 01456.

Envir. : Loch Ness★★ – Loch Ness Monster Exhibition★ *AC.*

◆Edinburgh 172 – ◆Inverness 16 – Kyle of Lochalsh 66.

- **Polmaily House** ⛰, IV3 6XT, W : 2 m. on A 831 ☎ 450343, Fax 450813, « Country house atmosphere », ⛱, 🌳, park, 🎾 – ⛔ TV ☎ P. VISA
  Meals 7.75/17.50 **t.** and dinner a la carte 7.00 – **10 rm** ☐ 29.50/105.00 **t.** – SB.

DRYMEN Stirling. (Central) 401 G 15 **Scotland G.** – pop. 1 565 – ECD : Wednesday – ☎ 01360.

Envir. : Loch Lomond★★, W : 3 m.

ℹ Drymen Library, The Square J63 0BL ☎ 60751 (summer only).

◆Edinburgh 64 – ◆Glasgow 18 – Stirling 22.

- **Buchanan Arms,** Main St., G63 0BQ, ☎ 60588, Fax 60943, Ⅎ₅, ≘s, ⛱, 🌳, squash – ⛔ TV ☎ P – 🏛 150. AE ⓓ VISA
  Meals 9.50/18.50 **st.** and a la carte 4.75 – **51 rm** ☐ 78.00/114.00 **st.**

DULNAIN BRIDGE Inverness. (Highland) 401 J 12 – ECD : Wednesday – ✉ Grantown-on-Spey (Moray Highland) – ☎ 01479.

◆Edinburgh 140 – ◆Inverness 31 – Perth 96.

- **Muckrach Lodge,** PH26 3LY, W : ½ m. on A 938 ☎ 851257, Fax 851325, ←, 🌳 – TV ☎ ♿ P. AE ⓓ VISA. ✻
  closed November – **Meals** 10.95/25.00 **t.** and a la carte 4.75 – **12 rm** ☐ 43.00/108.00 **t.** – SB.
- **Auchendean Lodge,** PH26 3LU, S : 1 m. on A 95 ☎ 851347, Fax 851347, ← Spey Valley and Cairngorms, 🌳 – ⛔ rest TV P. AE ⓓ VISA
  Meals (dinner only) 23.50 **st.** 3.50 – **8 rm** ☐ 36.00/69.00 **st.** – SB.

DUMBARTON Dunbarton. (Strathclyde) 401 G 16 **Scotland G.** – pop. 77 173 – ☎ 01389.

See : Dumbarton Castle (site★) *AC.*

Envir. : Loch Lomond★★, N : 5½ m. by A 82.

18 Vale of Leven, Northfield Rd, Bonhill ☎ 52351.

ℹ Milton, by Dumbarton A 82 (northbound) ☎ 742306 (summer only).

◆Edinburgh 64 – ◆Glasgow 12 – Greenock 17.

- **Forte Travelodge** without rest., Milton, G82 2TY, E : 3 m. by A 814 on A 82 ☎ 65202, Reservations (Freephone) 0800 850950 – TV ♿ P. AE VISA. ✻
  32 rm 33.50 **t.**

DUMFRIES Dumfries. (Dumfries and Galloway) 401 402 J 18 **Scotland G.** – pop. 21 164 – ECD : Thursday – 01387.

See : Town★ – Midsteeple★ A **A**.

Envir. : Lincluden College (Tomb★) *AC*, N : 1½ m. by College St. A.

Exc. : Drumlanrig Castle★★ (cabinets★) *AC*, NW : 16½ m. by A 76 A – Shambellie House Museum of Costume (Costume Collection★) S : 7¼ m. by A 710 A – Sweetheart Abbey★ *AC*, S : 8 m. by A 710 A – Caerlaverock Castle★ (Renaissance façade★★) *AC*, SE : 9 m. by B 725 B – Glenkiln (Sculptures★) W : 9 m. by A 780 - A - and A 75 – Ruthwell Cross★, SE : 12 m. by A 780 - B - A 75 and B 724.

18 Dumfries & Galloway, Laurieston Av., Maxwelltown ☎ 53582 A – 9 Crichton Royal, Bankend Rd ☎ 41122, B.

Whitesands, DG1 4TH ☎ 53862, Fax 50462 B.

◆Edinburgh 80 – ◆Ayr 59 – ◆Carlisle 34 – ◆Glasgow 79 – ◆Manchester 155 – ◆Newcastle upon Tyne 91.

DUMFRIES

High Street . . . . . A 18
Loreburn Centre . . . . . A 20

Aldermanhill Road . . . . . B 2
Bank Street . . . . . A 3
Buccleuch Street . . . . . A 4
Cardoness Street . . . . . B 5
Cassalands . . . . . A 6
Castle Street . . . . . A 7
Castle Douglas Road . . . . . A 8
Catherine Street . . . . . B 9
Corberry Avenue . . . . . A 10
Cornwall Mount Rd . . . . . B 12
Friars Vennel . . . . . A 13
Galloway Street . . . . . A 14
Glebe Street . . . . . B 15
Great King Street . . . . . A 16
Hermitage Drive . . . . . A 17
Loreburn Street . . . . . A 21
Nith Street . . . . . AB 22
Queen Street . . . . . B 23
Queensberry Street . . . . . A 24
Rae Street . . . . . B 26
St. Mary's Street . . . . . B 27
St. Michael Street . . . . . B 28
St. Michael's Bridge Road . . . . . A 30
Shakespeare Street . . . . . B 31
Union Street . . . . . A 32
Whitesands . . . . . A 34

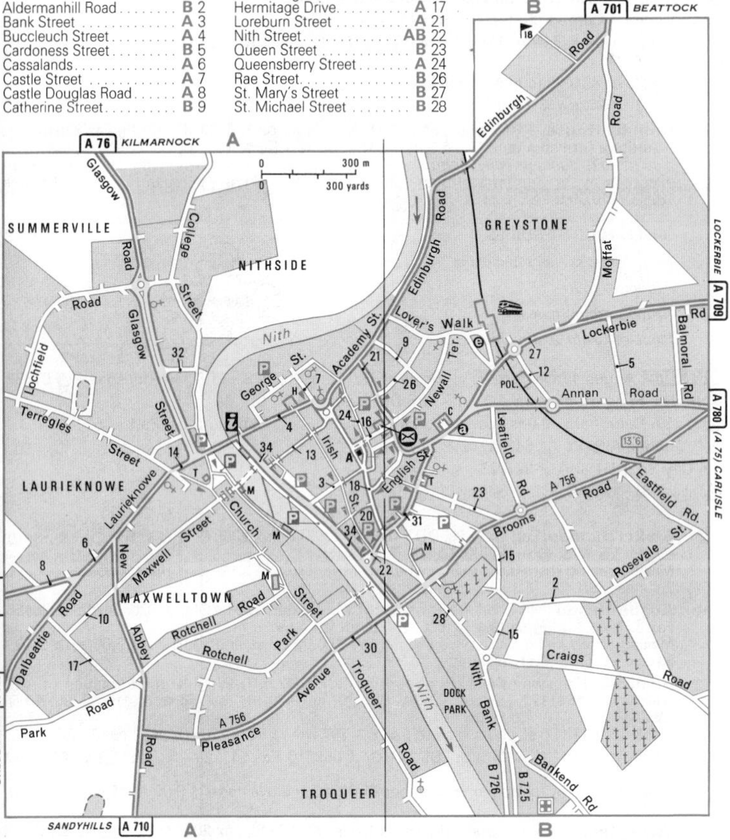

Cairndale, English St., DG1 2DF, ☎ 54111, Fax 50555, – – AE VISA. B **a**
Meals 9.50/17.00 **st.** and a la carte 5.00 – **76 rm** 75.00/95.00 **st.** – SB.

Station, 49 Lovers Walk, DG1 1LT, ☎ 54316, Fax 50388 – – 70. AE VISA B **e**
Meals (bar lunch)/dinner 14.50 **st.** and a la carte 4.00 – **32 rm** 65.00/80.00 **st.** – SB.

ATS Glasgow St. ☎ 63837/8

DUNAIN PARK Inverness. (Highland) – see Inverness.

DUNBAR E. Lothian. (Lothian) 401 M 15 **Scotland G.** – pop. 5 812 – ECD : Wednesday – 01368.

See : Tolbooth★ – John Muir's Birthplace★.

Exc. : Tantallon Castle★★ (clifftop site★★★) *AC*, NW : 10 m. by A 1087, A 1 and A 198 – Preston Mill★, W : 6 m. by A 1087, A 1 and B 1407 – Tyninghame★, NW : 6 m. by A 1 and A 198 – Museum of Flight★, W : 7 m. by A 1087, A 1 and B 1377.

East Links 862317 – Winterfield, St. Margarets, North Rd 862280.

143 High St. EH42 1ES 863353.

◆Edinburgh 28 – ◆Newcastle upon Tyne 90.

Courtyard, Woodbush Brae, EH42 1HB, 864169 – TV. AE VISA
Meals 12.50/15.00 **st.** and a la carte 5.50 – **7 rm** 24.50/62.00 **st.** – SB.

St. Laurence, North Rd, EH42 1AU, 862527, – rest
Meals (by arrangement) – **3 rm** 18.00/36.00 **st.**

Marine without rest., 7 Marine Rd, EH42 1AR, 863315,
March-October – **10 rm** 14.00/32.00 **st.**

DUNBLANE Perth. (Central) 401 I 15 **Scotland G.** – pop. 8 007 – ECD : Wednesday – 01786.

See : Town★ – Cathedral★ (west front★★).

Envir. : Doune★ (castle★ *AC*) W : 4½ m. by A 820 – Doune Motor Museum★ *AC*, W : 5½ m. by A 820 and A 84.

Stirling Rd 824428 (summer only).

◆Edinburgh 42 – ◆Glasgow 33 – Perth 29.

Cromlix House , Kinbuck, FK15 9JT, N : 3½ m. on B 8033 822125, Fax 825450, , « Antique furnishings », , , park, – rest TV – 30. AE VISA
closed mid January-early February – **Meals** (booking essential)(lunch by arrangement except May to September)/dinner 36.00 **t.** 6.00 – **6 rm** 100.00/160.00 **t.**, **8 suites** 180.00/240.00 **t.** – SB.

DUNDEE Angus. (Tayside) 401 L 14 **Scotland G.** – pop. 165 873 – ECD : Wednesday – 01382.

See : The Frigate Unicorn★ *AC* Y **A** – RRS Discovery★ *AC* Y B.

, (2x) Caird Park, Mains Loan Caird Park 453606 – Camperdown Park 623398.

Dundee Airport : 643242, SW : 1½ m. Z.

4 City Sq. DD1 3BA 227723.

◆Edinburgh 63 – ◆Aberdeen 67 – ◆Glasgow 83.

Plan opposite

Stakis Dundee, Earl Grey Pl., DD1 4DE, 229271, Fax 200072, , , , – rm rest TV – 400. AE VISA JCB Y **a**
Meals (carving rest.) 9.95/16.50 **t.** and a la carte 6.00 – 8.95 – **104 rm** 85.00/165.00 **t.**, 2 suites – SB.

Angus Thistle (Mt. Charlotte Thistle), 101 Marketgait, DD1 1QU, 226874, Telex 76456, Fax 322564 – TV – 500. AE VISA JCB Y **c**
Meals *(closed lunch Saturday and Sunday)* 8.00/13.60 **st.** and a la carte 5.60 – 9.40 – **53 rm** 78.75/93.50 **st.**, 5 suites.

Swallow, Kingsway West (Dundee Ring Rd), DD2 5JT, W : 4¾ m. at junction of A 85 with A 90 641122, Fax 568340, , , , – rest TV – 90. AE VISA Z
Meals 12.00/18.50 **st.** and a la carte 4.00 – **107 rm** 85.00/105.00 **st.**, 1 suite – SB.

Shaftesbury, 1 Hyndford St., DD2 1HQ, 669216, Fax 641598 – rest TV . AE VISA Z **e**
Meals (lunch by arrangement)/dinner 21.00 **st.** and a la carte 9.00 – **12 rm** 49.50/72.00 **st.** – SB.

Travel Inn, Discovery Quay, Riverside Drive, 203240, Fax 203237, – TV . AE VISA. Z **a**
Meals (grill rest.) a la carte approx. 16.00 **t.** – 4.95 – **40 rm** 33.50 **t.**

Travel Inn, Kingsway West, Invergowrie, DD2 5JU, NW : on A 90 561115, Fax 568431 – rm TV . AE VISA. Z
Meals (Beefeater grill) a la carte approx. 16.00 **t.** – 4.95 – **40 rm** 33.50 **t.**

Invermark without rest., 23 Monifieth Rd, DD5 2RN, 739430, Fax 739430, – TV . VISA. by A 930 Z
closed October – **4 rm** 30.00/40.00 **st.**

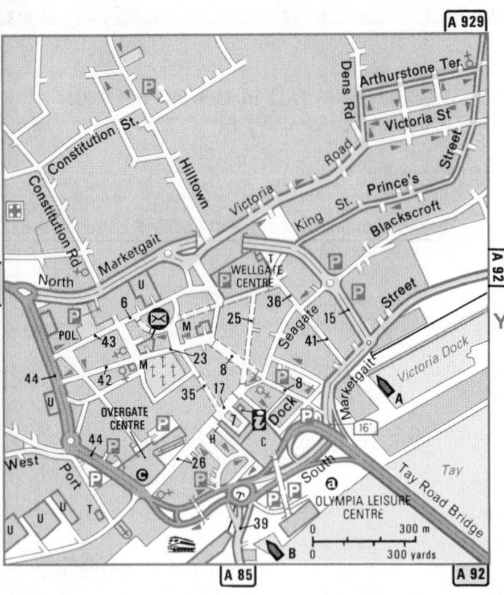

DUNDEE

Commercial Street . . . . Y 8
High Street . . . . Y 17
Murraygate . . . . Y 25
Nethergate . . . . Y 26
Overgate Centre . . . . Y
Reform Street . . . . Y 35
Wellgate Centre . . . . Y

Albert Street . . . . Z 2
Ancrum Road . . . . Z 5
Bell Street . . . . Y 6
City Square . . . . Y 7
Coupar Angus Road . . . . Z 9
Douglas Road . . . . Z 10
Drumgeith Road . . . . Z 12
Dudhope Terrace . . . . Z 13
East Dock Street . . . . Z 14
East Marketgait . . . . Y 15
Greendykes Road . . . . Z 16
Logie Street . . . . Z 18
Longtown Road . . . . Z 20
Mains Road . . . . Z 21
Meadowside . . . . Y 23
Moncur Crescent . . . . Z 24
Old Glamis Road . . . . Z 32
Provost Road . . . . Z 34
St. Andrews Street . . . . Y 36
South Union Street . . . . Y 39
Strathmartine Road . . . . Z 40
Trades Lane . . . . Y 41
Ward Road . . . . Y 42
West Bell Street . . . . Y 43
West Marketgait . . . . Y 44

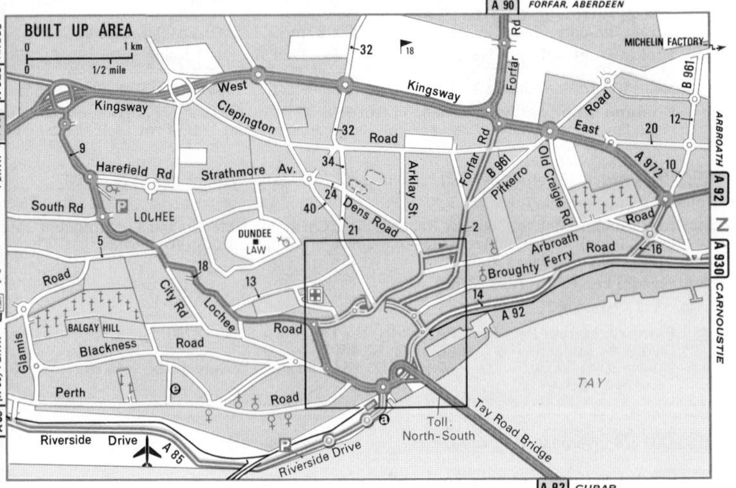

at Broughty Ferry E : 4½ m. by A 930 – Z – (Dundee Rd) – ✉ Dundee – ☎ 01382 :

- **Tayview** without rest., 71-73 Vincent St., DD5 2EZ, ☎ 779438 – ⇆. VISA. ✻
  11 rm ☕ 40.00/65.00 **t.**
- **Beach House,** 22 Esplanade, DD5 2EN, ☎ 776614, Fax 480241 – ⇆ rest TV ☎. VISA. ✻
  Meals 12.00 **s.** 4.00 – **5 rm** ☕ 38.00/45.00 **s.**

ATS 332 Clepington Rd ☎ 858327

DUNDONNELL Ross and Cromarty. (Highland) 401 E 10 **Scotland G.** – ✉ Garve – ☎ 01854.

Envir. : Loch Broom★★, N : 4½ m. via Alt na h–Airbhe.

Exc. : Falls of Measach★★, SE : 10 m. by A 832 – Corrieshalloch Gorge★, SE : 11½ m. by A 832 and A 835.

◆Edinburgh 215 – ◆ Inverness 59.

- **Dundonnell,** IV23 2QR, ☎ 633204, Fax 633366, ≤ Dundonnell Valley – ⇆ rest TV ☎ P – 60. VISA
  mid March-mid November and Christmas-New Year – **Meals** (bar lunch)/dinner 22.75 **st.** and a la carte 4.00 – **30 rm** ☕ 45.00/79.00 – SB.

DUNFERMLINE Fife. (Fife) 401 J 15 **Scotland G.** – pop. 29 436 – ECD : Wednesday – ☎ 01383.

See : Abbey★ (Abbey Church★★) *AC*.

Envir. : Forth Bridges★★, S : 5 m. by A 823 and B 980.

Exc. : Culross★★★ (Village★★★, Palace★★ *AC*, Study★ *AC*) W : 7 m. by A 994 and B 9037.

18 Canmore, Venturefair ✆ 724969 – 18 Pitreavie, Queensferry Rd ✆ 722591 – 9 Saline, Kinneddar Hill ✆ 852591.

13-15 Maygate KY12 7NE ✆ 720999 (summer only).

♦Edinburgh 16 – ♦Dundee 48 – Motherwell 39.

King Malcolm Thistle (Mt. Charlotte Thistle), Queensferry Rd, KY11 5DS, S : 1 m. on A 823 ✆ 722611, Fax 730865 – rm rest – 150
48 rm.

at Crossford SW : 1 ¾ m. on A 994 – ✉ Dunfermline – ☎ 01383 :

Keavil House, Main St., KY12 8QW, ✆ 736258, Fax 621600, – 150. AE VISA
Meals (bar lunch)/dinner 19.50 **st.** – **30 rm** 55.00/98.00 **t.** – SB.

ATS 14 Dickson St., Elgin St. Est. ✆ 722802

DUNKELD Perth. (Tayside) 401 J 14 **Scotland G.** – ECD : Thursday – ☎ 01350.

See : Village★ – Cathedral Street★.

9 Dunkeld & Birnam, Fungarth ✆ 727524.

The Cross PH8 0AN ✆ 727688 (summer only).

♦Edinburgh 58 – ♦Aberdeen 88 – ♦Inverness 98 – Perth 14.

Kinnaird, Dalguise, PH8 0LB, NW : 6 ¾ m. by A 9 on B 898 ✆ (01796) 482440, Fax 482289, ≤ Tay valley and hills, « Sporting estate, antique furnishings », park, – rest . AE VISA.
closed February – **Meals** 25.00/40.00 **t.** 8.50 – **8 rm** 175.00/225.00 **t.**, 1 suite.

Stakis Dunkeld, PH8 0HX, ✆ 727771, Fax 728924, ≤, « Tayside setting », park, – rm – 85. AE VISA
Meals (light lunch)/dinner 24.00 **st.** and a la carte – 9.75 – **83 rm** 92.00 **st.**, 3 suites – SB.

Bheinne Mhor, Perth Rd, Birnam, PH8 0DH, S : ¾ m. by A 923 ✆ 727779, – .
closed mid December-mid January – **Meals** (by arrangement) 12.00 **4 rm** 18.00/38.00 **st.** – SB.

DUNOON Argyll. (Strathclyde) 401 F 16 – pop. 13 781 – ECD : Wednesday – ☎ 01369.

9 Innellan, Knockamillie Rd ✆ 3546.

from Dunoon Pier to Gourock Railway Pier (Caledonian MacBrayne Ltd) frequent services daily (20 mn) – from Hunters Quay to McInroy's Point, Gourock (Western Ferries (Clyde) Ltd) frequent services daily (20 mn).

7 Alexandra Par. PA23 8AB ✆ 3785.

♦Edinburgh 73 – ♦Glasgow 27 – ♦Oban 77.

Enmore, Marine Par., Kirn, PA23 8HH, N : 1 m. on A 815 ✆ 2230, Fax 2148, ≤ Firth of Clyde, squash – rest . VISA
closed 20 to 30 December – **Meals** 10.00/25.00 **st.** and a la carte 5.50 – **10 rm** 39.00/120.00 **st.** – SB.

ATS 247 Argyll St. ✆ 2853

DUNVEGAN Inverness. (Highland) 401 A 11 – see Skye (Isle of).

DUROR Argyll. (Strathclyde) 401 E 14 – ✉ Appin – ☎ 0163 174.

♦Edinburgh 125 – Fort William 19 – ♦Oban 31.

Stewart, Glen Duror, PA38 4BW, ✆ 268, Fax 328, ≤, – rest . AE VISA
April-mid October – **Meals** (bar lunch Monday to Saturday)/dinner 25.00 **t.** 5.30 – **19 rm** 40.00/80.00 **t.** – SB.

DYCE Aberdeen. (Grampian) 401 N 12 – see Aberdeen.

EASDALE Argyll. (Strathclyde) 401 D 15 – see Seil (Isle of).

EAST KILBRIDE Lanark. (Strathclyde) 401 402 H 16 – pop. 73 378 – ECD : Wednesday – ☎ 0135 52 (5 fig.) and 01355 (6 fig.).

18 Torrance House, Strathaven Rd ✆ 48638.

♦Edinburgh 46 – ♦Ayr 35 – ♦Glasgow 10.

Westpoint, Stewartfield Way, G74 5LA, NW : 2 ¼ m. on A 726 ✆ 36300, Fax 33552, squash – rm rest – 150. AE VISA.
Meals 14.50/24.00 **t.** and a la carte – ***Point Grill* : Meals** *(closed Saturday and Sunday)* 22.50 **t.** – (see also ***Simpsons*** below) – **73 rm** 95.00/115.00 **t.**, 1 suite.

Bruce Swallow, 34 Cornwall St., G74 1AF, ✆ 29771, Fax 42216 – |♦| ⇔ rm TV ☎ P – 🏛 250. AE ⓓ VISA
Meals (bar lunch)/dinner 14.50 **st.** and a la carte – **78 rm** ☐ 57.00/80.00 **st.** – SB.

Stuart, 1 Cornwall Way, G74 1JR, ✆ 21161, Fax 64410 – |♦| TV ☎ – 🏛 200. AE ⓓ VISA
closed 25 December and 1 January – **Meals** 10.00/20.00 **t.** and a la carte – **38 rm** ☐ 57.00/100.00 **t.**, 1 suite – SB.

Crutherland ⛶, Strathaven Rd, G75 0QZ, SE : 2 m. on A 726 ✆ 37633, Fax 37633, ⛶, park – TV ☎ P – 🏛 40. AE ⓓ VISA
Meals 9.95 **t.** (lunch) and a la carte 8.75/22.00 **t.** 🍷 5.95 – **18 rm** ☐ 55.00/80.00 **st.**, 1 suite.

Travel Inn, Brunel Way, The Murray, G75 0JY, ✆ 22809, Fax 30517 – ⇔ rm TV ♿ P. AE ⓓ VISA. ✱
Meals (Beefeater grill) a la carte approx. 16.00 **t.** – ☐ 4.95 – **40 rm** 33.50 **t.**

XXX **Simpsons** (at Westpoint H.), Stewartfield Way, G74 5LA, NW : 2¼ m. on A 726 ✆ 36300, Fax 33552 – ⇔ ▤ P. AE ⓓ VISA
closed Monday dinner – **Meals** (booking essential) (dinner only) 24.00 **t.** and a la carte 🍷 5.50.

Se cercate un albergo tranquillo,
oltre a consultare le carte dell'introduzione,
rintracciate nell'elenco degli esercizi quelli con il simbolo ⛶ o ⛶.

EDINBURGH Midlothian. (Lothian) 401 K 16 **Scotland G.** – pop. 418 914 – ☎ 0131.

See : City★★★ – Edinburgh International Festival★★★ (August) – National Gallery of Scotland★★★ DY **M4** – Royal Botanic Garden★★★ AV – The Castle★★ *AC* DYZ : Site★★★ – Palace Block (Honours of Scotland★★★) – St. Margaret's Chapel (✱★★★) – Great Hall (Hammerbeam Roof★★) – ≤★★ from Argyle and Mill's Mount DZ – Abbey and Palace of Holyroodhouse★★ *AC* (Plasterwork Ceilings★★★, ✱★★ from Arthur's Seat) BV – Royal Mile★★ : St. Giles' Cathedral★★ (Crown Spire★★★) EYZ – Gladstone's Land★ *AC* EYZ **A** – Canongate Talbooth★ EY **B** – New Town★★ (Charlotte Square★★★ CY **14** – Royal Museum of Scotland (Antiquities)★★ EZ **M2** – The Georgian House★ *AC* CY **D** – National Portrait Gallery★ EY **M3** – Dundas House★ EY **E**) – Victoria Street★ EZ **84** – Scott Monument★ (≤★) *AC* EY **F** – Craigmillar Castle★ *AC* BX – Calton Hill (✱★★★ *AC* from Nelson's Monument) EY.

Envir. : Edinburgh Zoo★★ *AC* AV – Hill End Ski Centre (✱★★) *AC*, S : 5½ m. by A 702 BX – The Royal Observatory (West Tower ≤★) *AC* BX – Ingleston, Scottish Agricultural Museum★, W : 6½ m. by A 8 AV.

Exc. : Rosslyn Chapel★★ *AC* (Apprentice Pillar★★★) S : 7½ m. by A 701 - BX - and B 7006 – Forth Bridges★★, NW : 9½ m. by A 90 AV – Hopetoun House★★ *AC*, NW : 11½ m. by A 90 - AV - and A 904 – Dalmeny★ – Dalmeny House★ *AC*, St. Cuthbert's Church★ (Norman South Doorway★★) NW : 7 m. by A 90 AV – Crichton Castle (Italianate courtyard range★) *AC*, SE : 10 m. by A 7 - X - and B 6372.

18, 18 Braid Hills, Braid Hills Rd ✆ 447 6666, BX – 18 Craigmillar Park, 1 Observatory Rd ✆ 667 2837, BX – 18 Carrick Knowe, Glendevon Park ✆ 337 1096, AX – 18 Duddingston Road West ✆ 661 1005, BV – 18 Silverknowes, Parkway ✆ 336 3843, AV – 18 297 Gilmerton Rd ✆ 664 8580, BX – 9 Portobello Stanley St. ✆ 669 4361, BV – 18 (2x) Dalmahoy, Kirknewton ✆ 333 4105/1845, AX.

✈ Edinburgh Airport : ✆ 333 1000, W : 6 m. by A 8 AV – **Terminal** : Waverley Bridge.

🚗 ✆ 0345 090700.

🅘 Edinburgh & Scotland Information Centre, 3 Princes St., EH2 2QP ✆ 557 1700 – Edinburgh Airport, Tourist Information Desk ✆ 333 2167.

♦Glasgow 46 – ♦Newcastle upon Tyne 105.

Plans on following pages

Caledonian (Q.M.H.), Princes St., EH1 2AB, ✆ 225 2433, Telex 72179, Fax 225 6632 – |♦| ⇔ rm ▤ rest TV ☎ ♿ P – 🏛 300. AE ⓓ VISA JCB. ✱ CY **n**
Carriages :* Meals** 17.95/24.50 **t.** 🍷 5.75 (see also ***Pompadour below) – ☐ 14.95 – **228 rm** 125.00/285.00 **t.**, 11 suites – SB.

Balmoral (Forte), Princes St., EH2 2EQ, ✆ 556 2414, Telex 727282, Fax 557 3747, ⛶, ⛶, ⛶ – |♦| ⇔ rm ▤ rest TV ☎ ♿ 🚗 – 🏛 380. AE ⓓ VISA JCB. ✱ EY **n**
Bridges :* Meals** 20.00 **st.** (dinner) and a la carte 16.00/20.25 **st.** 🍷 7.00 - (see also ***Grill below) – ☐ 12.95 – **168 rm** 125.00/225.00 **st.**, 21 suites – SB.

Sheraton Grand, 1 Festival Sq., EH3 9SR, ✆ 229 9131, Telex 72398, Fax 228 4510, ⛶, ⛶, ⛶ – |♦| ⇔ rm ▤ TV ☎ ♿ P – 🏛 485. AE ⓓ VISA JCB. ✱ CDZ **v**
***Grill :* Meals** 23.00**t.** (lunch) and a la carte approx. 34.00 **t.** 🍷 7.00 – ***Terrace :* Meals** 19.50**t.** (lunch) and a la carte approx. 17.00 **t.** 🍷 7.00 – ☐ 13.00 – **255 rm** 145.00/195.00 **st.**, 6 suites.

George Inter-Continental, 19-21 George St., EH2 2PB, ✆ 225 1251, Fax 226 5644 – |♦| ⇔ rm TV ☎ P – 🏛 200. AE ⓓ VISA JCB. ✱ DY **z**
Meals 13.95/15.95 **t.** and a la carte 🍷 6.50 – ☐ 12.95 – **193 rm** 130.00/150.00 **t.**, 2 suites – SB.

Dalmahoy H. Golf & Country Club (Country Club) ⛶, Kirknewton, EH27 8EB, SW : 7 m. on A 71 ✆ 333 1845, Fax 335 3203, ≤, ⛶, ⛶, 18, ⛶, park, ⛶, squash – |♦| ⇔ ▤ rest TV ☎ ♿ P – 🏛 200. AE ⓓ VISA. ✱ AX
Meals 14.00/23.50 **t.** and dinner a la carte – ☐ 9.95 – **114 rm** ☐ 105.00/140.00 **t.**, 1 suite – SB.

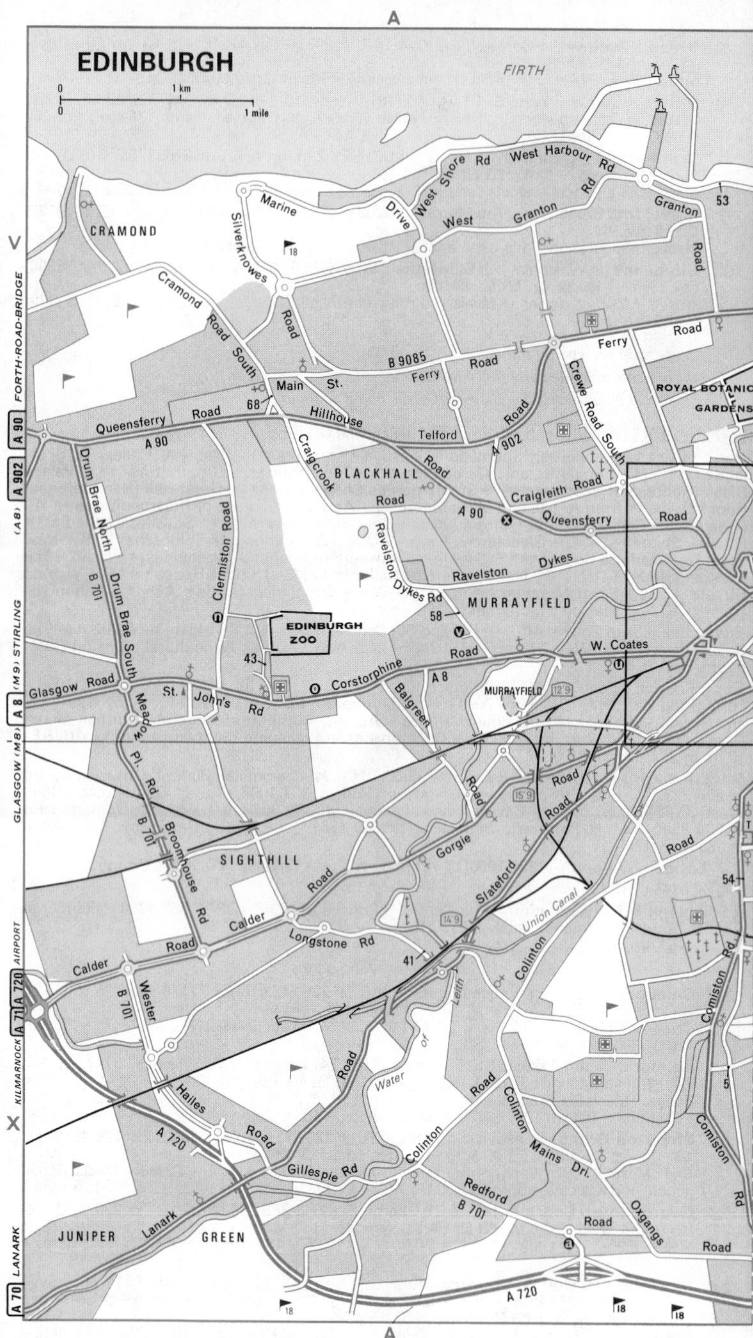
EDINBURGH
0
1 km
0
1 mile
FIRTH
CRAMOND
Marine Drive
West Shore Rd
West Harbour Rd
West Granton Rd
Granton Road
Silverknowes Road
Cramond Road South
B 9085
Ferry Road
Main St.
Queensferry Road
A 90
Hillhouse Road
Telford Road
A 902
Crewe Road South
ROYAL BOTANIC GARDENS
Craigcrook Road
BLACKHALL
Craigleith Road
Queensferry Road
Drum Brae North
Clermiston Road
Ravelston Dykes Rd
Ravelston Dykes
MURRAYFIELD
B 701
Drum Brae South
EDINBURGH ZOO
Corstorphine Road
A 8
W. Coates
Glasgow Road
St. John's Rd
Balgreen Road
MURRAYFIELD
Meadow Pl. Rd
Broomhouse Rd
SIGHTHILL
Gorgie Road
Slateford Road
Union Canal
Calder Road
Longstone Rd
Colinton Road
Comiston Rd
Calder Wester
Water of Leith
Hailes Road
A 720
Gillespie Rd
Colinton Road
Colinton Mains Dri.
Redford Road
B 701
Oxgangs Road
Comiston Rd
JUNIPER
Lanark
GREEN
A 720
FORTH-ROAD-BRIDGE
A 90
A 902
(A8)
(M9) STIRLING
A 8
GLASGOW (M8)
AIRPORT
A 720
A 71
KILMARNOCK
LANARK
A 70
A
V
X
A
53
68
58
43
41
54
18

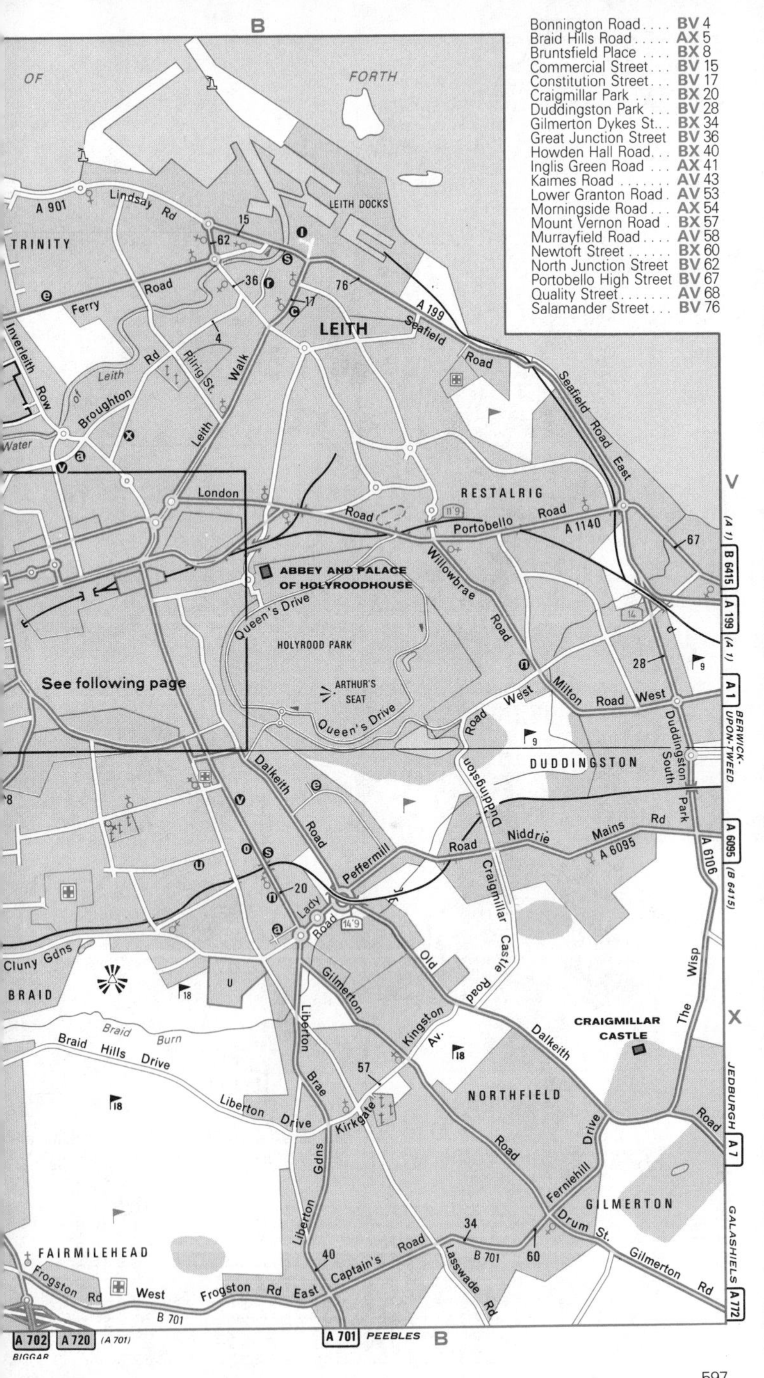

Bonnington Road	BV 4
Braid Hills Road	AX 5
Bruntsfield Place	BX 8
Commercial Street	BV 15
Constitution Street	BV 17
Craigmillar Park	BX 20
Duddingston Park	BV 28
Gilmerton Dykes St.	BX 34
Great Junction Street	BV 36
Howden Hall Road	BX 40
Inglis Green Road	AX 41
Kaimes Road	AV 43
Lower Granton Road	AV 53
Morningside Road	AX 54
Mount Vernon Road	BX 57
Murrayfield Road	AV 58
Newtoft Street	BX 60
North Junction Street	BV 62
Portobello High Street	BV 67
Quality Street	AV 68
Salamander Street	BV 76

EDINBURGH
CENTRE

Street	Grid	No.
Castle Street	DY	
Frederick Street	DY	
George Street	DY	
Hanover Street	DY	
High Street	EYZ	37
Lawnmarket	EYZ	46
Princes Street	DY	
St. James Centre	EY	
Waverley Market	EY	
Bernard Terrace	EZ	3
Bread Street	DZ	6
Bristo Place	EZ	7
Candlemaker Row	EZ	9
Castlehill	DZ	10
Chambers Street	EZ	12
Chapel Street	EZ	13
Charlotte Square	CY	14
Deanhaugh Street	CY	23
Douglas Gardens	CY	25
Drummond Street	EZ	27
Forrest Road	EZ	31
Gardner's Crescent	CZ	32
George IV Bridge	EZ	33
Grassmarket	DZ	35
Home Street	DZ	38
Hope Street	CY	39
Johnston Terrace	DZ	42
King's Bridge	DZ	44
King's Stables Road	DZ	45
Leith Street	EY	47
Leven Street	DZ	48
Lothian Street	EZ	51
Mound (The)	DY	55
North Bridge	EY	61
North St. Andrew Street	EY	66
Raeburn Place	CY	69
Randolph Crescent	CY	71
St. Andrew Square	EY	73
St. Mary's Street	EY	75
Shandwick Place	CYZ	77
South Charlotte Street	DY	78
South St. David Street	DEY	79
Spittal Street	DZ	83
Victoria Street	EZ	84
Waterloo Place	EY	87
Waverley Bridge	EY	89
West Maitland Street	CZ	92

Howard, 32-36 Gt. King St., EH3 6QH, 557 3500, Fax 557 6515, « Georgian town houses » – rest – 45. AE VISA DY **s**
closed first week January – **Meals** (dinner only) 18.95 **st.** and a la carte – **16 rm** 110.00/255.00 **st.** – SB.

Scandic Crown, 80 High St., EH1 1TH, 557 9797, Telex 727298, Fax 557 9789, – rm rest – 220 EY **z**
228 rm, 10 suites.

Swallow Royal Scot, 111 Glasgow Rd, EH12 8NF, W : 4 ½ m. on A 8 334 9191, Fax 316 4507, – rm rest – 300. AE VISA AV
Meals 14.75/18.75 **st.** and dinner a la carte – **255 rm** 105.00/130.00 **st.**, 4 suites – SB.

Hilton National, 69 Belford Rd, EH4 3DG, 332 2545, Telex 727979, Fax 332 3805 – rm – 140. AE VISA JCB CY **i**
Meals (bar lunch Saturday) 12.50/16.50 **t.** and dinner a la carte 6.00 – 11.25 – **144 rm** 85.00/195.00 **st.** – SB.

Capital Moat House (Q.M.H.), Clermiston Rd, EH12 6UG, 334 3391, Fax 334 9712, – rm – 300. AE VISA AV **n**
Meals (buffet lunch)/dinner 15.95 **t.** – 9.50 – **111 rm** 82.50/125.00 **st.** – SB.

Mount Royal (Jarvis), 53 Princes St., EH2 2DG, 225 7161, Telex 727641, Fax 220 4671, – – 50 DY **a**
156 rm.

Royal Terrace, 18 Royal Terrace, EH7 5AQ, 557 3222, Fax 557 5334, – – 100. AE VISA. EY **i**
Meals *(closed lunch Saturday and Sunday)* a la carte 23.00 approx. – 8.50 – **92 rm** 105.00/190.00 **st.**, 1 suite – SB.

Malmaison, 1 Tower Pl., Leith, EH6 7DB, 555 6868, Fax 555 6999 – – 25. AE VISA BV **i**
Meals - Brasserie a la carte approx. 17.50 **st.** 7.95 – 10.00 – **19 rm** 70.00/85.00 **st.**, 6 suites.

Forte Posthouse Edinburgh, Corstorphine Rd, EH12 6UA, 334 0390, Fax 334 9237 – rm – 120. AE VISA. AV **o**
Meals a la carte approx. 15.00 **t.** – **200 rm** 59.50 **t.**

King James Thistle (Mt. Charlotte Thistle), 107 Leith St., EH1 3SW, 556 0111, Telex 727200, Fax 557 5333 – rm – 250. AE VISA. EY **u**
Meals 15.00/18.50 **t.** and a la carte – 8.75 – **142 rm** 79.00/99.00 **st.**, 5 suites.

Stakis Edinburgh Grosvenor, Grosvenor St., EH12 5EF, 226 6001, Fax 220 2387 – – 300. AE VISA JCB CZ **a**
Meals *(closed lunch Saturday and Sunday)* 9.50/14.95 **t.** and a la carte – 8.50 – **135 rm** 89.00/109.00 **t.**, 1 suite – SB.

Channings, South Learmonth Gdns, EH4 1EZ, 315 2226, Fax 332 9631 – rest . AE VISA. CY **e**
Meals (light lunch Saturday and Sunday) 9.95/16.50 and dinner a la carte 4.80 – **48 rm** 89.00/128.00 **st.** – SB.

Ellersly Country House (Jarvis), 4 Ellersly Rd, EH12 6HZ, 337 6888, Fax 313 2543, – rm – 70 AV **v**
57 rm.

Holiday Inn Garden Court, 107 Queensferry Rd, EH4 3HL, 332 2442, Telex 72541, Fax 332 3408, – rm rest – 60 AV **x**
119 rm.

Thrums, 14-15 Minto St., EH9 1RQ, 667 5545, Fax 667 8707, – . VISA BX **v**
Meals a la carte 4.65/12.65 **t.** – **15 rm** 37.00/70.00 **t.** – SB.

Lodge, 6 Hampton Terr., West Coates, EH12 5JD, 337 3682, Fax 313 1700 – . VISA. AV **u**
Meals *(closed Sunday)* (dinner only) a la carte 11.00/18.90 **t.** 4.95 – **12 rm** 40.00/80.00 **st.** – SB.

Travel Inn, 228 Willowbrae Rd, EH8 7NG, 661 3396, Fax 652 2789 – rm . AE VISA. BV **n**
Meals (Beefeater grill) a la carte approx. 16.00 **t.** – 4.95 – **40 rm** 33.50 **t.**

Forte Travelodge without rest., 48 Dreghorn Link, City Bypass, EH13 9QR, 441 4296, Reservations (Freephone) 0800 850950 – . AE VISA. AX **a**
40 rm 33.50 **t.**

Sibbet House without rest., 26 Northumberland St., EH3 6LS, 556 1078, Fax 557 9445, « Georgian town house » – . VISA. DY **x**
closed Christmas and New Year – **3 rm** 58.00/70.00 **st.**

28 Northumberland Street without rest., 28 Northumberland St., EH3 6LS, 557 8036, Fax 558 3453, « Georgian town house » – . VISA. DY **x**
3 rm 35.00/70.00 **s.**

Drummond House without rest., 17 Drummond Pl., EH3 6PL, 557 9189, Fax 557 9189, « Georgian town house » – . VISA DY **e**
closed Christmas – **3 rm** 65.00/70.00.

⌂ **Stuart House** without rest., 12 East Claremont St., EH7 4JP, ✆ 557 9030, Fax 557 0563 – ⊬ TV ☎. EN AE VISA. ✻ BV x
closed 1 week Christmas – **7 rm** ☕ 32.00/68.00 **t.**

⌂ **Dorstan,** 7 Priestfield Rd, EH16 5HJ, ✆ 667 6721, Fax 668 4644 – ⊬ rest TV ☎ P. EN VISA. ✻ BX e
Meals (by arrangement) 13.00 **t.** – **14 rm** ☕ 38.00/70.00 **st.** – SB.

⌂ **International** without rest., 37 Mayfield Gdns, EH9 2BX, ✆ 667 2511, Fax 667 1109 – TV ✻ BX s
8 rm ☕ 25.00/62.00 **s.**

⌂ **Greenside** without rest., 9 Royal Terr., EH7 5AB, ✆ 557 0022, Fax 557 0022, ☘ – ✻ EY a
12 rm ☕ 25.00/60.00 **t.**

⌂ **Teviotdale,** 53 Grange Loan, EH9 2ER, ✆ 667 4376, Fax 667 4376 – ⊬ TV ☎. EN AE VISA ✻ BX u
Meals (by arrangement) 18.50 – **7 rm** ☕ 45.00/56.00 **t.**

⌂ **Ravensdown** without rest., 248 Ferry Rd, EH5 3AN, ✆ 552 5438 – ⊬ TV. ✻ BV e
7 rm ☕ 33.00/36.00.

⌂ **Parklands** without rest., 20 Mayfield Gdns, EH9 2BZ, ✆ 667 7184 TV. ✻ BX o
6 rm ☕ 36.00/50.00.

⌂ **Galloway** without rest., 22 Dean Park Cres., EH4 1PH, ✆ 332 3672 – TV CY a
10 rm ☕ 30.00/50.00 **t.**

⌂ **Glenisla,** 12 Lygon Rd, EH16 5QB, ✆ 667 4877, Fax 667 4098 – EN VISA BX a
Meals 12.50 **st.** ⅰ 3.20 – **7 rm** ☕ 22.50/50.00 **t.**

⌂ **St. Margaret's** without rest., 18 Craigmillar Park, EH16 5PS, ✆ 667 2202 – ⊬ rm TV P. EN VISA. ✻ BX n
closed January and February – **8 rm** ☕ 25.00/44.00 **st.**

XXXX **Pompadour** (at Caledonian H.), Princes St., EH1 2AB, ✆ 225 2433, Telex 72179, Fax 225 6632 – P. EN AE ⓓ VISA JCB CY n
closed lunch Saturday and Sunday – **Meals** 22.50/35.00 **t.** and a la carte ⅰ 5.95.

XXXX **Grill** (at Balmoral H.), Princes St., EH2 2EQ, ✆ 557 6727, Telex 727282, Fax 557 3747 – ▤. EN AE ⓓ VISA JCB EY n
closed lunch Saturday and Sunday – **Meals** 21.50/35.00 **st.** and a la carte ⅰ 7.00.

XX **Vintners Room,** The Vaults, 87 Giles St., Leith, EH6 6BZ, ✆ 554 6767, Fax 554 8423 – ▤. EN AE VISA BV r
closed Sunday and 2 weeks Christmas – **Meals** 11.75/28.00 **t.** and a la carte ⅰ 4.50.

XX **Martins,** 70 Rose St., North Lane, EH2 3DX, ✆ 225 3106 – ⊬. EN AE ⓓ VISA DY n
closed Saturday lunch, Sunday, Monday, 10 days late June, 10 days late September and 24 December-23 January – **Meals** (booking essential) 15.90 **t.** and a la carte.

XX **L'Auberge,** 56 St. Mary's St., EH1 1SX, ✆ 556 5888, Fax 556 2588 – ▤. EN AE ⓓ VISA JCB EYZ c
closed 25-26 December and 1-3 January – **Meals** - French 10.00/19.85 **t.** and a la carte ⅰ 4.50.

XX **Raffaelli,** 10-11 Randolph Pl., EH3 7TA, ✆ 225 6060, Fax 225 8830 – EN AE ⓓ VISA CY c
closed Saturday lunch, Sunday, 25-26 December, 1-2 January and Bank Holidays – **Meals** - Italian a la carte 15.65/24.40 **t.** ⅰ 4.95.

XX **Lancer's Brasserie,** 5 Hamilton Pl., Stockbridge, EH3 5BA, ✆ 332 3444 – EN AE ⓓ VISA CY r
Meals - North Indian a la carte 11.95/15.95 **t.**

XX **Indian Cavalry Club,** 3 Atholl Pl., EH3 8HP, ✆ 228 3282, Fax 225 1911 – EN AE ⓓ VISA CZ c
Meals - Indian 16.95 **t.** and a la carte.

XX **Merchants,** 17 Merchant St.,, EH1 2QD, off Candlemaker Row, (under bridge) ✆ 225 4009, Fax 557 9318 – EN AE ⓓ VISA JCB EZ x
closed 25 and 26 December – **Meals** (booking essential) a la carte 11.95/20.75 **t.** ⅰ 4.90.

XX **Denzler's 121,** 121 Constitution St., EH6 7AE, ✆ 554 3268 – EN AE ⓓ VISA JCB BV c
closed Saturday lunch, Sunday, Monday, first week January and 2 weeks July – **Meals** 14.30/22.55 **st.** ⅰ 5.35.

X **Atrium,** 10 Cambridge St., EH1 2ED, ✆ 228 8882, Fax 459 1060 – ▤. EN AE VISA DZ c
closed Saturday lunch, Sunday and 1 week Christmas – **Meals** a la carte 20.00/26.50 **t.**

X **Silvio's,** 54 The Shore, Leith, EH6 6RA, ✆ 553 3557 – EN AE VISA BV s
closed Sunday – **Meals** - Italian 9.50 **t.** (lunch) and a la carte 15.00/19.20 **t.** ⅰ 4.80.

X **Duncan's Land,** Gloucester St., Stockbridge, EH3 6EG, ✆ 225 1037 – EN VISA CY s
closed Saturday lunch, Sunday and Monday – **Meals** - Italian a la carte 13.50/20.50 **t.**

X **Le Marche Noir,** 2-4 Eyre Pl., EH3 5EP, ✆ 558 1608, Fax 556 0798 – EN AE VISA BV v
closed lunch Saturday and Sunday, 25-26 December and 1-2 January – **Meals** (booking essential) 11.50/25.50 **t.** ⅰ 4.25.

X **Indian Cavalry Club,** 8-10 Eyre Pl., New Town, EH3 5EP, ✆ 556 2404 – EN AE ⓓ VISA BV a
Meals - Indian 6.95/15.95 **st.** and a la carte ⅰ 5.50.

at Ingliston W : 7 3/4 m. on A 8 – AV – ✉ Edinburgh – ☎ 0131 :

Norton House ⚘, EH28 8LX, on A 8 ℘ 333 1275, Fax 333 5305, ≤, ☂, park – ⇎ rm TV ☎ & P – 🏛 250. AE ⓓ VISA
Meals 14.75/20.50 **t.** and a la carte 5.25 – **46 rm** ☐ 99.00/120.00 **st.**, 1 suite – SB.

ATS 167 Bonnington Rd, Leith ℘ 554 6617 ATS 6 Gylemuir Rd, Corstorphine ℘ 334 6174

EDZELL Angus. (Tayside) 401 M 13 **Scotland G.** – pop. 830 – ECD : Thursday – ☎ 01356.

Envir. : Castle★ *AC* (The Pleasance★★★) W : 2 m.

Exc. : Glen Esk★, NW : 7 m.

18 Trinity, Brechin ℘ 622383.

♦Edinburgh 94 – ♦Aberdeen 36 – ♦Dundee 31.

Glenesk, High St., DD9 7TF, ℘ 648319, Fax 647333, ≘s, ⛶, ☂ – TV ☎ P – 🏛 100. AE ⓓ VISA
Meals 10.50/14.50 **t.** and a la carte – **25 rm** ☐ 46.00/78.00 **t.** – SB.

ELGIN Moray. (Grampian) 401 K 11 **Scotland G.** – pop. 11 855 – ECD : Wednesday – ☎ 01343.

See : Town★ – Cathedral★ (Chapter house★★)*AC*.

Exc. : Glenfiddich Distillery★, SE : 10 m. by A 941.

18, 18 Moray, Stotfield Rd, Lossiemouth ℘ 812018 – 18 Hardhillock, Birnie Rd ℘ 542338 – 18 Hopeman, Moray ℘ 830578.

ℹ 17 High St. IV30 1EJ ℘ 542666.

♦Edinburgh 198 – ♦Aberdeen 68 – Fraserburgh 61 – ♦Inverness 39.

Mansion House, The Haugh, IV30 1AW, via Haugh Rd and Murdocks Wynd ℘ 548811, Fax 547916, Fø, ≘s, ⛶, ☂ – TV ☎ P. AE ⓓ VISA. ⋇
Meals 12.50/27.50 **t.** and a la carte 6.00 – **22 rm** ☐ 75.00/140.00 **st.** – SB(weekends only) 120.00/150.00.

Mansefield House, 2 Mayne Rd, IV30 1NY, ℘ 540883, Fax 552491 – |‡| ⇎ TV ☎ P. AE VISA. ⋇
Meals 12.00 **t.** (lunch) and a la carte 17.50/24.75 **t. t.** 4.95 – **16 rm** ☐ 55.00/90.00 **t.**

Lodge, 20 Duff Av., IV30 1QS, ℘ 549981, ☂ – ⇎ TV P. ⋇
Meals (by arrangement) 13.50 **s.** – **8 rm** ☐ 22.00/42.00 **s.** – SB.

ATS Moycroft ℘ 546333

ELIE Fife. (Fife) 401 L 15 – pop. 903 – ☎ 01333.

♦Edinburgh 41 – ♦Dundee 29 – Dunfermline 29.

Bouquet Garni, 51 High St., KY9 1BZ, ℘ 330374, Fax 330374 – AE VISA
closed Sunday, 2 weeks January and 1 week November – **Meals** a la carte 17.60/26.90 **t.** 6.40.

ERBUSAIG Ross and Cromarty (Highland) 401 C 12 – ✉ Kyle of Lochalsh – ☎ 01599.

♦Edinburgh 206 – ♦Dundee 184 – ♦Inverness 84 – ♦Oban 127.

Old Schoolhouse with rm, IV40 8BB, ℘ 534369, ☂ – TV P. VISA. ⋇
Easter-October – **Meals** (booking essential)(dinner only) a la carte 14.00/23.50 **t.** 4.00 – **2 rm** ☐ 30.00/50.00 **t.**

ERISKA (Isle of) Argyll. (Strathclyde) 401 D 14 – ✉ Oban – ☎ 01631.

Isle of Eriska ⚘, PA37 1SD, ℘ 720371, Fax 720531, ≤ Lismore and mountains, « Country house atmosphere », Fø, ≘s, ⛶, 9, ⚘, ☂, park, ⚔ – TV ☎ & P. VISA
closed January and February – **Meals** (dinner only) 35.00 **st.** 4.00 – **17 rm** ☐ 135.00/195.00 **st.** – SB.

ERROL Perth. (Tayside) 401 K 14 – ☎ 01821.

Waterybutts Lodge ⚘, Grange, PH2 7SZ, NE : 2 1/4 m. by B 958 ℘ 642894, Fax 642523, « Sporting lodge », ☂ – P. AE VISA
Meals (residents only)(communal dining)(dinner only) 16.50 **t.** 3.00 – **8 rm** ☐ 33.50/57.00 **t.**

ERSKINE Renfrew. (Strathclyde) 401 402 G 16 – ☎ 0141.

♦Edinburgh 55 – ♦Glasgow 9.

Forte Posthouse ⚘, Erskine Bridge, PA8 6AN, on A 726 ℘ 812 0123, Fax 812 7642, ≤, Fø, ≘s, ⛶, ☂ – |‡| ⇎ rm TV ☎ P – 🏛 600. AE ⓓ VISA
Meals a la carte approx. 15.00 **t.** 5.50 – **166 rm** 56.00 **st.**

We suggest:

For a successful tour, that you prepare it in advance.
Michelin **maps** *and* **guides** *will give you much useful information on route planning, places of interest, accommodation, prices etc.*

FALKIRK Stirling. (Central) 401 I 16 – pop. 42 353 – ECD : Wednesday – ☎ 01324.
Polmonthill, Grangemouth ☎ 711500 – Polmont, Manuel Rigg, Maddiston ☎ 711277.
2-4 Glebestreet, SK1 1HU ☎ 620244.
♦Edinburgh 26 – Dunfermline 18 – ♦Glasgow 25 – Motherwell 27 – Perth 43.

Grange Manor, Glensburgh Rd, FK3 8XJ, NE : 2 m. by A 904 on A 905 ☎ 474836, Fax 665861 – TV ☎ P – 120. AE VISA.
closed first week January – **Meals** *(closed Sunday dinner)* 13.25/19.25 **t.** and a la carte 4.85 – **6 rm** 61.00/84.00 **t.** – SB.

Stakis Falkirk, Camelon Rd, Arnothill, FK1 5RY, ☎ 628331, Fax 611593 – rm TV ☎ P – 300. AE VISA
Meals (bar lunch)/dinner 13.95 **st.** and a la carte – 8.50 – **55 rm** 69.00/79.00 **st.** – SB.

at Polmont SE : 3 m. on A 803 – ✉ Polmont – ☎ 01324 :

Inchyra Grange, Grange Rd, FK2 0YB, Kirk entry via Boness Rd ☎ 711911, Fax 716134, – rm TV ☎ P – 220. AE VISA
Meals (closed Saturday lunch) 8.20/18.75 **t.** and a la carte 4.95 – 8.50 – **43 rm** 80.00/125.00 **t.**

ATS Burnbank Rd ☎ 622958

FINSTOWN Orkney. (Orkney Islands) 401 K 6 – see Orkney Islands.

FIONNPHORT Argyll. (Strathclyde) 401 A 15 – Shipping Services : see Mull (Isle of).

FLODIGARRY Inverness. (Highland) - see Skye (Isle of).

FORFAR Angus. (Tayside) 401 L 14 – pop. 14 159 – ECD : Thursday – ☎ 01307.
Cunninghill ☎ 462120.
40 East High Street, DD8 2ES ☎ 467876 (summer only).
♦Edinburgh 75 – ♦Aberdeen 55 – ♦Dundee 12 – Perth 31.

Chapelbank House, 69 East High St., DD8 2EP, ☎ 463151, Fax 461922 – TV ☎ P. VISA.
Meals *(closed Sunday dinner and Monday)* 10.50/18.00 **t.** and a la carte 3.95 – **4 rm** 50.00/70.00 **t.** – SB.

ATS Queenswell Rd ☎ 464501

FORRES Moray. (Grampian) 401 J 11 **Scotland G.** – pop. 5 559 – ECD : Wednesday – ☎ 01309.
See : Town★.
Envir. : Brodie Castle★ *AC*, W : 3 m. by A 96.
Exc. : Elgin★ (Cathedral★, Chapter House★★ *AC*) E : 10¼ m. by A 96.
Muiryshade ☎ 672949.
116 High Styreet, IV6 0NP ☎ 672938 (summer only).
♦Edinburgh 165 – ♦Aberdeen 80 – ♦Inverness 27.

Ramnee, Victoria Rd, IV36 0BN, ☎ 672410, Fax 673392, – TV ☎ P – 100. AE VISA
closed 25 December and 1 to 3 January – **Meals** 10.50/18.00 **t.** and dinner a la carte 4.00 – **19 rm** 47.50/85.00 **st.** – SB.

Knockomie, Grantown Rd, IV36 0SG, S : 1½ m. on A 940 ☎ 673146, Fax 673290, – TV ☎ P – 50. AE VISA
Meals 8.00/25.00 **st.** and a la carte 6.00 – **14 rm** 65.00/160.00 **st.** – SB.

Parkmount House, St. Leonards Rd, IV36 0DW, ☎ 673312, Fax 673312, – rest TV ☎ P
8 rm.

FORT AUGUSTUS Inverness. (Highland) 401 F 12 **Scotland G.** – pop. 902 – ☎ 01320.
Exc. : Loch Ness★★ – The Great Glen★.
Markethill ☎ 366460.
Car Park ☎ 366367 (summer only).
♦Edinburgh 166 – Fort William 32 – ♦Inverness 36 – Kyle of Lochalsh 57.

Lovat Arms, PH32 4DU, ☎ 366206, Fax 366677, – TV ☎ P. VISA
Meals (bar lunch)/dinner 18.50 **t.** 4.75 – **21 rm** 26.50/67.00 **st.** – SB.

Inchnacardoch Lodge, PH32 4BL, NE : ¾ m. on A 82 ☎ 366258, – TV ☎ P. AE VISA
closed November and December – **Meals** (dinner only) 20.00 **t.** – **12 rm** 55.00/70.00 **t.** – SB.

Brae, PH32 4DG, ☎ 366289, Fax 366289, – TV P
8 rm.

Sonas without rest., PH32 4BA, on A 82 ☎ 366291, – P
3 rm 20.00/30.00.

FORT WILLIAM Inverness. (Highland) 401 E 13 **Scotland G.** – pop. 10 805 – ECD : Wednesday except summer – ☎ 01397.

See : Town★.

Exc. : Road to the Isles★★★ ≤★★ (Glenfinnan★ ≤★, Arisaig★, Silver Sands of Morar★, Mallaig★, Ardnamurchan Peninsula★★, Ardnamurchan Point ≤★★) NW : 46 m. by A 830 – SE : Glen Nevis★ (Ben Nevis★★ ≤★★ *AC*).

North Rd ✆ 704464.

✆ 0345 090700.

Cameron Centre, Cameron Sq., PH33 6AJ ✆ 703781.

♦Edinburgh 133 – ♦Glasgow 104 – ♦Inverness 68 – ♦Oban 50.

- **Inverlochy Castle**, Torlundy, PH33 6SN, NE : 3 m. on A 82 ✆ 702177, Fax 702953, ≤ loch and mountains, « Victorian castle in extensive park », – rest. VISA.
  March-November – **Meals** (booking essential) 25.00/42.50 – **16 rm** 150.00/260.00 **t.**, 1 suite
  Spec. Salad of roasted scallops with a lemon olive oil dressing, Baked escalope of wild Scottish salmon with a buttery court bouillon, Hot chocolate tart with an orange sauce.
- **Factor's House,** Torlundy, PH33 6SN, NE : 3½ m. on A 82 ✆ 705767, Fax 702953, – . VISA.
  April-November – **Meals** *(closed Sunday)* (booking essential)(dinner only) 23.00 **st.** 6.00 – **4 rm** 65.00/110.00 **st.** – SB.
- **Distillery House** without rest., Nevis Bridge, North Rd, PH33 6TQ, ✆ 700103, Fax 706277 – . VISA
  7 rm 55.00/60.00 **st.**
- **Grange** without rest., Grange Rd, PH33 6JF, by Ashburn Lane ✆ 705516, ≤, –
  April-October – **3 rm** 46.00/66.00 **t.**
- **Crolinnhe** without rest., Grange Rd, PH33 6JF, by Ashburn Lane ✆ 702709, ≤, – .
  April-November – **5 rm** 46.00/66.00 **st.**
- **Cabana House** without rest., Union Rd, PH33 6RB, ✆ 705991, – .
  closed February and November – **3 rm** 30.00/45.00.

at Banavie N : 3 m. by A 82 and A 830 on B 8004 – ✉ Fort William – ☎ 01397 :

- **Moorings,** PH33 7LY, ✆ 772797, Fax 772441, ≤, – rest . VISA.
  closed 24 to 26 December – ***Jacobean*** **: Meals** (lunch by arrangement)/dinner 25.00 and a la carte 6.00 – **24 rm** 46.00/88.00 **t.** – SB.

FOYERS Inverness (Highland) 401 G 12 – ✉ Loch Ness – ☎ 01456.

♦Edinburgh 175 – ♦Inverness 19 – Kyle of Lochalsh 63 – ♦Oban 96.

- **Craigdarroch**, IV1 2XU, N : ¼ m. on B 852 ✆ 486400, Fax 486444, ≤, park – . VISA
  Meals 12.00/25.00 **st.** and a la carte 8.00 – **15 rm** 32.50/65.00 **669** – SB.
- **Foyers Bay House,** Lower Foyers, IV1 2YB, W : 1 ¼ m. by B 852 on Lower Foyers rd ✆ 486624, Fax 486337, ≤, – . VISA
  Meals 13.00 **t.** dinner and a la carte 7.40/14.25 – **3 rm** 35.00/60.00 **t.** – SB.

GAIRLOCH Ross and Cromarty. (Highland) 401 C 10 **Scotland G.** – ECD : Wednesday except summer – ☎ 01445.

Envir. : Loch Maree★★★, E : 5½ m. by A 832.

Exc. : Inverewe Gardens★★★ *AC*, NE : 8 m. by A 832 – Wester Ross★★★ – S : from Gairloch to Kyle of Lochalsh★★★ (vista★★, ≤★★★) – N : from Gairloch to Ullapool★★ (≤★★★).

Gairloch ✆ 712407.

Auchtercairn ✆ 712130.

♦Edinburgh 228 – ♦Inverness 72 – Kyle of Lochalsh 68.

- **Creag Mor,** Charleston, IV21 2AH, ✆ 712068, Fax 712044, ≤, – . VISA
  March-November – **Meals** (bar lunch)/dinner 23.00 **st.** and a la carte 4.50 – **18 rm** 51.00/80.00 **st.**, 1 suite.
- **Little Lodge**, North Erradale, IV21 2DS, NW : 5½ m. on B 8021 ✆ 771237, ≤ Torridon Mountains and Skye, –
  closed mid December-January – **3 rm** (dinner included) 55.00/85.00 **s.** – SB.
- **Birchwood** without rest., IV21 2AH, ✆ 712011, ≤ –
  April-October – **6 rm** 23.00/46.00.

GALSON Western Isles (Outer Hebrides) 401 A 8 – see Lewis and Harris (Isle of).

GATEHOUSE OF FLEET Kirkcudbright. (Dumfries and Galloway) 401 402 H 19 – pop. 894 – ECD : Thursday – 01557.

Gatehouse of Fleet 814734.

Car Park DJ7 2AE 814212 (summer only).

◆Edinburgh 113 – ◆Dumfries 33 – Stranraer 42.

Cally Palace, DG7 2DL, E : ½ m. on B 727 814341, Fax 814522, park, – rest. VISA
closed 3 January-February – **Meals** 10.50/24.00 **t.** and a la carte 7.50 – **50 rm** 62.00/135.00, 6 suites – SB.

Murray Arms, Ann St., DG7 2HY, 814207, Fax 814370, – . AE VISA
Meals (bar lunch)/dinner a la carte 9.50/19.00 **st.** 4.65 – **13 rm** 39.50/80.00 **st.** – SB.

GATTONSIDE Roxburgh. (Borders) – see Melrose.

GIFFNOCK Renfrew. (Strathclyde) 401 ㊶ – see Glasgow.

GIFFORD E. Lothian. (Lothian) 401 L 16 **Scotland G.** – pop. 665 – ECD : Monday and Wednesday – Haddington – 01620.

See : Village★.

Exc. : Northern foothills of the Lammermuir Hills★★, S : 10½ m. by B 6355 and B 6368.

Edinburgh Rd 810591.

◆Edinburgh 20 – Hawick 50.

Tweeddale Arms, High St., EH41 4QU, 810240, Fax 810488 – . AE VISA
Meals 12.50/19.75 **t.** 3.75 – **15 rm** 47.50/75.00 **t.** – SB.

GIGHA (Isle of) Argyll. (Strathclyde) 401 C 16 – 01583.

◆Edinburgh 168.

Gigha, PA41 7AD, 505245, Fax 505244, Sound of Gigha and Kintyre Peninsula, – . VISA
mid March-mid October – **Meals** (bar lunch)/dinner 18.00 **t.** – **13 rm** 48.50/97.00 **t.** – SB.

GIRVAN Ayr (Strathclyde) 401 402 F 18 – 01465.

Brunston Castle, Dailly 81471 – Golf Course Rd 4272/4346.

◆Edinburgh 100 – ◆Ayr 20 – ◆Glasgow 56 – Stranraer 31.

Glendrissaig without rest., KA26 0HJ, S : 1¾ m. by A 77 on A 714 4631,
April-October – **3 rm** 21.00/44.00 **st.**

GLAMIS Angus. (Tayside) 401 K 14 **Scotland G.** – Forfar – 01307.

See : Village★ - Castle★★ *AC* – Angus Folk Museum★ *AC*.

Exc. : Meigle Museum★★ (early Christian Monuments★★) *AC*, SW : 7 m. by A 94.

◆Edinburgh 60 – ◆Dundee 11 – Perth 25.

Castleton House with rm, Eassie, DD8 1SJ, W : 3¾ m. on A 94 840340, Fax 840506, – rest . AE VISA.
Meals 11.75/19.50 **t.** and a la carte – **6 rm** 60.00/90.00 **t.** – SB.

GLASGOW Lanark. (Strathclyde) 401 402 H 16 **Scotland G.** – pop. 662 853 – ☎ 0141.

See : City★★★ – Cathedral★★★ (<★) DZ – The Burrell Collection★★★ AX **M1** – Hunterian Art Gallery★★ (Whistler Collection★★★ – Mackintosh Wing★★★) *AC* CY **M4** – Museum of Transport★★ (Scottish Built Cars★★★, The Clyde Room of Ship Models★★★) AV **M3** – Art Gallery and Museum Kelvingrove★★ CY – Pollok House★ (The Paintings★★) AX **D** – Tolbooth Steeple★ DZ **A** – Hunterian Museum (Coin and Medal Collection★) CY **M1** – City Chambers★ DZ **C** – Glasgow School of Art★ *AC*, CY **B** – Necropolis (<★ of Cathedral) DYZ.

Exc. : The Trossachs★★★, N : 31 m. by A 879 - BV - A 81 and A 821 – Loch Lomond★★, NW : 19 m. by A 82 AV.

18 Littlehill, Auchinairn Rd, Bishopbriggs ✆ 772 1916, BV – 18 Deaconsbank, Rouken Glen Park, Stewarton Rd, Eastwood ✆ 638 7044, AX – 18 Linn Park, Simshill Rd ✆ 637 5871, BX – 18 Lethamhill, Cumbernauld Rd ✆ 770 6220, BV – 9 Alexandra Park, Sannox Gdns, Alexandra Parade ✆ 556 3991, BV – 9 King's Park, 150a Croftpark Av., Croftfoot, ✆ 637 1066, BX – 9 Knightswood, Lincoln Av. ✆ 959 2131, AV - 9 Ruchill, Brassey St. ✆ 946 7676, BV.

Access to Oban by helicopter.

✈ Glasgow Airport : ✆ 887 1111, W : 8 m. by M 8 AV – **Terminal :** Coach service from Glasgow Central and Queen Street main line Railway Stations and from Anderston Cross and Buchanan Bus Stations – ✈ see also Prestwick – 🚗 ✆ 0345 090700.

ℹ 35 St. Vincent Pl. G1 2ER ✆ 204 4400 – Glasgow Airport, Paisley ✆ 848 4440.

◆Edinburgh 46 – ◆Manchester 221.

Plans on following pages

Glasgow Hilton, 1 William St., G3 8HT, ✆ 204 5555, Fax 204 5004, <, Ls, ≘s, ▣ – |‡| ⇔ rm ▤ TV ☎ ♿ P – 🔔 1 000. AE ① VISA JCB CZ **s**
Minsky's : **Meals** 18.95 **st.** (dinner) and a la carte - (see also ***Camerons*** below) – ☐ 13.75 – **315 rm** 115.00/140.00 **st.**, 4 suites.

Moat House International (Q.M.H.), Congress Rd, G3 8QT, ✆ 204 0733, Telex 776244, Fax 221 2022, <, Ls, ≘s, ▣ – |‡| ⇔ rm ▤ TV ☎ ♿ P – 🔔 100. AE ① VISA. ✻ CZ **r**
Mariners : **Meals** *(closed Saturday lunch and Sunday)* 16.50/32.50 and a la carte – *Pointhouse :* **Meals** 15.95/18.95 and a la carte – ☐ 10.95 – **267 rm** 112.00 **st.**, 16 suites.

Glasgow Marriott, 500 Argyle St., Anderston, G3 8RR, ✆ 226 5577, Fax 221 7676, Ls, ≘s, ▣, squash – |‡| ⇔ rm ▤ TV ☎ ♿ P – 🔔 720. AE ① VISA CZ **a**
Meals 11.95/14.95 **st.** and a la carte 🍷 7.00 – ☐ 10.25 – **293 rm** 89.00 **st.**, 5 suites – SB.

Forte Crest, Bothwell St., G2 7EN, ✆ 248 2656, Telex 77440, Fax 221 8986, < – |‡| ⇔ rm ▤ TV ☎ P – 🔔 800 CZ **z**
248 rm, 3 suites.

One Devonshire Gardens, 1 Devonshire Gdns, G12 OUX, ✆ 339 2001, Fax 337 1663, « Opulent interior design » – TV ☎ – 🔔 50. AE ① VISA AV **a**
Meals *(closed Saturday lunch)* 21.50/37.50 **t.** 🍷 8.00 – ☐ 12.50 – **25 rm** 125.00/160.00 **t.**, 2 suites.

Glasgow Thistle (Mt. Charlotte Thistle), 36 Cambridge St., G2 3HN, ✆ 332 3311, Telex 777334, Fax 332 4050 – |‡| ⇔ rm TV ☎ ♿ P – 🔔 1 500. AE ① VISA JCB DY **z**
Meals *(closed Saturday lunch and Sunday)* (carving rest.) 15.50/13.50 **st.** and a la carte – ☐ 10.25 – **304 rm** 90.00/115.00 **st.**, 3 suites – SB.

Devonshire, 5 Devonshire Gdns, G12 0UX, ✆ 339 7878, Fax 339 3980 – TV ☎ – 🔔 50. AE ① VISA. ✻ AV **a**
Meals (residents only) 15.00/35.00 **st.** and a la carte 🍷 6.95 – ☐ 10.50 – **14 rm** 95.00/150.00 **st.** – SB.

Malmaison, 278 West George St., G2 4LL, ✆ 221 6400, Fax 221 6411 – TV ☎. AE ① VISA CY **c**
Meals - Brasserie a la carte 13.00/17.95 **t.** – ☐ 10.00 – **17 rm** 70.00 **st.**, 4 suites.

Copthorne Glasgow, George Sq., G2 1DS, ✆ 332 6711, Telex 778147, Fax 332 4264 – |‡| ⇔ rm TV ☎ – 🔔 100 DZ **n**
136 rm, 4 suites.

Swallow Glasgow, 517 Paisley Rd West, G51 1RW, ✆ 427 3146, Fax 427 4059, Ls, ≘s, ▣ – |‡| ▤ rest TV ☎ P – 🔔 350. AE ① VISA AX **a**
Meals *(closed lunch Saturday and Bank Holiday)* (carving lunch) 7.95/15.95 **st.** and a la carte 🍷 5.50 – **117 rm** ☐ 80.00/130.00 **st.** – SB.

Tinto Firs Thistle (Mt. Charlotte Thistle), 470 Kilmarnock Rd, G43 2BB, ✆ 637 2353, Fax 633 1340 – TV ☎ P – 🔔 50. AE ① VISA JCB AX **c**
Meals (bar lunch Monday and Saturday) 18.50 **t.** and a la carte 🍷 4.95 – **26 rm** ☐ 75.00/85.00 **st.**, 2 suites – SB.

Carrick (Forte), 377 Argyle St., G2 8LL, ✆ 248 2355, Fax 221 1014 – |‡| ⇔ rm TV ☎ – 🔔 80. AE ① VISA. ✻ CZ **x**
closed 1-4 January – **Meals** *(closed lunch Saturday and Sunday)* (bar lunch)/dinner a la carte 13.30/21.50 **t.** 🍷 6.60 – ☐ 8.95 – **121 rm** 60.00 **t.** – SB.

Terrace House, 14 Belhaven Terr., G12 0TG, (off Great Western Rd) ✆ 337 3377, Fax 337 3377 – ⇔ rest TV ☎. AE ① VISA. ✻ AV **x**
Meals (dinner only) a la carte 14.20/22.65 **t.** 🍷 3.95 – **15 rm** ☐ 52.00/68.00 **t.** – SB.

Town House, 4 Hughenden Terr., G12 9XR, ✆ 357 0862, Fax 339 9605 – ⇔ rest TV ☎. VISA. ✻ AV **a**
Meals (dinner only) a la carte 15.50/20.45 **st.** 🍷 5.25 – **10 rm** ☐ 52.00/62.00 **st.**

GLASGOW
BUILT UP AREA

Aikenhead Road .... **BX** 3
Alexandra Parade .... **BV** 4
Balgrayhill Road .... **BV** 5
Ballater Street .... **BX** 6
Balornock Road .... **BV** 8
Balshagray Avenue .... **AV** 9
Battlefield Road .... **BX** 12
Berryknowes Road .... **AX** 15
Bilsland Drive .... **BV** 16
Blairbeth Road .... **BX** 18
Braidcraft Road .... **AX** 20
Broomloan Road .... **AV** 26
Burnhill Chapel Street .... **BX** 28
Byres Road .... **AV** 29
Caledonia Road .... **BX** 30
Carmunnock Road .... **BX** 33
Cook Street .... **BV** 38
Cumbernauld Road .... **BV** 40
Edmiston Drive .... **AV** 48
Farmeloan Road .... **BX** 53
Fenwick Road .... **AX** 55
Glasgow Road (PAISLEY) .... **AX** 62
Gorbals Street .... **BX** 63
Grange Road .... **BX** 67

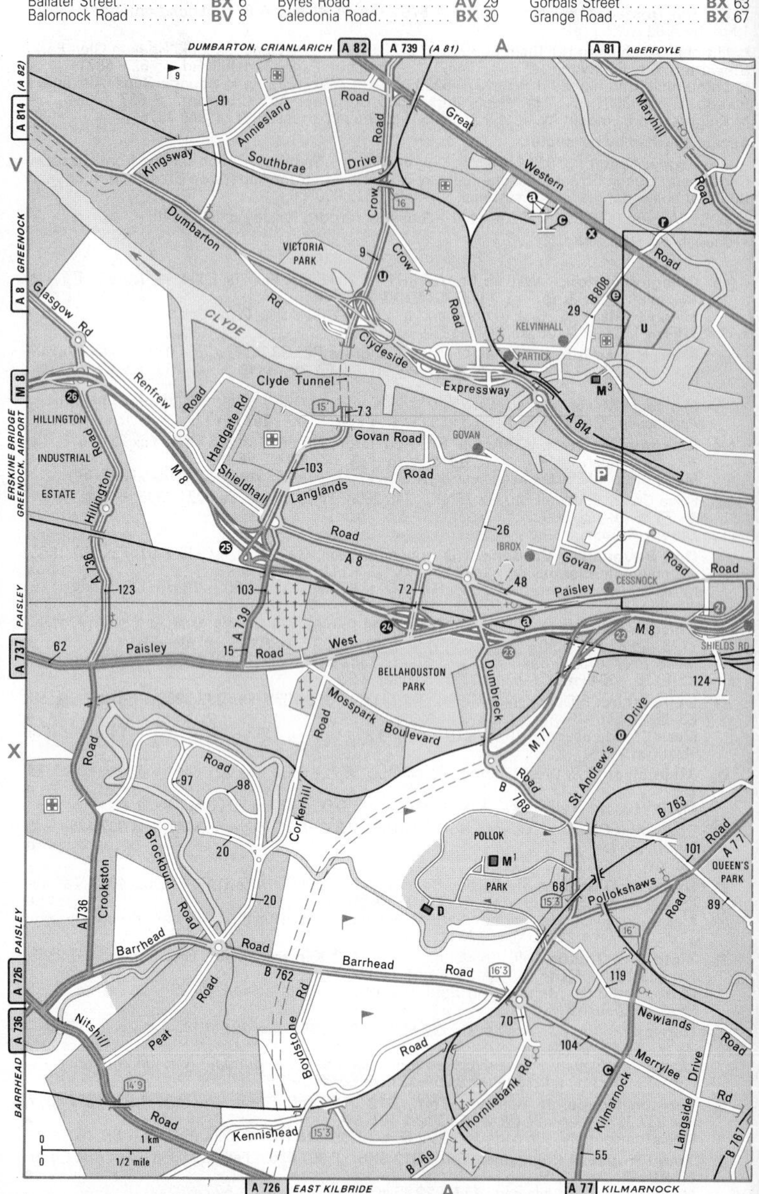

Haggs Road . . . . AX 68
Harriet Street . . . . AX 70
Helen Street . . . . AV 72
Holmfauld Road . . . . AV 73
Holmlea Road . . . . BX 74
Hospital Street . . . . BX 75
James Street . . . . BX 79
King's Drive . . . . BX 83
King's Park Road . . . . BX 84
Lamont Road . . . . BV 88
Langside Av. . . . . AX 89
Langside Road . . . . BX 90
Lincoln Avenue . . . . AV 91
Lyoncross Road . . . . AX 97
Meiklerig Crescent . . . . . . AX 98
Minard Rd . . . . AX 101
Moss Road . . . . AV 103
Nether Auldhouse Road . AX 104
Prospecthill Road . . . . BX 112
Provan Road . . . . BV 114
Red Road . . . . BV 118
Riverford Road . . . . AX 119
Sandwood Road . . . . AV 123
Shields Road . . . . AX 124
Todd Street . . . . BV 131
Westmuir Place . . . . BX 136
Westmuir Street . . . . BX 138

For Street Index see Glasgow p. 6

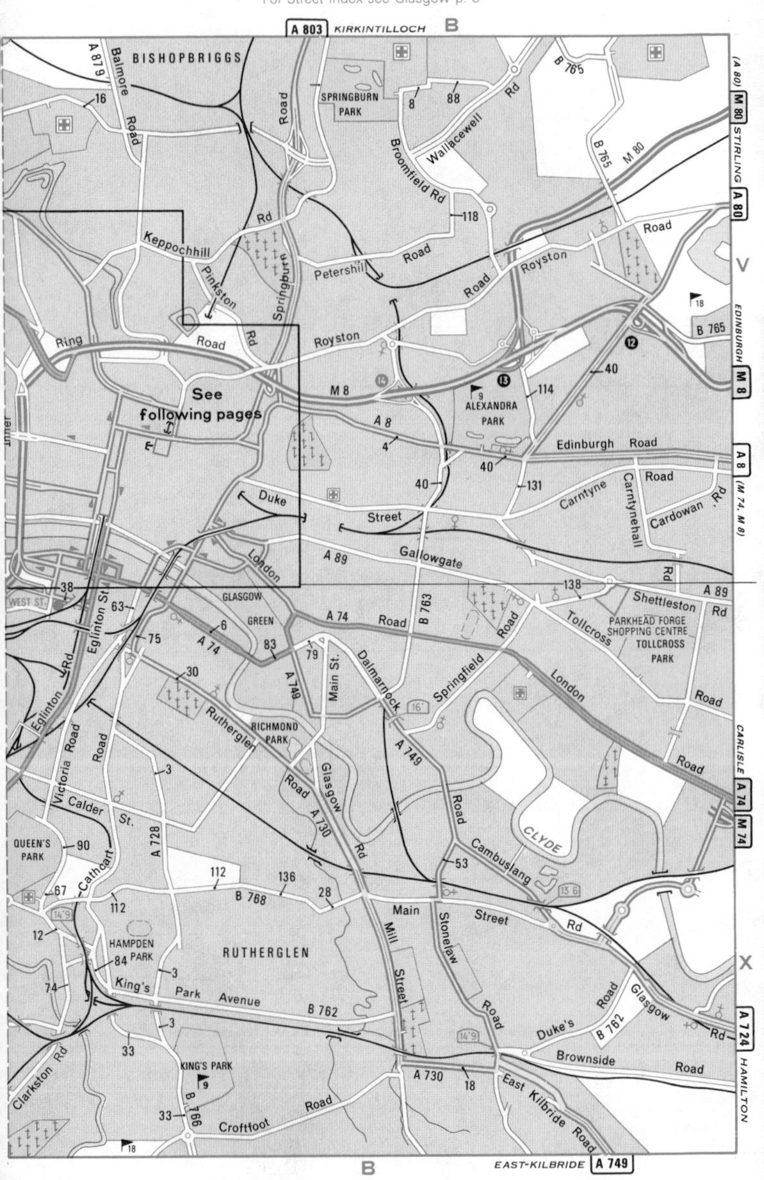

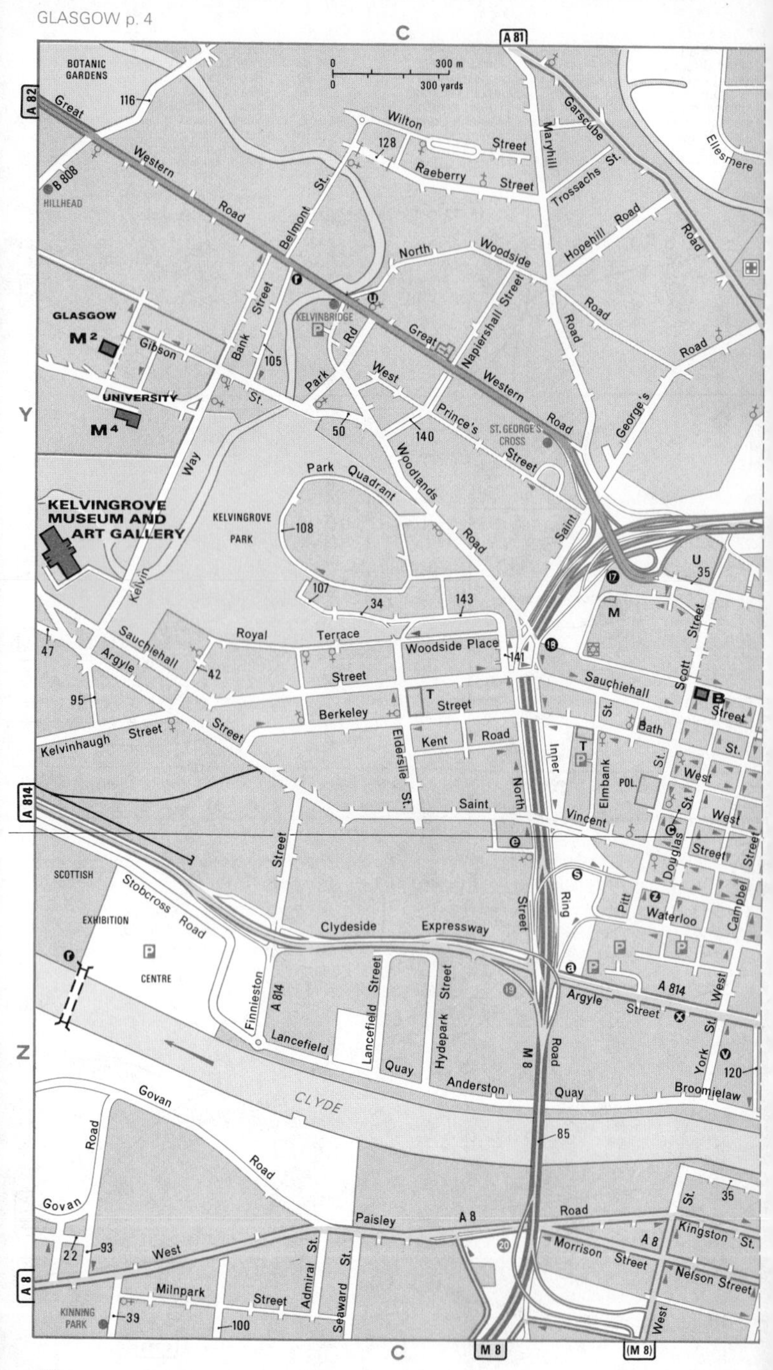
C
A 81
BOTANIC GARDENS
Great Western Road
Wilton Street
Raeberry Street
Maryhill Road
Garscube Road
Ellesmere
Trossachs St.
Hopehill Road
North Woodside Road
Belmont St.
Bank Street
HILLHEAD
GLASGOW
UNIVERSITY
Gibson St.
KELVINBRIDGE
Park Rd
West Prince's Street
Napiershall Street
ST. GEORGE'S CROSS
St. George's Road
Kelvin Way
KELVINGROVE MUSEUM AND ART GALLERY
KELVINGROVE PARK
Park Quadrant
Woodlands Road
Saint George's Road
Royal Terrace
Woodside Place
Sauchiehall Street
Argyle Street
Berkeley Street
Kent Road
Elderslie St.
Kelvinhaugh Street
Saint Vincent Street
North Street
Inner Ring Road
Elmbank St.
Bath St.
West Regent St.
West George Street
Scott Street
Douglas St.
Pitt St.
Waterloo St.
Campbell Street
SCOTTISH EXHIBITION CENTRE
Stobcross Road
Clydeside Expressway
Finnieston Street
Lancefield Street
Lancefield Quay
Hydepark Street
Anderston Quay
Broomielaw
York St.
West St.
A 814
CLYDE
Govan Road
Paisley Road West
Milnpark Street
Admiral St.
Seaward St.
Morrison Street
Kingston St.
Nelson Street
KINNING PARK
M 8
(M 8)
A 82
A 814
A 8
Y
Z
300 m
300 yards

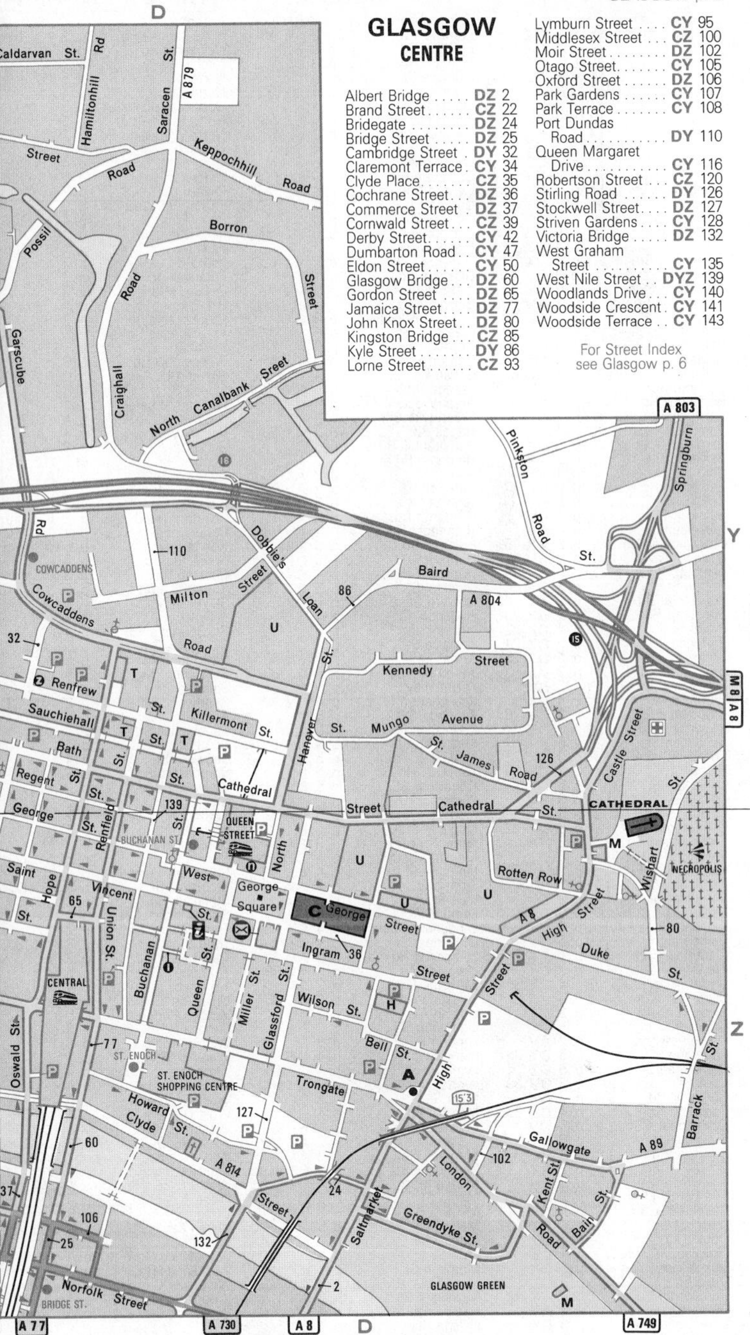
GLASGOW
CENTRE
Albert Bridge ..... DZ 2
Brand Street ...... CZ 22
Bridegate .... DZ 24
Bridge Street ..... DZ 25
Cambridge Street . DY 32
Claremont Terrace . CY 34
Clyde Place .... CZ 35
Cochrane Street ... DZ 36
Commerce Street .. DZ 37
Cornwald Street ... CZ 39
Derby Street ...... CY 42
Dumbarton Road .. CY 47
Eldon Street ...... CY 50
Glasgow Bridge ... DZ 60
Gordon Street .... DZ 65
Jamaica Street .... DZ 77
John Knox Street .. DZ 80
Kingston Bridge ... CZ 85
Kyle Street .... DY 86
Lorne Street ...... CZ 93
Lymburn Street .... CY 95
Middlesex Street ... CZ 100
Moir Street .... DZ 102
Otago Street .... CY 105
Oxford Street ...... DZ 106
Park Gardens ...... CY 107
Park Terrace .... CY 108
Port Dundas Road .... DY 110
Queen Margaret Drive .... CY 116
Robertson Street ... CZ 120
Stirling Road ...... DY 126
Stockwell Street .... DZ 127
Striven Gardens .... CY 128
Victoria Bridge ..... DZ 132
West Graham Street .... CY 135
West Nile Street .. DYZ 139
Woodlands Drive ... CY 140
Woodside Crescent . CY 141
Woodside Terrace .. CY 143
For Street Index see Glasgow p. 6
D
Y
Z
A 803
A 879
M 8 A 8
A 804
A 77
A 730
A 8
A 749
A 89
A 814
Caldarvan St.
Hamiltonhill Rd
Saracen St.
Keppochhill Road
Possil Road
Borron Street
Garscube Rd
Craighall Road
North Canalbank Street
Pinkston Road
Springburn
Baird St.
Dobbie's Loan
Milton Street
Cowcaddens
COWCADDENS
Cowcaddens Road
Kennedy Street
Mungo Avenue
St. James Road
Castle Street
Renfrew St.
Sauchiehall St.
Killermont St.
Hanover St.
Bath St.
Regent St.
Cathedral St.
CATHEDRAL
NECROPOLIS
George St.
Renfield St.
QUEEN STREET
BUCHANAN ST.
North
West George St.
George Square
Rotten Row
Wishart St.
Saint Vincent St.
Hope St.
Union St.
Buchanan St.
Queen St.
Ingram Street
High Street
Duke St.
Miller St.
Glassford St.
Wilson St.
Bell St.
CENTRAL
Oswald St.
ST. ENOCH
ST. ENOCH SHOPPING CENTRE
Trongate
Howard St.
Clyde Street
Gallowgate
London Road
Kent St.
Bain St.
Barrack St.
Saltmarket
Greendyke St.
GLASGOW GREEN
Norfolk Street
BRIDGE ST.

Argyle St. . . . . p. 4 CZ
Buchanan St. . . . . p. 5 DZ
Gordon St. . . . . p. 5 DZ 65
Jamaica St. . . . . p. 5 DZ 77
Oswald St. . . . . p. 5 DZ
Parkhead Forge
Shopping Centre . . p. 3 BX
Renfield St. . . . . p. 5 DZ
St. Enoch
Shopping Centre. . . . . . DZ
St. Vincent St. . . . . . p. 5 DZ
Sauchiehall St. . . . . . p. 5 DY
Trongate . . . . p. 5 DZ
Union St. . . . . p. 5 DZ

Albert Bridge . . . . p. 5 DZ 2
Admiral St. . . . . p. 4 CZ
Aikenhead Rd . . . . p. 3 BX 3
Alexandra Par. . . . . . . p. 3 BV 4
Anderston Quay . . . . . p. 4 CZ
Anniesland Rd . . . . . . p. 2 AV
Argyle St. . . . . p. 4 CZ
Bain St. . . . . p. 5 DZ
Baird St. . . . . p. 5 DY
Balgrayhill . . . . p. 3 BV 5
Ballater St. . . . . p. 3 BX 6
Balmore Rd. . . . . p. 3 BV
Balornock Rd . . . . p. 3 BV 8
Balshagray Av. . . . . . . p. 2 AV 9
Bank St. . . . . p. 4 CY
Barrack St. . . . . p. 5 DZ
Barrhead Rd . . . . p. 2 AX
Bath St. . . . . p. 4 CY
Battlefield Rd . . . . p. 3 BX 12
Bell St. . . . . p. 5 DZ
Belmont St. . . . . p. 4 CY
Berkeley St. . . . . p. 4 CY
Berryknowes Rd . . . . . p. 2 AX 15
Bilsland Drive . . . . . . p. 3 BV 16
Blairbeth Rd . . . . p. 3 BX 18
Borron St. . . . . p. 5 DY
Boydstone Rd. . . . . . . p. 2 AX
Braidcraft Rd. . . . . p. 2 AX 20
Brand St. . . . . p. 4 CZ 22
Bridegate. . . . . p. 5 DZ 24
Bridge St. . . . . p. 5 DZ 25
Brockburn Rd . . . . p. 2 AX
Broomfield Rd . . . . . . p. 3 BV
Broomielaw. . . . . p. 4 CZ
Broomloan Rd . . . . . . p. 2 AV 26
Brownside Rd. . . . . . . p. 3 BX
Buchanan St. . . . . p. 5 DZ
Burnhill Chapel St. . . . p. 3 BX 28
Byres Rd . . . . p. 2 AV 29
Caldarvan St. . . . . p. 5 DY
Calder St. . . . . p. 3 BX
Caledonia Rd . . . . p. 3 BX 30
Cambridge St. . . . . . . p. 5 DY 32
Cambuslang Rd . . . . . p. 3 BX
Cardowan Rd . . . . p. 3 BV
Carmunnock Rd . . . . . p. 3 BX 33
Carntyne Rd . . . . p. 3 BV
Carntynehall Rd . . . . . p. 3 BV
Castle St. . . . . p. 5 DY
Cathcart Rd. . . . . p. 3 BX
Cathedral St. . . . . p. 5 DY
Claremont Ter. . . . . . . p. 4 CY 34
Clarkston Rd . . . . p. 3 BX
Clyde Place. . . . . p. 4 CZ 35
Clyde St. . . . . p. 5 DZ
Clyde Tunnel. . . . . p. 2 AV
Clydeside
Expressway. . . . . . . p. 2 AV
Cochrane St. . . . . p. 5 DZ 36
Commerce St. . . . . . . p. 5 DZ 37
Cook St. . . . . p. 3 BV 38
Corkerhill Rd . . . . p. 2 AX
Cornwald St. . . . . p. 4 CZ 39
Cowcaddens St. . . . . . p. 5 DY
Craighall Rd . . . . p. 5 DY
Croftfoot Rd . . . . p. 3 BX
Crookston Rd . . . . p. 2 AX
Crow Rd . . . . p. 2 AV
Cumbernauld Rd . . . . p. 3 BV 40
Dalmarnock Rd. . . . . . p. 3 BX
Derby St. . . . . p. 4 CY 42
Dobbie's Loan . . . . . . p. 5 DY
Douglas St. . . . . p. 4 CZ
Duke's Rd . . . . p. 3 BX
Duke St. . . . . p. 5 DZ
Dumbarton Rd . . . . . . p. 4 CY 47
Dumbreck Rd. . . . . p. 2 AX
East Kilbride Rd . . . . . p. 3 BX

Edinburgh Rd . . . . p. 3 BV
Edmiston Drive. . . . . . p. 2 AV 48
Eglinton Rd. . . . . p. 3 BX
Eglinton St. . . . . p. 3 BX
Elderslie St. . . . . p. 4 CY
Eldon St. . . . . p. 4 CY 50
Elmbank St. . . . . p. 4 CY
Farmeloan Rd. . . . . . . p. 3 BX 53
Fenwick Rd. . . . . p. 2 AX 55
Finnieston St. . . . . . . p. 4 CZ
Gallowgate . . . . p. 5 DZ
Garscube Rd. . . . . p. 5 DY
George Square . . . . . . p. 5 DZ
George St. . . . . p. 5 DZ
Gibson St. . . . . p. 4 CY
Glasgow Bridge . . . . . p. 5 DZ 60
Glasgow Rd
(PAISLEY) . . . . p. 2 AX 62
Glasgow Rd
(RENFREW) . . . . . . p. 2 AV
Glasgow Rd
(RUTHERGLEN) . . p. 3 BX
Glassford St. . . . . p. 5 DZ
Gorbals St. . . . . p. 3 BX 63
Gordon St. . . . . p. 5 DZ 65
Govan Rd . . . . p. 4 CZ
Grange Rd . . . . p. 3 BX 67
Great Western Rd . . . p. 4 CY
Greendyke St. . . . . . . p. 5 DZ
Haggs Rd . . . . p. 2 AX 68
Hamiltonhill Rd. . . . . . p. 5 DY
Hardgate Rd . . . . p. 2 AV
Harriet St. . . . . p. 2 AX 70
Helen St. . . . . p. 2 AV 72
High St. . . . . p. 5 DZ
Hillington Rd. . . . . p. 2 AV
Holmfauld Rd . . . . p. 2 AV 73
Holmlea Rd. . . . . p. 3 BX 74
Hope St. . . . . p. 5 DZ
Hopehill Rd. . . . . p. 4 CY
Hospital St. . . . . p. 3 BX 75
Howard St. . . . . p. 5 DZ
Hydepark St. . . . . p. 4 CZ
Ingram St. . . . . p. 5 DZ
Jamaica St. . . . . p. 5 DZ 77
James St. . . . . p. 3 BX 79
John Knox St. . . . . p. 5 DZ 80
Kelvin Way . . . . p. 4 CY
Kelvinhaugh St. . . . . . p. 4 CY
Kennedy St. . . . . p. 5 DY
Kennishead Rd . . . . . . p. 2 AX
Kent Rd. . . . . p. 4 CY
Kent St. . . . . p. 5 DZ
Keppoch Hill Rd. . . . . p. 5 DY
Killermont St. . . . . p. 5 DY
Kilmarnock Rd . . . . . . p. 2 AX
King's Drive . . . . p. 3 BX 83
King's Park Av. . . . . . . p. 3 BX
Kings Park Rd. . . . . . . p. 3 BX 84
Kingston Bridge . . . . . p. 4 CZ 85
Kingston St. . . . . p. 4 CZ
Kingsway . . . . p. 2 AV
Kyle St. . . . . p. 5 DY 86
Lamont Rd . . . . p. 3 BV 88
Lancefield Quay . . . . . p. 4 CZ
Lancefield St. . . . . p. 4 CZ
Langlands Rd . . . . p. 2 AV
Langside Av. . . . . p. 2 AX 89
Langside Drive . . . . . . p. 2 AX
Langside Rd . . . . p. 3 BX 90
Lincoln Av. . . . . p. 2 AV 91
Linthaugh Rd . . . . p. 2 AX
London Rd . . . . p. 3 BX
Lorne St. . . . . p. 4 CZ 93
Lymburn St. . . . . p. 4 CY 95
Lyoncross Rd . . . . p. 2 AX 97
Main St. . . . . p. 3 BX
Maryhill Rd . . . . p. 4 CY
Meiklerig
Crescent . . . . p. 2 AX 98
Merrylee Rd . . . . p. 2 AX
Middlesex St. . . . . p. 4 CZ 100
Milnpark St. . . . . p. 4 CZ
Milton St. . . . . p. 5 DY
Mill St. . . . . p. 3 BX
Miller St. . . . . p. 5 DZ
Minard Rd. . . . . p. 2 AX 101
Moir St. . . . . p. 5 DZ 102
Morrison St. . . . . p. 4 CZ
Moss Rd . . . . p. 2 AV 103
Mosspark Blvd. . . . . . . p. 2 AX
Napiershall St. . . . . . . p. 4 CY
Nelson St. . . . . p. 4 CZ

Nether
Auldhouse Rd . . . . p. 2 AX 104
Newlands Rd. . . . . p. 2 AX
Nitshill Rd . . . . p. 2 AX
Norfolk St. . . . . p. 5 DZ
North St. . . . . p. 4 CY
North Canalbank St. . . p. 5 DY
North Hanover St. . . . p. 5 DY
North Woodside Rd . . p. 4 CY
Oswald St. . . . . p. 5 DZ
Otago St. . . . . p. 4 CY 105
Oxford St. . . . . p. 5 DZ 106
Paisley Rd . . . . p. 2 AV
Paisley Rd West . . . . . p. 2 AX
Park Gdns . . . . p. 4 CY 107
Park Quadrant . . . . p. 4 CY
Park Ter . . . . p. 4 CY 108
Peat Rd . . . . p. 2 AX
Petershill Rd . . . . p. 3 BV
Pinkston Rd . . . . p. 5 DY
Pitt St. . . . . p. 4 CZ
Pollokshaws Rd. . . . . . p. 2 AX
Port Dundas Rd . . . . . p. 5 DY 110
Possil Rd . . . . p. 5 DY
Prospecthill Rd . . . . . . p. 3 BX 112
Provan Rd . . . . p. 3 BV 114
Queen St. . . . . p. 5 DZ
Queen Margaret
Drive . . . . p. 4 CY 116
Raeberry St. . . . . p. 4 CY
Red Rd. . . . . p. 3 BV 118
Renfield St. . . . . p. 5 DZ
Renfrew Rd . . . . p. 2 AV
Renfrew St. . . . . p. 5 DY
Ring Rd . . . . p. 3 BV
Riverford Road . . . . . . p. 2 AX 119
Robertson St. . . . . p. 4 CZ 120
Rotten Row . . . . p. 5 DZ
Royal Ter . . . . p. 4 CY
Royston Rd . . . . p. 3 BV
Rutherglen Rd. . . . . . . p. 3 BX
St. Andrew's
Drive . . . . p. 2 AX
St. George's Rd . . . . . p. 4 CY
St. James Rd. . . . . p. 5 DY
St. Mungo Av. . . . . p. 5 DY
St. Vincent St . . . . p. 5 DZ
Saltmarket . . . . p. 5 DZ
Sandwood Rd . . . . p. 2 AV 123
Saracen St. . . . . p. 5 DY
Sauchiehall St. . . . . . . p. 5 DY
Scott St. . . . . p. 4 CY
Seaward St. . . . . p. 4 CZ
Shettleston Rd . . . . . . p. 3 BX
Shieldhall Rd . . . . p. 2 AV
Shields Rd. . . . . p. 2 AX 124
Southbrae Drive . . . . . p. 2 AV
Springburn Rd. . . . . . . p. 3 BV
Springfield Rd . . . . p. 3 BX
Stirling Rd . . . . p. 5 DY 126
Stobcross Road. . . . . . p. 4 CZ
Stockwell St. . . . . p. 5 DZ 127
Stonelaw Rd . . . . p. 3 BX
Striven Gdns . . . . p. 4 CY 128
Thornliebank Rd . . . . . p. 2 AX
Todd St. . . . . p. 3 BV 131
Tollcross Rd. . . . . p. 3 BX
Trongate . . . . p. 5 DZ
Trossachs St. . . . . p. 4 CY
Union St. . . . . p. 5 DZ
Victoria Bridge. . . . . . . p. 5 DZ 132
Victoria Rd. . . . . p. 3 BX
Wallacewell Rd . . . . . . p. 3 BV
Waterloo St. . . . . p. 4 CZ
West St. . . . . p. 4 CZ
West Campbell St. . . . p. 4 CZ
West George St. . . . . . p. 5 DZ
West Graham St. . . . . p. 4 CY 135
Westmuir Place. . . . . . p. 3 BX 136
Westmuir St. . . . . p. 3 BX 138
West Nile St. . . . . . . p. 5 DYZ 139
West Paisley Rd . . . . . p. 4 CZ
West Prince's St. . . . . p. 4 CY
West Regent St. . . . . . p. 5 DY
Wilson St. . . . . p. 5 DZ
Wilton St. . . . . p. 4 CY
Wishart St. . . . . p. 5 DZ
Woodlands Drive . . . . p. 4 CY 140
Woodlands Rd . . . . p. 4 CY
Woodside Crescent . . p. 4 CY 141
Woodside Place . . . . . p. 4 CY
Woodside Ter . . . . p. 4 CY 143
York St. . . . . p. 4 CZ

Manor Park, 28 Balshagray Drive, G11 7DD, ☎ 339 2143, Fax 339 5842 – TV ☎ AV **u**
9 rm.

Albion, 405-407 North Woodside Rd, G20 6NN, ☎ 339 8620, Fax 334 8159 – TV ☎
16 rm. CY **u**

Drumlin without rest., 4 Kelvin Drive, G20 8QG, ☎ 945 4877, Fax 945 5152 – TV ☎
7 rm. AV **r**

Kirklee without rest., 11 Kensington Gate, G12 9LG, ☎ 334 5555, Fax 339 3828 – TV ☎. VISA. AV **c**
9 rm 45.00/59.00 **st.**

XXXX **Camerons** (at Glasgow Hilton H.), 1 William St., G3 8HT, ☎ 204 5555, Fax 204 5004 – P. AE VISA JCB CZ **s**
Meals (booking essential) 17.50 **st.** (lunch) and a la carte 7.00.

XXX **Buttery,** 652 Argyle St., G3 8UF, ☎ 221 8188, Fax 204 4639 – P. AE VISA
closed Saturday lunch, Sunday and Bank Holidays – **Meals** 14.95 **st.** (lunch) and a la carte 20.35/28.55. CZ **e**

XXX **Rogano,** 11 Exchange Pl., G1 3AN, ☎ 248 4055, Fax 248 2608, « Art Deco » – AE VISA DZ **i**
closed Sunday lunch and Bank Holidays – **Meals** - Seafood 16.50 **t.** (lunch) and a la carte 24.95/41.50.

XX Ho Wong, 82 York St., G2 3LE, ☎ 221 3550 – CZ **v**
Meals (Chinese, Peking).

XX **Sepoy Club** (at Dalmeny House H.), 62 St. Andrews Drive, Nithsdale Cross, Pollokshields, G41 5EZ, ☎ 427 6288 – P. AE VISA AX **o**
Meals - Indian a la carte 9.45/14.95 3.95.

X **Ubiquitous Chip,** 12 Ashton Lane, off Byres Rd, G12 8SJ, ☎ 334 5007, Fax 337 1302 – AE VISA AV **e**
closed 25 December and 1-2 January – **Meals** a la carte 19.20/30.85 **t.**

X **La Parmigiana,** 447 Great Western Rd, Kelvinbridge, G12 8HH, ☎ 334 0686, Fax 332 3533 – AE VISA CY **r**
closed Sunday and Bank Holidays – **Meals** - Italian 6.80 **st.** (lunch) and a la carte 14.25/24.15 **st.**

at Stepps NE : 5 ½ m. by M 8 on A 80 – BV – ✉ Glasgow – ☎ 0141 :

Garfield House, Cumbernauld Rd, G33 6HW, ☎ 779 2111, Fax 779 2111 – TV ☎ & P – 120. AE VISA
Meals 7.95/15.95 **t.** and dinner a la carte 6.05 – **46 rm** 66.00/82.50 **t.**

at Giffnock (Renfrew.) (Strathclyde) S : 5 ¼ m. by A 77 – AX – ✉ Glasgow – ☎ 0141 :

MacDonald Thistle (Mt. Charlotte Thistle), Eastwood Toll, G46 6RA, at junction of A 77 with A 726 ☎ 638 2225, Telex 779138, Fax 638 6231, – TV ☎ P – 160. AE VISA JCB.
Meals (bar lunch Saturday and Bank Holidays) 9.50/19.50 **t.** and a la carte 4.90 – **52 rm** 70.00/85.00 **t.**, 4 suites – SB.

X **Turban Tandoori,** 2 Station Rd, G46 6JF, ☎ 638 0069 – AE VISA
Meals - Indian (dinner only) a la carte 8.55/12.70 **t.** 6.95.

at Busby S : 7 ¼ m. by A 77 – AX – on A 726 – ✉ Glasgow – ☎ 0141 :

Busby, 1 Field Rd, Clarkston, G76 8RX, ☎ 644 2661, Fax 644 4417 – rm TV ☎ P – 150. AE VISA.
Meals 9.25/15.95 **t.** and a la carte 6.50 – **32 rm** 55.00/80.00 **t.** – SB.

at Glasgow Airport W : 8 m. by M 8 – ✉ Paisley – ☎ 0141 :

Travel Inn, Whitecart Rd, PA3 2TH, M8 junc. 28 ☎ 842 1563, Fax 842 1570 – rm TV & P – 30. AE VISA.
Meals (grill rest.)(dinner only) a la carte approx. 16.00 **t.** – 4.95 – **81 rm** 33.50 **t.**

ATS 192 Finnieston St. ☎ 248 6761
ATS Rutherglen Ind. Est., Glasgow Rd, Rutherglen ☎ 647 9341
ATS 1 Sawmillfield St., off Garscube Rd ☎ 332 1945

GLASGOW AIRPORT Lanark. (Strathclyde) 401 402 G 16 – see Glasgow.

GLENCARSE Perth. (Tayside) 401 K 14 -see Perth.

GLENELG Ross and Cromarty (Highland) 401 D 12 – ☎ 01599.
♦Edinburgh 229 – ♦Inverness 75 – Kyle of Lochalsh 25.

Glenelg Inn, IV40 8JR, ☎ 522273, Fax 522373, ≤ Glenelg Bay, – rest P
Easter-October – **Meals** (bar lunch)/dinner 19.00 **t.** 4.50 – **6 rm** (dinner included) 90.00/150.00 **t.**

GLENFINNAN Inverness. (Highland) 401 D 13 – ✉ Fort William – ☎ 01397.
♦Edinburgh 150 – ♦Inverness 85 – ♦Oban 66.

Prince's House, PH37 4LT, W : ¾ m. on A 830 ☎ 722246, Fax 722307, ≤ – TV P. AE VISA
April-December – **Meals** (in bar) a la carte 16.15/25.95 **st.** – **9 rm** 39.95/79.90 **st.** – SB.

GLENLIVET Banff. (Grampian) 401 J 11 – ✉ Ballindalloch – ☎ 01807.

♦Edinburgh 180 – ♦Aberdeen 59 – Elgin 27 – ♦Inverness 49.

- **Minmore House** ⛰, AB37 9DB, S : ¾ m. on Glenlivet Distillery rd ☎ 590378, Fax 590472, ≤, 🌳 – ⊁ rest ☎ P. VISA
  May-October – **Meals** (dinner only) 22.00 **st.** 4.50 – **10 rm** 35.00/70.00 **st.** – SB.

GLENLUCE Wigtown. 401 F 19 – ✉ Newton Stewart – ☎ 01581.

18 Wigtownshire County, Mains of Park, Newton Stewart ☎ 300420,.

♦Edinburgh 126 – ♦Ayr 62 – Dumfries 65 – Stranraer 9.

- **Kelvin House,** 53 Main St., DG8 0PP, ☎ 300303, Fax 300258 – TV.
  Meals (bar lunch Monday to Saturday)/dinner 20.00 **t.** and a la carte 4.25 – **5 rm** 28.50/50.00 **t.**

GLENROTHES Fife. (Fife) 401 K 15 **Scotland G.** – pop. 33 639 – ECD : Tuesday – ☎ 01592.

Envir. : Falkland★ (Village★, Palace of Falkland★ *AC*, Gardens★ *AC*) N : 5½ m. by A 92 and A 912.

18 Thornton, Station Rd ☎ 771111 – 18 Golf Course Rd ☎ 754561/758686 – 18 Balbirnie Park, Markinch ☎ 752006 – 9 Auchterderran, Woodend Rd, Cardenden ☎ 721579 – 9 The Myre, Falkland ☎ (01337) 57404 – 9 Leslie, Balsillie Laws ☎ 620040.

Rothes Square, Kingddom Centre, ☎ 754954.

♦Edinburgh 33 – ♦Dundee 25 – Stirling 36.

- **Balbirnie House** ⛰, Markinch, KY7 6NE, NE : 1 ¾ m. by A 911 and A 92 on B 9130 ☎ 610066, Fax 610529, « Part 18C mansion », 🌳, park – ⊁ rest TV ☎ & P – 150. AE VISA
  Meals 17.50/45.00 **st.** and lunch a la carte – **28 rm** 85.00/180.00 **st.**, 2 suites – SB.

  at Leslie W : 3 m. by A 911 – ✉ Leslie – ☎ 01592 :

- **Rescobie,** 6 Valley Drive, KY6 3BQ, ☎ 742143, Fax 620231, 🌳 – TV ☎ P. AE VISA.
  closed 25 to 27 December – **Meals** 17.00 **t.** and a la carte 4.95 – **10 rm** 48.00/70.00 **t.** – SB.

GOLSPIE Sutherland. (Highland) 401 I 10 – pop. 1 385 – ECD : Wednesday – ☎ 01408.

18 Ferry Rd ☎ 633266.

♦Edinburgh 228 – ♦Inverness 72 – ♦Wick 54.

- **Sutherland Arms,** Old Bank Rd, KW10 6RS, ☎ 633234, Fax 633234, 🌳 – TV ☎ P – 30. VISA
  Meals (bar lunch)/dinner a la carte 9.75/17.95 **st.** 4.00 – **16 rm** 30.00/50.00 **st.** – SB.

GRANTOWN-ON-SPEY Moray. (Highland) 401 J 12 – pop. 1 800 – ECD : Thursday – ☎ 01479.

– 9 Abernethy, Nethy Bridge ☎ 821305.

High St. PH26 3EH ☎ 872773 (summer only).

♦Edinburgh 143 – ♦Inverness 34 – Perth 99.

- Ravenscourt House, Seafield Av., PH26 3JG, ☎ 872286, Fax 873260 – ⊁ rest TV P
  9 rm.
- **Garth,** The Square, PH26 3HN, ☎ 872836, Fax 872116, 🌳 – ⊁ rest TV ☎ P. AE VISA.
  Meals (bar lunch)/dinner 24.00 **t.** and a la carte 6.00 – **14 rm** 38.00/76.00 **t.** – SB.
- **Culdearn House,** Woodlands Terr., PH26 3JU, ☎ 872106, Fax 873641, 🌳 – ⊁ TV P. VISA.
  March-October – **Meals** (residents only) (dinner only) 3.95 – **9 rm** (dinner included) 48.00/96.00 **st.** – SB.
- **Ardlarig,** Woodlands Terr., PH26 3JU, ☎ 873245, 🌳 – ⊁ TV P
  closed 22 to 29 December – **Meals** 10.50 **st.** 5.95 – **7 rm** 17.50/35.00 **st.** – SB.
- **Ardconnel,** Woodlands Terr., PH26 3JU, ☎ 872104, Fax 872104, 🌳 – ⊁ TV P. VISA.
  Easter-October – **Meals** 15.00 **st.** 3.50 – **7 rm** 28.50/52.00 **st.**

GRETNA Dumfries. (Dumfries and Galloway) 401 402 K 19 – pop. 2 678 – ECD : Wednesday – ☎ 01461.

The Old Headless Cross DJ16 5EF ☎ 337834 (summer only) – Gateway to Scotland, M 74 Service Area ☎ 338500.

♦Edinburgh 91 – ♦Carlisle 10 – ♦Dumfries 24.

- Garden House, Sarkfoot Rd, DG16 5EP, on B 7076 ☎ 337621, Fax 37692, Iб, ≘s, – TV ☎ & P
  21 rm.

Gretna Chase, DG16 5JB, S : ¼ m. on B 7076 ℘ 337517, Fax 337766, « Gardens » – TV P. VISA
Meals *(closed Sunday)* (bar lunch)/dinner a la carte 14.85/22.40 **t.** 4.50 – **8 rm** 38.00/60.00 **t.**

Forte Travelodge without rest., DG16 5HQ, ℘ 337566, Fax 37752, Reservations (Freephone) 0800 850950 – TV P. AE VISA.
64 rm 33.50 **t.**

GRIMSAY Western Isles (Outer Hebrides) 401 Y 11 – see Uist (Isles of).

GULLANE E. Lothian. (Lothian) 401 L 15 **Scotland G.** – pop. 2 124 – ECD : Wednesday – 01620.

Envir. : Dirleton★ (Castle★) NE : 2 m. by A 198.

18, 18, 18 Gullane ℘ 843115.

♦Edinburgh 19 – North Berwick 5.

Greywalls , Duncur Rd, Muirfield, EH31 2EG, ℘ 842144, Fax 842241, ≤ gardens and golf course, « Lutyens house, gardens by Gertrude Jekyll », – rest TV P. AE VISA
April-October – **Meals** 20.00/33.00 **t.** and lunch a la carte 6.00 – **22 rm** 95.00/160.00 **t.**

La Potinière (Hilary Brown), Main St., EH31 2AA, ℘ 843214
closed 1 week June and October – **Meals** *(closed lunch Friday and Saturday, dinner Sunday to Thursday and Wednesday)* (booking essential) 20.00/30.00 **t.** 5.00
Spec. Sole with pesto and sauce vierge, Breast of duck with barley and wild mushrooms, Soft centred warm chocolate pudding.

at Dirleton NE : 2 m. by A 198 – ✉ Dirleton – 01620 :

Open Arms with rm, EH39 5EG, ℘ 850241, Fax 850570, « Tastefully converted stone cottages », – TV P. VISA
Meals *(closed dinner 31 December and 1 January)* (light lunch)/dinner 15.50/30.00 **st.** and a la carte 6.50 – **7 rm** 70.00/130.00 **st.** – SB.

HADDINGTON E. Lothian. (Lothian) 401 L 16 **Scotland G.** – pop. 7 342 – ECD : Thursday – 0162 082 (4 fig.) and 01620 (6 fig.).

See : Town★ – High Street★.

Envir. : Lennoxlove★ *AC*, S : 1 m.

Exc. : Tantallon Castle★★ (clifftop site★★★) *AC*, NE : 12 m. by A 1 and A 198 – Northern foothills of the Lammermuir Hills★★, S : 14 m. by A 6137 and B 6368 – Stenton★, E : 7 m.

18 Amisfield Park ℘ 3627.

♦Edinburgh 17 – Hawick 53 – ♦Newcastle upon Tyne 101.

Maitlandfield House, 24 Sidegate, EH41 4BZ, ℘ 6513, Fax 6713, – TV P – 200. AE VISA
Meals a la carte 8.30/19.70 **st.** 4.50 – **22 rm** 55.00/90.00 **st.** – SB.

Brown's with rm, 1 West Rd, EH41 3RD, ℘ 822254, Fax 822254, – rest TV P. AE VISA.
Meals (booking essential) (dinner only and Sunday lunch)/dinner 18.50/25.50 **t.** – **5 rm** 55.00/78.00 **t.**

HALKIRK Caithness. (Highland) 401 J 8 – 0184 784.

♦Edinburgh 285 – Thurso 8 – ♦Wick 17.

Bannochmore Farm , (The Bungalow) Harpsdale, KW12 6UN, S : 3 ¼ m. ℘ 216, « Working farm », park – P.
Meals (communal dining) 9.50 – **3 rm** 16.00/32.00 **t.** – SB.

HAMILTON SERVICE AREA Lanark. (Strathclyde) – 01698.

9 Larkhall, Burnhead Rd ℘ 881113 – 9 Strathclyde park, Mote Hill ℘ 266155.

Road Chef Services, M 74 northbound ML3 6JW ℘ 285590.

♦Edinburgh 38 – ♦Glasgow 12.

Road Chef Lodge without rest., ML3 6JW, M 74 between junctions 6 and 5 (northbound carriageway) ℘ 891904, Fax 891682 – TV P – 25
36 rm.

HARRIS (Isle of) Inverness. (Outer Hebrides) (Western Isles) 401 Z 10 – see Lewis and Harris (Isle of).

HAWICK Roxburgh. (Borders) 401 402 L 17 **Scotland G.** – pop. 16 127 – ECD : Tuesday – 01450.

Exc. : Jedburgh Abbey★★ *AC*, SW : 12½ m. by A 698 – Waterloo Monument (✻★★) NE : 12 m. by A 698, A 68 and B 6400 – Hermitage Castle★, S : 16 m. by B 6399.

18 Hawick, Vertish Hill ℘ 372293 – 18 Minto, Denholm ℘ 387220.

Common Haugh TD9 7AR ℘ 372547.

♦Edinburgh 51 – ♦Ayr 122 – ♦Carlisle 44 – ♦Dumfries 63 – Motherwell 76 – ♦Newcastle upon Tyne 62.

Kirklands, West Stewart Pl., TD9 8BH, ☎ 372263, Fax 370404, – TV ☎ P. VISA JCB
Meals (bar lunch)/dinner 10.95/19.50 **t.** and dinner a la carte 4.50 – **12 rm** 48.50/80.00 **t.** – SB.

Rubislaw, Newhouses, TD9 8PR, N : 3 m. by A 7 ☎ 377693, ← Rubers law and Cheviot hills, – TV P. VISA.
March-October – **Meals** (communal dining) 18.00 **st.** 4.75 – **3 rm** 34.00/56.00 **st.**

ATS Victoria Rd ☎ 373369

HEITON Roxburgh. (Borders) – see Kelso.

HELENSBURGH Dunbarton. (Strathclyde) 401 F 15 **Scotland G.** – pop. 12 972 – ECD : Wednesday – 01436.

See : Hill House★ *AC.*

Envir. : Loch Lomond★★, NE : 4½ m. by B 832.

Exc. : The Clyde Estuary★.

to Gourock via Kilcreggan (Caledonian MacBrayne Ltd) 2-10 daily (except Sunday).

The Clock Tower J84 7NY ☎ 672642 (summer only).

◆Edinburgh 68 – ◆Glasgow 22.

Commodore Toby, 112-117 West Clyde St., G84 8ER, ☎ 676924, Fax 676233, ← – rm TV ☎ P – 200
Meals (grill rest.) **44 rm**, 1 suite.

HUMBIE E. Lothian (Lothian) 401 L 16 – 01875.

◆Edinburgh 19 – Hawick 44 – ◆Newcastle upon Tyne 92.

Johnstounburn House (Mt. Charlotte Thistle), EH36 5PL, S : 1 m. on B 6368 ☎ 833696, Fax 833626, ←, « Part 17C country house in extensive gardens », park – TV ☎ P – 30. VISA
Meals 15.00/27.50 **t.** 5.30 – **20 rm** 95.00/160.00 **t.** – SB.

INSCH Aberdeen (Grampian) 401 M 11 **Scotland G.** – pop. 1 247 – ECD : Thursday – 01464.

Exc. : Huntly Castle (elaborate Heraldic carvings★★★) *AC*, NW : 14½ m. by B 9002 and A 97.

Golf Terr. ☎ 820363.

◆Edinburgh 55 – ◆Aberdeen 25.

Leslie Castle, Leslie, AB52 6NX, SW : 3¾ m. by B 992 ☎ 820869, Fax 821076, « 17C fortified baronial house » – TV ☎ P. VISA.
Meals (lunch by arrangement)/dinner 30.00 **st.** 5.50 – **4 rm** 83.00/138.00 **st.** – SB.

INGLISTON Midlothian. (Lothian) 401 K 16 – see Edinburgh.

INNERLEITHEN Peebles. 401 402 K 17 – 01896.

The Ley, EH44 6NL, N : 2¼ m. on B 709 ☎ 830240, Fax 830240, park – P.
mid February - mid October – **Meals** (by arrangement) (residents only) (dinner only) 19.50 4.25 – **3 rm** 47.00/74.00 **s.**

INVERCRERAN Argyll. (Strathclyde) 401 E 14 – ✉ Appin – 0163 173.

◆Edinburgh 142 – Fort William 29 – ◆Oban 19.

Invercreran Country House, Glen Creran, PA38 4BJ, ☎ 414, Fax 532, ← Glen Creran and mountains, park – rest TV ☎ P. VISA.
March-October – **Meals** 28.00 **t.** (dinner) and lunch a la carte 14.00/24.50 7.85 – **9 rm** 62.00/140.00 **t.** – SB.

INVERGARRY Inverness (Highland) 401 F 12 – ✉ Inverness – 01809.

◆Edinburgh 159 – Fort William 25 – ◆Inverness 43 – Kyle of Lochalsh 50.

Glengarry Castle, PH35 4HW, on A 82 ☎ 501254, Fax 501207, ←, park, – rest TV ☎ P. VISA
early April to late October – **Meals** (dinner only and Sunday lunch)/dinner 22.00 **st.** 5.25 – **26 rm** 42.50/87.00 **st.** – SB.

Ardochy Lodge, Glengarry, PH35 4HR, W : 7 ½ m. by A 87 on Tomdoun rd ☎ 511232, Fax 511233, ←, park – rest P
14 April-20 October – **Meals** (dinner only)(residents only) – **8 rm** (dinner included) 50.00/74.00.

Invergarry, PH35 4HG, ☎ 501206, Fax 501207, – rest TV ☎ P. VISA
Meals (dinner only)a la carte 9.30/17.80 **st.** 4.30 – **10 rm** 36.00/64.00 **st.** – SB.

INVERMORISTON Inverness. (Highland) 401 G 12 **Scotland G.** – 01320.

Envir. : Loch Ness★★.

◆Edinburgh 168 – ◆Inverness 29 – Kyle of Lochalsh 56.

Glenmoriston Arms, IV3 6YA, ☎ 351206, Fax 351206, – TV ☎ P. VISA
Meals (bar lunch)/dinner 18.00 **st.** and a la carte 4.85 – **8 rm** 45.00/66.00 **st.** – SB.

INVERNESS Inverness. (Highland) **401** H 11 **Scotland G.** – pop. 62 186 – ECD : Wednesday – ☏ 01463.

See : Town★ – Museum and Art Gallery★ **M**.

Exc. : Loch Ness★★, SW : by A 82 – Clava Cairns★, E : 9 m. by Culcabock Rd, B 9006 and B 851 – Cawdor Castle★ *AC*, NE : 14 m. by A 96 and B 9090.

⛳18 Culcabock Rd ✆ 239882 – ⛳18 Torvean, Glenurquhart Rd ✆ 711434.

✈ Dalcross Airport : ✆ 232471, NE : 8 m. by A 96.

🚗 ✆ 0345 090700.

ℹ Castle Wynd IN2 3BJ ✆ 234353.

♦Edinburgh 156 – ♦Aberdeen 107 – ♦Dundee 134.

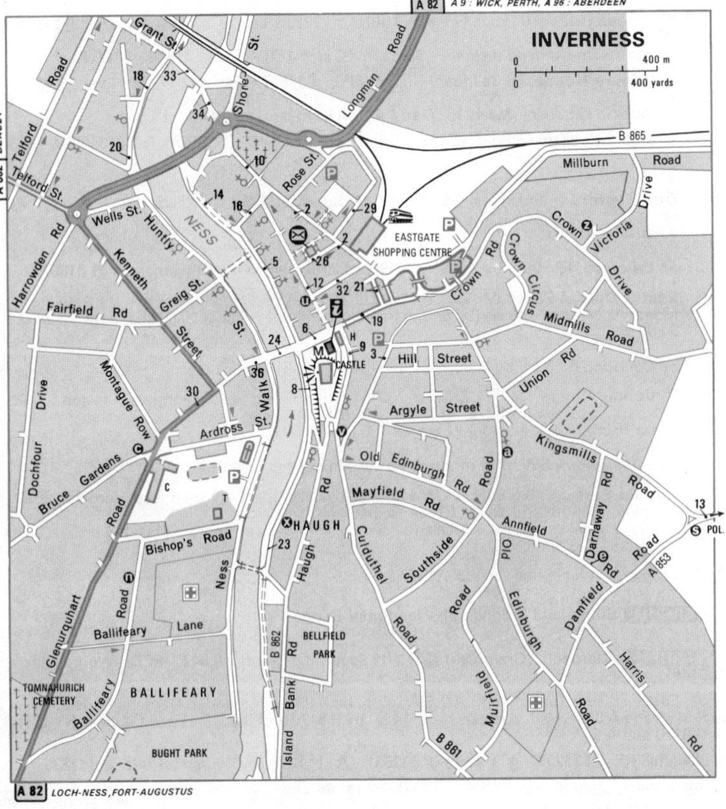

Academy Street 2
Bridge Street 6
Church Street 12
Eastgate Shopping Centre
High Street 19
Union Street 32

Ardconnel Street 3
Bank Street 5
Castle Road 8
Castle Street 9
Chapel Street 10
Culcabock Road 13
Douglas Row 14
Friars Lane 16
Gilbert Street 18
Huntly Place 20
Inglis Street 21
Ness Bank 23
Ness Bridge 24
Queensgate 26
Strothers Lane 29
Tomnahurich Street 30
Waterloo Bridge 33
Waterloo Place 34
Young Street 36

Kingsmills (Swallow), Culcabock Rd, IV2 3LP, ✆ 237166, Fax 225208, ⚒, ≘s, ▢, 🌳 – |♦| ⊭ rm ▢ ☎ ♿ **P** – 🏛 70. AE ① VISA **s**
Meals 12.00/20.50 **st.** and dinner a la carte 🍷 6.00 – **83 rm** ▭ 95.00/125.00 **st.**, 1 suite – SB.

Caledonian (Jarvis), 33 Church St., IV1 1DX, ✆ 235181, Fax 711206, ⚒, ≘s, ▢ – |♦| ▢ ☎ ♿ **P** – 🏛 300. AE ① VISA **u**
Meals (bar lunch Monday to Saturday)/dinner 18.00 **t.** and a la carte 🍷 5.50 – ▭ 8.50 – **103 rm** 79.00/99.00 **st.**, 3 suites – SB.

Craigmonie, 9 Annfield Rd, IV2 3HX, ☏ 231649, Fax 233720, ⛶, ⛶, ⛶ – ⛶ TV ☎ P – ⛶ 140. ⛶ AE ⛶ VISA. ⛶ **e**
Meals 11.25/21.50 **t.** and a la carte 5.50 – **32 rm** 68.00/115.00 **t.**, 3 suites.

Glenmoriston, 20 Ness Bank, IV2 4SF, ☏ 223777, Fax 712378 – TV ☎ P. ⛶ AE VISA. ⛶ **x**
closed 24 December-5 January – **Meals** (dinner only) 21.50 **t.** and a la carte 5.95 – **20 rm** 51.00/100.00 **t.** – SB.

Glendruidh House ⛶, Old Edinburgh Rd, IV1 2AA, SW : 2 m. ☏ 226499, Fax 710745, ⛶ – ⛶ TV ☎ P. ⛶ AE ⛶ VISA JCB. ⛶
Meals (residents only) 12.50/17.50 **t.** 5.50 – **7 rm** 50.00/72.00 **t.**

Braemore without rest., 1 Victoria Drive, IV2 3QB, ☏ 243318, ⛶ – ⛶ P. ⛶ **z**
3 rm 35.00/50.00 **st.**

Moyness House, 6 Bruce Gdns, IV3 5EN, ☏ 233836, Fax 233836, ⛶ – ⛶ rest TV P. ⛶ AE VISA **c**
closed 23 December-4 January – **Meals** 15.00 **st.** 4.50 – **7 rm** 29.00/58.00 **st.**

Ballifeary House, 10 Ballifeary Rd, IV3 5PJ, ☏ 235572, Fax 235572, ⛶ – ⛶ TV P. ⛶ VISA. ⛶ **n**
Easter-mid October – **Meals** 15.50 **st.** 4.10 – **8 rm** 32.00/64.00 **st.**

Craigside Lodge without rest., 4 Gordon Terr., IV2 3HD, ☏ 231576, Fax 713409, ← – TV. ⛶ **v**
6 rm 20.00/36.00 **st.**

Old Rectory without rest., 9 Southside Rd, IV2 3BG, ☏ 220969, ⛶ – ⛶ TV P. ⛶ **a**
4 rm 20.00/38.00.

at Dalcross NE : 9 m. by A 96, B 9039 and Ardersier rd – ✉ Inverness – ☏ 01667 :

Easter Dalziel Farm, IV1 2JL, on B 9039 ☏ 462213, « Working farm », ⛶ – P
March-November – **Meals** (by arrangement) (communal dining) 10.00 **st.** – **3 rm** 24.00/34.00 **st.**

at Culloden E : 3 m. by A 96 – ✉ Inverness – ☏ 01463 :

Culloden House ⛶, IV1 2NZ, ☏ 790461, Fax 792181, ←, « Georgian mansion », ⛶, ⛶, park, ⛶ – ⛶ rm TV ☎ P. ⛶ AE ⛶ VISA. ⛶
Meals 16.50/35.00 **t.** 5.10 – **22 rm** 125.00/175.00 **t.**, 1 suite.

at Dunain Park SW : 2½ m. on A 82 – ✉ Inverness – ☏ 01463 :

Dunain Park ⛶, IV3 6JN, ☏ 230512, Fax 224532, ←, « Country house, gardens », ⛶, ⛶, park – ⛶ rest TV ☎ P. ⛶ AE ⛶ VISA JCB
closed 3 weeks January – **Meals** (dinner only) a la carte approx. 24.85 **t.** 6.00 – **8 rm** 45.00/130.00 **t.**, 6 suites.

ATS Carsegate Rd North, The Carse ☏ 236167

INVERSHIN Sutherland. (Highland) – see Bonar Bridge.

INVERURIE Aberdeen. (Grampian) 401 M 12 **Scotland G.** – pop. 8 647 – ECD : Wednesday – ☏ 01467.

Exc. : Castle Fraser★ (exterior★★) *AC*, SW : 6 m. by B 993 – Pitmedden Gardens★★, NE : 10 m. by B 9170 and A 920 – Haddo House★, N : 14 m. by B 9170 and B 9005 – Fyvie Castle★, N : 13 m. by B 9170 and A 947.

⛳18 Blackhall Rd ☏ 620207 – ⛳18 Kintore ☏ 632631 – ⛳18, ⛳9 Kemnay, Monymusk Rd ☏ 642225.

ℹ Town Hall, Market Pl. AB51 9SN ☏ 620600 (summer only).

♦Edinburgh 147 – ♦Aberdeen 17 – ♦Inverness 90.

Thainstone House H. & Country Club ⛶, AB51 9NT, S : 2 m. by B 993 on A 96 ☏ 621643, Fax 625084, ⛶, ⛶, park – ⛶ ⛶ rest TV ☎ P – ⛶ 400
47 rm, 1 suite.

Strathburn, Burghmuir Drive, AB51 4GY, NW : 1¼ by A 96 ☏ 624422, Fax 625133 – ⛶ TV ☎ ♿ P – ⛶ 30. ⛶ AE VISA. ⛶
Meals 16.75/20.75 **st.** and a la carte 4.25 – **25 rm** 55.00/85.00 **st.** – SB.

IRVINE Ayr. (Strathclyde) 401 402 F 17 **Scotland G.** – pop. 23 275 – ☏ 01294.

Envir. : Kilmarnock (Dean Castle, arms and armour★, musical instruments★) *AC*, E : 5½ m. by A 71 and B 7038.

⛳18 Western Gailes, Gailes ☏ 311649 – ⛳18 Irvine Ravenspark, Kidsneuk Lane ☏ 271293 – ⛳18 Bogside ☏ 78139.

♦Edinburgh 75 – Ayr 14 – ♦Glasgow 29.

Hospitality Inn (Mt. Charlotte Thistle), 46 Annick Rd, KA11 4LD, SE : 1 m. on B 7081 ☎ 274272, Telex 777097, Fax 277287, « Exotic indoor garden with 🏊 », 9 – ⇔ rm TV ☎ ♿ P – 🏛 300. AE ① VISA
Meals (carving lunch) 5.25/19.95 **st.** and a la carte 5.10 – ☐ 8.75 – **127 rm** 85.00/200.00 **st.** – SB.

ATS 9 Kyle Rd, Ind. Est. ☎ 278727

ISLAY (Isle of) Argyll. (Strathclyde) 401 B 16 – pop. 3 840.

18 Machrie Hotel, Port Ellen ☎ (01496) 302310.

✈ Port Ellen Airport : ☎ (01496) 302361.

⛴ from Port Askaig to Isle of Jura (Feolin) (Western Ferries (Argyll) Ltd) (5 mn) – from Port Ellen and Port Askaig to Kintyre Peninsula (Kennacraig) (Caledonian MacBrayne Ltd) 1-3 daily – from Port Askaig to Oban via Isle of Colonsay (Scalasaig) (Caledonian MacBrayne Ltd) (3 h 30 mn).

ℹ at Bowmore, The Square ☎ (01496) 810254.

Ballygrant – ✉ Ballygrant – ☎ 01496.

Ballygrant Inn, PA45 7QR, ☎ 840277, Fax 840277, 🌳 – ⇔ P. VISA. ✗
Meals (bar lunch)/dinner 16.50 **st.** – **3 rm** ☐ 23.50/50.00 **st.** – SB.

Bridgend – ✉ Bowmore – ☎ 01496.

Bridgend, PA44 7PJ, ☎ 810212, Fax 810673, 🌳 – TV ☎ P
Meals (lunch by arrangement)/dinner 19.50 **t.** and a la carte 4.60 – **10 rm** ☐ 39.00/78.00 **t.** – SB.

ISLE of WHITHORN Wigtown. (Dumfries and Galloway) 401 402 G 19 **Scotland G.** – pop. 1 448 – ECD : Wednesday – ✉ Newton Stewart – ☎ 01988.

Envir. : Priory Museum (Early Christian Crosses★★) NW : 3 m. by A 750.

◆Edinburgh 152 – ◆Ayr 72 – ◆Dumfries 72 – Stranraer 34.

Steam Packet, Harbour Row, DG8 8LL, ☎ 500334, ← – TV ☎. VISA
closed 25 December – **Meals** (bar lunch)/dinner 21.50/13.50 **t.** and a la carte 4.75 – **5 rm** ☐ 22.50/45.00 **t.**

ISLEORNSAY Inverness. (Highland) 401 C 12 – see Skye (Isle of).

JEDBURGH Roxburgh. (Borders) 401 402 M 17 **Scotland G.** – pop. 4 768 – ECD : Thursday – ☎ 01835.

See : Town★ – Abbey★★ *AC* – Mary Queen of Scots House Visitor Centre★ *AC* – The Canongate Bridge★.

Envir. : Waterloo Monument (※★★) N : 4 m. by A 68 and B 6400.

9 Jedburgh, Dunion Rd ☎ 863587.

ℹ Murray's Green TD8 6BE ☎ 863435/863688.

◆Edinburgh 48 – ◆Carlisle 54 – ◆Newcastle upon Tyne 57.

Glenfriars, The Friars, TD8 6BN, ☎ 862000, 🌳 – TV P. AE VISA
closed Christmas-New Year – **Meals** (lunch by arrangement)/dinner 16.50 3.50 – **6 rm** ☐ 35.00/64.00 **t.** – SB.

Hundalee House without rest., TD8 6PA, S : 1 ½ m. by A 68 ☎ 863011, ←, 🌳, park – ⇔ TV P. ✗
April-October – **4 rm** ☐ 30.00/40.00 **st.**

Spinney without rest., Langlee, TD8 6PB, S : 2 m. on A 68 ☎ 863525, Fax 863525, 🌳 – ⇔ P. ✗
March-October – **3 rm** ☐ 30.00/40.00 **st.**

JOHN O'GROATS Caithness. (Highland) 401 K 8 – Shipping Services : see Orkney Islands.

JURA (Isle of) Argyll. (Strathclyde) 401 C 15 – pop. 196.

⛴ from Feolin to Isle of Islay (Port Askaig) (Western Ferries (Argyll) Ltd) (5 mn).

Craighouse – ECD : Tuesday – ✉ Jura – ☎ 0149 682.

Jura, PA60 7XU, ☎ 243, Fax 249, ← Small Isles Bay, 🌳 – P
16 rm, 1 suite.

When visiting Great Britain,
use the Michelin Green Guide **"Great Britain".**
- *Detailed descriptions of places of interest*
- *Touring programmes*
- *Maps and street plans*
- *The history of the country*
- *Photographs and drawings of monuments, beauty spots, houses...*

KELSO Roxburgh. (Borders) 401 402 M 17 **Scotland G.** – pop. 6 167 – ECD : Wednesday – ☎ 01573.

See : Town★ – Market Square★★ – ≤★ from Kelso Bridge.

Envir. : Floors Castle★ *AC*, NW : 1½ m. by A 6089.

Exc. : Mellerstain★★ (Ceilings★★★, Library★★★) *AC*, NW : 6 m. by A 6089 – Waterloo Monument (※★★) SW : 7 m. by A 698 and B 6400 – Jedburgh Abbey★★ *AC*, SW : 8½ m. by A 698 - Dryburgh Abbey★★ *AC* (setting★★★), SW : 10½ m. by A 6089, B 6397 and B 6404 – Scott's View★★, W : 11 m. by A 6089, B 6397, B 6404 and B 6356 – Smailholm Tower★ (※★★) NW : 6 m. by A 6089 and B 6397 – Lady Kirk (Kirk o'Steil★) NE : 16 m. by A 698, A 697, A 6112 and B 6437.

18 Berrymoss Racecourse Rd ☎ 223009.

Town House, The Square PD5 7HC ☎ 223464 (summer only).

◆Edinburgh 44 – Hawick 21 – ◆Newcastle upon Tyne 68.

Ednam House, Bridge St., TD5 7HT, ☎ 224168, Fax 226319, ≤, « 18C house », – TV ☎ P – 150. VISA
closed 24 December-7 January – **Meals** (bar lunch Monday to Saturday)/dinner 18.00 **st.** 3.75 – **32 rm** 44.50/88.50 **st.** – SB.

at Heiton SW : 3 m. by A 698 – ✉ Kelso – ☎ 01573 :

Sunlaws House, TD5 8JZ, ☎ 450331, Fax 450611, ≤, « Victorian country house », park, – rest TV ☎ P. AE VISA
Meals 16.00/38.00 **t.** 8.00 – **22 rm** 95.00/150.00 **t.** – SB.

ATS The Butts ☎ 224997/8

KENMORE Perth. (Tayside) 401 I 14 **Scotland G.** – ECD : Thursday except summer – ☎ 01887.

See : Village★.

Envir. : Loch Tay★★.

Exc. : Ben Lawers★★, SW : 8 m. by A 827.

18 Taynmouth Castle ☎ 830228 – 9 Mains of Taynmouth ☎ 830226.

◆Edinburgh 82 – ◆Dundee 60 – ◆Oban 71 – Perth 38.

Kenmore, PH15 2NU, ☎ 830205, Fax 830262, 18, – rest TV ☎ P. AE VISA.
Meals (bar lunch)/dinner 25.00 **st.** 8.50 – **38 rm** (dinner included) 66.50/127.00 **st.** – SB.

KENTALLEN Argyll. (Highland) 401 E 14 – ✉ Appin – ☎ 0163 174 (01631 from mid April).

◆Edinburgh 123 – Fort William 17 – ◆Oban 33.

Ardsheal House, PA38 4BX, SW : ¾ m. by A 828 ☎ 227 (740227 from April), Fax 342 (740342 from mid April),
Fax ≤, « Country house atmosphere », park, – rest ☎ P. AE VISA
closed 3 weeks January – **Meals** 17.50/32.50 **t.** 4.50 – **13 rm** (dinner included) 85.00/180.00 **t.**

Holly Tree, Kentallen Pier, PA38 4BY, ☎ 292 (740292 from April), Fax 345(740345 from April), ≤ Loch Linnhe and mountains, – rest TV ☎ P. VISA
Meals (bar lunch)/dinner 23.50 **st.** and a la carte 5.50 – **10 rm** 44.00/79.00 **st.** – SB.

KILCHOAN Argyll. (Strathclyde) 401 B 13 – ✉ Acharacle – ☎ 0197 23 (01972 from April).

◆Edinburgh 163 – ◆Inverness 120 – ◆Oban 84.

Meall Mo Chridhe, PH36 4LH, ☎ 238 (510238 from April), Fax 238(510238 from April), ≤ Sound of Mull, park – P
April-October – **Meals** *(closed Sunday to non residents)* (booking essential) (communal dining) (dinner only)(unlicensed) 23.95 **st.** – **4 rm** (dinner included) 56.00/119.00 **st.** – SB.

KILCHRENAN Argyll. (Strathclyde) 401 E 14 **Scotland G.** – ✉ Taynuilt – ☎ 0186 63 (3 fig.) and 01866 (6 fig.).

Envir. : Loch Awe★★, E : 1¼ m.

◆Edinburgh 117 – ◆Glasgow 87 – ◆Oban 18.

Ardanaiseig, PA35 1HE, NE : 4 m. ☎ 333, Fax 222, ≤ gardens and Loch Awe, « Country house in extensive informal gardens beside Loch Awe », park, – rest TV ☎ P. AE VISA.
April-mid October – **Meals** 12.50/30.00 **t.** 5.00 – **13 rm** 78.00/160.00 **t.**, 1 suite.

Taychreggan, PA35 1HQ, SE : 1 ¼ m. ☎ 833211, Fax 833244, ≤ Loch Awe and mountains, park – rest ☎ P. AE VISA
Meals (bar lunch)/dinner 31.50 **t.** 4.00 – **15 rm** (dinner only) 72.50/150.00 **t.**

KILDRUMMY Aberdeen. (Grampian) 401 L 12 **Scotland G.** – ✉ Alford – ☎ 0197 55.

See : Castle★ *AC*.

Exc. : Huntly Castle (Heraldic carvings★★★) N : 15 m. by A 97 – Craigievar Castle★, SE : 13 m. by A 97, A 944 and A 980.

◆Edinburgh 137 – ◆Aberdeen 35.

Kildrummy Castle ⛰, AB33 8RA, S : 1 ¼ m. on A 97 ☎ 71288, Fax 71345, ≤ gardens and Kildrummy castle, « 19C mansion in extensive park », 🐟 – ⇔ rest TV ☎ P. AE VISA JCB
closed January – **Meals** 16.50/27.00 **st.** and a la carte 🍷 4.50 – **15 rm** ☐ 70.00/140.00 **st.** – SB.

KILFINAN Argyll. (Strathclyde) 401 E 16 – ✉ Tighnabruaich – ☎ 0170 082 (01700 from March).

◆Edinburgh 124 – ◆Glasgow 78 – ◆Oban 78.

Kilfinan ⛰, PA21 2EP, ☎ 201 (821201 from March), Fax 205 (821205 from March), 🌳 – ⇔ rest TV ☎ P. AE VISA. ✱
closed February – **Meals** (bar lunch)/dinner 25.00 **st.** 🍷 3.90 – **11 rm** ☐ 48.00/82.00 **st.** – SB.

KILLIECRANKIE Perth. (Tayside) 401 I 13 – see Pitlochry.

KILLIN Perth. (Central) 401 H 14 **Scotland G.** – pop. 1 108 – ECD : Wednesday – ☎ 01567.

Exc. : Loch Tay★★, Ben Lawers★★, NE : 8 m. by A 827 – Loch Earn★★, SE : 7 m. by A 827 and A 85.

⛳9 ☎ 820312.

ℹ Main St. ☎ 820254 (summer only).

◆Edinburgh 72 – ◆Dundee 65 – Perth 43 – ◆Oban 54.

Dall Lodge Country House, Main St., FK21 8TN, ☎ 820217, Fax 820726, 🌳 – TV ☎ ♿ P. ⊙ VISA
closed 25 and 26 December – **Meals** (dinner only) 15.00 **t.** – **10 rm** ☐ 20.00/40.00 **t.** – SB.

Morenish Lodge Highland House ⛰, FK21 8TX, NE : 2 ½ m. on A 827 ☎ 820258, Fax 820258, ≤ Loch Tay and hills, 🐟, 🌳 – P. VISA. ✱
Easter-early October – **Meals** (dinner only) 14.00 **t.** 🍷 4.40 – **13 rm** ☐ (dinner included) 39.00/78.00 **st.** – SB.

Breadalbane House, Main St., FK21 8UT, ☎ 820386, Fax 820386 – ⇔ TV P. VISA
Meals (by arrangement) – **5 rm** ☐ 28.00/38.00 – SB.

Fairview House, Main St., FK21 8UT, ☎ 820667 – P. VISA
Meals 8.00 **st.** – **7 rm** ☐ 15.00/34.00 **s.**

at Ardeonaig NE : 6 ¾ m. – ✉ Killin – ☎ 01567 :

Ardeonaig ⛰, South Lochtayside, FK21 8SU, ☎ 820400, Fax 820282, ≤, 🐟, 🌳 – ⇔ rest P
closed mid November-Christmas – **Meals** (bar lunch)/dinner 21.50 **t.** 🍷 4.05 – **14 rm** ☐ 57.50/115.00 **t.**

Le Guide change, changez de guide Michelin tous les ans.

KILMARNOCK Ayr. (Strathclyde) 401 402 G 17 – ☎ 01563.

Forte Travelodge without rest., Kilmarnock Bypass, Bellfield Interchange, KA1 5LQ, at junc. of A 71 with A 76 and A 77 ☎ 73810, Reservations (Freephone) 0800 850950 – TV ♿ P. AE VISA
40 rm 33.50 **t.**

KILMORE Argyll. (Strathclyde) 401 D 14 – see Oban.

KILNINVER Argyll. (Strathclyde) 401 D 14 – see Oban.

KINCARDINE Fife (Central) 401 I 15 **Scotland G.** – ☎ 01259.

Envir. : Culross★★★ (Village★★★, Palace★★ *AC*, Study★ *AC*) E : 4 m. by B 9037.

⛳18 Tulliallan ☎ 730396.

◆Edinburgh 30 – Dunfermline 9 – ◆Glasgow 25 – Stirling 12.

Unicorn Inn, 15 Excise St., FK10 4LN, ☎ 730704 – AE VISA
closed Monday and Tuesday – **Meals** a la carte 12.60/27.25 **t.** 🍷 4.95.

KINCLAVEN Perth. (Tayside) 401 J 14 – ✉ Stanley – ☎ 01250.

◆Edinburgh 56 – Perth 12.

Ballathie House ⛰, PH1 4QN, ☎ 883268, Fax 883396, ≤, « Country house in extensive grounds on banks of River Tay », 🐟, 🌳, park, 🎾 – ⇔ rest TV ☎ ♿ P. AE ⊙ VISA
Meals 12.95/26.00 **t.** 🍷 4.40 – **26 rm** ☐ (dinner included) 97.50/210.00 **t.**, 1 suite – SB.

KINCRAIG Inverness. (Highland) 401 I 12 **Scotland G.** – ECD : Wednesday – ✉ Kingussie – ☎ 01540.

See : Highland Wildlife Park★ *AC*.

Exc. : The Cairngorms★★ (≤★★★) – ✱★★★ from Cairn Gorm, E : 14 m. by A 9 and B 970.

◆Edinburgh 119 – ◆Inverness 37 – Perth 75.

Ossian with rm, PH21 1NA, ☎ 651242, Fax 651633, ≤, 🐟, 🌳 – ⇔ rest TV ☎ P. VISA
closed mid November-mid December and last 3 weeks January – **Meals** (bar lunch)/dinner a la carte 13.70/20.90 **t.** 🍷 4.50 – **9 rm** ☐ 27.50/55.00 **st.**

KINGUSSIE Inverness. (Highland) 401 H 12 **Scotland G.** – pop. 2 557 – ECD : Wednesday – ☎ 01540.

Envir. : Highland Wildlife Park★ *AC*, NE : 4 m. by A 9.

Exc. : Aviemore★, NE : 11 m. by A 9 – The Cairngorms★★ (≤★★★) - ✳★★★ from Cairn Gorm, NE : 18 m. by B 970.

Gynack Rd ☎ 661374.

King St. PH21 1HP ☎ 661297 (summer only).

♦Edinburgh 117 – ♦Inverness 41 – Perth 73.

Scot House, Newtonmore Rd, PH21 1HE, ☎ 661351, Fax 661111 – rest TV ☎ P. VISA
closed November – **Meals** (bar lunch)/dinner 17.50 **t.** and a la carte 5.75 – **9 rm** (dinner included) 50.00/90.00 **st.** – SB.

Columba House, Manse Rd, PH21 1JF, ☎ 661402, – rest TV ☎ P
Meals (bar lunch)/dinner 17.00 **t.** 3.50 – **7 rm** 31.00/50.00 **t.** – SB.

St. Helens without rest., Ardbroilach Rd, PH21 1JX, ☎ 661430 – P.
3 rm 42.00 **s.**

Homewood Lodge, Newtonmore Rd, PH21 1HD, ☎ 661507, ≤, – P.
Meals (by arrangement) 10.50 **st.** – **4 rm** 19.50/39.00.

XXX **The Cross** with rm, Tweed Mill Brae, Ardbroilach Rd, PH21 1TC, ☎ 661166, Fax 661080 – ☎ P. VISA.
March-November and 27 December-7 January – **Meals** *(closed Tuesday)* (booking essential) 30.00/35.00 **st.** 5.00 – **9 rm** (dinner included) -/170.00 **t.**

KINLOCHBERVIE Sutherland. (Highland) 401 E 8 **Scotland G.** – ECD : Wednesday – ✉ Lairg – ☎ 01971.

Exc. : Cape Wrath★★★ (≤★★) *AC*, N : 28½ m. (including ferry crossing) by B 801 and A 838.

♦Edinburgh 276 – Thurso 93 – Ullapool 61.

Kinlochbervie, IV27 4RP, ☎ 521275, Fax 521438, ≤ Loch Inchard and sea – rest TV ☎ P. AE VISA
April-October – **Meals** (booking essential)(bar lunch)/dinner 27.50 **t.** 4.50 – **14 rm** 52.00/84.00 **t.** – SB.

Old School, Inshegra, IV27 4RH, SE : 1½ m. ☎ 521383, ≤ – rest TV ☎ P. VISA
closed 25-26 December and 1 January – **Meals** a la carte approx. 12.00 **t.** – **6 rm** 28.00/52.00 **t.**

KINLOCHMOIDART Inverness. (Highland) 401 C 13 – ✉ Lochailort – ☎ 01967.

X **Kinacarra,** PH38 4ND, ☎ 431238 – P
Easter-October – **Meals** *(closed Monday)* (booking essential) (light lunch) a la carte 8.80/18.25.

KINROSS Kinross. (Tayside) 401 J 15 – pop. 5 047 – ECD : Thursday – ☎ 01577.

Green Hotel, 2 The Muirs ☎ 863407 – Milnathort, South St. ☎ 864069 – Bishopshire, Kinnesswood ☎ (01592) 780203.

Kinross Service Area (junction 6, M 90) KY13 7BA ☎ 863680.

♦Edinburgh 28 – Dunfermline 13 – Perth 18 – Stirling 25.

Windlestrae, KY13 7AS, ☎ 863217, Fax 864733, – rm TV ☎ P – 250. AE VISA
Meals 11.95/27.00 **st.** and a la carte 4.95 – **43 rm** 64.50/120.00 **st.**, 2 suites – SB.

Green, 2 The Muirs, KY13 7AS, ☎ 863467, Fax 863180, squash – TV ☎ P – 140. AE VISA
Meals (bar lunch)/dinner 22.00 **st.** and a la carte 4.95 – **47 rm** 70.00/125.00 **st.** – SB.

Granada Lodge without rest., Kincardine Rd, KY13 7NQ, W : 1 m. by A 922 on A 977 ☎ 864646, Fax 864108, Reservations (Freephone) 0800 555300 – TV ☎ P. AE VISA.
4.00 – **35 rm** 39.95 **st.**

Lomond Country Inn, Kinnesswood, KY13 7HN, E : 4 ½ m. by A 922 on A 911 ☎ (01592) 840253, Fax 840693, ≤ – TV ☎ P
Meals (bar lunch) 8.00/10.00 **st.** and a la carte 3.50 – **12 rm** 35.00/55.00 **st.** – SB.

X **Croftbank House,** Station Rd, KY13 7TG, ☎ 863819 – P
closed Monday, 25 December and 1 to 4 January – **Meals** 12.50/22.00 6.00.

at Cleish SW : 4½ m. by B 996 off B 9097 – ✉ Kinross – ☎ 01577 :

Nivingston House, KY13 7LS, ☎ 850216, Fax 850238, ≤, park – TV ☎ P. AE VISA
Meals 16.50/26.00 **t.** and a la carte 6.00 – **17 rm** 70.00/100.00 **t.** – SB.

Bitte beachten Sie die Geschwindigkeitsbeschränkungen in Großbritannien
- 60 mph (= 96 km/h) außerhalb geschlossener Ortschaften
- 70 mph (= 112 km/h) auf Straßen mit getrennten Fahrbahnen und Autobahnen.

KINTYRE (Peninsula) Argyll. (Strathclyde) 401 D 16 **Scotland G.**.

See : Carradale★ – Saddell (Collection of grave slabs★).

18, 9 Campbeltown, Machrihanish ℘ (01586) 810213.

at Campbeltown (Machrihanish Airport) : ℘ (01586) 553021.

from Claonaig to Isle of Arran (Lochranza) (Caledonian MacBrayne Ltd) (summer only) frequent services daily (30 mn) – from Kennacraig to Isle of Islay (Port Ellen and Port Askaig) (Caledonian MacBrayne Ltd).

Campbeltown – ECD : Wednesday – ✉ Campbeltown – 01586.

MacKinnon House, The Pier PA28 6EF ℘ 552056.

♦Edinburgh 176.

Seafield, Kilkerran Rd, PA28 6JL, ℘ 554385, Fax 552741 – TV ☎ P. VISA
Meals 10.50/16.50 **t.** and a la carte – **9 rm** 35.00/57.00 **t.**

Rosemount without rest, Low Askomil, PA28 6EN, ℘ 553552, ≤, – TV P
3 rm 20.00/36.00 **s.**

Ballegreggan House , Ballegreggan Rd, PA28 6NN, NE : 1 m. by A 83 ℘ 552062, ≤, – TV P
Meals 20.00 **s.** – **4 rm** 30.00/50.00 **s.** – SB.

Machrihanish – pop. 540 – ✉ Campbeltown – 01586.

♦Edinburgh 182 – ♦Oban 95.

Ardell House without rest., PA28 6PT, ℘ 810235, ≤, – TV P
March-October – **10 rm** 21.00/48.00.

Tarbert – ✉ Tarbert – 01880.

9 Kilberry Rd, Tarbert ℘ 820565.

Harbour St. ℘ 820429 (summer only).

Columba, East Pier Rd, PA29 6UF, E : ¾ m. ℘ 820808, Fax 820808, ≤, – rest TV P. VISA
Meals (bar lunch Monday to Saturday)/dinner 16.95 **t.** 4.75 – **11 rm** 29.95/55.90 **t.** – SB.

Anchorage, Quayside, Harbour St., PA29 6UD, ℘ 820881 – VISA
March-October – **Meals** - Seafood *(closed Monday lunch and Sunday)* a la carte 13.65/23.85 **t.** 4.95.

ATS Burnside St., Campbeltown ℘ 554404

KIRKBEAN Dumfries (Dumfries and Galloway) 401 402 J 19 – ✉ Dumfries – 0138 788.

♦Edinburgh 89 – Carlisle 41 – ♦Dumfries 12.

Cavens House , DG2 8AA, ℘ 234, , park – rest TV P. VISA
Meals (by arrangement) 18.50 4.75 – **6 rm** 30.00/56.00 **st.** – SB.

KIRKCUDBRIGHT Kirkcudbright. (Dumfries and Galloway) 401 402 H 19 **Scotland G.** – pop. 4 188 – ECD : Thursday – 01557.

See : Town★.

Envir. : Dundrennan Abbey★ *AC*, SE : 5 m. by A 711.

18 Stirling Cres. ℘ 330314.

Harbour Sq. DJ6 4HY ℘ 330494 (summer only).

♦Edinburgh 108 – ♦Dumfries 28 – Stranraer 50.

Selkirk Arms, Old High St., DG6 4JG, ℘ 330402, Fax 331639, – TV ☎ P. AE VISA
Meals (bar lunch)/dinner 17.50 **st.** and a la carte 3.75 – **15 rm** 45.00/70.00 **st.** – SB.

Gladstone House without rest., 48 High St., DG6 4JX, ℘ 331734, – TV. VISA.
3 rm 32.00/50.00 **st.**

KIRKHILL Inverness (Highland) 401 G 11 – ✉ Inverness – 01463.

♦Edinburgh 164 – ♦Inverness 8 – ♦Wick 130.

Inchberry House , Lentran, IV3 6RJ, E : 2½ m. by B 9164 off A 862 ℘ 831342, ≤, – rest P
closed February and March – **Meals** (dinner only) 14.50 **s.** 4.50 – **6 rm** 32.00/42.00 **s.**

KIRKMICHAEL Perth. (Tayside) 401 J 13 **Scotland G.** – ✉ Blairgowrie – 01250.

Envir. : Glenshee (★★).

♦Edinburgh 74 – Perth 30 – Pitlochry 12.

Log Cabin , PH10 7NB, W : 1 m. ℘ 881288, Fax 881402, ≤, « Scandinavian pine chalet », – P. AE VISA
Meals (bar lunch)/dinner 18.95 **t.** 5.05 – **13 rm** (dinner included) 52.75/95.50 **t.**

KIRKWALL Orkney. (Orkney Islands) 401 L 7 – see Orkney Islands (Mainland).

KIRRIEMUIR Angus. (Tayside) 401 K 13 – ☎ 01575.

Purgavie Farm, Lintrathen, DD8 5HZ, W : 6 ¾ m. on B 951 ℘ 560213, Fax 560213, ≤ – ⅍ TV P
Meals (communal dining) 8.50 – **3 rm** 20.00/30.00 **st.**

KYLE OF LOCHALSH Ross and Cromarty. (Highland) 401 C 12 **Scotland G.** – pop. 862 – ECD : Thursday – ☎ 01599.

Exc. : N : from Kyle of Lochalsh to Gairloch*** (Vista**, ≤***) – Eilean Donan Castle* *AC*, (Site**) E : 8 m. by A 87.

to Isle of Skye (Kyleakin) (Caledonian MacBrayne Ltd) frequent services daily (5 mn).

to Mallaig (Caledonian MacBrayne Ltd) (summer only) (5 mn).

Car Park YV40 8DA ℘ 534276 (summer only).

♦Edinburgh 204 – ♦Dundee 182 – ♦Inverness 82 – ♦Oban 125.

Lochalsh, Ferry Rd, IV40 8AF, ℘ 534202, Fax 534881, ≤ Skye ferry and hills – ⅍ rm TV ☎ P. AE VISA JCB
Meals 12.50/28.00 **t.** and dinner a la carte 7.50 – **36 rm** 75.00/110.00 **t.**, 2 suites – SB.

KYLESKU Sutherland. (Highland) – ☎ 01971.

♦Edinburgh 256 – ♦Inverness 100 – Ullapool 34.

Newton Lodge, IV27 4HW, S : 2 m. on A 894 ℘ 502070, ≤ Loch Glencoul and mountains – ⅍ TV P. VISA.
April-September – **Meals** (residents only) (dinner only) 12.00 **t.** 5.20 – **7 rm** -/50.00 **t.**

Kylesku, IV27 4HW, ℘ 502231, Fax 502313, ≤ Loch Glencoul and mountains, – TV. VISA
March-November – **Meals** 12.50/25.00 **t.** and a la carte 3.95 – **7 rm** 25.00/48.00 **st.** – SB.

LADYBANK Fife (Fife) 401 K 15 – pop. 1 357 – ☎ 01337.

♦Edinburgh 38 – ♦Dundee 20 – Stirling 40.

Redlands Country Lodge, KY7 7SH, E : 1 m. on B 938 ℘ 831091, Fax 831091, – ⅍ TV P
closed February – **Meals** (by arrangement) 15.00 **st.** 5.00 – **4 rm** 28.00/46.00 **st.** – SB.

LAGGAN Inverness. (Highland) 401 H 12 – ✉ Newtonmore – ☎ 01528.

♦Edinburgh 110 – ♦Inverness 52 – Perth 66.

Gaskmore House, PH20 1BS, E : ¾ m. on A 86 ℘ 544250, Fax 544350, ≤ Grampian mountains, – TV ☎ ♿ P. AE VISA
Meals (see below) – **24 rm** dinner included 68.50/117.00 **st.** – SB.

XX **Gaskmore House** (at Gaskmore House H.), PH20 1BS, E : ¾ m. on A 86 ℘ 544250, Fax 544350 – ⅍ P. AE VISA
Meals (light lunch)/dinner 22.50/30.00 **st.** and dinner a la carte **st.** 4.50.

LAID Sutherland. (Highland) 401 F 8 – ✉ Lairg – ☎ 01971.

Balnakeil, Durness ℘ 511364.

♦Edinburgh 242 – Thurso 59 – Ullapool 95.

Port-na-Con House, by Altnaharra, IV27 4UN, ℘ 511367, ≤ Loch Eribol – ⅍. VISA
mid March-October – **Meals** approx. 11.00 **s.** – **4 rm** 23.00/36.00 **s.**

LAIRG Sutherland. (Highland) 401 G9 – pop. 857 – ECD : Wednesday – ☎ 01549.

♦Edinburgh 218 – ♦Inverness 61 – ♦Wick 72.

Sutherland Arms, IV27 4AT, ℘ 402291, Fax 402261, ≤, – TV ☎ P. AE VISA
April-October – **Meals** (bar lunch Monday to Saturday)/dinner 18.00 **st.** and a la carte 4.20 – **25 rm** (dinner included) 60.00/110.00 **t.** – SB.

LAMLASH Bute. (Strathclyde) 401 E 17 – see Arran (Isle of).

LANARK Lanark. (Strathclyde) 401 402 I 16 – pop. 11 682 – ECD : Thursday – ☎ 01555.

Horsemarket, Ladyacre Rd ML11 7LQ ℘ 661661.

♦Edinburgh 34 – ♦Carlisle 78 – ♦ Glasgow 28.

XX **Ristorante La Vigna,** 40 Wellgate, ML11 9DT, ℘ 664320, Fax 661400 – AE VISA
closed Sunday lunch – **Meals** - Italian (booking essential) 15.50 **t.** (lunch) and a la carte 18.20/25.70 4.95.

LANGBANK Renfrew. (Strathclyde) 401 G 16 – ECD : Saturday – ☎ 01475.

♦Edinburgh 63 – ♦Glasgow 17 – Greenock 7.

Gleddoch House, PA14 6YE, SE : 1 m. by B 789 ℘ 540711, Fax 540201, ≤ Clyde and countryside, 18, park, squash – ⅍ rm TV ☎ P – 80. AE VISA JCB
Meals 20.00/29.50 **t.** and a la carte 4.95 – **39 rm** 90.00/170.00 **t.**, 1 suite – SB.

I prezzi Per ogni chiarimento sui prezzi qui riportati, consultate le spiegazioni alle pagine dell'introduzione.

LARGS Ayr. (Strathclyde) 401 402 F 16 **Scotland G.** – pop. 11 297 – ECD : Wednesday – ☎ 01475.
See : Largs Old Kirk★ *AC*.
Irvine Rd ✆ 673594 – Routenburn, Greenock Rd ✆ 673230.
to Great Cumbrae Island (Cumbrae Slip) (Caledonian MacBrayne Ltd) frequent services daily (10 mn).
Promenade KA30 8BG ✆ 673765.
◆Edinburgh 76 – ◆Ayr 32 – ◆Glasgow 30.

- **Brisbane House,** 14 Greenock Rd, Esplanade, KA30 8NF, ✆ 687200, Fax 676295, ← – TV ☎ P – 50. AE VISA JCB.
Meals 15.00 **t.** (dinner) and a la carte 8.50/31.25 4.75 – **23 rm** 50.00/86.00 **st.** – SB.
- **Glen Eldon,** 2 Barr Cres., KA30 8PX, ✆ 673381, Fax 673381 – rest TV ☎ P. AE VISA.
closed January-mid March – **Meals** (dinner only) 14.00 **st.** 4.50 – **9 rm** 34.00/58.00 **st.**

LERWICK Shetland. (Shetland Islands) 401 Q 3 – see Shetland Islands (Mainland).

LETHAM Fife. (Fife) 401 K 15 – ✉ Cupar – ☎ 01337.

- **Fernie Castle**, KY7 7RU, NE : ½ m. on A 914 ✆ 810381, Fax 810422, « Part 14C Castle », park – TV ☎ P – 120. AE VISA
Meals 10.50/18.50 **t.** and dinner a la carte 5.00 – **15 rm** 45.00/95.00 **t.** – SB.

LESLIE Fife. (Fife) 401 K 15 – see Glenrothes.

LEVEN Fife. (Fife) 401 K 15 – ☎ 01333.

- **Old Manor,** Leven Rd, Lundin Links, KY8 6AJ, E : 2 m. on A 915 ✆ 320368, Fax 320911, ←, – rest TV ☎ P. AE VISA
Meals 14.50/21.50 **t.** and a la carte 4.95 – **20 rm** 60.00/95.00 **st.** – SB.

Prices For full details of the prices quoted in the guide, consult the introduction.

LEWIS and HARRIS (Isle of) Western Isles (Outer Hebrides) 401 A 9 **Scotland G.**.
See : Callanish Standing Stones★★ – Carloway Broch★ – St. Clement's Church, Rodel (tomb★).
from Stornoway to Ullapool (Caledonian MacBrayne Ltd) (3 h 30 mn) – from Kyles Scalpay to the Isle of Scalpay (Caledonian MacBrayne Ltd) 6-12 daily (except Sunday 1 daily) (10 mn) – from Tarbert to Isle of Skye (Uig) (Caledonian MacBrayne Ltd) 1-3 weekly (1 h 45 mn) – from Tarbert to Isle of Uist (Lochmaddy) (Caledonian MacBrayne Ltd) 1-2 weekly – from Tarbert to Portavadie (Caledonian MacBrayne Ltd) (summer only) 8-11 daily (30 mn).

LEWIS

Breasclete – ☎ 01851.

- **Eschol**, 21 Breasclete, PA86 9ED, ✆ 621357, ←, – TV P
March-October – **Meals** 14.00 – **4 rm** (dinner included) 36.00/100.00 – SB.
- **Corran View** without rest, 22A Breasclete, PA86 9EF, ✆ 621300, ←, – TV P. VISA
3 rm 42.50/73.00 **st.**

Galson – ☎ 01851.

- **Galson Farm**, South Galson, PA86 0SH, ✆ 850492, ←, , park – P. VISA
Meals (communal dining)(by arrangement) 18.00 **s.** 3.75 – **3 rm** 24.00/48.00 **s.**

Stornoway – ✉ Stornoway – ☎ 01851.
Lady Lever Park ✆ 702240.
26 Cornwell Street,PA7 2DD ✆ 703088.

- **Cabarfeidh,** Manor Park, PA87 2EU, N : ½ m. on A 859 ✆ 702604, Fax 705572 – rest TV ☎ P – 300. AE VISA
Meals 9.75/30.00 **st.** and a la carte 6.00 – **47 rm** 68.00/140.00 **st.** – SB.
- **County,** Francis St., PA87 2XB, ✆ 703250, Fax 706008 – TV ☎. VISA
Meals (bar lunch)/dinner a la carte 5.90/21.20 **t.** 4.50 – **18 rm** 40.00/60.00 **t.**
- **Hebron** without rest., 14 Maclean Terr., PA87 2QZ, NW : 1 m. by A 859 and McDonald Rd ✆ 702890 – TV
3 rm 15.00/30.00 **st.**

HARRIS

Ardvourlie – ☎ 01859.

- **Ardvourlie Castle**, PA85 3AB, ✆ 502307, ← Loch Seaforth and mountains, « 19C former hunting lodge on shore of Loch Seaforth », – rest P
March-October – **Meals** (dinner only) 25.00 **st.** – **4 rm** (dinner included) 70.00/140.00 **st.**

Scarista – pop. 2 363 – ECD : Thursday – ✉ Scarista – ☎ 01859.

Scarista House 🐎, PA85 3HX, from Tarbert, SW : 15 m. on A 859 ℘ 550238, Fax 550277, ≤ Scarista beach and mountains, 🌲 – 🚭 ☎ 🅿
May-September – **Meals** (booking essential) (dinner only) 26.00 **st.** 🍷 5.50 – **8 rm** ⊆ 43.00/94.00 **st.**

Tarbert – pop. 479 – ECD : Thursday – ✉ Harris – ☎ 01859.

Harris, PA85 3DL, ℘ 502154, Fax 502281, 🌲 – 🅿. VISA
Meals (bar lunch) 15.75 **t.** – **25 rm** ⊆ 29.60/65.50 **t.** – SB.

Leachin House 🐎, PA85 3AH, ℘ 502157, ≤ Loch Tarbert, 🌲 – 🚭 TV 🅿. ✻
closed 18 December-4 January – **Meals** (communal dining) 17.00 **st.** – **3 rm** ⊆ 33.00/66.00 **st.** – SB.

Allan Cottage, PA85 3DJ, ℘ 502146 – 🚭 TV
May-September – **Meals** 14.00 **s. 3 rm** 26.00/42.00 **s.**

Two Waters 🐎, Lickisto, PA85 3EL, S : 10 m. by A 859 on C 79 ℘ 530246, ≤, 🎣, 🌲 – 🚭 rest 🅿
May-September – **Meals** 13.00 **s.** – **4 rm** ⊆ 31.00/52.00 **s.**

LEWISTON Inverness. (Highland) 401 G 12 **Scotland G.** – ☎ 01456.

Envir. : Loch Ness★★.

♦Edinburgh 173 – ♦Inverness 17.

Glen Rowan without rest., West Lewiston, IV3 6UW, ℘ 450235, 🌲 – 🚭 TV 🅿
closed Christmas – **Meals** 10.00 **st.** – **3 rm** ⊆ 25.00/36.00 **st.**

LINICLATE Inverness (Western Isles) 401 XY 11 /12 – see Uist (Isles of).

LINLITHGOW W. Lothian. (Lothian) 401 J 16 **Scotland G.** – pop. 13 689 – ☎ 01506.

See : Town★★ – Palace★★ *AC* : Courtyard (fountain★★), Great Hall (Hooded Fireplace★★), Gateway★ – Old Town★ – St. Michaels★.

Envir. : Cairnpapple Hill★ *AC*, SW : 5 m. by A 706 – House of the Binns (plasterwork ceilings★) *AC*, NE : 4½ m. by A 803 and A 904.

Exc. : Hopetoun House★★ *AC*, E : 7 m. by A 706 and A 904 – Abercorn Parish Church (Hopetoun Loft★★) NE : 7 m. by A 803 and A 904.

18 Braehead ℘ 842585 – 18 West Lothian, Airngath Hill ℘ 826030.

Burgh Halls, The Cross EH49 7EJ ℘ 844600.

♦Edinburgh 19 – Falkirk 9 – ♦Glasgow 35.

XXX **Champany Inn,** Champany, EH49 7LU, NE : 2 m. on A 803 at junction with A 904 ℘ 834532, Fax 834302, « Converted horse mill », 🌲 – 🅿. AE VISA JCB
closed Saturday lunch, Sunday, 25-26 December and 1-2 January – **Meals** (Beef Specialities) 13.75/35.00 **st.** and a la carte 🍷 5.25.

LIVINGSTON Midlothian. (Lothian) 401 J 16 – pop. 22 357 – ☎ 01506.

18 Bathgate, Edinburgh Rd ℘ 652232 – 18 Deer Park C.C., Knightsbridge ℘ 438843.

♦Edinburgh 16 – Falkirk 23 – ♦Glasgow 32.

Hilton National, Almondview, Almondvale, EH54 6QB, ℘ 431222, Fax 434666, 🏋, 🏊, – 🚭 rm TV ☎ ♿ 🅿 – 🧑‍🏫 100. AE VISA
Meals (bar lunch)/dinner 14.95 **t.** and a la carte 🍷 5.95 – ⊆ 8.75 – **120 rm** 70.00/80.00 **st.** – SB.

LOCHBOISDALE Western Isles (Outer Hebrides) 401 Y 12 – see Uist (Isles of).

LOCHCARRON Ross and Cromarty (Highland) 401 D 11 **Scotland G.** – ECD : Thursday – ☎ 01520.

Envir. : Loch Earn★★.

Main St. ℘ 722357 (summer only).

♦Edinburgh 221 – ♦Inverness 65 – Kyle of Lochalsh 23.

Lochcarron, IV54 8YS, ℘ 722226, Fax 722612, ≤ Loch Carron – TV ☎ 🅿. VISA
accommodation closed Christmas to New Year – **Meals** (bar lunch Monday to Saturday)/dinner 6.90/16.50 **t.** and a la carte – **10 rm** ⊆ 35.00/80.00 **t.** – SB.

Rockvilla, IV54 8YB, ℘ 722379, ≤ Loch Carron – 🚭 rest TV. VISA. ✻
closed 25 December and 1 January – **Meals** (bar lunch)/dinner a la carte 10.50/18.50 **st.** 🍷 4.65 – **4 rm** ⊆ 27.00/54.00 **st.**

LOCHEARNHEAD Perth. (Central) 401 H 14 – ECD : Wednesday – ☎ 01567.

♦Edinburgh 65 – ♦Glasgow 56 – ♦Oban 57 – Perth 36.

Mansewood Country House, FK19 8NS, S : ½ m. on A 84 ℘ 830213, 🌲 – 🚭 🅿. VISA
Meals 14.00 **st.** 🍷 4.80 – **8 rm** ⊆ 20.00/46.00 **st.** – SB.

LOCHEPORT Western Isles (Outer Hebrides) 401 Y 11 – see Uist (Isles of).

LOCHGILPHEAD Argyll. (Strathclyde) 401 D 15 **Scotland G.** – pop. 2 391 – ECD : Tuesday – ☎ 01546.

Envir. : Loch Fyne★★, E : 3½ m. by A 83.

Blarbuie Rd ☎ 602340.

Lochnell St. PA31 8JN ☎ 602344 (summer only).

♦Edinburgh 130 – ♦Glasgow 84 – ♦Oban 38.

- **Stag,** Argyll St., PA31 8NE, ☎ 602496, Fax 603549 – TV ☎. VISA
  Meals (bar lunch)/dinner 15.00 **st.** and a la carte 3.50 – **17 rm** 35.00/65.00 **st.** – SB.
- **Empire Travellers Lodge** without rest., Union St., PA31 8JS, ☎ 602381 – TV ♿ P. VISA.
  9 rm 18.50/37.00 **st.**

at Cairnbaan NW : 2¼ m. by A 816 on B 841 – ✉ Lochgilphead – ☎ 01546.

- **Cairnbaan,** PA31 8SJ, ☎ 603668, Fax 606045 – TV ☎ P. AE VISA.
  Meals (bar lunch)/dinner a la carte 9.20/17.90 **t.** 5.50 – **7 rm** 45.00/90.00 **st.** – SB.

LOCH HARRAY Orkney. (Orkney Islands) 401 K 6 – see Orkney Islands (Mainland).

LOCHINVER Sutherland. (Highland) 401 E 9 **Scotland G.** – ECD : Tuesday – ✉ Lairg – ☎ 01571.

See : Village★.

Exc. : Loch Assynt★★, E : 6 m. by A 837.

Main St. ID27 4LF ☎ 844330 (summer only).

♦Edinburgh 251 – ♦Inverness 95 – ♦Wick 105.

- **Inver Lodge**, IV27 4LU, ☎ 844496, Fax 844395, ≤ Lochinver Bay, Suilven and Canisp mountains, park – TV ☎ P. AE VISA JCB
  April-October – **Meals** (bar lunch Monday to Saturday)/dinner 26.00 **st.** and a la carte 4.50 – **20 rm** 60.00/140.00 **st.** – SB.
- **Albannach**, Baddidarroch, IV27 4LP, W : 1 m. by Baddidarroch rd ☎ 844407, ≤, – P. VISA.
  Meals *(closed Monday lunch)* 20.00 **t.** (dinner) and a la carte 10.00/16.00 6.00 – **4 rm** (dinner included) -/45.00 **t.**
- **Veyatie** without rest., 66 Baddidarroch, IV27 4LP, W : 1 ¼ m. by Baddidarroch rd ☎ 844424, ≤ Lochinver Bay, Suilven and Canisp mountains, – P
  April-October – **3 rm** -/46.00 **s.**

LOCHMADDY Western Isles (Outer Hebrides) 401 Y 11 – see Uist (Isles of).

LOCHRANZA Bute. (Strathclyde) 401 402 E 16 – see Arran (Isle of).

LOCKERBIE Dumfries. (Dumfries and Galloway) 401 402 J 18 – pop. 2 301 – ECD : Tuesday – ☎ 01576.

18 Corrie Rd ☎ 203363 – 9 Lochmaben, Castlehill Gate ☎ (01387) 810552.

♦Edinburgh 74 – ♦Carlisle 27 – ♦Dumfries 13 – ♦Glasgow 73.

- **Dryfesdale,** DG11 2SF, NW : 1 m. by A 74 ☎ 202427, Fax 204187, ≤, – TV ☎ ♿ P. AE VISA
  Meals 11.00/17.00 **t.** and a la carte – **15 rm** 46.00/75.00 **st.** – SB.

LUSS Dunbarton. (Strathclyde) 401 G 15 **Scotland G.** – ☎ 01436.

See : Village★.

Envir. : E : Loch Lomond★★.

♦Edinburgh 89 – ♦Glasgow 26 – Oban 65.

- **Lodge on Loch Lomond,** G83 8NT, ☎ 860201, Fax 860203, ≤ Loch Lomond, – TV ☎ P. AE VISA
  Meals (bar lunch)/dinner 19.95 **t.** and a la carte 4.95 – 7.00 – **10 rm** 65.00 **t.** – SB.

LYBSTER Caithness. (Highland) 401 K 9 – ☎ 0159 32.

- **Portland Arms,** KW3 6BS, on A 9 ☎ 208, Fax 446 – TV ☎ P. AE VISA
  Meals 11.00/18.50 **st.** and lunch a la carte – **19 rm** 38.50/58.00 **st.** – SB.

MACHRIHANISH Argyll. (Strathclyde) 401 C 17 – see Kintyre (Peninsula).

MARNOCH Aberdeen. (Grampian) 401 L 11 **Scotland G.** – ✉ Huntly – ☎ 01466.

Exc. : Huntly Castle (elaborate Heraldic Carvings★★★) *AC*, SW : 10½ m. by B 9117, B 9118 and B 9022.

♦Edinburgh 170 – ♦Aberdeen 40 – Fraserburg 39 – ♦Inverness 77.

- **Old Manse of Marnoch**, AB54 5RS, on B 9117 ☎ 780873, Fax 780873, – rest TV P. VISA
  closed 2 weeks October-November – **Meals** 20.00 3.50 – **5 rm** 60.00/80.00 – SB.

MARYCULTER Aberdeen. (Grampian) 401 N 12 – see Aberdeen.

MAYBOLE Ayr. (Strathclyde) 401 402 F 17 **Scotland G.** – ☏ 0165 54.

Envir. : Culzean Castle★ *AC* (setting★★★, Oval Staircase★★) W : 5 m. by B 7023 and A 719.

- **Ladyburn** ⑤, KA19 7SG, S : 5½ m. by B 7023 off B 741 (Girvan rd) ✆ 585, Fax 580, ≤, 🌳, park – ⇔ TV ☎ P. AE VISA. ✗
closed 4 weeks January-February – **Meals** *(closed Sunday dinner and Monday to non-residents)* (booking essential) (lunch by arrangement)/dinner 30.00 **t.** 6.50 – **8 rm** 90.00/150.00 **t.** – SB.

MEIGLE Perth. (Tayside) 401 K 14 **Scotland G.** – ☏ 01828.

See : Museum★★ (early Christian Monuments★★) *AC.*

Exc. : Glamis Castle★★, NE : 7 m. by A 94.

◆Edinburgh 62 – ◆Dundee 13 – Perth 18.

- Kings of Kinloch ⑤, Coupar Angus Rd, PH12 8QX, W : 1 m. on A 94 ✆ 640273, Fax 640347, ≤, 🌳, park – TV ☎ P – 🏛 80
6 rm.

MELROSE Roxburgh. (Borders) 401 402 L 17 **Scotland G.** – pop. 2 414 – ECD : Thursday – ☏ 0189 682 (4 fig.) and 01896 (6 fig.).

See : Town★ - Abbey★★ (decorative sculptures★★★) *AC.*

Envir. : Eildon Hills (※★★★) – Scott's View★★ – Abbotsford★★ *AC*, W : 4½ m. by A 6091 and B 6360 – Dryburgh Abbey★★ *AC* (setting★★★) SE : 4 m. by A 6091.

Exc. : Bowhill★★ *AC*, SW : 11½ m. by A 6091, A 7 and A 708 – Thirlestane Castle (plasterwork ceilings★★) *AC*, NE : 21 m. by A 6091 and A 68.

18 Ladhope Recreation Ground, Galashiels ✆ 3724 – 9 Melrose, Dingleton ✆ 2855 – 9 Torwoodlee, Galashiels ✆ 2260.

Abbey House, Abbey Street, TD6 9LG ✆ 2555 (summer only).

◆Edinburgh 38 – Hawick 19 – ◆Newcastle upon Tyne 70.

- **Burts,** Market Sq., TD6 9PN, ✆ 822285, Fax 822870, 🌳 – TV ☎ P. AE ⓓ VISA
Meals 13.75/19.95 **t.** and dinner a la carte 4.95 – **22 rm** 45.00/74.00 **t.** – SB.
- Bon Accord, Market Sq., TD6 9PQ, ✆ 822645, Fax 823474 – ⇔ rest TV ☎
10 rm.
- **Dunfermline House** without rest., Buccleuch St., TD6 9LB, ✆ 822148 – ⇔ TV. ✗
5 rm 20.00/40.00 **st.**

at Gattonside NW : 2¼ m. by A 6091 on B 6360 – ✉ Melrose – ☏ 0189 682 (4 fig.) and 01896 (6 fig.) :

- **Hoebridge Inn,** TD6 9LZ, ✆ 3082 – P. VISA
closed Monday, 2 weeks April and 2 weeks October – **Meals** (dinner only) a la carte 12.95/20.90 **t.** 4.00.

MEY Caithness. (Highland) 401 K 8 – ☏ 0184 785.

◆Edinburgh 302 – ◆Inverness 144 – Thurso 13 – ◆Wick 21.

- **Castle Arms,** KW14 8XH, ✆ 244, Fax 244, 🌳 – TV ☎ ♿ P. VISA
Meals (bar lunch)/dinner 16.00 **st.** 3.95 – **8 rm** 33.00/52.00 **st.** – SB.

MILNGAVIE Lanark. (Strathclyde) 401 H 16 – pop. 12 030 – ECD : Tuesday and Saturday – ✉ Glasgow – ☏ 0141.

18, 18 Hilton Park, Auldmarroch Est., Stockiemuir Rd ✆ 956 5124/1215 – 18 Dougalston ✆ 956 5750.

◆Edinburgh 53 – ◆Glasgow 7.

- **Black Bull Thistle** (Mt.Charlotte Thistle), Main St., G62 6BH, ✆ 956 2291, Fax 956 1896 – TV ☎ P – 🏛 100. AE ⓓ VISA JCB
Meals *(closed lunch Saturday and Bank Holiday Mondays)* 18.00 **t.** (dinner) and a la carte 22.00/31.20 4.95 – 8.95 – **27 rm** 62.00/85.00 **t.** – SB.

MOFFAT Dumfries. (Dumfries and Galloway) 401 402 J 17 **Scotland G.** – pop. 2 647 – ECD : Wednesday – ☏ 01683.

Exc. : Grey Mare's Tail★★, NE : 9 m. by A 708.

18 Coatshill ✆ 20020.

Churchgate DJ10 9EG ✆ 20620 (summer only).

◆Edinburgh 61 – ◆Dumfries 22 – ◆Carlisle 43 – ◆Glasgow 60.

- **Moffat House,** High St., DG10 9HL, ✆ 20039, Fax 21288, 🌳 – ⇔ rest TV ☎ P. AE ⓓ VISA
Meals (bar lunch)/dinner 18.50 **t.** 5.00 – **20 rm** 52.00/75.00 **t.**
- **Beechwood Country House** ⑤, Harthope Pl., by Academy Rd, DG10 9RS, ✆ 20210, Fax 20889, ≤, 🌳 – ⇔ rest TV ☎ P. AE VISA
closed 2 January-16 February – **Meals** *(closed lunch Monday to Wednesday)* 13.00/20.50 **t.** 4.25 – **7 rm** (dinner included) 63.50/105.00 **t.** – SB.
- **Buccleuch Arms,** High St., DG10 9ET, ✆ 20003, Fax 21291, 🌳 – TV ☎. AE ⓓ VISA
Meals a la carte 10.75/19.00 **t.** 3.75 – **11 rm** 39.00/58.00 **t.** – SB.

Hartfell House, Hartfell Cres., DG10 9AL, by Well St. and Old Well Rd ✆ 20153, – rest
March-October – **Meals** (by arrangement) 12.50 **st.** 3.50 – **7 rm** 25.00/50.00 **st.**

Fernhill without rest., Grange Rd, DG10 9HT, ✆ 20077, –
May-August – **3 rm** 20.00/30.00 **s.**

Well View with rm, Ballplay Rd, DG10 9JU, E : ¾ m. by Selkirk Rd (A 708) ✆ 20184, – VISA
Meals *(closed Saturday lunch)* 11.50/24.00 **st.** – **6 rm** 42.00/76.00 **st.**, 1 suite.

MONTROSE Angus. (Tayside) 401 M 13 **Scotland G.** – pop. 8 473 – ECD : Wednesday – 01674.

Exc. : Edzell Castle★ (The Pleasance★★★) *AC*, NW : 17 m. by A 935 and B 966 – Cairn O'Mount Road★ (≤★★) N : 17 m. by B 966 and B 974 – Brechin (Round Tower★) W : 7 m. by A 935 – Aberlemno (Aberlemno Stones★, Pictish sculptured stones★) W : 13 m. by A 935 and B 9134.

18, 18 Traill Drive ✆ 672932.

The Library, Bridge Street ✆ 672000 (summer only).

♦Edinburgh 92 – ♦Aberdeen 39 – ♦Dundee 29.

Park, 61 John St., DD10 8RJ, ✆ 673415, Fax 677091, – – 180. AE VISA
Meals 7.50/14.50 **t.** and a la carte 5.20 – 7.50 – **57 rm** 65.00/85.00 **t.** – SB.

Oaklands without rest., 10 Rossie Island Rd, DD10 9NN, on A 92 ✆ 672018, Fax 672018 – VISA
7 rm 18.00/35.00 **s.**

Es ist empfehlenswert, ***in der Hauptsaison*** *und vor allem in Urlaubsorten, Hotelzimmer im voraus zu bestellen.*
Benachrichtigen Sie sofort das Hotel, wenn Sie ein bestelltes Zimmer nicht belegen können.

Wenn Sie an ein Hotel im Ausland schreiben, fügen Sie Ihrem Brief einen internationalen Antwortschein bei (im Postamt erhältlich).

MOTHERWELL Lanark. 401 I 16 – 01698.

Library, Hamilton Rd ML1 3DZ ✆ 251311.

♦Edinburgh 38 – ♦Glasgow 12.

Travel Inn without rest., Glasgow Rd, Newhouse, ML1 5SY, NE : 4 ¼ m. by A 723 and A 73 on A 775 ✆ 860277, Fax 861353 – – 100. AE VISA
4.95 – **40 rm** 33.50 **t.**

MUIR OF ORD Ross and Cromarty. (Highland) 401 G 11 – pop. 1 693 – 01463.

18 Great North Rd ✆ 870825.

♦Edinburgh 173 – ♦Inverness 10 – Wick 121.

Dower House, Highfield, IV6 7XN, N : 1 m. on A 862 ✆ 870090, Fax 870090, « Part 17C house », – VISA
closed 1 week March and 1 week November – **Meals** (lunch by arrangement)/dinner 28.00 **st.** 6.50 – **4 rm** 75.00/100.00 **st.**, 1 suite – SB.

MULL (Isle of) Argyll. (Strathclyde) 401 C 14 **Scotland G.** – pop. 2 838.

See : Island★ - Calgary Bay★★ – Torosay Castle *AC* (Gardens★ ≤★).

Envir. : Isle of Iona★ (Madean's Cross★, St. Oran's Chapel★, St. Martin's High Cross★, Infirmary Museum★ *AC*).

9 Craignure, Scallastle ✆ (01680) 812370.

from Craignure to Oban (Caledonian MacBrayne Ltd) (40 mn) – from Fishnish to Lochaline (Caledonian MacBrayne Ltd) frequent services daily (15 mn) – from Tobermory to Isle of Coll (Arinagour) (Caledonian MacBrayne Ltd) 3 weekly (1 h 20 mn) – from Tobermory to Isle of Tiree (Scarinish) (Caledonian MacBrayne Ltd) 3 weekly (2 h 30 mn) – from Tobermory to Kilchoan (Caledonian MacBrayne Ltd) 5-11 daily (summer only) (35 mn) – from Tobermory to Oban (Caledonian MacBrayne Ltd) 3 weekly (2 h).

from Fionnphort to Isle of Iona (Caledonian MacBrayne Ltd) frequent services daily in summer (5 mn).

Main St., Tobermory ✆ 01688 (Tobermory) 302182.

Bunessan – ✉ Fionnphort – 01681.

Ardfenaig House, PA67 6DX, W : 3 m. by A 849 ✆ 700210, Fax 700210, ≤, , park – rm VISA
April-October – **Meals** (dinner only) 25.00 **st.** 4.50 – **5 rm** (dinner included) 85.00/170.00 **st.**

Calgary – ✉ Tobermory – 01688.

Calgary Farmhouse, PA75 6QW, on B 8073 ✆ 400256, –
9 rm.

Dervaig – ✉ Tobermory – ☎ 01688.

Druimard Country House ⛰, PA75 6QW, on Salen rd ☎ 400345, ≤, – rest TV ☎ P. VISA
April-October – **Meals** (booking essential) (dinner only) 19.50 **t.** – **6 rm** ☕ 49.50/85.00 **t.**, 1 suite – SB.

Druimnacroish Country House ⛰, PA75 6QW, S : 2 m. by B 8073 and Salen rd ☎ 400274, Fax 400311, ≤ Bellart Glen, – rest TV ☎ P. AE VISA
mid April-mid October – **Meals** (dinner only) 25.00 **st.** 3.25 – **6 rm** ☕ (dinner included) 78.00 **st.**

Pennyghael – ✉ Pennyghael – ☎ 01681.

Pennyghael, PA70 6HB, ☎ 704288, ≤, – TV ☎ P. VISA
April-October – **Meals** (in bar)/dinner 21.75 4.75 – **6 rm** ☕ (dinner included) 60.00/100.00 **st.** – SB.

Tiroran – ✉ Tiroran – ☎ 01681.

Tiroran House ⛰, PA69 6ES, ☎ 705232, Fax 705232, ≤ Loch Scridain, « Country house atmosphere », , park – rest P.
mid May-early October – **Meals** (light lunch residents only)/dinner 28.50 **st.** 4.75 – **9 rm** ☕ (dinner included) 125.00/220.00 **st.**

Tobermory – pop. 843 – ECD : Wednesday – ✉ Tobermory – ☎ 01688.

Tobermory ☎ 302020.

Western Isles, PA75 6PR, ☎ 302012, Fax 302297, ≤ Tobermory harbour and Calve Island – rest TV ☎ P. VISA
closed 2-21 January and 19-28 December – **Meals** (bar lunch)/dinner 24.00 **st.** 5.50 – **26 rm** ☕ 41.00/170.00 **st.** – SB.

Tobermory, 53 Main St., PA75 6NT, ☎ 2091, Fax 2091, ≤ TV ♿. VISA
Meals (dinner only) 21.00 4.50 – **17 rm** ☕ 25.00/76.00 **st.**

Ulva House, Strongarbh, PA75 6PR, ☎ 302044, ≤ Tobermory harbour and Calve Island, – P
March-October – **Meals** 14.50 **t.** 4.80 – **6 rm** ☕ 24.95/64.90 **st.**

MURCAR Aberdeen. (Grampian) 401 N 12 – see Aberdeen.

MUSSELBURGH E. Lothian. (Lothian) 401 K 16 – pop. 18 425 – ☎ 0131.

Monktonhall ☎ 665 2005 – Royal Musselburgh, Prestongrange House, Prestonpans ☎ (01875) 810276 – Musselburgh Old Course, Silver Ring Clubhouse, Millhill ☎ 665 6981.

Brunton Hall EH21 6AF ☎ 665 6597 (summer only).

♦Edinburgh 6 – Berwick 54 – ♦Glasgow 53.

Granada Lodge without rest., Old Craighall, EH21 8RE, S : 1½ m. by B 6415 at junction with A 1 ☎ 653 6070, Fax 653 6106, Reservations (Freephone) 0800 555300 – TV ☎ ♿ P. AE VISA.
☕ 4.00 – **44 rm** 39.95 **t.**

NAIRN Nairn. (Highland) 401 I 11 **Scotland G.** – pop. 3 367 – ECD : Wednesday – ☎ 01667.

Envir. : Forres (Sueno's Stone★★) E : 11 m. by A 96 and B 9011 – Cawdor Castle★ *AC*, S : 5½ m. by B 9090 – Brodie Castle★ *AC*, E : 6 m. by A 96.

Exc. : Fort George★, W : 7 m. by A 96, B 9092 and B 9006.

18, 9 Seabank Rd ☎ 452103 – 18 Nairn Dunbar, Lochloy Rd ☎ 452741.

62 King St. ☎ 452753 (summer only).

♦Edinburgh 172 – ♦Aberdeen 91 – ♦Inverness 16.

Golf View, 63 Seabank Rd, IV12 4HD, ☎ 452301, Fax 455267, ≤, heated, , – TV ☎ P – 100. AE VISA
Meals 12.50/12.50 **st.** and a la carte 4.50 – **46 rm** ☕ 75.00/140.00 **st.**, 1 suite – SB.

Clifton House ⛰, Viewfield St., IV12 4HW, ☎ 453119, Fax 452836, ≤, – P. AE VISA
closed December and January – **Meals** (booking essential) a la carte 17.50/25.50 **st.** 5.00 – **12 rm** ☕ 54.00/96.00 **st.** – SB.

Lochloy House ⛰, Lochloy Rd, Lochloy, IV12 5LE, NE : 2½ m. ☎ 455355, Fax 454809, ≤ Moray Firth, « Country house atmosphere », , , park, – rest P.
mid March-October (booking essential) – **Meals** (lunch by arrangement)/dinner 25.00 **st.** and a la carte 30.00/43.00 **st.** 6.50 – **8 rm** ☕ 48.00/96.00 **st.**

Links, 1 Seafield St., IV12 4HN, ☎ 453321, Fax 453321, – TV ☎ P. AE VISA
Meals *(closed Sunday in winter)* (dinner only) 15.00 **st.** 4.15 – **10 rm** ☕ 32.50/60.00 **st.**

Claymore House, 45 Seabank Rd, IV12 4EY, ☎ 453731, Fax 455290, – TV ☎ P. AE VISA JCB
Meals 10.00/20.00 **st.** and a la carte 4.00 – **15 rm** ☕ 37.50/65.00 **st.** – SB.

Sunny Brae, Marine Rd, IV12 4EA, ☎ 452309, ≤, – rest TV P
April-September – **Meals** 9.00 **t.** – **10 rm** ☕ 21.00/46.00 **st.**

✗ **Longhouse,** 8 Harbour St., IV12 4NU, ℘ 455532 – VISA
closed Monday, January and February – **Meals** *(booking essential in winter)* (dinner only) a la carte 11.25/17.95 **t.** 5.50.

NETHERLEY Kincardine. (Grampian) 401 N 12 **Scotland G.** – ✉ Stonehaven – 01569.

Envir. : Muchalls Castle (plasterwork ceilings★★) *AC*, SE : 5 m. by B 979 – Deeside★★, N : 2 m. by B 979 – Aberdeen★★, NE : 3 m. by B 979 and B 9077.

Exc. : Aberdeen★★, NE : 12 m. by B 979 and B 9077 – Dunnottar Castle★★ (site★★★) *AC*, S : 7 m. by B 979 – Crathes Castle★★ (Gardens★★★) *AC*, NW : 13 m. by B 979, B 9077 and A 93.

♦Edinburgh 117 – ♦Aberdeen 12 – ♦Dundee 54.

✗✗ **Lairhillock,** AB3 2QS, NE : 1 ½ m. by B 979 on Portlethan rd ℘ 730001, Fax 731175 – Ⓟ. VISA
Meals (bar lunch Monday to Saturday)/dinner 18.50 **t.** and a la carte 6.50.

NEWBURGH Aberdeen. (Grampian) 401 N 12 **Scotland G.** – 01358.

Exc. : Pitmedden Gardens★★ *AC*, W : 6½ m. by B 9000 – Haddo House★ *AC*, NW : 14 m. by B 900, A 92 and B 9005.

18 McDonald, Ellon ℘ 720576 – 9 Newburgh-on-Ythan, Ellon ℘ 789438.

♦Edinburgh 144 – ♦Aberdeen 14 – Fraserburgh 33.

Udny Arms, Main St., AB41 0BL, ℘ 789444, Fax 789012, – TV Ⓟ – 80. VISA
Meals (see below) – 8.50 – **24 rm** 49.95/59.95 **st.** – SB.

✗✗ **Udny Arms** (at Udny Arms H.), Main St., AB41 0BL, ℘ 789444, Fax 789012 – Ⓟ. VISA
Meals a la carte 11.30/28.90 **st.** 6.00.

NEW GALLOWAY Kirkcudbright. (Dumfries and Galloway) 401 402 H 18 **Scotland G.** – pop. 290 – 0164 42 (changing to 01644).

Envir. : Galloway Forest Park★, Queen's Way★ (Newton Stuart to New Galloway) SW : 19 m. by A 712.

9 New Galloway ℘ 737.

♦Edinburgh 88 – ♦Ayr 36 – Dumfries 25.

Leamington, High St., DG7 3RN, ℘ 327 (420327 during 1995) – rest TV Ⓟ. VISA.
closed November – **Meals** (by arrangement) 12.15 3.50 – **9 rm** 14.00/40.00 **t.**

NEWPORT-ON-TAY Fife. (Fife) 401 L 14 – 01382.

Forgan House, DD6 8RB, SE : 2 ½ m. by B 995 and A 92 on Tayport rd ℘ 542760, Fax 542760, – TV Ⓟ. VISA.
Meals (by arrangement)(communal dining) 17.50 **s.** 5.00 – **4 rm** 35.00/60.00 **s.**

NEW SCONE Perth. (Tayside) 401 J 14 – see Perth.

NEWTONMORE Inverness. (Highland) 401 H 12 – pop. 1 010 – ECD : Wednesday – 01540.

18 Newtonmore ℘ 673328.

♦Edinburgh 113 – ♦Inverness 43 – Perth 69.

Ard-na-Coille, Kingussie Rd, PH20 1AY, ℘ 673214, Fax 673453, ≤, – rest Ⓟ. VISA
closed 1 week April, 1 week September and mid November-December – **Meals** (booking essential) (dinner only) 28.50 **t.** 7.00 – **7 rm** (dinner included) 65.00/160.00 **t.** – SB.

Pines, Station Rd, PH20 1AR, ℘ 673271, ≤, – Ⓟ.
mid April-mid October – **Meals** 11.00 **s.** 2.20 – **6 rm** (dinner included) 34.00/68.00 **st.**

NEWTON STEWART Wigtown. (Dumfries and Galloway) 401 402 G 19 **Scotland G.** – pop. 2 543 – ECD : Wednesday – 01671.

Envir. : Galloway Forest Park★, Queen's Way★ (Newton Stewart to New Galloway) N : 19 m. by A 712 – 18, Kirroughtree Av., Minnigaff ℘ 402172.

Dashwood Sq. DG8 6DQ ℘ 402431 (summer only).

♦Edinburgh 131 – ♦Dumfries 51 – ♦Glasgow 87 – Stranraer 24.

Kirroughtree, DG8 6AN, NE : 1 ½ m. on A 712 ℘ 402141, Fax 402425, ≤ woodland and River Cree, « Country house, gardens », park, – TV Ⓟ. VISA
closed 3 January-3 March – **Meals** 12.00/25.00 **t.** and lunch a la carte 5.75 – **17 rm** 70.00/144.00 **st.**, 1 suite – SB.

Creebridge House, Minnigaff, DG8 6NP, ℘ 402121, Fax 403258, – rest TV Ⓟ. VISA
Meals (bar lunch Monday to Saturday)/dinner 19.50 **st.** and a la carte 5.95 – **20 rm** 40.00/80.00 **t.** – SB.

Crown, 101 Queen St., DG8 6JW, ℘ 402727 – TV Ⓟ. VISA.
Meals (bar lunch)/dinner 13.50 **t.** 4.60 – **11 rm** 22.00/50.00 **t.** – SB.

Rowallan House, Corsbie Rd, DG8 6JB, ℘ 402520, – rest TV Ⓟ.
Meals (by arrangement) 13.00 **t.** 4.20 – **6 rm** 27.50/55.00 **t.** – SB.

NORTH BERWICK E. Lothian. (Lothian) 401 L 15 **Scotland G.** – pop. 5 871 – ECD : Thursday – ☎ 01620.

Envir. : North Berwick Law (※★★★) S : 1 m. - Tantallon Castle★★ (clifftop site★★★) *AC*, E : 3½ m. by A 198 – Dirleton★ (Castle★ *AC*) SW : 2½ m. by A 198.

Exc. : Museum of Flight★, S : 6 m. by B 1347 – Preston Mill★, S : 8½ m. by A 198 and B 1047 – Tyninghame★, S : 7 m. by A 198 – Coastal road from North Berwick to Portseton★, SW : 13 m. by A 198 and B 1348.

18 North Berwick, Bass Rock, Tantallon, West Links, Beach Rd ℘ 892135 – 18 Glen, Burgh Links, Glen East Links ℘ 892221.

Quality St. EH39 4HJ ℘ 892197.

◆Edinburgh 24 – ◆Newcastle upon Tyne 102.

- **Marine** (Forte), 18 Cromwell Rd, EH39 4LZ, ℘ 892406, Fax 894480, ≤ golf course and Firth of Forth, heated, – – 250. VISA JCB
Meals 12.50/22.95 **st.** and dinner a la carte 6.45 – **74 rm** 65.00/130.00 **st.**, 5 suites – SB.
- **Point Garry,** 20 West Bay Rd, EH39 4AW, ℘ 892380, Fax 892848, ≤ – TV. VISA
May-October – **Meals** 6.95/13.95 **t.** and a la carte 4.95 – **16 rm** 30.00/94.00 **t.**
- **Craigview** without rest., 5 Beach Rd, EH39 4AB, ℘ 892257 – TV.
2 rm 20.00/40.00 **st.**, 1 suite.

OBAN Argyll. (Strathclyde) 401 D 14 **Scotland G.** – pop. 7 476 – ECD : Thursday – ☎ 01631.

Exc. : Loch Awe★★, SE : 17 m. by A 85 – Bonawe Furnace★, E : 12 m. by A 85 – Cruachan Power Station★ *AC*, E : 16 m. by A 85 – Sea Life Centre★ *AC*, N : 14 m. by A 828.

18 Glencruitten Rd ℘ 62868/64115.

Access to Glasgow by helicopter.

to Isle of Mull (Craignure) (Caledonian MacBrayne Ltd) (40 mn) – to Isle of Barra (Castlebay) via South Uist (Lochboisdale) (Caledonian MacBrayne Ltd) (summer only) – to Isle of Tiree (Scarinish) via Isle of Mull (Tobermory) and Isle of Coll (Arinagour) (Caledonian MacBrayne Ltd) 3 weekly (4 h 15 mn) – to Isle of Islay (Port Askaig) and Kintyre Peninsula (Kennacraig) (Caledonian MacBrayne Ltd) (summer only) – to Isle of Lismore (Achnacroish) (Caledonian MacBrayne Ltd) 2-4 daily (50 mn) – to Isle of Colonsay (Scalasaig) (Caledonian MacBrayne Ltd) (2 h 15 mn).

Boswell House, Argyll Sq. PA34 4AR ℘ 63122.

◆Edinburgh 123 – ◆Dundee 116 – ◆Glasgow 93 – ◆Inverness 118.

- **Manor House,** Gallanach Rd, PA34 4LS, ℘ 62087, Fax 63053, ≤, – rest TV. VISA
closed 26 December-1 February – **Meals** (lunch by arrangement)/dinner 20.90 **t.** and a la carte 4.00 – **11 rm** (dinner included) 78.00/140.00 **t.** – SB.
- **Kilchrenan House** without rest., Corran Esplanade, PA34 5AU, ℘ 62663, ≤ – TV. VISA
April-October – **10 rm** 24.00/60.00 **t.**
- **Barriemore,** Corran Esplanade, PA34 5AQ, ℘ 66356, ≤ – TV. VISA
closed February and November – **Meals** *(closed Monday)* (dinner only) 20.00 **st.** – **13 rm** 54.00 **st.**

at Kilmore S : 4 m. on A 816 – ✉ Oban – ☎ 01631 :

- **Glenfeochan House**, PA34 4QR, S : ½ m. on A 816 ℘ 770273, Fax 770624, ≤, « Victorian country house in extensive gardens », park – TV. VISA.
March-October – **Meals** (residents only) (communal dining) (dinner only) 30.00 **st.** 6.00 – **3 rm** 128.00 **st.**

at Kilninver SW : 8 m. by A 816 on B 844 – ✉ Oban – ☎ 018526 :

- **Knipoch,** PA34 4QT, NE : 1½ m. on A 816 ℘ 316251, Fax 316249, ≤, – rest TV. VISA.
mid February-mid November – **Meals** (lunch by arrangement)/dinner 28.50 **t.** 6.20 – **17 rm** 65.00/130.00 **st.**

ONICH Inverness. (Highland) 401 E 13 – ECD : Saturday except summer – ✉ Fort William – ☎ 01855.
♦Edinburgh 123 – ♦Glasgow 93 – ♦Inverness 79 – ♦Oban 39.

The Lodge on the Loch, Creag Dhu, PH33 6RY, on A 82 ✆ 821237, Fax 821463, ≤ Loch Linnhe and mountains, – rest TV ☎ ♿ P. VISA
closed 4 to 31 January and Monday to Thursday in February – **Meals** 15.75/25.50 **t.** and lunch a la carte 5.50 – **20 rm** (dinner included) 68.00/151.00 **st.** – SB.

Onich, PH33 6RY, on A 82 ✆ 821214, Fax 821484, ≤ Loch Linnhe and mountains, « Lochside setting », – rest TV ☎ P. AE VISA
closed 21 to 29 December – **Meals** (bar lunch)/dinner 19.50 **t.** 4.25 – **27 rm** 45.00/80.00 **st.** – SB.

Allt-Nan-Ros, PH33 6RY, on A 82 ✆ 821210, Fax 821462, ≤ Loch Linnhe and mountains, – rest TV ☎ P. AE VISA
closed 6 January-10 February and 10 October-6 December – **Meals** 19.50 **t.** (dinner) and lunch a la carte 8.50/14.50 – **21 rm** (dinner included) 65.00/130.00 **st.** – SB.

Cuilcheanna House, PH33 6SD, ✆ 226, ≤, , park – rest P
8 rm.

ORD Inverness (Highland) 401 C 12 – see Skye (Isle of).

ORKNEY ISLANDS Orkney. (Orkney Islands) 401 KL 6/7 **Scotland G.** – pop. 19 612.

See : Islands★★.

Envir. : Old Man of Hoy★★★ – Maes Howe★★ *AC* – Skara Brae★★ *AC* – Corrigal Farm Museum★ *AC* – Brough of Birsay★ *AC* – Birsay (≤★) – Ring of Brodgar★ – Stromness★ (Pier Arts Centre, collection of abstract art★) – Unston Cairn★.

✈ see Kirkwall.

service between Isle of Hoy (Longhope), Isle of Hoy (Lyness), Isle of Flotta and Houton (Orkney Islands Shipping Co. Ltd) frequent services daily (except Sundays) – from Stromness to Scrabster (P & O Scottish Ferries) (1 h 45 mn) – from Stromness to Shetland Islands (Lerwick) via Aberdeen (P & O Scottish Ferries) – from Kirkwall to Westray, Stronsay via Eday and Sanday (Orkney Islands Shipping Co. Ltd) 2 daily – from Tingwall via Eglisay, Wyre and Rousay (Orkney Islands Shipping Co. Ltd) 5 daily – from Kirkwall to Shapinsay (Orkney Islands Shipping Co. Ltd) (25 mn) – from Stromness to Graemsay, Houton and Isle of Hoy (Lyness) (Orkney Islands Shipping Co. Ltd) 1 weekly – from Kirkwall to North Ronaldsay (Orkney Islands Shipping Co. Ltd) 1 weekly (2 h 30 mn).

from Burwick (South Ronaldsay) to John O'Groats (John O'Groats Ferries) (summer only) 4 daily (45 mn).

Burray – ✉ Burray – ☎ 01856.

Ankersted, KW17 2SS, E : ½ m. on A 961 ✆ 731217, ≤ – TV P.
Meals (by arrangement) 9.00 **st.** – **4 rm** 15.00/36.00 **st.**

Dounby – ✉ Dounby – ☎ 0185 677.

Smithfield, KW17 2HT, ✆ 215, Fax 494 – TV P.
May-October – **Meals** (bar lunch)/dinner 15.00 **st.** and a la carte – **7 rm** 25.00/50.00.

Finstown – ✉ Finstown – ☎ 01856.

Atlantis Lodges, KW17 2EH, ✆ 76581, ≤ – TV ☎ P. VISA
Meals (by arrangement) (dinner only) 15.00 4.00 – **2 rm** 46.00/66.00, **8 suites** 46.00/66.00.

Kirkwall **Scotland G.** – pop. 5 947 – ECD : Wednesday – ✉ Kirkwall – ☎ 01856 Kirkwall.

See : Kirkwall★★ – St. Magnus Cathedral★★ – Earl's Palace★ *AC* – Tankerness House Museum★ *AC*.

Exc. : Western Mainland★★ – Italian Chapel★ *AC*.

18 Grainbank ✆ 872457.

✈ Kirkwall Airport : ✆ 872421, S : 3½m.

6 Broad St., Kirkwall KW15 1NX ✆ 872856.

Ayre, Ayre Rd, KW15 1QX, ✆ 873001, Fax 876289 – TV ☎ P – 150. AE VISA
Meals 8.50/18.00 **st.** and dinner only 4.25 – **33 rm** 50.00/75.00 **st.** – SB.

Foveran, St. Ola, KW15 1SF, SW : 3 m. on A 964 ✆ 872389, Fax 876430, ≤, « Overlooking Scapa Flow », – TV ☎ P. VISA
closed January – **Meals** *(closed Sunday to non-residents)* (dinner only) 25.00/30.00 **t.** and a la carte **t.** 4.50 – **8 rm** 43.50/68.00 **st.**

Albert, Mounthoolie Lane, KW15 1GZ, pedestrian area off Junction Rd ✆ 876000, Fax 875397 – TV ☎. AE VISA
closed 25 December and 1 January – **Meals** (bar lunch)/dinner 18.00 **t.** and a la carte 4.65 – **19 rm** 48.00/81.00 – SB.

Queens, Shore St., KW15 1LG, ✆ 872200, Fax 873871 – TV ☎. VISA.
Meals (in bar) 10.00/20.00 **t.** – **9 rm** 26.00/40.00 **t.**

West End, Main St., KW15 1BU, ✆ 872368, Fax 876181 – TV ☎ P
16 rm.

Polrudden, Pickaquoy Rd, KW15 1RR, W : ¾ m. ☎ 874761, Fax 874761 – rest TV P
Meals (by arrangement) 11.00 **s.** – **7 rm** 26.00/42.00.

Brekk-Ness, Muddisdale Rd, KW15 1RS, W : 1 m. by Pickaquoy Rd ☎ 874317 – rest TV P.
Meals (by arrangement) – **11 rm** 27.00/44.00 **t.**

St. Ola, Harbour St., KW15 1LE, ☎ 875090, Fax 875090 – TV ☎. VISA.
Meals 10.00 **t.** – **6 rm** 26.00/40.00 **t.**

ATS Junction Rd, Kirkwall ☎ 872361/872158

Loch Harray – ✉ Loch Harray – ☎ 01856.

Merkister, KW17 2LF, off A 986 ☎ 771366, Fax 771515, ≤, – TV ☎ P. AE VISA
Meals (bar lunch Monday to Saturday)/dinner 14.00 **t.** and a la carte 5.00 – **14 rm** 32.50/71.00 **st.**

St. Margaret's Hope – ✉ St. Margaret's Hope – ☎ 01856.

Anchorage, Back Rd, KW17 2SP, ☎ 831456 – TV
Meals (communal dining) a la carte 8.00/17.00 – **4 rm** 17.00/30.00 **st.**

Murray Arms, Back Rd, KW17 2SP, ☎ 831205 – P
5 rm.

Creel with rm, Front Rd, KW17 2SL, ☎ 831311, ≤ – rm TV P. VISA.
closed Sunday to Thursday October-May and January – **Meals** (dinner only) a la carte 19.00/26.50 **t.** 4.50 – **3 rm** 27.00/50.00 **t.**

Stenness – ✉ Stenness – ☎ 01856.

Standing Stones, KW16 3JX, on A 965 ☎ 850449, Fax 851262, – rm TV ☎ P. VISA.
Meals (booking essential) (bar lunch)/dinner 17.50 **st.** and a la carte 4.30 – **17 rm** 35.00/64.00 **st.** – SB.

Stromness – ✉ Stromness – ☎ 01856.

Thira without rest, Innertown, KW16 3JP, W : 1½ m. by Back Rd, Outertown rd, then first right onto unmarked road and left turn after ½ m. ☎ 851181, ≤ Hoy Island and Sound, – TV P
closed December – **4 rm** 22.00/44.00 **st.**

Stenigar, Ness Rd, KW16 3DW, ☎ 850438, ≤, – TV P.
May-September – **Meals** (by arrangement) (communal dining) – **4 rm** 30.00/44.00 **st.**

Hamnovoe, 35 Graham Pl., KW16 3BY, ☎ 850606
May-October – **Meals** (dinner only) a la carte 11.60/16.10 **s.** 3.50.

PEAT INN Fife. (Fife) 401 L 15 – ✉ Cupar – ☎ 01334.

♦Edinburgh 45 – Dundee 21 – Perth 28.

The Peat Inn with rm, KY15 5LH, ☎ 840206, Fax 840530, – rest TV ☎ & P. AE VISA
Meals *(closed Sunday, Monday, 25 December and 1 January)* (booking essential) 18.50/45.00 **st.** and dinner a la carte 7.00 – **1 rm** 95.00 **st.**, **7 suites** 135.00 **st.**.

PEEBLES Peebles. (Borders) 401 402 K 17 **Scotland G.** – pop. 7 065 – ECD : Wednesday – ☎ 01721.

Exc. : Traquair House★★ *AC*, SE : 7 m. by B 7062 – Rosslyn Chapel★★ *AC*, N : 16½ m. by A 703, A 6094, B 7026 and B 7003 – The Tweed Valley★★, SE : 11 m. by A 72.

18 Kirkland St. ☎ 720197.

Chambers Institute, High St. EH45 8AG ☎ 720138 (summer only).

♦Edinburgh 24 – Hawick 31 – ♦Glasgow 53.

Peebles Hydro, Innerleithen Rd, EH45 8LX, ☎ 720602, Fax 722999, ≤, park, squash – TV ☎ P – 450. AE VISA.
Meals 14.50/19.50 **st.** 6.00 – **135 rm** (dinner included) 62.50/117.50 **st.**, 2 suites – SB.

Cringletie House, EH45 8PL, N : 3 m. on A 703 ☎ 730233, Fax 730244, ≤, « Victorian country house in extensive grounds », park, – rest TV ☎ P. VISA
closed 2 January-10 March – **Meals** (light lunch)/dinner 24.50 **t.** 5.75 – **13 rm** 52.50/98.00 **t.** – SB.

Park, Innerleithen Rd, EH45 8BA, ☎ 720451, Fax 723510, – TV ☎ P. AE VISA
Meals (bar lunch)/dinner 24.00 **t.** 6.25 – **24 rm** (dinner included) 61.50/141.00 **t.** – SB.

PENNAN Aberdeen. (Grampian) 401 N 10 – pop. 92 – ✉ New Aberdour – ☎ 01346.

♦Edinburgh 181 – ♦Aberdeen 51 – Fraserburgh 12 – ♦Inverness 85.

Pennan Inn, 17-19 Main St., AB43 4JB, ☎ 561201, Fax 561437 – TV ☎. AE VISA.
Meals (bar lunch)/dinner a la carte 8.50/25.00 **st.** 6.50 – 5.00 – **7 rm** 40.00 **st.**

PENNYGHAEL Argyll (Strathclyde) – see Mull (Isle of).

PERTH Perth. (Tayside) **401** J 14 **Scotland G.** – pop. 123 495 – ECD : Wednesday – ☎ 01738.

See : City★ – Black Watch Regimental Museum★ Y **M1** – Georgian Terraces★ Y – Museum and Art Gallery★ Y **M2.**

Envir. : Scone Palace★★ *AC*, N : 2 m. by A 93 Y – Branklyn Garden★ *AC*, SE : 1 m. by A 85 Z – Kinnoull Hill (≤★) SE : 1¼ m. by A 85 Z – Huntingtower Castle★ *AC*, NW : 3 m. by A 85 Y – Elcho Castle★ *AC*, SE : 4 m. by A 912 - Z - and Rhynd rd.

Exc. : Abernethy (11C Round Tower★), SE : 8 m. by A 912 - Z - and A 913.

18 Craigie Hill, Cherrybank ☏ 624377, Z – 18 King James VI, Moncreiffe Island ☏ 625170/632460, Z – 18 Murrayshall, New Scone ☏ 651171, Y – 18 North Inch, c/o Perth & Kinross District Council, 3 High St. ☏ 636481, Y.

i 45 High Street PH1 5TJ ☏ 638353 – Caithness Glass Car Park, A 9 Western City by-pass ☏ 638481 (summer only).

◆Edinburgh 44 – ◆Aberdeen 86 – ◆Dundee 22 – Dunfermline 29 – ◆Glasgow 64 – ◆Inverness 112 – ◆Oban 94.

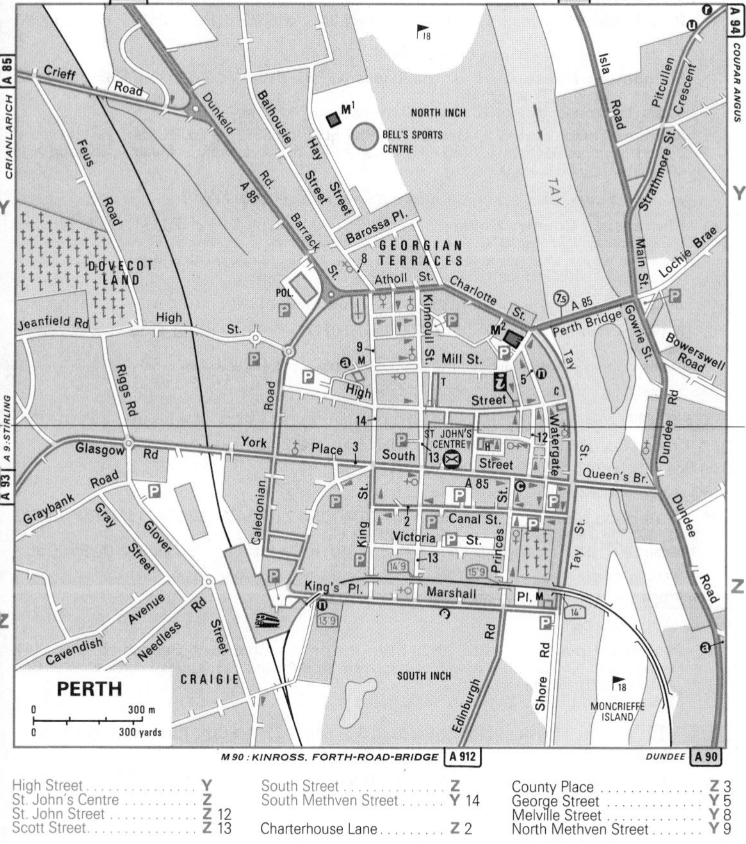

High Street . . . . Y	South Street . . . . Z	County Place . . . . Z 3
St. John's Centre . . . . . . Z	South Methven Street . . . . Y 14	George Street . . . . Y 5
St. John Street . . . . Z 12		Melville Street . . . . Y 8
Scott Street . . . . Z 13	Charterhouse Lane . . . . . . Z 2	North Methven Street . . . . Y 9

Dupplin Castle ⑤, SW : 6 ¼ m. by A 93 – Z – on A 9 ☏ 623224, Fax 444140, ≤, « Country house atmosphere, gardens », park – ⇆ rm ☎ **P**. VISA. ✻ Z
Meals (residents only)(booking essential)(communal dining)(dinner only) 28.00 **st.** – **4 rm** ☐ 45.00/90.00 **st.**

Hunting Tower ⑤, Crieff Rd, PH1 3JT, W : 3½ m. by A 85 ☏ 583771, Fax 583777, ⚘ – TV ☎ **P** – 🔬 180 Y
Meals 12.00/19.95 ₰ 6.00 – **15 rm** ☐ 65.00/84.00 **t.**, 10 suites – SB.

Parklands, St. Leonard's Bank, PH2 8EB, ℘ 622451, Fax 622046, – rest. Z **n**
closed Christmas and New Year – **Meals** 15.50/24.95 **st.** and a la carte – **14 rm** 70.00/120.00 **st.** – SB.

Stakis Perth, West Mill St., PH1 5QP, ℘ 628281, Fax 643423 – rm – 120. Y **a**
Meals 15.50 **st.** and a la carte – 8.50 – **76 rm** 65.00/90.00 **st.** – SB.

Salutation, 34 South St., PH2 8PH, ℘ 630066, Fax 633598 – – 300 Z **c**
69 rm.

Sunbank House, 50 Dundee Rd, PH2 7BA, ℘ 624882, Fax 442515, – . Z **a**
Meals (dinner only) 16.95 **t.** 5.75 – **9 rm** 38.00/60.00 **t.** – SB.

Lochiel House without rest., Pitcullen Cres., PH2 7HT, ℘ 633183 – . Y **u**
3 rm 30.00/38.00.

Pitcullen without rest, 17 Pitcullen Cres., PH2 7HT, ℘ 626506, Fax 628265 – . Y **r**
6 rm 20.00/40.00 **t.**

Park Lane without rest., 17 Marshall Pl., PH2 8AG, ℘ 637218, Fax 643519 – . Z **e**
21 January-15 November – **6 rm** 19.00/42.00 **s.**

Ellengowan House, Crieff Rd, Almondbank, PH1 3NG, W : 3½ m. on A 85 ℘ 583372, – rm . Y
Meals (communal dining) 15.00 **st.** – **3 rm** 20.00/40.00 **st.** – SB.

Number Thirty Three, 33 George St., PH1 5LA, ℘ 633771 – Y **n**
closed Sunday, Monday, 25-26 December and 1 to 24 January – **Meals** - Seafood a la carte 11.00/19.50 **t.** 5.00.

at New Scone NE : 2½ m. on A 94 – Y – ✉ Perth – 01738 :

Murrayshall Country House, PH2 7PH, E : 1½ m. by A 94 ℘ 551171, Fax 552595, park, – – 60. .
Meals (lunch by arrangement Monday to Saturday)/dinner 18.50 **st.** and a la carte – **16 rm** 75.00/130.00, 3 suites – SB.

at Glencarse E : 6¼ m. on A 85 – Y – ✉ Perth – 01738 :

Newton House, PH2 7LX, ℘ 860250, Fax 860717, – rest – 30.
Meals 10.50/19.50 **t.** and a la carte 6.00 – **10 rm** 55.00/86.00 **st.** – SB.

ATS Inveralmond Ind. Est., Ruthvenfield Rd ℘ 629481

PETERHEAD Aberdeen. (Grampian) 401 O 11 – pop. 20 789 – ECD : Wednesday – 01779.

Cruden Bay ℘ 812285 – Craigewan Links ℘ 472149.

54 Broad St. AB42 ℘ 471904 (summer only).

♦Edinburgh 165 – ♦Aberdeen 35 – Fraserburgh 18.

Waterside Inn, Fraserburgh Rd, AB42 7BN, NW : 2 m. on A 952 ℘ 471121, Fax 470670, – – 50.
Meals 9.00/19.95 **st.** and a la carte 4.75 – **110 rm** (dinner included) 65.00/93.00 **st.** – SB.

PITCAPLE Aberdeen. (Grampian) 401 M 12 – 01467.

♦Edinburgh 51 – ♦Aberdeen 21.

Pittodrie House, AB51 9HS, SW : 1 ¾ m. by Chapel of Garioch rd ℘ 681444, Fax 681648, « Country house atmosphere », park, squash – – 100.
Meals 11.00 **t.** 5.75 – **27 rm** 65.00/110.00 **t.** – SB.

PITLOCHRY Perth. (Tayside) 401 I 13 **Scotland G.** – pop. 3 126 – ECD : Thursday – 01796.

See : Town★.

Exc. : Blair Castle★★ *AC*, NW : 7 m. by A 9 – Queen's View★★, W : 7 m. by B 8019 – Falls of Bruar★, NW : 11 m. by A 9.

Golf Course Rd ℘ 472792.

22 Atholl Rd Ph16 5BX ℘ 472215/472751.

♦Edinburgh 71 – ♦Inverness 85 – Perth 27.

Pine Trees, Strathview Terr., PH16 5QR, ℘ 472121, Fax 472460, park – rm .
Meals 12.50/21.00 **t.** 8.50 – **20 rm** 50.00/90.00 **t.**

Green Park, Clunie Bridge Rd, PH16 5JY, ℘ 473248, Fax 473520, – rest .
3 April-29 October – **Meals** (bar lunch)/dinner 19.50 **t.** and a la carte – **37 rm** 42.00/95.00 **t.** – SB.

- **Dunfallandy House** ⚘, Logierait Rd, Dunfallandy, PH16 5NA, S : 1 ¼ m. by Bridge Rd ℘ 472648, Fax 472017, ≤, ⚘ – ⊬ TV P. AE VISA. ✗
  February-October and Christmas-New Year – **Meals** (bar lunch)/dinner 15.95 **st.** 3.50 – **8 rm** 37.00/60.00 **st.** – SB.
- **Knockendarroch,** 2 Higher Oakfield, PH16 5HT, ℘ 473473, Fax 474068, ≤, ⚘ – ⊬ TV P. AE ⓞ VISA
  April-November – **Meals** (residents only) (dinner only) 12.50 **st.** 4.00 – **12 rm** (dinner included) 50.00/100.00 **st.** – SB.
- **Westlands,** 160 Atholl Rd, PH16 5AR, ℘ 472266, Fax 473994, ⚘ – TV ☎ P. VISA
  Meals (bar lunch)/dinner 15.00 **st.** and a la carte 3.95 – **15 rm** 33.00/76.00 **st.** – SB.
- **Claymore,** 162 Atholl Rd, PH16 5AR, ℘ 472888, Fax 474037, ⚘ – ⊬ TV ☎ P. VISA
  closed January – **Meals** (bar lunch)/dinner 16.95 **st.** 4.70 – **12 rm** 32.00/64.00 **st.** – SB.
- **Acarsaid,** 8 Atholl Rd, PH16 5BX, ℘ 472389 – ⊬ rest TV ☎ P. VISA. ✗
  March-November – **Meals** (light lunch)/dinner 16.00 **t.** 4.00 – **18 rm** (dinner included) 48.50/97.00 **t.** – SB.
- **Castlebeigh,** 10 Knockard Rd, PH16 5HJ, ℘ 472925, Fax 474068, ≤, ⚘ – ⊬ rest TV P. VISA
  Meals (dinner only) 15.00 **t.** 3.60 – **21 rm** 39.00/78.00 **t.**
- **Balrobin,** Higher Oakfield, PH16 5HT, ℘ 472901, Fax 474200, ≤, ⚘ – ⊬ rest TV P. VISA
  March-October and New Year – **Meals** (residents only) (dinner only) 16.50 **t.** 6.75 – **16 rm** 25.00/55.00 **t.** – SB.
- **Birchwood,** 2 East Moulin Rd, PH16 5DW, ℘ 472477, Fax 473951, ⚘ – ⊬ rest TV ☎ P. VISA
  March-October – **Meals** 16.00/17.50 **t.** and dinner a la carte 5.00 – **12 rm** 35.00/67.00 **t.** – SB.
- **Torrdarach,** Golf Course Rd, PH16 5AU, ℘ 472136, ⚘ – ⊬ TV P. ✗
  Easter-mid October – **Meals** (by arrangement) 15.00 – **7 rm** 20.00/54.00 **st.** – SB.
- **Dundarave,** Strathview Terr., PH16 5AT, ℘ 473109, ≤, ⚘ – ⊬ rest TV P
  March-October – **Meals** 13.95 **st.** 4.00 – **7 rm** 28.00/56.00 **st.**
- XX **East Haugh House** with rm, East Haugh, PH16 5JS, SE : 2 m. by A 924 ℘ 473121, Fax 472473, ⚘ – ⊬ rest TV ☎ P. VISA
  Meals (bar lunch)/dinner 21.95 **t.** 6.00 – **8 rm** 39.00/82.00 **t.** – SB.

at Killiecrankie NW : 4 m. by A 924 and B 8019 on B 8079 – ✉ Pitlochry – ☎ 01796 :

- **Killiecrankie,** PH16 5LG, ℘ 473220, Fax 472451, ≤, ⚘ – ⊬ rest TV ☎ P. VISA
  closed January and February – **Meals** (bar lunch)/dinner 26.50 **st.** 7.00 – **9 rm** (dinner included) 72.00/165.00 **st.**, 1 suite – SB.

PLOCKTON Ross and Cromarty. (Highland) 401 D 11 **Scotland G.** – pop. 425 – ☎ 01599.

See : Village★.

◆Edinburgh 210 – ◆Inverness 88.

- **Haven,** Innes St., IV52 8TW, ℘ 544223, Fax 544467, ≤, ⚘ – ⊬ rest TV ☎ P. VISA
  closed 18 December-1 February – **Meals** (dinner only) 25.00 **t.** 4.00 – **13 rm** (dinner included) 53.00/106.00 **t.**
- **Plockton,** Harbour St., IV52 8TN, ℘ 544274, Fax 544274, ≤ Loch Carron, ⚘ – TV. VISA
  Meals (in bar) a la carte 9.80/18.75 **t.** 3.75 – **6 rm** 30.00/50.00 **t.** – SB.

POLLOCHAR Western Isles (Outer Hebrides) – see Uist (Isles of).

POLMONT Stirling. (Central) 401 402 I 16 – see Falkirk.

POOLEWE Ross and Cromarty. (Highland) 401 D 10 – ☎ 01445.

◆Edinburgh 234 – ◆Inverness 78 – Kyle of Lochalsh 74.

- **Pool House,** IV22 2LE, ℘ 781272, Fax 781403, ≤ Loch Ewe – ⊬ rest TV P. VISA. ✗
  March-October – **Meals** (bar lunch)/dinner 21.50 **st.** 5.60 – **13 rm** 30.00/72.00 **t.** – SB.

PORT APPIN Argyll. (Strathclyde) 401 D 14 – ECD : Thursday – ✉ Appin – ☎ 0163 173 (changing to 01631).

◆Edinburgh 136 – Ballachulish 20 – ◆Oban 24.

- ✿ **Airds** (Allen) ⚘, PA38 4DF, ℘ 236 (changing to 730236), Fax 535, ≤ Loch Linnhe and hills of Kingairloch, « Former ferry inn », ⚘ – ⊬ rest TV ☎ P. AE VISA. ✗
  Meals (light lunch)/dinner 35.00 **t.** 6.00 – **12 rm** 85.00/190.00 **t.**
  Spec. Sautéed scallops with ceps and a sweet and sour sauce, Roast monkfish tail on honeyed aubergines with a chive and tarragon sauce, Caramel parfait with toasted almonds and a caramel and lime sauce.

PORT OF MENTEITH Perth. (Central) 401 H15 – ☎ 01877.

◆Edinburgh 53 – ◆Glasgow 30 – Stirling 17.

- **Lake** ⚘, FK8 3RA, ℘ 385258, Fax 385671, ≤, « Lakeside setting » – ⊬ rest TV ☎ P. VISA
  Meals 14.95/20.90 **t.** and a la carte 4.00 – **12 rm** 85.00/150.00 **t.** – SB.

PORTPATRICK Wigtown. (Dumfries and Galloway) 401 402 E 19 – pop. 842 – ECD : Thursday – ✉ Stranraer – ☎ 01776.

18, 9 Portpatrick Dunskey, Golf Course Rd ☎ 810273.

♦Edinburgh 141 – ♦Ayr 60 – ♦Dumfries 80 – Stranraer 9.

- ❀ **Knockinaam Lodge** ♨, DG9 9AD, SE : 5 m. by A 77 off B 7042 ☎ 810471, Fax 810435, ≤, « Country house in picturesque coastal setting », ♘, ♐, park – ⅙ rest TV ☎ P. ⋈ AE ⊙ VISA
  closed 2 January-27 March – **Meals** (booking essential) (light lunch)/dinner 25.00/32.00 ₰ 5.85 – **10 rm** ⇨ 70.00/140.00 **st.** – SB
  Spec. Assiette de homard écossais aux épices parfumées, Pièce de boeuf poêlée à la moelle et au vin de Bordeaux, Croustade fine aux pommes et Drambuie son romarin grillé.
- **Fernhill,** Heugh Rd, DG9 8TD, ☎ 810220, Fax 810596, ≤, ♐ – TV ☎ ♿ P. ⋈ AE ⊙ VISA
  closed 25 and 26 December – **Meals** 8.50/17.50 **t.** and a la carte ₰ 3.95 – **20 rm** ⇨ 50.00/99.00 – SB.
- **Crown,** DG9 8SX, ☎ 810261, Fax 810551, ≤ Portpatrick Harbour – TV ☎. ⋈ VISA
  Meals a la carte 12.60/30.75 **t.** ₰ 4.00 – **12 rm** ⇨ 35.00/70.00 **t.** – SB.
- **Broomknowe,** School Brae, DG9 8LG, ☎ 810365, ≤, ♐ – ⅙ TV P
  April-September – **Meals** (by arrangement) – **3 rm** ⇨ 21.00/32.00 **st.**
- **Blinkbonnie,** School Brae, DG9 8LG, ☎ 810282, ≤, ♐ – ⅙ rest TV P. ⅙
  Meals (by arrangement) 10.50 **st.** – **6 rm** ⇨ 18.00/36.00 **st.** – SB.

PORTREE Inverness. (Highland) 401 B 11 – see Skye (Isle of).

PRESTWICK Ayr. (Strathclyde) 401 402 G 17 – pop. 13 355 – ECD : Wednesday – ☎ 01292.

✈ Prestwick Airport : ☎ 79822 – BY – **Terminal :** Buchanan Bus Station.

✈ see also Glasgow.

ℹ Prestwick Airport, KA9 2PL ☎ 79822 (summer only) BY.

♦Edinburgh 78 – ♦Ayr 2 – ♦Glasgow 32.

Plan of Built up Area : see Ayr

- Carlton Toby, 187 Ayr Rd, KA9 1TP, ☎ 76811, Fax 74845 – TV ☎ P — BY **v**
  37 rm.
- **Kincraig,** 39 Ayr Rd, KA9 1SY, ☎ 79480 – TV P. ⅙ — BY **c**
  Meals (by arrangement) – **6 rm** ⇨ 16.00/38.00 **st.**

QUOTHQUAN Lanark. (Strathclyde) 401 J 27 **Scotland G.** – ✉ Biggar – ☎ 01899.

Envir. : Biggar★ (Gladstone Court Museum★ *AC* – Greenhill Covenanting Museum★ *AC*) SE : 4½ m. by B 7016.

♦Edinburgh 32 – ♦Dumfries 50 – ♦Glasgow 36.

- **Shieldhill** ♨, ML12 6NA, NE : ¾ m. ☎ 20035, Fax 21092, ≤, « Victorian country house, 12C origins », ♐ – ⅙ TV ☎ P – 🏛 30. ⋈ AE ⊙ VISA. ⅙
  Meals (dinner only) 14.50/25.50 **st.** and lunch a la carte ₰ 4.50 – **11 rm** ⇨ 64.00/108.00 **st.** – SB.

RENFREW Renfrew. (Strathclyde) 401 G 16 **Scotland G.** – pop. 21 456 – ECD : Wednesday – ☎ 0141.

Envir. : Paisley Museum and Art Gallery (Paisley Shawl Section★) SW : 2¾ m. by A 741.

♦Edinburgh 53 – ♦Glasgow 7.

- **Glynhill,** 169 Paisley Rd, PA4 8XB, ☎ 886 5555, Fax 885 2838, Ls, ≘s, ⊠ – ⅙ rm TV ☎ P – 🏛 450. ⋈ AE ⊙ VISA JCB. ⅙
  Meals 9.75/29.00 **st.** and a la carte ₰ 4.75 – **125 rm** ⇨ 72.00/164.00 – SB.

ROCKCLIFFE Kirkcudbright. (Dumfries and Galloway) 401 402 I 19 – ✉ Dalbeattie – ☎ 01556.

♦Edinburgh 100 – ♦Dumfries 20 – Stranraer 69.

- Millbrae, DG5 4QG, ☎ 630217 – ⅙ rest TV P
  5 rm.
- **Torbay Farmhouse** ♨, DG5 4QE, E : ¼ m. ☎ 630403, ≤, ♐ – ⅙ P
  March-October – **Meals** (by arrangement) (communal dining) 8.50 **st.** – **3 rm** ⇨ 25.00/38.00 **st.** – SB.

ROGART Sutherland. (Highland) 401 H 9 – ☎ 01408.

♦Edinburgh 229 – ♦Inverness 73 – ♦Wick 63.

- **Rovie Farm** ♨, IV28 3TZ, W : ¾ m. by A 839 ☎ 641209, ≤, « Working farm », ♐, park – ⅙ P. ⅙
  Easter-November – **6 rm** ⇨ (dinner included) 27.00/54.00 **s.**

Europe

Wenn der Name eines Hotels dünn gedruckt ist,
hat uns der Hotelier Preise
und Öffnungszeiten nicht angegeben.

ROTHES Moray. (Grampian) 401 K 11 **Scotland G.** – pop. 1 520 – ECD : Wednesday – 01340.
Exc. : Glenfiddich Distillery★, SE : 7 m. by A 941.
Dufftown ✆ 820325.
◆Edinburgh 192 – ◆Aberdeen 62 – Fraserburgh 58 – ◆Inverness 49.

Rothes Glen, AB38 7AH, N : 3 m. on A 941 ✆ 831254, Fax 831566, ←, « Country house atmosphere », park – P. AE VISA
April-October – **Meals** 12.50/23.75 **t.** and a la carte 4.00 – **16 rm** 55.00/80.00 **t.**

ROTHESAY Bute. (Strathclyde) 401 402 E 16 – see Bute (Isle of).

ST. ANDREWS Fife. (Fife) 401 L 14 **Scotland G.** – pop. 11 136 – ECD : Thursday – 01334.
See : City★★ – Cathedral★ (★★) *AC* – West Port★.
Exc. : The East Neuk★★, SE : 9 m. by A 917 and B 9131 – Crail★★ (Old Centre★★, Upper Crail★) SE : 9 m. by A 917 – Kellie Castle★ *AC*, S : 9 m. by B 9131 and B 9171 – Ceres★, SW : 9 m. by B 939 - E : Inland Fife★.
(x5), Eden, Jubilee, New, Old, Strathtyrum and Balgove Courses ✆ 475757 – St. Michael's, Leuchars ✆ 839365.
Market Street, KY16 9NU ✆ 472021.
◆Edinburgh 51 – ◆Dundee 14 – Stirling 51.

St. Andrews Old Course, Old Station Rd, KY16 9SP, ✆ 474371, Telex 76280, Fax 477668, ← golf courses and sea, – rm rest P – 300. AE VISA JCB
Conservatory : **Meals** 14.00 **t.** 7.25 – ***Grill*** : **Meals** (closed lunch in Summer) 15.00/34.50 **t.** 7.25 – **108 rm** 170.00/290.00 **st.**, 17 suites – SB.

Rusacks (Forte), 16 Pilmour Links, KY16 9JQ, ✆ 474321, Fax 477896, ←, – rest P – 100. AE VISA JCB
Meals 12.50/27.00 **t.** and dinner a la carte – 9.50 – **48 rm** 80.00/155.00 **st.**, 2 suites – SB.

Rufflets, Strathkinness Low Rd, KY16 9TX, W : 1 ½ m. on B 939 ✆ 472594, Fax 478703, ←, « Country house, gardens » – P – 30. AE VISA.
Meals (bar lunch Monday to Friday in winter) 15.00/25.00 **st.** and a la carte 7.50 – **25 rm** 65.75/150.00 **st.** – SB.

St. Andrews Golf, 40 The Scores, KY16 9AS, ✆ 472611, Fax 472188, ← – rest P – 200. AE VISA JCB
Meals 13.75/25.00 **t.** and a la carte 5.00 – **23 rm** 74.00/148.00 **t.** – SB.

The Scores, 76 The Scores, KY16 9BB, ✆ 472451, Fax 473947, ←, – rest P – 180. AE VISA JCB.
closed 24 to 27 December – **Meals** (bar lunch)/dinner 21.50 **t.** 6.50 – **30 rm** 72.00/136.00 **st.** – SB.

Aslar House without rest., 120 North St., KY16 9AF, ✆ 473460, Fax 473460, – . VISA.
5 rm 25.00/50.00 **s.**

ST. BOSWELLS Roxburgh. (Borders) 401 402 L 17 **Scotland G.** – pop. 2 092 – 01835.
Envir. : Dryburgh Abbey★★ *AC* (setting★★★) NW : 4 m. by B 6404 and B 6356.
Exc. : Bowhill★★ *AC*, SW : 11 ½ m. by A 699 and A 708.
St. Boswells ✆ 822359/823527.
◆Edinburgh 39 – ◆Glasgow 79 – Hawick 17 – ◆Newcastle upon Tyne 66.

Dryburgh Abbey, TD6 0RQ, N : 3 ½ m. by B 6404 on B 6356 ✆ 822261, Fax 823945, ←, , , – rest P – 140. VISA JCB
Meals (dinner only and Sunday lunch)/dinner 19.95 **t.** 5.50 – **24 rm** 47.00/150.00 **t.**, 2 suites – SB.

ST. CATHERINES Argyll. (Strathclyde) 401 E 15 **Scotland G.** – ✉ Cairndow – 01499.
Envir. : Loch Fyne★★.
Exc. : Inveraray★★ : Castle★★ (interior★★★) *AC*, NW : 12 m. by A 815 and A 83 – Auchindrain★, NW : 18 m. by A 815 and A 83.
◆Edinburgh 99 – ◆Glasgow 53 – ◆Oban 53.

Thistle House without rest., PA25 8AZ, on A 815 ✆ 302209, ←, – P
Easter-October – **5 rm** 21.00/42.00 **t.**

ST. FILLANS Perth. (Tayside) 401 H 14 – ECD : Wednesday – 01764.
◆Edinburgh 67 – ◆Glasgow 57 – ◆Oban 64 – Perth 30.

Four Seasons, PH6 2NF, ✆ 685333, Fax 685333, ← Loch Earn and mountains – rest P. AE VISA
March-mid December – **Meals** (dinner only and Sunday lunch)/dinner 22.00 **t.** and a la carte 4.75 – **12 rm** 40.00/82.00 **t.**

Achray House, PH6 2NF, ✆ 685231, Fax 685320, ← Loch Earn and mountains, – P. VISA.
March-October – **Meals** (bar lunch Monday to Saturday)/dinner 15.00/21.30 **t.** and a la carte 4.50 – **10 rm** 37.00/59.00 **t.**

ST. MARGARET'S HOPE Orkney. (Orkney Islands) 401 K 6 – see Orkney Islands.

SANDYHILLS Kirkcudbright. (Dumfries and Galloway) 401 402 I 19 – ✉ Dalbeattie – ☎ 0138 778.

◆Edinburgh 99 – ◆Ayr 62 – ◆Dumfries 19 – Stranraer 68.

Cairngill House ⛰, DG5 4NZ, ☎ 681, ≤, 🌳, 🎾 – TV P
Meals 8.00/18.00 **st.** and a la carte 3.00 – **7 rm** ☕ 28.00/50.00 **st.**

SANQUHAR Dumfries (Dumfries and Galloway) 401 402 I 17 – ☎ 01659.

⛳9 Blackaddie Rd ☎ 50577.

ℹ Tolbooth High St. ☎ 50185.

◆Edinburgh 58 – Dumfries 27 – ◆Glasgow 24.

Blackaddie House, Blackaddie Rd, DG4 6JJ, N : 1/4 m. by A 76 ☎ 50270, « Riverside setting », 🎣, 🌳 – TV P. VISA.
Meals 8.95/9.50 **t.** and dinner a la carte 4.50 – **10 rm** ☕ 32.00/54.00 **t.** – SB.

SCALASAIG Argyll. (Strathclyde) 401 B 15 – see Colonsay (Isle of).

SCALLOWAY Shetland. (Shetland Islands) 401 Q 3 – see Shetland Islands (Mainland).

SCARISTA Inverness. (Outer Hebrides) (Western Isles) 401 Y 10 – see Lewis and Harris (Isle of).

SCOURIE Sutherland. (Highland) 401 E 8 **Scotland G.** – ✉ Lairg – ☎ 01971.

Exc. : Cape Wrath*** (≤**) *AC*, N : 31 m. (including ferry crossing) by A 894 and A 838 – Loch Assynt**, S : 17 m. by A 894.

◆Edinburgh 263 – ◆Inverness 107.

Eddrachilles ⛰, Badcall Bay, IV27 4TH, S : 2 1/2 m. on A 894 ☎ 502080, Fax 502477, ≤ Badcall Bay and islands, 🌳 – TV ☎ P. VISA.
March-October – **Meals** (bar lunch)/dinner 10.60 **t.** and a la carte 3.30 – **11 rm** ☕ 46.00/72.00 **t.** – SB.

Scourie ⛰, IV27 4SX, ☎ 502396, Fax 502423, ≤, 🎣 – ☎ P. AE VISA
April-24 October – **Meals** (bar lunch)/dinner 14.00 **t.** – **20 rm** ☕ 42.00/74.00 **t.** – SB.

Die Preise — Einzelheiten über die in diesem Führer angegebenen Preise finden Sie in der Einleitung.

SEIL (Isle of) Argyll. (Strathclyde) 401 D 15 – ✉ Oban – ☎ 01852.

Clachan Seil – ✉ Oban – ☎ 01852.

Willowburn ⛰, PA34 4TJ, ☎ 300276, ≤, 🌳 – TV P. VISA
April-October – **Meals** (bar lunch)/dinner 18.00 **t.** and a la carte 4.50 – **6 rm** ☕ (dinner included) 45.00/90.00 **t.** – SB.

Easdale – ✉ Oban – ☎ 01852.

Inshaig Park ⛰, PA34 4RF, ☎ 300256, ≤ Inner Hebridean Islands, 🌳 – 🚭 rest TV P
Easter-October – **Meals** (bar lunch)/dinner 20.00 **st.** and a la carte – **6 rm** ☕ 32.00/54.00 **st.**

SELKIRK Selkirk. (Borders) 401 402 L 17 **Scotland G.** – pop. 6 469 – ☎ 017505.

Envir. : Bowhill** *AC*, W : 3 1/2 m. by A 708 – Abbotsbury** *AC*, NE : 5 1/2 m. by A 7 and B 6360.

Exc. : Melrose Abbey** (decorative sculptures***) *AC*, NE : 8 1/2 m. by A 7 and A 6091 – Eildon Hills (✻***) NE : 7 1/2 m. by A 699 and B 6359 – The Tweed Valley**, NW : 7 1/2 m. by A 707 and A 72.

⛳9 The Hill ☎ 20621.

ℹ Halliwell's House TD7 4BL ☎ 20054 (summer only).

◆Edinburgh 40 – ◆Glasgow 73 – Hawick 11 – ◆Newcastle upon Tyne 73.

Philipburn House ⛰, TD7 5LS, W : 1 m. at junction of A 707 with A 708 ☎ 20747, Fax 21690, 🏊 heated, 🌳 – TV ☎ P – 🏛 30. VISA JCB
Meals 9.85/22.50 **t.** and a la carte 5.95 – **16 rm** ☕ 45.00/120.00 **t.** – SB.

SHETLAND ISLANDS Shetland. (Shetland Islands) 401 PQ 3 **Scotland G.** – pop. 22 522.

See : Islands* - Up Helly Aa** (last Tuesday in January) – Jarlshof** *AC*.

✈ Tingwall Airport : ☎ (01595) 84306, NW : 6 1/2m. of Lerwick by A 971.

✈ Unst Airport : at Baltasound ☎ (0195 781) 404.

⛴ from Lerwick to Aberdeen via Orkney Islands (Stromness) (P & O Scottish Ferries) – from Lerwick to Republic of Ireland (Skerries) (Shetland Islands Council) booking essential 2 weekly (2 h 30 mn) – from Lerwick (Mainland) to Bressay (Shetland Islands Council) frequent services daily (5 mn) – from Laxo (Mainland) to Isle of Whalsay (Symbister) (Shetland Islands Council) frequent services daily (30 mn) – from Toft (Mainland) to Isle of Yell (Ulsta) (Shetland Islands Council) frequent services daily (20 mn) – from Isle of Yell (Gutcher) to Isle of Unst (Belmont) via Isle of Fetlar (Oddsta) (Shetland Islands Council) (booking essential) – from Fair Isle to Sumburgh (Gruntness) (Shetland Islands Council) 1-2 weekly.

MAINLAND

Brae – ✉ Brae – ☎ 01806.

🏨 **Busta House** 🐦, ZE2 9QN, SW : 1½ m. ☏ 522506, Fax 522588, ≤, « Part 16C and 18C country house », 🌳 – ⇆ rest 📺 ☎ Ⓟ. 🄽 AE ⓓ VISA
closed 21 December-3 January – **Meals** (bar lunch)/dinner 22.50 **t.** – **20 rm** ☐ 63.00/110.00 **t.** – SB.

Lerwick **Scotland G.** – pop. 7 223 – ECD : Wednesday – ✉ Lerwick – ☎ 01595.

Envir. : Gulber Wick (≤★) S : 2 m. by A 970.

Exc. : Mousa Broch★★★ *AC* (Mousa Island) S : 14 m. – Lerwick to Jarlshof★, S : 22 m. by A 970 – Shetland Croft House Museum★ *AC*, SW : 6 m. by A 970 and A 9073.

⛳18 Lerwick ☏ 695369.

• ℹ Market Cross, Lerwick ZE1 0LU ☏ 3434.

🏨 **Shetland,** Holmsgarth Rd, ZE1 0PW, ☏ 695515, Fax 695828, ≤ – 🛗 ⇆ 📺 ☎ ♿ Ⓟ – 🏛 250. 🄽 AE ⓓ VISA
Meals (bar lunch)/dinner 20.00 **st.** and a la carte 🍷 3.40 – **64 rm** ☐ 71.00/90.00 **st.**, 1 suite – SB.

🏨 **Kveldsro House,** Greenfield Pl., ZE1 0AQ, ☏ 2195, Fax 6595 – ⇆ rest 📺 ☎ Ⓟ – 🏛 35. 🄽 AE ⓓ VISA. ✗
closed 24 December - 5 January – **Meals** (bar lunch)/dinner 18.50 **st.** 🍷 4.00 – **17 rm** ☐ 82.50/110.00 **st.** – SB.

⌂ **Whinrig** without rest., 12 Burgh Rd, ZE1 0LB, ☏ 3554, 🌳 – ⇆ 📺 Ⓟ. ✗
3 rm ☐ 16.00/36.00 **s.**

⌂ **Breiview,** 43 Kanterstead Rd, ZE1 0RJ, SW : 1 m. by A 970 ☏ 695956 – 📺 Ⓟ. ✗
Meals (communal dining) 8.00 **st.** – **6 rm** ☐ 24.00/40.00 **st.**

ATS 3 Gremista Ind. Est., Lerwick ☏ 3857

Scalloway – ✉ Scalloway – ☎ 01595.

⌂ **Broch House** without rest., Upper Scalloway, ZE1 0UP, NE : ½ m. by A 70 taking unmarked road on left after school ☏ 880767, Fax 880731 – 📺 Ⓟ. ✗
3 rm ☐ 19.00/34.00.

Walls – ✉ Walls – ☎ 0159 571.

✕ **Burrastow House** 🐦 with rm, ZE2 9PB, SW : 2½ m. ☏ 307, Fax 213, ≤, « 18C house overlooking Vaila Sound », 🐟 – ⇆ Ⓟ
closed January-early March – **Meals** *(closed Sunday dinner and Monday to non-residents)* (lunch by arrangement)/dinner 25.00 – **2 rm** ☐ (dinner included) 66.00/122.00 – SB.

SHIELDAIG Ross and Cromarty. (Highland) 401 D 11 **Scotland G.** – ✉ Strathcarron – ☎ 01520.

Exc. : Wester Ross★★★.

◆Edinburgh 226 – ◆Inverness 70 – Kyle of Lochalsh 36.

🏨 **Tigh-An Eilean,** IV54 8XN, ☏ 755251, Fax 755321, ≤ Shieldaig Islands and Loch, « Attractively furnished inn », 🐟 – ⇆ rest. 🄽 VISA
Meals (dinner only) 19.50 **t.** 🍷 4.25 – **11 rm** ☐ (dinner included) 58.90/126.00 **t.**

SKEABOST Inverness. (Highland) 401 B 11 – see Skye (Isle of).

SKELMORLIE Ayr. (Strathclyde) 401 F 16 **Scotland G.** – pop. 1 606 – ECD : Wednesday – ☎ 01475.

Exc. : Greenock (≤★★) NE : 8½ m. by A 78 off A 770.

⛳9 Skelmorlie ☏ 520152.

◆Edinburgh 78 – ◆Ayr 39 – ◆Glasgow 32.

🏨 **Redcliffe House,** 25 Shore Rd, PA17 5EH, on A 78 ☏ 521036, Fax 521894, ≤, 🌳 – 📺 ☎ Ⓟ. 🄽 AE ⓓ VISA
Meals 12.95 **st.** (dinner) and a la carte 9.00/18.00 **st.** 🍷 3.50 – **10 rm** ☐ 45.00/90.00 **st.** – SB.

SKYE (Isle of) Inverness. (Highland) 401 B 11 /12 **Scotland G.** – pop. 8 139.

See : Island★★ – The Cuillins★★★ – Skye of Island's Life Museum★ *AC*.

Envir. : N : Trotternish Peninsula★★ – W : Duirinish Peninsula★ – Portree★.

⛴ from Kyleakin to Kyle of Lochalsh (Caledonian MacBrayne Ltd) frequent services daily (5 mn) – from Armadale to Mallaig via Isles of Eigg, Muck, Rhum and Canna (Caledonian MacBrayne Ltd) 3-6 daily (except Sunday) (30 mn) – from Uig to Isle of Harris (Tarbert) (Caledonian MacBrayne Ltd) 1-3 daily (1 h 45 mn) – from Uig to North Uist (Lochmaddy) via Isle of Harris (Tarbert) (Caledonian MacBrayne Ltd) 1-2 daily – from Sconser to Isle of Raasay (Caledonian MacBrayne Ltd) 5 daily (except Sunday) (15 mn).

Ardvasar – ✉ Ardvasar – ☎ 01471.

🏨 **Ardvasar,** IV45 8RS, ☏ 844223, 🌳 – 📺 Ⓟ. 🄽 VISA. ✗
closed January and February – **Meals** a la carte 12.00 approx. – **10 rm** ☐ 32.00/65.00 – SB.

Breakish – ☎ 01471.

✕ **Seagull,** IV42 8PY, ☏ 822001 – Ⓟ. 🄽 VISA
Easter-early October – **Meals** (dinner only) a la carte 9.35/21.70 **st.**

Broadford – 01471.

Dunollie, IV49 9AE, 822253, Fax 822060 – rest.
April-October – **Meals** (bar lunch)/dinner 15.00 **t.** and a la carte – **87 rm** 35.00/70.00 **st.** – SB.

Ptarmigan without rest., Harrapool, IV49 9AQ, E : 3/4 m. on A 850 822744, Fax 822745, Broadford Bay and islands, « Waterside setting », –
closed 2 weeks winter – **3 rm** 35.00/48.00.

Earsary without rest., Harrapool, IV49 9AQ, E : 3/4 m. on A 850 822697, park –
3 rm 18.00/40.00 **t.**

Westside without rest., Elgol Rd, IV49 9AB, on A 881 822320, –
3 rm 16.00/36.00 **st.**

Culnaknock – Portree – 01470.

Glenview Inn, IV51 9JH, 652248, –
Meals a la carte 10.00/22.50 **t.** 3.25 – **5 rm** 18.00/36.00 **t.**

Dunvegan – Dunvegan – 01470.

Harlosh House, IV55 8ZG, SE : 6 m. by A 863 521367, Fax 521367, Loch Bracadale and Islands –
Easter-mid October – **Meals** (dinner only) a la carte 18.15/27.45 **t.** 5.50 – **6 rm** 65.00/90.00 **t.**

Dunorin House, Herebost, IV55 8GZ, SE : 2½ m. by A 863 on Roag rd 521488, –
April-October – **Meals** (dinner only) a la carte 14.55/22.15 **t.** 3.75 – **10 rm** 38.00/68.00 **t.** – SB.

Three Chimneys, Colbost, IV55 8ZT, NW : 5¾ m. by A 863 on B 884 511258 –
closed Sunday and November-March – **Meals** (booking essential)/dinner a la carte 13.50/27.95 **t.**

Flodigarry – Staffin – 01470.

Flodigarry Country House, IV51 9HZ, 552203, Fax 552301, Staffin Island and coastline, –
Meals (bar lunch Monday to Saturday)/dinner 28.00 **st.** 4.25 – **23 rm** 36.00/92.00 **st.** – SB.

Isleornsay – Sleat – 01471.

Kinloch Lodge, IV43 8QY, N : 3½ m. by A 851 833333, Fax 833277, Loch Na Dal, « 17C former shooting lodge », park –
closed 10 December-28 February – **Meals** (dinner only) 35.00 **t.** 4.00 – **10 rm** 40.00/110.00 **t.** – SB.

Eilean Iarmain, Camus Cross, IV43 8QR, 833332, Fax 833275, « 19C inn », –
Meals 15.00/25.00 **t.** 6.00 – **12 rm** 55.00/78.00 **t.** – SB.

Ord – Sleat – 01471.

Fiordhem, IV43 8QN, 855226, Loch Eishort and Cuillin mountains, « Idyllic setting on shore of Loch Eishort », –
April-October – **3 rm** (dinner included) 35.00/70.00.

Portree – pop. 1 533 – ECD : Wednesday – Portree – 01478.
Meall House, Portree IV51 9BZ 612137.

Cullin Hills, IV51 9LU, NE : 3/4 m. by A 855 612003, Fax 613092, park – rest – 40.
Meals (bar lunch Monday to Saturday)/dinner 19.50 **t.** and a la carte 5.75 – **26 rm** (dinner included) 60.00/120.00 **t.** – SB.

Bosville, Bosville Terr., IV51 9DG, 612846, Fax 613434, –
closed January-early February – **Meals** *(closed Sunday lunch)* 9.00/15.50 **st.** and a la carte 5.45 – **11 rm** 35.00/70.00 **st.**, 3 suites – SB.

Rosedale, Beaumont Cres., IV51 9DB, 613131, Fax 612531, harbour, – rest
May-September – **Meals** (dinner only) 24.00 – **23 rm** 40.00/75.00 **t.** – SB.

Kings Haven without rest., 11 Bosville Terr., IV51 9DJ, 612290 –
closed Christmas – **6 rm** -/54.00 **t.**

Burnside without rest., 5 Budmhor, IV51 9DJ, NE : ½ m. by A 855 612669, –
3 rm 15.00/34.00 **st.**

Skeabost – ECD : Wednesday – Skeabost Bridge – 01470.
Skeabost 532202.

Skeabost House, IV51 9NP, 532202, Fax 532454, Loch Snizort Beag, park – rest
April-October – **Meals** (buffet lunch)/dinner 17.50 **t.** and a la carte 4.50 – **26 rm** 42.00/96.00 **t.** – SB.

Uig – ✉ Uig – ☎ 01470.

Ferry Inn, IV51 9XP, ℘ 542242 – ⊭ rm TV P. VISA
closed 1 January – **Meals** a la carte 9.00/17.00 **4.70 – 6 rm** 35.00/56.00 **t.** – SB.

Woodbine, Kilmiur Rd, IV51 9XP, ℘ 542243 – TV P
Meals 11.00 **st.** – **4 rm** 22.00/37.00 **st.**

SPEAN BRIDGE Inverness. (Highland) 401 F 13 – ☎ 01397.
♦Edinburgh 143 – Fort William 10 – ♦Glasgow 94 – ♦Inverness 58 – ♦Oban 60.

Corriegour Lodge, Loch Lochy, PH34 4EB, N : 8¾ m. on A 82 ℘ 712685, Fax 712696, ≤, – ⊭ rest TV P. AE VISA.
March-October and weekends in winter – **Meals** (dinner only) 19.00 **t.** and a la carte 4.90 – **9 rm** 28.00/80.00 **t.** – SB.

Old Pines, PH34 4EG, NW : 1½ m. by A 82 on B 8004 ℘ 712324, Fax 712433, ≤, park – ⊭ & P. VISA.
closed 2 weeks November – **Meals** (by arrangement) 18.50 **st.** – **8 rm** (dinner included) 40.00/90.00 **st.** – SB.

Old Station, Station Rd, PH34 4EP, ℘ 712535 – ⊭ P. VISA
closed 25 December, 1 January, 2 weeks March, 2 weeks October and Sunday-Tuesday November-March – **Meals** (booking essential) a la carte 12.60/19.25 **t.** 5.75.

"Short Breaks" (SB)

De nombreux hôtels proposent des conditions avantageuses pour un séjour de deux nuits comprenant la chambre, le dîner et le petit déjeuner.

SPITTAL OF GLENSHEE Perth. (Tayside) 401 J 13 **Scotland G.** – ✉ Blairgowrie – ☎ 01250.
Envir. : Glenshee (※★★) (chairlift *AC*).
♦Edinburgh 69 – ♦Aberdeen 74 – ♦Dundee 35.

Dalmunzie House, PH10 7QG, ℘ 885224, Fax 885225, ≤, 9, park, – P. VISA
closed 1 November-28 December – **Meals** (bar lunch)/dinner 19.00 **t.** – **17 rm** 53.00/86.00 **t.**

STENNESS Orkney. (Orkney Islands) 401 K 7 – see Orkney Islands.

STEPPS Lanark. (Strathclyde) 401 H 16 – see Glasgow.

STEWARTON Ayr. (Strathclyde) 401 402 G 16 **Scotland G.** – pop. 6 319 – ECD : Wednesday and Saturday – ☎ 01560.
Envir. : Kilmarnock (Dean Castle, arms and armour★, musical instruments★ *AC*) S : 5½ m. by A 735 and B 7038.
♦Edinburgh 68 – ♦Ayr 21 – ♦Glasgow 22.

Chapeltoun House with rm, KA3 3ED, SW : 2½ m. by A 735 off B 769 ℘ 482696, Fax 485100, « Country house in extensive grounds », park – ⊭ rest TV ☎ P. AE VISA.
Meals 15.50/26.30 5.20 – **8 rm** 69.75/139.00 **t.**

STIRLING Stirling. (Central) 401 I 15 **Scotland G.** – pop. 36 640 – ECD : Wednesday – ☎ 01786.
See : Town★★ – Castle★★ *AC* (Site★★★, external elevations★★★, Stirling Heads★★, Argyll and Sutherland Highlanders Regimental Museum★) B – Argyll's Lodging★ (Renaissance decoration★) B A – Church of the Holy Rude★ B **B.**
Envir. : Wallace Monument (※★★) NE : 2½ m. by A 9 - A - and B 998.
Exc. : Dunblane★ (Cathedral★★, West Front★★), N : 6½ m. by A 9 A.
41 Dumbarton Rd FK8 2LQ ℘ 475019 – Royal Burgh of Stirling Visitor Centre, Broad St. ℘ 479901 (summer only) – Motorway Service Area, M 9/M 80, junction 9 ℘ 814111 (summer only).
♦Edinburgh 37 – Dunfermline 23 – Falkirk 14 – ♦Glasgow 28 – Greenock 52 – Motherwell 30 – ♦Oban 87 – Perth 35.

Plan on next page

Stirling Highland, Spittal St., FK8 1DU, ℘ 475444, Fax 462929, squash – ⊭ rm TV ☎ & P – 150. AE VISA B **e**
Scholars : **Meals** 19.75 and a la carte **t.** 5.95 – *Rizzios* : **Meals** 20.50 **t.** 5.95 – **72 rm** 87.00/124.00 **t.**, 4 suites – SB.

Park Lodge without rest., 32 Park Terr., FK8 2JS, ℘ 474862, « Tastefully decorated Georgian house, antiques », – TV ☎ P – 100. VISA. B **a**
10 rm 45.00/110.00 **st.**

Granada Lodge without rest., Pirnhall roundabout, Snabhead, FK7 8EU, S : 3 m. by A 872 ℘ 813614, Fax 815900, Reservations (Freephone) 0800 555300 – ⊭ TV ☎ & P. AE VISA. A
4.00 – **37 rm** 39.95 **st.**

STIRLING

Dumbarton Road . . . . . B 10
Leisure Centre . . . . . B
Murray Place . . . . . B 15
Port Street . . . . . B
Thistle Centre . . . . . B
Upper Craigs . . . . . B 29

Barnton Street . . . . . B 2
Borestone Crescent . . . . . A 3
Causewayhead Road . . . . A, B 4
Corn Exchange Road . . . . . B 5
Cornton Road . . . . . A 7
Coxithill Road . . . . . A 8
Drummond Place . . . . . B 9
Goosecroft Road . . . . . B 12
King Street . . . . . B 13
Newhouse . . . . . A 16

Park Place . . . . . A 18
Queen Street . . . . . B 20
Randolph Terrace . . . . . A 22
St. John Street . . . . . B 23
St. Mary's Wynd . . . . . B 24
Seaforth Place . . . . . B 25
Shirra's Brae Road . . . . . A 26
Spittal Street . . . . . B 27
Union Street . . . . . B 28
Weaver Row . . . . . A 31

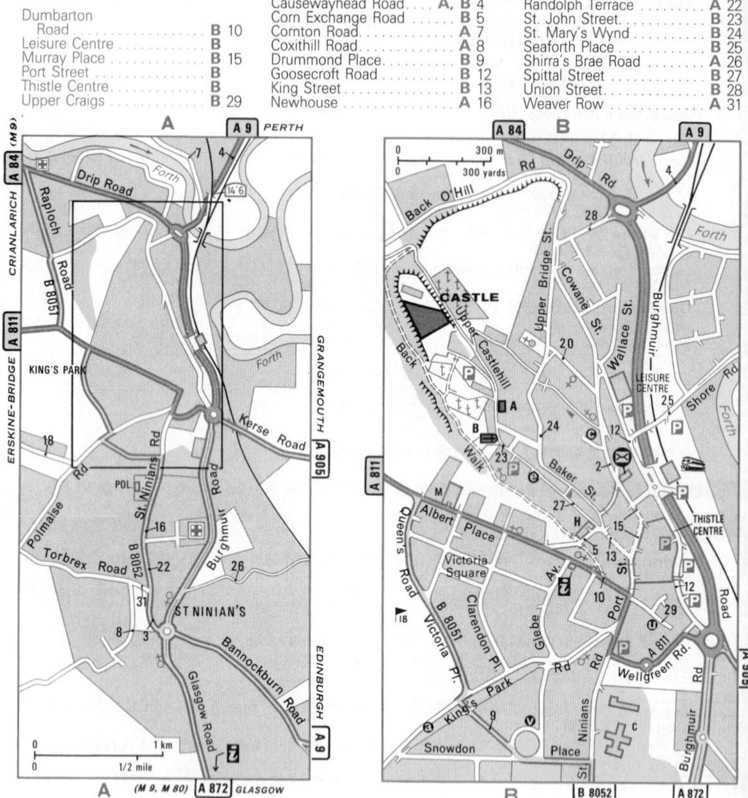

⌂ **Number 10,** Gladstone Pl., FK8 2NN, ☏ 472681, ⚘ – ⊭ rm TV. ✻ — B **v**
Meals (by arrangement) 6.00 **st.** – **3 rm** ⊐ 20.00/35.00 **st.**

⌂ **West Plean House** without rest., FK7 8HA, S : 3 ½ m. on A 872 (Denny rd) ☏ 812208, « Working farm », ⚘, park – ⊭ Ⓟ — A
closed 2 weeks Christmas-New Year – **3 rm** ⊐ 25.00/44.00 **st.**

⌂ **Fairfield,** 14 Princes St., FK8 1HQ, ☏ 472685 – ⊭ TV. ✻ — B **c**
Meals (by arrangement) 7.00 **st.** – **6 rm** ⊐ 20.00/40.00 **st.** – SB.

XX **Regent,** 30 Upper Craigs, FK8 2DG, ☏ 472513 – ▤. AE VISA — B **u**
Meals - Chinese (Canton, Peking) 5.60/23.00 **t.** and a la carte 🍷 5.50.

at Blairlogie NE : 4 ½ m. by A 9 on A 91 – A – ✉ Stirling – ☎ 01259 :

⌂ **Blairlogie House,** FK9 5QE, ☏ 761441, Fax 761441, ⚘, park – TV ☎ Ⓟ. VISA
Meals *(closed Sunday to non-residents)* 7.50/16.50 **t.** and dinner a la carte 🍷 4.15 – **7 rm** ⊐ 49.00/68.00 **t.** – SB.

ATS 45 Drip Rd ☏ 450770

STONEHAVEN Kincardine. (Grampian) **401** N 13 – ☎ 01569.

◆ Edinburgh 114 – ◆ Aberdeen 16 – ◆ Dundee 51.

⌂ **Muchalls Castle** ⛰, AB3 2RS, N : 5 m. by B 979 and A 92 on Netherley rd ☏ 731170, Fax 731480, « Early 17C laird's house, plasterwork ceilings », ⚘ – ⊭ rm Ⓟ. ✻
closed January and Christmas – **Meals** (booking essential) (communal dining) (dinner only) 25.00 **st.** 🍷 9.50 – **8 rm** ⊐ 75.00/120.00 **st.**

ATS 64-72 Barclay St. ☏ 762077

En haute saison, et surtout dans les stations, il est prudent de retenir à l'avance.

STORNOWAY Ross and Cromarty. (Outer Hebrides) (Western Isles) 401 A 9 – see Lewis and Harris (Isle of).

STRACHUR Argyll. (Strathclyde) 401 E 15 **Scotland G.** – ECD : Wednesday – ✉ Cairndow – ☎ 0136 986.

Exc. : Inveraray** : Castle** (interior***) *AC*, NW : 17 m. by A 185 and A 83 – Loch Fyne**.

♦Edinburgh 104 – ♦Glasgow 58 – ♦Oban 58.

Creggans Inn, PA27 8BX, on A 815 ☏ 279, Fax 637, ≤ Loch Fyne, – rest TV ☎ P. VISA
Meals 18.50 **st.** and a la carte – **21 rm** 49.00/98.00 **st.** – SB.

STRANRAER Wigtown. (Dumfries and Galloway) 401 402 E 19 **Scotland G.** – pop. 10 766 – ECD : Wednesday – ☎ 01776.

Exc. : Logan Botanic Garden* *AC*, S : 11 m. by A 77, A 716 and B 7065.

18 Creachmore, Leswalt ☏ 870245.

to Northern Ireland (Larne) (Stena Sealink Line) frequent services daily (2 h 20 mn) – to Northern Ireland (Belfast) (Hoverspeed Ltd) 4-5 daily (1 h 30 mn).

1 Bridge St., DG9 7JA ☏ 702595 (summer only).

♦Edinburgh 132 – ♦Ayr 51 – ♦Dumfries 75.

North West Castle, Portrodie, DG9 8EH, ☏ 704413, Fax 702646, – TV ☎ P – 100.
Meals 19.50 **t.** (dinner) and a la carte 9.45/20.25 6.95 – **71 rm** 55.00/138.00 **t.** – SB.

Kildrochet House , DG9 9BB, S : 3¼ m. by A 77 on A 716 ☏ 820216, « Former 18C dower house », – P.
Meals (by arrangement) (communal dining) 14.00 **s.** – **3 rm** 26.00/46.00 **s.**

ATS Commerce Rd, Ind. Est. ☏ 702131

I prezzi Per ogni chiarimento sui prezzi qui riportati, consultate le spiegazioni alle pagine dell'introduzione.

STRATHBLANE Stirling. (Central) 401 H 16 – pop. 2 355 – ECD : Wednesday – ✉ Glasgow – ☎ 01360.

♦Edinburgh 52 – ♦Glasgow 11 – Stirling 26.

Kirkhouse Inn, G63 9AA, ☏ 770621, Fax 770896 – TV ☎ P – 40. VISA JCB
Meals 12.95/18.95 **st.** and a la carte 4.95 – **15 rm** 55.25/82.00 **st.** – SB.

STRATHCONON Ross and Cromarty. (Highland) 401 F 11 **Scotland G.** – ✉ Muir of Ord – ☎ 01997.

Exc. : Wester Ross***.

♦Edinburgh 184 – ♦Inverness 28.

East Lodge , IV6 7QQ, W : 11 m. from Marybank off A 832 ☏ 7222 (477222 early 1995), Fax 7243 (477243 early 1995), ≤, – TV ☎ P. VISA
Meals (lunch by arrangement)/dinner 20.00/25.00 **st.** 3.75 – **10 rm** 43.50/90.00 **st.** – SB.

STRATHPEFFER Ross and Cromarty. (Highland) 401 G 11 – pop. 1 244 – ECD : Thursday – ☎ 01997.

18 Strathpeffer Spa ☏ 421219.

The Square IV14 9DW ☏ 421415 (summer only).

♦Edinburgh 174 – ♦Inverness 18.

Holly Lodge, Golf Course Rd, IV14 9AR, ☏ 421254, – TV P. VISA
Meals 8.95/15.00 **st.** 4.00 – **8 rm** 27.50/55.00 **st.**

Craigvar without rest., The Square, IV14 9DL, ☏ 421622, – TV ☎ P. VISA
Easter-October – **3 rm** 25.00/40.00 **st.**

STRATHYRE Perth. (Central) 401 H 15 **Scotland G.** – ✉ Callander – ☎ 01877.

Exc. : The Trossacks*** (Loch Katherine**) SW : 14 m. by A 84 and A 821 – Hilltop viewpoint*** (***) SW : 16½ m. by A 84 and A 821.

♦Edinburgh 62 – ♦Glasgow 53 – Perth 42.

Creagan House with rm, FK18 8ND, on A 84 ☏ 384638, Fax 384638, ≤ – P. VISA
closed February and 1 week October – **Meals** (booking essential) (dinner only and Sunday lunch)/dinner 21.00 **t.** 6.25 – **5 rm** 34.25/61.00 **t.** – SB.

at Balquhidder NW : 4 m. by A 84 – ✉ Lochearnhead – ☎ 01877 :

Stronvar Country House , FK19 8PB, ☏ 384688, Fax 384230, ≤ Loch Voil and Braes of Balquhidder, « Bygones Museum », – rest TV P. VISA
March-October – **Meals** (restricted lunch)/dinner 17.50 **st.** 4.25 – **4 rm** 39.50/59.00 **st.**

STROMNESS Orkney. (Orkney Islands) 401 K 7 – see Orkney Islands.

STRONTIAN Argyll. (Highland) 401 D 13 – ☎ 01967.
ℹ Village Square, PH36 ℘ 402131 (summer only).
♦Edinburgh 139 – Fort William 23 – ♦Oban 66.

Kilcamb Lodge ⚘, PH36 4HY, ℘ 402257, Fax 402041, ≤, ⛾, park – ⇆ P. VISA
March-November – **Meals** (light lunch)/dinner 25.00 **st.** 4.50 – **10 rm** 43.00/86.00 **st.** – SB.

STRUY Inverness (Highland) 401 F 11 – ✉ Beauly – ☎ 01465.
♦Edinburgh 191 – ♦Inverness 21 – Kyle of Lochalsh 61.

Cnoc ⚘, IV4 7JU, ℘ 761264, Fax 761264, ≤, ⛾ – ⇆ rest P
8 rm.

TAIN Ross and Cromarty. (Highland) 401 H 10 – pop. 4 540 – ECD : Thursday – ☎ 01862.
⛳18 Tain ℘ 892314.
♦Edinburgh 191 – ♦Inverness 35 – ♦Wick 91.

Morangie House, Morangie Rd, IV19 1PY, ℘ 892281, Fax 892872 – TV ☎ P. AE VISA.
Meals (bar lunch Monday to Saturday)/dinner 22.00 **t.** and a la carte 4.60 – **13 rm** 45.00/70.00 **t.** – SB.

TALLADALE Ross and Cromarty (Highland) 401 D 10 **Scotland G.** – ✉ Achnasheen – ☎ 01445.
Envir. : Loch Maree★★★ – Victoria Falls★, N : 2 m. by A 832.
Exc. : Wester Ross★★★.
♦Edinburgh 218 – ♦Inverness 62 – Kyle of Lochalsh 58.

Old Mill Highland Lodge ⚘, IV22 2HL, ℘ 760271, ⛾ – ⇆ P.
Meals 18.50 **t.** – **5 rm** 35.00/70.00 **st.** – SB.

TARBERT Argyll. (Strathclyde) 401 D 16 – see Kintyre (Peninsula).

TARBERT Inverness. (Outer Hebrides) (Western Isles) 401 Z 10 – see Lewis and Harris (Isle of).

TAYVALLICH Argyll. (Strathclyde) 401 D 15 – ✉ Lochgilphead – ☎ 0154 67.
♦Edinburgh 141 – ♦Glasgow 95 – ♦Oban 40.

Tayvallich Inn, PA31 8PR, ℘ 282, ≤ – P. VISA
closed Monday November-Easter – **Meals** a la carte 9.00/17.50 **t.** 4.50.

THORNHILL Dumfries. (Dumfries and Galloway) 401 402 I 18 **Scotland G.** – pop. 1 449 – ECD : Thursday – ☎ 01848.
Envir. : Drumlanrig Castle★★ (cabinets★) *AC*, NW : 2½ m. by A 76.
♦Edinburgh 64 – ♦Ayr 44 – ♦Dumfries 15 – ♦Glasgow 63.

Trigony House, Closeburn, DG3 5EZ, S : 1½ m. on A 76 ℘ 331211, ⛾ – TV ☎ P. VISA.
Meals (bar lunch)/dinner 19.00 **t.** 5.50 – **8 rm** 37.00/64.00 **t.** – SB.

THORNHILL Stirling. (Central) 401 H 15 – pop. 1 435 – ✉ Stirling – ☎ 01786.
♦Edinburgh 46 – ♦Glasgow 36.

Corshill Cottage ⚘, FK8 3QD, E : 1 m. on A 873 ℘ 850270, ⛾ – ⇆ P
April-September – **Meals** (by arrangement) – **3 rm** 22.00/40.00 **st.**

THURSO Caithness. (Highland) 401 J 8 **Scotland G.** – pop. 9 110 – ECD : Thursday – ☎ 01847.
Exc. : Strathy Point★ (≤★★★) W : 22 m. by A 836.
⛳18 Newlands of Geise ℘ 63807.
⛴ from Scrabster to Stromness (Orkney Islands) (P & O Scottish Ferries) (1 h 45 mn).
ℹ Riverside KW14 8BU ℘ 62371 (summer only).
♦Edinburgh 289 – ♦Inverness 133 – ♦Wick 21.

Forss House ⚘, Bridge of Forss, KW14 7XY, W : 5½ m. on A 836 ℘ 86201, Fax 86301, ≤, ⛾, park – TV ☎ P. AE VISA.
Meals (dinner only) 18.50 **t.** 4.30 – **7 rm** 45.00/80.00 **t.**

TIRORAN Argyll. (Strathclyde) 401 B 14 – see Mull (Isle of).

TOBERMORY Argyll. (Strathclyde) 401 B 14 – see Mull (Isle of).

TONGUE Sutherland. (Highland) 401 G 8 **Scotland G.** – ECD : Saturday – ✉ Lairg – ☎ 01847.
Exc. : Cape Wrath★★★ (≤★★) W : 44 m. (including ferry crossing) by A 838 – Ben Loyal★★, S : 8 m. by A 836 – Ben Hope★ (≤★★★) SW : 15 m. by A 838 – Strathy Point★ (≤★★★) E : 22 m. by A 836 – Torrisdale Bay★ (≤★★) NE : 8 m. by A 836.
♦Edinburgh 257 – ♦Inverness 101 – Thurso 43.

Ben Loyal, Main St., IV27 4XE, ℘ 611216, Fax 611216, ≤ – ⇆ rest TV P. VISA
closed 25 December-23 February – **Meals** (bar lunch)/dinner 18.50 **t.** and a la carte 6.95 – **12 rm** (dinner included) 48.50/97.00 **t.** – SB.

TORRIDON Ross and Cromarty (Highland) 401 D 11 – ✉ Achnasheen – ☎ 01445.

♦Edinburgh 234 – ♦Inverness 62 – Kyle of Lochalsh 44.

Loch Torridon ⊗, IV22 2EY, S : 1 ½ m. on A 896 ℘ 791242, Fax 791296, ≤ Upper Loch Torridon and mountains, ↘, ⌘, park – |♦| ⇌ TV ☎ ♿ P
restricted service January-February – **Meals** (bar lunch)/dinner 35.00 **st.** 5.00 – **19 rm** 60.00/160.00 **st.**, 1 suite.

TROON Ayr. (Strathclyde) 401 402 G 17 – pop. 15 116 – ECD : Wednesday – ☎ 01292.

(3x) Troon Municipal, Harling Drive ℘ 312464.

Municipal Buildings, South Beach ℘ 317696 (summer only).

♦Edinburgh 77 – ♦Ayr 7 – ♦Glasgow 31.

Marine Highland, 8 Crosbie Rd, KA10 6HE, ℘ 314444, Fax 316922, ≤, ⚡, ≘s, ⊠, squash – |♦| TV ☎ P – 200. AE VISA
Meals 14.50/22.50 **t.** and a la carte 4.95 – **66 rm** 88.00/140.00 **t.**, 6 suites – SB.

Lochgreen House ⊗, Monktonhill Rd, Southwood, KA10 7EN, SE : 2 m. on B 749 ℘ 313343, Fax 318661, ⌘, park, ✂ – ⇌ rest TV ☎ P. AE VISA.
Meals 12.50/25.00 **st.** 5.00 – **7 rm** 90.00/105.00 **st.**, 1 suite – SB.

Piersland House, 15 Craigend Rd, KA10 6HD, ℘ 314747, Fax 315613, ⌘ – TV ☎ P – 100. AE VISA
Meals 10.95/18.50 **t.** and a la carte 5.00 – **22 rm** 56.00/125.00 **st.**, 4 suites – SB.

Ardneil, 51 St. Meddans St., KA10 6NU, ℘ 311611, Fax 318111 – TV P. AE VISA
Meals 8.95/13.25 **st.** and a la carte 3.90 – **9 rm** 25.00/50.00 **t.**

Highgrove House with rm, Old Loans Rd, Loans, KA10 7HL, E : 2 ½ m. by A 759 ℘ 312511, Fax 318228, ≤, ⌘ – TV ☎ P. AE VISA
Meals 15.00/21.50 **t.** and a la carte 6.95 – **9 rm** 55.00/90.00 **t.** – SB.

Great Britain and Ireland are covered entirely at a scale of 16 miles to 1 inch by our map « Main roads » 986.

TURNBERRY Ayr. (Strathclyde) 401 402 F 18 **Scotland G.** – ECD : Wednesday – ✉ Girvan – ☎ 01655.

Envir. : Culzean Castle★ *AC* (setting★★★, Oval Staircase★★) NE : 5 m. by A 719.

♦Edinburgh 97 – ♦Ayr 15 – ♦Glasgow 51 – Stranraer 36.

Turnberry H. & Golf Courses ⊗, KA26 9LT, on A 719 ℘ 31000, Telex 777779, Fax 31706, « Edwardian country house, ≤ golf course, bay and Ailsa Craig », ⚡, ≘s, ⊠, 18, ⌘, ✂, squash – |♦| TV ☎ ♿ P – 150. AE VISA JCB
Turnberry : **Meals** *(closed lunch Monday to Saturday, October to March)* a la carte 19.50/37.50 **st.** 9.00 – ***Bay at Turnberry*** : **Meals** a la carte 18.00/30.00 **t.** 9.00 – **122 rm** 170.00/235.00 **t.**, 10 suites – SB.

TWYNHOLM Kirkcudbright. (Dumfries and Galloway) 402 H 19 – ☎ 0155 76 (01557 from Summer).

♦Edinburgh 107 – ♦Ayr 54 – ♦Dumfries 27 – Stranraer 48.

Fresh Fields ⊗, Arden Rd, DG6 4PB, SW : ¾ m. by Burn Brae ℘ 221 (860221 from summer), Fax 221 (860221 from summer), ⌘ – ⇌ P.
March-October – **5 rm** (dinner included) 39.00/78.00 **st.**

UDDINGSTON Lanark. (Strathclyde) 401 402 H 16 – pop. 5 367 – ECD : Wednesday – ✉ Glasgow – ☎ 01698.

18 Coatbridge, Townhead Rd ℘ (01236) 28975.

♦Edinburgh 41 – ♦Glasgow 10.

Redstones, 8-10 Glasgow Rd, G71 7AS, ℘ 813774, Fax 815319 – TV ☎ P. AE VISA.
closed 25 December and 1-2 January – **Meals** (in bar lunchtime and Sunday dinner)/dinner 15.50 **t.** and a la carte 4.95 – **18 rm** 52.00/74.50 **t.**

Il Buongustaio, 84 Main St., G71 7LR, ℘ 816000 – AE VISA
closed Sunday dinner and Tuesday – **Meals** - Italian 5.95/40.45 **t.** (lunch) and a la carte 14.00/38.45 4.50.

UIG Inverness. (Highland) 401 B 11 and 12 – see Skye (Isles of).

UIST (Isles of) Western Isles (Outer Hebrides) 401 XY 11 /12 – pop. 3 677.

see Liniclate.

from Lochboisdale to Isle of Barra (Castlebay) and Oban (Caledonian MacBrayne Ltd) (summer only) – from Lochmaddy to Isle of Skye (Uig) (Caledonian MacBrayne Ltd) – from Lochmaddy to Isle of Harris (Tarbert) (Caledonian MacBrayne Ltd) (1 h 45 mn).

NORTH UIST

Grimsay – ☎ 01870.

Glendale ⊗, 7 Kallin, PA82 5HY, ℘ 602029, ≤ – ⇌ P
Meals 10.00 – **3 rm** 18.00/30.00 **st.**

Locheport – 01876.

Langass Lodge, PA82 5HP, NW : 4½ m. by B 894 off A 867 580285, ≤, – P
6 rm.

Lochmaddy – 01876.

Lochmaddy, PA82 5AA, 500331, Fax 500210 – TV ☎ P. AE VISA
Meals (bar lunch)/dinner 17.00 **t.** 3.80 – **15 rm** 38.00/72.00 **t.** – SB.

BENBECULA

Liniclate – 01870.

Benbecula Airport : 602051.

Dark Island, PA88 5PJ, 603030, Fax 602347 – TV ☎ P. VISA
Meals 9.75/16.50 **t.** and a la carte 4.50 – **42 rm** 45.00/80.00 **t.** – SB.

SOUTH UIST

Daliburgh – ✉ Lochboisdale – 01878.

Askernish 700541.

Borrodale, PA81 5SS, 700444, Fax 700611, – TV P. VISA
Meals 9.50/14.50 **t.** and a la carte 5.00 – **14 rm** 34.00/59.00 **st.**

Ard-na-Mara, Kilpheder, PA81 5TP, SW : 1½ m. on Cille Pheadair rd 700452, – P
3 rm.

Lochboisdale – 01878.

Brae Lea, Lasgair, PA81 5TH, NW : 1 m. by A 865 700497, – P
4 rm.

Pollachar – 01878.

Polochar Inn, PA81 5TT, 700215, ≤ Sound of Barra – TV ☎ P
11 rm.

ULLAPOOL Ross and Cromarty. (Highland) 401 E 10 **Scotland G.** – pop. 1 006 – ECD : Tuesday except summer – 01854.

See : Town★.

Envir. : Loch Broom★★.

Exc. : Falls of Measach★★, S : 11 m. by A 835 and A 832 - Corrieshalloch Gorge★, SE : 10 m. by A 835 – Northwards to Lochinver★★, Morefield (≤★★ of Ullapool), ≤★ Loch Broom – S : from Ullapool to Gairloch★★ (≤★★★).

to Isle of Lewis (Stornoway) (Caledonian MacBrayne Ltd) (3 h 30 mn).

West Shore St. IV26 2UR 612135 (summer only).

♦Edinburgh 215 – ♦Inverness 59.

✿✿ **Altnaharrie Inn** (Gunn Eriksen), IV26 2SS, SW : ½ m. by private ferry 633230, ≤ Loch Broom and Ullapool, « Idyllic setting on banks of Loch Broom », – . VISA.
Easter-October – **Meals** (booking essential)(dinner only) 50.00 **st.** 5.70 – **8 rm** (dinner included) 125.00/310.00 **st.**
Spec. Warm salad of scallops and green lentils, Champagne vinegar butter sauce, A 'clear' soup of shellfish and sherry with vermicelli of vegetables, Quail stuffed with mushrooms, grapes and foie gras, served with two sauces.

Harbour Lights, Garve Rd, IV26 2SX, 612222, Fax 612222, ≤ Loch Broom, – TV ☎ P. AE VISA
accommodation closed 4 days Christmas – **Meals** (bar lunch)/dinner 19.50 **t.** and a la carte 4.50 – **19 rm** 35.00/68.00 **t.** – SB.

Ardvreck without rest., Morefield Brae, IV26 2TH, NW : 2 m. by A 835 612561, Fax 612028, ≤ Loch Broom and mountains, – TV P
10 rm 24.00/46.00 **st.**

Ladysmith House, Pulteney St., IV26 2UP, 612185 – TV. VISA.
Meals (dinner only) a la carte 11.75/20.50 **t.** 4.75 – **6 rm** 16.00/40.00 **t.**

Sheiling without rest., Garve Rd, IV26 2SX, 612947, ≤ Loch Broom, – P.
closed Christmas and New Year – **7 rm** 25.00/40.00 **st.**

Dromnan without rest., Garve Rd, IV26 2SX, 612333, ≤ – TV P.
7 rm 25.00/38.00 **st.**

UPHALL W. Lothian. (Lothian) 401 J 16 – ECD : Wednesday – 01506.

Uphall 856404.

♦Edinburgh 13 – ♦Glasgow 32.

Houstoun House, EH52 6JS, 853831, Fax 854220, « Gardens », park – TV ☎ P. AE VISA
Meals 15.50/27.50 **st.** and a la carte **st.** 6.00 – 8.00 – **30 rm** 92.00/140.00 **t.** – SB.

WALKERBURN Peebles. (Borders) 401 402 K 17 **Scotland G.** – pop. 1 038 – ☎ 01896.

Envir. : The Tweed Valley** – Traquair House**, W : 4 m. by A 72 and B 709.

Exc. : Abbotsbury** *AC*, W : 10½ m. by A 72, A 6091 and B 6360.

Innerleithen, Leithen Water, Leithen Rd ☎ 830951.

♦Edinburgh 32 – Galashiels 10 – Peebles 8.

Tweed Valley, Galashiels Rd, EH43 6AA, ☎ 870636, Fax 870639, ←, – rest . VISA
closed 25 and 26 December – **Meals** (in bar) 12.50/27.00 **t.** and a la carte 6.00 – **16 rm** 40.00/92.00 **t.** – SB.

WALLS Shetland. (Shetland Islands) 401 PQ 3 – see Shetland Islands (Mainland).

WESTHILL Aberdeen. (Grampian) 401 N 12 – see Aberdeen.

WHITEBRIDGE Inverness. (Highland) 401 G 12 – ☎ 01456.

♦Edinburgh 171 – ♦Inverness 23 – Kyle of Lochalsh 67 – ♦Oban 92.

Knockie Lodge, IV1 2UP, SW : 3 ½ m. by B 862 ☎ 486276, Fax 486389, ← Loch Nanlann and mountains, « Tastefully converted hunting lodge », park – rest . AE VISA
May-October – **Meals** (residents only) (dinner only) 28.00 **t.** 4.00 – **10 rm** 55.00/140.00 **t.**

WHITING BAY Bute. (Strathclyde) 401 402 E 17 – see Arran (Isle of).

WICK Caithness. (Highland) 401 K 8 **Scotland G.** – pop. 9 713 – ECD : Wednesday – ☎ 01955.

Exc. : Duncansby Head* (Stacks of Duncansby**) N : 14 m. by A 9 – Grey Cairns of Camster* (Long Cairn**) S : 17 m. by A 9 – The Hill O'Many Stanes*, S : 10 m. by A 9.

Reiss ☎ 602726.

Wick Airport : ☎ 602215, N : 1 m.

Whitechapel Rd KW1 4EA ☎ 602596.

♦Edinburgh 282 – ♦Inverness 126.

Clachan without rest., South Rd, KW1 5NH, on A 9 ☎ 605384, – .
3 rm 25.00/40.00 **st.**

WIGTOWN Wigtown. (Dumfries and Galloway) 401 G 19 **Scotland G.** – pop. 1 344 – ECD : Wednesday – ✉ Newton Stewart – ☎ 01988.

Exc. : Whithorn Museum (early Christian crosses**) S : 10 m. by A 746.

Wigtown & Bladnoch, Lightlands Terr. ☎ 403354.

♦Edinburgh 137 – ♦Ayr 61 – ♦Dumfries 61 – Stranraer 26.

Corsemalzie House, DG8 9RL, SW : 6 ½ m. by A 714 on B 7005 ☎ 860254, Fax 860213, park – . VISA
closed 12 January-5 March – **Meals** 11.75/18.50 **t.** and a la carte 3.95 – **14 rm** 41.50/86.00 **t.** – SB.

WORMIT Fife. (Fife) 401 L 14 – ECD : Wednesday – ✉ Newport-on-Tay – ☎ 01382.

Scotscraig, Golf Rd, Tayport ☎ 552515.

♦Edinburgh 53 – ♦Dundee 6 – St. Andrews 12.

Sandford, DD6 8RG, S : 2 m. at junction of A 914 with B 946 ☎ 541802, Fax 542136, ←, – – 60. AE VISA
Meals (bar lunch)/dinner 23.95 **t.** and a la carte 4.95 – **16 rm** 80.00/95.00 **st.** – SB.

Northern Ireland

Place with at least :

a hotel or restaurant .... ● Londonderry
a pleasant hotel or restaurant .. 🏨, ⌂, ✕
a quiet, secluded hotel .... 🐴
a restaurant with .... ✿, ✿✿, ✿✿✿, **Meals** (**M**)
See this town for establishments located in its vicinity .... **BELFAST**

Localité offrant au moins :

une ressource hôtelière ...... ● Londonderry
un hôtel ou restaurant agréable 🏨, ⌂, ✕
un hôtel très tranquille, isolé .... 🐴
une bonne table à ✿, ✿✿, ✿✿✿, **Meals** (**M**)
Localité groupant dans le texte les ressources de ses environs .... **BELFAST**

La località possiede come minimo :

una risorsa alberghiera ...... ● Londonderry
Albergo o ristorante ameno .... 🏨, ⌂, ✕
un albergo molto tranquillo, isolato ...... 🐴
un'ottima tavola con . ✿, ✿✿, ✿✿✿, **Meals** (**M**)
La località raggruppa nel suo testo le risorse dei dintorni .... **BELFAST**

Ort mit mindestens :

einem Hotel oder Restaurant ● Londonderry
ein angenehmes Hotel oder Restaurant . 🏨, ⌂, ✕
einem sehr ruhigen und abgelegenen Hotel 🐴
einem Restaurant mit ✿, ✿✿, ✿✿✿, **Meals** (**M**)
Ort mit Angaben über Hotels und Restaurants in seiner Umgebung .... **BELFAST**

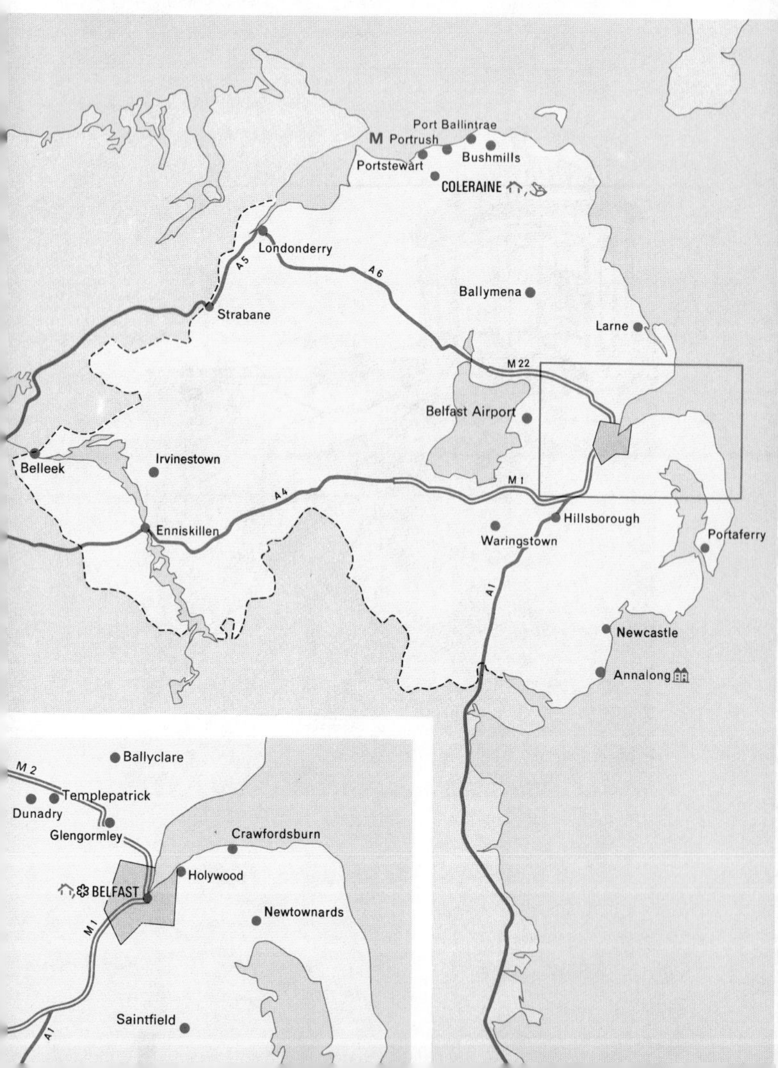

ANNALONG (Áth na Long) Down 405 O 5 **Ireland G.** – pop. 1 823 – ☎ 0139 67.

Exc. : W : Mourne Mountains★★ : Bryansford, Tollymore Forest Park★★ *AC*, Annalong Marine Park and Cornmill★ *AC* – Silent Valley Reservoir★ (≤★) – Spelga Pass and Dam★ – Drumena Cashel and Souterrain★ – Kilbroney Forest Park (viewpoint★).

♦Belfast 37 – ♦Dundalk 36.

Glassdrumman Lodge ⛰, 85 Mill Rd, BT34 4RH, ☎ 68451, Fax 67041, ≤ Irish Sea and Mourne mountains, « Working farm », park – TV ☎ P. VISA.
Meals (communal dining) (dinner only) (booking essential) 25.00/30.00 **t.** and dinner a la carte 5.00 – **8 rm** 65.00/95.00 **t.**, 2 suites – SB.

BALLYCLARE (Bealach Cláir) Antrim 405 N/O 3 – ☎ 01232.

18 25 Springvale Rd ☎ (019603) 42352.

♦Belfast 10 – Ballymena 14 – Larne 10.

XX **Ginger Tree,** 29 Ballyrobert Rd, BT39 9RY, S : 3¼ m. by A 57 on B 56 ☎ 848176 – P. AE VISA
closed Saturday lunch, Sunday, 12-13 July and 24 to 26 December – **Meals** - Japanese 6.50/26.00 **t.** and a la carte 3.75.

BALLYMENA (An Baile Meánach) Antrim 405 N 3 **Ireland G.** – pop. 28 166 – ☎ 01266.

Exc. : Antrim Glens★★★ : Murlough Bay★★★ (Fair Head ≤★★★) Glengariff Forest Park★★ *AC* (Waterfall★★) Glengariff★, Glendun★, Rathlin Island★ – Antrim (Shane's Castle Railway★ *AC*, Round Tower★) S : 9½ m. by A 26.

18 128 Raceview Rd ☎ 861207/861487.

Ardeevin, Ballymena Council Offices, 80 Galgorm Rd, BT42 1AB ☎ 44111 – Morrows Shop, 13-15 Bridge St. BT42 1AB ☎ 653663 (summer only).

♦Belfast 28 – ♦Dundalk 78 – Larne 21 – ♦Londonderry 51 – ♦Omagh 53.

Country House ⛰, 20 Doagh Rd, BT42 3LZ, SE : 6 m. by A 36 on B 59 ☎ 891663, Fax 891477, – TV ☎ P – 150. AE VISA.
closed 25 and 26 December – **Meals** 10.95 **t.** (lunch) and dinner a la carte 15.50/19.00 4.00 – **40 rm** 60.00/120.00 **t.** – SB.

Adair Arms, 1-5 Ballymoney Rd, BT43 5BS, ☎ 653674, Fax 40436 – TV ☎ P – 100. AE VISA
closed 25 December – **Meals** 7.95/15.95 **t.** and a la carte 5.00 – **40 rm** 58.00/80.00 **t.** – SB.

ATS Antrim Rd ☎ 652888

BELFAST (Béal Feirste) Antrim 405 O 4 **Ireland G.** – pop. 279 237 – ☎ 01232.

See : City★ – Ulster Museum★★ (Spanish Armada Treasure★★, Shrine of St. Patrick's Hand★) AZ **M1** – City Hall★ BZ – Donegall Square★ BZ **20** – Botanic Gardens (Palm House★) AZ – St Anne's Cathedral★ BY – Crown Liquor Saloon★ BZ – Sinclair Seamen's Church★ BY – St Malachy's Church★ BZ.

Envir. : Belfast Zoological Gardens★★ *AC*, N : 5 m. by A 6 AY.

Exc. : Carrickfergus (Castle★★ *AC*, St. Nicholas' Church★) NE : 9½ m. by A 2 – Talnotry Cottage Bird Garden, Crumlin★ *AC*, W : 13½ m. by A 52.

18 Balmoral, 518 Lisburn Rd ☎ 381514, AZ – 18 Belvoir Park, Newtonbreda ☎ 641159/692817, AZ – 18 Fortwilliam, Downview Av. ☎ 370770, AY – 18 The Knock, Summerfield, Dundonald ☎ 482249, AZ – 18 Shandon Park, 73 Shandon Park ☎ 793730, AZ – 9 Cliftonville, Westland Rd ☎ 744158, AY – 9 Ormeau, 50 Park Rd ☎ 641069, AZ.

Belfast Airport : ☎ (01849) 422888, W : 15½ m. by A 52 AY – Belfast City Airport : ☎ 457745 – **Terminal** : Coach service (Ulsterbus Ltd.) from Great Victoria Street Station (40 mn).

to Isle of Man (Douglas) (Isle of Man Steam Packet Co. Ltd) (summer only) (4 h 30 mn) – to Stranraer (SeaCat Scotland) (1 h 30 mn) – to Liverpool (Norse Irish Ferries Ltd) (11 h).

St. Annes Court, 59 North St., BT1 1NB ☎ 246609 – City Hall, BT1 5GS ☎ 320202 – Belfast City Airport, Sydenham Bypass, BT3 9JH ☎ 457745.

♦Dublin 103 – ♦Londonderry 70.

Plans on following pages

Stormont, 587 Upper Newtownards Rd, BT4 3LP, E : 4½ m. by A 2 on A 20 ☎ 658621, Fax 480240 – rm TV ☎ P – 400. AE VISA. AZ
closed 24 and 25 December – **Meals** *(closed Saturday lunch and Sunday dinner)* 14.50/19.50 **t.** and a la carte 6.50 – 8.50 – **106 rm** 83.00/160.00 **t.**

Dukes, 65 University St., BT7 1HL, ☎ 236666, Fax 237177, – rm rest TV ☎ – 150. AE VISA. AZ **a**
closed 12-13 July and 25-26 December – **Meals** (bar lunch Saturday) 8.50 **st.** (lunch) and a la carte 8.50/18.95 **st.** 4.00 – 6.50 – **21 rm** 75.00/85.00 **st.** – SB.

Plaza, 15 Brunswick St., BT2 7GE, ☎ 333555, Fax 232999 – rm TV ☎ – 90. AE VISA. BZ **a**
Meals 8.50/11.95 **st.** and a la carte 4.00 – 3.50 – **69 rm** 65.00/86.00 **st.**

Stranmillis Lodge without rest., 14 Chlorine Gdns, BT9 5DJ, ☎ 682009, Fax 682009 – TV ☎ P. VISA. AZ **x**
6 rm 40.00/56.00 **st.**

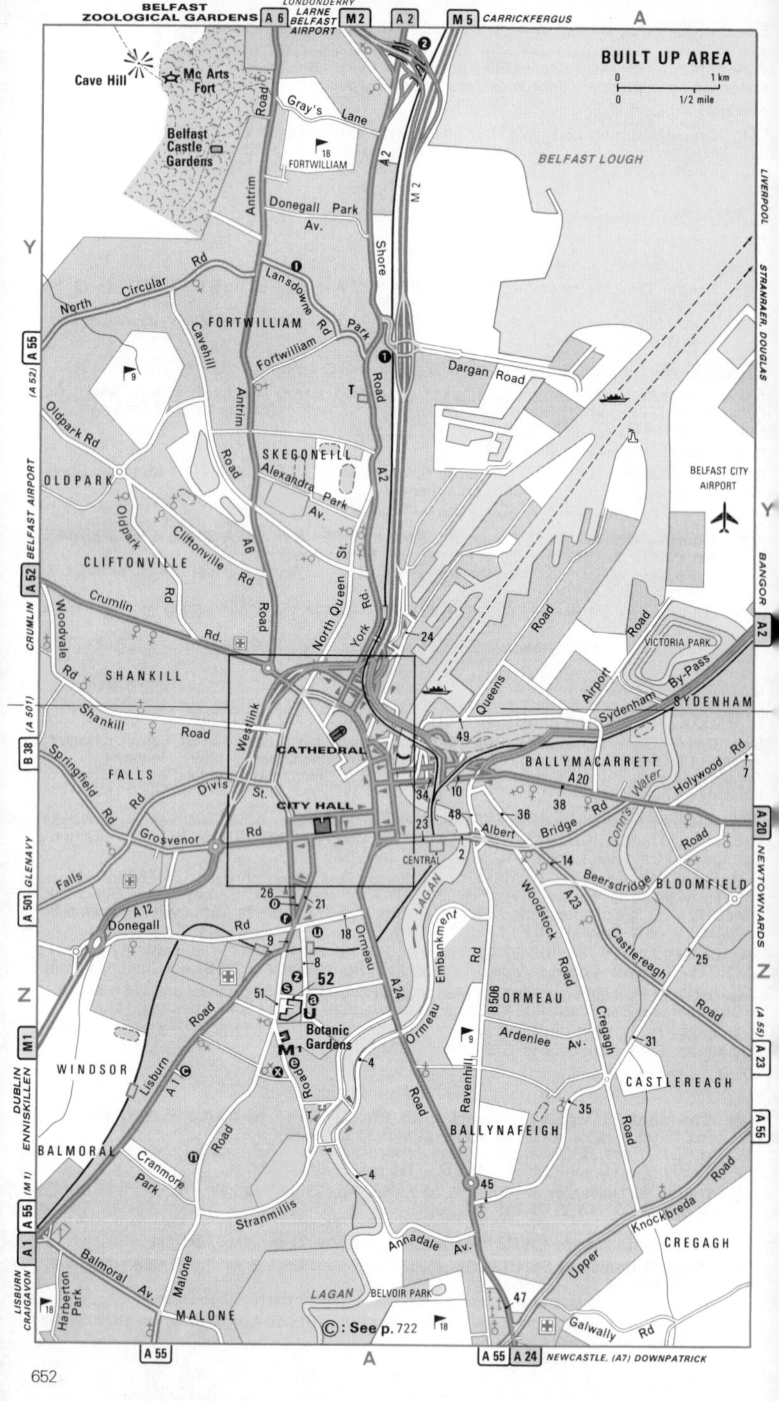

BUILT UP AREA
BELFAST ZOOLOGICAL GARDENS
LONDONDERRY LARNE BELFAST AIRPORT
CARRICKFERGUS
Cave Hill
Mc Arts Fort
Belfast Castle Gardens
FORTWILLIAM
BELFAST LOUGH
LIVERPOOL
STRANRAER, DOUGLAS
BELFAST CITY AIRPORT
BANGOR
VICTORIA PARK
SYDENHAM
BALLYMACARRETT
CATHEDRAL
CITY HALL
CENTRAL
SKEGONEILL
OLDPARK
CLIFTONVILLE
SHANKILL
FALLS
BLOOMFIELD
NEWTOWNARDS
ORMEAU
CASTLEREAGH
BALLYNAFEIGH
WINDSOR
BALMORAL
Botanic Gardens
MALONE
CREGAGH
BELVOIR PARK
LAGAN
CRUMLIN
BELFAST AIRPORT
GLENAVY
DUBLIN ENNISKILLEN
LISBURN CRAIGAVON
NEWCASTLE, (A7) DOWNPATRICK
©: See p. 722

BELFAST

Castlecourt Shopping Centre . . . . BYZ
Castle Place . . . . BZ
Donegal Place . . . . BZ
Royal Avenue . . . . BYZ

Albert Bridge . . . . AZ 2
Albert Square . . . . BY 3
Annadale Embankment . . . . AZ 4
Ann Street . . . . BZ 5
Belmont Road . . . . AZ 7
Botanic Avenue . . . . AZ 8
Bradbury Place . . . . AZ 9
Bridge End . . . . AZ 10
Bridge Street . . . . BZ 12
Castlereagh Street . . . . AZ 14
Clifton Street . . . . BY 15
Corporation Square . . . . BY 16
Donegall Pass . . . . AZ 18
Donegall Quay . . . . BYZ 19
Donegall Square . . . . BZ 20
Dublin Road . . . . AZ 21
East Bridge Street . . . . AZ 23
Garmoyle Street . . . . AY 24
Grand Parade . . . . AZ 25
Great Victoria Street . . . . . . AZ 26
High Street . . . . BYZ 28
Howard Street . . . . BZ 29
Ladas Drive . . . . AZ 31
Lagan Bridge . . . . BY 32
Middlepath St. . . . . AZ 34
Mount Merrion Avenue . . . AZ 35
Mountpottinger Road . . . . . AZ 36
Newtownards Road . . . . AZ 38
Queen Elizabeth Bridge . . . BZ 40
Queen's Bridge . . . . BZ 41
Queen's Square . . . . BY 42
Rosemary Street . . . . BZ 44
Rosetta Park . . . . AZ 45
Saintfield Road . . . . AZ 47
Short Strand . . . . AZ 48
Sydenham Road . . . . AZ 49
University Road . . . . AZ 51
University Square . . . . AZ 52
Waring Street . . . . BY 54
Wellington Place . . . . BZ 55

See p. 722

In Northern Ireland traffic and parking are controlled in the town centres. No vehicle may be left unattended in a Control Zone.

The names of main shopping streets are indicated in red at the beginning of the list of streets.

Ash Rowan without rest., 12 Windsor Av., BT9 6EE, ✆ 661758, Fax 663227, – . VISA. AZ c
closed 23 December-1 January – **4 rm** 40.00/66.00 **t.**

Malone without rest., 79 Malone Rd, BT9 6SH, ✆ 669565 – . AZ n
closed mid July, Christmas and New Year – **8 rm** 31.00/46.00 **st.**

Somerton, 22 Lansdowne Rd, BT15 4DB, by Fortwilliam Park ✆ 370717, – AY i
8 rm.

XX ✿ **Roscoff** (Rankin), 7 Lesley House, Shaftesbury Sq., BT2 7DB, ✆ 331532, Fax 312093, « Art Deco influenced interior » – . AE VISA AZ r
closed Saturday lunch, Sunday, Easter Monday, 11-12 July and 25-26 December – **Meals** 14.50/19.50 **t.** and a la carte 18.20/26.95
Spec. Crispy duck confit with balsamic lentils, Spiced sole tempura with a lobster and coriander aïoli, White chocolate and raspberry trifle.

XX **Antica Roma,** 67/69 Botanic Av., BT7 1JL, ✆ 311121 – AE VISA AZ z
closed Sunday and 25 December – **Meals** 8.95 **st.** (lunch) and a la carte 14.70/22.85.

X **Nick's Warehouse,** 35-39 Hill St. (1st Floor), BT1 2LB, ✆ 439690 – . AE VISA BY a
closed Saturday lunch, Monday dinner, Sunday, 17 March, Easter Monday, 12 July and 25-26 December – **Meals** 18.50 **t.** and a la carte.

X **La Belle Epoque,** 61-63 Dublin Rd, BT2 7HE, ✆ 323244, Fax 323244 – AE VISA AZ o
closed Saturday lunch, Sunday, 12-13 July and 25-26 December – **Meals** a la carte 12.25/21.90 **st.** 7.95.

X **Manor House,** 43-47 Donegall Pass, BT7 1DQ, ✆ 238755 – VISA AZ u
closed 12-13 July and 25-26 December – **Meals** - Chinese (Canton) 5.50/8.75 **t.** and a la carte 3.95.

X **Strand,** 12 Stranmillis Rd, BT9 5AA, ✆ 682266, Fax 663189 – AE VISA AZ e
closed 12-13 July and 25-26 December – **Meals** - Bistro a la carte 8.15/17.35 **t.** 4.25.

X Saints and Scholars, 3 University St., BT7 1FY, ✆ 325137, Fax 323240 AZ s

at Dundonald E : 5 ½ m. by A 2 – AZ – on A 20 – ✉ Belfast – 01247 :

Cottage without rest., 377 Comber Rd, BT16 0XB, SE : 1 ¾ m. on Comber Rd ✆ 878189, – .
3 rm 18.00/34.00 **st.**

at Dunmurry SW : 5 ½ m. on A 1 – AZ – ✉ Belfast – 01232 :

Forte Crest, 300 Kingsway, BT17 9ES, ✆ 612101, Fax 626546, , park, squash – rm rest – 400
80 rm, 2 suites.

MICHELIN Distribution Centre, Mallusk Park, 40 Mallusk Rd, Newtonabbey, BT36 8FS, ✆ 842616, Fax 342732 by A6 AY

ATS 4 Duncrue St. ✆ 749531 ATS 37 Boucher Rd ✆ 663623

Es ist empfehlenswert, in der Hauptsaison und vor allem in Urlaubsorten, Hotelzimmer im voraus zu bestellen.

BELFAST AIRPORT **(Aerphort Béal Feirste)** Antrim 405 N 4 – ✉ Aldergrove – 01849.
Belfast Airport : ✆ 422888.
♦Belfast 15 – Ballymena 20 – Larne 23.

Aldergrove Airport H., Aldergrove, BT29 4AB, ✆ 422033, Fax 423500, , – rm – 250
108 rm.

BELLEEK **(Béal Leice)** Fermanagh 405 H 4 – 0136 56.
♦Belfast 117 – ♦Londonderry 56.

Moohan's Fiddlestone without rest., Main St., BT93 3FY, ✆ 58008 – .
5 rm 15.00/30.00 **st.**

BUSHMILLS **(Muileann na Buaise)** Antrim 405 M 2 **Ireland G.** – pop. 1 348 – ✉ Bushmills – 0126 57.

Exc. : Causeway Coast★★ : Giant's Causeway★★★ (Hamilton's Seat ≤★★), Carrick-a-rede Rope Bridge★★★, Dunluce Castle★★ *AC*, Gortmore Viewpoint★★ – Magilligan Strand★★, Downhill★ (Mussenden Temple★).

9 Bushfoot, Portballintrae ✆ 31317.
♦Belfast 57 – Ballycastle 12 – Coleraine 10.

Bushmills Inn, 25 Main St., BT57 8QA, ✆ 32339, Fax 32048 – – 100. VISA
Meals 13.95 **t.** and a la carte 4.95 – **11 rm** 48.00/78.00 **st.** – SB.

CASTLEROCK **(Carraig Ceasail)** Londonderry – see Coleraine.

COLERAINE (Cîil Raithin) Londonderry 405 L 2 **Ireland G.** – pop. 20 721 – ☎ 01265.

Exc. : Antrim Glens★★★ : Murlough Bay★★★ (Fair Head ≤★★★), Glenariff Forest Park★★ *AC* (Waterfall★★) – Glenariff★, Glendun★, Rathlin Island★ – Causeway Coast★★ : Giant's Causeway★★★ (Hamilton's Seat ≤★★) – Carrick-a-rede Rope Bridge★★★ – Dunluce Castle★★ *AC* – Gortmore Viewpoint★★ – Magilligan Strand★★ – Downhill★ (Mussenden Temple★).

18, 9 Castlerock, Circular Rd ✆ 848314 – 9 Brown Trout, 209 Agivey Rd ✆ 868209.

Railway Rd, BT52 1PE ✆ 44723.

♦Belfast 53 – Ballymena 25 – ♦Londonderry 31 – ♦Omagh 65.

Blackheath House , 112 Killeague Rd, Blackhill, BT51 4HH, S : 8 m. by A 29 on Macosquin rd ✆ 868433, Fax 868433, – rest TV P. VISA. *closed Christmas* – ***Macduffs* : Meals** *(closed Sunday and Monday)* (booking essential) (dinner only) a la carte 14.00/18.00 **t.** – **5 rm** 30.00/60.00 **t.**

Greenhill House , 24 Greenhill Rd, Aghadowey, BT51 4EU, S : 9 m. by A 29 on B 66 ✆ 868241, – TV P. VISA. *March-October* – **Meals** (by arrangement) 13.00 – **6 rm** 26.00/42.00 – SB.

Camus House without rest., 27 Curragh Rd, BT51 3RY, SE : 3¾ m. on A 54 ✆ 42982, , park – TV P. **3 rm** 23.00/35.00.

at Castlerock NW : 6 m. by A 2 on B 119 – ✉ Castlerock – ☎ 01265 :

Maritima without rest., 43 Main St., BT51 4RA, ✆ 848388, ≤, – TV P. **3 rm** 20.00/36.00.

ATS Loguestown Ind. Est., Bushmills Rd ✆ 42329

CRAWFORDSBURN (Sruth Chráfard) Down 405 O 4 **Ireland G.** – pop. 2 561 – ☎ 01247.

Envir. : Heritage Centre, Bangor★, E : 3 m. by B 20.

♦Belfast 10 – Bangor 3.

Old Inn, 15 Main St., BT19 1JH, ✆ 853255, Fax 852775, – TV ☎ P – 25. AE VISA. **Meals** 10.50/25.00 **t.** and a la carte – **33 rm** 70.00/120.00 **t.** – SB.

DUNADRY (Dîn Eadradh) Antrim 405 N 3 **Ireland G.** – ☎ 01849.

Envir. : Antrim (Round tower★, Shane's Castle Railway★ *AC*) NW : 4 m. by A 6.

Exc. : Crumlin : Talnotry Cottage Bird Garden★ *AC*, SW : 10½ m. by A 5, A 26 and A 52.

♦Belfast 15 – Larne 18 – ♦Londonderry 56.

Dunadry Inn, 2 Islandreagh Drive, BT41 2HA, ✆ 432474, Fax 433389, , , , – TV ☎ P – 300 **67 rm.**

DUNDONALD (Dún Dónaill) Antrim 405 O 4 – see Belfast.

DUNMURRY (Dún Muirígh) Antrim 405 N 4 – see Belfast.

ENNISKILLEN (Inis Ceithleann) Fermanagh 405 J 4 **Ireland G.** – pop. 11 436 – ☎ 01365.

Envir. : Castle Coole★★★ *AC*, SE : 1 m..

Exc. : NW : Lough Erne★★ : Cliffs of Magho Viewpoint★★★ *AC* – Devenish Island★ *AC* – Castle Archdale Country Park★ – White Island★ – Janus Figure★ – Tully Castle★ *AC* – Florence Court★★ *AC*, SW : 8 m. by A 4 and A 32 – Marble Arch Caves and Forest Nature Reserve★★ *AC*, SW : 10 m. by A 4 and A 32.

18 Castlecoole ✆ 325250.

Lakeland Visitors Centre, Wellington Rd, BT74 7EF ✆ 323110.

♦Belfast 87 – ♦Londonderry 59.

Killyhevlin, Dublin Rd, BT74 4AU, SE : 1¾ m. on A 4 ✆ 323481, Fax 324726, ≤, , park – TV ☎ P – 400. AE VISA. **Meals** (carving lunch Sunday) a la carte 12.00/16.75 **st.** – **25 rm** 45.00/95.00 **st.** – SB.

GLENGORMLEY (Gleann Ghormlaithe) Antrim 405 O 3 – ✉ Newtownabbey – ☎ 01232.

9 Doagh Rd ✆ 848287.

♦Belfast 6 – Larne 15.

XX Sleepy Hollow, 15 Kiln Rd, Ballyhenry, BT36 8SU, N : 2 m. by A 8 (M) off B 56 ✆ 342042 – P

HILLSBOROUGH (Cromghlinn) Down 405 N 4 Ireland G. – 01846.
See : Town★ – Fort★.
The Square, BT26 6AH 682477.
♦Belfast 13.

White Gables, 14 Dromore Rd, BT26 6HU, SW : ½ m. on A 1 682755, Fax 689532 – rm rest – 120. VISA.
Meals *(closed Saturday lunch and Sunday)* 12.75/22.50 **t.** and a la carte 4.95 – 7.75 – **31 rm** 66.00/94.00 **t.**

Hillside, 21 Main St., BT26 6AE, 682765 – VISA
closed Sunday – **Meals** (dinner only) a la carte 16.60/18.75 **t.** 5.15.

HOLYWOOD (Ard Mhic Nasca) Down 405 O 4 Ireland G. – pop. 9 252 – 01232.
Envir. : Cultra : Ulster Folk and Transport Museum★★ *AC*, NE : 1 m. by A 2.
♦Belfast 5 – Bangor 6.

Culloden, 142 Bangor Rd, BT18 0EX, E : 1½ m. on A 2 425223, Fax 426777, ≤, , park, , squash – rm – 500. VISA.
closed 24 and 25 December – **Meals** *(closed Saturday lunch)* 14.00/17.00 **t.** and a la carte – 8.50 – **83 rm** 104.00/135.00 **t.**, 6 suites.

Rayanne , 60 Demesne Rd, BT18 9EX, by High St. and Downshire Rd 425859, Fax 425859, – . VISA.
Meals (by arrangement) 15.00 **t.** – **6 rm** 49.50/75.00 **st.**

IRVINESTOWN (Baile an Irbhinigh) Fermanagh 405 J 4 Ireland G. – pop. 2 244 – 0136 56.
Exc. : NW : Lough Erne★★ : Cliffs of Magho Viewpoint★★★ *AC* – Devenish Island★ *AC* – Castle Archdale Country Park★ – White Island★ – Janus Figure★ – Tully Castle★ *AC*.
♦Belfast 78 – ♦Dublin 132 – Donegal 27.

Mahon's, 2-10 Mill St., BT94 1GS, 21656, Fax 28344 – – 300. VISA.
Meals 8.75/14.00 **st.** and a la carte 4.95 – **18 rm** 29.50/55.00 **st.** – SB.

Prices For full details of the prices quoted in the guide, consult the introduction.

LARNE (Latharna) Antrim 405 O 3 Ireland G. – pop. 17 575 – 01574.
Envir. : Glenoe Waterfall★, S : 5 m. by A 2 and B 99 – SE : Island Magee (Ballylumford Dolmen★).
Exc. : NW : Antrim Glens★★★ – Murlough Bay★★★ (Fair Head ≤ ★★★), Glenariff Forest Park★★ *AC* (Waterfall★★), Glenariff★, Glendun★, Rathlin Island★.
Cairndhu, 192 Coast Rd, Ballygally 583248.
to Stranraer (Stena Sealink Line) frequent services daily (2 h 20 mn) – to Cairnryan (P & O European Ferries Ltd) 4-6 daily (2 h 15 mn).
Sir Thomas Dixon Buildings, Victoria Rd, BT40 1RU 260088 – Carnfunnock County Park, Coast Road 270541 – Larne Harbour, BT40 1AQ 270517 Interpretative Centre, Narrow Guage Rd BT40 1XB 260088.
♦Belfast 23 – Ballymena 20.

Magheramorne House , 59 Shore Rd, Magheramorne, BT40 3HW, S : 3½ m. on A 2 279444, Fax 260138, ≤, , park – – 50. VISA.
Meals (bar lunch Monday to Saturday)/dinner 15.75 **st.** and a la carte – **22 rm** 53.50/76.00 – SB.

Derrin House without rest., 2 Prince's Gdns, BT40 1RQ, off Glenarm Rd (A 2) 273269 – . VISA
closed 25 and 26 December – **7 rm** 18.00/34.00 **s.**

ATS Narrow Gauge Rd 274491

LONDONDERRY (Doire) Londonderry 405 K 2-3 Ireland G. – pop. 72 334 – 01504.
See : Town★ – City Walls and Gates★★ – Guildhall★ – St. Columb's Cathedral★ *AC* – Long Tower Church★.
Envir. : Grianan of Aileach★★ (≤ ★) (Republic of Ireland) NW : 5 m. by A 2 and N 13.
Exc. : SE : by A 6 – Sperrin Mountains★ : Ulster-American Folk Park★★ – Glenshane Pass★★ (★★) – Sawel Mountain Drive★ (≤★★) – Roe Valley Country Park★ – Ness Wood Country Park★ – Sperrin Heritage Centre★ *AC* – Beaghmore Stone Circles★ – Ulster History Park★ – Oak Lough Scenic Road★ – Eglinton★ – Gortin Glen Forest Park★ *AC*.
18, 9 City of Derry, 49 Victoria Rd 311610/46369.
Eglinton Airport : 810784, E : 6 m. by A 2.
8 Bishop St., BT48 6PW 267284.
♦Belfast 70 – ♦Dublin 146.

Everglades, Prehen Rd, BT47 2PA, S : 1½ m. by A 5 46722, Fax 49200 – – 300. VISA.
closed 25 December – **Meals** *(closed Saturday lunch)* 8.50/20.00 **st.** and a la carte 6.50 – **51 rm** 62.00/80.00 **st.**, 1 suite – SB.

Beech Hill House ⑤, 32 Ardmore Rd, BT47 3QP, SE : 3 ½ m. by A 6 ℘ 49279, Fax 45366, ←, ⚘, park, ✗ – TV ☎ P – 🏛 100. VISA ✻ *closed 24 and 25 December* – **Meals** 12.95/26.60 **st.** and a la carte – **17 rm** ☕ 52.50/ 100.00 **st.** – SB.

White Horse, 68 Clooney Rd, BT47 3PA, NE : 6 ½ m. on A 2 (Coleraine rd) ℘ 860606, Fax 860371 – TV ☎ P – 🏛 500. AE VISA ✻ *closed 25 December* – **Meals** (grill rest.) 9.90/18.00 **st.** and a la carte 5.00 – ☕ 5.25 – **44 rm** 42.50 **st.** – SB.

Waterfoot, 14 Clooney Rd, Caw Roundabout, BT47 1TB, NE : 3 ¾ m. at junction of A 39 with A 5 and A 2 ℘ 45500, Fax 311006 – TV ☎ ♿ P. AE VISA ✻ *closed 25 and 26 December* – **Meals** 7.00/19.00 **st.** and a la carte – ☕ 4.75 – **48 rm** 47.00/ 57.00 **st.** – SB.

NEWCASTLE (An Caisleán Nua) Down 405 O 5 Ireland G. – pop. 7 214 – ☎ 0139 67.

Envir. : Castlewellan Forest Park★★ *AC*, NW : 4 m. by A 50 – Dundrum Castle★ *AC*, NE : 4 m. by A 2.

Exc. : SW : Mourne Mountains★★ : Bryansford, Tollymore Forest Park★★ *AC* – Annalong Marine Park and Cornmill★ *AC* – Silent Valley Reservoir★ (←★) – Spelga Pass and Dam★ – Drumena Cashel and Souterrain★ – Kilbroney Forest Park (viewpoint★) – Loughinisland Churches★, NE : 10 m. by A 2 and A 24.

ℹ The Newcastle Centre, 10-14 Central Promenade, BT33 0AA ℘ 22222 (summer only).

♦Belfast 30 – ♦Londonderry 101.

Burrendale H. & Country Club, 51 Castlewellan Rd, BT33 0JY, N : 1 m. on A 50 ℘ 22599, Fax 22328, Fō, ≘s, ⛱, ⚘ – 🛗 TV ☎ ♿ P – 🏛 150. AE VISA JCB. ✻ **Meals** 10.00/20.00 st. and dinner a la carte 4.95 – **51 rm** ☕ 65.00/90.00 **st.** – SB.

The Guide is updated annually so renew your Guide every year.

NEWTOWNARDS (Baile Nua na hArda) Down 405 O 4 Ireland G. – pop. 23 869 – ☎ 01247.

See : Priory (Cross Slabs★).

Envir. : Mount Stewart★★★ *AC*, SE : 5 m. by A 20 – Scrabo Tower (← ★★★) SW : 1 m. – Ballycopeland Windmill★ *AC*, E : 6 m. by B 172.

Exc. : Strangford Lough★ (Castle Espie Centre★ *AC* - Nendrum Monastery★) – Grey Abbey★ *AC*, SE : 7 m. by A 20.

⛳18 Broadway, Bangor ℘ 270922 – ⛳18 Carnalea, Station Rd, Bangor ℘ 465004 – ⛳18 Scrabo, 233 Scrabo Rd ℘ 812355 – ⛳9 Helen's Bay, Golf Rd, Bangor ℘ 852601.

ℹ 2 Church St., BT23 4AP ℘ 812215 – Regent Street (summer only).

♦Belfast 10 – Bangor 5.

Strangford Arms, 92 Church St., BT23 4AL, ℘ 814141, Fax 818846 – ⇔ rm ▤ rest TV ☎ P – 🏛 100. AE VISA ✻ **Meals** a la carte 9.45/14.45 **st.** 2.95 – ☕ 6.75 – **40 rm** 61.00/76.00 **st.** – SB.

PORTAFERRY (Port an Pheire) Down 405 P 4 Ireland G. – pop. 3 508 – ☎ 0124 77.

See : Aquarium★.

Envir. : Castle Ward★★ *AC*, SW : 4 m. by boat and A 25.

Exc. : SE : Lecale Peninsula★★ – Struell Wells★, Quoile Pondage★, Ardglass★, Strangford★, Audley's Castle★.

♦ Belfast 29 – Bangor 24.

Portaferry, 10 The Strand, BT22 1PE, ℘ 28231, Fax 28999, ← – TV ☎. AE VISA ✻ *closed 24 and 25 December* – **Meals** 12.95/17.50 **t.** and dinner a la carte 4.85 – **14 rm** ☕ 45.00/85.00 **t.** – SB.

PORT BALLINTRAE (Port Bhaile an Trá) Antrim 405 M 2 Ireland G. – pop. 586 – ✉ Bushmills – ☎ 0126 57.

Exc. : Causeway Coast★★ : Giant's Causeway★★★ (Hamilton's Seat ←★★) – Carrick-a-rede Rope Bridge★★★ – Dunluce Castle★★ *AC* – Gortmore Viewpoint★★ – Magilligan Strand★★ – Downhill★ (Mussenden Temple★).

♦Belfast 68 – Coleraine 15.

Bayview, 2 Bayhead Rd, BT57 8RT, ℘ 31453, Fax 32360, ←, ≘s, ⛱, ✗ – TV ☎ P – 🏛 300. VISA ✻ **Meals** 8.75/18.50 **t.** and a la carte 6.50 – **16 rm** ☕ 40.00/67.50 **t.** – SB.

PORTRUSH (Port Rois) Antrim 405 L 2 Ireland G. – pop. 5 598 – ☎ 01265.

Exc. : Causeway Coast★★ : Giant's Causeway★★★ (Hamilton's Seat ←★★) – Carrick-a-rede Rope Bridge★★★ – Dunluce Castle★★ *AC* – Gortmore Viewpoint★★ – Magilligan Strand★★ – Downhill★ (Mussenden Temple★).

⛳18, ⛳18, ⛳9 Royal Portrush, Dunluce Rd ℘ 822311.

ℹ Dunluce Centre, BT56 8DW ℘ 823333 (summer only).

♦Belfast 58 – Coleraine 4 – ♦Londonderry 35.

Magherabuoy House, 41 Magheraboy Rd, BT56 8NX, SW : 1 m. by A 29 ℘ 823507, Fax 824687, ←, ≘s, ⛱ – TV ☎ P – 🏔 300. VISA.
closed Christmas Day – **Meals** (bar lunch Monday to Saturday)/dinner 18.00 **t.** and a la carte 5.00 – **38 rm** 50.00/75.00 **t.** – SB.

Causeway Coast, 36 Ballyreagh Rd, BT56 8LR, NW : 1 ¼ m. on A 2 (Portstewart rd) ℘ 822435, Fax 824495, ← – TV ☎ P – 🏔 500. AE VISA.
Meals (bar lunch)/dinner 16.00 **st.** 5.50 – **21 rm** 53.00/70.00 **st.** – SB.

Glencroft, 95 Coleraine Rd, BT56 8HN, ℘ 822902, ⛱ – TV P.
closed 2 weeks November and 2 weeks Christmas – **Meals** (by arrangement) 14.00 – **5 rm** 16.00/36.00 **st.**

Ramore, The Harbour, BT56 8DQ, ℘ 824313, ← – P. VISA
closed Sunday and Monday – **Meals** (booking essential) (dinner only) a la carte 12.70/23.45 **t.** 4.25.

PORTSTEWART (Port Stíobhaird) Londonderry 405 L 2 **Ireland G.** – pop. 2 250 – 01265.

Exc. : Causeway Coast** : Giant's Causeway*** (Hamilton's Seat ←**) – Carrick-a-rede Rope Bridge*** – Dunluce Castle** *AC* – Gortmore Viewpoint** – Magilligan Strand** – Downhill* (Mussenden Temple*).

Town Hall, The Crescent, BT55 7AB ℘ 832286 (summer only).

♦Belfast 67 – Coleraine 6.

Edgewater, 88 Strand Rd, BT55 7LZ, ℘ 833314, Fax 832224, ←, ≘s – TV ☎ P. AE VISA.
Meals 10.00/15.00 **t.** and dinner a la carte – **31 rm** 41.00/80.00 **t.** – SB.

SAINTFIELD (Tamhnaigh Naomh) Down 405 O 4 – 01238.

♦Belfast 11 – Downpatrick 11.

The Barn, 120 Monlough Rd, BT24 7EU, NW : 1 ¾ m. by A 7 ℘ 510396, ⛱ – P. VISA
closed Sunday to Tuesday – **Meals** (dinner only) 25.00 **t.** 5.50.

STRABANE (An Srath Bán) Tyrone 405 J 3 **Ireland G.** – pop. 11 670 – 01504.

Exc. : Sperrin Mountains* : Ulster-American Folk Park** – Glenshane Pass** (✳**) – Sawel Mountain Drive* (←**) – Roe Valley Country Park* – Ness Wood Country Park* – Sperrin Heritage Centre* *AC* – E : Beaghmore Stone Circles* – Ulster History Park* – Oak Lough Scenic Road* – Eglinton* – Gortin Glen Forest Park* *AC*.

18 Ballycolman ℘ 382271/382007.

Abercorn Square BT82 8DY ℘ 883735 (summer only) – Council Offices, 47 Derry Rd ℘ 382204.

♦Belfast 87 – Donegal 34 – ♦Dundalk 98 – ♦Londonderry 14.

Fir Trees, Melmount Rd, BT82 9JT, S : 1 ¼ m. on A 5 ℘ 382382, Fax 885932 – TV ☎ P
26 rm.

TEMPLEPATRICK (Teampall Phádraig) Antrim 405 N 3 – pop. 1 383 – ✉ Ballyclave – 0184 94.

♦Belfast 12 – Ballymena 16 – ♦Dundalk 65 – Larne 16.

Templeton, 882 Antrim Rd, BT39 0AH, ℘ 432984, Fax 433406, ⛱ – TV ☎ P – 🏔 300. AE VISA JCB.
closed 25 December – **Meals** (bar lunch Monday to Saturday)/dinner 15.95 **st.** and a la carte 5.25 – **20 rm** 85.00/125.00 **st.**

WARINGSTOWN (Baile an Bhairínigh) Armagh 405 N 4 **Ireland G.** – pop. 1 167 – 01762.

Exc. : The Argory*, W : 20 m. by A 26, A 76 and M 1.

♦Belfast 26 – Craigavon 4.

Grange, Main St., BT66 7QH, ℘ 881989, ⛱ – P
closed Saturday lunch, Sunday dinner, Monday and 1 week mid July – **Meals** a la carte 17.40/20.40 **t.** 4.20.

Channel Islands

Place with at least :

a hotel or restaurant ● Catel
a pleasant hotel or restaurant 🏨, 🏠, ✗
a quiet, secluded hotel 🐴
a restaurant with ✿, ✿✿, ✿✿✿, **Meals** (M)

La località possiede come minimo :

una risorsa alberghiera ● Catel
Albergo o ristorante ameno 🏨, 🏠, ✗
un albergo molto tranquillo, isolato 🐴
un'ottima tavola con ✿, ✿✿, ✿✿✿, **Meals** (M)

Localité offrant au moins :

une ressource hôtelière ● Catel
un hôtel ou restaurant agréable 🏨, 🏠, ✗
un hôtel très tranquille, isolé 🐴
une bonne table à ✿, ✿✿, ✿✿✿, **Meals** (M)

Ort mit mindestens :

einem Hotel oder Restaurant ● Catel
ein angenehmes Hotel oder Restaurant 🏨, 🏠, ✗
einem sehr ruhigen und abgelegenen Hotel 🐴
einem Restaurant mit ✿, ✿✿, ✿✿✿, **Meals** (M)

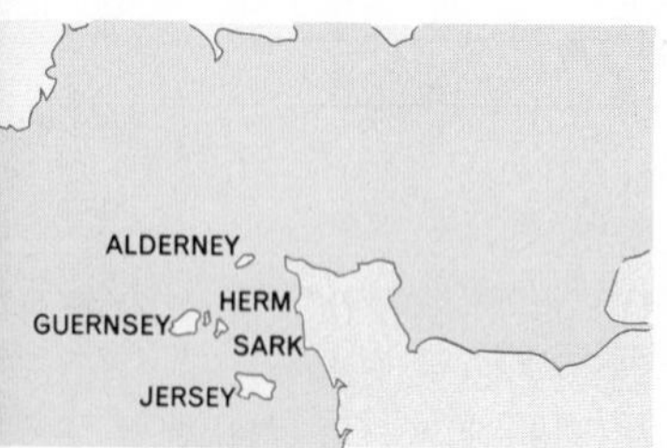

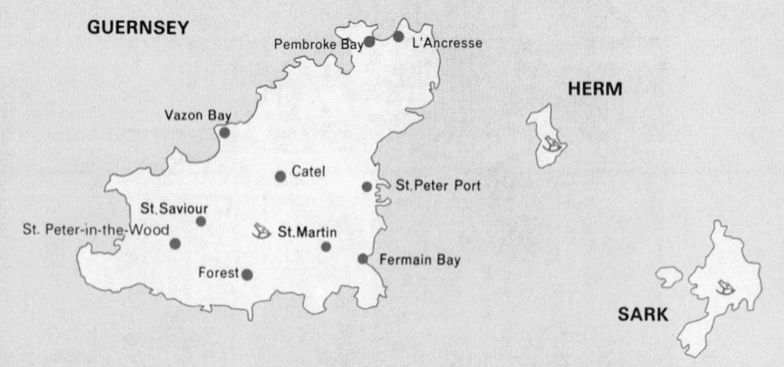

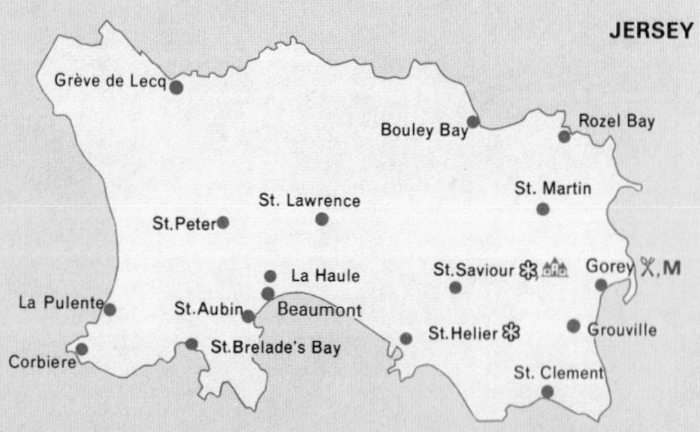

ALDERNEY 403 Q 33 and 230 ⑨ **The West Country G.** – pop. 2 297 – ECD : Wednesday – 01481.

See : Braye Bay★ – Mannez Garenne (≤★ from Quesnard Lighthouse) – Telegraph Bay★ – Vallee des Trois Vaux★ – Clonque Bay★.

822551 - Booking Office : Aurigny Air Services 822889,.

to Guernsey (St. Peter Port) (Condor Ltd) (45 mn) – to Jersey (St. Helier) (Condor Ltd) (1 h 50 mn) – to France (St. Malo) (Condor Ltd) (4 h 20 mn).

States Office, Queen Elizabeth II St. JY9 3AA 822994/823737.

St. Anne – St. Anne – 01481.

Route des Carrières 822835.

Chez André, Victoria St., 822777, Fax 822962 – TV. AE VISA
Meals (closed Sunday dinner in winter) 12.00/13.50 **s.** and dinner a la carte 4.00 – **11 rm** 32.50/90.00 **s.** – SB.

Inchalla, Le Val, GY9 3UL, 823220, Fax 823551, – rm TV. AE VISA.
closed 21 December-3 January – **Meals** *(closed Sunday dinner)* (dinner only and Sunday lunch)/dinner 12.00 and a la carte 3.50 – **9 rm** 48.00/77.50.

Rose and Crown, Le Huret, 823414, Fax 823615, – TV. AE VISA.
Meals *(closed Sunday)* (in bar) a la carte approx. 10.00 **s.** – **6 rm** 35.00/50.00 **s.**

Belle Vue, The Butes, 822844, Fax 823601 – rest TV. AE VISA.
closed 24 to 26 December – **Meals** 12.00/18.00 **s.** and a la carte 4.50 – **27 rm** 33.00/76.00 – SB.

Maison de la Paix without rest., Petit Val, GY9 3DF, NW: 3/4 m. by Les Mouriaux 823369, Fax 823369, ≤ Platte Saline – TV.
closed Christmas - New Year – **3 rm** 24.00/48.00 **s.**

Chez Nous without rest., Les Venelles, GY9 3TW, 823633, Fax 823732 – TV.
closed February – **3 rm** 24.00/40.00.

Georgian House, Victoria St., GY9 3UF, 822471, Fax 822471 – AE VISA
Meals (bar lunch Monday to Saturday)/dinner 21.00 and a la carte 3.75.

Braye – Braye – 01481.

First and Last, 823162, ≤ harbour – AE VISA JCB
Easter to October – **Meals** (closed Sunday dinner and Monday except Bank Holidays) (dinner only) 15.00/35.00 and a la carte 3.95.

GUERNSEY 403 OP 33 and 230 ⑨ ⑩ **The West Country G.** – pop. 58 867 – 01481.

See : Island★ – Pezeries Point★★ – Icart Point★★ – Côbo Bay★★ – St. Martins Point★★ – St. Apolline's Chapel★ – Vale Castle★ – Fort Doyle★ – La Gran'mere du Chimquiere★ – Moulin Huet Bay★ – Rocquaine Bay★ – Jerbourg Point★.

Service Air 37682, Aurigny Air 37426, Midland Airport Services 37785.

to France (St. Malo) via Jersey (St. Helier) (Emeraude Lines) summer only – from St. Peter Port to Jersey (St. Helier) (Condor Ltd) 3 daily – from St. Peter Port to Weymouth (Condor Ltd) 3 daily – from St. Peter Port to Herm (Herm Seaway) (25 mn).

from St. Peter Port to France (Portbail and Carteret) (Service Maritime Carteret) (summer only) (1 h 5 mn) – from St. Peter Port to France (St. Malo and St. Quay Portrieux) via Jersey (St. Helier) (Emeraude Lines) (summer only) – from St. Peter Port to Weymouth (Condor Ltd : hydrofoil) 2 daily – from St. Peter Port to Sark (Isle of Sark Shipping Co. Ltd) (summer only) (40 mn) – from St. Peter Port to Alderney (Condor Ltd) (45 mn) – from St. Peter Port to Jersey (Channiland) (summer only) (50 mn).

North Esplanade, GY1 3AN 723552 – The Airport, La Villiaze, Forest 37267.

L'Ancresse – Vale – 01481.

Lynton Park, Hacse Lane, Clos du Valle, GY3 5DS, 45418, Fax 43581, – TV. VISA.
closed January – **Meals** (bar lunch)/dinner 19.90 and a la carte 3.50 – **13 rm** 31.00/62.00 **s.** – SB.

Catel/Castel – Catel – 01481.

Belvoir Farm, Rue de la Hougue, GY5 7DY, 56004, Fax 56349, heated, – rest TV.
mid April-early September – **Meals** (by arrangement) – **14 rm** (dinner included) 44.00/64.00 **s.**

Fermain Bay – St. Peter Port – 01481.

La Favorita, Fermain Lane, GY4 6SD, 35666, Fax 35413, ≤, – rest TV. AE VISA.
closed December-6 January – **Meals** 20.00 **s.** and a la carte approx. 10.50 **s.** 4.25 – **36 rm** 45.00/87.00 **s.** – SB.

Le Chalet, GY4 6SD, 35716, Fax 35718 – TV. AE VISA.
26 May-14 October – **Meals** (bar lunch Monday to Saturday)/dinner 13.50 and a la carte 3.75 – **40 rm** 38.00/96.00 **s.** – SB.

Forest – ✉ Forest – ☎ 01481.

Tudor Lodge Deer Farm without rest., Forest Rd, GY8 0AG, ℘ 37849, Fax 35662, park – TV ☎ P. VISA.
closed December-mid January – **5 rm** 30.00/55.00.

Mon Plaisir without rest., Rue des Landes, GY8 0DY, ℘ 64498, Fax 63493, – TV P.
closed 2 weeks December-January – **4 rm** 24.00/40.00.

Pembroke Bay – ✉ Vale – ☎ 01481.
St. Peter Port 5.

Pembroke, GY3 5BY, ℘ 47573, Fax 48838, heated, – TV ☎ P. VISA
Ludwig's : **Meals**- Bavarian 10.55/17.20 **s.** 2.90 – **12 rm** 40.00/77.00 **s.**

St. Martin – pop. 6 082 – ECD : Thursday – ✉ St. Martin – ☎ 01481.
St. Peter Port 2.

Green Acres, Les Hubits, GY4 6LS, ℘ 35711, Fax 35978, heated, – rest rest TV ☎ P – 40. AE VISA.
Meals (bar lunch)/dinner 14.50 and a la carte 3.50 – **48 rm** 48.00/75.00.

Idlerocks, Jerbourg Point, GY4 6BJ, ℘ 37711, Fax 35592, ≤ sea and neighbouring Channel Islands, heated, – rm TV ☎ P. AE VISA
Meals (bar lunch)/dinner 14.50 and a la carte 4.50 – **28 rm** (dinner included) 47.50/175.00 – SB.

Saints Bay, Icart, GY4 6JG, ℘ 38888, Fax 35558, heated, – TV ☎ P. VISA.
Meals (bar lunch)/dinner 17.50 and a la carte 3.80 – **34 rm** (dinner included) 55.00/90.00.

Bella Luce, La Fosse, Moulin Huet, GY4 6EB, ℘ 38764, Fax 39561, heated, – TV ☎ P. AE VISA
Meals (bar lunch)/dinner 14.00 and a la carte 4.00 – **31 rm** 44.50/86.00 – SB.

St. Margarets Lodge, Forest Rd., GY4 6UE, ℘ 35757, Fax 37594, heated, – rest TV ☎ P – 80
46 rm, 1 suite.

Bon Port, Moulin Huet Bay, GY4 6EW, ℘ 39249, Fax 39596, ≤ Moulin Huet Bay and Jerbourg Point, – rest TV ☎ P. VISA.
Meals 9.95/14.95 and a la carte 3.95 – **14 rm** 57.20/98.00 **s.**, 4 suites.

La Cloche, Les Traudes, GY4 6LR, ℘ 35421, Fax 38258, heated, – TV ☎ P. VISA.
Easter-October – **Meals** (residents only) (bar lunch)/dinner 12.00 **s.** 3.20 – **10 rm** (dinner included) 50.00/80.00 **s.**

La Barbarie, Saints Bay, GY4 6ES, ℘ 35217, Fax 35208, heated, – TV ☎ P. VISA.
closed 8 January-6 February – **Meals** (bar lunch Monday to Saturday)/dinner 11.95 **s.** and a la carte 3.95 – **14 rm** 41.00/62.00, 1 suite – SB.

Farnborough without rest., Les Damonettes Lane, GY1 1ZN, off Les Hubits ℘ 37756, Fax 36067, – TV P. VISA.
April-September – **11 rm** 27.00/44.00 **s.**

La Michele, Les Hubits, GY4 6NB, ℘ 38065, Fax 39492, heated, – rest TV ☎ P. AE VISA.
April-October – **Meals** (residents only) (dinner only) 7.50 3.50 – **13 rm** (dinner included) 26.00/69.00 – SB.

Ambassador, Route De Sausmarez, GY4 6SQ, ℘ 38356, Fax 39280, – rest TV ☎ P
19 rm.

Wellesley without rest., Route De Sausmarez, GY4 6SE, ℘ 38028, Fax 39501, – TV ☎ P.
May-October – **10 rm** 33.00/60.00.

St. Peter in the Wood – ✉ St. Peters – ☎ 01481.
St. Peter Port 6.

XX **Café Du Moulin,** Rue du Quanteraine, GY7 9DP, ℘ 65944, Fax 66468 – VISA
closed Sunday dinner, Monday, and last 2 weeks February – **Meals** 13.50 (lunch) and a la carte 20.75/24.45 4.50.

St. Peter Port The West Country G. – pop. 16 648 – ECD : Thursday – ✉ St. Peter Port – ☎ 01481.

See : Town★★ – St. Peter's Church★ Z – Hauteville House (Victor Hugo's House)★ *AC* Z – Castle Cornet★ (≤★) *AC* Z.

Envir. : Saumarez Park★, W : 2 m. by road to Catel Z – Little Chapel★, SW : 2¼ m. by Mount Durand road Z.

18 St. Pierre Park ℘ 727039, Z.

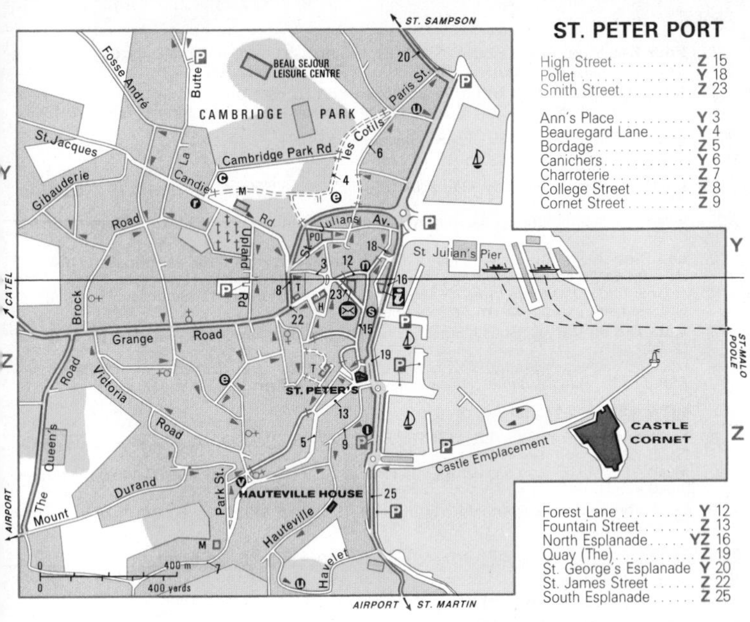

St. Pierre Park, Rohais, GY1 1FD, ℘ 728282, Telex 4191662, Fax 712041, ≤, park, – rm – 200. VISA.
Café Renoir : **Meals** 15.00 ₰ 5.50 (see also ***Victor Hugo*** below) – **134 rm** 95.00/150.00 **s.**, 3 suites – SB. by Grange Rd Z

Duke of Richmond, Cambridge Park, GY1 1UY, ℘ 726221, Fax 728945, heated – rest – 100. VISA Y **c**
Meals 8.50/15.00 **s.** and a la carte ₰ 3.50 – **73 rm** 45.00/110.00, 1 suite – SB.

De Havelet, Havelet, GY1 1BA, ℘ 722199, Fax 714057, – VISA. Z **u**
Wellington Boot : **Meals** (closed Sunday to non-residents) (dinner only) 15.00 and a la carte ₰ 3.25 – ***Havelet Grill :*** **Meals** *(closed Sunday lunch and Monday dinner)* 10.95/14.50 ₰ 3.25 – **34 rm** 38.50/107.00 – SB.

Moore's Central, Le Pollet, GY1 1WH, ℘ 724452, Fax 714037 – VISA. Y **n**
Meals 17.50 and a la carte ₰ 3.00 – **50 rm** 29.50/150.00 – SB.

Midhurst House, Candie Rd, GY1 1UP, ℘ 724391, Fax 729451, – VISA. Y **r**
Easter-mid October – **Meals** (residents only) (dinner only) 10.00 ₰ 3.20 – **8 rm** 39.00/56.00 – SB.

Kenwood House without rest., Allez St., GY1 1NG, ℘ 726146, Fax 725632 – VISA. Z **e**
6 rm 27.50/44.00 **s.**

Marine without rest., Well Rd, GY1 1WS, ℘ 724978 – VISA. Y **u**
11 rm 23.50/44.00 **s.**

XXXX **Victor Hugo** (at St. Pierre Park H.), Rohais, GY1 1FD, ℘ 728282, Telex 4191662, Fax 712041 – VISA by Grange Rd Z
closed Saturday lunch and Sunday dinner – **Meals** - Seafood 9.95/17.95 **s.** and a la carte ₰ 6.50.

XX **La Frégate** with rm, Les Cotils, GY1 1UT, ℘ 724624, Fax 720443, ≤ town and harbour, – VISA. Y **e**
Meals 12.50/18.00 **s.** and a la carte ₰ 4.50 – 8.50 – **13 rm** 55.00/95.00 **s.**

XX **The Absolute End,** Longstore, GY1 2BG, N : ¾ m. by St. George's Esplanade ℘ 723822, Fax 729129 – VISA Y
closed Sunday and January – **Meals** - Seafood 11.00 **s.** (lunch)and a la carte 13.00/24.75 **s.** ₰ 4.00.

XX **Le Nautique,** Quay Steps, GY1 2LE, ℘ 721714, Fax 721786, ≤ – VISA Z **s**
closed Sunday and first 2 weeks January – **Meals** a la carte 16.50/22.00 ₰ 4.50.

XX **Four Seasons,** Albert House, South Esplanade, GY1 1AJ, ℘ 727444 – VISA Z i
closed Sunday and February – **Meals** 9.00/11.75 **s.** and a la carte 3.75.

XX **La Piazza,** Trinity Sq., GY1 1LX, ℘ 725085 – AE VISA Z v
closed Sunday and 25 December-25 January – **Meals** - Italian a la carte 11.60/21.70 3.50.

St. Saviour – pop. 2 419 – ✉ St. Saviour – ☎ 01481.

St. Peter Port 4.

L'Atlantique, Perelle Bay, GY7 9NA, ℘ 64056, Fax 63800, ≤, heated, – TV ☎ P. AE VISA.
Meals (bar lunch Monday to Saturday) /dinner 13.90 and a la carte 3.75 – **23 rm** 38.50/83.00.

Les Piques , Rue des Piques, ℘ 64515, Fax 65857, « Part 15C farmhouse », , , – TV ☎ P. VISA.
closed mid January-February – **Meals** (bar lunch Monday to Saturday)/dinner 15.00 and a la carte 3.25 – **25 rm** 35.00/85.00 **s.**

Auberge du Val , Sous L'Eglise, GY7 9FX, ℘ 63862, Fax 64835, , – TV ☎ P. AE VISA.
closed 2 weeks February, 2 weeks October and 25 to 26 December – **Meals** *(closed Monday)* (bar lunch)/dinner a la carte approx. 14.45 – **8 rm** 27.00/54.00 **s.**

Vazon Bay – ✉ Catel – ☎ 01481.

La Grande Mare, GY5 7LL, ℘ 56576, Fax 56532, ≤, heated, 18, , – TV ☎ P. AE VISA JCB.
Meals 11.00/19.95 and a la carte – **11 rm** (dinner included) 109.00/146.00, **13 suites** 205.00/250.00 – SB.

Les Embruns House, Route de la Margion, GY5 7LG, ℘ 64834, Fax 66024, heated, – TV ☎ P – **16 rm.**

HERM ISLAND 403 P 33 and 230 ⑩ **The West Country G.** – pop. 45 – ☎ 01481.

See : Le Grand Monceau★.

to Guernsey (St. Peter Port) (Herm Seaway) (25 mn).

Administrative Office, ℘ 722377.

Herm – ✉ Herm – ☎ 01481.

White House , GY1 3HR, ℘ 722159, Fax 710066, ≤ Belle Greve Bay and Guernsey, , , park, – rest. VISA.
April-early October – **Meals** 10.25/16.25 – **38 rm** (dinner included) 50.00/128.00 **s.**

JERSEY 403 OP 33 and 230 ⑪ **The West Country G.** – pop. 84 082 – ☎ 01534.

See : Island★★ – Jersey Zoo★★ *AC* – St. Catherine's Bay★ (≤★★) – Grosnez Point★ – Devil's Hole★ – St. Matthews Church, Millbrook (glasswork★) – La Hougue Bie (Neolithic tomb★ *AC*, Chapels★, German Occupation Museum★ *AC*) – St. Catherine's Bay★ (≤★★) – Noirmont Point★.

States of Jersey Airport : ℘ 46111 (846111 from April).

to France (St. Malo) (Emeraude Lines) – from St. Helier to Weymouth via Guernsey (St. Peter Port) 3 daily.

from St. Helier to France (St. Quay Portrieux (Emeraude Lines), Granville and St. Malo (Emeraude Lines and Channiland)) (summer only) – from Gorey to France (Portbail and Carteret) (Emeraude Lines) (summer only) (30 mn) – from St. Helier to Alderney (Condor Ltd) (1 h 55 mn) – from St. Helier to Sark (Emeraude Lines) (summer only) – from St. Helier to Guernsey (St. Peter Port) (Emeraude Lines) (summer only) – from St. Helier to Weymouth via Guernsey (St. Peter Port) (Condor Ltd) – from St. Helier to Guernsey (St. Peter Port) (50 mn), to Sark (45 mn) (Channiland) (summer only).

Liberation Square, St. Helier, JE1 1BB ℘ 500700.

Beaumont – ✉ Beaumont – ☎ 01534.

L'Hermitage, JE3 7BR, on A 12 ℘ 33314, Fax 21207, , , , – rest TV P
119 rm.

Bouley Bay – ✉ Trinity – ☎ 01534.

St. Helier 5.

Water's Edge, JE3 5AS, ℘ 862777, Fax 863645, ≤ Bouley Bay, , heated, – rest TV ☎ P. AE VISA
April-October – **Meals** 13.50/17.50 and a la carte 5.60 – **44 rm** 55.00/115.00, 7 suites – SB.

Corbiere – ✉ St. Brelade – ☎ 01534.

St. Helier 8.

XXX **Sea Crest** with rm, Petit Port, JE3 8HH, ℘ 46353, Fax 47316, ≤, , – rest TV ☎ P. AE VISA.
closed 3 weeks January-February – **Meals** *(closed Sunday dinner October-March and Monday)* 11.00/25.00 and a la carte 4.00 – **7 rm** 57.50/95.00.

Gorey The West Country G. – ✉ St. Martin – ☎ 01534.

See : Mont Orgueil Castle★ (≤★★) *AC* – Jersey Pottery★.

St. Helier 4.

Old Court House, Gorey Village, JE3 9EX, ☎ 854444, Fax 853587, ≘s, ⛱ heated, ⛱ – |‡| TV ☎ ♿ P. AE VISA
closed January-mid March – **Meals** (bar lunch)/dinner 13.00 ₰ 3.60 – **58 rm** 46.00/100.00.

Moorings, Gorey Pier, JE3 6EW, ☎ 853633, Fax 857618 – ≡ rest TV ☎. AE VISA. ✂
Meals 9.50/14.50 **s.** and la carte ₰ 3.50 – **17 rm** ☐ 32.00/96.00 – SB.

Maison Gorey, Gorey Village, JE3 9EP, ☎ 857775, Fax 857779 – ⇆ rest TV ☎
30 rm.

Trafalgar Bay, Gorey Village, JE3 9ES, ☎ 856643, Fax 856922, ⛱ heated, ⛱ – TV P. AE VISA. ✂
May-October – **Meals** (bar lunch)/dinner 11.00 **s.** – **27 rm** ☐ (dinner included) 43.00/90.00 **s.**

Jersey Pottery (Garden Restaurant), Gorey Village, JE3 9EP, ☎ 851119, Fax 856403, « Working Pottery », ⛱ – ⇆ P. AE VISA
closed Saturday October-March, Sunday and 10 days Christmas – **Meals** - Seafood (lunch only) a la carte 16.95/25.45 ₰ 5.50.

Village Bistro, Gorey Village, JE3 9EP, ☎ 853429. VISA
closed Monday, first two weeks March, last two weeks November and Bank Holidays – **Meals** 8.50 (lunch) and a la carte 16.30/22.70 ₰ 2.75.

Grève De Lecq – ✉ St. Ouen – ☎ 01534.

Des Pierres, JE3 2DT, on B 65 ☎ 481858, Fax 485273 – TV P. AE VISA. ✂
closed 15 December-15 January – **Meals** (dinner only) ₰ 2.95 – **16 rm** ☐ (dinner included) 37.00/76.00.

Grouville – ☎ 01534.

Lavender Villa, Rue a Don, JE3 9DA, on A 3 ☎ 854937, Fax 856147, ⛱, ⛱ – ⇆ rest TV P. AE VISA. ✂
mid March-October – **Meals** (dinner only) 7.00 ₰ 2.50 – **21 rm** ☐ (dinner included) 32.00/64.00.

Mon Desir House without rest., La Rue Des Prés, JE3 9DJ, ☎ 854718, Fax 857798, ⛱ – TV P. VISA. ✂
closed 2 weeks Christmas – **13 rm** ☐ 17.00/52.00 **s.**

La Haule – ✉ St. Brelade – ☎ 01534.

La Place ⛰, Route du Coin, JE3 8BF, by B 25 on B 43 ☎ 44261, Fax 45164, ≘s, ⛱ heated – TV ☎ P. AE VISA. ✂
16 April-October – **Meals** 11.50/19.00 and a la carte ₰ 4.50 – **40 rm** ☐ 80.00/120.00 – SB.

Au Caprice, JE3 8BA, on A 1 ☎ 22083, Fax 26199 – TV. VISA. ✂
mid April-mid October – **Meals** (by arrangement) – **13 rm** ☐ 16.00/49.00 **s.**

La Pulente – ✉ St. Brelade – ☎ 01534.

⛳9 Les Mielles, The Mount, Val de la Mare, St. Ouens ☎ 81947/82787.

St. Helier 7.

Atlantic ⛰, La Moye, JE3 8HE, ☎ 44101, Fax 44102, ≤, Fō, ≘s, ⛱ heated, ⛱, ⛱, 🎾 – |‡| TV ☎ P – 🏛 60. AE VISA. ✂
closed January and February – **Meals** 14.50/19.50 **s.** and a la carte – **49 rm** ☐ 95.00/220.00 **s.**, 1 suite – SB.

Rozel Bay – ✉ St. Martin – ☎ 01534.

St. Helier 6.

Chateau La Chaire ⛰, Rozel Valley, JE3 6AJ, ☎ 863354, Fax 865137, ⛱ – TV ☎ P. AE VISA JCB. ✂
Meals (see below) – **13 rm** ☐ 90.00/135.00, 1 suite – SB.

Le Couperon de Rozel, JE3 5BN, ☎ 865522, Fax 865332, ≤, ⛱ heated – TV ☎ P. AE VISA. ✂
27 April-8 October – **Meals** 11.00/17.50 **s.** and a la carte – **35 rm** ☐ (dinner included) 75.00/115.00 **s.**

Chateau La Chaire (at Chateau La Chaire H.), Rozel Valley, JE3 6AJ, ☎ 863354, Fax 865137 – P. AE VISA JCB
Meals 14.75/25.50 and a la carte ₰ 4.75.

St. Aubin – ✉ St. Aubin – ☎ 01534.
St. Helier 4.

Somerville, Mont du Boulevard, JE3 8AD, S : 3/4 m. via harbour ☎ 41226, Fax 46621, ≤ St. Aubin's Bay, heated, – TV ☎ P. AE VISA.
April-October – **Meals** (dancing 3 evenings a week) (bar lunch Monday to Saturday)/ dinner 15.00 and a la carte 3.25 – **59 rm.**

La Tour, High St., JE3 8BR, ☎ 43770, Fax 47143, ≤ St. Aubin's Fort and Bay – rest TV ☎ P. VISA.
March-November – **Meals** (dinner only) 7.50 and a la carte 3.50 – **19 rm** 37.00/81.00, 1 suite.

Panorama without rest., High St., JE3 8BR, ☎ 42429, Fax 45940, ≤ St. Aubin's Fort and Bay, – TV. AE VISA.
April-October – **17 rm** 38.00/66.00.

Bon Viveur, The Bulwarks, JE3 8AB, ☎ 41049, Fax 47540, ≤ – TV. AE VISA.
March-October – **Meals** 9.10 and a la carte 3.00 – **19 rm** 22.00/48.00.

St. Magloire, High Street, JE3 8BR, ☎ 41302, Fax 44148 – rest TV
12 rm.

Sabots d'or, High St., JE3 8BR, ☎ 43732 – TV.
March-October – **Meals** (by arrangement) 8.00 3.50 – **12 rm** (dinner included) 26.00/60.00 **s.**

St. Magloire, High St., JE3 8BR, ☎ 41302, Fax 44148 – rest TV. AE VISA.
March 16-October 28 – **Meals** (by arrangement) 6.00 – **12 rm** 30.00/44.00 **s.** – SB.

Old Court House Inn with rm, St. Aubin's Harbour, ☎ 46433, Fax 45103 – TV ☎. AE VISA.
Meals 15.50 **s.** (lunch) and a la carte 3.75 – **8 rm** 40.00/80.00, 1 suite – SB.

St. Brelade's Bay The West Country G. – pop. 8 566 – ✉ St. Brelade – ☎ 01534.
See : Fishermen's Chapel (frescoes★).
St. Helier 6.

L'Horizon, JE3 8EF, ☎ 43101, Telex 4192281, Fax 46269, ≤ St. Brelade's Bay, – rest TV ☎ P – 150. AE VISA.
Crystal Room : **Meals** 14.00/23.75 **s.** 5.00 (see also ***Star Grill*** below) – **104 rm** 70.00/ 190.00 **s.**, 3 suites – SB.

St. Brelade's Bay, JE3 8EP, ☎ 46141, Fax 47278, ≤ St. Brelade's Bay, heated, – TV ☎ P. AE VISA.
mid April-mid October – **Meals** 12.00/18.00 and a la carte 3.00 – **81 rm** (dinner included) 95.00/220.00 **s.**, 1 suite.

Golden Sands, La Route de la Baie, JE3 8EF, ☎ 41241, Fax 499366, ≤ – TV ☎. AE VISA
12 April-October – **Meals** (residents only)(dinner only) 10.00 **s.** and a la carte 3.00 – **62 rm** 42.00/80.00 **s.**

Chateau Valeuse, Rue de la Valeuse, JE3 8EE, ☎ 46281, Fax 47110, heated, – TV ☎ P. VISA.
late March-late October – **Meals** *(closed Sunday dinner to non-residents)* 9.00/15.50 and dinner a la carte – **33 rm** (dinner included) 50.00/118.00 **s.**

Three Bay View without rest., La route de Noirmont, JE3 8AJ, on B 57 ☎ 42028 – P.
7 rm 16.00/34.00.

Star Grill (at L'Horizon H.), JE3 8EF, ☎ 43101, Fax 46269 – P. VISA
Meals 13.50 **s.** (lunch) and a la carte23.45/37.20 5.00.

St. Clement – pop. 7 393 – ✉ St. Clement – ☎ 01534.
St. Clements ☎ 21938.
St. Helier 2.

Playa D'Or, Greve d'Azette, JE2 6PL, W : 2 m. on A 4 ☎ 22861, Fax 69668 – TV P. VISA.
closed December and January – **Meals** (by arrangement) 7.50 – **15 rm** 27.50/55.00 **s.** – SB.

Rocque-Berg View without rest., Rue de Samares, JE2 6LS, ☎ 852642, Fax 851694, heated – TV P.
April-October – **9 rm** 35.00/40.00 **s.**

Les Grandes Vaques, Pontac, JE2 6SE, E: 1 m. on A 4 ☎ 851198, Fax 856120, – rest TV P
12 rm.

St. Helier The West Country G. – pop. 29 941 – ECD : Thursday and Saturday – ✉ St. Helier – ☎ 01534.
See : Jersey Museum★ *AC* Z – Elizabeth Castle (≤★) *AC* Z – Fort Regent (≤★ *AC*) Z.
Envir. : St. Peter's Valley (Living Legend★ *AC*) NW : 4 m. by A 1, A11 St. Peter's Valley rd and C 112.

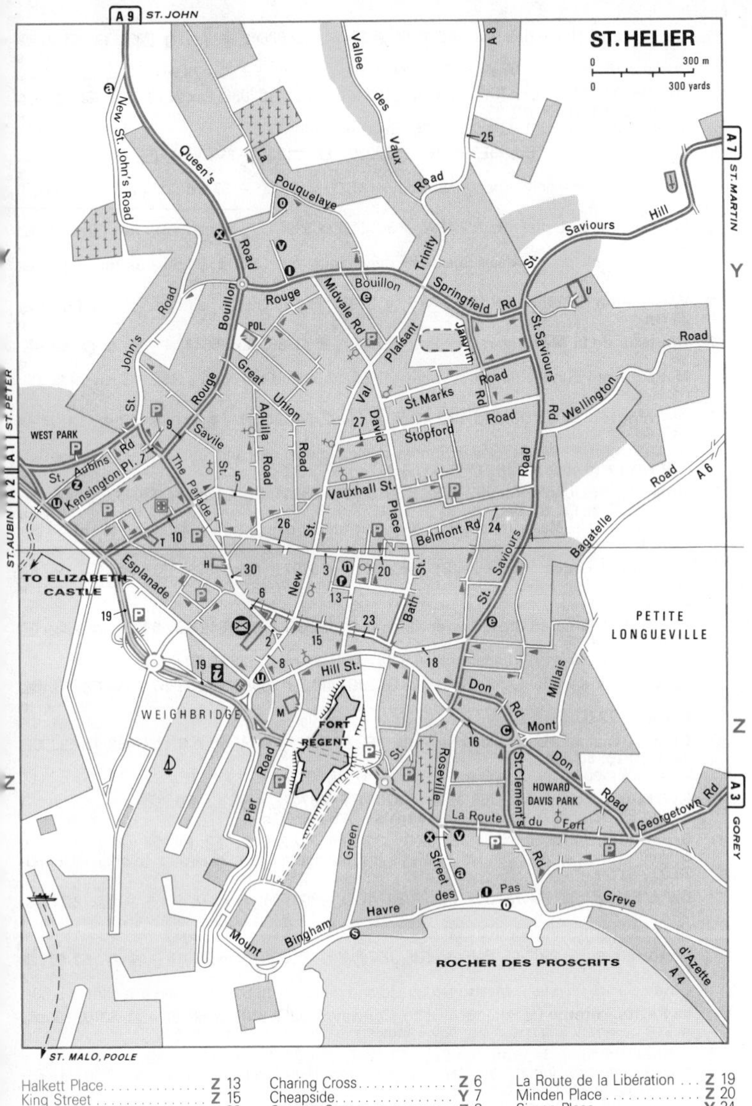

Halkett Place . . . . Z 13	Charing Cross . . . . Z 6	La Route de la Libération . . . Z 19
King Street . . . . Z 15	Cheapside . . . . Y 7	Minden Place . . . . Z 20
Queen Street . . . . Z 23	Conway Street . . . . Z 8	Simon Place . . . . Y 24
	Elizabeth Place . . . . Y 9	Trinity Hill . . . . Y 25
Broad Street . . . . Z 2	Gloucester Street . . . . Y 10	Union Street . . . . Y 26
Burrard Street . . . . Z 3	La Colomberie . . . . Z 16	Victoria Street . . . . Y 27
Cannon Street . . . . Y 5	La Motte Street . . . . Z 18	York Street . . . . Z 30

De Vere Grand, Esplanade, JE4 8WD, ✆ 22301, Fax 37815, ≤, Fs, ≘s, ☒ – |♦| ▤ rest TV ☎ ♿ P – 🚗 180. AE ① VISA. ✂ Y **u**
Meals (dinner only) 21.00 ♁ 5.50 – (see also ***Victoria's*** below) – **110 rm** ☕ 60.00/110.00, 5 suites – SB.

Pomme d'Or, Liberation Sq., JE2 3NR, ✆ 78644, Telex 4192309, Fax 37781 – |♦| ⊁ rm ▤ rest TV ☎ – 🚗 180. AE ① VISA. ✂ Z **u**
Harbour Room* : Meals** (carving rest.) 8.00/15.50 **s.** ♁ 3.45 (see also ***La Petite Pomme below) – **145 rm** ☕ 65.00/130.00 **s.**, 2 suites – SB.

De la Plage, Havre des Pas, JE2 4UQ, 23474, Fax 68642, ←, – . Z s
30 April-15 October – **Meals** 14.00/16.50 **s.** and a la carte 3.60 – **78 rm** 35.00/108.00 **s.**

Apollo, 9 St. Saviour's Rd, JE2 4LA, 25441, Telex 4192086, Fax 22120, – . Z e
Meals (dinner only) 11.00 6.50 – **85 rm** 61.50/90.00 **s.**

Queens, Queens Rd, JE2 3JR, 22239, Fax 21930 – rest . Y x
Meals (residents only) (bar lunch)/dinner 16.00 **s.** 3.50 – **37 rm** (dinner included) 44.00/88.00 **s.** – SB.

Laurels, La route du Fort, JE2 4PA, 36444, Fax 59904, heated – rest . Z v
mid March-October – **Meals** (residents only)(dinner only) 9.50 **s.** 4.50 – **37 rm** (dinner included) 52.50/85.00.

Washington, Clarendon Rd, JE2 3YS, 37981, Fax 89899, heated – rest Y e
36 rm.

Chateau de la Mer, Havre Des Pas, JE2 4PX, 33366, Fax 36544, ← – . Z o
Meals (closed Sunday dinner in winter) 10.00/17.50 and a la carte 3.50 – **5 rm** 52.00/84.00 **s.** – SB.

Mornington, 60-68 Don Rd, JE2 4QD, 24452, Fax 34131 – rest . Z c
April-December – **Meals** *(closed Sunday dinner)* (dinner only and Sunday lunch)/dinner 9.00 – **31 rm** (dinner included) 41.00/68.00.

Uplands, St. John's Rd, JE2 3LE, 30151, Fax 68804, Reservations 73006, heated – rest . Y a
April-October – **Meals** (residents only) (bar lunch)/dinner 8.75 **s.** 4.95 – **43 rm** 38.50/77.00 **s.**

Greenwood Lodge, Roseville St., JE2 4PL, 67073, Fax 67876, heated – Z x
33 rm.

Almorah, 1 Almorah Cres., Lower Kings Cliff, JE2 3GU, 21648, Fax 68600, – . Y o
Meals (residents only) (dinner only) 9.50 3.00 – **14 rm** 32.00/64.00 **s.**

La Bonne Vie without rest., Roseville St., JE2 4PL, 35955, Fax 33357 – . Z a
10 rm 23.00/46.00 **s.**

Glen without rest., Vallee des Vaux, JE2 3GB, N : 1¼ m. off A 8 32062, Fax 32062, – . Y
closed 22 December-3 January – **7 rm** 17.00/50.00 **s.**

Kaieteur, 4 Ralegh Av., JE2 3ZG, 37004, Fax 67423 – . Y i
closed 25 October-9 November – **10 rm** 24.50/49.00 **s.**

Brookfield, 24 Raleigh Av., JE2 3ZG, 23168, Fax 21543 – . Y v
closed December and January – **Meals** (by arrangement) – **20 rm** (dinner included) 28.00/56.00 **s.**

De L'Etang, 33 Havre des Pas, JE2 4UQ, 21996, Fax 37829, ← – . Z i
13 rm (dinner included) 27.00/54.00.

XXX **Victoria's** (at Grand H.), Peirson Rd, JE4 8WD, 22301, Fax 37815 – . Y z
closed Sunday dinner – **Meals** (live music and dancing) 15.50/22.50 and a la carte 5.50.

XXX **La Petite Pomme** (at Pomme d'Or H), Conway St., JE2 3NR, 66608 – . Z u
closed Saturday lunch and Sunday – **Meals** a la carte 17.60/25.45 **s.** 3.45.

XX ✿ **Shai** (Broome), 8a Waterloo St., JE2 4WT, 617434 – . Z r
closed Saturday lunch, Sunday, January and Bank Holidays – **Meals** 12.50 (lunch) and a la carte 21.40/25.40 4.75
Spec. Crab gateau, lime and shallot salsa, Crisp red mullet, braised salsify, vanilla sauce, White chocolate tart.

XX **La Capannina,** 65-67 Halkett Pl., JE2 4WG, 34602, Fax 77628 – Z n
closed Sunday and Bank Holidays – **Meals** - Italian 17.00 (dinner) and a la carte 12.00/21.00 4.90.

St. Lawrence – pop. 4 561 – ✉ St. Lawrence – 01534.

St. Helier 3.

Elmdale Farm, Ville Emphrie, JE3 1EA, 34779, heated, – .
Meals *(closed Mondays except Bank Holidays)* 8.50/14.50 and a la carte 3.75 – **13 rm** 32.50/65.00.

Villa d'Oro without rest., La Grande Route de St. Laurent, JE3 1FA, on A 10 862262, Fax 863012 – .
early April-mid October – **12 rm** 18.00/40.00 **s.**

St. Martin – pop. 3 258 – ✉ St. Martin – ☎ 01534.

St. Helier 4.

Le Relais de St. Martin, JE3 6EA, ✆ 853271, Fax 855241, heated pool, garden – rest TV P. VISA.
Meals *(closed November-March)* 8.75 **s.** 3.00 – **11 rm** 25.00/50.00 **s.**

La Franchise Farm without rest., JE3 6HU, NW : ¾ m. by B 30 on C 110 ✆ 862224, garden – P.
April-October – **7 rm** 19.00/48.00 **s.**

St. Peter – pop. 3 713 – ✉ St. Peter – ☎ 01534.

St. Helier 5.

Mermaid, Airport Rd, JE3 7BN, on B 36 ✆ 41255, Fax 45826, heated, garden, – TV P – 80. AE VISA.
Meals 10.00/12.00 and a la carte 7.50 – **68 rm** 63.00/95.00.

Greenhill Country, Coin Varin, Mont de l'Ecole, JE3 7EL, on C 112 ✆ 481042, Fax 485322, heated – TV P. AE VISA.
closed January-March – **Meals** 10.00/20.00 **s.** and a la carte 5.00 – **19 rm** 40.00/90.00 **s.** – SB.

St. Saviour – pop. 12 747 – ECD : Thursday – ✉ St. Saviour – ☎ 01534.

St. Helier 1.

✿ **Longueville Manor,** Longueville Rd, JE2 7SA, on A 3 ✆ 25501, Fax 31613, « Former manor house with Jacobean panelling », heated, garden, park, – rest rest TV P. AE VISA
Meals 18.50/28.50 **s.** and dinner a la carte 31.50/34.50 5.00 – **30 rm** 130.00/215.00 **s.**, 2 suites – SB
Spec. Grilled suprême of turbot and calamari with a green vegetable salad, Steamed Jersey sea bass with a cucumber and caviar sauce, Grilled scallop salad with a Provencale vinaigrette and crispy vegetables.

Champ Colin without rest., Rue du Champ Colin, Hougè Bie, JE2 7UN, ✆ 851877, garden – TV P. AE VISA.
3 rm 36.00/44.00.

SARK 403 P 33 and 230 ⑩ **The West Country G.** – pop. 560 – ☎ 01481.

See : Island★★ – La Coupee★★★ – Port du Moulin★★ – Creux Harbour★ – La Seigneurie★ *AC* – Pilcher Monument★ – Hog's Back★.

to France (St. Malo) via Jersey (St. Helier) (Emeraude Lines) (summer only) – to Guernsey (St. Peter Port) (Isle of Sark Shipping Co. Ltd) (summer only) (40 mn) – to Jersey (St. Helier) (Channiland) (45 mn).

ℹ ✆ 832345.

Dixcart, GY9 0SD, ✆ 832015, Fax 832164, garden, park
15 rm.

Petit Champ, GY9 0SF, ✆ 832046, Fax 832469, ≤ coast, Herm, Jetou and Guernsey, « Country house atmosphere », heated, garden – rest. AE VISA.
Easter-early October – **Meals** 16.50 **s.** (dinner) and a la carte 8.95/22.75 **s.** 3.60 – **16 rm** (dinner included) 46.00/96.00 **s.**

Stocks, GY9 0SD, ✆ 832001, Fax 832130, garden. AE VISA
April-September – **Meals** 7.95/16.95 and a la carte 5.00 – **24 rm** 34.00/78.00 **s.** – SB.

Les Quatre Vents, GY9 0SE, off Harbour Hill ✆ 832247, Fax 832332, ≤, garden – rm TV.
closed 14 October-2 January – **Meals** (by arrangement) – **4 rm** 20.00/40.00 **s.**

La Sablonnerie with rm, Little Sark, GY9 OSD, ✆ 832061, Fax 832408, garden – AE VISA.
mid April-early October – **Meals** 17.50/23.00 and a la carte 4.50 – **21 rm** (dinner included) 45.50/101.00, 1 suite.

Founiais, Harbour Hill, GY9 0SB, ✆ 832626, Fax 832642 – AE VISA
closed Mondays (except Bank Holidays) and November-February – **Meals** a la carte 11.70/16.40 **s.** 2.50.

Isle of Man

Place with at least :

a hotel or restaurant .... ● Douglas
a pleasant hotel or restaurant ..... 🏨, 🏠, ✕
a quiet, secluded hotel .... 🐎
a restaurant with ..... ✿, ✿✿, ✿✿✿, **Meals** (M)

Localité offrant au moins :

une ressource hôtelière .... ● Douglas
un hôtel ou restaurant agréable ... 🏨, 🏠, ✕
un hôtel très tranquille, isolé .... 🐎
une bonne table à ... ✿, ✿✿, ✿✿✿, **Meals** (M)

La località possiede come minimo :

una risorsa alberghiera .... ● Douglas
Albergo o ristorante ameno .... 🏨, 🏠, ✕
un albergo molto tranquillo, isolato .... 🐎
un'ottima tavola con .. ✿, ✿✿, ✿✿✿, **Meals** (M)

Ort mit mindestens :

einem Hotel oder Restaurant .... ● Douglas
ein angenehmes Hotel oder Restaurant 🏨, 🏠, ✕
einem sehr ruhigen und abgelegenen Hotel . 🐎
einem Restaurant mit . ✿, ✿✿, ✿✿✿, **Meals** (M)

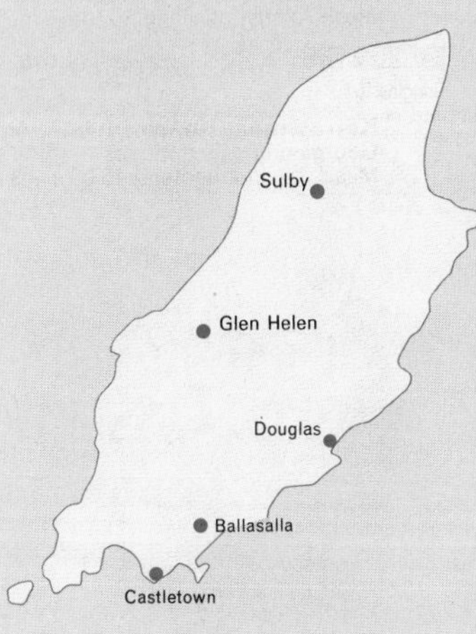

BALLASALLA 402 G 21 – ☎ 01624.

ℹ Airport Information Desk, Ronaldsway IM9 2AF ✆ 823311.

Douglas 8.

XX **Silverburn Lodge,** IM9 3DA, ✆ 822343 – Ⓟ. VISA
closed Sunday dinner, Monday and 25 December – **Meals** 12.50/20.00 **t.** and a la carte 5.00.

CASTLETOWN 402 G 21 **Great Britain G.** – pop. 3 152 – ECD : Thursday – ☎ 01624.

Exc. : Cregneash Folk Museum★ *AC*, W : 6½ m. by A 5 and A 31.

Douglas 10.

Castletown Golf Links, Derbyhaven, E : 2 m. ✆ 822201, Fax 824633, ≤ sea and golf links, , , 18, park – TV ☎ & Ⓟ – 200. AE VISA
Meals (dinner only and Sunday lunch)/dinner 18.50 **st.** and a la carte 5.50 – **50 rm** 50.00/95.00 **st.**, 8 suites – SB.

X Chablis Cellar, 21 Bank St., ✆ 823527.

DOUGLAS 402 G 21 **Great Britain G.** – pop. 22 214 – ECD : Thursday – ☎ 01624.

Exc. : Snaefell★ (✻★★★) N : 8 m. by A 2 and mountain tramcar from Laxey – Laxey Wheel★★, NE : 8 m. by A 2.

18 Douglas Municipal, Pulrose Park ✆ 661558 – 18 King Edward Bay, Groudle Rd, Onchan ✆ 620430/673821.

✈ Ronaldsway Airport : ✆ 823311, SW : 7 m. – **Terminal** : Coach service from Lord St.

⛴ to Belfast (Isle of Man Steam Packet Co. Ltd) (summer only) (4 h 30 mn) – to Republic of Ireland (Dublin) (Isle of Man Steam Packet Co. Ltd) (4 h 30 mn) – to Fleetwood (Isle of Man Steam Packet Co. Ltd) (summer only) (3 h 20 mn) – to Heysham (Isle of Man Steam Packet Co. Ltd) (3 h 45 mn) – to Liverpool (Isle of Man Steam Packet Co. Ltd) (4 h).

ℹ Sefton Tourist Information Centre, Harris Promenade ✆ 686766.

Palace, Central Promenade, ✆ 662662, Fax 670848, ≤, , , – rm rest TV ☎ Ⓟ – 320. AE VISA JCB
Meals 17.50 **t.** (dinner) and a la carte **st.** 5.00 – **130 rm** 70.00/95.00 **t.**, 3 suites – SB.

Empress, Central Promenade, IM2 4RA, ✆ 661155, Fax 673554, , – rest TV ☎ – 200. AE VISA.
Meals 12.50 **t.** and a la carte – 7.50 – **99 rm** 59.00/65.00 **t.**, 3 suites – SB.

Sefton, Harris Promenade, IM1 2RW, ✆ 626011, Fax 676004, ≤, , , – TV ☎ Ⓟ – 80. AE VISA.
Meals 8.00/13.00 **st.** and dinner a la carte 3.75 – **79 rm** 35.00/67.50 **st.**, 1 suite.

Admirals House, 12 Loch Promenade, IM1 2LX, ✆ 629551, Fax 675021 – TV ☎. AE VISA.
***Boncompte* : Meals** *(closed Sunday)* 10.50/15.95 **t.** – **12 rm** 50.00/110.00 **t.**

ATS Mount Vernon, Peel Rd ✆ 622661 ATS 5-7 South Quay ✆ 676532

GLEN HELEN – ☎ 01624.

XX **Swiss Chalet,** IM4 3NP, ✆ 801657 – Ⓟ
closed Sunday dinner, Monday, 27 January-10 February and 23 October-1 November – **Meals** (dinner only and Sunday lunch)/dinner 11.95 **st.** and a la carte 5.50.

SULBY 402 G 21 – ✉ Lezayre – ☎ 01624.

Douglas 16.

Kerrowmoar House, IM7 2AX, E : ½ m. on Ramsey rd ✆ 897543, Fax 897927, « Part Georgian house, antiques », , , park, – rm TV ☎ Ⓟ.
Meals (by arrangement) 25.00 **s.** – **3 rm** 35.00/70.00 **s.**

Republic of Ireland

Prices quoted in this section of the guide are in Irish pounds (punt)

Dans cette partie du guide, les prix sont indiqués en monnaie irlandaise « Punts »

In questa parte della guida, i prezzi sono indicati in livres irlandesi « Punts »

In diesem Teil des Führers sind die Preise in irländischer Währung « Punts » angegeben

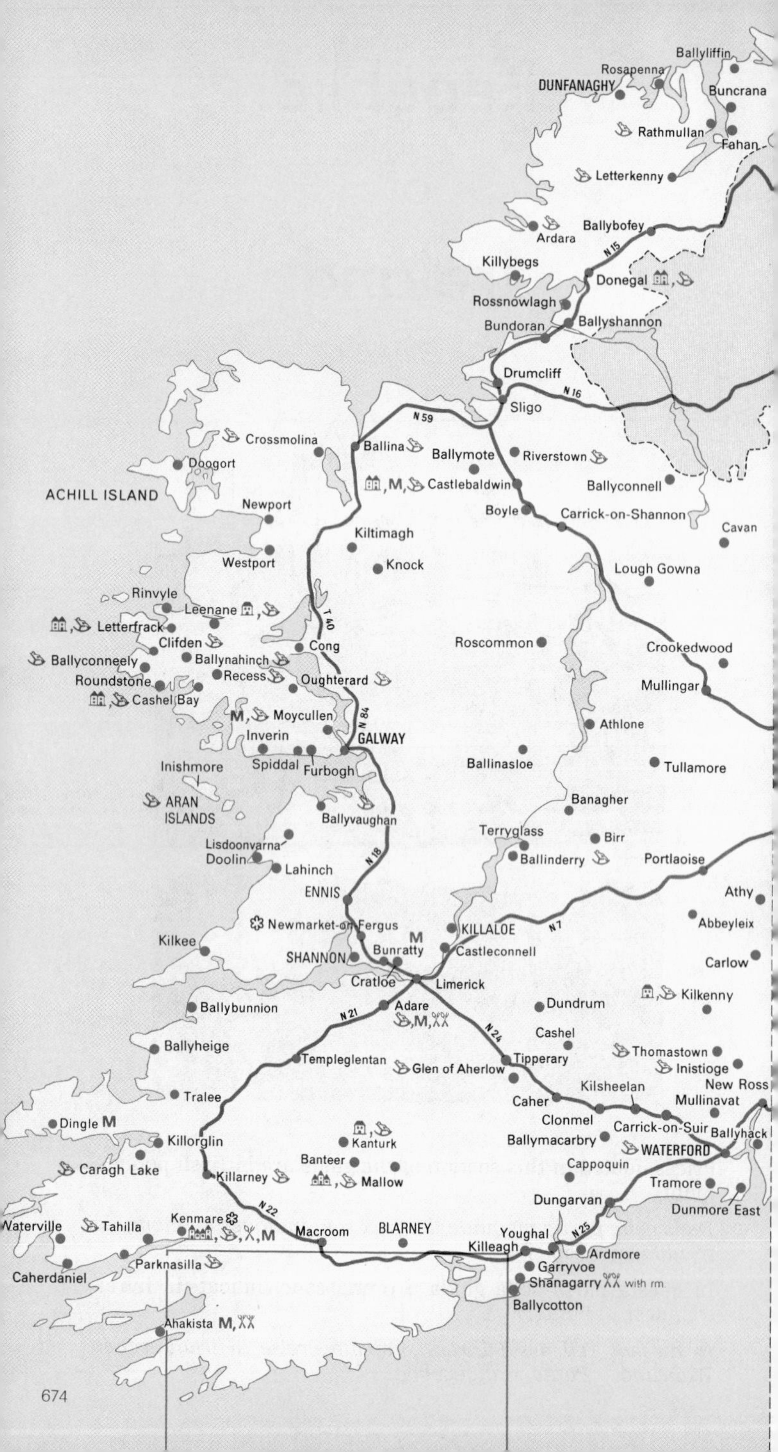
Ballyliffin
Rosapenna
DUNFANAGHY
Buncrana
Rathmullan
Fahan
Letterkenny
Ballybofey
Ardara
N 15
Killybegs
Donegal
Rossnowlagh
Bundoran
Ballyshannon
Drumcliff
N 16
Sligo
N 59
Crossmolina
Ballina
Ballymote
Riverstown
Doogort
Castlebaldwin
Ballyconnell
ACHILL ISLAND
Newport
Boyle
Carrick-on-Shannon
Cavan
Kiltimagh
Westport
Knock
Lough Gowna
Rinvyle
Leenane
Letterfrack
T 40
Clifden
Cong
Roscommon
Crookedwood
Ballyconneely
Ballynahinch
Recess
Roundstone
Oughterard
Mullingar
Cashel Bay
M
Moycullen
N 84
Athlone
Inverin
GALWAY
Inishmore
Spiddal
Furbogh
Ballinasloe
Tullamore
ARAN ISLANDS
Banagher
Ballyvaughan
Terryglass
Birr
Lisdoonvarna
Doolin
N 18
Ballinderry
Portlaoise
Lahinch
ENNIS
Athy
Newmarket-on-Fergus
KILLALOE
N 7
Abbeyleix
Kilkee
Bunratty
Castleconnell
SHANNON
Carlow
Cratloe
Limerick
Kilkenny
Ballybunnion
Adare
Dundrum
N 21
N 24
Cashel
Ballyheige
Thomastown
Templeglentan
Glen of Aherlow
Tipperary
Inistioge
Tralee
Kilsheelan
New Ross
Caher
Mullinavat
Dingle M
Clonmel
Carrick-on-Suir
Ballyhack
Killorglin
Kanturk
Ballymacarbry
WATERFORD
Banteer
Cappoquin
Caragh Lake
Killarney
Mallow
Tramore
Dungarvan
N 22
Dunmore East
Kenmare
Macroom
BLARNEY
N 25
Waterville
Tahilla
Youghal
Killeagh
Ardmore
Parknasilla
Garryvoe
Caherdaniel
Shanagarry with rm.
Ballycotton
Ahakista M,

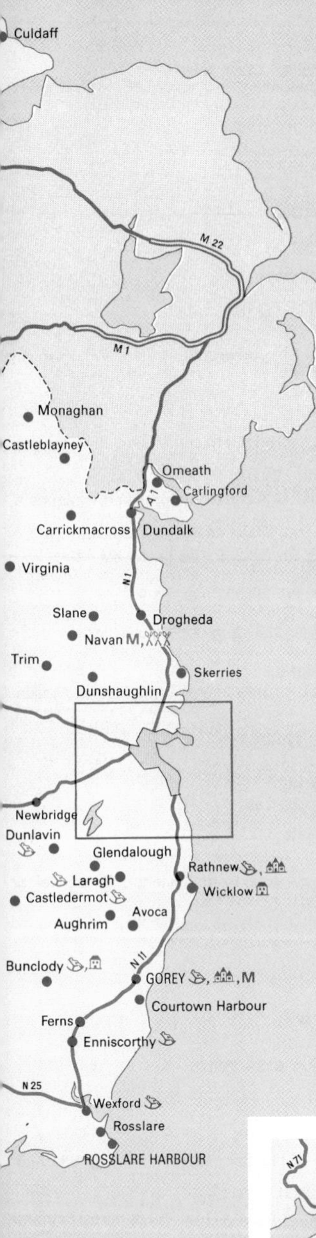

Place with at least :

a hotel or restaurant .... ● Adare

a pleasant hotel or restaurant .... 🏨, ⌂, ✗

a quiet, secluded hotel .... 🐎

a restaurant with .... ✿, ✿✿, ✿✿✿, **Meals (M)**

See this town for establishments located in its vicinity .... **DUBLIN**

Localité offrant au moins :

une ressource hôtelière .... ● Adare

un hôtel ou restaurant agréable .. 🏨, ⌂, ✗

un hôtel très tranquille, isolé .... 🐎

une bonne table à ... ✿, ✿✿, ✿✿✿, **Meals (M)**

Localité groupant dans le texte les ressources de ses environs .... **DUBLIN**

La località possiede come minimo :

una risorsa alberghiera .... ● Adare

Albergo o ristorante ameno ...... 🏨, ⌂, ✗

un albergo molto tranquillo, isolato .... 🐎

un'ottima tavola con . ✿, ✿✿, ✿✿✿, **Meals (M)**

La località raggruppa nel suo testo le risorse dei dintorni .... **DUBLIN**

Ort mit mindestens :

einem Hotel oder Restaurant .... ● Adare

ein angenehmes Hotel oder Restaurant ... 🏨, ⌂, ✗

einem sehr ruhigen und abgelegenen Hotel 🐎

einem Restaurant mit ✿, ✿✿, ✿✿✿, **Meals (M)**

Ort mit Angaben über Hotels und Restaurants in seiner Umgebung .... **DUBLIN**

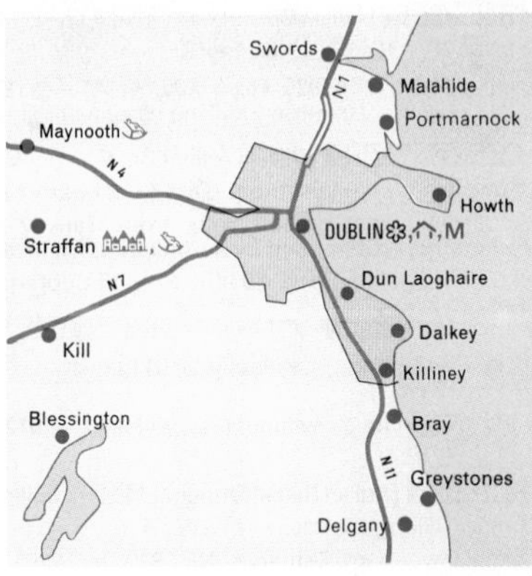

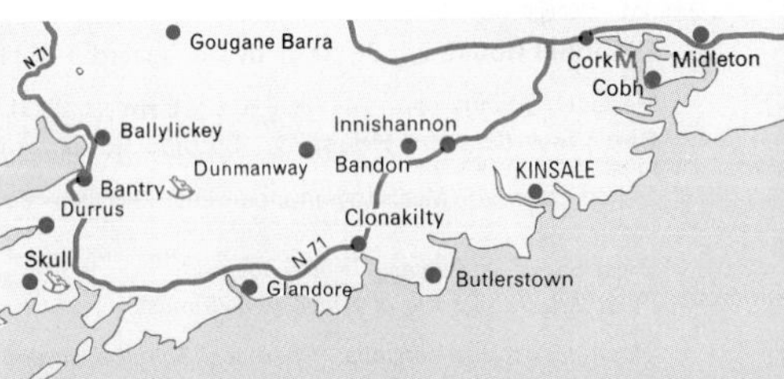

ABBEYLEIX **(Mainistir Laoise)** Laois 405 J 9 – pop. 1 299 – ECD : Wednesday – ☎ 0502.

♦Dublin 64 – Kilkenny 21 – ♦Limerick 65 – ♦Tullamore 30.

Hibernian House, Lower Main St., ✆ 31252 – TV ☎. VISA. *closed 25 to 27 December* – **Meals** 8.00 **st.** (lunch) and dinner a la carte 5.55/16.00 **st.** 6.00 – **10 rm** 25.00/50.00 **st.** – SB.

ACHILL ISLAND **(Acaill)** Mayo 405 B 5/6 **Ireland G.**

See : Island★.

Achill Sound ✆ 45384 (1 July-31 August).

Doogort (Dumha Goirt) – ✉ Achill Island – ☎ 098.

Keel ✆ 43202.

Gray's, ✆ 43244, – **Meals** (by arrangement) 15.00 **t.** – **17 rm** 18.00/36.00 **t.**

ADARE **(Áth Dara)** Limerick 405 F 10 **Ireland G.** – pop. 899 – ☎ 061.

See : Town★ – Adare Friary★.

Exc. : Rathkeale (Castle Matrix★ *AC*) W : 7½ m. by N 21 – Newcastle West★, W : 16 m. by N 21 – Glin Castle★ *AC*, W : 29 m. by N 21, R 518 and N 69.

✆ 396255 (mid April-30 October).

♦Dublin 131 – ♦Killarney 59 – ♦Limerick 10.

Adare Manor, ✆ 396566, Fax 396124, ≤, « 19C Gothic mansion in extensive parkland », – TV ☎ – 200. AE VISA. **Meals** 15.00/40.00 **t.** and a la carte 7.00 – 10.50 – **64 rm** 195.00/350.00 **st.**

Dunraven Arms, Main St., ✆ 396633, Fax 396541, « Attractively furnished, antiques », – TV ☎ – 150. AE VISA. *Maigue* : **Meals** 16.00/26.00 **t.** and a la carte 4.50 – 9.50 – **44 rm** 69.00/99.00 **t.**

Abbey Villa without rest., Kildimo Rd, ✆ 396113, Fax 396969 – TV. VISA. **6 rm** 17.00/34.00 **st.**

Village House without rest., Main St., ✆ 396554, Fax 396903 – . VISA. *March-October* – **5 rm** 16.00/34.00 **st.**

Adare Lodge without rest., Kildimo Rd, ✆ 396629 – TV. VISA JCB. **6 rm** 20.00/34.00 **st.**

Mustard Seed, Main St., ✆ 396451 – AE VISA *closed Sunday, Monday and 25 January-1 March* – **Meals** (dinner only) (booking essential) 25.00/27.00 **t.** 6.00.

AHAKISTA **(Áth an Chiste)** Cork 405 D 13 – ✉ Bantry – ☎ 027.

♦Dublin 217 – ♦Cork 63 – ♦Killarney 59.

Shiro, ✆ 67030, Fax 67206, ≤, – . AE VISA **Meals** - Japanese (booking essential) (dinner only) 33.00 **st.**

ARAN ISLANDS **(Oileáin Árann)** Co. Galway 405 CD 8 **Ireland G.**

See : Islands★ – Inishmore (Dun Aenghus★★★).

Access by boat or aeroplane from Galway city or by boat from Kilkieran, Rossaneel or Fisherstreet (Clare) and by aeroplane from Inverin.

✆ 099 (Inishmore) 61263 (30 May-15 September).

Inishmore – ✉ Aran Islands – ☎ 099.

Ard Einne, Killeany, ✆ 61126, ≤ **12 rm.**

Tigh Fitz without rest., Killeany, ✆ 61213, ≤ – ☎ **6 rm.**

ARDARA **(Ard an Rátha)** Donegal 405 G 3 **Ireland G.** – pop. 653 – ☎ 075.

Envir. : Glengesh Pass★★★, SW : 5 m.

Exc. : Gweebarra Estuary★, NE : 9 m. by R 262.

♦Dublin 188 – Donegal 24 – ♦Londonderry 58.

Woodhill House, SE : ¼ m. by Donegal rd ✆ 41112, Fax 41516, ≤, – . AE VISA. **Meals** (by arrangement) 24.00 **t.** 5.00 – **6 rm** 18.00/52.00 **t.** – SB.

Bay View Country House, Portnoo Rd, N : ¾ m. ✆ 41145, ≤ Loughros Bay and hills, – . VISA. *March-October* – **Meals** (by arrangement) 12.00 **st.** – **6 rm** 14.50/29.00 **st.**

ARDMORE (Aird Mhór) Waterford 405 I 12 **Ireland G.** – pop. 375 – ☎ 024.

See : Town★ – Round Tower★ – Church★ (arcade★).

Envir. : Whiting Bay★, W : 2 m. by the coast road.

Community Office ☎ 94444 (May-September).

♦Dublin 139 – ♦Cork 34 – ♦Waterford 43.

Cliff House, ☎ 94106, Fax 94496, ←, – ☎ **P**. VISA.
Meals (bar lunch Monday to Saturday)/dinner 19.50 **t.** and a la carte 5.00 – **20 rm** 31.00/68.00 **t.** – SB.

ATHLONE (Baile Átha Luain) Westmeath 405 I 7 **Ireland G.** – pop. 8 170 – ECD : Thursday – ☎ 0902.

Exc. : Clonmacnois★★★ (Grave Slabs★, Cross of the Scriptures★) S : 13 m. by N 6 and N 62 – N : Lough Ree (Ballykeeran Viewpoint★★, Glassan★) – Clonfinlough Stone★, S : 11½ m. by N 6 and N 62.

Hodson Bay ☎ 92073/92235.

Tourist Office, The Castle ☎ 94630 (Easter-mid October).

♦Dublin 75 – ♦Galway 57 – ♦Limerick 75 – Roscommon 20 – ♦Tullamore 24.

Hodson Bay,, NW : 4¾ m. by N 61 ☎ 92444, Fax 92688, ←, – ☎ **P** – 500. VISA.
Meals 10.50/19.50 **st.** and dinner a la carte 7.50 – **44 rm** 75.00/80.00 **st.**, 2 suites – SB.

Shelmalier House, Retreat Rd, Cartrontroy, E : 2½ m. by Dublin rd ☎ 72245, Fax 73190, – ☎ **P**. VISA.
Meals 14.00 **st.** – **7 rm** 18.50/30.00 **st.**

ATHY (Baile Átha Á) Kildare 405 L 9 – ☎ 0507.

♦Dublin 40 – Kilkenny 29 – Wexford 59.

Tonlegee House,, SW : 2¼ m. by N 78 ☎ 31473, Fax 31473 – ☎ **P**. VISA.
Meals *(closed Sunday to non-residents)* (dinner only) 23.00 **t.** – **5 rm** 40.00/60.00 **t.** – SB.

AUGHRIM (Eachroim) Wicklow 405 N 9 – ☎ 0402.

☎ 73939 (1 May-2 October).

♦Dublin 46 – ♦Waterford 77 – Wexford 60.

Lawless's, ☎ 36146, Fax 36384, – ☎ **P**. VISA.
closed 24-28 December – **Meals** (bar lunch Monday to Saturday)/dinner 17.00 **st.** and a la carte – **10 rm** 30.00/57.00 **t.** – SB.

AVOCA (Abhóca) Wicklow 405 N 9 – pop. 494 – ☎ 0402.

♦Dublin 47 – ♦Waterford 72 – Wexford 55.

Woodenbridge, Vale of Avoca, SW : 2¼ m. on R 752 ☎ 35146, Fax 35573, – ☎ **P**. VISA.
Meals 9.950/17.95 **t.** and dinner a la carte 6.00 – **12 rm** 33.00/56.00 **t.** – SB.

BALLINA (Béal an Átha) Mayo 405 E 5 **Ireland G.** – pop. 6 563 – ECD : Thursday – ☎ 096.

Envir. : Rosserk Abbey★, N : 4 m. by R 314.

Exc. : Moyne Abbey★, N : 7 m. by R 314 – Downpatrick Head★, N : 20 m. by R 314.

Mosgrove, Shanaghy ☎ 21050.

☎ 70848 (3 May-30 September).

♦Dublin 150 – ♦Galway 73 – Roscommon 64 – ♦Sligo 37.

Mount Falcon Castle, Foxford Rd, S : 4 m. on N 57 ☎ 21172, Fax 71517, ←, « Country house atmosphere », park, – ☎ **P**. VISA
closed February and 20-27 December – **Meals** (by arrangement) (communal dining) (dinner only) 22.00 4.50 – **10 rm** 49.00/98.00 **st.**

BALLINASLOE (Béal Átha na Sluaighe) Galway 405 H 8 **Ireland G.** – pop. 5 793 – ECD : Thursday – ☎ 0905.

Exc. : Turoe Stone, Bullaun★, SW : 18 m. by R 348 and R 350.

Ballinasloe ☎ 42126 – Mountbellew ☎ 79259.

Main Street ☎ 42131 (July and August).

♦Dublin 91 – ♦Galway 41 – ♦Limerick 66 – Roscommon 36 – ♦Tullamore 34.

Haydens, Dunlo St., ☎ 42347, Fax 42895, – rest ☎ **P** – 30. VISA.
closed 24 to 26 December – **Meals** 9.50/18.50 **t.** and dinner a la carte 4.95 – 5.50 – **48 rm** 30.00/50.00 **t.** – SB.

BALLINCLASHET Cork 405 G 12 – see Kinsale.

BALLINDERRY (Baile an Doire) Tipperary 405 H 8 Ireland G. – ✉ Nenagh – ☎ 067.

Exc. : Portumna★ (castle★) N : 9½ m. by R 493 and N 65.

♦Dublin 111 – ♦Galway 53 – ♦Limerick 41.

- **Gurthalougha House** ⛰, W : 1¾ m. ☎ 22080, Fax 22154, ≤, « Country house on banks of Lough Derg », ⛵, ⛱, park, 🎾 – ☎ 🅿. VISA
  closed February and 1 week Christmas – **Meals** (dinner only) 23.00 **st.** 5.50 – **8 rm** 34.00/80.00 **st.** – SB.

BALLYBOFEY (Bealach Féich) Donegal 405 I 3 – pop. 2 972 – ECD : Wednesday – ☎ 074.

⛳18 Ballybofey & Stranorlar ☎ 31093.

♦Dublin 148 – ♦Londonderry 30 – ♦Sligo 58.

- **Kee's,** Main St., Stranorlar, NE : ½ m. on N 15 ☎ 31018, Fax 31917, ⛹, ≘s, 🏊 – 📺 ☎ 🅿. AE VISA
  Meals 9.00/17.00 **t.** and dinner a la carte 5.60 – **36 rm** 32.50/75.00 **t.**

BALLYBUNNION (Baile an Bhuinneánaigh) Kerry 405 D 10 Ireland G. – pop. 1 346 – ☎ 068.

Exc. : Carrigafoyle Castle★, NE : 13 m. by R 551 – Glin Castle★ *AC*, E : 19 m. by R 551 and N 69.

⛳18, ⛳18 Ballybunnion ☎ 27146.

♦Dublin 176 – ♦Limerick 56 – Tralee 26.

- **Marine,** Sandhill Rd, ☎ 27139, Fax 27666, ≤ – 📺 ☎ 🅿. AE VISA
  early March-October – **Meals** (bar lunch Monday to Saturday)/dinner 20.00 **t.** and a la carte 6.25 – **12 rm** 45.00/66.00 **t.** – SB.

BALLYCONNEELY (Baile Conaola) Galway 405 B 7 – ✉ Clifden – ☎ 095.

♦Dublin 189 – ♦Galway 54.

- **Erriseask House** ⛰, ☎ 23553, Fax 23639, ≤ – ☎ 🅿. AE VISA. ⛔
  April-October – **Meals** (light lunch)/dinner 21.90 **t.** and a la carte 6.00 – **8 rm** 35.00/80.00 **st.**

BALLYCONNELL (Béal Atha Conaill) Cavan 405 J 5 – pop. 465 – ☎ 049.

♦Dublin 89 – Drogheda 76 – Enniskillen 23.

- Slieve Russell,, SE : 1¾ m. on R 200 ☎ 26444, Fax 26474, ≤, ⛹, ≘s, 🏊, ⛳18, ⛱, park, 🎾, squash – 🛗 ▤ rest 📺 ☎ ♿ 🅿 – 🏛 800
  145 rm.

BALLYCOTTON (Baile Choitán) Cork 405 H 12 – ☎ 021.

♦Dublin 165 – ♦Cork 27 – ♦Waterford 66.

- **Bayview,** ☎ 646746, Fax 646824, ≤, ⛱ – 🛗 📺 ☎ 🅿 – 🏛 40. AE VISA. ⛔
  April-October – **Meals** 12.00/22.00 **st.** and dinner a la carte 5.50 – **33 rm** 50.00/80.00 **st.**, 2 suites – SB.
- **Spanish Point,** ☎ 646177, Fax 646179, ≤ – 📺 ☎ 🅿. AE VISA
  Meals (restricted service in winter) 9.50/19.00 **t.** and a la carte 5.50 – **5 rm** 22.00/72.00 **st.** – SB.

BALLYEDMUND Wexford – see Gorey.

BALLYHACK (Baile Hac) Wexford 405 L 11 – pop. 221 – ✉ New Ross – ☎ 051.

♦Dublin 105 – ♦Waterford 8.5.

- **Neptune,** Ballyhack Harbour, ☎ 389284, Fax 389284 – AE VISA
  April-October – **Meals** - Seafood *(closed Sunday and Monday September-May)* (dinner only) 13.50 **st.** and a la carte 6.50.

BALLYHEIGE (Baile Uí Thaidhg) Kerry 405 C 10 – ☎ 066.

♦Dublin 186 – ♦Limerick 73 – Tralee 11.

- **White Sands,** ☎ 33102, Fax 33357 – 📺 ☎ 🅿. VISA
  April-September – **Meals** (dinner only and Sunday lunch)/dinner 15.00 **s.** and a la carte 5.00 – **57 rm** 36.00/62.00 **st.** – SB.

BALLYLICKEY (Béal Átha Leice) Cork 405 D 12 Ireland G. – ✉ Bantry – ☎ 027.

Exc. : Glengarriff★ (Garinish Island★★, access by boat) NW : 8 m. by N 71 – Healy Pass★★ (≤★★) W : 23 m. by N 71, R 572 and R 574 – Slieve Miskish Mountains (≤★★) W : 29 m. by N 71 and R 572 – Lauragh (Derreen Gardens★ *AC*) NW : 27½ m. by N 71, R 572 and R 574 – Allihies (copper mines★) W : 41½ m. by N 71, R 572 and R 575 – Garnish Island (≤★) W : 44 m. by N 71 and R 572.

⛳9 Bantry Park, Donemark ☎ 50579.

♦Dublin 216 – ♦Cork 55 – ♦Killarney 45.

Ballylickey Manor House ⑤, ℘ 50071, Fax 50124, ≤, « Extensive gardens », heated, park – rest TV ☎ P. AE VISA.
April-October – **Meals** *(closed Wednesday lunch)* (dinner residents only) (light lunch)/ dinner 30.00 **t.** 8.00 – **7 rm** -/90.00 **t.**, 4 suites – SB.

Sea View House ⑤, ℘ 50462, Fax 51555, ≤, – TV ☎ & P. AE VISA JCB
mid March-mid November – **Meals** (bar lunch Monday to Saturday)/dinner 22.50 **t.** 6.50 – **17 rm** 45.00/100.00 **st.** – SB.

Reendesert, ℘ 50153, Fax 50597 – TV ☎ P. AE VISA
10 April-October – **Meals** (bar lunch Monday to Saturday)/dinner 16.00 **st.** and a la carte 4.25 – **19 rm** 31.00/58.00 **st.** – SB.

XX Tra Amici, Coomhola Rd, N : ½ m. on Coohane Church rd ℘ 50235, Fax 50958 – P
Meals - Italian.

BALLYLIFFIN (Baile Lifín) Donegal 405 J 2 Ireland G. – pop. 334 – ✉ Carndonagh – ✆ 077.

Exc. : Inishowen Peninsula★★ : Malin Head★★★ (≤★★★) N : 19 m. by R 238 and R 242 – Carndonagh High Cross★, SE : 6 m. by R 238 – Gap of Mamore★, SW : 8 m. by R 238 – Lag Sand Dunes★, NE : 12 m. by R 238 and R 242.

18 Clonmany ℘ 76119.

♦Dublin 180 – Donegal 83 – ♦Londonderry 35.

Strand, ℘ 76107, Fax 76486, – TV ☎ P. VISA.
closed 24 to 26 December – **Meals** 8.50/16.00 **t.** 4.15 – **12 rm** 30.00/45.00 **t.**

BALLYMACARBRY (Baile Mhac Cairbre) Waterford 405 I 11 Ireland G. – pop. 240 – ✉ Clonmel – ✆ 052.

Exc. : W : Nier Valley Scenic Route★★.

♦Dublin 118 – ♦Cork 49 – Waterford 39.

Hanora's Cottage ⑤, Nire Valley, E : 4 m. by Nire Drive rd and Nire Valley Lakes rd ℘ 36134, Fax 36540, – TV ☎ P. VISA.
Meals (closed Sunday dinner to non-residents) (dinner only and Sunday lunch)/dinner a la carte 18.00/23.00 **st.** 5.95 – **8 rm** 30.00/40.00 **st.**

Clonanav Farm ⑤, N : 1 m. by T 27 ℘ 36141, Fax 36141, ≤, , park – rm ☎ P. AE VISA.
February-mid November – **Meals** 12.00 **st.** 3.85 – **10 rm** 20.00/40.00 **st.**

BALLYMOTE (Baile an Mhóta) Sligo 405 G 5 – ✉ Sligo – ✆ 071.

♦Dublin 124 – Longford 48 – ♦Sligo 15.

Mill House without rest., Keenaghan, ℘ 83449, – P.
closed 18 December-8 January – **5 rm** 15.00/28.00.

BALLYNAHINCH (Baile na hInse) Galway 405 C 7 – ✉ Recess – ✆ 095.

♦Dublin 140 – ♦Galway 41 – Westport 49.

Ballynahinch Castle ⑤, Ballinafad, ℘ 31006, Fax 31085, ≤ Owenmore river and woods, , park, – TV ☎ P. AE VISA.
closed February – **Meals** (bar lunch)/dinner 23.00 **t.**and a la carte 7.00 – **28 rm** 69.00/ 104.00 **t.**

BALLYSHANNON (Béal Atha Seanaion) Donegal 405 M 4 Ireland G. – pop. 2 573 – ✆ 072.

Envir. : Rossnowlagh Strand★★, N : 6 m. by R 231.

♦Dublin 157 – Donegal 13 – ♦Sligo 27.

Dorrian's Imperial, Main St., ℘ 51147, Fax 51001 – TV ☎ P – 30. AE VISA.
closed 23 to 31 December – **Meals** 9.50/16.50 **t.** and a la carte – **26 rm** 40.00/70.00 **t.** – SB.

BALLYVAUGHAN (Baile Uí Bheacháin) Clare 405 E 8 Ireland G. – pop. 181 – ✆ 065.

Envir. : The Burren★★ (Cliffs of Moher★★★, Scenic Routes★★, Aillwee Cave★ *AC* (Waterfall★), Corcomroe Abbey★, Kilfenora Crosses★).

♦Dublin 149 – Ennis 34 – ♦Galway 29.

Gregans Castle ⑤, SW : 3 ¾ m. on N 67 ℘ 77005, Fax 77111, ≤ countryside and Galway Bay, – ☎ P. VISA JCB.
6 April-October – **Meals** (bar lunch)/dinner 27.00 **t.** and a la carte 7.85 – **18 rm** 76.00/ 99.00 **t.**, 4 suites.

Hyland's, ℘ 77037, Fax 77131 – TV ☎ P. AE VISA.
closed 6 January-5 February – **Meals** a la carte 19.00 approx. 6.50 – **19 rm** 24.00/ 60.00 **t.**

Rusheen Lodge without rest., Knocknagrough, SW : ¾ m. on N 67 ℘ 77092, Fax 77152, – TV ☎ P. AE VISA.
closed 16 December-1 February – **6 rm** 30.00/40.00 **st.**

BANAGHER **(Beannchar) Offaly** 405 I 8 **Ireland G.** – pop. 1 428 – 0902.

Envir. : Clonfert Cathedral★ (West doorway★★).

◆Dublin 83 – ◆Galway 54 – ◆Limerick 56 – ◆Tullamore 24.

- **Brosna Lodge,** Main St., ℘ 51350, Fax 51521, – TV ☎ P. VISA
closed February – **Meals** (bar lunch Monday to Saturday)/dinner 14.95 **st.** and a la carte 4.50 – **14 rm** 24.00/48.00 **st.** – SB.
- **Old Forge,** West End, ℘ 51504 – P.
closed 25 December – **Meals** (by arrangement) (communal dining) – **4 rm** 16.00/32.00 **st.** – SB.

BANDON **(Droichead na Bandan) Cork** 405 F 12 – 023.

◆Dublin 174 – ◆Cork 19.

- **Munster Arms,** Oliver Plunkett St., ℘ 41562, Fax 41562 – TV ☎. AE ① VISA.
closed 25 December – **Meals** 8.95/19.00 **st.** and a la carte 6.50 – **29 rm** 30.00/50.00 **st.** – SB.
- **St. Anne's** without rest., Clonakilty Rd, SW : 3/4 m. on N 71 ℘ 44239, – P. VISA.
5 rm 18.00/30.00 **st.**

BANTEER **(Bántár) Cork** 405 F 11 – 029.

◆Dublin 158 – ◆Cork 30 – ◆Killarney 29 – ◆Limerick 48.

- **Clonmeen Lodge**, E : 2 m. on Mallow rd ℘ 56238, Fax 56294, , , park – P. VISA.
Meals (booking essential) (dinner only) a la carte 18.00 approx. 5.50 – **6 rm** 30.00/60.00 **st.** – SB.

BANTRY **(Beanntraí) Cork** 405 D 12 **Ireland G.** – pop. 2 777 – ECD : Wednesday – 027.

See : Bantry House★ *AC* – The Square ℘ 50229 (June-September).

◆Dublin 218 – ◆Cork 57 – ◆Killarney 48.

- **Bantry House**, ℘ 50047, Fax 50795, ≤, « Early 18C stately home with formal gardens » – ☎ P. AE ① VISA.
closed 23-27 December – **Meals** *(closed Saturday and Sunday)* (residents only) (dinner only) 25.00 **t.** 6.50 – **9 rm** 50.00/100.00 **t.** – SB.
- **Dunauley** without rest., Seskin, NE : 1 m. by Vaughan's Pass rd ℘ 50290, ≤ – P.
May-September – **5 rm** 20.50/36.00 **st.**
- XX **Larchwood House** with rm, Pearsons Bridge, NE : 4 1/4 m. by N 71 ℘ 66181, ≤, – P. AE ① VISA.
closed Sunday and 4 days Christmas – **Meals** (dinner only) 25.00 **t.** 6.00 – **4 rm** 20.00/40.00 **t.**

BAREFIELD **(Gort Lomán) Clare** 405 F 9 – see Ennis.

BIRR **(Biorra) Offaly** 405 I 8 **Ireland G.** – pop. 3 280 – 0509.

See : Town★ – Birr Castle Demesne★★ *AC* (Telescope★) – **Exc.** : Roscrea★ (Damer House★ *AC*) S : 12 m. by N 62 – Slieve Bloom Mountains★, E : 13 m. by R 440.

18 The Glenns ℘ 20082 – ℘ 20110 (10 May-12 September).

Athlone 28 – ◆Dublin 87 – Kilkenny 49 – ◆Limerick 49.

- Dooly's, Emmet Sq., ℘ 20032, Fax 21332 – TV ☎ – 300
18 rm.
- **County Arms,** Station Rd, ℘ 20791, Fax 21234, , squash – TV ☎ P – 80. AE ① VISA JCB.
Meals 8.00/19.00 **t.** and a la carte 6.50 – **18 rm** 36.00/72.00 **t.** – SB.

BLACKROCK **(An Charraig Dhubh) Dublin** 405 N 8 – see Dublin.

BLARNEY **(An Bhlarna) Cork** 405 G 12 **Ireland G.** – pop. 2 043 – ✉ Cork – 021.

See : Blarney Castle★★ *AC* – Blarney House★ *AC*.

◆Dublin 167 – ◆Cork 6.

- **Blarney Park,** ℘ 385281, Fax 381506, , , , , – TV ☎ & P – 300. AE ① VISA.
Meals 11.00/18.00 **t.** 6.00 – **75 rm** 56.00/104.00 **t.** – SB.

at Tower W : 2 m. on R 617 – ✉ Cork – 021.

- **Ashlee Lodge** without rest., ℘ 385346 – P.
April-October – **5 rm** 20.00/32.00 **st.**

BLESSINGTON **(Baile Coimán) Wicklow** 405 M 8 – 045.

◆Dublin 19 – Kilkenny 56 – Wexford 70.

- **Tulfarris House**, S : 6 m. by N 81 ℘ 64574, Fax 64423, ≤, , , , 9, , , park, – TV ☎ P. AE ① VISA JCB
closed 4 days Christmas – **Meals** (bar lunch Monday to Saturday)/dinner 21.00 – **21 rm** 61.50/102.00 **st.** – SB.

BOYLE (Mainistir na Búille) Roscommon 405 H 6 Ireland G. – pop. 1 695 – 079.

See : Boyle Abbey* AC.

Envir. : Lough Key Forest Park** AC, E : 2 m.

Roscommon Rd 62594.

Patrick Street 62145 (1 June-17 September).

Dublin 107 – Ballina 40 – Galway 74 – Roscommon 26 – Sligo 24.

Forest Park, Dublin Rd, E : ½ m. on N 4 62229, Fax 63113, – . VISA.
Meals 11.00/20.00 **t.** and dinner a la carte 5.00 – **12 rm** 35.00/60.00 **st.** – SB.

BRAY (Bré) Wicklow 405 N 8 Ireland G. – pop. 25 096 – ECD : Wednesday – 01.

Envir. : Powerscourt** (Waterfall*** AC) W : 4 m. - Killruddery House and Gardens* AC, S : 2 m. by R 761.

Woodbrook, Dublin Rd 282 4799 – Old Conna, Ferndale Rd 282 6055 – Ravenswell Rd 286 2484.

286 7128 (mid June-August).

Dublin 13 – Wicklow 20.

Tree of Idleness, Seafront, 286 3498 – VISA
closed Monday, first 2 weeks September and Christmas – **Meals** - Greek-Cypriot (dinner only) 20.00 **t.** and a la carte 6.75.

BUNCLODY (Bun Clóidí) Wexford 405 M 10 Ireland G. – pop. 1 316 (inc. Carrickduff) – 054.

Envir. : Mount Leinster*, SW : 4 m..

Dublin 63 – Kilkenny 32 – Wexford 27.

Clohamon House, Clohamon, SE : 1 ¾ m. by Carnew rd 77253, Fax 77956, « 18C country house », park – rm . VISA.
March-mid November (booking essential) – **Meals** *(closed Sunday except Bank Holidays)* (residents only) (communal dining) (dinner only) 22.50 **t.** 6.00 – **5 rm** 42.00/84.00 **st.**

BUNCRANA (Bun Crannacha) Donegal 405 J 2 – 077.

Dublin 160 – Londonderry 15 – Sligo 99.

Lake of Shadows, Grianan Park, 61005 –
23 rm.

BUNDORAN (Bun Dobhráin) Donegal 405 H 4 – 072.

Main St. 41350 (June-September).

Dublin 161 – Donegal 17 – Sligo 23.

Great Northern, N :¼ m. 41204, Fax 41114, – . VISA
closed 5 January-17 March – **Meals** 9.00/22.00 **t.** 5.00 – **94 rm** 48.00/90.00 **t.**

Holyrood, 41232, Fax 41100, – . VISA
closed 23-26 December – **Meals** (carving rest.)(bar lunch Monday to Saturday)/dinner 16.00 **st.** and a la carte 4.25 – **85 rm** 35.00/52.00 **st.**

Allingham Arms, 41075, Fax 41171 – . VISA.
Meals 8.00/17.00 **t.** and dinner a la carte 4.50 – **88 rm** 35.00/65.00 **t.** – SB.

Bay View without rest., Main St., 41296, Fax 41147, – . VISA
19 rm 23.00/32.00 **st.**

BUNRATTY (Bun Raite) Clare 405 F 9 Ireland G. – 061.

See : Castle and Folk Park** AC.

360133 (29 April-September).

Dublin 129 – Ennis 15 – Limerick 8.

Fitzpatrick's Bunratty Shamrock, 361177, Telex 72114, Fax 471252, – rm rest – 200. VISA.
Meals 10.50/20.50 **t.** and dinner a la carte – 8.50 – **115 rm** 75.00/256.00 **t.** – SB.

Shannon View without rest., NW : 1 m. on N 18 364056, Fax 364056, – .
March-November – **4 rm** 16.00/32.00 **st.**

Bunratty Lodge without rest.,, N : 1½ m. 369402, – .
April-October – **6 rm** 23.00/33.00 **st.**

MacCloskey's, Bunratty House Mews, 364082, « Cellars of Georgian house » – . VISA
closed Sunday, Monday and 20 December-25 January – **Meals** (dinner only) 26.00 **t.** 7.50.

BUTLERSTOWN (Baile an Bhuitléaraigh) Cork 405 F 13 Ireland G. – Bandon – 023.

Envir. : Courtmacsherry*, N : 3 m.

Dublin 193 – Cork 32.

Dunworley Cottage, Dunworley, S : 2 m. 40314 – . VISA
closed Monday, Tuesday and November-mid March except Christmas – **Meals** a la carte 16.00/24.50 **t.**

CAHERDANIEL (Cathair Dónall) Kerry 405 B 12 – ✉ Waterville – ☎ 0667.
♦Dublin 238 – ♦Killarney 48.

XX **Loaves and Fishes,** ☎ 75273 – VISA
April-September – **Meals** *(closed Tuesday except June-August and Monday)* (dinner only) 22.50/24.25 **t.** and a la carte 5.00.

CAHIR/CAHER (An Chathair) Tipperary 405 I 10 **Ireland G.** – pop. 2 055 – ECD : Thursday – ☎ 052.
See : Caher Castle★★ *AC* – Town Square★ – St. Paul's Church★.
Envir. : Swiss Cottage★ *AC*, S : 1 m. by R 670.
Exc. : Clonmel★ (County Museum★, St. Mary's Church★, Riverside★, Quay★) E : 10 m. by N 24.
Cahir Park, Kilcommon ☎ 41474.
Castle Street ☎ 41453 (1 May-1 October).
♦Dublin 112 – ♦Cork 49 – Kilkenny 41 – ♦Limerick 38 – ♦Waterford 39.

Kilcoran Lodge, SW : 4¾ m. on N 8 ☎ 41288, Fax 41994, park – ☎ – 200
23 rm.

CAPPOQUIN (Ceapach Choinn) Waterford 405 I 11 **Ireland G.** – pop. 829 – ☎ 058.
Envir. : Lismore★ (Lismore Castle Gardens★ *AC*, St. Carthage's Cathedral★), W : 4 m. by N 72 – Mount Melleray Abbey★, N : 4 m. by R 669.
Exc. : The Gap★ (←★) NW : 9 m. by R 669.
♦Dublin 136 – ♦Cork 31 – ♦Waterford 40.

Richmond House, SE : ½ m. on N 72 ☎ 54278, Fax 54988, park – ☎. VISA.
closed 24 to 31 December – **Meals** *(closed Sunday and Monday to non-residents)* (dinner only) 22.00 **st.** and a la carte 5.00 – **10 rm** 25.00/56.00 **st.** – SB.

Le Guide change, changez de guide Michelin tous les ans.

CARAGH LAKE (Loch Cárthaí) Kerry 405 C 11 **Ireland G.** – ☎ 066.
See : Lough Caragh★.
Exc. : Iveragh Peninsula★★★ (Ring of Kerry★★).
Dooks, Glenbeigh ☎ 68205/68200.
♦Dublin 212 – ♦Killarney 22 – Tralee 25.

Ard-Na-Sidhe, ☎ 69105, Fax 69282, ←, « Country house atmosphere », park – ☎. AE VISA.
May-September – **Meals** (dinner only) 25.00 **st.** and a la carte 8.80 – **20 rm** 64.00/125.00 **st.**

Caragh Lodge, ☎ 69115, Fax 69316, ←, « Country house atmosphere », – ☎. VISA.
April-14 October – **Meals** (dinner only) 24.00 **t.** 6.00 – **10 rm** 60.00/95.00 **t.**

CARLINGFORD (Cairlinn) Louth 405 N 5 **Ireland G.** – pop. 850 – ☎ 042.
See : Town★.
Exc. : Windy Gap★, NW : 8 m. by R 173.
♦Dublin 66 – ♦Dundalk 13.

McKevitt's Village, Market Sq., ☎ 73116, Fax 73144, – TV ☎. AE VISA.
Meals 12.50/17.50 **st.** and a la carte 4.50 – **14 rm** 28.00/56.00 **st.** – SB.

Carlingford House without rest., ☎ 73118, – TV
April-October – **5 rm** 18.00/30.00.

CARLOW (Ceatharlach) Carlow 405 L 9 – ☎ 0503.
♦Dublin 50 – Kilkenny 23 – Wexford 47.

Barrowville Town House without rest., Kilkenny Rd, ☎ 43324, Fax 41953, – TV ☎.
7 rm 17.50/40.00 **st.**

Goleen without rest., Milford, SW : 5¼ m. on N 9 ☎ 46132, – TV ☎. VISA.
closed March-November – **6 rm** 15.00/36.00 **st.**

CARRICKMACROSS (Carraig Mhachaire Rois) Monaghan 405 L 6 **Ireland G.** – pop. 1 678 – ☎ 042.
Envir. : Dún a' Rá Forest Park★, SW : 5 m. by R 179 – St. Mochta's House★, E : 7 m. by R 178.
Nuremore ☎ 61438.
♦Dublin 57 – Dundalk 14.

Nuremore, S : 1 m. on N 2 ☎ 61438, Fax 61853, ←, park, squash – rest TV ☎ – 250. AE VISA.
Meals 15.50/27.50 **st.** and dinner a la carte 6.50 – **69 rm** 75.00/150.00 **st.** – SB.

CARRICK-ON-SHANNON (Cora Droma Rúisc) Leitrim 405 H 6 – ☎ 078.

♦Dublin 97 – Ballina 50 – ♦Galway 74 – Roscommon 26 – ♦Sligo 34.

Hollywell without rest., Liberty Hill, ☎ 21124, Fax 21124, ←, – P.
9 January-15 December – **4 rm** 30.00/50.00 **t.**

CARRICK-ON-SUIR (Carraig na Siûire) Tipperary 405 J 10 – pop. 5 143 – ☎ 051.

Garravone ☎ 40047.

☎ 40726 (May-7 September).

♦Dublin 95 – ♦Cork 68 – ♦Limerick 62 – ♦Waterford 16.

Carraig, Main St., ☎ 641455, Fax 641604 – rest TV ☎ P – 50. AE VISA.
closed Good Friday and Christmas Day – **Meals** 7.35/14.95 **st.** and a la carte – **14 rm** 30.00/50.00 **st.** – SB.

CASHEL (Caiseal) Tipperary 405 I 10 **Ireland G.** – pop. 2 473 – ECD : Wednesday – ☎ 062.

See : Town★★★ – Rock of Cashel★★★ *AC* – Cormac's Chapel★★ – Round Tower★ – Museum★ – Cashel Palace Gardens★ – Cathedrals★ – GPA Bolton Library★ *AC* – Hore Abbey★ – Dominican Friary★.

Envir. : Holy Cross Abbey★★, N : 9 m. by R 660 – Athassel Abbey★, W : 5 m. by N 74.

Bolton Library ☎ 61333 (1 April-1 October).

♦Dublin 101 – ♦Cork 60 – Kilkenny 34 – ♦Limerick 36 – ♦Waterford 44.

Cashel Palace, Main St., ☎ 61411, Fax 61521, « Former Archbishop's palace, gardens » – TV ☎ P – 25. AE VISA JCB.
closed 23 to 26 December – **Meals** 18.00/26.00 **t.** 6.75 – 11.00 – **20 rm** 85.00/225.00 **t.** – SB.

Ros Guill House without rest., NE : ¾ m. on R 691 ☎ 61507, – P. VISA.
April-October – **5 rm** 25.00/33.00 **st.**

Chez Hans, Rockside, ☎ 61177, « Converted 19C church » – P. VISA
closed Sunday, Monday and first 3 weeks January – **Meals** (dinner only) a la carte 22.50/26.50 **t.** 6.50.

La guida cambia, cambiate la guida ogni anno.

CASHEL BAY (Cuan an Chaisil) Galway 405 C 7 **Ireland G.** – ☎ 095.

See : Town★.

♦Dublin 173 – Galway 41.

Cashel House, ☎ 31001, Fax 31077, ←, « Country house atmosphere, gardens », park, – TV ☎ P. AE VISA
closed 10 to 31 January – **Meals** (bar lunch)/dinner 19.95/29.00 **t.** and a la carte 7.00 – **32 rm** 46.00/160.00 **t.** – SB.

Zetland House, ☎ 31111, Fax 31117, ← Cashel Bay, « Country house, gardens », – ☎ P. AE VISA
10 April-October – **Meals** (dinner only) 30.00 **st.** 8.50 – **19 rm** 75.00/150.00 **st.** – SB.

Glynsk House, SW : 4½ m. on R 340 ☎ 32279, Fax 32342, ← – TV ☎ P. VISA
Meals 18.00 **t.** (dinner) and a la carte 12.25/17.00 **t.** 6.00 – **12 rm** 27.00/50.00 **st.** – SB.

CASTLEBALDWIN (Béal Átha na gCarraigíní) Sligo 405 G 5 **Ireland G.** – ✉ Boyle (Roscommon) – ☎ 071.

Envir. : Carrowkeel Megalithic Cemetery (←★★) S : 3 m.

♦Dublin 118 – Longford 42 – ♦Sligo 15.

Cromleach Lodge, Ballindoon, SE : 3½ m. ☎ 65155, Fax 65455, ← Lough Arrow, , park – TV ☎ P. AE VISA.
closed 15 December-28 January – **Meals** (dinner only) 35.00 **t.** 5.95 – **10 rm** 90.00/170.00 **t.** – SB.

CASTLEBLAYNEY (Baile na Lorgan) Monaghan 405 L 5 – pop. 2 029 – ☎ 042.

Muchno Park ☎ 40197.

♦Dublin 68 – ♦Belfast 58 – ♦Drogheda 39 – ♦Dundalk 17 – ♦Londonderry 80.

Glencarn, Monaghan Rd, ☎ 46666, Fax 46521, , – TV ☎ P. AE VISA.
Meals (bar lunch)/dinner 16.00 **t.** and a la carte 5.00 – **27 rm** 32.00/64.00 **t.** – SB.

CASTLECONNELL (Caisleán Uí Chonaill) Limerick 405 G 9 **Ireland G.** – pop. 1 053 – ✉ Limerick – ☎ 061.

See : Town★.

♦Dublin 111 – ♦Limerick 9.

Castle Oaks House, ☎ 377666, Fax 377717, ←, , , , , , park, – TV ☎ P. AE VISA.
closed 24 and 25 December – **Meals** (bar lunch Monday to Saturday)/dinner 16.95 **st.** and a la carte 4.75 – **11 rm** 54.00/90.00 **t.** – SB.

CASTLEDERMOT (Díseart Diarmada) Kildare 405 L 9 **Ireland G.** – pop. 741 – ☎ 0503.

Exc. : Carlow Cathedral (Marble Monument*) NE : 7 m. by N 9.

♦Dublin 44 – Kilkenny 30 – Wexford 54.

Kilkea Castle ⛰, Kilkea, NW : 3 ¾ m. on R 418 ☎ 45156, Fax 45187, ←, « Part 12C castle », ⛳, ⛳, park, – ⛶ rm ☎ 🅿 – 200. AE VISA.
closed 22 to 27 December – **Meals** 14.50/30.00 **t.** 6.00 – 10.00 – **39 rm** 150.00/170.00 **t.**, 1 suite – SB.

CAVAN (An Cabhán) Cavan 405 J 6 **Ireland G.** – pop. 3 332 – ☎ 049.

Envir. : Killykeen Forest Park*, W : 6 m. by R 198.

Farnham St. ☎ 31942 (May-September).

♦Dublin 71 – Drogheda 58 – Enniskillen 40.

Kilmore, Dublin Rd, E : 2 m. on N 3 ☎ 32288, Fax 32458 – ☎ & 🅿 – 550. AE VISA.
Meals 9.50/18.50 **t.** and dinner a la carte 4.80 – **39 rm** 36.00/66.00 **t.** – SB.

CLIFDEN (An Clochán) Galway 405 B 7 – pop. 808 – ECD : Thursday – ☎ 095.

Market Street ☎ 21163 (3 May-30 September).

♦Dublin 181 – Ballina 77 – ♦Galway 49.

Rock Glen Manor House ⛰, S : 1 ¼ m. by L 102 ☎ 21035, Fax 21737, – ☎ 🅿. AE VISA JCB.
15 March-October – **Meals** (bar lunch)/dinner 24.75 **st.** and a la carte 6.00 – **29 rm** 62.00/180.00 **st.**

Abbeyglen Castle ⛰, Sky Rd, W : ½ m. ☎ 21201, Fax 21797, ←, heated, – rm ☎ 🅿. AE VISA
closed 10 January-1 February – **Meals** (bar lunch)/dinner 19.50 **st.** 7.00 – **38 rm** 52.50/99.00 **st.**, 2 suites – SB.

Ardagh ⛰, Ballyconneely rd, S : 1 ¾ m. on L 102 ☎ 21384, Fax 21314, ← Ardbear Bay, – ☎ 🅿. AE VISA JCB.
April-October – **Meals** (bar lunch)/dinner 23.00 **t.** and a la carte 7.00 – **21 rm** 52.00/99.00 **st.** – SB.

Sunnybank House without rest., Sunny Bank, Church Hill, ☎ 21437, Fax 21976, heated, – ☎ 🅿. AE VISA.
March-October – **11 rm** 25.00/60.00 **st.**

Failte ⛰ without rest., S : 1 ¼ m. by L 102 ☎ 21159, ← – 🅿. AE VISA.
April-September – **5 rm** 13.50/30.00 **st.**

Mal Dua without rest., Galway Rd, E : ½ m. on N 59 ☎ 21171, Fax 21739 – ☎ 🅿. VISA.
closed December – **9 rm** 21.00/44.00 **st.**

Quay House, Beach Rd, ☎ 21369, Fax 41168, ←. VISA
closed 20-29 December – **Meals** *(closed Sunday and Monday December-March)* (light lunch May to September) 7.50/19.00 **st.** and a la carte 5.50.

CLONAKILTY (Cloich na Coillte) Cork 405 F 13 **Ireland G.** – ☎ 023.

See : West Cork Regional Museum* *AC.*

Envir. : Timoleague* (Franciscan Friary*) E : 5 m. by R 600.

♦Dublin 193 – ♦Cork 32.

Árd na Gréine Farm House ⛰, Ballinascarthy, NW : 5 ¾ m. by N 71 ☎ 39104, Fax 39397, – 🅿. AE VISA
Meals 14.00 **st.** and a la carte – **6 rm** 21.00/32.00 **st.** – SB.

CLONEA STRAND Waterford – see Dungarvan.

CLONMEL (Cluain Meala) Tipperary 405 I 10 – pop. 14 531 – ECD : Thursday – ☎ 052.

⛳18 Lyreanearla, Mountain Rd ☎ 21138.

Community Office, Nelson St. ☎ 22960 (17 June-7 September).

♦Dublin 108 – ♦Cork 59 – Kilkenny 31 – ♦Limerick 48 – ♦Waterford 29.

Minella ⛰, Coleville Rd, ☎ 22388, Fax 24381, park – ☎ 🅿 – 600
45 rm.

Clonmel Arms, Sarsfield St., ☎ 21233, Fax 21526 – ☎ – 400. AE VISA
closed 24-26 December – **Meals** a la carte 10.15/21.40 **t.** 4.50 – 6.50 – **31 rm** 53.00/76.00 **t.** – SB.

Jasmine Court, 36 Gladstone St., ☎ 24888 – AE VISA
Meals - Chinese 8.50/16.50 **t.** and dinner a la carte 5.95.

COBH (An Cóbh) Cork 405 H 12 – ☎ 021.

♦Dublin 173 – ♦Cork 13 – ♦Waterford 71.

Tearmann ⛰, Ballynde, N : 2½ m. by R 624 ☎ 813182, – 🅿.
March-October – **Meals** (by arrangement) 11.00 **s.** – **3 rm** 18.00/28.00 **s.**

CONG (Conga) Mayo 405 E 7 **Ireland G.** – pop. 183 – ☎ 092.

See : Town★.

Envir. : Lough Corrib★★.

Exc. : Ross Abbey★★ (Tower ≤★) – Joyce Country★★ (Lough Nafooey★★) W : by R 345.

♦Dublin 160 – Ballina 49 – ♦Galway 28.

Ashford Castle ⛰, ℘ 46003, Fax 46260, ≤, « Part 13C and 18C castle, in extensive formal gardens on shores of Lough Corrib », 9, park, – ‖ TV ☎ P – 140. AE VISA.
George V Room : **Meals** *(closed Christmas and New Year)* 20.00/33.00 and a la carte 9.00 – (see also *Connaught Room below*) – 13.80 – **77 rm** 198.00 **st.**, 6 suites.

Danagher's, ℘ 46028, Fax 46495 – TV ☎. VISA.
Meals 10.00/18.00 **st.** and a la carte 7.00 – **11 rm** 25.00/50.00 **st.** – SB.

XXXX **Connaught Room** (at Ashford Castle H.), ℘ 46003, Fax 46260, ≤ gardens, Lough Corrib and islands – P. AE VISA
Meals (booking essential) (dinner only) a la carte 35.00/46.00 12.50.

For the quickest route use the Michelin Main Road Maps:

970 Europe, 980 Greece, 984 Germany, 985 Scandinavia-Finland,

986 Great Britain and Ireland, 987 Germany-Austria-Benelux, 988 Italy,

989 France, 990 Spain-Portugal and 991 Yugoslavia.

CORK (Corcaigh) Cork 405 G 12 **Ireland G.** – pop. 174 400 – ☎ 021.

See : City★★ – Shandon Bells★★ EY, St. Fin Barre's Cathedral★★ *AC* Z, Cork Public Museum★★ X **M** – Grand Parade★ Z, South Mall★ Z, St. Patrick Street★ Z, Crawford Art Gallery★ Y – Christ the King Church★ X **D**, Elizabethan Fort★ Z, Cork Lough★ X.

Envir. : Dunkathel House★ *AC*, E : 5¾ m. by N 8 and N 25 X.

Exc. : Fota Island★★ (Fota House★★) E : 8 m. by N 8 and N 25 X – Cobh★ (St. Colman's Cathedral★, Lusitania Memorial★) SE : 15 m. by N 8, N 25 and R 624 X.

18 Douglas ℘ 891086, X – 18 Mahon, Cloverhill, Blackrock, X – 18 Monkstown, Parkgarriffe ℘ 841376, X – 18 Harbour Point, Clash, Little Island ℘ 353094, X.

Cork Airport : ℘ 313131, S : 4 m. by L 42 X – **Terminal** : Bus Station, Parnell Pl..

to France (Cherbourg and Le Harve) (Irish Ferries) 1 weekly (summer only), (Roscoff and St. Malo) (Brittany Ferries) 3 weekly (summer only) – to Swansea (Swansea Cork Ferries) (10 h).

Tourist House, Cork City, Grand Parade ℘ 273251 – Cork Ferryport, Ringaskiddy (1 June-30 September).

♦Dublin 154.

CORK
BUILT UP AREA

Baker's Road . . . . X 4
Commons Road . . . . X 12
Curragh Road . . . . X 14
Dublin Street . . . . X 16
Gardiner's Hill . . . . X 20
Great William O'Brien Street . . . . X 22
Horgan Quay . . . . X 23
Lower Mayfield Road . . . . X 31
Thomas Davis Street . . . . X 49
Victoria Cross Rd . . . . X 50
Watercourse Road . . . . X 52
Western Road . . . . X 53
Wilton Road . . . . X 55

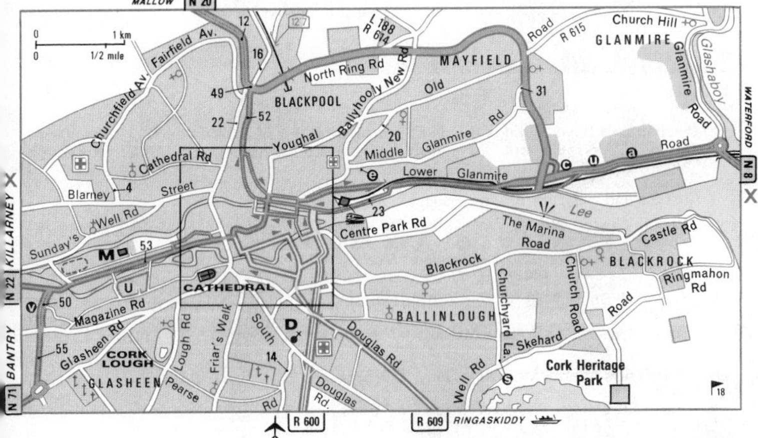

CORK

Merchant's Quay Shopping Centre . . . . Y
Oliver Plunkett Street. . . . . . . Z
St. Patrick's Street . . . . Z

Camden Place . . . . Y 5
Coburg Street. . . . . Y 10
Corn Market Street . . . . Y 13
Dominick Street. . . . . Y 15
Eason's Hill. . . . . Y 17
Emmet Place . . . . Y 18
Gerald Griffin St. . . . . Y 21
Infirmary Road . . . . Z 24
John Redmond Street . . . . . . Y 26
Lancaster Quay . . . . Z 28
Langford Row. . . . . Z 29
Lower Glanmire Road . . . . . . Y 30
Merchant's Quay. . . . . Y 32
Newsom's Quay . . . . Y 34
North Mall . . . . Y 35
O'Connell's Square . . . . Y 36
Parnell Place. . . . . Z 38
Pembroke Street . . . . Z 39
Proby's Quay . . . . Z 40
Roman Street. . . . . Y 42
St Patrick's Quay . . . . Y 44
Southern Road . . . . Z 45
South Link. . . . . Z 46
South Main Street . . . . Z 47
Summer Hill. . . . . Y 48
Wolfe Tone Street . . . . Y 56

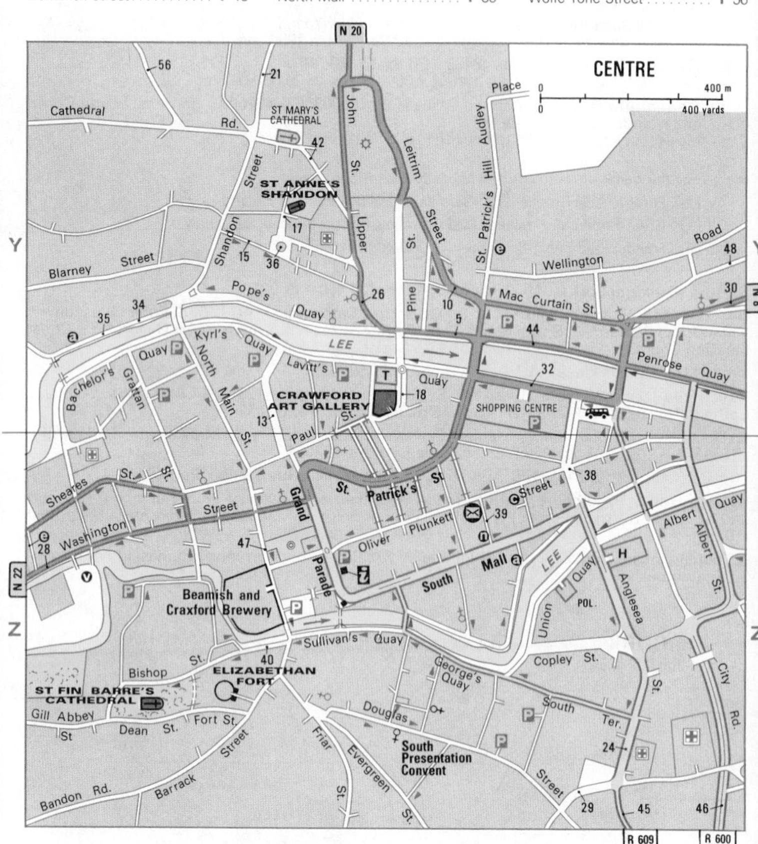

Fitzpatrick's Silver Springs, Tivoli, E : 2½ m. on N 8 ☎ 507533, Telex 76111, Fax 507641, park, squash – rest – 800. AE VISA JCB. X c
closed 25 December – **Meals** *(closed Sunday dinner except July and August)* 9.50/19.50 **t.** and a la carte **107 rm**, 2 suites – SB.

Jurys, Western Rd, by Washington St., ☎ 276622, Fax 274477, heated, squash – rest – 500. AE VISA. Z v
closed 24 to 26 December – ***Glandore :*** **Meals** 15.50 **t.** (dinner) and a la carte 15.15/26.60 **t.** 5.85 – 9.75 – **184 rm** 90.50/105.00 **t.**, 1 suite – SB.

Imperial, South Mall, ☎ 274040, Telex 75126, Fax 274040 – 600. AE VISA. Z n
closed 1 week Christmas – **Meals** 15.00/25.00 **t.** and a la carte 5.50 – **101 rm** 63.00/150.00 **t.** – SB.

Morrisons Island, Morrisons Quay, ☎ 275858, Fax 275833, – rm. AE VISA. Z a
closed Christmas – ***Riverbank :*** **Meals** (bar dinner Sunday) 12.50/18.95 **t.** and a la carte 6.50 – 6.50 – **8 rm** 75.00/110.00 **t.**, **32 suites** 110.00 **st.** – SB.

Rochestown Park, Rochestown Rd, SE : 3 m. by R 609 ℘ 892233, Fax 892178, – 150. X
Meals 12.00/22.00 **t.** and a la carte 5.50 – **63 rm** 57.00/85.00 **t.** – SB.

Arbutus Lodge, Middle Glanmire Rd, Montenotte, ℘ 501237, Fax 502893, – rest. X e
closed 24 to 30 December – **Meals** (see ***Arbutus Lodge*** below) – **20 rm** 45.00/115.00 **st.** – SB.

Lotamore House without rest., Tivoli, E : 3¼ m. on N 8 ℘ 822344, Fax 822219, park –. X a
closed Christmas – **20 rm** 30.00/50.00 **st.**

Victoria Lodge without rest., Victoria Cross, ℘ 542233, Fax 542572, –. X v
29 rm 28.00/50.00 **st.**

Forte Travelodge without rest., Blackash, S : 2¼ m. by R 600 ℘ 310722, Reservations (Freephone) 0800 850950 (UK) - 1800 709709 (Republic of Ireland) –. X
40 rm 33.50 **t.**

Seven North Mall without rest., 7 North Mall, ℘ 397191, Fax 300811 –. Y a
closed 9 December-15 January – **5 rm** 40.00/60.00 **st.**

Acorn House without rest., 14 St. Patricks Hill, ℘ 502474 – Y e
9 rm.

Cliffords, 18 Dyke Par., ℘ 275333 – Z e
closed lunch Saturday and Monday, Sunday, last week August and 1 week Christmas – **Meals** 13.50/29.00 **t.**

Arbutus Lodge (at Arbutus Lodge H.), Middle Glanmire Rd, Montenotte, ℘ 501237, Fax 502893, –. X e
closed Sunday to non-residents and 24 to 30 December – **Meals** 12.50/21.50 **st.** and a la carte 6.95.

Flemings with rm, Silver Grange House, Tivoli, E : 2¾ on N 8 ℘ 821621, Fax 821800, –. X u
closed 24 to 27 December – **Meals** 12.50/20.00 **t.** and a la carte 6.00 – **5 rm** 37.00/55.00 **t.** – SB.

Lovett's, Churchyard Lane, off Well Rd, Douglas, ℘ 294909 –. X s
closed Saturday lunch, Sunday and 24 to 30 December – **Meals** 14.50/21.00 **t.** and dinner a la carte.

Michael's Bistro, 4 Mardyke St., ℘ 276887 – Z e
closed Monday and Saturday lunch, Sunday and 1 week Christmas – **Meals** a la carte 10.65/18.70 **t.**

Jacques 9 Phoenix St., ℘ 277387, Fax 270634 –. Z c
closed Monday dinner, Sunday, 24 December-2 January and Bank Holidays – **Meals** a la carte 11.00/22.05 **t.** 6.00.

COURTOWN HARBOUR (Cuan Bhaile na Cúirte) Wexford 405 N 10 – pop. 343 – ✉ Gorey – ☎ 055.

♦Dublin 62 – ♦Waterford 59 – Wexford 42.

Courtown, ℘ 25108, Fax 25304, –.
17 March-October – **Meals** 10.00/19.00 **t.** and a la carte – **21 rm** 45.00/70.00 – SB.

CRATLOE (An Chreatalach) Clare 405 F 9 – ✉ Bunratty – ☎ 061.

♦Dublin 127 – Ennis 17 – ♦Limerick 7.

Bunratty View, ℘ 87352, Fax 87491, –
8 rm.

CROOKEDWOOD (Tigh Munna) Westmeath 405 K 7 – ✉ Mullingar – ☎ 044.

♦Dublin 55 – ♦Drogheda 30 – Mullingar 6.

Crookedwood House, E : 1½ m. on Delvin rd ℘ 72165, Fax 72166, « 18C rectory », –.
closed Sunday dinner, Monday and first 2 weeks November – **Meals** (dinner only and Sunday lunch)/dinner 18.50 and a la carte 5.95.

CROSSMOLINA (Crois Mhaoilíona) Mayo 405 E 5 **Ireland G.** – pop. 1 202 – ☎ 096.

Envir. : Errew Abbey*, SE : 6 m. by R 315.

Exc. : Broad Haven*, NW : 27 m. by N 59 and R 313.

♦Dublin 157 – ♦Ballina 6.5.

Enniscoe House, Castlehill, S : 2 m. on L 140 ℘ 31112, Fax 31773, « Georgian country house, antiques », park –.
April-14 October and January – **Meals** (dinner only) 20.00 **st.** 7.00 – **6 rm** 54.00/100.00 **st.** – SB.

CULDAFF (Cúil Dabhcha) Donegal 405 K 2 – ✉ Inishowen – ☎ 077.

♦Dublin 170 – ♦Londonderry 21 – ♦Sligo 115.

Culdaff House ⑤, NW : ½ m. by Beach rd ☎ 79103, ≤, « Working farm », – Ⓟ.
Meals (by arrangement) 13.00 – **6 rm** 20.00/30.00 **s.**

DALKEY (Deilginis) Dublin 405 N 8 **Ireland G.** – ☎ 01.

Envir. : ≤★★ of Killiney Bay from coast road south of Sorrento Point.

♦Dublin 11.

Guinea Pig, 17 Railway Rd, ☎ 285 9055 – AE VISA JCB
Meals - Seafood (booking essential) (dinner only) 21.95 **t.** and a la carte 6.00.

DELGANY (Deilgne) Wicklow 405 N 8 – pop. 7 442 (inc. Greystones) – ✉ Bray – ☎ 01.

Delganny ☎ 287 4645/287 4833.

♦Dublin 19.

Glenview ⑤, Glen of the Downs, NW : 2 m. by L 164 on N 11 ☎ 287 3399, Fax 287 7511, ≤, park – TV ☎ Ⓟ – 250. AE VISA.
closed 25 December – **Meals** 15.00/24.00 **t.** and dinner a la carte 5.50 – **40 rm** 62.00/170.00 **t.** – SB.

DINGLE (An Daingean) Kerry 405 B 11 **Ireland G.** – pop. 1 272 – ECD : Thursday – ☎ 066.

See : Town★ – Pier★, St. Mary's Church★.

Envir. : Gallarus Oratory★★★, NW : 5 m. by R 559 – NE : Connor Pass★★ – Kilmalkedar★, NW : 5½ m. by R 559.

Exc. : Mount Eagle (Beehive Huts★★) W : 9 m. by R 559 – Slea Head★★, W : 10½ m. by R 559 – Stradbally Strand★★, NE : 10½ m. via Connor Pass – Ballyferriter Heritage Centre★ *AC*, NW : 8 m. by R 559 – Mount Brandon★, N : 12½ m. by R 559 via Kilmalkedar – Blasket Islands★, W : 13 m. by R 559 and ferry from Dunquin.

Main Street ☎ 51188 (5 April- 31 October).

♦Dublin 216 – ♦Killarney 51 – ♦Limerick 95.

Dingle Skellig, SE : ½ m. by T 68 ☎ 51144, Fax 51501, ≤, – TV ☎ Ⓟ. AE VISA.
mid March-mid November – **Meals** 9.75/19.95 and a la carte 6.00 – **99 rm** 45.00/90.00 **t.**, 1 suite – SB.

Benners, Main St., ☎ 51638, Fax 51412, – TV ☎ Ⓟ
24 rm.

Greenmount House without rest., Gortonora, by John St. ☎ 51414, Fax 51974, ≤ – TV ☎ Ⓟ. VISA.
closed 20-28 December – **8 rm** -/40.00 **st.**

Milltown House ⑤ without rest., W : ¾ m. by Slea Head Drive ☎ 51372, Fax 51095, ≤, – TV ☎ Ⓟ. VISA.
March-mid November – **7 rm** 40.00/44.00 **st.**

Alpine House without rest., Mail Rd, E : on T 68 ☎ 51250, – TV ☎ Ⓟ. VISA.
14 rm 35.00.

Bambury's without rest., Mail Rd, E : on T 68 ☎ 51244, Fax 51786, ≤ – TV ☎ Ⓟ
12 rm.

Captains House without rest., The Mall, ☎ 51531, – TV ☎. AE VISA.
closed 5 January-16 March – **8 rm** 25.00/40.00 **t.**

Cleevaun without rest., Lady's Cross, Milltown, W : 1¼ m. on R 559 ☎ 51108, Fax 51108, ≤, – TV ☎ Ⓟ. VISA.
closed mid December-mid February – **9 rm** 33.00/39.00.

Beginish, Green St., ☎ 51588, Fax 51591, – AE VISA
mid March-mid November – **Meals** - Seafood *(closed Monday)* (light lunch)/dinner a la carte 16.45/23.45 **t.** 5.00.

Doyle's Seafood Bar with rm, 4 John St., ☎ 51174, Fax 51816 – TV ☎. VISA.
mid March-mid November – **Meals** *(closed Sunday)* (dinner only) 13.95/22.00 **t.** and a la carte 18.00/24.00 7.20 – **8 rm** 39.00/62.00 **t.**

DONEGAL (Dún na nGall) Donegal 405 H 4 **Ireland G.** – pop. 2 193 – ECD : Wednesday – ☎ 073.

See : Donegal Castle★ *AC*.

Exc. : Cliffs of Bunglass★★★, W : 30 m. by N 56 and R 263 – Glencolumbkille Folk Village★★ *AC*, W : 33 m. by N 56 and R 263 – Trabane Strand★★, W : 36 m. by N 56 and R 263 – Glenmalin Court Cairn★, W : 37 m. by N 56 and R 263 at Malin Beg.

Donegal Airport ☎ (075) 48232.

The Quay ☎ 21148 (April-October).

♦Dublin 164 – ♦Londonderry 48 – ♦Sligo 40.

St. Ernan's House ⑤, St. Ernan's Island, SW : 2 ¼ m. by N 15 ☎ 21065, Fax 22098, « Wooded island setting ≤ Donegal Bay », park – ⇔ rest TV ☎ P. VISA.
mid April-October – **Meals** (dinner only) 25.00 **st.** 6.00 – **12 rm** -/138.00 **st.** – SB.

Harvey's Point Country ⑤, NE : 4 ½ m. by T 27 (Killibegs rd) ☎ 22208, Fax 22352, ≤, « Loughside setting », ⑤, park, % – ⇔ rm TV ☎ P – 100. AE VISA
April-October – **Meals** (see Harvey's Point Country below) – **20 rm** 55.00/100.00 **t.** – SB.

Island View House without rest., Ballyshannon rd, SW : ¾ m. ☎ 22411, ≤ – TV P
closed January and February – **4 rm** 22.00/30.00 **st.**

Harvey's Point Country (at Harvey's Point Country H.), NE : 4½ m. by T 27 (Killibegs rd) ☎ 22208, Fax 22352, ≤, « Loughside setting », – P. AE VISA
April-October – **Meals** 9.50/25.00 **t.** and a la carte 5.80.

DOOLIN (Dúlainm) Clare 405 D 8 – ☎ 065.

♦Dublin 171 – ♦Galway 43 – ♦Limerick 50.

Aran View House ⑤, NE : ½ m. ☎ 74061, Fax 74540, ≤, « Working farm », park ⇔ rm TV ☎ P. AE VISA.
March-October – **Meals** (bar lunch Monday to Saturday)/dinner 18.00 **t.** and a la carte 4.95 – **19 rm** 30.00/60.00 **t.** – SB.

Doonmacfelim House without rest., ☎ 74503, % – ☎ P
8 rm.

DROGHEDA (Droichead Átha) Louth 405 M 6 – ☎ 041.

Envir. : Monasterboice★★, N : 6½ m. by N 1 – Termonfeckin (Tower House★) NE : 5 m. by R 166.

♦Dublin 29 – ♦Dundalk 22.

Boyne Valley, on N 1 ☎ 37737, Fax 39188, park ⇔ rm TV ☎ P – 150. AE VISA.
Meals 10.00/20.00 **st.** and dinner a la carte 4.50 – **37 rm** 30.00/120.00 **st.** – SB.

DRUMCLIFF (Droim Chliabh) Sligo 405 G 5 – ☎ 071.

♦Dublin 178 – Donegal 34 – ♦Sligo 6.

Mountain View ⑤ without rest., Carney, NW : 1 m. ☎ 63290, ≤, « Working farm », – P
April-October – **5 rm** 18.00/30.00 **st.**

DUBLIN (Baile Átha Cliath) Dublin 405 N 7 **Ireland G.** – pop. 859 976 – ☎ 01.

See : City★★★ – Trinity College★★★ (Library★★★ *AC*) EY – Chester Beatty Library★★★ CV – Phoenix Park★★★ AU – Dublin Castle★★ DY – Christ Church Cathedral★★ DY – St. Patrick's Cathedral★★ DZ – March's Library★★ DZ – National Museum★★ (Treasury★★), FZ – National Gallery★★ FZ – Merrion Square★★ FZ – Rotunda Hospital Chapel★★ EX – Kilmainham Hospital★★ AV – Kilmainham Gaol Museum★★ AV **M6** – National Botanic Gardens★★ BU – No 29★ FZ **D** – Liffey Bridge★ EY – Taylors' Hall★ DY – City Hall★ DY **H** – St. Audoen's Gate★ DY **B** – St. Stephen's Green★ EZ – Grafton Street★ EYZ – Powerscourt Centre★ EY – Civic Museum★ EY **M1** – Bank of Ireland★ EY – O'ConnelStreet★ (Anna Livia Fountain★) EX – St. Michan's Church★ DY **E** – Hush Lane Municipal Gallery of Modern Art★ EX **M4** – Pro-Cathedral★ EX – Garden of Remembrance★ EX – Custon House★ FX – Bluecoat School★ BU **F** – Guinness Museum★ BV **M7** – Marino Casino★ CU – Zoological Gardens★ AU – Newman House★ *AC* EZ.

Exc. : Powerscourt★★ (Waterfall★★★ *AC*), S : 14 m. by N 11 and R 117 BV – Russborough House★★★, SW : 22 m. by N 81 BV.

18 Elm Park G. & S.C., Nutley House, Donnybrook ☎ 2693438, CV – 18 Milltown, Lower Churchtown Rd ☎ 977060/976090, BV – 18 Royal Dublin, Bull Island ☎ 336346, CU – 18 Forrest Little ☎ 8401183/8401763, BU – 18 Lucan, Hermitage ☎ 626 5396, AU – 18 Edmondstown, Rathfarnham ☎ 4932461, BV.

Dublin Airport : ☎ 8444900, N : 5½m. by N 1 BU – **Terminal** : Busaras (Central Bus Station) Store St.

to Holyhead (B & I Line) 2 daily (3 h 30 mn) – to the Isle of Man (Douglas) (Isle of Man Steam Packet Co. Ltd) (4 h 30 mn).

Bus Eireann Desk, 14 Upper O'Connell St. ☎ 874 7733 – Dublin Airport ☎ 844 5387.

Baggot St., Bridge ☎ 874 7733.

♦Belfast 103 – ♦Cork 154 – ♦Londonderry 146.

Plans on following pages

Conrad Dublin, Earlsfort Terr., D2, ☎ 676 5555, Telex 91872, Fax 676 5424 – ⇔ rm TV ☎ & P – 300. AE VISA JCB. EZ **z**
Alexandra **: Meals** *(closed Saturday lunch, Sunday and Bank Holidays)* 16.95/28.00 **st.** and a la carte 6.00 – ***Plurabelle*** **: Meals** 13.50 **t.** and a la carte 6.00 – 11.00 – **182 rm** 155.00/180.00 **t.**, 9 suites.

Berkeley Court, Lansdowne Rd, Ballsbridge, D4, ☎ 660 1711, Fax 661 7238, – ⇔ rm rest TV ☎ & P – 500. AE VISA. CV **c**
Meals 11.00/26.00 **t.** and a la carte 5.50 – 8.00 – **181 rm** 99.00/140.00 **t.**, 5 suites.

Westbury, Grafton St., D2, 679 1122, Telex 91091, Fax 679 7078 – rm rest – 200 EY **z**
195 rm, 8 suites.

Shelbourne (Forte), 27 St. Stephen's Green, D2, 676 6471, Telex 93653, Fax 661 6006 – rm – 400 EZ **s**
155 rm, 9 suites.

Jurys H. & Towers, Pembroke Rd, Ballsbridge, D4, 660 5000, Telex 93723, Fax 660 5540, heated – rm rest – 850.
***Kish* : Meals** Seafood (dinner only) 16.00/21.00 **t.** – ***Embassy Garden* : Meals** a la carte approx. 27.50 **t.** 6.00 – 9.75 – **378 rm** 110.00/185.00 **t.**, 6 suites – SB. CV **c**

Gresham, O'Connell St., D1, 874 6881, Telex 32473, Fax 878 7175 – rest – 300. EX **s**
closed 24 and 25 December – **Meals** 17.00 **st.** (dinner) and a la carte 11.45/20.00 **t.** 4.75 – 9.55 – **194 rm** 75.00/110.00 **t.**, 6 suites.

Burlington, Upper Leeson St., D4, 660 5222, Telex 93815, Fax 660 8496 – – 1000 BV **o**
448 rm, 4 suites.

Doyle Montrose, Stillorgan Rd, D12, SE : 4 m. by N 11 269 3311, Telex 91207, Fax 269 1164 – rest – 80. CV **n**
Meals 11.00/15.00 **t.** and a la carte 5.30 – 6.75 – **179 rm** 76.00/160.00 **t.**

Royal Dublin, O'Connell St., D1, 873 3666, Fax 873 3120 – rm – 220. EX **e**
closed 25 December – **Meals** 10.95/18.50 **st.** and a la carte 4.65 – **114 rm** 78.00/99.00 **st.**, 3 suites – SB.

Hibernian, Eastmoreland Pl., Ballsbridge, D4, 668 7666, Fax 660 2655 – . BV **x**
closed 23-30 December – **Meals** *(closed Saturday lunch)* 14.95/26.95 **t.** and dinner a la carte 5.95 – **29 rm** 87.00/135.00 **st.** – SB.

Central, 1-5 Exchequer St., D2, 679 7302, Fax 679 7303 – rm – 80 EY **u**
69 rm, 1 suite.

Stephens Hall, Earlsfort Centre, 14-17 Lower Leeson St., D2, 661 0585, Fax 661 0606 – . EZ **o**
closed 24-28 December – **Meals** *(closed Saturday lunch and Sunday)* 9.50/16.50 **st.** and a la carte 5.00 – 7.00 – **3 rm** 95.00/134.00 **st.**, 34 suites 134.00 **st.** – SB.

Temple Bar, Fleet St., D2, 677 3333, Fax 677 3088 – rm – 30. EY **e**
closed 22 to 28 December – **Meals** 10.25/14.00 **st.** and a la carte – 5.00 – **108 rm** 85.00/110.00 **st.**

Grafton Plaza without rest., Johnsons Pl., D2, 475 0888, Fax 475 0908 – . EZ **c**
closed 24-26 December – 7.50 – **75 rm** 55.00/75.00 **st.**

Doyle Tara, Merrion Rd, D4, SE : 4 m. on T 44 269 4666, Fax 269 1027 – rest – 400. CV **a**
Meals 9.30/13.25 **t.** and a la carte – 7.50 – **114 rm** 76.00/99.00 **t.**

Russell Court, 21-25 Harcourt St., D2, 478 4066, Fax 478 1576 – – 100. EZ **v**
closed 24 December-2 January – **Meals** 12.00/16.00 **t.** and dinner a la carte 6.00 – 6.50 – **42 rm** 60.00/120.00 **t.** – SB.

Skylon, Upper Drumcondra Rd, N : 2 ½ m. on N 1 837 9121, Fax 837 2778 – rest . BU **e**
Meals 9.30/11.30 **t.** and a la carte 4.60 – 7.50 – **92 rm** 76.00/99.00.

DUBLIN
BUILT UP AREA

Adelaide Road	BV	2
Bath Avenue	CV	5
Benburb Street	BU	6
Berkeley Road	BU	7
Botanic Road	BU	8
Bow Street	BU	9

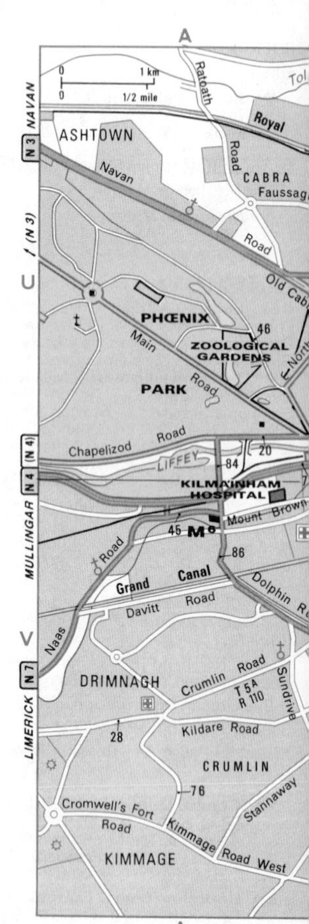

Ariel House without rest., 52 Lansdowne Rd, Ballsbridge, D4, 668 5512, Fax 668 5845, – . AE VISA. CV **c**
closed 23 December-10 January – 7.50 – **28 rm** 55.00/130.00 **t.**

Jurys Christchurch Inn, Christchurch Pl., 475 0111, Fax 475 0488 – AE VISA. DY **e**
Meals (bar lunch)/dinner 13.50 **st.** and a la carte – 5.50 – **183 rm** 49.00 **st.**

Longfield's, 10 Lower Fitzwilliam St., D2, 676 1367, Fax 676 1542 – . AE VISA. FZ **i**
closed 24 December-2 January – **Meals** *(closed lunch Saturday, Sunday and Bank Holidays)* 12.00/17.50 **t.** and a la carte 6.00 – **26 rm** 79.50/140.00 **st.** – SB.

Aberdeen Lodge, 53-55 Park Av., D4, 283 8155, Fax 283 7877, – CV **e**
16 rm.

Canal Road	**BV**	15	James' Street	**BV**	48	St John's Road West	**AU**	78
Clanbrassil Street	**BV**	17	Leeson Street Upper	**BV**	54	Sandford Road	**BV**	81
Conyngham Road	**AU**	20	Macken Street	**BUV**	56	Shelbourne Road	**CV**	82
Denmark Street	**BU**	24	Morehampton Road	**BV**	60	Shrewsbury Road	**CV**	83
Donnybrook Road	**CV**	26	Mount Street Upper	**BV**	61	South Circular Road	**AU**	84
Dorset Street	**BU**	27	Palmerston Park	**BV**	66	Suir Road	**AV**	86
Drimnagh Road	**AV**	28	Phibsborough Road	**BU**	70	Terenure Road East	**BV**	90
Eglinton Road	**CV**	33	Rathmines Road Upper	**BV**	73	Thomas Street West	**BV**	91
Grand Parade	**BV**	40	Ringsend Road	**CV**	74	Victoria Quay	**BU**	93
Inchicore Road	**AV**	45	St Agnes Road	**AV**	76	Western Way	**BU**	97
Infirmary Road	**AU**	46	St Alphonsus Road	**BU**	77	Wolfe Tone Quay	**BU**	102

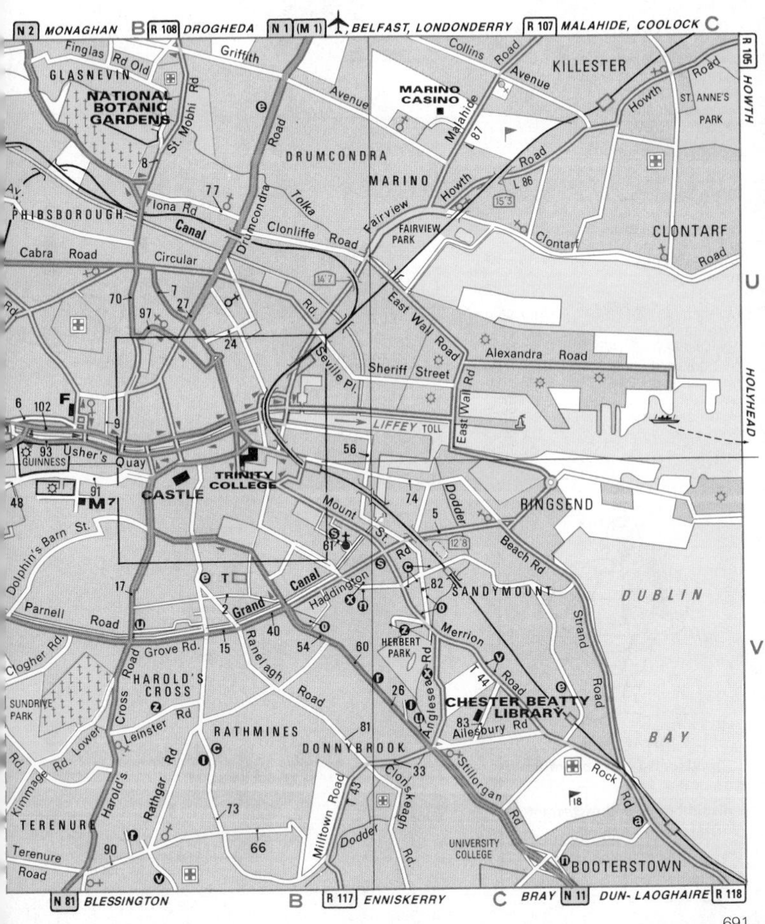

DUBLIN
CENTRE

Street	Grid	No.
Anne Street South	EYZ	3
Dawson Street	EYZ	
Duke Street	EY	29
Grafton Street	EYZ	
Henry Street	EX	
Ilac Centre	DEX	
Irish Life Mall Centre	EFX	
O'Connell Street	EX	
Brunswick Street North	DX	10
Buckingham Street	FY	12
Bull Alley	DZ	13
Chancery Street	DY	16
Clanbrassil Street	DZ	17
College Green	EY	18
College Street	EY	19
Cornmarket	DY	21
D'Olier Street	EY	25
Earlsfort Terrace	EZ	32
Essex Quay	DY	34
Fishamble Street	DY	36
George's Quay	FY	38
Golden Lane	DZ	39
Henrietta Street	DX	42
High Street	DY	43
Kevin Street Upper	DZ	50
Kildare Street	EFZ	51
King Street South	EZ	52
Marlborough Street	EX	57
Merchants Quay	DY	58
Montague Street	EZ	59
Mount Street Upper	FZ	61
Nicholas Street	DY	64
Parnell Square East	EX	67
Parnell Square North	EX	68
Parnell Square West	DEX	69
St Mary's Abbey St.	DY	79
St Patrick Close	DZ	80
Stephen Street	DEY	85
Tara Street	FY	89
Wellington Quay	DEY	95
Werburgh Street	DY	96
Westland Row	FY	98
Westmoreland Street	EY	99
Wexford Street	DEZ	100
Winetavern Street	DY	101
Wolfe Tone Quay	DX	103
Wood Quay	DY	104

Town plans:
roads most used by traffic and those on which guide-listed hotels and restaurants stand are fully drawn; the beginning only of lesser roads is indicated.

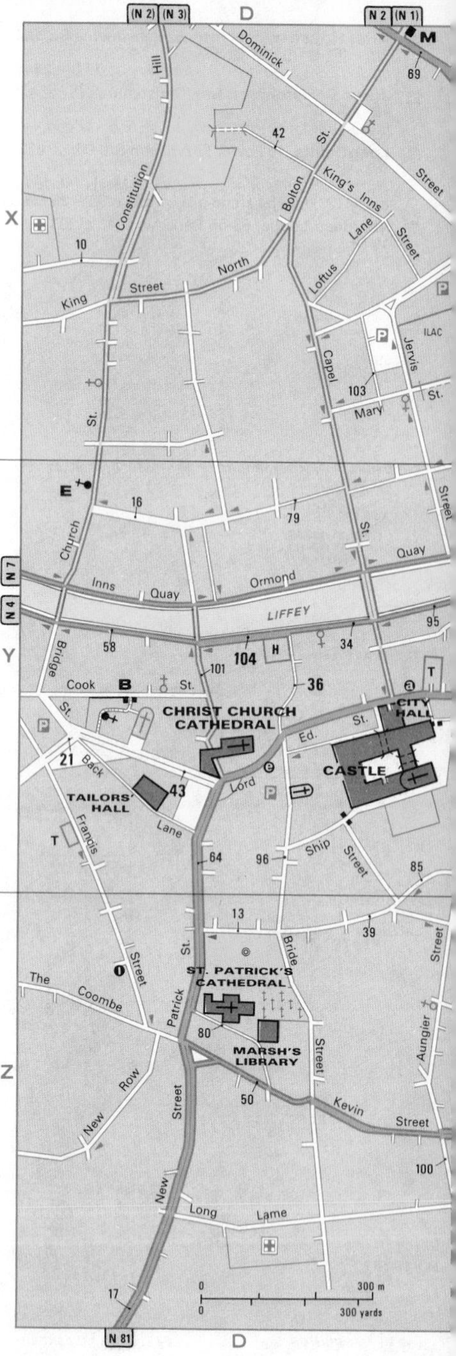

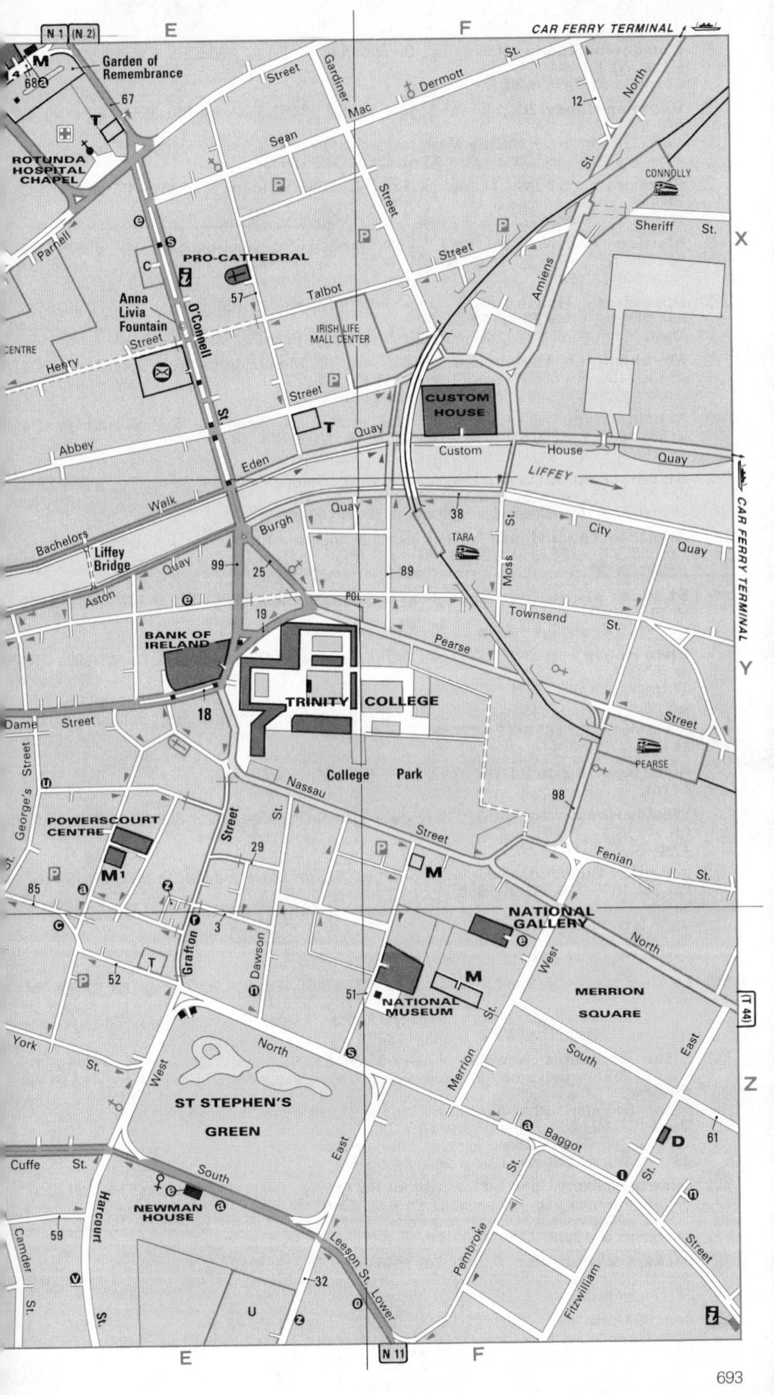
CAR FERRY TERMINAL
Garden of Remembrance
ROTUNDA HOSPITAL CHAPEL
PRO-CATHEDRAL
Anna Livia Fountain
O'Connell St.
Henry Street
Talbot Street
Sean Mac Dermott St.
Gardiner Street
IRISH LIFE MALL CENTER
CONNOLLY
Sheriff St.
Amiens Street
North St.
CUSTOM HOUSE
Abbey Street
Eden Quay
Custom House Quay
LIFFEY
Bachelors Walk
Liffey Bridge
Aston Quay
Burgh Quay
City Quay
TARA
Moss St.
Townsend St.
Pearse Street
BANK OF IRELAND
TRINITY COLLEGE
College Park
PEARSE
Dame Street
George's Street
Nassau Street
Fenian St.
POWERSCOURT CENTRE
Grafton Street
Dawson St.
NATIONAL GALLERY
NATIONAL MUSEUM
MERRION SQUARE
Merrion Square North
Merrion Square South
Merrion Square West
Merrion Square East
Merrion St.
York St.
ST STEPHEN'S GREEN
St Stephen's Green North
St Stephen's Green West
St Stephen's Green South
St Stephen's Green East
Cuffe St.
Harcourt St.
NEWMAN HOUSE
Camden St.
Leeson St. Lower
Baggot Street
Pembroke St.
Fitzwilliam St.
CAR FERRY TERMINAL
E
F
X
Y
Z
N 1
N 2
N 11
T 44

Lansdowne Lodge without rest., Shelbourne Rd, D4, ℘ 660 5755, Fax 660 5662, – TV ☎. VISA. CV **o**
12 rm 45.00/70.00 **st.**

Georgian House, 20-21 Lower Baggot St., D2, ℘ 661 8832, Fax 661 8834 – TV ☎ P. VISA. FZ **a**
closed 24 and 25 December – **Meals** *(closed Saturday and Sunday lunch)* (bar lunch)/dinner a la carte 16.50/18.50 **t.** 7.50 – **33 rm** 40.00/89.00 **t.** – SB.

Glenogra without rest., 64 Merrion Rd, D4, ℘ 668 3661, Fax 668 3661 – TV ☎ P. AE VISA. CV **v**
closed 20 December-2 January and 2 weeks February – **9 rm** 35.00/70.00 **st.**

Merrion Hall without rest., 54-56 Merrion Rd, Ballsbridge, D4, ℘ 668 1426, Fax 668 4280, – TV ☎ P. VISA. CV **v**
closed 22 December-2 January – **15 rm** 40.00/70.00 **st.**

Uppercross House, 26-30 Upper Rathmines Rd, Rathmines, D6, ℘ 4975486, Fax 4975361 – TV ☎. AE VISA BV **c**
Meals (dinner only) 16.00 **st.** and a la carte 5.00 – **15 rm** 30.00/55.00 **st.**

Morehampton Townhouse without rest., 46 Morehampton Rd, Donnybrook, D4, ℘ 660 2106, Fax 660 2566 – TV ☎ P. VISA. CV **r**
closed 15 December-15 January – **6 rm** 40.00/60.00.

Raglan Lodge without rest., 10 Raglan Rd, off Pembroke Rd, Ballsbridge, D4, ℘ 660 6697, Fax 660 6781, – TV ☎ P. AE VISA. CV **z**
closed 22 to 31 December – **7 rm** 48.00/85.00 **st.**

Stauntons on the Green without rest., 83 St. Stephen's Green South, D2, ℘ 478 2300, Fax 478 2263, – TV ☎. AE VISA EZ **a**
closed 25 and 26 December – **30 rm** 53.00/130.00.

Anglesea Town House without rest., 63 Anglesea Rd, Ballsbridge, D4, ℘ 668 3877, Fax 668 3461 – TV ☎. AE VISA. CV **x**
closed 24-26 December – **7 rm** 45.00/90.00 **t.**

St. Aiden's without rest., 32 Brighton Rd, Rathgar, D6, ℘ 4906178, Fax 4920234 – TV ☎ P. VISA. BV **r**
closed 25 December – **8 rm** 25.00/66.00 **t.**

Clara House without rest., 23 Leinster Rd, Rathmines, D6, ℘ 4975904, Fax 4975904 – TV ☎. VISA BV **z**
13 rm 30.00/54.00 **st.**

Glenveagh Town House without rest., 31 Northumberland Rd, Ballsbridge, D4, ℘ 668 4612, Fax 668 4559 – TV ☎ CV **s**
11 rm.

Abrae Court, 9 Zion Rd, D6, ℘ 922242 – TV ☎ P BV **v**
14 rm.

Wesley House without rest., 113 Anglesea Rd, Ballsbridge, D4, ℘ 668 1201, – TV P. CV **u**
3 rm 40.00/50.00 **st.**

XXX ✿ **Patrick Guilbaud,** 46 James' Pl., James' St., off Lower Baggot St., D2, ℘ 676 4192, Fax 660 1546 – ▤. AE VISA FZ **n**
closed Sunday, Monday and first 2 weeks January – **Meals** - French 18.50/25.00 **t.** and a la carte 28.00/38.00
Spec. Warm wild Irish salmon with a potato blinis and a lemon butter sauce, Fillet of lamb with Guerande salt, a parsley purée and herb salad, Stuffed crubeens with a mushroom pudding.

XXX **Le Coq Hardi,** 35 Pembroke Rd, D4, ℘ 668 9070, Fax 668 9887 – P. AE VISA JCB BV **n**
closed Saturday lunch, Sunday, 2 weeks August, 1 week Christmas-New Year and Bank Holidays – **Meals** 16.00/28.00 **t.** and a la carte.

XXX ✿ **The Commons,** Newman House, 85-86 St. Stephen's Green, D2, ℘ 475 2597, Fax 478 0551, « Contemporary collection of James Joyce inspired Irish Art » – AE VISA JCB EZ **e**
closed Saturday lunch, Sunday dinner, 24 December-3 January and Bank Holidays – **Meals** 17.00/27.50 **t.** and a la carte 27.50/36.50 7.50
Spec. Foie gras and black pudding, warm pear dressing, Roast monkfish in bacon with colcannon, red wine sauce, Poached pear and peach with a brandy snap basket of sorbet.

XXX **Ernie's,** Mulberry Gdns, off Donnybrook Rd, Donnybrook, D4, ℘ 269 3300, Fax 269 3260, « Contemporary Irish Art collection » – ▤. AE VISA CV **i**
closed Saturday lunch, Sunday, Monday and 1 week Christmas – **Meals** 13.95/22.50 **t.** and dinner a la carte 23.50/33.90 6.25.

XX **Locks,** 1 Windsor Terr., Portobello, ℘ 4543391, Fax 4538352 – AE VISA BV **u**
closed Saturday lunch, Sunday, 1 week Christmas and Bank Holidays – **Meals** 13.95/21.00 **t.** and a la carte 5.95.

XX **Zen,** 89 Upper Rathmines Rd, D6, ℘ 4979428 – ▤. AE VISA BV **i**
closed lunch Monday, Tuesday, Wednesday and Saturday – **Meals** - Chinese (Szechuan) 8.00/22.50 **t.** and a la carte 5.50.

XX **La Stampa,** 35 Dawson St., D2, ☎ 677 8611, Fax 677 3336 – AE VISA EZ n
closed lunch Saturday and Sunday, Good Friday and 25-26 December – **Meals** 12.50 **t.** (lunch) and a la carte 16.15/24.05 ₫ 5.00.

XX **Les Frères Jacques,** 74 Dame St., D2, ☎ 679 4555, Fax 679 4725 – AE VISA DY a
closed Saturday lunch, Sunday, 25-30 December and Bank Holidays – **Meals** - French 13.00/20.00 **t.** and dinner a la carte ₫ 5.50.

XX Chandni, 174 Pembroke Rd, Ballsbridge, D4, ☎ 668 1458 – CV o
Meals - Indian.

XX **Old Dublin,** 90-91 Francis St., D8, ☎ 4542028, Fax 4541406 – AE VISA DZ i
closed Sunday and Bank Holidays – **Meals** - Russian-Scandinavian 9.50/19.00 **t.** and dinner a la carte ₫ 5.50.

XX **Chapter One,** 18-19 Parnell Sq., D2, ☎ 873 2266, Fax 873 2330 – P. AE VISA EX a
closed Saturday lunch, Monday dinner and Sunday – **Meals** 11.50/15.50 **t.** and dinner a la carte.

XX **Kapriol,** 45 Lower Camden St., D2, ☎ 475 1235 – AE VISA JCB BV e
closed Sunday, 3 weeks August and Bank Holidays – **Meals** - Italian (dinner only) 18.00 **t.** and a la carte 18.50/29.50 **t.** ₫ 5.40.

XX **Eastern Tandoori,** 34-35 South William St., D2, ☎ 671 0428, Fax 677 9232 – AE VISA EY a
closed Sunday lunch, Good Friday, 25-26 December and Bank Holiday lunch – **Meals** - Indian 7.50/19.50 **t.** and a la carte.

XX **Dobbin's,** 15 Stephen's Lane, off Lower Mount St., D2, ☎ 676 4679, Fax 661 3331 – AE VISA BV s
closed Saturday lunch, Monday dinner, Sunday and Bank Holidays – **Meals** - Bistro 14.50/28.00 **st.** and a la carte ₫ 6.25.

XX Fitzers, National Gallery, Merrion Sq., ☎ 668 9733 – P FZ e

X **Roly's Bistro,** 7 Ballsbridge Terr., Ballsbridge, D4, ☎ 668 2611, Fax 660 8535 – AE VISA CV z
closed Good Friday and 25-26 December – **Meals** 9.50 **t.** (lunch) and a la carte 15.15/20.40 **t.** ₫ 4.50.

X **Chili Club,** 1 Anne's Lane, South Anne St., D2, ☎ 677 3721, Fax 493 8284 – AE VISA EZ r
closed lunch Saturday and Bank Holidays, Sunday, 25-26 December and 1 January – **Meals** - Thai (booking essential) 7.95/17.50 **t.** and dinner a la carte ₫ 4.95.

at Blackrock SE : 4 ½ m. by T 44 – V – ✉ Blackrock – ☎ 01 :

XX **Clarets,** 63-65 Main St., D18, ☎ 288 2008 – AE VISA
closed Saturday lunch, Sunday, Monday, 24 to 31 December and Bank Holidays – **Meals** 13.95/22.95 **t.** and dinner a la carte 21.95/34.40 ₫ 6.00.

MICHELIN Distribution Centre, Spilmak Pl., Bluebell Industrial Estate, Naas Rd, Dublin 12, ☎ 509096, Fax 504302 by N7 AZ

DUNDALK (Dun Dealgan) Louth 405 M 5/6 – ☎ 042.

◆Dublin 51 – Drogheda 22.

Carrickdale, Carrickcarnon, N : 8 m. on N 1 ☎ 71208, Fax 71740, park – rm TV ☎ P. AE VISA JCB.
closed 25 December – **Meals** 6.00/18.50 **st.** and a la carte ₫ 5.50 – **47 rm** 35.00/60.00 **st.** – SB.

DUNDRUM (Dún Droma) Tipperary 405 H 10 – ✉ Cashel – ☎ 062.

◆Dublin 104 – ◆Cork 66 – ◆Limerick 33.

Dundrum House, SE : ¾ m. on R 505 ☎ 71116, Fax 71366, park – TV ☎ P – 350
54 rm.

DUNFANAGHY (Dún Fionnachaidh) Donegal 405 I 2 Ireland G. – pop. 390 – ✉ Letterkenny – ☎ 074.

Envir. : Horn Head Scenic Route★, N : 2½ m.

Exc. : Doe Castle★, SE : 7 m. by N 56 – The Rosses★, SW : 25 m. by N 56 and R 259.

◆Dublin 172 – Donegal 54 – ◆Londonderry 43.

Arnold's, Main St., ☎ 36208, Fax 36352 – TV ☎ P. AE VISA.
April-October – **Meals** 10.00/19.00 **t.** and lunch a la carte ₫ 6.50 – **34 rm** 33.00/66.00 **t.** – SB.

Carrig Rua, Main St., ☎ 36133, Fax 36277 – TV ☎ P. AE VISA.
17 March-early November – **Meals** (bar lunch)/dinner 19.50 **t.** and a la carte ₫ 4.50 – **22 rm** 25.00/60.00 **t.** – SB.

at Portnablahy/Portnablagh E : 1 ½ m. on T 72 – ✉ Letterkenny – ☎ 074 :

Port-na-Blagh, ✆ 36129, Fax 36379, ≤ Sheephaven Bay and harbour, ⛳, ✗, ✗ – TV ☎ P. AE VISA
April-September – **Meals** 6.95/23.50 **t.** and a la carte 5.50 – **45 rm** ☐ 32.00/64.00 **t.** – SB.

DUNGARVAN **(Dún Garbháin)** Waterford 405 J 11 – ☎ 058.

♦Dublin 118 – ♦Cork 44 – Waterford 30.

at Clonea Strand E : 3 ¾ m. by Clonea Strand rd – ✉ Dungarvan – ☎ 058.

Clonea Strand, ✆ 42416, Fax 42880, ≤, Ꝭ, ☐, ☐, 9 – ☐ TV ☎ P – 200. AE VISA. ✗
Meals 9.00/17.00 **t.** and dinner a la carte 4.65 – **58 rm** ☐ 48.50/77.00 **st.** – SB.

En saison, *surtout dans les stations fréquentées, il est prudent de retenir à l'avance. Cependant, si vous ne pouvez pas occuper la chambre que vous avez retenue, prévenez immédiatement l'hôtelier.*

Si vous écrivez à un hôtel à l'étranger, joignez à votre lettre un coupon-réponse international (disponible dans les bureaux de poste).

DUN LAOGHAIRE **(Dún Laoghaire)** Dublin 405 N 8 – pop. 55 540 – ☎ 01.

⛴ to Holyhead (Stena Sealink Line) 2-4 daily (3 h 30 mn).

ℹ St. Michaels Wharf ✆ 2844768.

♦Dublin 9.

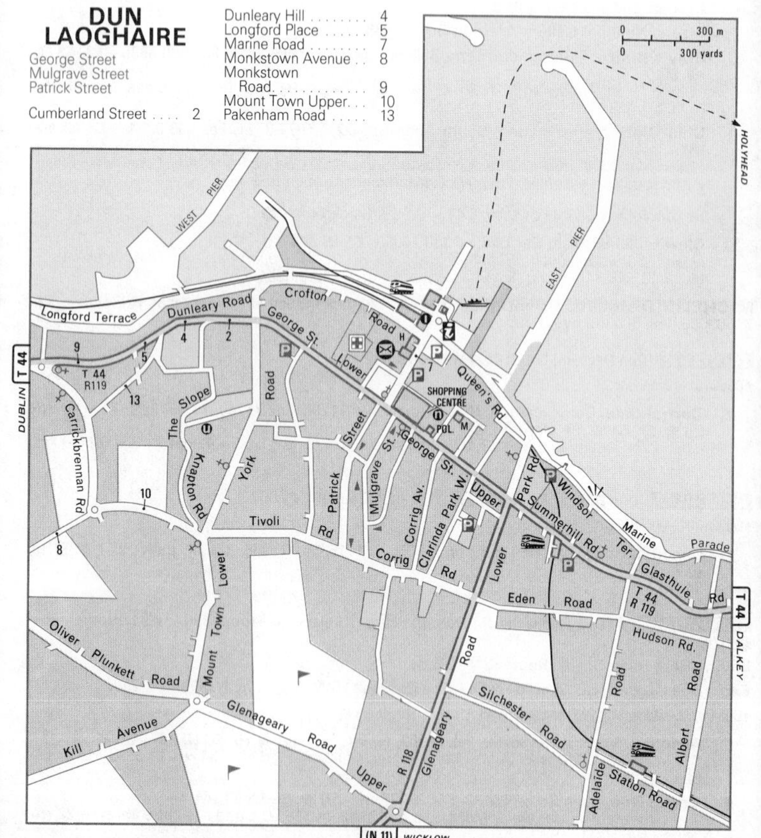

Royal Marine, Marine Rd, ☎ 280 1911, Fax 280 1089, ≤, 🌳 – |‡| ▤ rest TV ☎ P – 🎪 500. AE VISA. 🐕 **n**
Meals *(closed Saturday lunch)* 6.95/17.95 **st.** and a la carte – **104 rm** 72.00/115.00 **st.** – SB.

Chestnut Lodge without rest., 2 Vesey Pl., Monkstown, ☎ 280 7860, Fax 280 1466, « Regency house, antiques », 🌳 – TV ☎. VISA. 🐕 **u**
4 rm 37.50/55.00.

XXX **Na Mara,** 1 Harbour Rd, ☎ 280 6767, Fax 284 4649 – AE VISA **i**
closed Sunday and 1 week Christmas – **Meals** - Seafood 13.50/23.00 **t.** 6.00.

DUNLAVIN (Dún Luáin) Wicklow 405 L 8 – pop. 720 – ☎ 045.

♦Dublin 31 – ♦Kilkenny 44 – Wexford 61.

Rathsallagh House 🐦, SW : 2 m. on Grangecon Rd ☎ 53112, Fax 53343, ≤, « 18C converted stables, walled garden », 🧖, 🏊, 18, park, 🎾 – ☎ P – 🎪 25. AE VISA JCB. 🐕
closed 24 to 26 December – **Meals** (dinner only) 27.00/35.00 **st.** 6.00 – **17 rm** 75.00/230.00 **st.** – SB.

DUNMANWAY (Dún Mánmhaí) Cork 405 E 12 – pop. 1 404 – ☎ 023.

♦Dublin 191 – ♦Cork 37 – ♦Killarney 49.

Dun Mhuire,, W : ½ m. by T 65 ☎ 45162, 🌳 – TV ☎ P. VISA. 🐕
Meals (by arrangement) 17.00 **t.** 5.00 – **5 rm** 26.00/40.00 **st.** – SB.

DUNMORE EAST (Dún Mór) Waterford 405 L 11 **Ireland G.** – pop. 1 038 – ✉ Waterford – ☎ 051.

See : Village★.

♦Dublin 108 – ♦Waterford 12.

X **Ship,** Bayview, ☎ 383141 – VISA
closed lunch October-April and Sundayand Monday November to April – **Meals** - Seafood a la carte 10.00/17.50 5.75.

Europe

Se il nome di un albergo è stampato in carattere magro, chiedete arrivando le condizioni che vi saranno praticate.

DUNSHAUGHLIN (Dún Seachlainn) Meath 405 M 7 – ☎ 01.

♦Dublin 17 – Drogheda 19.

Gaulstown House 🐦, NE : 1 ½ m. by Ratoath rd ☎ 825 9147, « Working farm », 🌳, park – 🚭 P. 🐕
April-October – **Meals** (by arrangement) 13.00 – **3 rm** 20.00/34.00 **st.** – SB.

DURRUS (Dúras) Cork 405 D 13 – pop. 188 – ☎ 027.

♦Dublin 210 – ♦Cork 56 – ♦Killarney 53.

XX **Blairs Cove.**, SW : 1 m. on L 56 ☎ 61127, « Converted barn », 🌳 – P. AE VISA
closed Sunday, Monday except July and August and November-March – **Meals** (booking essential) (dinner only) 24.00 **t.**

ENNIS (Inis) Clare 405 F 9 **Ireland G.** – pop. 13 730 – ECD : Thursday – ☎ 065.

See : Ennis Friary★ *AC*.

Envir. : Clare Abbey★, SE : 1 m. by R 469.

Exc. : Quin Franciscan Friary★, SE : 6½ m. by R 469 – Knappogue Castle★ *AC*, SE : 8 m. by R 469 – Carrofin (Clare Heritage Centre★ *AC*), N : 8½ m. by N 85 and R 476 – Craggaunowen Centre★ *AC*, SE : 11 m. by R 469 – Kilmacduagh Churches and Round Tower★, NE : 11 m. by N 18 – Scattery Island★, SW : 27 m. by N 68 and boat from Kilrush – Bridge of Ross, Kilkee★, SW : 35½ m. by N 68 and N 67.

18 Drumbiggle Rd ☎ 24074.

Clare Road ☎ 28366.

♦Dublin 142 – ♦Galway 42 – ♦Limerick 22 – Roscommon 92 – ♦Tullamore 93.

Old Ground (Forte), O'Connell St., ☎ 28127, Fax 28112, 🌳 – TV ☎ P – 🎪 200
58 rm.

Auburn Lodge, Galway Rd, N : 1 ½ m. on N 18 ☎ 21247, Fax 21202, 🌳, 🎾 – TV ☎ P. AE VISA. 🐕
Meals 9.00/19.00 **t.** and a la carte 4.50 – **75** 27.00/80.00 **t.** – SB.

Cill Eoin House without rest., Killadysert Cross, Clare Rd, SE : 1 ½ m. at junction of N 18 with R 473 ☎ 41668, Fax 20224, 🌳, 🎾 – 🚭 TV ☎ P
14 rm.

Magowna House 🐦, Inch, Kilmaley, SW : 5 m. by R 474 (Kilmaley rd) ☎ 39009, Fax 39258, ≤, 🌳 – ☎ P. AE VISA. 🐕
closed 24-26 December – **Meals** 16.00 **st.** 5.00 – **5 rm** 22.00/34.00 **st.** – SB.

at Barefield NE : 3 ½ m. on N 18 – ✉ Ennis – ☎ 065 :

⌂ **Carraig Mhuire,** Bearnafunshin, NE : 1 ¾ m. on N 18 ☎ 27106, Fax 27375, 🌳 – 🅿. ✗
Meals 11.00 – **4 rm** ☕ 13.50/26.00 **s.** – SB.

ENNISCORTHY (Inis Córthaidh) Wexford 405 M 10 – ☎ 053.
♦Dublin 76 – Kilkenny 46 – Waterford 34 – Wexford 15.

🏠 **Ballinkeele House** 🐦, Ballymurn, SE : 6 ½ m. by unmarked rd and Curracloe rd ☎ 38105, Fax 38468, « 19C country house, antiques », 🌳, park, 🎾 – 🚭 rm 🅿. VISA JCB. ✗
Booking essential mid November-February – **Meals** (communal dining) (dinner only) 18.00 **st.** – **5 rm** ☕ 32.00/60.00 **st.**

FAHAN (Fathain) Donegal 405 J 2 **Ireland G.** – pop. 309 – ✉ Inishowen – ☎ 077.
Exc. : Inishowen Peninsula★★ : (Dun Ree Fort★ *AC*), N : 11 m. by R 238.
⛳18 North West, Lisfannon ☎ 61027.
♦Dublin 156 – ♦Londonderry 11 – ♦Sligo 95.

XX **St. John's,** ☎ 60289, « Loughside setting », 🌳 – 🚭 🅿. AE ⓓ VISA JCB
closed Monday and 25-26 December – **Meals** (dinner only) 20.00 **t.** 🍷 5.95.

FERNS (Fearna) Wexford 405 M 10 – ✉ Enniscorthy – ☎ 054.
♦Dublin 69 – Kilkenny 53 – Waterford 41 – Wexford 22.

⌂ **Clone House,** S : 2 m. by Boolavogue rd and Monageer rd ☎ 66113, Fax 66113, « Working farm », 🌳, park – 🚭 TV 🅿. ✗
March-October – **Meals** (communal dining) 14.00 **st.** 🍷 5.00 – **5 rm** ☕ 23.00/36.00 **s.**

We suggest:

For a successful tour, that you prepare it in advance.
Michelin maps and guides will give you much useful information on route planning, places of interest, accommodation, prices etc.

FURBOGH/FURBO (Na Forbacha) Galway 405 E 8 – ☎ 091.
♦Dublin 42 – ♦Galway 7.

🏨 **Connemara Coast,** ☎ 92108, Fax 92065, ≤, 🏋, ≘s, 🏊, 🎾 – 🚭 rm TV ☎ 🅿 – 🏛 500. AE ⓓ VISA. ✗
Meals (bar lunch)/dinner 23.50 **st.** and a la carte 🍷 6.25 – **111 rm** ☕ 50.00/125.50 **st.**, 1 suite – SB.

GALWAY (Gaillimh) Galway 405 E 8 **Ireland G.** – pop. 50 855 – ECD : Monday – ☎ 091.
See : City★★ – Lynch's Castle★ BY – St. Nicholas' Church★ BY – Roman Catholic Cathedral★ AY – Eyre Square : Bank of Ireland Building (Mace★) BY **D.**
Envir. : NW : Lough Corrib★★.
Exc. : W : by boat, Aran Islands (Inishmore - Dun Aenghus★★★) BZ – Thoor Ballylee★★, SE : 21 m. by N 6 and N 18 BY – Athenry★, E : 14 m. by N 6 and R 348 BY – Dunguaire Castle, Kinvarra★ *AC*, S : 16 m. by N 6, N 18 and N 67 BY – Knockmoy Abbey★, NE : 19 m. by N 17 and N 63 BY – Coole Park (Autograph Tree★), SE : 21 m. by N 6 and N 18 BY – St. Mary's Cathedral, Tuam★, NE : 21 m. by N 17 BY – Loughrea (St. Brendan's Cathedral★) SE : 22 m. by N 6 BY.
⛳18 Galway, Salthill ☎ 22169/27622.
✈ Carnmore Airport : ☎ 752874, NE : 4 m..
ℹ Aras Faiva, Victoria Pl., Eyre Sq. ☎ 63081.
♦Dublin 135 – ♦Limerick 64 – ♦Sligo 90.

Plan opposite

🏨 **Glenlo Abbey,** Bushypark, NW : 3 ¼ m. on N 59 ☎ 26666, Fax 27800, « Restored part 18C house and church », ≘s, ⛳9, 🎣, park, 🎾 – 🛗 🚭 rm ▤ rest TV ☎ ♿ 🅿 – 🏛 70. AE ⓓ VISA. ✗
Meals 10.75/21.75 **t.** and a la carte 🍷 8.00 – ☕ 8.00 – **38 rm** 80.00/115.00 **t.**, 4 suites – SB.

🏨 **Great Southern,** Eyre Sq., ☎ 64041, Fax 66704, ≘s, 🏊 – 🛗 🚭 rm TV ☎ – 🏛 450. AE ⓓ VISA. ✗ BY **a**
Meals (carving lunch Monday to Saturday)/dinner 18.00 **t.** and a la carte 🍷 5.50 – ☕ 7.50 – **116 rm** 70.50/190.00 **t.** – SB.

🏨 **Corrib Great Southern,** Dublin Rd, E : 1 ¾ m. on N 6 ☎ 755281, Fax 751390, 🏊 – 🛗 🚭 rm ▤ rest TV ☎ ♿ 🅿 – 🏛 850. AE ⓓ VISA. ✗
closed 25 and 26 December – **Meals** *(closed Saturday lunch)* 10.00/16.00 **t.** and dinner a la carte 🍷 6.00 – **176 rm** ☕ 61.00/98.00 **t.**, 4 suites – SB.

🏨 **Ardilaun House,** Taylor's Hill, ☎ 21433, Fax 21546, 🏋, ≘s, 🌳 – 🛗 🚭 rm TV ☎ 🅿 – 🏛 450. AE ⓓ VISA JCB. ✗
closed Christmas – **Meals** (bar lunch Saturday) 9.75/22.00 **t.** and a la carte 🍷 7.00 – **89 rm** ☕ 40.00/105.00 **t.**, 1 suite – SB.

GALWAY

Claddagh Bridge	AZ 2
Dominick Street	AZ 3
Father Griffin Avenue	AZ 5
Forster Street	BY 6
High Street	BY 7
Market Street	BY 9
Mary Street	BY 10
New Dock Street	BZ 13
Newton Smith	BY 14
O'Brien Bridge	AY 15
Presentation Street	AY 17
Quay Street	BZ 18
St. Francis Street	BY 20
St. Vincent's Avenue	BY 21
Shantalia Road	AY 22
Shop Street	BY 24
William Street	BY 25

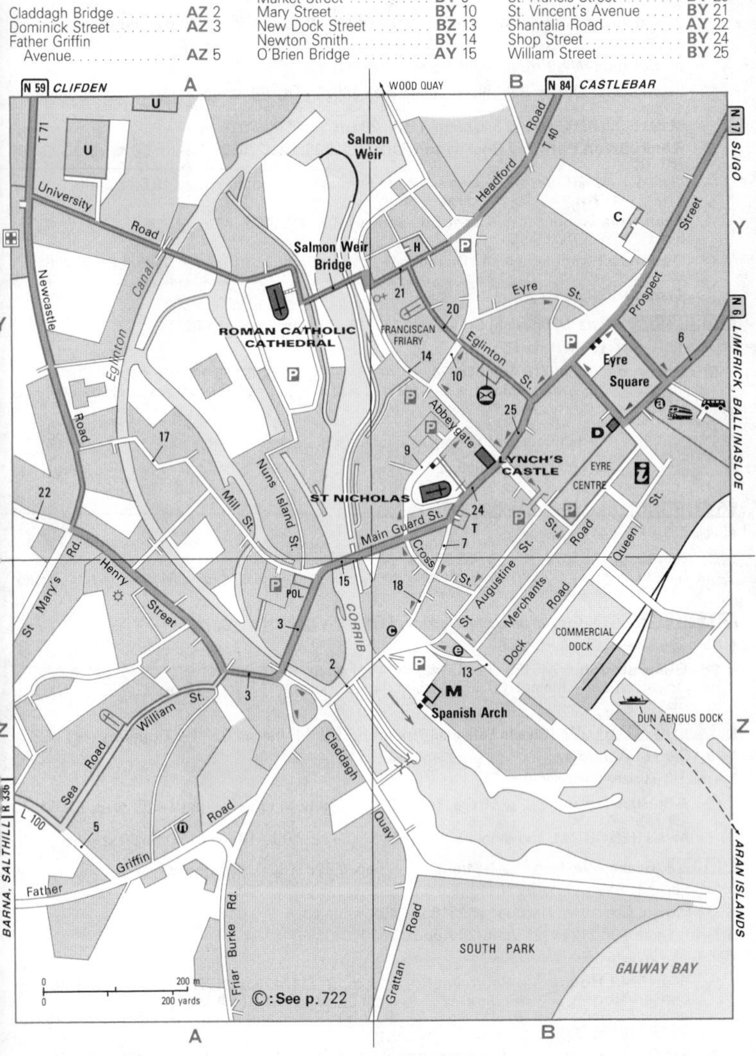

🏨 **Jurys Galway Inn,** Quay St., ✆ 66444, Fax 68415, ← – |♦| ⇆ rm 📺 ☎. AE ⓓ VISA. ✗ — BZ **c**
Meals (bar lunch)/dinner 17.50 **st.** and a la carte 4.75 – ☐ 5.00 – **129 rm** 53.00 **t.**

🏨 **Brennan's Yard,** Lower Merchants Rd, ✆ 68166, Fax 68262 – |♦| ⇆ rm 📺 ☎ Ⓟ. AE ⓓ VISA. ✗ — BZ **e**
Meals (booking essential) 9.95/16.50 **t.** and a la carte – **24 rm** ☐ 55.00/90.00 **t.** – SB.

🏨 **Galway Ryan,** Dublin Rd, E : 1 ¼ m. on N 6 ✆ 753181, Telex 50149, Fax 753187, ← – |♦| 📺 ☎ Ⓟ – 60. AE ⓓ VISA. ✗
Meals (bar lunch)/dinner 17.00 **t.** and a la carte 5.50 – ☐ 8.00 – **96 rm** 75.00/120.00 **st.** – SB.

⌂ **Adare House** without rest., 9 Father Griffin Pl., Lower Salthill, ✆ 582638, Fax 583963 – 📺 ☎ Ⓟ. VISA. ✗ — AZ **n**
closed 23 to 29 December – **11 rm** ☐ 22.00/35.00 **t.**

XX **Casey's Westwood,** Newcastle, NW : 1 3/4 m. on N 59 ℘ 21442, – P. VISA
closed Good Friday and 24 to 27 December – **Meals** 11.50/22.50 **t.** and dinner a la carte 5.80.

at Salthill SW : 2 m. AZ – ✉ Salthill – 091 :

Jamesons, Upper Salthill, ℘ 28666, Fax 28626 – – 50. VISA.
Meals 8.00/16.00 **st.** and a la carte 6.00 **20 rm** 45.00/70.00 **st.**

Rockbarton Park, 5-7 Rockbarton Park, ℘ 22286, Fax 27692 – rm P. VISA.
closed 1 week Christmas – **Meals** *(closed Sunday)* (bar lunch)/dinner 19.50 **t.** and a la carte 5.00 – **11 rm** 38.50/60.00 **st.** – SB.

Arch Villa without rest., Coast Rd, Gentian Hill, ℘ 21425, – P.
6 rm 25.00/30.00 **st.**

Devondell without rest., 47 Devon Park, Lower Salthill, off Lower Salthill Rd ℘ 23617 – .
4 rm 15.00/34.00.

GARRYVOE (Garraí Uí Bhuaigh) Cork 405 H 12 – ✉ Castlemartyr – 021.
◆Dublin 161 – ◆Cork 23 – Waterford 62.

Garryvoe, ℘ 646718, Fax 646824, <, – P. VISA.
closed 25 December – **Meals** 10.50/20.00 **st.** and a la carte 6.50 – **20 rm** 35.00/60.00 **st.** – SB.

Prices	For full details of the prices quoted in the guide, consult the introduction.

GLANDORE (Cuan Dor) Cork 405 E 13 – 028.
◆Dublin 196 – ◆Cork 44 – ◆Killarney 75.

XXX **Rectory,** ℘ 33072, < – P. VISA.
closed 4 days Christmas – **Meals** *(weekends only November - March)* (dinner only) 21.50 **st.** and a la carte 7.30.

GLENDALOUGH (Gleann dá Loch) Wicklow 405 M 8 – 0404.
◆Dublin 28 – Kilkenny 68 – Wexford 63.

Glendalough, ℘ 45135, Fax 45142, – P. VISA
April-October – **Meals** 9.00/19.00 **t.** and dinner a la carte 5.00 – **16 rm** 42.50/70.00 **t.** – SB.

GLEN OF AHERLOW (Gleann Eatharlaí) Tipperary 405 H 10 **Ireland G.** – ✉ Tipperary – 062.
See : Glen of Aherlow★.
◆Dublin 118 – Cahir 6 – Tipperary 9.

Aherlow House , ℘ 56153, Fax 56212, < Galty Mountains, park – P. VISA.
Meals 9.95/18.00 **t.** and dinner a la carte 5.00 – 7.00 – **10 rm** 31.00/95.00 **st.** – SB.

GOREY (Guaire) Wexford 405 N 9 **Ireland G.** – pop. 2 198 – ECD : Wednesday – 055.
Exc. : Ferns★, SW : 11 m. by N 11.
18 Courtown, Courtown Harbour ℘ 25166/25432.
Town Centre ℘ 21248 (28 June-28 August).
◆Dublin 58 – Waterford 55 – Wexford 38.

Marlfield House , Courtown Rd, E : 1 m. ℘ 21124, Fax 21572, <, « Regency house, conservatory », , , park, – rest P. VISA
closed 12 December -31 January – **Meals** 17.50/29.00 **t.** and lunch a la carte 6.50 – **18 rm** 85.00/145.00 **t.**, 1 suite – SB.

Kia Ora Farmhouse , Courteencurragh, ℘ 21166, « Working farm », , park – P
4 rm.

at Ballyedmund S : 10½ m. on R 741 – ✉ Gorey – 054 :

X **Eugenes,** on R 741 ℘ 89288 – P. VISA
closed Tuesday, 1-8 March, 5-20 September, 24-28 December and Good Friday – **Meals** (lunch by arrangement) 9.50/15.00 **t.** 7.00.

GOUGANE BARRA (Guagán Barra) Cork 405 D 12 **Ireland G.** – ✉ Ballingeary – 026.
See : Gougane Barra Forest Park★★.
◆Dublin 206 – ◆Cork 45.

Gougane Barra , ℘ 47069, Fax 47226, < lough and mountains, – P. VISA.
mid April-8 October – **Meals** 9.00/18.00 and lunch a la carte 5.50 – **28 rm** 36.00/70.00.

GREYSTONES (Na Clocha Liatha) Wicklow 405 N 8 – ☎ 01.

♦Dublin 22.

✕ **Hungry Monk,** Southview Church Rd, ✆ 287 5759, Fax 872 2809 – AE VISA
closed Monday, Tuesday, Good Friday and 24-26 December – **Meals** (dinner only and Sunday lunch)/dinner 14.95 **t.** and a la carte 9.95.

HOWTH (Binn Éadair) Dublin 405 N 7 **Ireland G.** – ✉ Dublin – ☎ 01.

See : Town★ – The Summit★.

9, 18 Deer Park ✆ 832 2624.

♦Dublin 10.

Marine, Sutton Cross, NW : 1½ m. ✆ 832 2613, Fax 839 0442, ←, – TV ☎ P – 220. AE VISA.
closed 25-27 December – **Meals** 12.00/20.50 **st.** and dinner a la carte 5.50 – **26 rm** 58.00/96.00 **st.** – SB.

Howth Lodge, ✆ 832 1010, Fax 832 2268, ←, – TV ☎ & P – 200. AE VISA.
closed 23 to 27 December – **Meals** *(closed Sunday dinner)* (bar lunch Monday to Saturday)/ dinner 23.00 **t.** and a la carte 4.50 – **46 rm** 50.00/90.00 **st.** – SB.

Deer Park, ✆ 832 2624, Fax 839 2405, ←, 18, 9, park – rest TV ☎ & P – 100. AE VISA JCB.
closed 24 and 25 December – **Meals** (bar lunch Monday to Saturday)/dinner 18.00 **st.** and a la carte 5.00 – **49 rm** 48.00/80.00 **st.** – SB.

✕✕✕ **King Sitric,** Harbour Rd, East Pier, ✆ 832 5235, Fax 839 2442 – AE VISA
closed Sunday, 1 week Easter, first week January and Bank Holidays – **Meals** - Seafood (light lunch Monday to Saturday May-September) (dinner only October-April)/dinner 22.00 **t.** and a la carte 6.00.

Les prix Pour toutes précisions sur les prix indiqués dans ce guide, reportez-vous à l'introduction.

INISHMORE (Inis Mór) Galway 405 CD 8 – see Aran Islands.

INISTIOGE (Inis Tíog) Kilkenny 405 K 10 – ☎ 056.

♦Dublin 82 – Kilkenny 16 – ♦Waterford 19 – Wexford 33.

Berryhill , SE : ½ m. by R 700 ✆ 58434, Fax 58434, ←, , park – P.
April-19 December – **Meals** (communal dining) (dinner only) 25.00 **st.** 6.50 – **3 rm** 30.00/70.00 **st.**

✕✕ **Motte,** ✆ 58655 – AE VISA
closed Monday and Bank Holidays – **Meals** (dinner only) 18.50 **t.** 5.50.

INNISHANNON (Inis Eonáin) Cork 405 G 12 – pop. 319 – ☎ 021.

♦Dublin 169 – ♦Cork 15.

Innishannon House , S : ¾ m. on R 605 ✆ 775121, Fax 775609, « Riverside setting », – TV ☎ P. AE VISA
Meals 12.00/22.50 **t.** and a la carte 6.50 – **13 rm** 65.00/125.00 **st.**, 1 suite – SB.

INVERIN (Indreabhán) Galway 405 D8 – ☎ 091.

♦Dublin 149 – ♦Galway 17.

Tigh Chualain without rest., Kilroe East, on L 100 ✆ 83609 – TV ☎ P
April-October – **9 rm** 20.00/30.00.

KANTURK (Ceann Toirc) Cork 405 F 11 **Ireland G.** – pop. 1 777 – ECD : Wednesday – ☎ 029.

See : Town★ – Castle★.

9 Fairy Hill ✆ 50534.

♦Dublin 161 – ♦Cork 33 – ♦Killarney 31 – ♦Limerick 44.

Assolas Country House , E : 3¼ m. by R 576 off R 580 ✆ 50015, Fax 50795, ←, « Part 17C and 18C country house, gardens, riverside setting », , park, – ☎ P. AE VISA.
mid March-October – **Meals** (booking essential) (dinner only) 28.00 **st.** 7.50 – **9 rm** 60.00/150.00 **st.** – SB.

KENMARE (Neidín) Kerry 405 D 12 **Ireland G.** – pop. 1 366 – ECD : Thursday – ☎ 064.

See : Site★.

Exc. : Iveragh Peninsula★★★ (Ring of Kerry★★) – Healy Pass★★ (←★★), SW : 19 m. by R 571 and R 574 – Mountain Road to Glengarriff (←★★) S : by N 71 - Slieve Miskish Mountains (←★★), SW : 30 m. by R 571 – Lauragh (Derreen Gardens★ *AC*) SW : 14½ m. by R 571 – Allihies (Copper Mines★), SW : 35½ m. by R 571 and R 575 – Garnish Island (←★), SW : 42½ m. by R 571, R 575 and R 572.

18 Kenmare ✆ 41291.

Heritage Centre, The Square ✆ 41233 (3 May-30 September).

♦Dublin 210 – ♦Cork 58 – ♦Killarney 20.

Park 🔇, ℘ 41200, Fax 41402, ≤ Kenmare Bay and hills, « Antiques, paintings », 18, park, – lift TV ☎ ♿ P – 35. AE VISA
16 April-5 November and 24 December-1 January – **Meals** 18.50/37.00 **st.** and a la carte 31.85/43.95 8.50 – 13.00 – **46 rm** 86.00/214.00 **t.**, 4 suites – SB
Spec. Pan fried goujons of Dover sole on wild rice and mango, ginger sauce, Grilled fillet of beef with truffles, wild mushrooms and a shallot sauce, Roulade of dark chocolate with a citrus salad and pistachio ice cream.

Sheen Falls Lodge 🔇, SE : 1¼ m. by N 71 ℘ 41600, Fax 41386, « Wooded setting on banks of Sheen River and Kenmare Bay, ≤ Sheen Falls », park, – lift rest TV ☎ ♿ P – 120. AE VISA JCB
closed 2 January-13 February and 2-20 December – **La Cascade : Meals** (bar lunch Monday to Saturday)/dinner 37.50 **t.** and a la carte 27.50/37.50 **t.** 8.50 – **33 rm** 175.00/230.00 **t.**, 7 suites – SB
Spec. Sauté of fresh langoustine with coriander and citrus dressing, Roast breast of pigeon with grilled polenta, truffle and Madeira essence, Pan fried scallops on a potato croustade with Sauternes and saffron.

Dromquinna Manor 🔇, Blackwater Bridge P.O., W : 3 m. by N 71 on N 70 ℘ 41657, Fax 41791, « Situated on the banks of Kenmare river », park, – TV ☎ P. AE VISA JCB
Meals (bar lunch Monday to Saturday in Winter) 8.50/16.50 **st.** and a la carte 5.00 – **27 rm** 37.50/120.00 **st.** – SB.

Sallyport House without rest., S : ¼ m. on N 71 ℘ 42066, Fax 41752, ≤, – TV ☎ P.
April-mid November – **4 rm** 40.00/60.00 **st.**

Dunkerron Lodge 🔇, Sneem Rd, W : 2½ m. on N 70 ℘ 41102, Fax 41102, park – ☎ P. VISA
April-October – **Meals** (lunch by arrangement)/dinner 18.00 and a la carte 5.50 – **10 rm** 32.00/52.00 **st.**

Foleys, Henry St., ℘ 41361, Fax 41799 – TV ☎. VISA
Meals (bar lunch)/dinner 13.95 **st.** and a la carte 5.75 – **10 rm** 20.00/40.00 **st.** – SB.

Mylestone House without rest., Killowen Rd, E : ¼ m. ℘ 41753, – P. VISA
mid February-mid November – **5 rm** 22.00/32.00 **st.**

Ceann Mara 🔇, E : 1 m. on Kilgarvan rd ℘ 41220, ≤ Kenmare Bay and hills, – P.
June-September – **Meals** (by arrangement) 14.00 – **4 rm** 19.00/32.00 **st.**

Ard Na Mara without rest., Pier Rd, ℘ 41399, Fax 41399, ≤ Kenmare Bay and hills, – P.
4 rm 20.00/28.00 **t.**

XX **d'Arcys Old Bank House,** Main St., ℘ 41589, Fax 41589 – AE VISA
closed Monday to Wednesday October-March, last 2 weeks January and 24-27 December – **Meals** (dinner only) 15.50/29.45 **st.** and a la carte 6.00.

X **Lime Tree,** Shelbourne St., ℘ 41225, Fax 41839, « Characterful former schoolhouse » – P. VISA
closed Sunday-Thursday November to December and January – **Meals** (dinner only) a la carte 19.00/24.00 **t.** 6.00.

X **Packies,** Henry St., ℘ 41508 – VISA
closed Sunday and 12 November-March – **Meals** (dinner only) a la carte 12.90/20.80 **st.** 4.95.

KILKEE (Cill Chaoi) Clare 405 D 9 – ☎ 065.

◆Dublin 177 – ◆Galway 77 – ◆Limerick 58.

Halpin's, Erin St., ℘ 56032, Fax 56317 – TV ☎. AE VISA
closed 4 January-15 March – **Meals** (bar lunch Monday to Saturday)/dinner 18.00 **t.** and a la carte 8.00 – **12 rm** 30.00/66.00 **t.** – SB.

KILKENNY (Cill Chainnigh) Kilkenny 405 K 10 Ireland G. – pop. 8 515 – ECD : Thursday – ☎ 056.

See : Town★★ – St. Canice's Cathedral★★ – Kilkenny Castle and Grounds★★ *AC* – Cityscope★ *AC* – Black Abbey★.

Exc. : Dunmore Cave★ *AC*, N : 7 m. by N 77 and N 78 – Kells Priory★, S : 9 m. by R 697.

18 Glendine ℘ 22125.

Shee Alms House, Rose Inn St. ℘ 51500.

◆Dublin 71 – ◆Cork 86 – ◆Killarney 115 – ◆Limerick 69 – ◆Tullamore 52 – ◆Waterford 29.

Kilkenny, College Rd, SW : 1½ m. on N 76 ℘ 62000, Fax 65984, – TV ☎ P – 400. AE VISA
Meals 8.95/22.50 **st.** and a la carte 4.95 – **60 rm** 55.00/150.00 **t.** – SB.

Newpark, Castlecomer Rd, N : ¾ m. on N 77 ℘ 22122, Fax 61111, park, – TV ☎ P – 600
60 rm.

Club House, Patrick St., ℘ 21994, Fax 21994 – TV ☎ P – 100. AE VISA
Meals (bar lunch Monday to Saturday)/dinner 17.50 **st.** and a la carte 4.95 – **38 rm** 40.00/95.00 **st.**

Blanchville House , Dunbell, Maddoxtown, SE : 7 1/2 m. by N 10 (eastbound) ℘ 27197, Fax 27636, ←, « Georgian house, working farm », , park – . *March-October* – **Meals** *(closed Sunday)* (communal dining) (dinner only) 17.50 **st.** 6.00 – **6 rm** 25.00/60.00 **st.** – SB.

Shillogher House without rest., Callan Rd, SW : 3/4 m. on N 76 ℘ 63249, – . *closed 23 to 25 December* – **5 rm** -/35.00.

Lacken House with rm, Dublin Rd, ℘ 61085, Fax 62435, – . *closed 1 week Christmas* – **Meals** *(closed Sunday and Monday)* (dinner only) 22.00 **t.** and a la carte 6.00 – **8 rm** 36.00/60.00 **t.** – SB.

KILL (An Chill) Kildare 405 M 8 – 045.

◆Dublin 15 – Carlow 36.

Ambassador, on N 7 ℘ 77064, Fax 77515 – – 250. **Meals** (bar lunch Monday to Saturday)/dinner 16.50 **st.** and a la carte – **36 rm** 45.00/100.00 **st.** – SB.

KILLALOE (Cill Dalua) Clare 405 G 9 **Ireland G.** – pop. 956 – ECD : Wednesday – 061.

See : Town★ – St. Flannan's Cathedral★.

Envir. : Graves of the Leinstermen★, N : 4 1/2 m. by R 494.

Exc. : Nenagh★ (Heritage Centre★★ *AC*, Castle★), NE : 12 m. by R 496 and N 7 – Holy Island★ *AC*, N : 8 m. by R 463 and boat from Tuamgraney.

Lock House, ℘ 376866 (1 June-11 September).

◆Dublin 109 – Ennis 32 – ◆Limerick 13 – ◆Tullamore 58.

Lakeside, ℘ 376122, Fax 376431, ←, , , , , , – . *closed 23 to 26 December* – **Meals** 9.00/18.50 **st.** and a la carte 5.00 – **36 rm** 45.00/85.00 **st.** – SB.

at Ogonnelloe N : 6 1/4 m. on R 463 – ✉ Ogonnelloe – 061 :

Lantern House , ℘ 923034, Fax 923139, ←, – . *mid February-October* – **Meals** (by arrangement) 15.00 **t.** 4.55 – **6 rm** 20.00/36.00 **t.**

Plans de ville : *Les rues sont sélectionnées en fonction de leur importance pour la circulation et le repérage des établissements cités.*

Les rues secondaires ne sont qu'amorcées.

KILLARNEY (Cill Airne) Kerry 405 D 11 **Ireland G.** – pop. 7 275 – ECD : Thursday – 064.

See : Town★★ – Knockreer Demesne★ – St. Mary's Cathedral★.

Envir. : Killarney National Park★★★ – Muckross House★★ *AC*, S : 3 1/2 m. by N 71 – Torc Waterfall★★, S : 5 m. by N 71 – Gap of Dunloe★★, SW : 6 m. by R 582 – Muckross Abbey★, S : 3 1/2 m. by N 71.

Exc. : Iveragh Peninsula★★★ (Ring of Kerry★★) – Ladies View★★, SW : 12 m. by N 71 – Moll's Gap★, SW : 15 1/2 m. by N 71.

18, 18 O'Mahoney's Point ℘ 31034.

Kerry (Farranfore) Airport : ℘ 066 (Farranfore) 64644, N : 9 1/2m. by N 22.

Town Hall ℘ 31633.

◆Dublin 189 – ◆Cork 54 – ◆Limerick 69 – ◆Waterford 112.

Europe , Fossa, W : 3 1/2 m. on T 67 ℘ 31900, Fax 32118, ← lake and mountains, , , , , , park, – – 500. *April-October* – **Meals** (bar lunch)/dinner 25.00 **st.** and a la carte 8.80 – **197 rm** 70.00/124.00 **st.**, 8 suites.

Dunloe Castle , Beaufort, W : 6 m. by R 562 ℘ 44111, Fax 44583, ← Gap of Dunloe, countryside and mountains, , , , , park, – – 400. *May-September* – **Meals** 18.50 **st.** and a la carte 8.80 – **119 rm** 62.00/125.00 **st.**, 1 suite.

Aghadoe Heights , NW : 3 1/2 m. by N 22 ℘ 31766, Fax 31345, ← countryside, lake and Macgillycuddy's Reeks, , , , – rest – 100. . *Fredrick's at the Heights :* **Meals** 17.50/29.50 **st.** and a la carte 6.95 – **57 rm** 110.00/155.00 **st.**, 3 suites – SB.

Great Southern, ℘ 31262, Fax 31642, , , , , park, – – 900. *closed 5 January-21 February* – ***Dining Room :*** **Meals** (dinner only) 16.95 **t.** 6.50 – ***Malton Room :*** **Meals** (dinner only) 23.95 **t.** and a la carte 6.50 – **178 rm** 78.00/122.00 **t.**, 2 suites – SB.

Muckross Park, S : 2 3/4 m. on N 71 ℘ 31938, Fax 31965, – . *mid March-November* – **Meals** (bar lunch)/dinner 25.00 **st.** and a la carte 5.25 – **25 rm** 73.00/110.00 **st.**, 2 suites – SB.

Killarney Park, Kenmare Pl., East Avenue Rd, 35555, Fax 35266, – rest
55 rm.

Randles Court, Muckross Rd, 35333, Fax 35206 – . VISA
closed 16 March-19 December – **Meals** (bar lunch Monday to Saturday)/dinner 12.00/22.00 **st.** and a la carte 5.50 – **37 rm** 45.00/120.00 **st.** – SB.

Cahernane, Muckross Rd, S : 1 m. on N 71 31895, Fax 34340, , , , – . VISA.
Easter-October – **Meals** (bar lunch)/dinner 25.00 **st.** and a la carte 7.50 – **48 rm** 80.00/150.00 **st.** – SB.

Torc Great Southern, Park Rd, 31611, Fax 31824, , , , –
Easter - mid October – 6.50 – **94 rm** 49.50/71.00 – SB.

Eviston House, 97 New St., 31640, Fax 33685 – . VISA
Meals (bar lunch)/dinner 16.00 **st.** and a la carte 7.00 – **40 rm** 45.00/70.00 **st.** – SB.

Ross, Kenmare Pl., 31855, Fax 31139, – rest rest
32 rm.

Royal, College St., 31853, Fax 34001 – . VISA
closed 22-28 December – **Meals** (bar lunch Monday to Saturday)/dinner 17.50 **t.** and a la carte – **49 rm** 50.00/100.00 **st.** – SB.

Foley's, 23 High St., 31217, Fax 34683 – rest . VISA.
March-October – **Meals** (bar lunch)/dinner 20.00 **st.** and a la carte 7.00 – **12 rm** 35.00/70.00 **t.** – SB.

Killeen House, Aghadoe, W : 4 m. by R 562 31711, Fax 31811, – . VISA.
closed 31 December-March – **Meals** (dinner only) 18.50/22.50 **st.** 6.00 – **15 rm** 36.30/72.60 **st.** – SB.

Whitegates, Muckross Rd, 31164, Fax 34850 – . VISA.
Meals (bar lunch Monday to Saturday)/dinner 15.00 **st.** and a la carte 4.90 – **23 rm** 42.00/68.00 **st.** – SB.

Kathleens Country House without rest., Tralee Rd, N : 2 m. on N 22 32810, Fax 32340, , – . VISA.
17 March-13 November – **17 rm** 60.00/70.00 **st.**

Park Lodge without rest., Cork Rd, E : ¾ m. 31539, Fax 34892, –
20 rm.

Victoria House without rest., Muckross Rd, S : 1¼ m. on N 71 35430, Fax 35439 – . VISA.
15 rm 22.00/40.00 **t.**

Lime Court without rest., Muckross Rd, S : ¾ m. on N 71 34547, Fax 34121 – . VISA.
closed 20-28 December – **12 rm** 21.00/25.00 **st.**

Beaufield House without rest., Cork Rd, E : 1 m. 34440, Fax 34663 – . VISA.
closed 15-30 December – **14 rm** 25.00/37.00 **t.**

Gleann Fia without rest., Deerpark, N : 1½ m. off N 22 bypass 35035, Fax 35000, « Riverside setting », – . VISA.
15 March-October – **8 rm** 23.00/35.00 **st.**

Fuchsia House without rest., Muckross Rd, 33743, Fax 33743, – . VISA.
closed January and February – **10 rm** 32.00/42.00 **t.**

Carriglea Farmhouse without rest., Muckross Rd, S : 1½ m. on N 71 31116, , – .
May-October – **8 rm** 32.00 **st.**

Lake Lodge without rest., Muckross Rd, S : ¾ m. on N 71 33333, Fax 35109 – . VISA.
closed 7 January-15 March – **13 rm** 20.00/36.00 **st.**

Gaby's, 27 High St., 32519, Fax 32747 – VISA
closed Monday lunch, Sunday, 1 week Christmas and February – **Meals** - Seafood a la carte 16.50/29.30 **t.** 6.10.

Strawberry Tree, 24 Plunkett St., 32688, Fax 32688 – VISA
closed January, February and Monday-Tuesday except July and August – **Meals** (dinner only) a la carte 22.25/26.45 **st.** 6.25.

KILLEAGH (Cill la) Cork 405 H 12 – 024.

♦Dublin 151 – ♦Cork 23 – ♦Waterford 53.

Ballymakeigh House, N : 1 m. 95184, Fax 95370, « Working farm », , park, – .
Meals 18.00 **st.** 7.00 – **5 rm** 25.00/40.00 **st.** – SB.

KILLINEY (Cill Iníon Léinín) Dublin 405 N 8 – ☎ 01.
Killiney ✆ 851983.
◆Dublin 8 – Bray 4.

- **Fitzpatrick Castle,** ✆ 284 0700, Telex 30353, Fax 285 0207, ←, squash – rm – 400. VISA JCB.
  Meals 12.50/20.00 **t.** and dinner a la carte – 8.50 – **84 rm** 75.00/124.00 **t.**, 6 suites – SB.
- **Court,** Killiney Bay, ✆ 285 1622, Fax 285 2085, ←, – rm rest – 250. VISA.
  Meals 11.50/20.95 **t.** and a la carte 5.50 – **86 rm** 65.00/85.00 **st.** – SB.

KILLORGLIN (Cill Orglan) Kerry 405 C 11 – ☎ 066.
◆Dublin 207 – ◆Killarney 12 – Tralee 16.

- **Bianconi,** ✆ 61146, Fax 61950, – rm. VISA
  closed 24 to 28 December – **Meals** (in bar lunchtime and Sunday dinner) 21.00 **t.** and a la carte 5.25 – **15 rm** 25.00/44.00 **t.** – SB.
- **Westfield House,** Glenbeigh Rd, W : ¾ m. by N 70 ✆ 61909, Fax 61996, – rm. VISA
  Meals 12.50 **st.** – **10 rm** 20.00/35.00 **st.** – SB.
- **Grove Lodge** without rest., Killarney Rd, E : ½ m. on R 562 ✆ 61157, Fax 61157, « Riverside setting », – . VISA
  closed December – **5 rm** 25.00/34.00 **st.**

KILLYBEGS (Na Cealla Beaga) Donegal 405 G 4 – ☎ 073.
◆Dublin 181 – Donegal 17 – ◆Londonderry 64 – ◆Sligo 57.

- **Bay View,** Main St., ✆ 31950, Fax 31856, ←, – . VISA
  Meals (bar lunch Monday to Saturday)/dinner 16.00 **t.** and a la carte 4.70 – **36 rm** 45.00/70.00 **t.**, 2 suites – SB.

When looking for a quiet hotel
use the maps found in the introductory pages
or look for establishments with the sign or .

KILSHEELAN (Cill Síoláin) Tipperary 405 J 10 – ✉ Clonmel – ☎ 052.
◆Dublin 97 – ◆Cork 66 – ◆Limerick 53 – ◆Waterford 24.

- **Highfield House** , E : 1¾ m. by N 24 ✆ 33192, , park – .
  April-September – **Meals** (by arrangement) (communal dining) – **3 rm** 20.00/35.00 **t.**

KILTIMAGH (Coillte Mach) Mayo 405 EF 6 – ☎ 094.
◆Dublin 138 – ◆Galway 52 – Westport 26.

- **Cill Aodain,** ✆ 81761, Fax 81838 – . VISA.
  Meals (carving lunch Monday to Saturday)/dinner 22.00 **st.** and a la carte 4.20 – **15 rm** 27.50/59.00 **st.** – SB.

KINSALE (Cionn Eitigh) Cork 405 G 12 **Ireland G.** – pop. 1 759 – ECD : Thursday – ☎ 021.
See : Town★★ – St. Multose Church★ – Kinsale Regional Museum★ *AC*.
Envir. : Summercove★ (←★) E : 1½ m. – Charles Fort★ *AC*, E : 1¾ m.
Pier Rd ✆ 774417 (March-November).
◆Dublin 178 – ◆Cork 17.

- **Acton's** (Forte), Pier Rd, ✆ 772135, Fax 772231, ←, – rm – 300. VISA.
  Meals (bar lunch Monday to Saturday)/dinner 17.00 **st.** and a la carte 5.50 – **57 rm** 60.00/110.00 **st.** – SB.
- **Old Bank House** without rest., 11 Pearse St., ✆ 774075, Fax 774296 – . VISA.
  closed 24 to 26 December – **9 rm** 50.00/120.00 **st.**
- **Blue Haven,** 3 Pearse St., ✆ 772209, Fax 774268 – . VISA.
  closed 25 December – **Meals** - (see ***Blue Haven*** below) – **18 rm** 63.00/110.00 **st.** – SB.
- **Scilly House Inn** without rest., Scilly, ✆ 772413, Fax 774629, ←, – . VISA.
  16 April-October – **7 rm** 65.00/115.00 **st.**
- **Moorings** without rest., Scilly, ✆ 772376, Fax 772675, ← Kinsale harbour – . VISA.
  closed 1 week Christmas – **8 rm** 50.00/90.00.
- **White Lady Inn,** Lower O'Connell St., ✆ 772737 – . VISA.
  Meals (grill rest.) (dinner only and Sunday lunch)/dinner a la carte 8.40/15.30 **t.** 5.75 – **10 rm** 35.00/50.00 **st.**
- **Old Presbytery,** Cork St., ✆ 772027, « Memorabilia », – rm .
  closed 23 to 30 December – **Meals** (by arrangement) 22.00 **st.** 6.00 – **6 rm** 34.00/50.00 **st.**
- **Lighthouse** without rest., The Rock, ✆ 772734 – . VISA.
  5 rm 30.00/50.00 **st.**

XX **Chez Jean Marc,** Lower O'Connell St., ☎ 774625, Fax 774680 – P. AE VISA
closed Sunday in winter, Monday and 15 February-15 March – **Meals** (dinner only) 18.00 **t.** and a la carte.

XX **Blue Haven** (at Blue Haven H.), 3 Pearse St., ☎ 772209, Fax 774268 – AE VISA
Meals - Seafood 25.00 **t.** (dinner) and a la carte 10.75/28.00 **t.** 5.00.

XX Billy Mackesy's Bawnleigh House,, N : 5 ½ m. on Old Cork Rd ☎ 771333 – P.

X **Max's,** Main St., ☎ 772243 – VISA
12 February-October – **Meals** 12.00 **t.** and a la carte.

at Ballinclashet E : 5 m. by R 600 – ✉ Kinsale – ☎ 021 :

XX **Oystercatcher,** ☎ 770822 – P. VISA
closed January-mid March – **Meals** *(closed Monday)* (dinner only) 28.00 **t.** 7.75.

KNOCK (An Cnoc) Mayo 405 F 6 **Ireland G.** – pop. 440 – ☎ 094.

See : Basilica of our Lady, Queen of Ireland★.

Knock (Connaught) Airport : ☎ 67222, NE : 9 m. by N 17.

Knock Airport ☎ 67247.

♦Dublin 132 – Galway 46 – Wesport 32.

Hotel and Restaurant see : Cong SW : 36 m. by N 17, R 331, R 334 and R 345.

LAHINCH (An Leacht) Clare 405 D 9 **Ireland G.** – pop. 550 – ☎ 065.

Envir. : Cliffs of Moher★★★.

18, 18 Lahinch ☎ 81003 – 9 Spanish Point, Miltown Malbay ☎ 84198.

☎ 81474 (27 May-1 September).

♦Dublin 162 – ♦Galway 49 – ♦Limerick 41.

Aberdeen Arms, ☎ 81100, Fax 81228, – rest TV ☎ P – 250. AE VISA.
Meals 9.50/23.00 **st.** and a la carte 5.50 – **55 rm** 54.00/84.00 **st.** – SB.

Atlantic House, Main St., ☎ 81049, Fax 81029 – TV ☎ P. VISA
closed January-Easter – **Meals** (bar lunch)/dinner a la carte 16.70/19.00 **t.** 6.50 – **14 rm** 29.15/55.10 **st.** – SB.

LARAGH (Láithreach) Wicklow 405 N 8 – ✉ Wicklow – ☎ 0404.

♦Dublin 26 – Kilkenny 70 – Wexford 61.

Laragh Trekking Centre , Laragh East, NW : 1 ½ m. on Sallygap rd ☎ 45282, Fax 45204, ←, – TV P. VISA
Meals 13.50 **st.** – **6 rm** 27.00/37.00 **st.** – SB.

LEENANE (An Líonán) Galway 405 C 7 **Ireland G.** – – ✉ Clifden – ☎ 095.

See : Killary Harbour★.

Envir. : Joyce Country★★ – Aasleagh Falls★, NE : 2½ m.

Exc. : Lough Nafooey★★, SE : 8 ½ m by R 336 – Doo Lough Pass★, NW : 9 m. by N 59 and R 335.

♦Dublin 173 – Ballina 56 – ♦Galway 41.

Delphi Lodge , NW : 8 ¼ m. by N 59 on Louisburgh rd ☎ 42211, Fax 42296, ←, « Georgian sporting lodge, loughside setting », , park – ☎ P – 30. VISA.
February-October – **Meals** (residents only) (communal dining) (dinner only) 25.00 **t.** 6.00 – **11 rm** 42.50/95.00 **t.**

Portfinn Lodge, ☎ 42265, Fax 42315 – ☎ P. VISA
April-October – **Meals** (by arrangement) 16.50 **t.** 7.00 – **8 rm** 22.50/35.00 **t.** – SB.

LETTERFRACK (Leitir Fraic) Galway 405 C 7 – ☎ 0195.

♦Dublin 189 – Ballina 69 – ♦Galway 57.

Rosleague Manor , W : 1 ½ m. on N 59 ☎ 41101, Fax 41168, ← Ballynakill harbour and Tully mountain, , , park, – rest ☎ P. AE VISA
April-October – **Meals** (bar lunch)/dinner 25.00 **st.** and a la carte 6.50 – **20 rm** 45.00/150.00 **t.** – SB.

LETTERKENNY (Leitir Ceanainn) Donegal 405 I 3 **Ireland G.** – pop. 7 166 – ECD : Monday – ☎ 074.

Exc. : Glenveagh National Park★★ (Gardens★★), NW : 12 m. by R 250, R 251 and R 254 – Grianan of Aileach★★ (←★) NE : 17 ½ m. by N 13 – Church Hill (Colmcille Heritage Centre★ *AC*, Glebe House and Gallery★ *AC*) NW : 10 m. by R 250.

18 Barnhill ☎ 21150 – 18 Dunfanaghy ☎ 36335.

Derry Rd ☎ 21160.

♦Dublin 150 – ♦Londonderry 21 – ♦Sligo 72.

Clanree, Derry Rd, E : 1 ¾ m. on N 13 ☎ 24369, Fax 25389 – TV ☎ P
21 rm.

Castlegrove House , Ramelton Rd, NE : 4 ½ m. by N 13 and R 245 ☎ 51118, Fax 51384, ←, , , park – ☎ . AE VISA.
closed 23 to 30 December and 9 January to 14 February – **Meals** *(closed Sunday and Monday October to May)* (dinner only) 19.00 **t.** and a la carte 5.00 – **8 rm** 40.00/ 160.00 **t.** – SB.

LIMERICK

Arthur Quay Shopping Centre . . . . Y
O'Connell Street . . . . Z
Patrick Street . . . . YZ 32
Roches Street . . . . Z
Sarfield Street . . . . Y 39
William Street . . . . Z

Arthur Quay . . . . Y 2
Baal's Bridge . . . . Y 4
Bank Place . . . . Y 5
Barrington Street . . . . Z 6
Bridge Street . . . . Y 7
Broad Street . . . . Y 8
Castle Street . . . . Y 10
Cathedral Place . . . . Z 12
Charlotte's Quay . . . . Y 13
The Crescent . . . . Z 14
Gerald Griffen St. . . . . Z 16
Grattan Street . . . . Y 17
High Street . . . . Z 18
Honan's Quay . . . . Y 19
John Square . . . . Z 20
Lock Quay . . . . Y 21
Lower Cecil Street . . . . Z 22
Lower Mallow St. . . . . Z 23
Mathew Bridge . . . . Y 24
Michael Street . . . . Y 25
Mount Kenneth . . . . Z 26
Newtown Mahon . . . . Z 28
North Circular Rd. . . . . Z 29
O'Dwyer Bridge . . . . Y 30
Penniwell Road . . . . Z 33
Rutland Street . . . . Y 34
St Alphonsus St. . . . . Z 35
St Gerard St. . . . . Z 36
St Lelia Street . . . . YZ 37
Sexton Street North . . . . Y 40
Shannon Street . . . . Z 42
South Circular Rd. . . . . Z 43
Thomond Bridge . . . . Y 45
Wickham Street . . . . Z 47

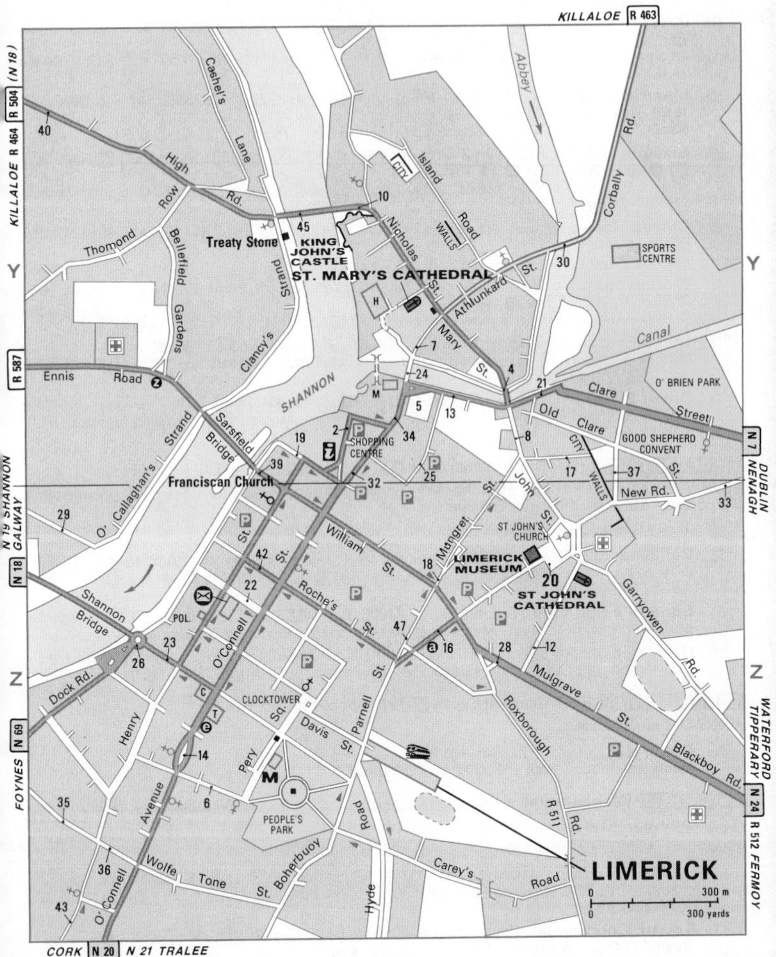

LIMERICK **(Luimneach)** Limerick 405 G 9 **Ireland G.** – pop. 52 083 – ECD : Thursday – 061.

See : City** – St Mary's Cathedral** Y – Limerick Museum** Z – King John's Castle* *AC* Y – John Square* Z **20** – St. John's Cathdral* Z.

Envir. : Hunt Museum, Limerick University* *AC*, E : 2 m. by N 7 Y – Cratloe Wood (<*) NW : 5 m. by N 18 Z.

Exc. : Lough Gur Interpretive Centre* *AC*, S : 11 m. by R 512 and R 514 Z – Clare Glens*, E : 13 m. by N 7 and R 503 Y – Monasteranenagh Abbey*, S : 13 m. by N 20 Z.

Shannon Airport : 061 (Shannon) 471444, W : 16 m. by N 18 Z – **Terminal** : Limerick Railway Station.

Arthur's Quay 317522 Y.

♦Dublin 120 – ♦Cork 58.

Plan on preceding page

- **Castletroy Park,** Dublin Rd, E : 2 ¼ m. on N 7 335566, Fax 331117, – rm – 250. Y
  closed 25 to 30 December and 1 to 3 January – **Meals** *(closed Saturday lunch and Sunday dinner)* 15.95/24.20 **st.** and dinner a la carte – 9.50 – **105 rm** 100.00/154.00 **st.**, 2 suites – SB.
- Limerick Inn, Ennis Rd, NW : 4 m. on N 18 326666, Fax 326281, – rest – 500 Y
  149 rm, 4 suites.
- **Jurys,** Ennis Rd, 327777, Telex 70766, Fax 326400, – rest – 200. Y **z**
  closed 24 to 27 December – **Meals** 12.50/15.00 **t.** and a la carte 6.05 – 8.00 – **94 rm** 74.00/92.00 **t.**, 1 suite – SB.
- **Limerick Ryan,** Ennis Rd, NW : 1¼ m. on N 18 453922, Fax 326333, – rest – 120. Y
  Meals 15.00/20.00 **t.** and a la carte 5.95 – 8.00 – **179 rm** 75.00/90.00 **t.**, 2 suites – SB.
- **Greenhills,** Ennis Rd, NW : 2 ¼ m. on N 18 453033, Fax 453307, – – 300. Y
  closed 25 December – **Meals** *(closed Sunday and Monday)* 9.75/20.00 **t.** and a la carte 5.25 – **60 rm** 52.50/115.00 **st.** – SB.
- **Clifton House** without rest., Ennis Rd, NW : 1 ¼ m. on N 18 451166, Fax 451224, – . Z
  closed 20 December-6 January – **16 rm** 22.00/32.00 **t.**
- **Clonmacken House** without rest., Clonmacken Rd, off Ennis Rd, NW : 2 m. by N 18 327007, – . Z
  closed 20 December-6 January – **10 rm** 20.00/36.00 **st.**
- **De La Fontaine,** 12 Upper Gerald Griffin St., 414461 – Z **a**
  closed Saturday lunch, Sunday and Bank Holidays – **Meals** - French 10.00/21.50 **t.** and a la carte 5.00.
- **Silver Plate,** 74 O'Connell St., 316311 – Z **e**
  closed Sunday, Monday and 24 to 26 December – **Meals** (dinner only) a la carte 13.30/20.80 **t.** 4.50.

LISDOONVARNA **(Lios Dîin Bhearna)** Clare 405 E 8 **Ireland G.** – pop. 842 – 065.

Envir. : The Burren** (Cliffs of Moher***, Scenic Routes**, Aillwee Cave* *AC* (Waterfall*), Corcomroe Abbey*, Kilfenora Crosses*).

♦Dublin 167 – ♦Galway 39 – ♦Limerick 47.

- **Ballinalacken Castle** , W : 2 m. on L 54 74025, < – rest .
  May-September – **Meals** (light lunch)/dinner a la carte approx. 20.45 **t.** 6.50 – **13 rm** 35.00/55.00 **st.**
- **Sheedy's Spa View,** Sulphir Hill, 74026, Fax 74555, – .
  mid March-mid October – **Meals** (see ***Orchid*** below) – **11 rm** 35.00/50.00 **t.**
- **Orchid** (at Sheedy's Spa View H.), Sulphir Hill, 74026, Fax 74555 – .
  mid March-mid October – **Meals** (dinner only) a la carte 18.40/23.75 **t.** 8.50.

LOUGH GOWNA **(Loch Gamhna)** Cavan 405 J 6 – pop. 125 – 043.

♦Dublin 81 – ♦Tullamore 54.

- **Robin Hill** , 83121, – .
  Meals (by arrangement) 14.00 **st.** 4.00 – **6 rm** 14.00/28.00 **s.**

MACROOM **(Maigh Chromtha)** Cork 405 F 12 – pop. 2 303 – ECD : Wednesday – 026.

Lackaduve 41072.

♦Dublin 186 – ♦Cork 25 – ♦Killarney 30.

- **Castle,** Main St., 41074, Fax 41505, , squash – .
  closed 24 to 26 December – **Meals** 8.50/18.50 **st.** and a la carte 6.50 – **26 rm** 28.00/50.00 **st.** – SB.
- **Bower,** Gortanaddan, Kilnamartyra, W : 8 m. by N 22 40192, – rm
  Meals 11.00 **st.** – **5 rm** 13.50/30.00 **st.**

MALAHIDE (Mullach Íde) Dublin 405 N 7 Ireland G. – pop. 12 088 – ☎ 01.

See : Castle★.

18, 9 Beechwood, The Grange ☎ 846 1611.

◆Dublin 9 – Drogheda 24.

Grand, ☎ 845 0000, Telex 31446, Fax 845 0987, ← – rm – 600
97 rm, 3 suites.

Liscara without rest, Malahide Rd, Kinsealy, S : 3 m. on Dublin rd ☎ 848 3751 –
closed December and January – **6 rm** 32.00.

Bon Appetit, 9 James's Terr., ☎ 8450314, Fax 8450314 – . AE VISA JCB
closed Saturday lunch, Sunday and 1 week Christmas – **Meals** 10.60/22.00 **t.** and a la carte 5.50.

MALLOW (Mala) Cork 405 F 11 Ireland G. – pop. 6 238 – ECD : Wednesday – ☎ 022.

See : Town★ – St. James' Church★.

Exc. : Doneraile Wildlife Park★ *AC*, NE : 6 m. by N 20 and R 581 – Buttevant Friary★, N : 7 m. by N 20.

18 Balleyellis ☎ 21145.

◆Dublin 149 – ◆Cork 21 – ◆Killarney 40 – ◆Limerick 41.

Longueville House , W : 3½ m. by N 72 ☎ 47156, Fax 47459, ←, « Georgian mansion in extensive grounds », – rest . AE VISA.
closed 17 December-16 March – ***Presidents* : Meals** (booking essential) (bar lunch Monday to Saturday)/dinner 38.00 **t.** and a la carte 7.00 – **16 rm** 53.00/158.00 **t.** – SB.

Springfort Hall, N : 4¾ m. by N 20 and R 581 ☎ 21278, Fax 21557, , park – .
AE VISA
closed 24 December-1 January – **Meals** *(closed Sunday)* (dinner only) 23.00 **st.** and a la carte 5.75 – **24 rm** 35.00/60.00 **st.** – SB.

Central, ☎ 21527, Fax 21527 – – 40
20 rm.

Die Preise Einzelheiten über die in diesem Führer angegebenen Preise finden Sie in der Einleitung.

MAYNOOTH (Maigh Nuad) Kildare 405 M 7 – pop. 6 027 – ECD : Wednesday – ☎ 01.

Envir. : Castletown House★★ *AC*, SE : 4 m. by R 405.

9 Kilcock ☎ 628 7283.

◆Dublin 15.

Moyglare Manor , Moyglare, N : 2 m. ☎ 628 6351, Fax 628 5405, ←, « Georgian country house, antique furnishings », , park, – – 35. AE VISA JCB.
closed 24 to 26 December – **Meals** *(closed Saturday lunch to non-residents)* 12.95/21.95 **t.** and a la carte 6.95 – **17 rm** 80.00/120.00 **t.**

MIDLETON (Mainistir na Corann) Cork 405 H 12 – ☎ 021.

18 East Cork, Gortacue ☎ 631687/631273.

Jameson Heritage Centre ☎ 613702 (8 April-20 September).

◆Dublin 161 – ◆Cork 12 – ◆Waterford 61.

Midleton Park, Old Cork Rd, ☎ 631767, Fax 631605, – rest – 400.
AE VISA.
Meals 9.95/16.50 **st.** and a la carte 4.95 – **39 rm** 50.00/75.00 **st.**, 1 suite – SB.

Bailick Cottage without rest., S : ½ m. by Broderick St. ☎ 631244, – .
6 rm 25.00/50.00 **s.**

MONAGHAN (Muineachán) Monaghan 405 L 5 – ☎ 047.

◆Dublin 83 – ◆Belfast 43 – Drogheda 54 – ◆Dundalk 22 – ◆Londonderry 75.

Hillgrove, Old Armagh Rd, SE : ¾ m. by N 2 ☎ 81288, Fax 84951 – rest –
800. AE VISA.
Meals (carving lunch)/dinner 18.00 **st.** and a la carte – **44 rm** 38.00/80.00 **st.** – SB.

MOYCULLEN (Maigh Cuilinn) Galway 405 E 7 – pop. 545 – ☎ 091.

◆Dublin 139 – ◆Galway 7.

Knockferry Lodge , Knockferry (on Lough Corrib), NE : 6½ m. ☎ 80122, Fax 80328, ←, , – rest . AE VISA.
May-September – **Meals** (dinner only) 16.00 **st.** – **10 rm** 27.00/40.00 **st.** – SB.

Moycullen House , SW : 1 m. on Spiddle rd ☎ 85566, Fax 85566, – . AE
VISA.
April-October – **Meals** (communal dining)(by arrangement) – **5 rm** 37.50/55.00 **st.**

Drimcong House, NW : 1 m. on N 59 ☎ 85115, « 17C estate house », – . AE
VISA
closed Sunday, Monday and Christmas-March – **Meals** (booking essential) (dinner only) 16.95 **t.** and a la carte 25.00/30.00 4.50.

MULLINAVAT **(Muileann an Bhata)** Kilkenny 405 K 10 – ☎ 051.
◆Dublin 88 – Kilkenny 21 – Waterford 8.

Rising Sun, Main St., ✆ 98173, Fax 98435 – TV ☎ P
10 rm.

MULLINGAR **(An Muileann gCearr)** Westmeath 405 JK 7 **Ireland G.** – pop. 8 003 – ☎ 044.
Envir. : Belvedere House and Gardens★ *AC*, S : 3½ m. by N 52.
Exc. : Multyfarnhan Franciscan Friary★, N : 8 m. by N 4 - Tullynally Castle★ *AC*, N : 13 m. by N 4 and R 394 – Fore Abbey★, NE : 17 m. by R 394.
Mullingar ✆ 48366/48629.
Dublin Road ✆ 48650.
◆Dublin 49 – ◆Drogheda 36.

Greville Arms, Pearse St., ✆ 48563, Fax 48052 – rest TV ☎ P – 100. AE VISA.
Meals 8.00/18.00 **st.** and a la carte 4.50 – **40 rm** 28.00/70.00 **st.**

Hilltop Country House, Rathconnell, NE : 2½ m. by R 52 ✆ 48958, Fax 48013, – P.
March-October – **Meals** (by arrangement) – **5 rm** 20.00/30.00 **st.**

NAVAN **(An Uaimh)** Meath 405 L 7 – ☎ 046.
Envir. : Bective Abbey★, S : 4 m. by R 161.
Exc. : Trim★ (castle★★) SW : 8 m. by R 161.
◆Dublin 29 – Drogheda 17.

XXX **Dunderry Lodge,** Dunderry, SW : 6 m. by N 51 off L 23 ✆ 31671, « Converted farm buildings » – P. AE VISA
closed Sunday dinner, Monday and Bank Holidays – **Meals** (dinner only and Sunday lunch)/dinner 15.95 **st.** and a la carte 5.50.

NEWBRIDGE **(An Droichead Nua)** Kildare 405 L 8 **Ireland G.** – pop. 11 778 – ECD : Tuesday – ☎ 045.
See : Town★.
Envir. : Tully★★★ (Japanese Gardens★★★ *AC*, Irish National Stud★★ *AC*) SW : 6 m. by N 7 - Kildare★ (Cathedral★★) SW : 5½ m. by N 7.
Curragh ✆ 41238/41714.
Main Street, ✆ 33835 (10 July-August).
◆Dublin 28 – Kilkenny 57 – ◆Tullamore 36.

Keadeen, Ballymany, SW : 1 m. on N 7 ✆ 31666, Fax 34402, – TV ☎ P – 350
36 rm, 1 suite.

NEWMARKET-ON-FERGUS **(Cora Chaitlín)** Clare 405 F 7 – pop. 1 583 – ☎ 061.
◆Dublin 136 – Ennis 8 – ◆Limerick 15.

Dromoland Castle, NW : 1 ½ m. on N 18 ✆ 368144, Telex 70654, Fax 363355, <, « Converted castle », 18, , , park, – TV ☎ P – 450. AE VISA.
Meals 20.00/33.00 **t.** and a la carte – 12.50 – **67 rm** 198.00 **st.**, 6 suites
Spec. Pan fried scallops with a marinade of vegetables and olive purée dressing, Fricassee of lobster with baby vegetables and Champagne sauce, Hot brown bread soufflé.

Clare Inn,, NW : 2 m. on N 18 ✆ 368161, Fax 368622, , , , 9, – rm TV ☎ P – 400. AE VISA.
closed January-24 February – **Meals** (bar lunch Monday to Saturday)/dinner 20.00 **st.** and a la carte – 7.00 – **121 rm** 45.00/99.00 **st.** – SB.

Carrygerry House, NW : 8 m. by N 18 ✆ 472339, Fax 472123, , park – rm TV ☎ P. AE VISA.
closed 4 days Christmas – **Meals** *(closed Sunday)* (bar lunch)/dinner 21.50 **t.** and a la carte 5.00 – **14 rm** 43.50/79.00 **t.** – SB.

NEWPORT **(Baile Uí Fhiacháin)** Mayo 405 D 6 **Ireland G.** – pop. 512 – ☎ 098.
Envir. : Burrishoole Abbey★, NW : 2 m. by N 59 – Furnace Lough★, NW : 3 m. by N 59.
◆Dublin 164 – Ballina 37 – ◆Galway 60.

Newport House, ✆ 41222, Fax 41613, « Country house atmosphere, antiques », , , park – rest ☎ P. AE VISA.
19 March-2 October – **Meals** (dinner only) 28.00 **st.** 7.00 – **19 rm** 63.00/126.00 **st.**

NEW ROSS (Ros Mhic Thriîin) Wexford 405 L 10 **Ireland G.** – pop. 5 018 – ECD : Wednesday – ✉ Newbawn – ☎ 051.

See : St. Mary's Church★.

Exc. : Kennedy Arboretum, Campile★ *AC*, S : 7½ m. by R 733 – Dunbrody Abbey★, S : 8 m. by R 733 – Inistiage★, NW : 10 m. by N 25 and R 700 – Graiguenamanagh★ (Duiske Abbey★) N : 11 m. by N 25 and R705.

Tinneranny ☎ 21433.

Town Centre ☎ 21857 (16 June-4 August).

♦Dublin 88 – Kilkenny 27 – ♦Waterford 15 – Wexford 23.

Cedar Lodge, Carrigbyrne, E : 8 m. on N 25 ☎ 28386, Fax 28222, – TV ☎ P. VISA.
closed mid December-mid January – **Meals** (lunch booking essential)/dinner 25.00 **t.** – **18 rm** 50.00/80.00 **st.** – SB.

OGONNELLOE (Tuath Ó gConaíle) Clare 405 G 9 – see Killaloe.

OMEATH (Û Méith) Louth 405 N 5 – ☎ 042.

♦Dublin 63 – ♦Dundalk 10.

Omeath Park, NW : ½ m. on B 79 ☎ 75116, ←, , park – TV ☎ P
13 rm.

Granvue House, ☎ 75109 – TV ☎ P
9 rm.

OUGHTERARD (Uachtar Ard) Galway 405 E 7 **Ireland G.** – pop. 711 – ☎ 091.

See : Town★.

Envir. : Lough Corrib★★ (Shore road - NW - ←★★) – Aughnanure Castle★ *AC*, SE : 2 m. by N 59.

Gurteeva ☎ 82131.

Main street ☎ 82808.

♦Dublin 149 – ♦Galway 17.

Connemara Gateway, SE : ¾ m. on N 59 ☎ 82328, Fax 82332, , , , – rest TV ☎ P. AE VISA.
closed December and January except New Year – **Meals** (bar lunch)/dinner 21.00 **st.** and a la carte 6.50 – **62 rm** 50.00/140.00 **st.**

Currarevagh House, NW : 4 m. ☎ 82313, Fax 82731, ←, « Country house atmosphere », , , park, – rest P.
April September – **Meals** (booking essential) (dinner only) 18.75 **t.** 4.70 – **15 rm** 42.00/84.00 **t.** – SB.

Ross Lake House, Rosscahill, SE : 4½ m. by N 59 ☎ 80109, Fax 80184, , – ☎ P. AE VISA.
closed November-mid March – **Meals** (dinner only) 19.00 **t.** 9.50 – **13 rm** 35.00/70.00 **t.** – SB.

Boat Inn, ☎ 82196, Fax 82694 – TV ☎
11 rm.

Cnoc na Curra without rest., Pier Rd, ☎ 82225, ←, , – P.
May-mid September – **4 rm** 18.00/36.00 **st.**

PARKNASILLA (Páirc na Saileach) Kerry 405 C 12 **Ireland G.** – ☎ 064.

Envir. : Sneem★, NW : 2½ m. by N 70.

Exc. : Iveragh Peninsula★★★ (Ring of Kerry★★) – Staigue Fort★, W : 13 m. by N 70.

♦Dublin 224 – ♦Cork 72 – ♦Killarney 34.

Great Southern, ☎ 45122, Telex 73899, Fax 45323, ← Kenmare river, bay and mountains, , , , , , park, – TV ☎ P – 50. AE VISA.
closed 3 January-16 March – **Meals** (bar lunch)/dinner 30.00 **st.** and a la carte 8.00 – 8.00 – **83 rm** 81.00/148.00 **st.**, 1 suite – SB.

PORTLAOISE (Port Laoise) Laois 405 K 8 **Ireland G.** – pop. 3 618 – ☎ 0502.

Envir. : Rock of Dunamase★ (←★), E : 4 m. by N 80 – Emo Court★ *AC*, NE : 7 m. by N 7.

Exc. : Stradbally★, E : 6½ m. by N 80 – Timahoe Round Tower★, SE : 8 m. by R 426.

The Heath ☎ 46533.

James Fintan Lawlor Av. ☎ 21178.

♦ Dublin 54 – Kilkenny 31 – ♦Limerick 67.

Aspen without rest., Dunamase, E : 4½ m. by N 80 ☎ 25405, Fax 25405, – P.
March-October – **4 rm** 20.00/34.00 **st.**

PORTMARNOCK (Port Mearnóg) Dublin 405 N 7 – pop. 9 173 – ☎ 01.

♦Dublin 5 – Drogheda 28.

Portmarnock H. & Country Club, ☎ 846 0611, Fax 846 2442, ←, – TV ☎ P – 750. AE VISA.
closed 24 and 25 December – **Meals** (dinner only and Sunday lunch)/dinner 18.75 **t.** 6.50 – 4.50 – **19 rm** 62.50/135.00 **t.** – SB.

PORTNABLAHY/ PORTNABLAGH (Port na Bláiche) Donegal 405 I 2 – see Dunfanaghy.

RATHMULLAN (Ráth Maoláin) Donegal 405 J 2 **Ireland G.** – pop. 536 – ✉ Letterkenny – ☎ 074.

Exc. : Knockalla Viewpoint★★, N : 8 m. by R 247 – Rathmelton★, SW : 7 m. by R 247.

Otway, Saltpans ☎ 58319.

♦Dublin 165 – ♦Londonderry 36 – ♦Sligo 87.

Rathmullan House 🐦, N : ½ m. on R 247 ☎ 58188, Fax 58200, ≤ Lough Swilly and hills, « Early 19C country house, gardens », ⛲, 🏊, 🎣, park, 🎾 – ⇔ rest TV ☎ P. AE ⓓ VISA. ✂
March-October – **Meals** (bar lunch Monday to Saturday)/dinner 22.50 **t.** 🍷 5.00 – **23 rm** ☕ 35.00/110.00 **t.** – SB.

Fort Royal 🐦, N : ½ m. on R 247 ☎ 58100, Fax 58103, ≤ Lough Swilly and hills, 🌳, park, 🎾, squash – ⇔ rest TV ☎ P. AE ⓓ VISA
April-October – **Meals** (bar lunch Monday to Friday)/dinner 21.00 **st.** 🍷 6.75 – **15 rm** ☕ 40.00/90.00 **t.** – SB.

Prices For full details of the prices quoted in the guide, consult the introduction.

RATHNEW (Ráth Naoi) Wicklow 405 N 8 **Ireland G.** – pop. 1 496 – ✉ Wicklow – ☎ 0404.

Exc. : Glendalough★★★, W : 13 m. by N 11, R 763, R 755 and R 756 – W : Wicklow Mountains★★.

♦Dublin 31 – ♦Waterford 82 – Wexford 65.

Tinakilly House 🐦, ☎ 69274, Fax 67806, ≤, « Part Victorian country house », 🌳, 🎾 – TV ☎ P – 🏛 60. AE ⓓ VISA JCB. ✂
Meals *(closed 24 to 27 December to non residents)* 17.50/28.50 **st.** 🍷 7.50 – **26 rm** ☕ 88.00/136.00 **st.**, 3 suites – SB.

Hunter's, Newrath Bridge, N : ¾ m. on L 29 ☎ 40106, Fax 40338, « Converted 18C inn, gardens » – ☎ P. AE ⓓ VISA. ✂
Meals 16.00/22.50 **t.** 🍷 4.50 – **16 rm** ☕ 42.50/62.50 **t.** – SB.

RECESS (Sraith Salach) Galway 405 C 7 – ☎ 095.

♦Dublin 173 – Ballina 72 – ♦Galway 36.

Lough Inagh Lodge 🐦, NW : 4 ¾ m. by N 59 ☎ 34706, Fax 34708, ≤ Lough Inagh and The Twelve Bens, 🎣 – TV ☎ P. AE ⓓ VISA. ✂
mid April-October – **Meals** (bar lunch)/dinner 23.00 **t.** and a la carte – **12 rm** ☕ 69.00/120.00 **t.** – SB.

RINVYLE/RENVYLE (Rinn Mhaoile) Galway 405 C 7 – ☎ 095.

♦Dublin 193 – Ballina 73 – ♦Galway 61.

Renvyle House 🐦, ☎ 43511, Fax 43515, ≤ Atlantic Ocean, 🏊 heated, 9, 🎣, 🌳, park, 🎾 – TV ☎ P. AE ⓓ VISA JCB. ✂
closed 3 January-mid March – **Meals** (light lunch Monday to Saturday)/dinner 21.00 **t.** 🍷 8.50 – **64 rm** ☕ 53.00/106.00 **t.**, 1 suite – SB.

RIVERSTOWN (Baile idir Dhá Abhainn) Sligo 405 G 5 – pop. 274 – ☎ 071.

♦Dublin 123 – ♦Sligo 13.

Coopershill 🐦, ☎ 65108, Fax 65466, ≤, 🌳, park, 🎾 – ⇔ ☎ P. AE ⓓ VISA JCB. ✂
15 March-October – **Meals** (residents only) (dinner only) 21.00 **t.** 🍷 5.00 – **7 rm** ☕ 55.00/90.00 **st.**

ROSAPENNA (Rosapenna) Donegal 405 I 2 **Ireland G.** – ☎ 074.

Envir. : N : Rosguill Peninsula Atlantic Drive★.

18 Downings ☎ 55301.

♦Dublin 216 – Donegal 52 – ♦Londonderry 47.

Rosapenna Golf, Downings, ☎ 55301, Fax 55128, ≤, 18, 🎾 – TV ☎ P. AE ⓓ VISA
31 March-28 October – **Meals** (bar lunch)/dinner 22.00 **t.** and a la carte 🍷 5.00 – **46 rm** ☕ 51.00/112.00 **st.** – SB.

ROSCOMMON (Ros Comáin) Roscommon 405 H 7 **Ireland G.** – pop. 1 314 – ☎ 0903.

See : Castle★.

Exc. : Castlestrange Stone★, SW : 7 m. by N 63 and R 362 – Strokestown Park House★ *AC*, N : 12 m. by N 61 and R 368 – Castlerea : Clonalis House★ *AC*, NW : 19 m. by N 60.

9 Moate Park ☎ 26382.

ℹ ☎ 26342 (20 June-4 September).

♦Dublin 94 – ♦Galway 57 – Limerick 94.

Abbey 🐦, on N 63 ☎ 26240, Fax 26021, 🌳 – TV ☎ ♿ P – 🏛 40. AE ⓓ VISA. ✂
Meals *(closed 25 December)* 15.00/22.50 **st.** and dinner a la carte 🍷 4.75 – **20 rm** ☕ 40.00/140.00 **st.** – SB.

ROSSLARE (Ros Láir) Wexford 405 M 11 – pop. 847 – ☎ 053.

Rosslare Strand ℘ 32113.

Rosslare Terminal ℘ 33622.

◆Dublin 104 – ◆Waterford 50 – Wexford 12.

Kelly's Resort, Strand Rd, ℘ 32114, Fax 32222, squash – rest ☎ ♿ P. AE VISA.
March-November – **Meals** 9.00/22.00 **t.** 10.00 – **99 rm** 41.00/88.00 **t.** – SB.

Cedars, Strand Rd, ℘ 32124, Fax 32243, – rest ☎ P. VISA.
April-December – **Meals** (bar lunch Monday to Saturday)/dinner 16.95 **t.** and a la carte 5.50 – **34 rm** 44.00/68.00 **st.** – SB.

ROSSLARE HARBOUR (Calafort Ros Láir) Wexford 405 N 11 **Ireland G.** – pop. 968 – ☎ 053.

Envir. : Lady's Island★, SW : 6 m. by N 25 and R 736 – Tacumshane Windmill★, SW : 6 m. by N 25 and R 736.

– to Fishguard (Stena Sealink Line) 2 daily (3 h 30 mn) – to Pembroke (B & I Line) 1-2 daily (4 h 15 mn).

Kilrane ℘ 33232 (May-mid September).

◆Dublin 105 – ◆Waterford 51 – Wexford 13.

Great Southern, ℘ 33233, Fax 33543, – ☎ ♿ P – 250. AE VISA
mid March-November – **Meals** (bar lunch Monday to Saturday)/dinner 19.50 **st.** and a la carte 6.50 – **99 rm** 60.00/90.00 **st.** – SB.

Rosslare, ℘ 33110, Fax 33386, ≤, squash – ☎ P. AE VISA
Meals 10.50/18.00 **st.** and a la carte – **25 rm** 25.00/75.00 **t.** – SB.

Tuskar House, St. Martins Rd, ℘ 33363, Fax 33363, ≤, – ☎ P. AE VISA.
Meals (bar lunch Monday to Saturday)/dinner 16.95 **st.** and a la carte 4.95 – 5.50 – **30 rm** 29.00/48.00 **t.** – SB.

Devereux, Wexford Rd, ℘ 33216, Fax 33301, ≤ – ☎ P. AE VISA JCB.
closed 24 and 25 December – **Meals** (bar lunch Monday to Saturday)/dinner a la carte 9.95/19.20 and a la carte 4.95 – **16 rm** 35.00/52.00 – SB.

at Tagoat W : 2 ½ m. on N 25 – ✉ Rosslare – ☎ 053 :

Churchtown House, N : ½ m. on Rosslare rd ℘ 32555, Fax 32555, – P. VISA
March-November – **Meals** (booking essential) (residents only) (unlicensed) 15.50 4.75 – **8 rm** 29.50/55.00 **st.** – SB.

ROSSNOWLAGH (Ros Neamhlach) Donegal 405 H 4 – ☎ 072.

◆Dublin 153 – Donegal 14 – ◆Sligo 31.

Sand House, ℘ 51777, Fax 52100, ≤ bay, beach and mountains, – ☎ P. AE VISA.
Easter-early October – **Meals** (bar lunch Monday to Friday)/dinner 22.50 **t.** 7.00 – **40 rm** 40.00/90.00 **t.**

ROUNDSTONE (Cloch na Rón) Galway 405 C 7 – ☎ 095.

◆Dublin 193 – ◆Galway 47.

Eldon's, ℘ 35933, Fax 35921, ≤, – ☎. AE VISA.
closed mid March-December – **Meals** 17.50 **t.** and a la carte 4.95 – **13 rm** 27.50/70.00 – SB.

SALTHILL (Bóthar na Trá) Galway 405 E 8 – see Galway.

SHANAGARRY (An Seangharraí) Cork 405 H 12 **Ireland G.** – pop. 242 – ✉ Midleton – ☎ 021.

Envir. : Ballycotton★, SE : 2 ½ m. by R 629 – Cloyne Cathedral★, NW : 4 m. by R 629.

Exc. : Rostellan Wood★, W : 9 m. by R 629 and R 631 on R 630.

◆Dublin 163 – ◆Cork 25 – ◆Waterford 64.

Ballymaloe House with rm, NW : 1 ¾ m. on L 35 ℘ 652531, Fax 652021, ≤, « Country house atmosphere », heated, park, – rest ☎ P. VISA.
closed 24 to 26 December – **Meals** (buffet Sunday) 20.00/35.00 **t.** 7.50 – **29 rm** 72.00/130.00 **t.**

SHANNON (Sionainn) Clare 405 F 9 – pop. 7 920 – ☎ 061.

Shannon ,Airport ℘ 471020.

Shannon Airport : ℘ 471444.

Shannon Airport ℘ 471664/471565.

◆Dublin 136 – Ennis 16 – ◆Limerick 15.

Oak Wood Arms, ℘ 361500, Fax 361414 – rm ☎ P – 250. AE VISA.
closed 24 and 25 December – **Meals** (buffet lunch)/dinner 17.50 **t.** and a la carte 5.75 – **45 rm** 50.00/80.00 **t.**, 1 suite – SB.

at Shannon Airport SW : 2½ m. on N 19 – ✉ Shannon – ☎ 061 :

Great Southern, ☎ 471122, Telex 72078, Fax 471982 – rm rest – 200. VISA.
Meals (bar lunch)/dinner 16.50 **st.** and a la carte 5.00 – 7.00 – **113 rm** 58.00/88.00 **st.**, 2 suites – SB.

SKERRIES (Na Sceirí) Dublin 405 N 7 – pop. 7 032 – ☎ 01.
Skerries ☎ 849 1204.
Community Office ☎ 849 0888.
♦Dublin 19 – Drogheda 15.

Red Bank, 7 Church St., ☎ 849 1005, Fax 849 1598 – AE VISA
closed Sunday dinner and 2 weeks early January – **Meals** - Seafood (dinner only and Sunday lunch)/dinner 21.00 **t.** and a la carte 5.75.

SKULL/SCHULL (An Scoil) Cork 405 D 13 – pop. 579 – ☎ 028.
♦Dublin 226 – ♦Cork 65 – ♦Killarney 64.

Corthna Lodge without rest., W : ¾ m. by R 592 ☎ 28517, Fax 28517, ←, –
April-October – **6 rm** 25.00/40.00 **t.**

SLANE (Baile Shláine) Meath 405 M 6 – ☎ 041.
♦Dublin 29 – Drogheda 9.

Conyngham Arms, ☎ 24155, Fax 24205, – rest – 120
16 rm.

SLIEVERUE (Sliabh Rua) Waterford – see Waterford.

Europe

If the name of the hotel
is not in bold type,
on arrival ask the hotelier his prices.

SLIGO (Sligeach) Sligo 405 G 5 **Ireland G.** – pop. 17 302 – ☎ 071.
See : Town★ - Abbey★.
Envir. : SE : Lough Gill★★ – Carrowmore Megalithic Cemetery★ *AC*, SW : 3 m. – Knocknarea★ (←★★★) SW : 6 m. by R 292.
Exc. : Parke's Castle★★ *AC*, E : 9 m. by R 286 – Glencar Waterfall★, NE : 9 m. by N 16 – Creevelea Abbey, Dromahair★, SE : 11½ m. by N 4 and R 287 – Creevykeel Court Cairn★, N : 16 m. by N 15.
Rosses Point ☎ 77134/77186.
Sligo Airport, Strandhill : ☎ 68280.
Aras Reddan, Temple St. ☎ 61201.
♦Dublin 133 – ♦Belfast 126 – ♦Dundalk 106 – ♦Londonderry 86.

Sligo Park, Pearse Rd, S : 1 m. on N 4 ☎ 60291, Fax 69556, , , , , – – 500
89 rm, 1 suite.

Tree Tops without rest., Cleveragh Rd, S : ¼ m. by Dublin rd ☎ 60160, Fax 62301, – . VISA.
closed 15 December-15 January – **5 rm** 19.00/31.00 **t.**

SPIDDAL (An Spidéal) Galway 405 E 8 – ☎ 091.
♦Dublin 143 – ♦Galway 11.

Bridge House, Main St., ☎ 83118, – rest . AE VISA.
closed 22 December-1 March – **Meals** 12.50/20.00 **t.** and a la carte 4.65 – **14 rm** 35.00/70.00 **t.** – SB.

Ardmor Country House without rest., W : ½ m. on L 100 ☎ 83145, Fax 83145, ←, – . VISA.
8 rm -/31.00.

STRAFFAN (Teach Srafáin) Kildare 405 M 8 – pop. 341 – ☎ 01.
Naas, Kerdiffstown ☎ (0145) 97509.
♦Dublin 15 – Mullingar 47.

Kildare H. & Country Club , ☎ 627 3333, Fax 627 3312, ←, « Part early 19C country house on banks of the River Liffey », , , , , , , park, , squash – – 70. AE VISA JCB.
Byerley Turk : **Meals** 18.00/45.00 **t.** and dinner a la carte 30.50/60.00 **t.** 8.00 – ***Legends*** (in K Club) : **Meals** 14.95/21.00 **t.** – **38 rm** 180.00/275.00 **t.**, 7 suites – SB.

Barberstown Castle, N : ½ m. ☎ 628 8157, Fax 627 7027, « Part Elizabethan, part Victorian house with 13C castle keep », – . AE VISA.
Meals 15.50/22.50 **t.** and dinner a la carte 6.50 – **10 rm** 65.00/110.00 **t.**

SWORDS **(Sord)** Dublin 405 N 7 – pop. 17 705 – ☎ 01.

Balcarrick, Corballis, Donabate ℘ 843 6228.

♦Dublin 8 – Drogheda 22.

Forte Travelodge, Miltons Field, S : ½ m. on N 1 ℘ 840 9233, Reservations (Freephone) 0800 850950 (UK), 1800 709709 (Republic of Ireland) – TV ♿ P. AE VISA. **Meals** (grill rest.) 16.00 **t.** – **40 rm** 33.50 **t.**

Le Chateau, River Mall, Main St., ℘ 840 6533, Fax 840 6533 – P.

TAGOAT Wexford 405 M 11 – see Rosslare Harbour.

TAHILLA **(Tathuile)** Kerry 405 C 12 **Ireland G.** – ☎ 0164.

Exc. : Iveragh Peninsula★★★ (Ring of Kerry★★).

♦Dublin 222 – ♦Cork 70 – ♦Killarney 32.

Tahilla Cove , ℘ 45204, ←, , – ☎ P. AE VISA *Easter-September* – **Meals** (bar lunch)/dinner 16.50 **st.** – **9 rm** 40.00/66.00 **st.** – SB.

TEMPLEGLENTAN **(Teampall an Ghleanntáin)** Limerick 405 E 10 **Ireland G.** – ☎ 069.

Exc. : Newcastle West★, NE : 4½ m. by N 21.

Newcastle West ℘ 76104.

♦Dublin 154 – ♦Killarney 36 – ♦Limerick 33.

Devon, on N 21 ℘ 84122, Fax 84122 – TV ☎ P. AE VISA. *closed 24 and 25 December* – **Meals** 8.50/13.00 **st.** and dinner a la carte 4.75 – **18 rm** 30.00/60.00 **st.** – SB.

TERRYGLASS **(Tír Dhá Ghlas)** Tipperary 405 H 8 – ✉ Nenagh – ☎ 067.

♦Dublin 114 – ♦Galway 51 – ♦Limerick 43.

Riverrun without rest., ℘ 22125, Fax 22187, , – ☎ P. AE VISA **6 rm** 25.00/45.00 **st.**

THOMASTOWN **(Baile Mhic Andáin)** Kilkenny 405 K 10 **Ireland G.** – ✉ Kilkenny – ☎ 056.

See : Ladywell Water Garden★ *AC*.

Envir. : Jerpoint Abbey★★, SW : 1½ m. by N9.

Thomastown ℘ 24725.

♦Dublin 77 – Kilkenny 11 – ♦Waterford 30 – Wexford 38.

Mount Juliet , NW : 1½ m. ℘ 24455, Fax 24522, « 18C manor and sporting estate, ← River Nore and park », , , , , , – TV ☎ P. AE VISA **Meals** 15.00/33.00 **st.** and a la carte – **30 rm** 150.00/215.00 **st.**, 2 suites.

Hunters Yard at Mount Juliet, NW : 1½ m. ℘ 24725, Fax 24522, « Converted 18C stables », , , , , , park, – TV ☎ P – 80. AE VISA. **Meals** 15.00/33.00 **st.** and a la carte – **13 rm** 125.00 **st.**, 8 suites.

TIPPERARY **(Tiobraid Árann)** Tipperary 405 H 10 **Ireland G.** – pop. 4 772 – ECD : Wednesday – ☎ 062.

Envir. : Glen of Aherlow★, S : by R 664.

Exc. : Kilmallock★★ : Abbey★, Collegiate Church★, Blossom's Gate★, Town Walls★, King's Castle★, W : 20 m. by R 515.

Rathanny ℘ 51119.

Community Office, James St. ℘ 51457.

♦Dublin 113 – ♦Cork 57 – ♦Limerick 24 – ♦Waterford 53.

Bansha House, Bansha, SE : 5½ m. by N 24 ℘ 54194, , park – P. VISA. *closed 20 December-1 January* – **Meals** 13.00 **t.** 5.00 – **8 rm** 20.00/35.00 **t.** – SB.

TOWER Cork 405 G 12 – see Blarney.

TRALEE **(Trá Lí)** Kerry 405 C 11 **Ireland G.** – pop. 17 225 – ECD : Wednesday – ☎ 066.

Envir. : Blennerville Windmill★★ *AC*, SW : 2 m. by N 86 – Ardfert Cathedral★, NW : 5½ m. by R 551.

Exc. : Banna Strand★★, NW : 8 m. by R 551 – Crag Cave★★ *AC*, W : 13 m. by N 21 – Rattoo Round Tower★, N : 12 m. by R 556.

Ashe Memorial Hall, Denny St. ℘ 21288.

♦Dublin 185 – ♦Killarney 20 – ♦Limerick 64.

Brandon, Princes St., ℘ 23333, Group Telex 73130, Fax 25019, , , – TV ☎ P – 1 000 **159 rm**, 1 suite.

Grand, Denny St., ℘ 21499, Fax 22877 – rm TV ☎ – 250. AE VISA. **Meals** 10.00/15.00 **t.** and a la carte 5.00 – **44 rm** 30.00/70.00 **st.** – SB.

Ballyseede Castle , SE : 3¼ m. by N 22 ℘ 25799, Fax 25287, , park – TV ☎ P. AE VISA. **Meals** (bar lunch Monday to Saturday)/dinner 20.00 **t.** and a la carte 5.75 – **15 rm** 35.00/125.00 **t.** – SB.

Kilteely House, Ballyard, Dingle Rd, S : 1 m. 23376, Fax 25766 – . VISA.
Meals (by arrangement) 15.00 **st.** – **11 rm** 22.50/45.00 **st.** – SB.

Knockanish House without rest., The Spa, W : 3 m. by R 551 on R 558 36268, –
6 rm.

TRAMORE (Trá Mhór) Waterford 405 K 11 – 051.
♦Dublin 105 – ♦Cork 69 – ♦Waterford 9.

O'Shea's, Strand St., 381246, Fax 390144 – . AE VISA
closed 22-29 December – **Meals** (bar lunch Monday to Saturday)/dinner 16.50 **t.** and a la carte 3.95 – **12 rm** 25.00/50.00 **t.** – SB.

TRIM (Baile Átha Troim) Co. Meath 405 L 7 – 046.

Crannmór without rest., Dunderry Rd, N : 1¼ m. 31635, – rm .
April-September – **4 rm** 18.50/29.00.

TULLAMORE (Tulach Mhór) Offaly 405 J 8 – 0506.
♦Dublin 65 – Kilkenny 52 – ♦Limerick 80.

Sea Dew House without rest., Clonminch Rd, on N 80 52054, Fax 52054, – . VISA.
closed 22 December-3 January – **10 rm** 26.00/50.00.

Pine Lodge, Screggan, SW : 4½ m. by N 52 and Mountbolus rd 51927, Fax 51927, , , – .
closed 15 December-15 February – **Meals** (by arrangement) 17.50 **st.** – **4 rm** 25.00/40.00 **st.** – SB.

VIRGINIA (Achadh an Iílr) Cavan 405 K 6 – 049.
♦Dublin 51 – Drogheda 39 – Enniskillen 60.

Sharkey's, 47561, –
11 rm.

WATERFORD (Port Láirge) Waterford 405 K 11 **Ireland G.** – pop. 40 328 – 051.
See : Town★ – City Walls★ – City Hall and Theatre Royal★.
Envir. : Waterford Crystal★, SW : 1½ m. by N 25.
Exc. : Tramore★, S : 9 m. by R 675 – Duncannon★, E : 12 m. by R 683, ferry from Passage East and R 374 (south) – Dunmore East★, SE : 12 m. by R 684 – Tintern Abbey★, E : 13 m. by R 683, ferry from Passage East, R 733 and R 734 (south).
18 Newrath 76748/74182.
Waterford Airport, Killowen : 75589.
41 The Quay 75788.
♦Dublin 96 – ♦Cork 73 – ♦Limerick 77.

Waterford Castle, The Island, Ballinakill, E : 2½ m. by R 683, Ballinakill Rd and private ferry 78203, Fax 79316, , « Part 15C and 19C castle, river island setting », , 18, , , park, – . AE VISA.
Meals 16.00/33.00 **t.** 7.50 – 10.00 – **14 rm** 150.00/200.00 **t.**, 5 suites.

Granville, Meagher Quay, 55111, Fax 70307 – rm rest – 250. AE VISA JCB.
closed 25 and 26 December – **Meals** 9.95/16.75 **st.** and a la carte 4.95 – ***Bells* : Meals** *(closed Sunday October-May)* (dinner only) a la carte 16.70/19.25 **st.** 4.95 – **74 rm** 45.00/124.00 **st.** – SB.

Jurys, Ferrybank, 32111, Telex 80684, Fax 32863, City, , , , , park, – rm – 700. AE VISA.
Meals 10.00/13.00 **st.** and a la carte 5.50 – 8.00 – **98 rm** 65.00/85.00 **t.**

Tower, The Mall, 75801, Fax 70129, , , – rest – 500. AE VISA.
closed 24 to 27 December – **Meals** 12.00/20.00 **st.** and a la carte 5.00 – **138 rm** 60.00/90.00 **st.**, 3 suites – SB.

Bridge, The Quay, 77222, Fax 77229 – – 50
75 rm.

Dooley's, The Quay, 73531, Fax 70262 – rm . AE VISA JCB.
closed 25 to 27 December – **Meals** 10.50/15.50 **t.** and dinner a la carte 5.50 – **35 rm** 35.20/64.90 **st.** – SB.

Foxmount Farm, SE : 4½ m. by R 683, off Cheekpoint rd 74308, Fax 54906, , « Working farm », , park, – .
March-October – **Meals** (by arrangement) 15.00 – **6 rm** 20.00/36.00 **st.** – SB.

Prendiville's, Cork Rd, SW : ¾ m. on N 25 78851, Fax 74062 – . AE VISA
closed Saturday lunch and Sunday – **Meals** 9.00/22.00 **t.** and dinner a la carte 5.00.

at Slieverue NE : 2¼ m. by N 25 – Waterford – 051 :

Diamond Hill without rest., 32855, Fax 32254, – . VISA.
10 rm 20.00/35.00 **t.**

WATERVILLE (An Coireán) Kerry 405 B 12 **Ireland G.** – pop. 463 – ☎ 066.

Exc. : Iveragh Peninsula★★★ (Ring of Kerry★★) – Skellig Islands★★, W : 8 m. by N 70 , R 567 and ferry from Ballinskelligs – Derrynane National Historic Park★★ *AC*, S : 9 m. by N70 – Leacanabuaile Fort (≤★★), N : 13 m. by N 70 – Cahergall Fort★, N : 12 m. by N 70.

18 Ring of Kerry ☎ 74102/74545.

◆Dublin 238 – ◆Killarney 48.

Butler Arms, ☎ 74144, Fax 74520, ≤, ⅋, ⅋, ⅋ – TV ☎ P. AE VISA. ⅋
mid April-mid October – **Meals** (bar lunch)/dinner 23.00 **t.** and a la carte 5.25 – **30 rm** 50.00/100.00 **t.** – SB.

Klondyke House without rest., N : ½ m. on N 70 ☎ 74119, Fax 74666, ≤ – P. VISA. ⅋
6 rm 19.00/30.00 **st.**

WESTPORT (Cathair na Mart) Mayo 405 D 6 **Ireland G.** – pop. 3 688 – ECD : Wednesday – ☎ 098.

See : Town★★ (Centre★) – Westport House★★ *AC*.

Exc. : SW : Murrisk Peninsula★★ – Silver Strand★★, SW : 21 m. by R 335 - Ballintubber Abbey★, SE : 13 m. by R 330 – Croagh Patrick★, W : 6 m. by R 335 – Bunlahinch Clapper Bridge★, W : 16 m. by R 335.

18 Carowholly ☎ 25113/27070.

The Mall ☎ 25711.

◆Dublin 163 – ◆Galway 50 – ◆Sligo 65.

Westport Woods, Louisburgh Rd, W : 1 m. ☎ 25811, Fax 26212, ⅋, ⅋ – ⅋ rest TV ☎ P. AE VISA. ⅋
Meals (dinner only) 15.00 **t.** and a la carte – **56 rm** 54.00/74.00 **t.** – SB.

Wilmaur ⅋ without rest., Rosbeg, W : 2 m. on R 335 ☎ 25784, Fax 26224, ≤, ⅋ – P. ⅋
April-mid October – **5 rm** 22.50/30.00 **s.**

Stadtpläne : *Die Auswahl der Straßen wurde unter Berücksichtigung des Verkehrs und der Zufahrt zu den erwähnten Häusern getroffen.*

Die weniger wichtigen Straßen wurden nur angedeutet.

WEXFORD (Loch Garman) Wexford 405 M 10 **Ireland G.** – pop. 13 232 – ECD : Thursday – ☎ 053.

See : Town★ – Main Street★ – Franciscan Friary★.

Envir. : Irish Agricultural Museum, Johnstown Castle★★ *AC*, SW : 4½ m. – Irish National Heritage Park, Ferrycarrig★ *AC*, NW : 2½ m. by N 11 – Curracloe★, NE : 5 m. by R 741 and R 743.

Exc. : Tacumshane Windmill★, S : 11 m. by N 25 – Lady's Island★, S : 11 m. by N 25 – Kilmore Quay★, SW : 15 m. by N 25 and R 739 (Saltee Islands★ - access by boat) – Enniscorthy Castle★ (County Museum★ *AC*) N : 15 m. by N 11.

18 Mulgannon ☎ 42238/45095.

Crescent Quay ☎ 23111 – Heritage Park ☎ 41911 (March-November).

◆Dublin 88 – Kilkenny 49 – ◆Waterford 38.

Ferrycarrig ⅋, Ferrycarrig Bridge, NW : 2¾ m. on N 11 ☎ 22999, Fax 41982, ≤, ⅋, ⅋, ⅋ – ⅋ ⅋ rest TV ☎ P – ⅋ 400. AE VISA. ⅋
Meals (bar lunch)/dinner a la carte 8.85/24.85 **st.** 4.75 – (see also ***Conservatory*** below) – **39 rm** 49.00/180.00 **st.** – SB.

Whitford House, New Line Rd, W : 2¼ m. on R 733 ☎ 43444, Fax 46399, ⅋, ⅋, ⅋ – ⅋ rest TV ☎ P. VISA. ⅋
closed 22 December-16 January – **Meals** (bar lunch)/dinner 18.75 **t.** 5.00 – **23 rm** 25.50/63.00 **st.** – SB.

White's, George St., ☎ 22311, Telex 80630, Fax 45000, ⅋, ⅋ – ⅋ TV ☎ P – ⅋ 50. AE VISA JCB
closed 25 December – **Meals** 8.50/18.00 **st.** and a la carte 6.00 – **81 rm** 50.00/76.00 **st.**, 1 suite – SB.

Gateway, Rosslare Rd, Drinagh, S : 2½ m. ☎ 43295, Fax 45827, ⅋, squash – TV ☎ P. AE VISA. ⅋
Meals (bar lunch Monday to Saturday)/dinner 18.00 **st.** and a la carte 5.00 – **11 rm** 28.00/48.00 **st.** – SB.

Ardruadh ⅋ without rest., Spawell Rd, ☎ 23194, « Gothic style Victorian house », ⅋ – TV P. VISA. ⅋
closed 10-25 November and 22 December-6 January – **5 rm** 19.00/35.00 **s.**

Rathaspeck Manor ⅋, Rathaspeck, SW : 4 m. by R 733 and N 25 ☎ 42661, « Georgian country house », 18, ⅋, ⅋ – ⅋ rm TV P. ⅋
June-October – **Meals** (by arrangement) (residents only) (dinner only) 14.00 – **7 rm** -/40.00 **st.** – SB.

Newbay Country House ⅋, W : 4 m. by N 25 and Clonard rd ☎ 42779, Fax 46318, ≤, ⅋, park – P. ⅋
March-October – **Meals** *(closed Sunday and Monday)* (by arrangement) (residents only) (communal dining) (dinner only) 25.00 **st.** 6.00 – **6 rm** 37.00/58.00 **st.**

Clonard House ⛰, Clonard Great, SW : 2 ½ m. by R 733 ☏ 43141, Fax 43141, ≤, « Working farm », park – ⅹ TV P. ✗
Easter-mid November – **Meals** (by arrangement) 13.00 **st.** – **9 rm** ☐ 19.00/32.00 **st.**

Slaney Manor ⛰, Ferrycarrig, ☏ 45751, Fax 46510, ⅹ TV ☎ P. VISA
closed December and January – **Meals** (by arrangement) 18.00 **st.** 5.00 – **11 rm** ☐ 40.00/70.00 **st.** – SB.

XXX **Conservatory** (at Ferrycarrig H.), Ferrycarrig Bridge, NW : 2 ¾ m. on N 11 ☏ 22999, Fax 41982, ≤, – ▤ P. AE ⓓ VISA
Meals 22.00 **st.** (dinner) and lunch a la carte 9.65/25.00.

WICKLOW (Cill Mhantáin) Wicklow 405 N 9 Ireland G. – pop. 5 847 – ECD : Thursday – ☏ 0404.

Envir. : Mount Usher Gardens, Ashford★ *AC*, NW : 4 m. by R 750 and N 11 – Devil's Glen★, NW : 8 m. by R 750 and N 11.

Exc. : Glendalough★★★ : Lower Lake★★★, Upper Lake★★, Cathedral★★, Round Tower★, St. Kevin's Church★, St. Kieran's Church★, St. Kevin's Cross★, St. Saviour's Priory★ – W : 14 m. by R 750, N 11, R 763, R 755 and R 756 – Wicklow Mountains★★ : Avondale Forest Park★★ *AC*, Wicklow Gap★★, Sally Gap★★, Meeting of the Waters★, Glenmacnass Waterfall★, Glenmalur★ – Loughs Tay and Dan★.

18 Blainroe ☏ 68168.

Fitzwilliam St. ☏ 69117.

◆Dublin 33 – ◆Waterford 84 – Wexford 67.

Grand, ☏ 67337, Fax 69607, – ⅹ rm ▤ rest TV ☎ P – 240. VISA. ✗
Meals 10.50/17.50 **t.** and a la carte 4.50 – **33 rm** ☐ 37.00/61.85 **st.** – SB.

Old Rectory, ☏ 67048, Fax 69181, – ⅹ rest TV ☎ P. AE ⓓ VISA. ✗
April-October – **Meals** (booking essential) (dinner only) 26.00 **st.** and a la carte 6.50 – **5 rm** ☐ 67.00/90.00 **st.** – SB.

YOUGHAL (Eochaill) Cork 405 I 12 Ireland G. – pop. 5 532 – ECD : Wednesday – ☏ 024.

See : Town★ – St. Mary's Collegiate Church★★ – Town Walls★★ – Clock Gate★ – The Red House★.

Exc. : Helvick Head★★ (≤★★), NE : 22 m. by N 25 and R 674 – Ringville (≤★★), NE : 20 m. by N 25 and R 674 – Dungarvan★ (King John's Castle★) NE : 19 m. by N 25.

18 Knockaverry ☏ 92787.

Heritage Centre ☏ 92390 (1 June-mid September).

◆Dublin 146 – ◆Cork 30 – ◆Waterford 47.

Devonshire Arms, Pearse Sq., ☏ 92827, Fax 92900 – TV ☎ P. AE ⓓ VISA. ✗
closed 24 and 25 December – **Meals** 12.00/18.50 **t.** and a la carte 6.50 – **10 rm** ☐ 30.00/66.00 **st.**

XX **Aherne's Seafood Bar** with rm, 163 North Main St., ☏ 92424, Fax 93633 – TV ☎ ♿ P. AE ⓓ VISA. ✗
closed 5 days at Christmas – **Meals** 13.50/22.50 **t.** and a la carte 6.00 – **10 rm** ☐ 60.00/100.00 **st.**

Major hotel groups

Abbreviations used in the Guide and central reservation telephone numbers

Principales chaînes hôtelières

Abréviations utilisées dans nos textes et centraux téléphoniques de réservation

Principali catene alberghiere

Abbreviazoni utilizzate nei nostri testi e centrali telefoniche di prenotazione

Die wichtigsten Hotelketten

Im Führer benutzte Abkürzungen der Hotelketten und ihre Zentrale für telefonische Reservierung

COPTHORNE HOTELS	COPTHORNE	0800 414741 (Freephone)
COUNTRY CLUB HOTEL GROUP *(Country Club Resorts/Lansbury Collection)*	COUNTRY CLUB	01582 562256
DE VERE HOTELS PLC	DE VERE	01925 265050
RADISSON EDWARDIAN HOTELS	RADISSON EDWARDIAN	0800 191991 (Freephone)
FORTE HOTELS	FORTE	(0345) 404040 or 0800 404040 (Freephone)
TRAVELODGES		0800 850950 (Freephone)
FRIENDLY HOTELS	FRIENDLY	0800 591910 (Freephone)
GRANADA HOTELS & LODGES	GRANADA	0800 555300 (Freephone)
HILTON HOTELS	HILTON	0171 7346000
HOLIDAY INN WORLDWIDE	HOLIDAY INN	0800 897121 (Freephone)
HYATT HOTELS	HYATT	0171 5808197
INTERCONTINENTAL HOTELS LTD	INTER-CON	0181 8472277 or calls from outside London 0345 581444
JARVIS HOTELS	JARVIS	(0345) 581811
MARRIOTT HOTELS	MARRIOTT	0800 221222 (Freephone)
MOUNT CHARLOTTE THISTLE HOTELS	MT. CHARLOTTE THISTLE	0171 9378033 01532 439111
NOVOTEL	NOVOTEL	0171 7241000
PREMIER LODGES & INNS	PREMIER	0800 118833 (Freephone)
QUEENS MOAT HOUSES PLC	Q.M.H.	0800 289330 (Freephone) or 01708 766677
RAMADA INTERNATIONAL	RAMADA	0800 181737 (Freephone)
SHERATON HOTELS	SHERATON	0800 353535 (Freephone)
STAKIS HOTELS	STAKIS	0800 262626 (Freephone)
SWALLOW HOTELS LTD	SWALLOW	0191 5294666
TOBY HOTELS *(No central reservations – Contact Hotels direct)*	TOBY	
TRAVEL INNS	TRAVEL INN	01582 414341

DISTANCES

All distances in this edition are quoted in miles. The distance is given from each town to other nearby towns and to the capital of each region as grouped in the guide. Towns appearing in the charts are preceded by a diamond ◆ text.

To avoid excessive repetition some distances have only been quoted once – you may therefore have to look under both town headings.

The distances in miles quoted are not necessarily the shortest but have been based on the roads which afford the best driving conditions and are therefore the most practical.

DISTANCES EN MILES

Pour chaque région traitée, vous trouverez au texte de chacune des localités sa distance par rapport à la capitale et aux villes environnantes. Lorsque ces villes sont celles des tableaux, leur nom est précédé d'un losange noir ◆.

La distance d'une localité à une autre n'est pas toujours répétée aux deux villes intéressées : voyez au texte de l'une ou de l'autre.

Ces distances ne sont pas nécessairement comptées par la route la plus courte mais par la plus pratique, c'est-à-dire celle offrant les meilleures conditions de roulage.

135 Miles

Dublin - Sligo

	Belfast	Cork	Dublin	Dundalk	Galway	Killarney	Limerick	Londonderry	Omagh	Sligo	Tullamore
Cork	259										
Dublin	107	153									
Dundalk	54	205	53								
Galway	197	124	139	156							
Killarney	285	54	179	232	135						
Limerick	224	57	118	170	67	68					
Londonderry	72	299	144	102	173	299	232				
Omagh	68	266	111	70	156	254	187	33			
Sligo	125	204	135	107	89	215	147	85	68		
Tullamore	138	126	59	84	83	139	72	160	127	96	
Waterford	204	72	98	150	136	112	78	244	211	178	82

DISTANZE IN MIGLIA

Per ciascuna delle regioni trattate, troverete nel testo di ogni località la sua distanza dalla capitale e dalle città circostanti. Quando queste città sono comprese nelle tabelle, il loro nome è preceduto da una losanga ◆.

Le distanza da una località all'altra non è sempre ripetuta nelle due città interessate : vedere nel testo dell'una o dell'atra.

Le distanze non sono necessariamente calcolate seguendo il percorso più breve, ma vengono stabilite secondo l'itinerario più pratico, che offre cioè le migliori condizioni di viaggio.

ENTFERNUNGSANGABEN IN MEILEN

Die Entfernungen der einzelnen Orte zur Landeshauptstadt und zu den nächstgrößeren Städten in der Umgebung sind im allgemeinen Ortstext angegeben. Die Namen der Städte in der Umgebung, die auf der Tabelle zu finden sind, sind durch eine Raute ◆ gekennzeichnet.

Die Entfernung zweier Städte voneinander können Sie aus den Angaben im Ortstext der einen oder der anderen Stadt ersehen.

Die Entfernungsangaben gelten nicht immer für den kürzesten, sondern für den günstigsten Weg.

Distances between major towns

Distances entre-principales villes

Distanze tra le principali città

Entfernungen zwischen den größeren Städten

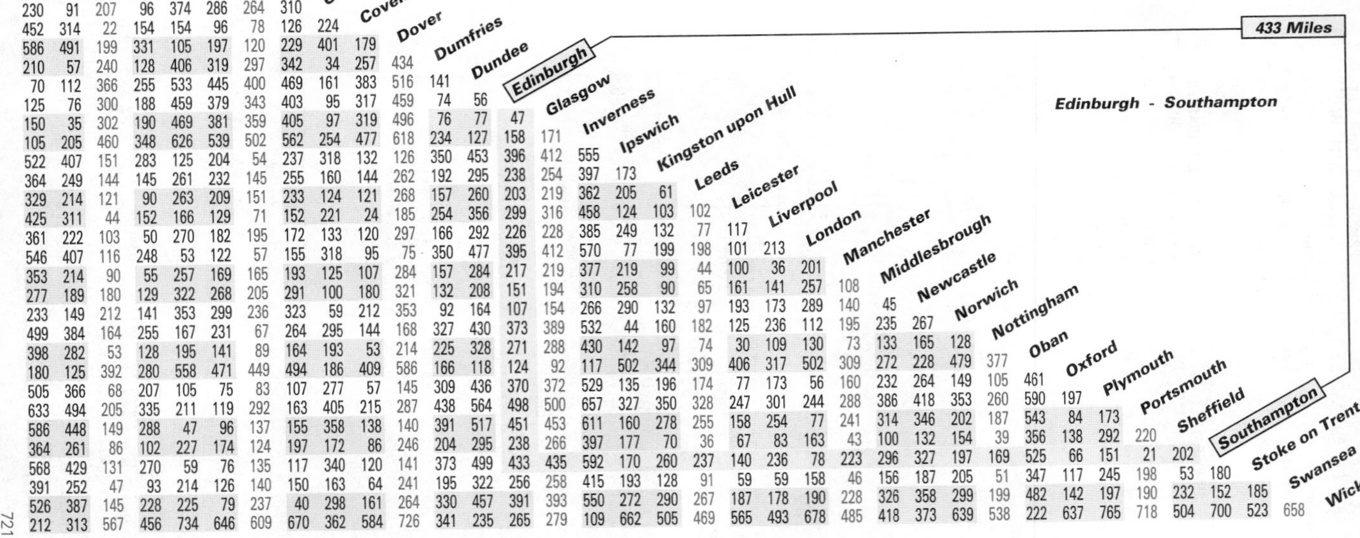

	Aberdeen	Ayr	Birmingham	Blackpool	Brighton	Bristol	Cambridge	Cardiff	Carlisle	Coventry	Dover	Dumfries	Dundee	Edinburgh	Glasgow	Inverness	Ipswich	Kingston upon Hull	Leeds	Leicester	Liverpool	London	Manchester	Middlesbrough	Newcastle	Norwich	Nottingham	Oban	Oxford	Plymouth	Portsmouth	Sheffield	Southampton	Stoke on Trent	Swansea
Ayr	184																																		
Birmingham	436	297																																	
Blackpool	324	185	138																																
Brighton	602	463	165	304																															
Bristol	515	376	86	216	157																														
Cambridge	469	354	98	230	120	169																													
Cardiff	538	399	110	240	190	44	202																												
Carlisle	230	91	207	96	374	286	264	310																											
Coventry	452	314	22	154	154	96	78	126	224																										
Dover	586	491	199	331	105	197	120	229	401	179																									
Dumfries	210	57	240	128	406	319	297	342	34	257	434																								
Dundee	70	112	366	255	533	445	400	469	161	383	516	141																							
Edinburgh	125	76	300	188	459	379	343	403	95	317	459	74	56																						
Glasgow	150	35	302	190	469	381	359	405	97	319	496	76	77	47																					
Inverness	105	205	460	348	626	539	502	562	254	477	618	234	127	158	171																				
Ipswich	522	407	151	283	125	204	54	237	318	132	126	350	453	396	412	555																			
Kingston upon Hull	364	249	144	145	261	232	145	255	160	144	262	192	295	238	254	397	173																		
Leeds	329	214	121	90	263	209	151	233	124	121	268	157	260	203	219	362	205	61																	
Leicester	425	311	44	152	166	129	71	152	221	24	185	254	356	299	316	458	124	103	102																
Liverpool	361	222	103	50	270	182	195	172	133	120	297	166	292	226	228	385	249	132	77	117															
London	546	407	116	248	53	122	57	155	318	95	75	350	477	395	412	570	77	199	198	101	213														
Manchester	353	214	90	55	257	169	165	193	125	107	284	157	284	217	219	377	219	99	44	100	36	201													
Middlesbrough	277	189	180	129	322	268	205	291	100	180	321	132	208	151	194	310	258	90	65	161	141	257	108												
Newcastle	233	149	212	141	353	299	236	323	59	212	353	92	164	107	154	266	290	132	97	193	173	289	140	45											
Norwich	499	384	164	255	167	231	67	264	295	144	168	327	430	373	389	532	44	160	182	125	236	112	195	235	267										
Nottingham	398	282	53	128	195	141	89	164	193	53	214	225	328	271	288	430	142	97	74	30	109	130	73	133	165	128									
Oban	180	125	392	280	558	471	449	494	186	409	586	166	118	124	92	117	502	344	309	406	317	502	309	272	228	479	377								
Oxford	505	366	68	207	105	75	83	107	277	57	145	309	436	370	372	529	135	196	174	77	173	56	160	232	264	149	105	461							
Plymouth	633	494	205	335	211	119	292	163	405	215	287	438	564	498	500	657	327	350	328	247	301	244	288	386	418	353	260	590	197						
Portsmouth	586	448	149	288	47	96	137	155	358	138	140	391	517	451	453	611	160	278	255	158	254	77	241	314	346	202	187	543	84	173					
Sheffield	364	261	86	102	227	174	124	197	172	86	246	204	295	238	266	397	177	70	36	67	83	163	43	100	132	154	39	356	138	292	220				
Southampton	568	429	131	270	59	76	135	117	340	120	141	373	499	433	435	592	170	260	237	140	236	78	223	296	327	197	169	525	66	151	21	202			
Stoke on Trent	391	252	47	93	214	126	140	150	163	64	241	195	322	256	258	415	193	128	91	59	59	158	46	156	187	205	51	347	117	245	198	53	180		
Swansea	526	387	145	228	225	79	237	40	298	161	264	330	457	391	393	550	272	290	267	187	178	190	228	326	358	299	199	482	142	197	190	232	152	185	
Wick	212	313	567	456	734	646	609	670	362	584	726	341	235	265	279	109	662	505	469	565	493	678	485	418	373	639	538	222	637	765	718	504	700	523	658

MAJOR ROADS AND PRINCIPAL SHIPPING ROUTES

Motorway ....

Road number .... A 4. T 35. N 2

Mileage 20

PRINCIPALES ROUTES ET LIAISONS MARITIMES

Autoroute ....

N° de route .... A 4. T 35. N 2

Distance en miles 20

PRINCIPALI STRADE E ITINERARI MARITTIMI

Autostrada ....

Numero di strada .... A 4. T 35. N 2

Distanza in miglia 20

HAUPTVERKEHRSSTRASSEN UND SCHIFFSVERBINDUNGEN

Autobahn ......

Straßennummer ...... A 4. T 35. N 2

Entfernung in Meilen ... 20

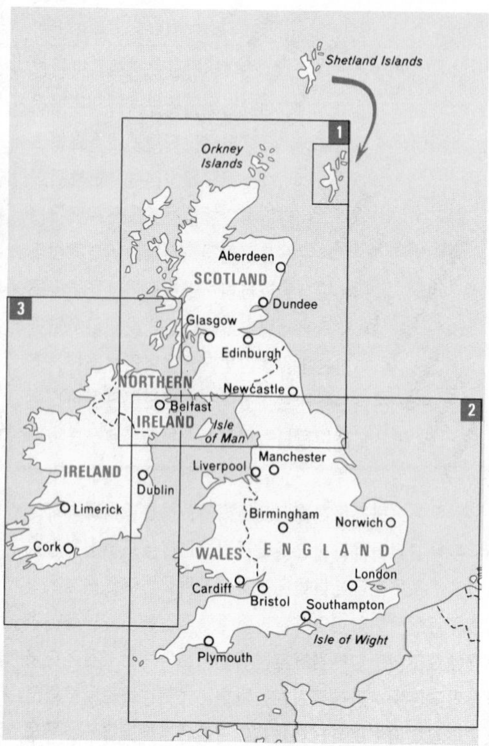

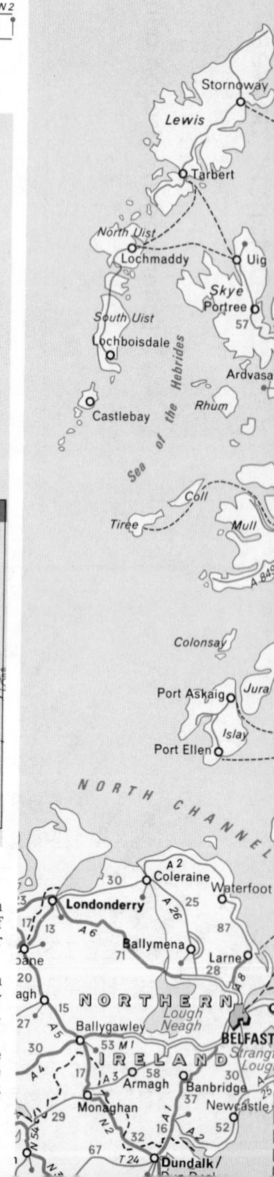

GREAT BRITAIN : the maps and town plans in the Great Britain Section of this Guide are based upon the Ordnance Survey of Great Britain with the permission of the Controller of Her Majesty's Stationery Office, Crown Copyright reserved.

NORTHERN IRELAND : the maps and town plans in the Northern Ireland Section of this Guide are based upon the Ordnance Survey of Northern Ireland with the sanction of the Controller of H.M. Stationery Office, Permit number 724.

REPUBLIC OF IRELAND : the maps and town plans in the Republic of Ireland Section of this Guide are based upon the Ordnance Survey of Ireland by permission of the Government of the Republic, Permit number 5942.

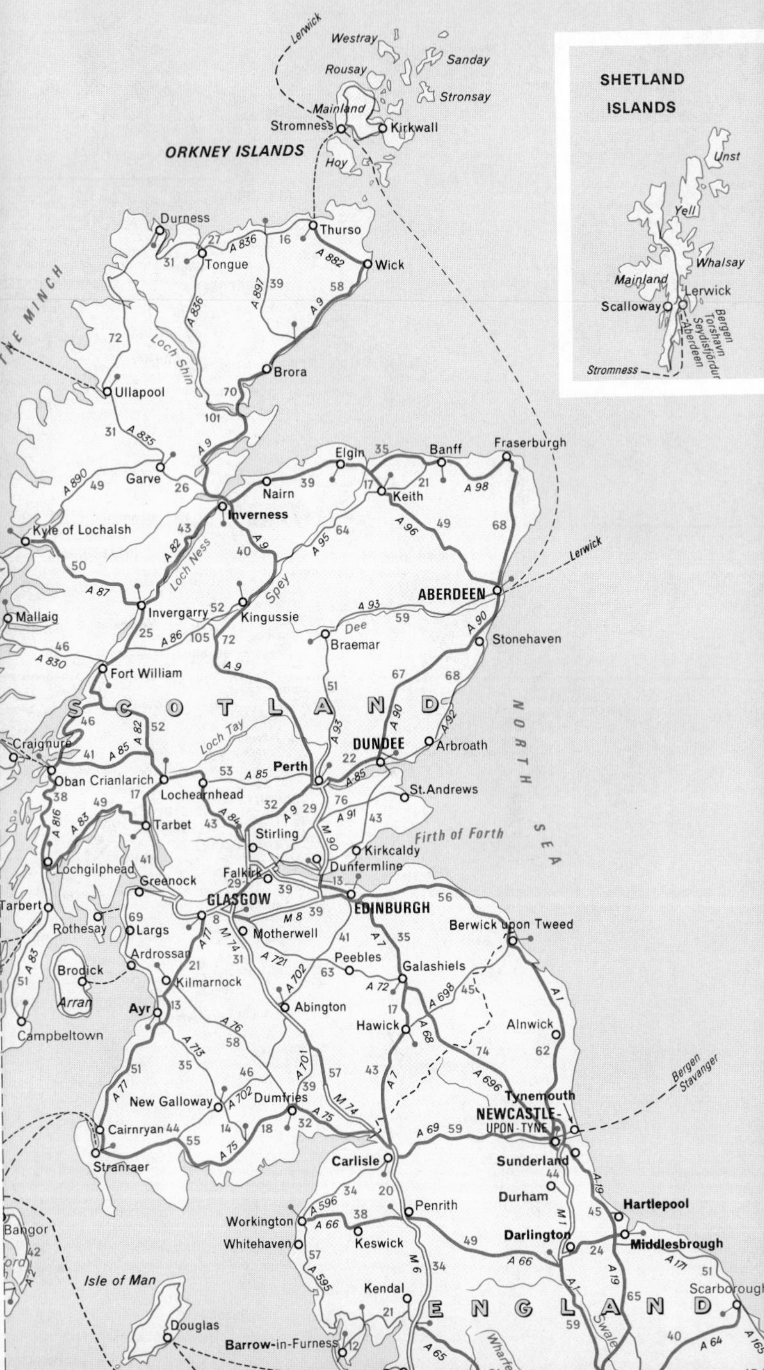
SHETLAND ISLANDS
Unst
Yell
Whalsay
Mainland
Lerwick
Scalloway
Stromness
Aberdeen
Seydisfjördur
Torshavn
Bergen
ORKNEY ISLANDS
Westray
Sanday
Rousay
Stronsay
Mainland
Stromness
Kirkwall
Hoy
Lerwick
Durness
Thurso
Tongue
Wick
Brora
Ullapool
Loch Shin
THE MINCH
Garve
Inverness
Nairn
Elgin
Banff
Fraserburgh
Keith
Kyle of Lochalsh
Loch Ness
Spey
ABERDEEN
Mallaig
Invergarry
Kingussie
Braemar
Dee
Stonehaven
Fort William
SCOTLAND
Loch Tay
DUNDEE
Arbroath
NORTH SEA
Craignure
Oban
Crianlarich
Lochearnhead
Perth
St. Andrews
Tarbet
Stirling
Firth of Forth
Kirkcaldy
Lochgilphead
Greenock
Falkirk
Dunfermline
GLASGOW
EDINBURGH
Tarbert
Rothesay
Largs
Motherwell
Berwick upon Tweed
Ardrossan
Peebles
Galashiels
Brodick
Arran
Kilmarnock
Ayr
Abington
Hawick
Alnwick
Campbeltown
New Galloway
Dumfries
Tynemouth
NEWCASTLE-UPON-TYNE
Bergen
Stavanger
Cairnryan
Stranraer
Carlisle
Sunderland
Durham
Hartlepool
Penrith
Workington
Whitehaven
Keswick
Darlington
Middlesbrough
Bangor
Isle of Man
Kendal
Scarborough
ENGLAND
Swale
Douglas
Barrow-in-Furness
Wharfe
Harrogate

NORTHERN IRELAND
Lough Neagh
BELFAST
Strangford Lough
Larne
Bangor
Ballygawley
Armagh
Banbridge
Newcastle
Monaghan
Dundalk/
Dun Dealgan
Kells
Drogheda/
Droichead Átha
Boyne
DUBLIN/
BAILE ÁTHA CLIATH
Dún Laoghaire
Naas
Bray
Wicklow
Carlow
Arklow
Enniscorthy
Wexford
Rosslare
Stranraer
Isle of Man
Douglas
IRISH SEA
ST GEORGE'S CHANNEL
Cherbourg
Carlisle
Workington
Whitehaven
Keswick
Penrith
Kendal
Barrow-in-Furness
Heysham
Lancaster
Sunderland
Durham
Darlington
ENGL
Wharfe
Harrogate
LEEDS
Bradford
Burnley
Halifax
Oldham
BLACKPOOL
Preston
Blackburn
Bolton
Southport
Wigan
LIVERPOOL
Birkenhead
MANCHESTER
Stockport
Warrington
Macclesfield
Chester
Matlock
Colwyn Bay/
Bae Colwyn
Holyhead/
Caergybi
Bangor
Caernarfon
Mold/
Yr Wyddgrug
Wrexham/
Wrecsam
STOKE-
ON TRENT
Dolgellau
Shrewsbury
Welshpool/
Y Trallwng
Wolverhampton
Walsall
Dudley
BIRMINGHAM
Aberystwyth
Llangurig
Ludlow
Severn
Warwick
Llandrindod
Wells
Worcester
Stratford-
upon-Avon
WALES
Wye
Hereford
Fishguard/
Abergwaun
Carmarthen/
Caerfyrddin
Brecon/
Aberhonddu
Ross
Cheltenham
Milford Haven/
Aberdaugleddau
Merthyr Tydfil
Gloucester
Pembroke Dock/
Doc Penfro
Newport/
Casnewydd
THAMES
Swansea/
Abertawe
Swindon
CARDIFF/
CAERDYDD
Bristol Channel
BRISTOL
Bath
Ilfracombe
Minehead
Wells
Barnstaple
Bridgwater
Taunton
Salisbury
Yeovil
Avon
Bude
EXETER
Honiton
Dorchester
Exmouth
Weymouth
BOURNEMOUTH
Newquay
Bodmin
PLYMOUTH
Torquay
Torbay
Truro
Penzance
Falmouth
Isles of Scilly
Santander
Roscoff
ENGLISH
Rosslare
Alderney
Cherbourg
Guernsey
Sark
St.Peter-Port
Jersey
St.Hélier

NORTH SEA
Hartlepool
Middlesbrough
Scarborough
York
KINGSTON UPON HULL
Immingham
Rotterdam
Zeebrugge
Wakefield
Scunthorpe
Barnley
Great Grimsby
Doncaster
Rotherham
SHEFFIELD
Lincoln
Skegness
Boston
Derby
NOTTINGHAM
Cromer
King's Lynn
NORWICH
Wisbech
LEICESTER
Stamford
Great Yarmouth
Peterborough
Lowestoft
Coventry
Ely
Rugby
Bury St.Edmunds
Northampton
CAMBRIDGE
Zeebrugge
Bedford
Ipswich
Felixstowe
Esbjerg
Göteborg
Hoek van Holland
Hamburg
Stevenage
Colchester
Harwich
Luton
Aylesbury
Harlow
Chelmsford
OXFORD
LONDON
Tilbury
Southend-on-Sea
THAMES
Reading
Windsor
Newbury
Margate
Sheerness
Ramsgate
Canterbury
Deal
Basingstoke
Guildford
Maidstone
Crawley
Royal-Tunbridge Wells
Dover
Winchester
Folkestone
Channel Tunnel
SOUTHAMPTON
BRIGHTON
Chichester
Hastings
Worthing
Eastbourne
PORTSMOUTH
Newhaven
Newport
Isle of Wight
St-Malo
CHANNEL
Rosslare
LE HAVRE
CAEN
Lisieux
ROUEN
Dieppe
FRANCE
Zeebrugge
OOSTENDE
BRUGGE
BELGIË
BELGIQUE
Dunkerque
Calais
St-Omer
Boulogne
LILLE
Arras
Cambrai
Abbeville
AMIENS
Somme
St-Quentin
Beauvais
Compiègne
Senlis
SEINE

3

Colonsay
Port Askaig
Jura
Tarbert
Islay
Port Ellen
ATLANTIC OCEAN
NORTH CHANNEL
Coleraine
Waterfoot
Letterkenny
Londonderry
Ballymena
Larne
Donegal
Strabane
Omagh
NORTHERN IRELAND
Lough Neagh
Bangor
BELFAST
Strangford Lough
Ballygawley
Enniskillen
Sligo/
Sligeach
Armagh
Banbridge
Newcastle
Ballina
L. Allen
Monaghan
Boyle
Cavan
Dundalk/
Dun Dealgan
Castlebar
Westport
L. Mask
Longford
Kells
Drogheda/
Droichead Átha
Clifden
L. Corrib
Roscommon
L. Ree
Boyne
Mullingar
Athlone
DUBLIN/
BAILE ÁTHA CLIATH
Galway/
Gaillimh
Ballinasloe
Tullamore
Naas
Dún Laoghaire
Bray
Lisdoonvarna
IRELAND
River Shannon
Roscrea
Wicklow
Ennis/
Inis
Kilkee
Thurles
Suir
Carlow
Arklow
LIMERICK/
LUIMNEACH
Kilkenny/
Cill Chainnigh
Barrow
Cashel/
Caiseal
Enniscorthy
Tralee
Dingle
Killarney/
Cill Airne
Caher
Carrick on Suir
Wexford
Fermoy
Waterford/
Port Lairge
Rosslare
R. Blackwater
Lismore
ST GEORGE'S CHANNEL
CORK/
CORCAIGH
Youghal
Cobh
Glengarriff
Bantry
Fishguard
Abergwaun
Milford Haven
Aberdaugleddau
Cherbourg

CELTIC SEA

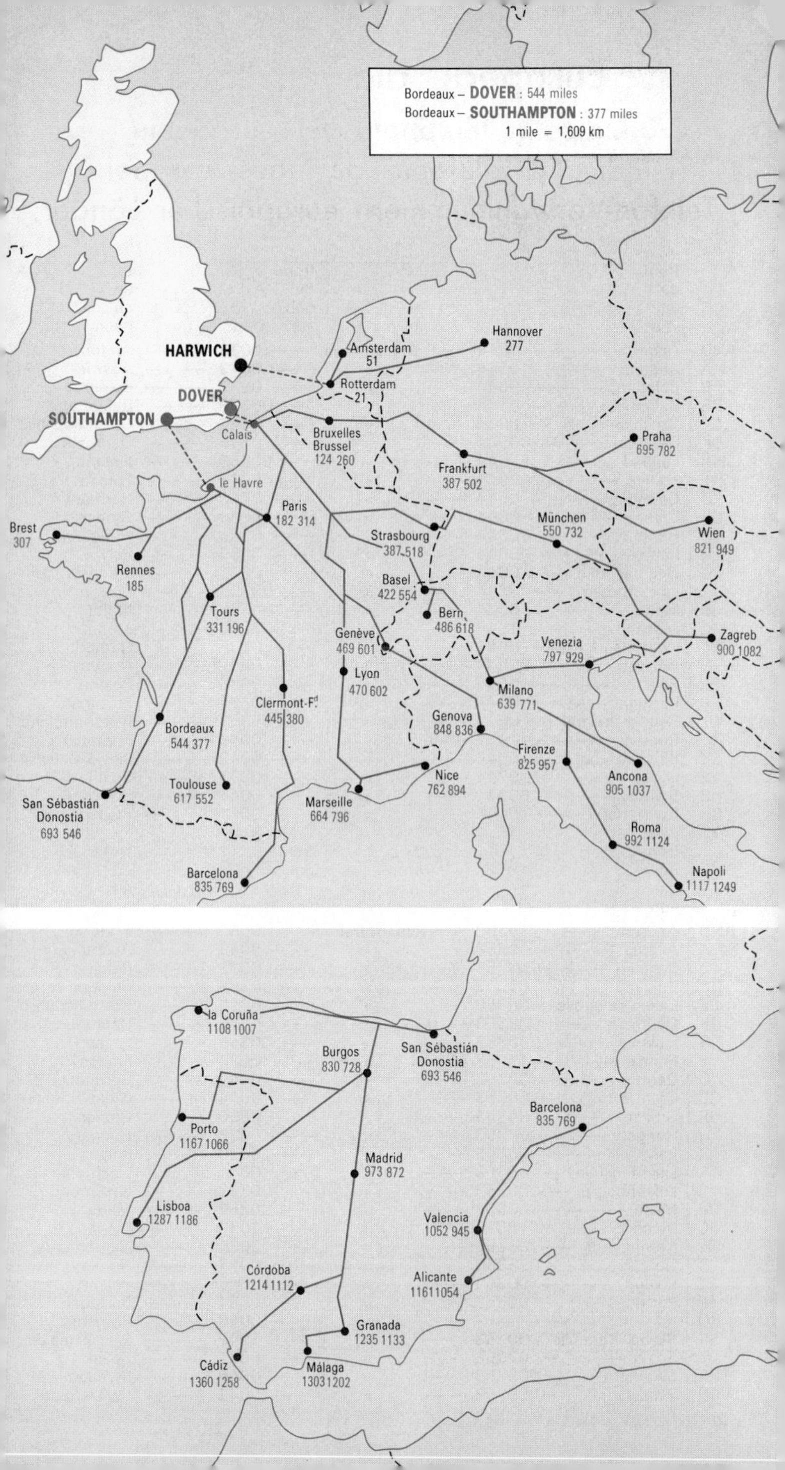
Bordeaux – DOVER : 544 miles
Bordeaux – SOUTHAMPTON : 377 miles
1 mile = 1,609 km
HARWICH
DOVER
SOUTHAMPTON
Calais
le Havre
Amsterdam 51
Rotterdam 21
Hannover 277
Bruxelles Brussel 124 260
Frankfurt 387 502
Praha 695 782
Paris 182 314
Strasbourg 387 518
München 550 732
Wien 821 949
Brest 307
Rennes 185
Tours 331 196
Basel 422 554
Bern 486 618
Genève 469 601
Lyon 470 602
Venezia 797 929
Zagreb 900 1082
Milano 639 771
Clermont-F^d 445 380
Bordeaux 544 377
Genova 848 836
Firenze 825 957
Ancona 905 1037
Toulouse 617 552
Nice 762 894
Marseille 664 796
San Sébastián Donostia 693 546
Roma 992 1124
Napoli 1117 1249
Barcelona 835 769
la Coruña 1108 1007
Burgos 830 728
San Sébastián Donostia 693 546
Porto 1167 1066
Barcelona 835 769
Madrid 973 872
Lisboa 1287 1186
Valencia 1052 945
Alicante 1161 1054
Córdoba 1214 1112
Granada 1235 1133
Cádiz 1360 1258
Málaga 1303 1202

European dialling codes
Indicatifs téléphoniques européens
Indicativi telefonici dei paesi europei
Telefon-Vorwahlnummern europäischer Länder

	from de dal von		to en in nach	from de dal von	to en en nach
AND	Andorra	1944	**Great Britain**	0033	Andorra
A	Austria	0044	»	0043	Austria
B	Belgium	0044	»	0032	Belgium
BG	Bulgaria	0044	»	00359	Bulgaria
CZ	Czech Republic	0044	»	0042	Czech Republic
DK	Denmark	00944	»	0045	Denmark
FIN	Finland	99044	»	00358	Finland
F	France	1944	»	0033	France
D	Germany	0044	»	0049	Germany
GR	Greece	0044	»	0030	Greece
H	Hungary	0044	»	0036	Hungary
I	Italy	0044	»	0039	Italy
FL	Liechtenstein	0044	»	0041	Liechtenstein
L	Luxembourg	0044	»	00352	Luxembourg
M	Malta	0044	»	00356	Malta
MC	Monaco	1944	»	003393	Monaco
NL	Netherlands	0944	»	0031	Netherlands
N	Norway	09544	»	0047	Norway
PL	Poland	0044	»	0048	Poland
P	Portugal	0044	»	00351	Portugal
IRL	Rep. of Ireland	0044	»	00353	Rep. of Ireland
RO	Romania	-	»	0040	Romania
SK	Slovak Republic	0044	»	0042	Slovak Republic
E	Spain	0744	»	0034	Spain
S	Sweden	00944	»	0046	Sweden
CH	Switzerland	0044	»	0041	Switzerland

	from de dal von		to en in nach	from de dal von	to en en nach
AND	Andorra	19353	**Rep. of Ireland**	0033	Andorra
A	Austria	00353	»	0043	Austria
B	Belgium	00353	»	0032	Belgium
BG	Bulgaria	00353	»	00359	Bulgaria
CZ	Czech Republic	00353	»	0042	Czech Republic
DK	Denmark	009353	»	0045	Denmark
FIN	Finland	990353	»	00358	Finland
F	France	19353	»	0033	France
D	Germany	00353	»	0049	Germany
GB	Great Britain	00353	»	0044	Great Britain
GR	Greece	00353	»	0030	Greece
H	Hungary	00353	»	0036	Hungary
I	Italy	00353	»	0039	Italy
FL	Liechtenstein	00353	»	0041	Liechtenstein
L	Luxembourg	00353	»	00352	Luxembourg
M	Malta	00353	»	00356	Malta
MC	Monaco	19353	»	0033	Monaco
NL	Netherlands	09353	»	0031	Netherlands
N	Norway	095353	»	0047	Norway
PL	Poland	00353	»	0048	Poland
P	Portugal	00353	»	00351	Portugal
RO	Romania	-	»	0040	Romania
SK	Slovak Republic	00353	»	0042	Slovak Republic
E	Spain	07353	»	0034	Spain
S	Sweden	009353	»	0046	Sweden
CH	Switzerland	00353	»	0041	Switzerland

Notes